ASTRODYNAMICS 2011
Part I

<u>Front Cover Photos</u>:

Top photo: Cassini looking back at an eclipsed Saturn, Astronomy picture of the day 2006 October 16, credit CICLOPS, JPL, ESA, NASA;
Bottom left photo: Shuttle shadow in the sunset (in honor of the end of the Shuttle Era), Astronomy picture of the day 2010 February 16, credit: Expedition 22 Crew, NASA;
Bottom right photo: Comet Hartley 2 Flyby, Astronomy picture of the day 2010 November 5, Credit: NASA, JPL-Caltech, UMD, EPOXI Mission.

American Astronautical Society

ASTRODYNAMICS 2011

Volume 142
Part I
ADVANCES IN THE ASTRONAUTICAL SCIENCES

Edited by
Hanspeter Schaub
Brian C. Gunter
Ryan P. Russell
William Todd Cerven

*Proceedings of the AAS/AIAA Astrodynamics
Specialist Conference held July 31 – August 4
2011, Girdwood, Alaska, U.S.A.*

*Published for the American Astronautical Society by
Univelt, Incorporated, P.O. Box 28130, San Diego, California 92198
Web Site: http://www.univelt.com*

Affiliated with the American Association for the Advancement of Science
Member of the International Astronautical Federation

First Printing 2012

Library of Congress Card No. 57-43769

ISSN 0065-3438

ISBN 978-0-87703-577-0 (Hard Cover Plus CD ROM)
ISBN 978-0-87703-578-7 (CD ROM)

Published for the American Astronautical Society
by Univelt, Incorporated, P.O. Box 28130, San Diego, California 92198
Web Site: http://www.univelt.com

Printed and Bound in the U.S.A.

FOREWORD

The 2011 Astrodynamics Conference was hosted by the American Astronautical Society (AAS) and co-sponsored by the American Institute of Aeronautics and Astronautics (AIAA). The conference was held July 31 – August 4, 2011, Girdwood, Alaska, U.S.A. There were some 220 papers presented in 28 technical sessions. Session topics included Asteroid & NEO; Orbital Debris; Dynamical Systems Theory; Special Topic: Autonomous Aerobraking; Trajectory Optimization; Formation Flying; Special Topic: Conjunction Assessment; Non-Earth Orbiting Missions; Orbit Estimation; Special Topic: ARTEMIS Mission; Planetary Mission Studies; Spacecraft GN&C; Satellite Constellations; Special Topic: MESSENGER at Mercury; Attitude D&C; Spacecraft Autonomy; Space Environment; Large Space Structures and Tethers; Optimal Control; and Rendezvous.

These astrodynamics conferences have been held annually since the mid-1960s, managed alternately by the American Astronautical Society and the American Institute of Aeronautics and Astronautics. Every second year the American Astronautical Society publishes the proceedings. The proceedings usually consist of a hard-copy volume or set of volumes plus a CD ROM (microfiche supplements in earlier years). This volume, *Astrodynamics 2011*, Volume 142, *Advances in the Astronautical Sciences*, consists of four parts totaling about 4,000 pages, plus a CD ROM which includes the papers in digital form. All of the available papers appear in full in Volume 142. A chronological index and an author index are appended to the fourth part of the volume. Papers which were not available for publication are listed on the divider pages of each section in the hard copy volume.

This volume is the latest in a sequence of Astrodynamics volumes which are published as a part of the American Astronautical Society series, *Advances in the Astronautical Sciences*. Several other sequences or subseries have been established in this series. Among them are: Space Flight Mechanics (annual), Guidance and Control (annual), International Space Conferences of Pacific-Basin Societies (ISCOPS, formerly PISSTA), and AAS Annual Conference proceedings. Proceedings volumes for earlier conferences are still available either in hard copy, CD ROM or in microfiche form. The appendix of the volume lists proceedings available through the American Astronautical Society.

In these proceedings volumes the technical accuracy and editorial quality are essentially the responsibility of the authors. The session chairs and the editors do not review all papers in detail; however, format and layout are improved when necessary by the editors.

We commend the general chairs, technical chairs, session chairs and the other participants for their role in making the conference such a success. A special word of thanks is also extended to those who assisted in organizational planning, registration and numerous other functions required for a successful conference.

The current proceedings are valuable in keeping specialists abreast of the state of the art; however, even older volumes contain some articles that have become classics and all volumes have archival value.

AAS/AIAA ASTRODYNAMICS VOLUMES

Astrodynamics 2011 appears as Volume 142, *Advances in the Astronautical Sciences*. This publication presents the complete proceedings of the AAS/AIAA Astrodynamics Conference 2011.

Astrodynamics 2009, Volume 135, *Advances in the Astronautical Sciences*, Eds. A.V. Rao et al., 2892p, three parts plus a CD ROM Supplement.

Astrodynamics 2007, Volume 129, *Advances in the Astronautical Sciences*, Eds. R.J. Proulx et al., 2892p, three parts plus a CD ROM Supplement.

Astrodynamics 2005, Volume 123, *Advances in the Astronautical Sciences*, Eds. B.G. Williams et al., 2878p, three parts plus a CD ROM Supplement.

Astrodynamics 2003, Volume 116, *Advances in the Astronautical Sciences*, Eds. J. de Lafontaine et al., 2746p, three parts plus a CD ROM Supplement.

Astrodynamics 2001, Volume 109, *Advances in the Astronautical Sciences*, Eds. D.B. Spencer et al., 2592p, three parts.

Astrodynamics 1999, Volume 103, *Advances in the Astronautical Sciences*, Eds. K.C. Howell et al., 2724p, three parts.

Astrodynamics 1997, Volume 97, *Advances in the Astronautical Sciences*, Eds. F.R. Hoots et al., 2190p, two parts.

Astrodynamics 1995, Volume 90, *Advances in the Astronautical Sciences*, Eds. K.T. Alfriend et al., 2270p, two parts; Microfiche Suppl., 6 papers (Vol. 72 *AAS Microfiche Series*).

Astrodynamics 1993, Volume 85, *Advances in the Astronautical Sciences*, Eds. A.K. Misra et al., 2750p, three parts; Microfiche Suppl., 9 papers (Vol. 70 *AAS Microfiche Series*)

Astrodynamics 1991, Volume 76, *Advances in the Astronautical Sciences*, Eds. B. Kaufman et al., 2590p, three parts; Microfiche Suppl., 29 papers (Vol. 63 *AAS Microfiche Series*)

Astrodynamics 1989, Volume 71, *Advances in the Astronautical Sciences*, Eds. C.L. Thornton et al., 1462p, two parts; Microfiche Suppl., 25 papers (Vol. 59 *AAS Microfiche Series*)

Astrodynamics 1987, Volume 65, *Advances in the Astronautical Sciences*, Eds. J.K. Soldner et al., 1774p, two parts; Microfiche Suppl., 48 papers (Vol. 55 *AAS Microfiche Series*)

Astrodynamics 1985, Volume 58, *Advances in the Astronautical Sciences*, Eds. B. Kaufman et al., 1556p, two parts; Microfiche Suppl. 55 papers (Vol. 51 *AAS Microfiche Series*)

Astrodynamics 1983, Volume 54, *Advances in the Astronautical Sciences*, Eds. G.T. Tseng et al., 1370p, two parts; Microfiche Suppl., 41 papers (Vol. 45 *AAS Microfiche Series*)

Astrodynamics 1981, Volume 46, *Advances in the Astronautical Sciences*, Eds. A.L. Friedlander et al., 1124p, two parts; Microfiche Suppl., 41 papers (Vol. 37 *AAS Microfiche Series*)

Astrodynamics 1979, Volume 40, *Advances in the Astronautical Sciences*, Eds. P.A. Penzo et al., 996p, two parts; Microfiche Suppl., 27 papers (Vol. 32 *AAS Microfiche Series*)

Astrodynamics 1977, Volume 27, *AAS Microfiche Series*, 73 papers

Astrodynamics 1975, Volume 33, *Advances in the Astronautical Sciences*, Eds., W.F. Powers et al., 390p; Microfiche Suppl., 59 papers (Vol. 26 *AAS Microfiche Series*)

Astrodynamics 1973, Volume 21, *AAS Microfiche Series*, 44 papers

Astrodynamics 1971, Volume 20, *AAS Microfiche Series*, 91 papers

AAS/AIAA SPACEFLIGHT MECHANICS VOLUMES

Spaceflight Mechanics 2011, Volume 140, *Advances in the Astronautical Sciences*, Eds. M.K. Jah et al., 2652p., three parts, plus a CD ROM supplement.

Spaceflight Mechanics 2010, Volume 136, *Advances in the Astronautical Sciences*, Eds. D. Mortari et al., 2622p., three parts, plus a CD ROM supplement.

Spaceflight Mechanics 2009, Volume 134, *Advances in the Astronautical Sciences*, Eds. A.M. Segerman et al., 2496p., three parts, plus a CD ROM supplement.

Spaceflight Mechanics 2007, Volume 127, *Advances in the Astronautical Sciences*, Eds. M.R. Akella et al., 2230p., two parts, plus a CD ROM supplement.

Spaceflight Mechanics 2006, Volume 124, *Advances in the Astronautical Sciences*, Eds. S.R. Vadali et al., 2282p., two parts, plus a CD ROM supplement.

Spaceflight Mechanics 2005, Volume 120, *Advances in the Astronautical Sciences*, Eds. D.A. Vallado et al., 2152p., two parts, plus a CD ROM supplement.

Spaceflight Mechanics 2004, Volume 119, *Advances in the Astronautical Sciences*, Eds. S.L. Coffey et al., 3318p., three parts, plus a CD ROM supplement.

Spaceflight Mechanics 2003, Volume 114, *Advances in the Astronautical Sciences*, Eds. D.J. Scheeres et al., 2294p, three parts, plus a CD ROM supplement.

Spaceflight Mechanics 2002, Volume 112, *Advances in the Astronautical Sciences*, Eds. K.T. Alfriend et al., 1570p, two parts.

Spaceflight Mechanics 2001, Volume 108, *Advances in the Astronautical Sciences*, Eds. L.A. D'Amario et al., 2174p, two parts.

Spaceflight Mechanics 2000, Volume 105, *Advances in the Astronautical Sciences*, Eds. C.A. Kluever et al., 1704p, two parts.

Spaceflight Mechanics 1999, Volume 102, *Advances in the Astronautical Sciences*, Eds. R.H. Bishop et al., 1600p, two parts.

Spaceflight Mechanics 1998, Volume 99, *Advances in the Astronautical Sciences*, Eds. J.W. Middour et al., 1638p, two parts; Microfiche Suppl., 2 papers (Vol. 78 *AAS Microfiche Series*).

Spaceflight Mechanics 1997, Volume 95, *Advances in the Astronautical Sciences*, Eds. K.C. Howell et al., 1178p, two parts.

Spaceflight Mechanics 1996, Volume 93, *Advances in the Astronautical Sciences*, Eds. G.E. Powell et al., 1776p, two parts; Microfiche Suppl., 3 papers (Vol. 73 *AAS Microfiche Series*).

Spaceflight Mechanics 1995, Volume 89, *Advances in the Astronautical Sciences*, Eds. R.J. Proulx et al., 1774p, two parts; Microfiche Suppl., 5 papers (Vol. 71 *AAS Microfiche Series*).

Spaceflight Mechanics 1994, Volume 87, *Advances in the Astronautical Sciences*, Eds. J.E. Cochran, Jr. et al., 1272p, two parts.

Spaceflight Mechanics 1993, Volume 82, *Advances in the Astronautical Sciences*, Eds. R.G. Melton et al., 1454p, two parts; Microfiche Suppl., 2 papers (Vol. 68 *AAS Microfiche Series*).

Spaceflight Mechanics 1992, Volume 79, *Advances in the Astronautical Sciences*, Eds. R.E. Diehl et al., 1312p, two parts; Microfiche Suppl., 11 papers (Vol. 65 *AAS Microfiche Series*).

Spaceflight Mechanics 1991, Volume 75, *Advances in the Astronautical Sciences*, Eds. J.K. Soldner et al., 1353p, two parts; Microfiche Suppl., 15 papers (Vol. 62 *AAS Microfiche Series*).

All of these proceedings are available from Univelt, Inc., P.O. Box 28130, San Diego, California 92198 (Web Site: http://www.univelt.com), publishers for the AAS.

Robert H. Jacobs,
Series Editor

PREFACE

The 2011 Astrodynamics Specialist Conference was held at The Hotel Alyeska in Girdwood, Alaska, from July 31 – August 4, 2011. The meeting was sponsored by the American Astronautical Society (AAS) Space Flight Mechanics Committee and co-sponsored by the American Institute of Aeronautics and Astronautics (AIAA) Astrodynamics Technical Committee. Approximately 270 people registered for the meeting; attendees included engineers, scientists, and mathematicians representing government agencies, the military services, industry, and academia from the United States and abroad.

There were 220 technical papers presented in 28 sessions on topics related to space-flight mechanics and astrodynamics. The 4 special sessions on Autonomous Aerobraking, Conjunction Assessment, the ARTEMIS Mission and MESSENGER at Mercury were well received and strongly attended.

The meeting included 4 social events. On Sunday the Early Bird Reception was held in the Kahiltna Court, on Monday evening there was a student social also in Kahiltna Court. On Tuesday evening the conference enjoyed a tram ride and dinner at the Glacier Express Restaurant, while on Wednesday evening the award ceremony and keynote address banquet was held in the Columbia conference rooms A/B/C. The keynote speaker was Dr. Robert D. Braun, the NASA Chief Technologist. The editors extend their gratitude to the Session Chairs who made this meeting successful: Ossama Abdelkhalik, Matthew Berry, Shyam Bhaskaran, Angela Bowes, Brent Buffington, Dennis Byrnes, David Dunham, Thomas Eller, David Folta, Ryan Frigm, Michael Gabor, Bob Glover, Yanping Guo, Felix Hoots, Alan Lovell, Don Mackison, James McAdams, Craig McLaughlin, Bo Naasz, Ryan Park, Chris Ranieri, Jon Sims, David Spencer, Thomas Starchville, Aaron Trask, Rao Vadali, Kenneth Williams, Roby Wilson, and Renato Zanetti. Our gratitude also goes to Tom Eller, Shannon Coffey, Felix Hoots, John Seago and James Kirkpatrick for their support and assistance.

Dr. Hanspeter Schaub
University of Colorado
AAS Technical Chair

Dr. Ryan P. Russell
Georgia Institute of Technology
AAS General Chair

Dr. Brian C. Gunter
Delft University of Technology
AIAA Technical Chair

Dr. William Todd Cerven
The Aerospace Corporation
AIAA General Chair

CONTENTS

SESSION 7: FORMATION FLYING I

Part II

SESSION 8: SPECIAL TOPIC: CONJUNCTION ASSESSMENT

Part IV

ASTEROID AND NEO I

SESSION 1

Chair:
Ryan Park
Jet Propulsion Laboratory

The following papers were not available for publication:

AAS 11-401
   (Paper Withdrawn)

AAS 11-407
   (Paper Withdrawn)

AN ANALYSIS OF MULTIPLE-REVOLUTION THIRD BODY DRIVEN PLANE CHANGE MANEUVERS

Eric Trumbauer[*] and Benjamin Villac[**]

Third-body forces can greatly affect the orbital elements of spacecraft orbiting moons and small bodies. These forces can be harnessed to induce controlled orbital maneuvers such as plane changes. Previous studies have focused on a single revolution to effect these maneuvers. This paper extends this by considering multiple periapsis passages before recircularization. The performance envelope is evaluated and compared to previous studies. While the gains are modest in feasible cases, interesting structures emerge in relation to escape, capture, and libration point dynamics. These present opportunities for mapping nearby regions suitable for transfers to and from scientifically interesting near-polar orbits.

INTRODUCTION

Multi-body models have been successfully used to find transfers beyond those of classical two body models.[1] Within this large body of work, *a recurring theme is mapping regions of phase space with different global behavior* such as transit between areas of interest or the number of revolutions around a body before moving on. These characteristics are shaped by invariant manifolds of periodic orbits and so, rather than being arbitrary, are tied to the global structures of the system in question.[2] Koon et al. have show intersections of these manifolds and their images form regions of phase space with specific transit behavior that may be used for mission planning.[1,3] These regions have been labelled with a sequence of symbols whose dynamics match the long term behavior of the trajectory. In other works, the 'neck' region near the secondary body in the Circular Restricted Three Body Problem was divided into lobes where trajectories having a periapsis in these regions shared the number of periapsis passages remaining until escape.[4,5]

However, properties such as transit are not the only ones of interest. Local orbital properties such as the inclination and altitude of trajectories near a massive body are important, yet the lack of a *direct* connection with global dynamical structures has made it difficult to analyze these feature in the same framework. Some steps have been made in this direction. For example, the range of inclination changes that could be achieved with a transfer to geostationary orbits from LEO using invariant manifolds has been investigated.[6] While not the authors' aim, this can be generalized to other such transfers, but would be limited in that inclination changes may be desired at low energies where invariant manifolds do not intersect the area of interest. An alternative approach was made by integrating forward potential third body driven transfer trajectories at every point near the surface of Europa.[7] This approach was also applied to Mars and Callisto.[8] This procedure has the benefit of being applicable for any apoapsis raising

---

* Graduate Student, Mechanical and Aerospace Engineering, University of California, Irvine. etrumbau@uci.edu
** Assistant Professor, Mechanical and Aerospace Engineering, University of California, Irvine. bvillac@uci.edu

maneuver, not just those that follow nearly asymptotic trajectories. However, the natural case of allowing multiple revolutions before recircularizing has not been considered in this way. In addition to lacking a more complete performance characterization, the restriction to a single periapsis passage makes it difficult to see the connections between the numerical results and key trajectories that order these results. *It is this link between the dynamical structures emphasized in (References 1,4) and the wide ranging numerical analysis of changes to orbital elements in (References 7,8) that will allow for a generalized method to find good initial guesses near optimal results rather than the current case-by-case basis.*

Multiple periapsis passages before recircularization are considered and compared to the single revolution case to gauge under which conditions they yield superior performance. This paper combines the emphasis on structure with the scope and methods of the numerical approaches mentioned in order to provide performance guidelines. Key features such as the existence of intersecting libration point orbits and singularity collision orbits are discussed as they are intimately linked with changes to the maxima of plane changes. This is a first step in determining how areas of interest may be mapped and given an expanded symbolic dynamics. This way end-to-end transfers may be found with not only desired transit characteristics, but with a natural tendency towards other mission critical attributes.

To illustrate the results, Europa and Ceres have been selected as test cases due to current interest and how differently the systems behave. There are many orbital characteristics that could be the subject of a specific investigation, but the focus here is on changes to inclination from polar orbits. Polar orbits are useful for mapping the surface of the body being orbited. However, even close to the smaller massive body where the perturbations from the larger, distant body are small, these orbits are unstable and result in impact without active thrusting.[9] Additionally, modern missions with multiple objectives may need the ability to transfer from such an orbit to accomplish other scientific goals. So, the ability for an outer moon or small body orbiter to transition between different inclinations (and possibly altitude) greatly increases both mission safety and flexibility.

The paper is organized in the following fashion. To begin, descriptions of classical orbital transfer maneuvers and third-body driven transfers and their geometries are given. Following this is a brief description of Hill's Model for a three body system. While simulations were done in both Hill's Model and the Circular Restricted Three Body Problem, the scalability and dimensionless form of the latter made it an attractive choice in presenting multiple examples. A reduction of variables allows for a two dimensional representation of performance results, and the method to generate these maps are given as well as a description of their features. These features are related to key types of trajectories and how these relationships determine the magnitude of the global extrema of inclination changes and can provide locations for initial guesses for optimization procedures. The examples Europa and Ceres are used to show when multiple revolutions yield superior results and example cases where the previously mentioned structures come in to play. The conclusion summarizes the results and links to other avenues of research.

BACKGROUND ON PLANE CHANGES

To begin, the types of maneuvers being considered are discussed along with their classical counterparts. Although many types of transfers can be considered in the context described above, the important case of changes to inclination are the focus of our attention.

4

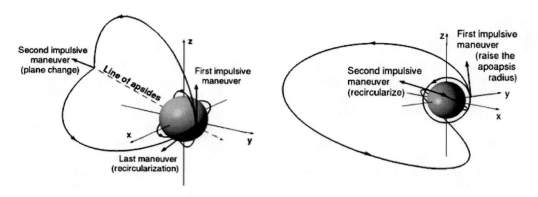

Figure 1: A bi-elliptic plane change   Figure 2: A Third-body driven plane change

Classical Plane Change Maneuvers

Within the framework of the restricted two body problem, optimal plane change maneuvers have been completely characterized. Given an initial and a final circular orbit, depending on the inclination there is an ideal sequence of one or more impulsive maneuvers to transfer between them.[10] Before taking third-body perturbations into account, two types of these transfers in the classical problem should be mentioned. While those cases where the altitude is allowed to change are considered, particular attention is paid to the case where given an initial orbit with radius r_0 and inclination i, we transfer to a final orbit with the same radius r_0 and final inclination $i + \Delta i$. These maneuvers where the final orbit has the same altitude as the initial orbit are called *plane changes*.

One such transfer requires a single burn to directly change the inclination, making sure the resulting magnitude of velocity is unchanged so as not to change the orbit's radius. More important for our purposes is the bi-elliptic plane change (See Figure 1). This involves three maneuvers: one tangential to transfer to an ellipse with a larger radius of apoapsis, a second to change the orbital plane at the farthest point, and then a third tangential maneuver to recircularize the orbit at the next periapsis. Although there are more maneuvers to be performed, for large (>39 degrees) plane changes the bi-elliptic method actually uses less fuel as the change to the orbital plane is much easier to perform at a larger distance from the body being orbited.[10] Note that in both of these cases, due to the spherical symmetry of the two body problem, the change of inclination is not dependent on the initial longitude of the ascending node Ω_0 or the argument from periapsis ω_0. Rather, these are selected to achieve a desired Ω_f, ω_f of the final orbit.

Third-body Driven Plane Changes

In a highly perturbed multi-body environment, bi-elliptic plane changes are no longer strictly possible. The gravitational influence of a larger massive body means that none of the orbital element values predicted by the bi-elliptic classical model correspond to the actual final result. Indeed, it is fairly likely that impact or escape will result. However, as is frequently the case in three body problems, what is initially seen to be a problem in many cases is actually an opportunity. In some cases, raising the apoapsis with a tangential maneuver will cause the perturbing forces to change the inclination upon a return to the moon or asteroid. A second tangential maneuver may then be used to recircularize into a desirable orbit around the moon or asteroid. In effect, the force of the larger body replaces the orbital plane changing maneuver in the bi-elliptic case. If the radius at this point is identical to that of the initial orbit, it is called a third body driven plane change. A diagram of this process is shown in Figure 2. It is clear that the position of the spacecraft relative to both the body being orbited and the larger perturbing body when the apoapsis raising maneuver occurs will affect the outcome. This is different from the two body case where $\Delta i, \Delta r_p$ were independent of Ω_0, ω_0. Thus in the case of third-body driven plane changes, we may state that we have functions $\Delta i(\Omega, \omega), \Delta r_p(\Omega, \omega)$.

Ω, ω are in this case in reference to the rotating axis connecting the two massive bodies, rather than a fixed direction in an inertial frame.

This is the type of plane change covered in (References 7,8), and in the case the apoapsis raising maneuver places the trajectory near an asymptotic trajectory of a libration point orbit, in (Reference 6). Aside from its visual similarity with the bi-elliptic plane change that it 'replaces', some results echo those from the classical maneuver. For example, it was shown that in the case distances on the order of the radius of Europa, this type of third-body driven plane change is optimal over a single maneuver direct plane change for inclination changes greater than 38 degrees.[7] This is remarkably similar to the optimality of the bi-elliptic plane change over the single maneuver at inclination changes greater than 39 degrees in the classical case. So indeed is large inclination changes are needed for a mission, third-body driven changes are something that should be considered.

In the previous papers, the trajectory was recircularized when the first periapsis was reached. However, there is nothing limiting the third-body driven plane change procedure to this single periapsis passage case. A trajectory could theoretically be allowed any number of extra revolutions until a periapsis passage is reached that allows an easy transfer to a desirable orbit. It is an obvious question to ask if going around once can lead to improved performance, might going around two or more times be better? This paper seeks to characterize conditions under which this is the case. Although there is no theoretical limit on the number of revolutions, simulations were limited to several periapsis passages. This is due to issues such as diminishing returns, increase in operational difficulty, and increasing effects of modeling error. Thus, the focus is on two periapsis passages, with three and four passages considered in some cases.

MODEL DESCRIPTION

The rather visual description of third body driven orbital transfers is important to gain intuitive understanding the process. However, to put this understanding on solid ground and obtain precise performance results, an appropriate model for the dynamics must be given. In this paper Hill's Model is used. One reason is that due to the scalability and dimensionless form of Hill's Model, it is easier to present multiple examples in a unified framework and with proportional length scales. Another is that this model turns some of the "almost-symmetries" of the CR3BP into true symmetries and this allowed a smaller area to be surveyed, leading to a finer resolution. And lastly, as this work should be compared to those of Villac and Scheeres[7,8], it seemed best to use the same model.

Hill's Model

Like the CR3BP, Hill's Model is a limiting case of the Three Body Problem. It was originally derived by Hill to describe the motion of the Moon around the Earth as perturbed by the Sun.[11] It has also come to be used as a model of a spacecraft orbiting a moon or asteroid under the influence of a more distant, larger massive object. Before moving to the equations of motion, the appropriateness of using a point mass model in this scenario should be discussed. If orbits very close to the moon/asteroid were to be considered in detail, certainly this approximation would be troublesome due to the lack of gravitational harmonics. However, our focus is not on the motion of the initial and final orbits themselves over a period of time, but rather the trajectories joining them. By raising the apoapsis to many times the radius of the body being orbited, the differences between the point mass model and a more fully developed gravitational model of the asteroid or small moon become small. Hill's Model also compares well with more developed models for the gravity of the larger perturbing body for distances within the Hill's Sphere, corresponding to 1 unit in the normalized model. The problem being analyzed is limited to this range, and so the model acceptable for initial analysis.

The model is defined by the following system of ordinary differential equations:

$$\ddot{x} - 2N\dot{y} = -(\mu/r^3)x + 3N^2x$$

$$\ddot{y} + 2N\dot{x} = -(\mu/r^3)y$$

$$\ddot{z} = -(\mu/r^3)z - N^2z$$

where x, y, and z are the Cartesian coordinates of the orbiter in the rotating frame centered on the body being orbited (See Figure 3), r is the magnitude of the distance vector from the body to the orbiter, N is the angular frequency of the asteroid/moon around the larger perturbing body (Sun or planet), and μ is the gravitational parameter of the asteroid/moon (mass x G, the gravitational constant). Note that unlike the CR3BP this gravitational parameter is not a ratio of masses. Example parameters for several systems are given in Table 1 for reference.

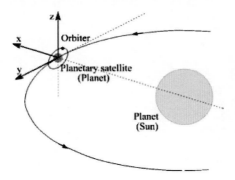

Orbited Body (Perturbing Body)	μ km^3/s^2	Radius, km	Length Scale km	Normalized Radius
Ceres (Sun)	6.293E+01	487.3	322710	0.0015
Europa (Jupiter)	3.193E+03	1569	19672.6	0.0797
Ganymede (Jupiter)	9.883E+03	2631	45733.4	0.0575
Callisto (Jupiter)	7.171E+03	2400	72283.6	0.0332
Moon (Earth)	4.903E+03	1738	88454.7	0.0196
Phobos (Mars)	6.4E-04	11	23.1	0.4859
Deimos (Mars)	1.3E-04	6	33.8	0.1881
Earth (Sun)	3.9860E+05	6371	2158322	0.0029

Figure 3: Geometry of Hill's Model   **Table 1: Example parameters in Hill's Model**

By adopting length and timescales of $l = (\mu/N^2)^{1/3}$ and $\tau = 1/N$, the equations can be reduced to a dimensionless and parameterless form:

$$\ddot{x} - 2\dot{y} = -x/r^3 + 3x$$

$$\ddot{y} + 2\dot{x} = -y/r^3$$

$$\ddot{z} = -z/r^3 - z$$

Because of this, results obtained in the dimensionless version can be scaled to any particular application by describing them with the correct length scales and timescales. All of the results in this paper are presented in the nondimensional form of the problem. This allows for the use of consistent units between multiple systems. So for example, a radius of $.69l$ corresponds to approximately the distance to the libration points in any example, allowing for easier comparison between similar situations across test cases.

Some Helpful Features

Hill's Model has many similarities and some slight differences with the CR3BP. There are two libration points *L1* and *L2* near the body being orbited. These lie along the *x*-axis at distance $(1/3)^{(1/3)}l \approx .69l$ on either side of the origin. This is an example of a repeating pattern whereby near symmetries in the CR3BP – *L1* and *L2* are not quite equidistant to the secondary – is a true symmetry in Hill's Model. These are unstable equilibria and there exist periodic orbits around them with stable and unstable manifolds consisting of trajectories asymptotic to the orbits forward or backward in time. As in the case of the Circular Restricted Three Body Problem, points in phase space lying in the interior of such a stable manifold transit through to the other side of the equilibrium region. We may define a region in the *xy*-plane where these trajectories have their periapsis. Trajectories inside this region escape before reaching another periapsis, while those exterior to any such region have at least one more periapsis before escaping, if at all. At sufficiently high energy levels where the transfer trajectories being considered might intersect these manifolds, escape then becomes a possibility. As can be seen in Figure 4, this also means these features can be leveraged to find trajectories with a large influence from the perturbing body.

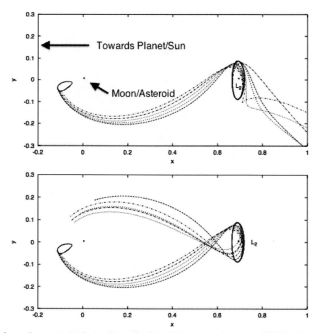

Figure 4: Example of nearly asymptotic trajectories bordering invariant manifolds of an unstable libration point orbit. On the left side of each image is the boundary created by points where the trajectories making up the manifolds attain periapsis. Top: Those trajectories attaining periapsis in the interior this region transit past the equilibrium region. Bottom: Those attaining periapsis in the exterior of this region do not transit and may be used as transfers to effect an inclination change.

Additionally, the equations of motion are invariant under several coordinates transformations. If $(x, y, z, \dot{x}, \dot{y}, \dot{z}, t)$ is a solution to the equations of motion, then valid solutions are also obtained with the following coordinate transformations:

$$(x, y, z, \dot{x}, \dot{y}, \dot{z}, t) \xrightarrow{S_1} (-x, y, z, \dot{x}, -\dot{y}, -\dot{z}, -t)$$

$$(x, y, z, \dot{x}, \dot{y}, \dot{z}, t) \xrightarrow{S_2} (x, -y, z, -\dot{x}, \dot{y}, -\dot{z}, -t)$$

$$(x, y, z, \dot{x}, \dot{y}, \dot{z}, t) \xrightarrow{S_3} (x, y, -z, \dot{x}, \dot{y}, -\dot{z}, t)$$

$$(x, y, z, \dot{x}, \dot{y}, \dot{z}, t) \xrightarrow{S_4} (-x, -y, z, -\dot{x}, -\dot{y}, \dot{z}, t)$$

In particular the last two transformations allow us to restrict our domain by only considering trajectories with apoapsis raising maneuvers occurring in the region defined by $y, z \geq 0$. This is helpful in a very practical way in that simulation times are reduced by this domain restriction so that finer resolution may be achieved.

MAPPING THE DYNAMICS

Now that the idea of third body driven orbital transfers and the properties of Hill's model have been discussed, the next step is to characterize the behavior of multiple revolution plane changes. A comprehensive selection of transfer trajectories from a given orbit are integrated forward to provide both data for finding optimal changes to orbital elements as well as to create a visual picture of these extrema and their surroundings. To create this picture, a series of maps are created which capture the changes to the dynamics as the energy/thrust increases and as the number of revolutions increases. Structures in the maps may then be linked to the quantitative performance characteristics such as changes to inclination and radius of periapsis. These structures can then assist in the goal to characterize the conditions under which multiple revolutions lead to superior performance in a general setting.

Defining Initial Conditions

For an example scenario, such as transfers from a near-Europa orbit, the initial r_p is fixed. Recall that since we are considering polar orbits and burns tangential to the orbit, the initial direction is fixed for each starting point. So, the magnitude is the defining feature once a position has been given. Earlier, a transfer trajectory's initial velocity was associated with the radius of apoapsis of an elliptical orbit such a velocity would create in a classical two-body problem. This is equivalent to Δv but fits in better with the labeling scheme of using orbital elements. Changes to this r_a make a good focus point for a couple of reasons. Given the limits on both fuel use and maximum impulse for distant missions, it is easy to relate to mission constraints. Also, from the simulations done for this work, increasing this value seems to best reveal the role of key trajectories in shaping the results.

For ease of visualization, it would be preferable to create planar maps. Thus, every trajectory in each plot needs to be represented with two variables. Consider the following details of the setup:

- The initial radius is the same for every trajectory in an example. For the case of Europa, near-Europa orbits with normalized radii equal to .08 are considered. For Ceres, orbits one asteroid radius away from the surface, $r = .003$, are considered.

- The initial inclination is fixed for each example. In this paper, transfers from polar orbit are the focus and so the initial inclination is 90 degrees.
- These transfer trajectories begin and end at periapsis conditions. Thus $\dot{r}=0, \ddot{r}>0$ at the beginning and end of each transfer.
- Using the longitude of the ascending node Ω (in our case relative to the x-axis and not a fixed direction in an inertial frame), the argument from periapsis ω, and the radius of periapsis r_p the position may be defined in a manner similar to spherical coordinates.
- The inclination and the periapsis condition determine the direction of the initial velocity which is tangential to the circular orbit.

For each map there isan associated $r_a(\Delta v)$, which is how large a radius of apoapsis would be produced by the maneuver in the two-body problem. By doing this, trajectories with equivalently large Δv at the start of the transfer are grouped together even though the perturbations may result in different behavior and distances by the end.

Thus if r_p, r_a, and i are all fixed, and since the periapsis condition holds for every such transfer we have enough information to represent an initial state with the addition of just Ω and ω. This means that as long as the above fixed values are known for a plot, we may graph changes of some feature as a function of these two orbital elements. Since r_p and i are fixed for each example, a sequence of two dimensional plots (each with an associated r_a) may be generated for $\Delta i(\Omega, \omega), \Delta r_p(\Omega, \omega)$ for each system considered. Also, thanks to the symmetries present in Hill's Model, only a range from 0 to 180 degrees need be considered for Ω and ω to cover every possible initial condition in this way. Of course, different pairs of variables could be considered as independent variables while others remain fixed, however this is a natural choice which corresponds to the notion of covering the entire sphere around the body being orbited.

Map Creation

A wide range of r_a values are considered, and for each of these values a map is created. Per the conditions discussed above, the independent variables Ω and ω then complete the definition of all of the initial conditions considered. These maps are then contour plots showing a desired characteristic as a function of Ω and ω. For this work, plots were created to determine *changes to inclination* and changes to *radius of periapsis*. As mentioned before, changes to inclination are the center of the analysis here, but in order to define plane changes and consider things like surface impacts, inclination must be linked to the radius of periapsis. Distinct maps are created for *one, two, and three* periapsis passages with the determination of the orbital elements taken at these milestones. Given the symmetries in Hill's Model, Ω and ω are each taken in the interval $[0,180]$. Starting points are .25 degrees apart giving 720 x 720 = 518,400 total trajectories per map. Figure 5 shows some examples for the case of Europa. Each column shows the change in inclination from one to three periapsis passages, and the rows have different r_a values. Series of maps like these allow a chance to find the features that explain the changing performance as thrust is increased. These features will now be discussed.

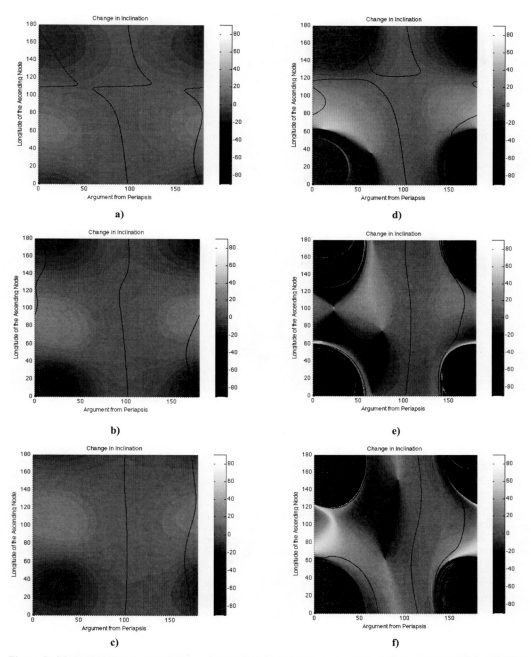

Figure 5: Maps of change to inclination as a function of orbital elements. Case of Europa with initial radius .08 units. a), b), c) Radius of apoapsis .4 units after 1, 2, and 3 passages. d), e), f) Radius of apoapsis .6 units after 1, 2, and 3 passages. Note the presence of the escape regions in the corners shaded black.

Organizing Dynamical Structures

In this section the roles of collision and escape trajectories are discussed. The existence of one of these features guarantees a global maximum inclination change occurs at or near these trajectories. As a result, neighborhood of these trajectories provide regions of interest for optimization methods.

One of these is the existence of *escaping trajectories among the trajectories considered.* That is to say when they appear on the maps of tangential maneuvers from the given initial orbit, not when escape in the system in general. At the energy levels considered, the existence of such trajectories implies that invariant manifolds of libration point orbits are intersecting the set of initial conditions so defined.[12,13] The boundaries of these escaping regions in the map are then asymptotic orbits, and non-escaping trajectories nearby present transfer opportunities with strong third body perturbations. For any number of periapsis passages, the existence of such trajectories cause a jump in the extrema of inclination change performance.

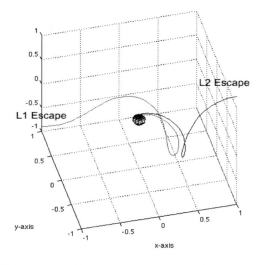

Figure 7: Example of an escaping trajectory and a non-escaping trajectory from neighboring nested escape regions in a map. The right trajectory is a direct escape through L2 which would appear in an inner circle in the contour maps. The left trajectory is an escape through L1, but one that lies in an outer annulus between the direct escapes in the center and non-escaping trajectories.

In the case of a single passage, the greatest magnitude negative inclination change (i.e. a minimum) occurs at the boundary, while the maximum occurred near but not on this area.[7,8] However the boundaries themselves did not contain the maximum positive inclination changes in the single passage case. When multiple periapsis passages are allowed, these boundary areas (see Figure 8) do indeed contain the maximum values for general inclination changes, if not plane changes. The full effects of the chaotic behavior associated with libration point dynamics can also be seen in this case. The escape regions are nested in these maps (As in Figure 5b) and the extrema containing boundaries between them exhibit a Cantor Set like structure as the number of periapsis passages is increased (Figure 8).[14] What does this have to do with practical performance? More passages may allow larger plane changes when escape is possible, but even nearby non-escaping trajectories exhibit wildly different behavior, increasing missions risks and complexity. So, in order to accurately compare performance, one must decide whether or not to include trajectories in these chaotic boundary regions in a search.

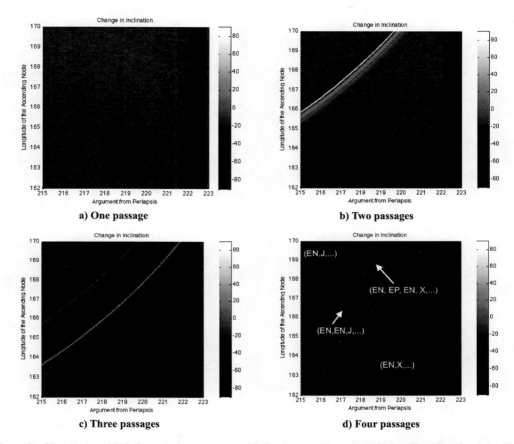

Figure 8: **Changes to orbital elements from a polar orbit for the case where the initial radius of periapsis is .08 and the Δv is equivalent to creating an elliptical orbit with radius of apoapsis .60 as above. Zoomed in to show details and structure in the escape regions as the number of periapsis passages is increased. For the last image, a simplification of the idea of labeling regions of space is illustrated. Here the possible states at each periapsis passage are escape towards Jupiter (J), escape to the exterior region (X), remaining in the Europa region with a positive inclination change (EP), and staying in the Europa region with a negative inclination change (EN). Inclusion of all of the performance data would be difficult to illustrate visually.**

The other key type of trajectory that shapes the nature of extrema are *collision trajectories*. By this we are referring to trajectories that approach the singularity of the model inside the body being orbited. This is a stronger condition than just impacting the surface. In the maps generated, these can be seen as points where regions of positive and negative plane change are pinched together in a discontinuous looking fashion. This is a result of scattering of trajectories at the singularity. Clearly colliding with a singularity does not constitute a transfer, however the existence of such a feature affects nearby trajectories so that near-global extrema may be found near these key trajectories (See Figure 9).

The way these two types of structure creating trajectories relate is worth discussing. Depending on the example being considered, none, one or both type of trajectories may be present at once. In the case of the near-Europa orbit example, both types appear at the same time. For the Ceres example with a lower normalized radius, collision trajectories are present at lower energies than escaping trajectories. One can expect for normalized body radii greater than Europa , escape would be possible before collision.

If one type of trajectory is present, initial guesses for finding extrema should take place near that group of transfers. What is somewhat surprising is that when both are present, neither option produces a maximum greater than the other, so both should be considered depending on mission circumstances. To emphasize the point, the maximum values for inclination changes (without restrictions on the change to radius of periapsis) appear to be nearly identical in the boundary of escaping trajectories and at collision trajectories when both are present. For true plane changes the situation is more nuanced as results depend both on the structure of the changes to inclination and how this intersects with lines of zero change to the radius of periapsis. However, as both types may yield large results depending on the situation, both areas should be searched. Further practical restrictions determine how close feasible transfers may come to these theoretical extrema will be discussed next.

So, these key trajectories and intersections of invariant manifolds with the initial state of the transfers give structure to the results. In particular, these transfers of theoretical importance provide us with regions of interest to limit the search space in the practical goal of finding the best performance.

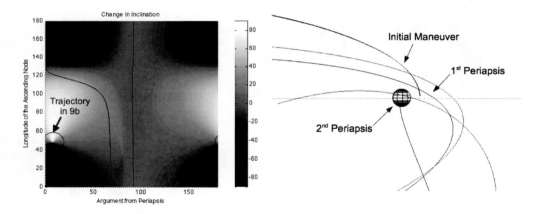

Figure 9a: Map with collision after two periapsis passages. Case of Ceres with $r_p = .003, r_a = .45$

Figure 9b: Example of collision trajectory and a neighboring plane change.

Physical Limitation and Mission Constraints

The previous section described features that order the results based solely on the dynamical properties of the model. However, there are practical issues due to the body being orbited and the mission constraints that affect the feasibility of attaining those theoretical extrema.

The most obvious additional piece of information is the *radius of the orbited body,* R_M. This determines which trajectories are invalid due to impacting the surface. Since periapsis is a (local) closest approach, only the radii of periapsis need be considered to determine if a trajectory is impacting. In the case of a single periapsis passage, plane changes are unaffected assuming the initial orbit is not inside the moon/asteroid since $\Delta r_p = 0$. For general inclination changes, impact is possible and so this may reduce the theoretical extrema as produced by the model. When multiple periapsis passages are allowed, both plane changes and general inclination changes can be affected. This is because transfer trajectories exist where the radius of periapsis after one passage is reduced before returning to the initial radius at the second (or third, fourth, etc.) passage. Impacting trajectories may be ignored after simulations have been run by setting $\Delta i = 0$ if $r_p \leq R_M$. This is useful because it allows the simulations to be run once for a given normalized radius (that may be relevant for multiple systems) and then adjusted for the specific case rather than needing to rerun at the same radius for each system considered. In relation to performance characteristics, even if an excluded impact region prevents a theoretical extrema from being achieved, the boundary of the impact region frequently contains transfers with impressive performance. This is especially true if the normalized radius is small, such as the case of Ceres. As such, trajectories passing near these boundaries should be considered when searching for feasible extrema.

Two other practical considerations that lead to similar restriction on the data are *constraints on navigation accuracy* and on *time of flight*. The restriction on the data is similar because both of these constraints make the escape region boundaries unfeasible. Since these regions contain the near-asymptotic trajectories that include the extrema of inclination changes, this is of great importance. Navigation accuracy is important due to the chaotic nature of these regions. Since a small error in timing the maneuver may lead to wildly different outcomes [Recall Figure 7], high accuracy or active control is necessary in these areas. Even with control added, fuel needed to correct the trajectory may be excessively high if this error is not quickly recognized. So, if highly accurate navigation is not possible in a given system, these boundary regions should perhaps be excluded from consideration. Another attribute of these near asymptotic trajectories is their long flight times. If this is not practical for a given mission, these regions might also be excluded from consideration.

To make the above more concrete, compare the situations in the Earth/Sun system and the Europa/Jupiter system. In the first case, accurate navigation methods have been established and the instability time scale is on the order of years. So, in this case boundary trajectories associated with asymptotic trajectories and libration point dynamics are rightly considered as they produce impressive results.[6] Now consider the case of Europa. Not only is navigation accuracy decreased relative to near Earth orbits, the much smaller size of the moon means that even greater accuracy would be needed. The instability time scale for the Europa/Jupiter system has been shown to be on the order of days.[10] Simultaneously, the high radiation environment near Jupiter makes long flight times undesirable. In this case, this class of trajectory ought to be excluded from consideration.

Excluding these areas from consideration can pose some difficulties with implementation. During simulations, a check for time of flight or proximity to the libration points may be used to eliminate a particular trajectory from consideration. This is clear-cut and effective, however this would require running a simulation anew depending on the mission restrictions. A method that operates on the simulation results themselves would be desirable to avoid this. One possibility is to take advantage of the fact that these boundaries are indeed chaotic regions. If closely neighboring points show many different types of transit outcomes after a few revolutions then it can be assumed the trajectory in question lies in the region that should be excluded. A sample result of this method is shown in Figure 10. In the examples considered, the two methods did not produce different values of extrema, at least in these simulations. Thus, an understanding of the chaotic nature of these regions are needed in order to restrict our consideration to feasible transfers. Otherwise, results obtained may not be applicable to the system being considered. As before, an understanding of the structure of areas containing extrema is necessarily to characterize and validate performance results.

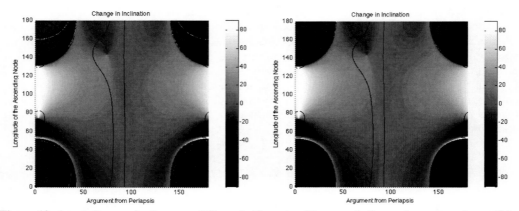

Figure 10: A sample map in the case of Ceres in the case of two revolutions when escape is possible. Note the presence of the boundaries containing near-asymptotic trajectories that look like rings between the escape regions. On the right is the same map with these trajectories excluded after the simulations are run by taking advantage of the chaotic nature of these regions.

The maps created allow for an understanding of the relationship between different performance characteristics and the presence of key trajectories that structure the results. The insights gained also provided a method to limit the search area based on practical mission restrictions. We are now in a position to see under what conditions multiple periapsis passages yield superior performance and why this is the case.

PERFORMANCE RESULTS

The plots in Figures 11 and 12 show the extremal inclination changes and plane changes of a sequence of maps as the r_a is increased. Thus, the Δv increases as one moves from left to right. For each data point, a scan over all points (every .25 degrees) is used. While this does not result in an exact optimal value, it allows for a more complete coverage of the Ω, ω field. This wide yet very fine resolution sweep is needed as there are many local extrema and disconnected regions in the boundaries and is sufficient for the goals of this paper. In a sense, the method selected results in best initial guesses. Since Hill's Model is itself only used to provide starting conditions for a search in a fully ephemeris model, there is little benefit in finding a perfectly accurate result for a model that is itself an approximation.

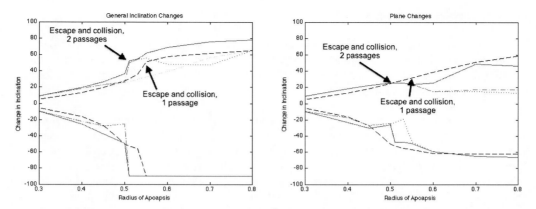

Figure 11: Europa: General Inclination Changes and true Plane Changes as a function of Radius of Apoapsis. Dark dashes (- -): Single periapsis passage. Light dashes (- -): Single Periapsis Passage, no impacting trajectories (general inclination changes only). Solid Line (–): Two periapsis passages, according to pure model. Dash/dot (- .): Two periapsis passages, no impacting trajectories. Dots (. . .): Two periapsis passages, no impacting trajectories nor trajectories at chaotic boundaries.

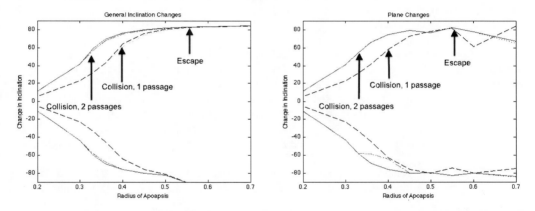

Figure 12: Ceres: General Inclination Changes and true Plane Changes as a function of Radius of Apoapsis. Dark dashes (- -): Single periapsis passage. Light dashes (- -): Single Periapsis Passage, no impacting trajectories (general inclination changes only). Solid Line (–): Two periapsis passages, according to pure model. Dash/dot (- .): Two periapsis passages, no impacting trajectories. Dots (. . .): Two periapsis passages, no impacting trajectories nor trajectories at chaotic boundaries.

The different curves correspond to the different restrictions discussed previously. The cases considered are: the theoretical extrema from Hill's Model alone, when impacting orbits are excluded, when trajectories in the chaotic boundary regions are excluded, and when both of these types are excluded. In Figures 11 and 12, the single periapsis passage case is compared to the two periapsis case. These restrictions are applied to both general inclination changes when the final radius of periapsis.

General Inclination Changes

Not restricting the radius of the final orbit to be exactly that of the initial circular orbit results in a case that is more simple to analyze. Because the values do not also depend on the location of the location of $\Delta r_p = 0$ lines, this case allows the effects of escape, collision, and other features to be seen more directly.

First consider the extrema of one and two periapsis passages without impact or boundary restrictions. Note that the general behavior as r_a is increased is similar. The magnitude of the extrema increase at a near linear rate until a r_a value is reached where one of the structural elements is involved. These can be seen where the values rise sharply and then the concavity changes. For the case of Europa, there are visible jumps when escape through libration point regions becomes possible at $r_a = .55$ for a single revolution and at $r_a = .51$ for two. For Ceres the increases occur when collision becomes possible at $r_a = .40$ for a single revolution and at $r_a = .33$ for two revolutions. In this case without restrictions, multiple passages always have at least one trajectory that produces larger extrema than the single passage case. However, as a percentage increase over the single passage case, multiple revolution have the largest improvement at lower values of r_a up to and immediately after the structural feature is reached. This is because the single revolution case will shortly thereafter have its own jump due to the existence of the same feature.

Figure 13 shows examples of the trajectories with the largest positive inclination changes at these values of r_a. As a trajectory can never truly flatten out, when a large plane change is possible for a single revolution, there is diminishing room for improvement for each succeeding periapsis passage. Also, it is after these events that the chances of escape or impact greatly increase. Thus, for r_a beyond these events, performance improvement is marginal while risks such as escape and impact increase (See Table 2). These principles can be extended to any number of passages for general, unrestricted inclination changes. The trends may be summarized as follows:

1)   For general inclination changes, extra revolutions can lead to sizable performance increases (often over 50% better than the single revolution) under certain conditions.

2)   These favorable conditions occur from relatively low values of r_a up to and including when collision or escape becomes possible for multiple revolutions, but not yet for a single revolution. After this point, performance improvements relative to fewer passage cases decreases as there is little room for improvement as Δi for the single passage case approaches ± 90 degrees.

3)   Because of this limit, each successive revolution added will have a smaller improvement than the revolution before it. Additionally, the range of r_a where the increases are large will itself be increasingly smaller.

Table 2: Percentages of trajectories that result in impact or escape as the number of periapsis passages increases. Case of Europa when $r_a = .60$, corresponding to Figure 5d, 5e, 5f.

	Number of Periapsis Passages		
	One	Two	Three
Impact Percentage	31.09%	46.39%	50.98%
Escape Percentage	11.34%	25.18%	27.30%
Total (Satellite Lost)	42.43%	71.57%	78.28%

18

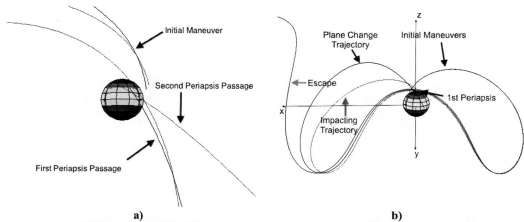

Figure 13: General inclination changing trajectories with positive change to inclination a) Ceres: Radius of apoapsis taken where collision first becomes possible, $r_a = .33$. An example of a two passage trajectory improving upon the optimal one passage trajectory. b) Europa: Radius of apoapsis taken where escape regions form, $r_a = .53$. Trajectories taken from boundary of escape region.

Adding restrictions not in the dynamical model such as not allowing impacting orbits or not allowing trajectories from the chaotic boundaries can complicate the picture above. For Ceres, this has only a small effect on the results. This is due to the fact that its normalized radius is quite small, so very few trajectories considered impact the surface. As a result, even those trajectories that are influenced by the existence of collisions can be non-impacting and so have values almost identical to those that pass within the asteroid. Due to this fact, excluding trajectories from boundary regions will also not have a great effect on the global extrema. Even if that class of trajectory is omitted, the Δi values at the near-impacting trajectories will be close to those of whatever extrema were lost.

For Europa, there are large differences in performance once impacting or boundary region trajectories are not allowed. For r_a values just below where escape is possible, impacting regions contain an increasing share of large inclination change trajectories; so much so that the performance is almost equivalent to the single revolution, non-impacting case. At higher energies, the trajectories in the boundaries of the escape regions become a dominant feature. Excluding just impacting trajectories does not change the global extrema alone, but by excluding both types there is a large drop in performance. For $r_a > .60$ if these boundary regions are not considered feasible due to mission constraints, the single periapsis passage case actually attains greater maximum values. *So, in some cases practical constraints not only limit the promise of the multiple revolution results from the dynamical model, but in fact causes a step backwards.* It is for cases like these that other methods such as allowing an extra impulse may produce better results without raising the radius high enough to have to deal with libration point complexities. Deciding whether or not an orbit impacts is simple enough, but without the understanding of the asymptotic nature of the trajectories and the chaotic structure of the boundaries that contain them, these potentially unfeasible trajectories would be difficult to exclude. Their features both inform the decision whether to omit them, and if so to provide a method for doing just that. While impact conditions may reduce the effectiveness of some of the region suggested by the guidelines for the unrestricted case, the area prescribed will still contain the r_a values with the greatest improvement versus the single periapsis passage case.

Plane Changes

Analyzing plane changes may be seen as a special case of the discussion above, with an extra restriction that $\Delta r_p = 0$. In particular, plane change results most closely resemble those of the non-impacting case. As a result of viewing plane changes as a subcase of non-impacting transfers, it should be clear that while plane change extrema may be smaller in magnitude, they can certainly be no greater. Since the initial circular orbit is near the body being orbited, there is little qualitative difference in most cases between a maximum non-impacting single periapsis passage inclination change and a single passage plane change. So at an r_a value where single passage general inclination change have performance comparable or better than the restricted multiple revolution cases, one can expect this trend to carry over to true plane changes. This prediction must now be borne out by the data.

In both systems, for r_a below the values where escape is possible, there is a very close concordance between the plane change extrema and those of non-impacting general inclination changes. This is in agreement with both the assumptions above and with the general principle that in the absence of escaping trajectories, the extrema should be sought near the boundary impacting trajectories. Since our initial circular orbits are close the the massive bodies, the plane change values are close to the boundary between impacting and non-impacting trajectories. One implication of this is that for Ceres where collision occurs before escape and the body radius is small, the large increase in the magnitude of extrema associated with general inclination changes carries over to the case of plane changes. Thus, the recommended range of r_a values where multiple revolutions are preferable over the single revolution case is the same for plane changes as it is for general inclination changes.

When escape regions open up, the picture becomes more complicated in both systems. For Ceres and Europa, the existence of escape regions changes the topology of the $\Delta r_p = 0$ curves. Compare the black curves in Figure 5 between the two r_a levels for Europa for all three revolutions shown. For Ceres compare Figures 9a and 10 to see changes in the number of connected contours. As the number and shape of these curves become more complex, the true extrema of plane change values may fluctuate more between different r_a values as curves fall over different parts of the maps. Admittedly, the increasing complexity in the curves and variation from point to point at higher energies makes it more likely that the grid of points used has a less accurate approximation of the extrema. Regardless of the causes of these fluctuations, it is a clear trend that adding another revolution does not improve the maximum plane change values allowed. In the case of Europa, it actually produces lower performance. From the general inclination changes and the large drop that occurs when chaotic boundary trajectories are excluded, it appears that general inclination extrema occur in these boundaries. Yet in the case of plane changes, even when these regions are allowed, the maximum values are much smaller than were present for general inclination changes. This is because even though extrema of inclination changes are found in these regions as well as plane change trajectories, the extrema do not lie on the $\Delta r_p = 0$ curves at these levels of r_a. Increasing the number of periapsis passages beyond two only makes the curve topology and hence results even more erratic.

To summarize, how well r_a values of superior performance for multiple revolution plane changes match up with those for general inclination changes depends on the type of dominant structural feature – collision, escape, or neither. Differences between general inclination changes and plane change, as well as fluctuations appear once escape is possible. So if collision trajectories are dominant as in the case of Ceres and appear at lower r_a than escape, the range of values should be similar. In this case the guidelines for both plane changes and general inclination changes are to expect a noticeable increase in performance for multiple plane changes up to and including the value of r_a where collision trajectories come into existence. For Europa, the large jump in magnitude for general inclination changes when the escape regions open up does not appear for plane changes due to a lack of correspondence between trajectories with very large Δi values and those that satisfy $\Delta r_p = 0$. While there may be systems where trajectories exist with both of these conditions, we see that such trajectories cannot be guaranteed for all such escape dominated systems.

CONCLUSION AND FUTURE DIRECTIONS

The notion of third body driven plane changes has been described and extended to allow multiple periapsis passages in the hopes of increasing performance. Rather than focusing too tightly on a particular example, the approach has been based on finding the features that govern the numerical results. The existence of two key structures from the dynamical model – singularity collision trajectories and escaping trajectories associated with libration point orbits and their invariant manifolds – creates neighborhoods where large inclination changes may be found. This results in trimming the search space for more effective optimization. In addition to providing locations for initial guesses for optimal Ω, ω to perform a maneuver, these features also shape a range of r_a where multiple revolutions provide better performance. Understanding of other features such as chaotic boundaries between escape regions have also proven necessary to decide on and eliminate certain trajectories from consideration based on practical mission constraints such as navigation accuracy and time of flight restrictions. Along with impact considerations and the complicated topology of $\Delta r_p = 0$ curves, these restrictions limit the promise of multiple-revolution plane change maneuvers when very large apoapsis raising maneuvers are performed. Generally, multiple revolution inclination and true plane changes create the greatest improvement from low r_a values up to those where the key trajectories like collisions are present for multiple passages but not for the single passage case.

A full classification of plane change maneuvers would need to be expanded in several ways. Due to their importance, polar orbits were the focus of this paper, however other initial inclinations should be considered. This flexibility would cause complications while focusing on structure as the extra independent variable added would make visualization more difficult. Another natural extension of this is to eliminate the restriction that the recircularization maneuvers be purely tangential. This would combine both classical and third-body driven plane change characteristics and allow for better performance for any number of revolutions.

The paper is a first step in mapping regions of phase space based on performance characteristics for applications to automated mission design. The role of structural elements and key trajectories in determining even practical performance results suggests an extension of the use of symbolic dynamics beyond labeling transit properties of a region. The ability to quickly search for areas whose natural dynamics – as represented symbolically – correspond to mission goals and provide an initial guess for a transfer using key trajectories will be investigated as a method to aid in autonomous trajectories redesigns.

ACKNOWLEDGEMENTS

Travel to present this work has been partially funded by the NASA Space Technology and Research Fellowship.

REFERENCES

[1]W.S. Koon, M.W. Lo, J.E. Marsden and S.D. Ross, *Dynamical Systems, the Three-Body Problem and Space Mission Design* (Marsden Books, 2008). ISBN 978-0-615-24095-4.

[2]C.C. Conley, "Low energy transit orbits in the restricted three-body problem," *SIAM J. Appl. Math.*, Vol. 16, 1968, pp. 732–746.

[3]M.W. Lo, B.G. Williams, W.E. Bollman, D.S. Han, Y.S. Hahn, J.L. Bell, E.A. Hirst, R.A. Corwin. P.E. Hong, K.C. Howell, B. Barden and R. Wilson, "Genesis Mission Design", *Journal of the Astronautical Sciences*, vol. 49, No.1, pp. 169-184.

[4]A.F. Haapala, K.C. Howell, "Trajectory Design Using Periapse Poincaré Maps and Invariant Manifolds," 21st AAS/AIAA Space Flight Mechanics Meeting, New Orleans, Louisiana, February 2011.

[5]M. E. Paskowitz and D. J. Scheeres, "Robust capture and transfer trajectories for planetary satellite orbiters," *Journal of Guidance, Control, and Dynamics*, Vol. 29, No.2, 2006, pp. 342–353.

[6]K.E. Davis, R.L. Anderson, G.H. Born, "Preliminary Study of Geosynchronous Orbit Transfers from LEO Using Invariant Manifolds," Preprint for 2011 Born Symposium.

[7]B.F. Villac, D.J. Sheeres, "New Class of Optimal Plane Change Maneuvers," *Journal of Guidance, Control, and Dynamics,* Vol. 26, No.5, 2003, pp. 750-757.

[8]B.F. Villac, D.J. Sheeres, "Third Body Driven vs. One Impulse Plane Change", *Proceedings of the 2003 AAS/AIAA Spaceflight Mechanics meeting,* Paper AAS 03-519.

[9]D.J. Scheeres, M.D. Guman, and B.F. Villac, "Stability Analysis of Planetary Satellite Orbiters: Application to the Europa Orbiter," *Journal of Guidance, Control, and Dynamics*, Vol. 24, No. 4, 2001, pp. 778–780.

[10]Chobotov, V. A. (ed.), Orbital Mechanics, AIAA Education Series, 3rd ed., AIAA, Reston, VA, 2002, pp. 99–103.

[11]G.W. Hill, "Researches in the Lunar Theory," American Journal of Mathematics, Vol. 1, No. 1, 1878, pp. 5–26.

[12]B.F. Villac, and D.J. Scheeres, "Escaping Trajectories in the Hill Three-Body Problem and Applications," Journal of Guidance, Control, and Dynamics, Vol. 26, No. 2, 2002, pp. 224–232.

[13]B.F. Villac, and D.J. Scheeres, "A Simple Algorithm to Compute Hyperbolic Invariant Manifolds near L1 and L2," AAS/AIAA Space Flight Mechanics Conference, AAS 04-243, Maui, Hawaii, February 8-12, 2004.

[14]J. Henrard and J.F. Navarro. "Spiral Structures and Chaotic Scattering in Coorbital Satellites," *Celestial Mechanics and Dynamical Astronomy*, 79:297–314, 2001.

APPLICATION OF WIDE-FIELD INTEGRATION OF OPTIC FLOW TO PROXIMITY OPERATIONS AND LANDING FOR SPACE EXPLORATION MISSIONS

Michael A. Shoemaker[*†] and Shinji Hokamoto[‡]

New advances in vision-based navigation for micro air vehicles (MAVs) have been inspired by the biological systems of flying insects and the use of optic flow. These biologically-inspired optical sensor systems for MAVs are computationally efficient and have low mass and low power consumption, which makes them attractive for small spacecraft. This study explores the applicability of the wide-field integration (WFI) of optic flow to a spacecraft operating in close proximity to an asteroid. In contrast with past WFI work, this study uses an asteroid-relative reference trajectory and known *a priori* environment model such that the optimal sensitivity functions are recalculated onboard the vehicle at each time step. Numerical simulations with computer-generated images of the asteroid surface are used to estimate the vehicle's translational and angular velocities. Although the accuracy of these state estimates are reasonable considering the noise in the optic flow measurements, the onboard recalculation of the sensitivity functions for this time-varying scenario add computational burden which negates the main advantage of the WFI method. Hence, future applications to time-invariant scenarios for small-body missions are also discussed.

INTRODUCTION

Biologically-inspired vision-based navigation and control is a topic that has seen many studies in recent years (see Reference 1 for a review), particularly related to micro air vehicles (MAVs) and the desire to mimic the behavioral heuristics of flying insects (*e.g.* collision avoidance in cluttered environments). Several flying insects (*e.g.* bees, flies) have nervous systems that process the optic flow (*i.e.* retinal motion patterns) across a wide field-of-view (FOV). This study expands on the biologically-inspired methods developed by Humbert *et al.*[2–4] for the wide-field integration (WFI) of optic flow, which have previously been applied to aerial and ground robotic vehicles.

Although there are many differences between MAVs and spacecraft, some space mission concepts or mission phases may benefit from applying WFI-based optic flow processing. First it is necessary to understand past vision-based navigation methods for space exploration missions. Typical systems use high-resolution images, which are also required to meet science mission objectives. Sometimes these high-resolution images are processed on the ground; this was the case for NEAR-Shoemaker, where optical observations of surface landmarks were combined with ground-based radiometric

---

[*]Doctoral Candidate, Dept. of Aeronautics and Astronautics, Kyushu University, West Zone Building 4, 744 Motooka, Nishi-ku, Fukuoka, Japan, 819-0395.

[†]Research Fellow, Japan Society for the Promotion of Science

[‡]Professor, Dept. of Aeronautics and Astronautics, Kyushu University, West Zone Building 4, 744 Motooka, Nishi-ku, Fukuoka, Japan, 819-0395.

measurements in a weighted least-squares orbit determination process.[5] Similar landmark identification and processing functions were performed on the ground for Hayabusa's orbit determination near asteroid Itokawa.[6] In the case of small-body missions, these high-quality measurements are useful for refining estimates of the target-body shape, spin-rate, spin-axis, etc. Kalman-filtering approaches have also been used with optical measurements: angles-only measurements obtained from correlating 2-D images with *a priori* 3-D landmark databases yield position-type information; and features correlated between pairs of images yield velocity-type information. Both methods have been studied for small-body missions[7,8] and planetary entry, descent, and landing missions.[9] For the terminal descent guidance of the Hayabusa asteroid landing, a Fast-Fourier-Transform algorithm was studied as a means of providing line-of-site rate information between image sequences.[10]

In contrast with the above methods, we wish to explore vision-based methods that use low-resolution images (*e.g.* from a small-sized camera) and optic flow measurements. This approach is more in line with a small spacecraft paradigm: rather than a small number of high-quality vision-based measurements, we seek to use a large number of low-quality measurements. Example applications where small systems may be beneficial for spacecraft include swarms of spacecraft for solar system exploration[11] or small landers released from larger spacecraft (*e.g.* Rosetta's Philae comet lander or Hayabusa's Minerva asteroid lander[12]). Of course, if high-resolution imagery is required to meet science objectives, then the methods explored in this paper may be less attractive.

Others have investigated the use of optic flow for space missions* in the past. Reference 13 uses an embedded optic flow correlator with an *a priori* digital elevation map for simulated landing on air-less planetary bodies. Reference 14 uses a nadir facing optic flow sensor in a simulated lunar landing scenario to estimate translational velocity. One potential advantage of the WFI approach in our study is that the optic flow is measured over a wide FOV, rather than a narrow patch (*e.g.* directly under the vehicle).

This paper also explores a few modifications to the standard WFI methods researched previously. The previous applications of WFI of optic flow have focused on specific scenarios where the assumed environment and vehicle states result in time-invariant control gains. These scenarios allow much of the computation to be done once off-line and then stored onboard, hence the low-computational requirements are suitable for MAVs. For example, References 3 and 15 simulate rotorcraft flight control for a desired reference state of level flight at constant speed. Reference 2 demonstrates the method on a robotic wheeled vehicle moving along the center of a tunnel at constant speed. In the examples given above, it is assumed that the vehicle does not have knowledge of the distribution of surfaces (*i.e.* obstacles) in the environment, but the desired control response is generated if the vehicle deviates from the time-invariant reference state.

We explore a different application in the present paper. For a spacecraft descending towards an irregularly shaped small-body, the combination of reference state and surface geometry result in time-varying sensitivity functions which must be recalculated onboard. We assume that the vehicle has an *a priori* model of the surface shape, and wishes to navigate relative the specified reference state. In these simulations, the state estimated using the WFI of optic flow is limited to the translational and angular velocities. Also, we show a different approach to deriving the linearized least-square estimation of the WFI measurements, which approximates the integral as a Riemann sum. This work builds on our previous two-dimensional simulations of asteroid proximity operations.[16]

---

*Many examples can be found in the literature for aircraft or other robotic systems as well. Reference 3 gives several of these references.

VEHICLE CONFIGURATION

Let there be a spacecraft* having body-fixed reference frame $\mathcal{F}_B$ operating in proximity to a target body (*e.g.* asteroid) having a rigidly attached reference frame $\mathcal{F}_T$. Because this study only treats motion relative to $\mathcal{F}_T$, we will disregard the inertial frame. The vehicle's motion is described relative to $\mathcal{F}_T$, and unless otherwise noted, vector quantities without subscripts are expressed in $\mathcal{F}_T$. Let the total sensor area be described by a spherical imaging surface S^2 centered on the origin of $\mathcal{F}_B$, with the azimuth γ and elevation β angles describing a point on this sphere. The angle γ is measured positive from the x_B axis and the angle β is measured positive from the z_B axis. Thus, the line-of-site (LOS) vector at sensor coordinates (γ, β) expressed in $\mathcal{F}_B$ is

$$[\hat{\mathbf{d}}]_B = \begin{bmatrix} \sin\beta\cos\gamma & \sin\beta\sin\gamma & \cos\beta \end{bmatrix}^T. \tag{1}$$

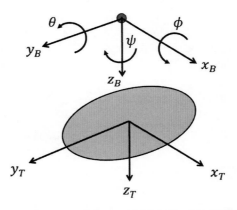

Figure 1. Vehicle-fixed and target-fixed reference frames.

OPTIC FLOW MODEL

The model relating the vehicle dynamics and ideal optic flow is the same as that used in Reference 3, but here the vehicle motion is referenced to $\mathcal{F}_T$ rather than a general inertial frame. The marker $\mathbf{Q} = \mathbf{d}/|\mathbf{d}| = \hat{\mathbf{d}}$ describes the line-of-sight to some fiducial point in the environment (*i.e.* in $\mathcal{F}_T$) relative to the observer fixed on $\mathcal{F}_B$. The motion parallax $\dot{\mathbf{Q}}$ is the time derivative of $\mathbf{Q}$ in the spherical imaging surface S^2, caused by the translational and angular velocity of $\mathcal{F}_B$ with respect to $\mathcal{F}_T$. The spatially continuous optic flow† can be written with

$$\dot{\mathbf{Q}} = -\boldsymbol{\omega} \times \mathbf{Q} - \lambda \left[\mathbf{v} - \langle \mathbf{v}, \mathbf{Q} \rangle \mathbf{Q} \right], \tag{2}$$

where $\langle \cdot, \cdot \rangle$ denotes the inner product, and the nearness function $\lambda(\gamma, \beta, \mathbf{q}) = 1/|\mathbf{d}|$ is the inverse of the distance to points in the environment, which depends on the sensor coordinates and vehicle pose $\mathbf{q} = (x, y, z, \phi, \theta, \psi)$. Note that although the WFI literature typically uses μ to denote the nearness function, we use λ to avoid confusion with the gravitational parameter used in astrodynamics. Let $\boldsymbol{\omega} = (p, q, r)$ be the angular velocity and $\mathbf{v} = (u, v, w)$ be the translational velocity, both expressed

---

*See the notation section at the end of this document for a list of mathematical symbols.

†The (ideal) optic flow can be treated synonymously with the motion parallax.

in the vehicle's body frame. Then the γ and β components of the optic flow $\dot{\mathbf{Q}} = \dot{Q}_\gamma \hat{\mathbf{e}}_\gamma + \dot{Q}_\beta \hat{\mathbf{e}}_\beta$ can be written as

$$\dot{Q}_\gamma = p \cos\beta \cos\gamma + q \cos\beta \sin\gamma - r \sin\beta + \lambda(u \sin\gamma - v \cos\gamma), \tag{3}$$

$$\dot{Q}_\beta = p \sin\gamma - q \cos\gamma + \lambda(-u \cos\beta \cos\gamma - v \cos\beta \sin\gamma + w \sin\beta). \tag{4}$$

WIDE-FIELD OPTIC FLOW INTEGRATION

Summarizing the WFI method from Reference 3, the measurement outputs $\mathbf{y}$ are the inner product between $\dot{\mathbf{Q}}$ and specified sensitivity functions $\mathbf{F} = F^\gamma \hat{\mathbf{e}}_\gamma + F^\beta \hat{\mathbf{e}}_\beta$:

$$\mathbf{y} = \langle \dot{\mathbf{Q}}, \mathbf{F} \rangle = \int_{S^2} \dot{\mathbf{Q}} \cdot \mathbf{F} d\Omega, \tag{5}$$

where Ω is the solid angle on the imaging surface sphere. The sensitivity functions $\mathbf{F}$ serve as analogs to the directionally sensitive tangential cells in a fly's lobula plate.[4] Writing the WFI measurement from sensitivity function $\mathbf{F}_j$, $j \in \{1, \ldots, M\}$ in component form:

$$y_j = \langle \dot{\mathbf{Q}}, \mathbf{F}_j \rangle = \int_{S^2} \dot{\mathbf{Q}} \cdot \mathbf{F}_j d\Omega = \int_{S^2} \left(\dot{Q}^\gamma F_j^\gamma + \dot{Q}^\beta F_j^\beta \right) d\Omega. \tag{6}$$

The real spherical harmonics with degree l and order m are used as the component weighting functions:

$$Y_{l,m} = N_l^m \Phi_l^m \begin{cases} \cos(m\gamma) & m \geq 0 \\ \sin(m\gamma) & m < 0 \end{cases} \tag{7}$$

where Φ_l^m is the associated Legendre function in terms of $\cos\beta$ and N_l^m is a normalization coefficient.

If we write Eq. 6 as a Riemann sum:

$$y_j = \Delta\Omega \sum_{k=1}^{K} \left(\dot{Q}^\gamma(k) F_j^\gamma(k) + \dot{Q}^\beta(k) F_j^\beta(k) \right), \tag{8}$$

then this is equivalent to

$$y_j = \Delta\Omega \left(\begin{bmatrix} F_j^\gamma(1) & \cdots & F_j^\gamma(K) \end{bmatrix} \begin{bmatrix} \dot{Q}^\gamma(1) \\ \vdots \\ \dot{Q}^\gamma(K) \end{bmatrix} + \begin{bmatrix} F_j^\beta(1) & \cdots & F_j^\beta(K) \end{bmatrix} \begin{bmatrix} \dot{Q}^\beta(1) \\ \vdots \\ \dot{Q}^\beta(K) \end{bmatrix} \right). \tag{9}$$

Including this for all M in the WFI measurement vector yields

$$\mathbf{y} = \Delta\Omega \left(\begin{bmatrix} F_1^\gamma(1) & \cdots & F_1^\gamma(K) \\ \vdots & \ddots & \vdots \\ F_M^\gamma(1) & \cdots & F_M^\gamma(K) \end{bmatrix} \begin{bmatrix} \dot{Q}^\gamma(1) \\ \vdots \\ \dot{Q}^\gamma(K) \end{bmatrix} + \begin{bmatrix} F_1^\beta(1) & \cdots & F_1^\beta(K) \\ \vdots & \ddots & \vdots \\ F_M^\beta(1) & \cdots & F_M^\beta(K) \end{bmatrix} \begin{bmatrix} \dot{Q}^\beta(1) \\ \vdots \\ \dot{Q}^\beta(K) \end{bmatrix} \right), \tag{10}$$

and by defining the matrices

$$[F^\gamma] \equiv \begin{bmatrix} F_1^\gamma(1) & \dots & F_1^\gamma(K) \\ \vdots & \ddots & \vdots \\ F_M^\gamma(1) & \dots & F_M^\gamma(K) \end{bmatrix}, \quad [F^\beta] \equiv \begin{bmatrix} F_1^\beta(1) & \dots & F_1^\beta(K) \\ \vdots & \ddots & \vdots \\ F_M^\beta(1) & \dots & F_M^\beta(K) \end{bmatrix} \quad (11)$$

$$\left[\dot{Q}^\gamma\right] \equiv \left[\ \dot{Q}^\gamma(1) \ \dots \ \dot{Q}^\gamma(K) \ \right]^T, \quad \left[\dot{Q}^\beta\right] \equiv \left[\ \dot{Q}^\beta(1) \ \dots \ \dot{Q}^\beta(K) \ \right]^T \quad (12)$$

then Eq. 10 becomes

$$\mathbf{y} = \Delta\Omega\Big([F^\gamma]\left[\dot{Q}^\gamma\right] + \left[F^\beta\right]\left[\dot{Q}^\beta\right] \Big). \quad (13)$$

Equation 13 can be further compacted with

$$\mathbf{y} = \Delta\Omega\ \big[\ [F^\gamma]\ \ [F^\beta]\ \big] \begin{bmatrix} \left[\dot{Q}^\gamma\right] \\ \left[\dot{Q}^\beta\right] \end{bmatrix} = \Delta\Omega\boldsymbol{\Gamma}\boldsymbol{\Pi}, \quad (14)$$

where $\boldsymbol{\Gamma} \equiv \big[\ [F^\gamma]\ \ [F^\beta]\ \big]$ is a $M \times 2K$ matrix, and $\boldsymbol{\Pi} \equiv \left[\ \left[\dot{Q}^\gamma\right]^T\ \ \left[\dot{Q}^\beta\right]^T\ \right]^T$ is a $2K \times 1$ matrix. Thus, $\boldsymbol{\Gamma}$ represents the sensitivity functions, and $\boldsymbol{\Pi}$ represents the optic flow component equations, both of which are evaluated at a each sensor point (γ_k, β_k).

STATE ESTIMATION

Let $B = 2K$ be the number of independent measurements over all sensor points K, such that $b \in \{1 \dots B\}$. Because $\partial\Gamma_{jb}/\partial x_n = 0$, where x_n is the n-th element of state vector $\mathbf{x}$, the measurement Jacobian is then

$$\frac{\partial\mathbf{y}}{\partial\mathbf{x}} = \Delta\Omega\boldsymbol{\Gamma}\boldsymbol{\Xi}, \quad (15)$$

where we introduce the term

$$\boldsymbol{\Xi} \equiv \left.\frac{\partial\boldsymbol{\Pi}}{\partial\mathbf{x}}\right|_{\mathbf{x}_0}. \quad (16)$$

For the linear least-squares estimator of the form $\mathbf{y} = \mathbf{Cx}$, the estimate is obtained with $\hat{\mathbf{x}} = \mathbf{C}^\dagger(\mathbf{y} - \mathbf{y}_0) + \mathbf{x}_0$, where $\mathbf{C}^\dagger \equiv (\mathbf{C}^T\mathbf{WC})^{-1}\mathbf{C}^T\mathbf{W}$. For the measurement equation given in Eq. 14, the $\mathbf{C}^\dagger$ term is written as

$$\mathbf{C}^\dagger = (\boldsymbol{\Xi}^T\boldsymbol{\Gamma}^T\Delta\Omega^2\mathbf{W}\boldsymbol{\Gamma}\boldsymbol{\Xi})^{-1}\boldsymbol{\Xi}^T\boldsymbol{\Gamma}^T\Delta\Omega\mathbf{W}. \quad (17)$$

The minimum-variance weight matrix $\mathbf{W}$ can be found by writing an appropriate expression for the WFI measurement noise covariance matrix. Let the optic flow be affected by the $B \times 1$ zero-mean additive noise vector $\boldsymbol{\eta}$ having variance σ_η^2. We assume this noise is uncorrelated in γ and β directions and is independent of sensor position k:

$$\mathbf{y} = \Delta\Omega\boldsymbol{\Gamma}(\boldsymbol{\Pi} + \boldsymbol{\eta}) = \Delta\Omega\boldsymbol{\Gamma}\boldsymbol{\Pi} + \boldsymbol{\epsilon}, \quad (18)$$

where the definition $\boldsymbol{\epsilon} \equiv \Delta\Omega\boldsymbol{\Gamma}\boldsymbol{\eta}$ is introduced. Then the measurement noise covariance matrix is defined as $\mathbf{R} = E(\boldsymbol{\epsilon}\boldsymbol{\epsilon}^T)$, which is formed with

$$\mathbf{R} = E(\Delta\Omega^2\boldsymbol{\Gamma}\boldsymbol{\eta}\boldsymbol{\eta}^T\boldsymbol{\Gamma}^T) = \Delta\Omega^2\sigma_\eta^2\boldsymbol{\Gamma}\boldsymbol{\Gamma}^T. \quad (19)$$

Because the spherical harmonics making up $\mathbf{\Gamma}$ comprise an orthonormal basis, it can be shown that $\Delta\Omega\mathbf{\Gamma}\mathbf{\Gamma}^T \approx \mathbf{I}_{M\times M}$. Thus, the minimum-variance weight matrix is found with

$$\mathbf{W} = \mathbf{R}^{-1} = \frac{1}{\Delta\Omega\sigma_\eta^2}\mathbf{I}_{M\times M}. \tag{20}$$

Substituting Eq. 20 into Eq. 17 gives

$$\mathbf{C}^\dagger = \{\mathbf{\Xi}^T\mathbf{\Gamma}^T(\Delta\Omega/\sigma_\eta^2)\mathbf{\Gamma}\mathbf{\Xi}\}^{-1}\mathbf{\Xi}^T\mathbf{\Gamma}^T(1/\sigma_\eta^2). \tag{21}$$

Finally the state estimate can be found with

$$\hat{\mathbf{x}} = \{\mathbf{\Xi}^T\mathbf{\Gamma}^T(\Delta\Omega/\sigma_\eta^2)\mathbf{\Gamma}\mathbf{\Xi}\}^{-1}\mathbf{\Xi}^T\mathbf{\Gamma}^T(\Delta\Omega/\sigma_\eta^2)\mathbf{\Gamma}\Delta\mathbf{\Pi} + \mathbf{x}_0, \tag{22}$$

where $\Delta\mathbf{\Pi} \equiv \mathbf{\Pi} - \mathbf{\Pi}(\mathbf{x}_0)$. By introducing the definition $\mathbf{W}' \equiv (\Delta\Omega/\sigma_\eta^2)\mathbf{\Gamma}^T\mathbf{\Gamma}$, Eq. 22 can be rewritten as

$$\hat{\mathbf{x}} = \{\mathbf{\Xi}^T\mathbf{W}'\mathbf{\Xi}\}^{-1}\mathbf{\Xi}^T\mathbf{W}'\Delta\mathbf{\Pi} + \mathbf{x}_0. \tag{23}$$

ENVIRONMENT MODEL

The vehicle's model of the environment is parameterized in the nearness function $\lambda(\gamma, \beta, \mathbf{q})$. Because the estimated state $\mathbf{x}$ in this paper does not include the pose terms $\mathbf{q} = (x, y, z, \phi, \theta, \psi)$, we do not need to define a continuous nearness function $\lambda(\gamma, \beta, \mathbf{q})$ for formulating the partial derivatives in the measurement Jacobian $\mathbf{\Xi}$. Instead, we just need to calculate a numeric value of λ for a given sensor coordinate (γ, β) and reference pose $\mathbf{q}_0$, which is used in the evaluation of $\mathbf{\Xi}$ and $\mathbf{\Pi}_0$. For the above reasons, and to allow applicability to an irregularly shaped target body, we use a faceted shape model.

There are two steps to this process of calculating λ: first, we use a ray-tracing algorithm to determine which facet is being intersected by the LOS vector $\hat{\mathbf{d}}$ at coordinate (γ_k, β_k); then we calculate λ using

$$\lambda = \frac{\langle\hat{\mathbf{n}}, \hat{\mathbf{d}}\rangle}{\kappa - \langle\hat{\mathbf{n}}, \mathbf{r}\rangle}, \tag{24}$$

where $\hat{\mathbf{n}}$ is the unit normal of the facet, and κ is the perpendicular distance from the $\mathcal{F}_T$ origin to the facet plane (where positive κ is measured in the direction of $\hat{\mathbf{n}}$). It is most convenient to leave the facet normal vector $\hat{\mathbf{n}}$ and spacecraft position $\mathbf{r}$ expressed in $\mathcal{F}_T$, and thus rotate only the sensor line-of-sight vector from $\mathcal{F}_B$ to $\mathcal{F}_T$: $\hat{\mathbf{d}} = \mathcal{R}^{TB}[\hat{\mathbf{d}}]_B$. Of course, the computational cost of this ray-tracing step increases as the number of facets in the model increases.

SIMULATION OVERVIEW

The simulations considered will estimate the vehicle's translational and rotational velocities. We assume that for an operational system other sensors would provide measurements useful for position and attitude estimation, like laser range finders, horizon sensors, etc. Thus, let the full state be denoted by $\mathbf{x}_{\text{full}} = (\phi, \theta, \psi, x, y, z, p, q, r, u, v, w)$, and the state estimated using the WFI method will be denoted by $\mathbf{x} = (p, q, r, u, v, w)$.

An overview of the simulation process is shown in Figure 2. First we define an initial reference state $\mathbf{x}_{\text{full},0}(t_0)$, and for a given simulation run generate a truth state $\mathbf{x}_{\text{full}}(t_0)$ which is a small offset from the reference state. Next, we propagate these states from t_{i-1} to t_i, and the simulated asteroid graphics are drawn using the true state. The optic flow is measured between frames t_{i-1} and t_i and populated in the vector $\mathbf{\Pi}$. Then the optic flow processing step: for each sensor point where the measured optic flow is nonzero, do the ray-tracing step and calculate $\lambda(\gamma_k, \beta_k, \mathbf{x}_{\text{full},0})$. Using $\lambda(\gamma_k, \beta_k, \mathbf{x}_{\text{full},0})$, calculate the reference optic flow $\mathbf{\Pi}(\mathbf{x}_0)$. Also using $\lambda(\gamma_k, \beta_k, \mathbf{x}_{\text{full},0})$, calculate $\mathbf{\Xi}(\mathbf{x}_0)$. Note that the estimated state $\hat{\mathbf{x}}$ is saved at each time step, but we do not use this to update the reference state $\mathbf{x}_0$ for the next iteration.

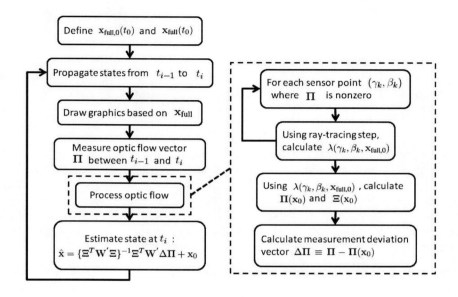

Figure 2. Flow chart of simulation process.

SIMULATION SETUP

The spacecraft is assumed to have six cameras, with one on each of side of the bus (Figure 3). Each camera has a 90 deg FOV, such that the entire imaging sphere is covered. This is a general setup, because for the simulations considered only cameras 1 through 5 are actually used.

The Gaskell[17] implicitly connected quadrilateral model of asteroid 25143 Itokawa is used for both the graphics simulation and the vehicle's simulated onboard knowledge of the environment. A model with 12,288 triangular facets is used to render the graphics (Figure 4). The vehicle's knowledge of the environment is implemented with a 192-facet model (Figure 5); the lower number of facets means there will be some error in the calculated λ, but the ray-tracing loop will have less computational cost. The gray-scale intensity on each facet in the graphics model is varied randomly to mimic the texture variation (*e.g.* craters, regolith types) typically seen on asteroids or other small bodies. A facet is drawn completely black if it is facing away from the specified sun direction (assumed constant in $\mathcal{F}_T$) to mimic shadowing.

Figure 6 shows the simulated camera images for two different heights above the surface, which illustrates how the wide-FOV sensors observe more of the environment as the vehicle gets closer

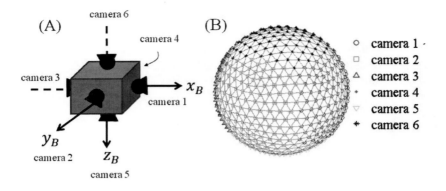

Figure 3. **(A) Illustration of spacecraft with six cameras (B) Icosahedral sensor grid with camera assignments.**

to the target. In this figure, the simulated images from cameras 1 through 5 are shown as if the sides of the cube have been folded flat. The scene is rendered by projecting each visible facet onto a given camera's focal plane using a perspective (pin-hole) projection. Each camera image is first drawn with a resolution of 500×500 pixels per camera, de-sampled to 100×100 pixels, and then blurred with a Gaussian point-spread-function. The resulting images are meant to simulate the performance of a low-resolution camera in accordance with the small-spacecraft paradigm discussed in the introduction.

The optic flow is measured (estimated) in each sequential pair of camera images using a hierarchal Lucas-Kanade algorithm, with 2 levels and 4 iterations. The resulting optic flow is further refined by rejecting any measurements that are physically unrealistic (*i.e.* having magnitude above a preset level), and then applying a median filter with 20×20 pixel window size. The optic flow is then

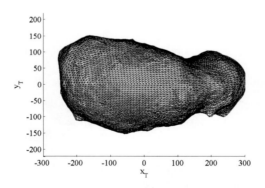

Figure 4. **Surface model used for rendering graphics having 12,288 facets.**

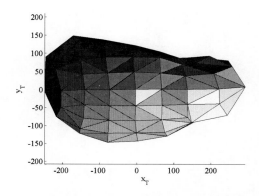

Figure 5. Vehicle's knowledge of surface having 192 facets.

transformed from the image plane (*i.e.* pixels/s) to the spherical imaging surface (*i.e.* rad/s) using a geometric projection. The final optic flow at each (γ_k, β_k) is then assigned as the measured value at the corresponding pixel in the image plane. The sensitivity functions used for the real spherical harmonics include up to $l = 10$ and $m = 10$, resulting in a total of $M = 242$ sensitivity functions.

The initial conditions at $t = 0$ are defined as

$$(\phi, \theta, \psi, x, y, z, p, q, r, u, v, w) = (0, 0, 0, 0, 0, -190 \text{ m}, 0, 0, 2 \text{ deg/s}, 0, 0, 1 \text{ m/s}), \qquad (25)$$

thus, the spacecraft has a small yaw rate and is descending towards the asteroid surface vertically at 1 m/s. The dynamics model in this simulation (*i.e.* used in the propagation step in Figure 2) is simplified by neglecting external accelerations or torques acting on the vehicle; the intent is to evaluate the performance of the WFI estimator without dependence on a specific dynamic environment. Monte Carlo (MC) simulations are conducted by randomly offsetting the initial truth state (used to generate the computer graphics). The 1-σ standard deviations of these offsets are

$$\sigma_\phi = \sigma_\theta = \sigma_\psi = 0.5 \text{ deg}, \qquad (26)$$

$$\sigma_x = \sigma_y = \sigma_z = 0.1 \text{ m}, \qquad (27)$$

$$\sigma_p = \sigma_q = \sigma_r = 1.0 \text{ deg/s}, \qquad (28)$$

$$\sigma_u = \sigma_v = \sigma_w = 0.1 \text{ m/s}. \qquad (29)$$

The standard deviation of the optic flow measurement noise, σ_η, was set to 3×10^{-3} rad/s during the numerical simulations. This value was determined by running the simulations with $\mathbf{x}_{\text{full},0} = \mathbf{x}_{\text{full}}$ and observing the noise in the measurement residuals. Figure 7 shows an example of the reference optic flow $\mathbf{\Pi}_0$ and measured optic flow $\mathbf{\Pi}$ for this sample case of $\mathbf{x}_{\text{full},0} = \mathbf{x}_{\text{full}}$; we can see in this figure that most of the optic flow is measurable along the horizon or in other regions of high contrast (*e.g.* near eclipse boundaries). Figures 8 and 9 show the RMS error between $\hat{\mathbf{x}}$ and the true $\mathbf{x}$ at each time step from 10 MC runs, with each simulation lasting for 15 seconds. The cameras are simulated at 1 frame/s. Note that the texture variation in the graphics model is also randomly generated in each MC run.

31

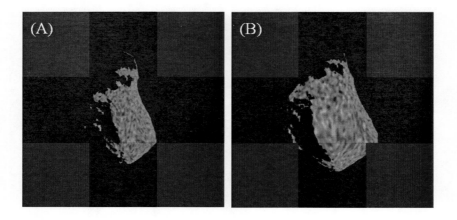

Figure 6. Simulated images from cameras 1-5 at (A) $(x, y, z) = (0\,\mathbf{m}, 0\,\mathbf{m}, -170\,\mathbf{m})$ **and (B)** $(x, y, z) = (0\,\mathbf{m}, 0\,\mathbf{m}, -130\,\mathbf{m})$.

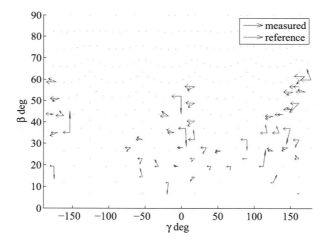

Figure 7. Example of reference and measured optic flow.

DISCUSSION

These preliminary simulations demonstrate that the translational and angular velocities can be estimated during the descent towards the asteroid surface, with a level of estimation error as shown in Figures 8 and 9. With regard to the practical utility of these state estimates, one would hope that

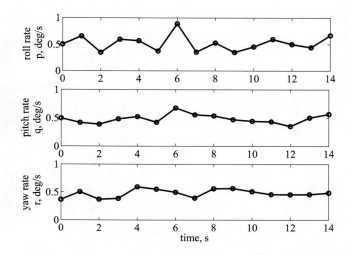

Figure 8. RMS error in angular velocity estimation, 10 MC runs.

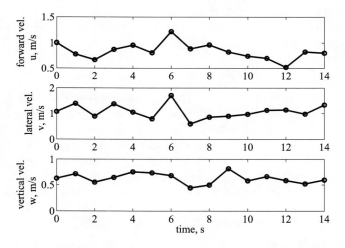

Figure 9. RMS error in translational velocity estimation, 10 MC runs.

the RMS errors in Figures 8 and 9 would be less than the random offsets between the truth and reference states (Eqs. 28 and 29), *i.e.* otherwise it is better to simply use the reference state than the estimated state. We can see in Figure 8 that the RMS error in the angular velocity is less than the 1.0 deg/s 1-σ offsets in Eq. 28. However, the translational velocity RMS errors in Figure 9 are not less than the 0.1 m/s 1-σ offsets in Eq. 29.

But, as in any estimator, the accuracy of the state estimates will depend on the accuracy of the measurements: it can be shown that these translational velocity estimation errors are expected, considering the measurement noise in the optic flow in these particular simulations. The RMS errors in the measured $\dot{\mathbf{Q}}$ (*i.e.* recall Figure 7) are approximately 1.0 deg/s. For this simulation scenario, we can approximate the optic flow due to translational velocity as

$$\frac{|\mathbf{v}|}{|\mathbf{d}|} = \frac{1 \text{ m/s}}{50 \text{ m}} = 1.15 \text{ deg/s}, \tag{30}$$

where $|\mathbf{d}| = 50$ m represents a nominal range to the surface points around the vehicle. Likewise, the optic flow due to translational velocity having a small offset of 0.1 m/s is

$$\frac{|\mathbf{v}| + \delta|\mathbf{v}|}{|\mathbf{d}|} = \frac{1.1 \text{ m/s}}{50 \text{ m}} = 1.26 \text{ deg/s}. \tag{31}$$

In order to detect a 0.1 m/s difference in velocity, the optic flow measurements would need to be accurate to $1.26 - 1.15 \approx 0.1$ deg/s, which is an order of magnitude below the accuracy of the current optic flow measurements. Thus, the estimation errors in Figures 8 and 9 are expected for this level of measurement noise; future simulations may be improved by decreasing this noise.

Regarding the overall performance of this estimation system: the primary advantage of the WFI of optic flow is the reduced computational cost for the specific time-invariant cases discussed in the introduction. In the time-varying scenarios we examined in this paper, the additional ray-tracing step and evaluation of $\mathbf{\Pi}_0$ at each time step add considerable computational cost. Thus, these WFI methods may be best applied by examining specific landing or proximity operations scenarios where the asteroid environment can be approximated by the time-invariant formulation (*e.g.* an irregularly shaped asteroid which can be approximated by a sphere).

CONCLUSION

The wide-field integration of optic flow is applied to a simulated scenario of a spacecraft descending towards the surface of an asteroid. The wide-field integration method is shown using a Riemann sum derivation rather than an exact formulation. The vehicle is assumed to have an *a priori* surface model of the irregularly-shaped asteroid having 192 facets, and uses this to calculate the reference nearness function onboard using a ray-tracing step. Thus, the optimal sensitivity functions must be calculated onboard the vehicle at each time step. Only the translational and angular velocities of the vehicle relative to the asteroid-fixed frame are estimated with the optic flow information. Monte Carlo simulations are performed using computer-generated images of the asteroid using a 12,288-facet model with variable texture and lighting. The RMS errors in the optic flow measurements from these image sequences are approximately 1.0 deg/s. In this surface descent scenario, the vehicle has a nominal yaw rate of 2.0 deg/s and vertical velocity of 1.0 m/s. The RMS estimation errors for each angular velocity component are approximately 0.5 deg/s. The RMS estimation errors in the forward and lateral velocity components are each 1.0 m/s, and the vertical component is approximately 0.8 m/s. It is shown that the translational velocity estimation errors may be improved by decreasing the optic flow measurement noise. The time-varying formulation discussed in this paper adds considerable computational cost, which negates the main advantage of the wide-field integration methods; future work will examine time-invariant scenarios appropriate for asteroid proximity operations and landing.

NOTATION

b	measurement index	κ	facet perpendicular distance from origin, m
B	number of measurements	λ	nearness, 1/m
$\mathbf{C}$	observation matrix	Φ	associated Legendre function
$\mathbf{C}^\dagger$	observation inversion matrix	ϕ	roll angle, rad
$\mathbf{d}$	position vector to fiducial point, m	ψ	yaw angle, rad
$E(\cdot)$	expectation operator	Ξ	optic flow Jacobian
$\mathbf{F}$	sensitivity function	$\mathbf{\Pi}$	optic flow matrix
$\mathcal{F}$	reference frame	Ω	solid angle, sr
i	discrete time index	$\boldsymbol{\omega}$	angular velocity vector, rad/s
j	sensitivity function index		
K	number of discrete sensor points		*Superscripts and Subscripts*
k	index of sensor point	B	body (vehicle) frame
l	spherical harmonic degree	full	full state
M	number of sensitivity functions	T	target frame
m	spherical harmonic order	0	reference
N	normalization coefficient	$\hat{}$	estimated value
$\mathbf{n}$	facet normal vector		
p	roll rate, rad/s		
$\mathbf{Q}$	marker vector to fiducial point		
$\dot{\mathbf{Q}}$	optic flow		
$\mathbf{q}$	vehicle pose vector		
q	pitch rate, rad/s		
$\mathbf{R}$	measurement noise covariance		
$\mathcal{R}^{TB}$	rotation matrix from $\mathcal{F}_B$ to $\mathcal{F}_T$		
r	yaw rate, rad/s		
u	forward velocity, m/s		
$\mathbf{v}$	translational velocity vector, m/s		
v	lateral velocity, m/s		
$\mathbf{W}$	minimum-variance weight matrix		
w	vertical velocity, m/s		
$\mathbf{x}$	state vector		
x_n	element of state vector		
$\mathbf{y}$	measurement vector		
y_j	element of measurement vector		
β	sensor elevation angle, rad		
$\mathbf{\Gamma}$	sensitivity function matrix		
γ	sensor azimuth angle, rad		
$\boldsymbol{\epsilon}$	measurement noise vector		
$\boldsymbol{\eta}$	optic flow noise vector		
θ	pitch angle, rad		

REFERENCES

[1] M. O. Franz and H. A. Mallot, "Biomimetic Robot Navigation," *Robotics and Autonomous Systems*, Vol. 30, 2000, pp. 133–153.

[2] J. S. Humbert and A. M. Hyslop, "Bioinspired Visuomotor Convergence," *IEEE Transactions on Robotics*, Vol. 26, Feb 2010, pp. 121–130.

[3] A. M. Hyslop and J. S. Humbert, "Autonomous Navigation in Three-Dimensional Urban Environments Using Wide-Field Integration of Optic Flow," *Journal of Guidance, Control, and Dynamics*, Vol. 33, No. 1, 2010, pp. 147–159.

[4] A. Hyslop, H. G. Krapp, and J. S. Humbert, "Control theoretic interpretation of directional motion preferencs in optic flow processing interneurons," *Biological Cybernetics*, Vol. 103, 2010, pp. 353–364.

[5] D. K. Yeomans *et al.*, "Radio Science Results During the NEAR-Shoemaker Spacecraft Rendezvous with Eros," *Science*, Vol. 289, 2000, pp. 2085–2088. doi:10.1126/science.289.5487.2085.

[6] T. Yoshimitsu, J. Kawaguchi, T. Hashimoto, T. Kubota, M. Uo, H. Morita, and K. Shirakawa, "Hayabsua-final autonomous descent and landing based on target marker tracking," *Acta Astronautica*, Vol. 65, 2009, pp. 657–665. doi:10.1016/j.actaastro.2009.01.074.

[7] T. Misu, T. Hashimoto, and K. Ninomiya, "Optical Guidance for Autonomous Landing of Spacecraft," *IEEE Transactions on Aerosapce and Electronic Systems*, Vol. 35, No. 2, 1999, pp. 459–473. doi:10.1109/7.766929.

[8] D. S. Bayard and P. B. Brugarolas, "On-Board Vision-Based Spacecraft Estimation Algorithm for Small Body Exploration," *IEEE Transactions on Aerospace and Electronic Systems*, Vol. 44, No. 1, 2008, pp. 243–260.

[9] A. I. Mourikis, N. Trawny, S. I. Roumeliotis, A. E. Johnson, A. Ansar, and L. Matthies, "Vision-Aided Inertial Navigation for Spacecraft Entry, Descent, and Landing," *IEEE Transactions on Robotics*, Vol. 25, No. 2, 2009, pp. 264–280.

[10] J. Kawaguchi, T. Hashimoto, T. Kubota, and S. Sawai, "Autonomous Optical Guidance and Navigation Strategy Around a Small Body," *Journal of Guidance, Control, and Dynamics*, Vol. 20, No. 5, 1997, pp. 1010–1017. doi:10.2514/2.4148.

[11] S. A. Curtis *et al.*, "Use of Swarm Intelligence in Spacecraft Constellations for the Resource Exploration of the Astroid Belt," *Proceedings of the Third International Workshop on Satellite Constellations and Formation Flying, Pisa, Italy*, 2003.

[12] S. Ulamec and J. Biele, "Surface elements and landing strategies for small bodies missions – Philae and beyond," *Advances in Space Research*, Vol. 44, 2009, pp. 847–858.

[13] K. Janschek, V. Tchernykh, and M. Beck, "Performance Analysis for Visual Planetary Landing Navigation Using Optical Flow and DEM Matching," *AIAA Guidance, Navigation, and Control Conference and Exhibit, 21 - 24 August 2006, Keystone, Colorado*. AIAA 2006-6706.

[14] F. Valette, F. Ruffier, S. Viollet, and T. Seidl, "Biomimetic optic flow sensing applied to a lunar landing scenario," *IEEE International Conference on Robotics and Automation, May 2010, Anchorage, Alaska*, 2010, pp. 2253–2260.

[15] J. S. Humbert, R. M. Murray, and M. H. Dickinson, "Pitch-Altitude Control and Terrain Following Based on Bio-Inspired Visuomotor Convergence," *Proceedings of the AIAA Guidance Navigation and Control Conference and Exhibit*, AIAA, Aug 2005. AIAA 2005-6280.

[16] M. Shoemaker and S. Hokamoto, "Relative Navigation Near Asteroids Using Wide-Field Integration of Optic Flow," *Proceedings of the 28th International Symposium on Space Technology and Science, Okinawa, Japan*, June 2011. paper no. 2011-d-38.

[17] R. Gaskell, O. Barnouin-Jha, D. Scheeres, T. Mukai, N. Hirata, S. Abe, J. Saito, M. Ishiguro, T. Kubota, T. Hashimoto, J. Kawaguchi, M. Yoshikawa, K. Shirakawa, and T. Kominato, "Landmark Navigation Studies and Target Characterization in the Hayabusa Encounter with Itokawa," *AAS/AIAA Astrodynamics Specialists Conference, Keystone, CO*, 2006. AIAA paper 2006-6660.

COMPARISON OF FRAGMENTATION/DISPERSION MODELS FOR ASTEROID NUCLEAR DISRUPTION MISSION DESIGN

Brian D. Kaplinger[*] and Bong Wie[†]

This paper considers the problem of developing statistical orbit predictions of near-Earth object (NEO) fragmentation for nuclear disruption mission design and analysis. The critical component of NEO fragmentation modeling is developed for a momentum-preserving hypervelocity impact of a spacecraft carrying nuclear payload. The results of the fragmentation process are compared to static models and results from complex hydrodynamic code simulations, developing benchmark initial conditions for orbital prediction algorithms. The problem is examined in a way that enables high-performance GPU acceleration of the resulting computational system, and the mission design fidelity is improved to allow for high throughput self-gravity and collision models of NEO fragments. Improvements to model efficiency are demonstrated using a range of orbits to assess disruption mission effectiveness.

INTRODUCTION

Asteroids have impacted the Earth in the past and threaten to do so in the future. While the most likely near-term threat is that of a low-altitude airburst, the expected energy of an event such as Tunguska would be devastating in a highly populated area. Additionally, though the population of catastrophic impactors has been well surveyed, it is estimated that thousands of bodies over 140 m in diameter remain undiscovered [1]. Many methods have been suggested for the mitigation of this threat, but most require substantial lead time in order to be effective. A study by the National Research Council suggests that nuclear explosive devices may be the only option for late warning cases [2]. Previous simulations show that disruption, once thought to be undesirable, may substantially reduce the amount of mass remaining on impact trajectories. This method could be available with as little as 10 days of lead time between intercept and the predicted impact date for an orbit like that of the asteroid Apophis [3].

This paper addresses a simulation framework for a disrupted near-Earth object (NEO) dispersing along the orbit. Initial simulations use a spherical NEO model with a dense granite core and an outer shell of tuff material, similar to the description in [1], the only difference being that a meshless particle description is used, with the mass distributed to best approximate the desired body. A formulation for adapting the procedure in [4] is given for a general NEO shape, allowing a wide range of initial conditions with a momentum-preserving fragmentation model. After simulation of the NEO breakup, individual fragments are identified and their resulting velocities mapped to a rotating orbital coordinate system. The trajectory of each fragment is then predicted using an improved version of the algorithms presented in [5], with special attention paid to the probability density of

---
[*] Graduate Research Assistant, Asteroid Deflection Research Center, Iowa State University.
[†] Vance Coffman Chair Professor, Asteroid Deflection Research Center, Iowa State University.

fragment given uncertain initial conditions. The results are then compared to fragmentation models in [6] and resulting from complex hydrodynamic code simulations.

A major bottleneck in determining appropriate mitigation methods for NEOs has been a lack of experimental data on the efficacy of each approach, forcing a reliance on simulations to determine mission effectiveness. As we move from the concept stage into true mission planning for effective NEO threat mitigation, we must depart from simulation of a few sample cases and instead use actual mission parameters to integrate modeling and simulation into the mission design cycle. This paper presents the development of simulation tools designed to be implemented as part of the mission design procedure for nuclear fragmentation and dispersion of an NEO. A brief history of general purpose GPU computing will be given, followed by the particulars of high-level language access to the GPU for this simulation. Motivation for the parallelization of the presented model lies in the decoupled nature of each hydrodynamic particle, relying only on information for its immediate neighbors. Improvements of the fragmentation model are shown to result in 60% cost savings for the simulation and a speedup of over 300x compared to serial CPU implementation. The adaptation of previously presented models to the memory and compute capability of the GPU architecture will be described, as well as steps taken to optimize performance in the presence of GPU limitations.

Past work [5,7] showed that a large amount of data can be processed using GPU simulation. Initial work was focused mostly on prediction of relative impacting mass. Disruption at different times along a given orbit can have a large effect on the resulting shape of the debris cloud. This paper looks at the fragmentation model to better address how uncertainty in the NEO breakup affects orbital prediction, using the model developed in [4]. This has allowed for a revolution in computing on a budget, allowing hundreds of complex simulations to be tested. While new high-performance computing (HPC) technology is shown to solve old problems faster, this paper also addresses the identification of new problems that were previously intractable without the use of a supercomputer or dedicated cluster.

SIMULATION MODEL

This section presents the equations of motion and target model used in the fragmentation and dispersion simulations. Two primary reference targets are used, to emphasize the differences between material composition. Both are 100 meters in diameter, but have different bulk densities and material strength properties. The first target is a rubble-pile asteroid, with a bulk density of 1.91 g/cm^3. This is a likely target for demonstrating the behavior of more porous material. The second target is a single granite boulder with a bulk density of 2.63 g/cm^3. A linear model for material strength is used in this target with a yield strength of 14.6 MPa and a shear modulus of 35 MPa, resulting in a more granulated fragmentation and slower dispersion velocities. Real asteroid targets are expected to fall within these two extremes, with variances for composition, distribution of mass, and orientation. A Smoothed Particle Hydrodynamics (SPH) model [4] is used for the asteroid fragmentation simulation under 3 initial conditions: a subsurface explosion of 100 kt buried at a 5 m depth, a surface blast of 100 kt surrounded by a 1 m thick aluminum impactor, and a standoff blast at 10 m above the surface. We assume an isotropic Weibull distribution of implicit flaws in the NEO material and conduct Monte Carlo simulation to establish a mean response of the target NEO to the fragmentation process. Resulting coherent masses are propagated through a model of solar system dynamics until the predetermined date of impact. Masses remaining on impact trajectories undergo a simulation of reentry into Earth's atmosphere, resulting in final tallies of mass missing the Earth, fragments on capture trajectories, airburst events, and impacts of reduced-mass fragments.

Hydrodynamic Equations

For the purposes of the present simulation study, a meshless hydrodynamics model was desired. This approach would eliminate the need for storing and updating a grid, simplify calculations for large deformations, and allow for contiguous memory access to local field properties. The SPH formulation [8,9] was chosen to satisfy the first two goals, while the latter will be discussed with regards to the GPU implementation. The core idea of SPH is to approximate a field property $f(x)$ by using a mollifier W (also known as an approximate identity) with compact support:

$$\langle f(x) \rangle = \int_\Omega f(s)W(x-s)ds, \quad W \in C_0^1(\mathbb{R}^n), \quad \Omega = \mathrm{supp}(W) \tag{1}$$

where the brackets indicate the SPH approximation [9], allowing the field variables to be computed as a sum over the nearest neighbor particles representing the flow. In the present formulation, W is taken as the cubic spline kernel [8,9], with a variable isotropic domain of support with radius h. Changing h in space and time allows for the simulation to respond to changes in flow conditions with a change in local resolution [8,9]. A mass m is assigned to each particle representative in the model, as well as initial position and velocity components (x^β and v^β) in each β direction. Material properties such as density, ρ, and specific energy, e, complete the state description. Similar to the above integral relationship, derivatives and integrals of field functions can be approximated, resulting in the following set of equations [8-10] involving the kernel derivative (a scalar valued function of vector position $\mathbf{x}$):

$$\frac{Dx_i^\alpha}{Dt} = v_i^\alpha \tag{2}$$

$$\frac{D\rho_i}{Dt} = \sum_{j=1}^N m_j \left(v_i^\beta - v_j^\beta \right) \frac{\partial W(\mathbf{x}_j - \mathbf{x}_i)}{\partial x^\beta} \tag{3}$$

$$\frac{Dv_i^\alpha}{Dt} = -\sum_{j=1}^N m_j \left(\frac{\sigma_i^{\alpha\beta}}{\rho_i^2} + \frac{\sigma_j^{\alpha\beta}}{\rho_j^2} + \Pi_{ij} \right) \frac{\partial W(\mathbf{x}_j - \mathbf{x}_i)}{\partial x^\beta} + F_i^\alpha \tag{4}$$

$$\frac{De}{Dt} = \frac{1}{2} \sum_{j=1}^N m_j \left(\frac{P_i}{\rho_i^2} + \frac{P_j}{\rho_j^2} + \Pi_{ij} \right) \left(v_i^\beta - v_j^\beta \right) \frac{\partial W(\mathbf{x}_j - \mathbf{x}_i)}{\partial x^\beta} + \frac{1}{\rho_i} S_i^{\alpha\beta} \epsilon_i^{\alpha\beta} + H_i \tag{5}$$

where repeated indices in a product indicate implied summation over all possible values, $\sigma^{\alpha\beta}$ is the stress tensor, P is the pressure, $S^{\alpha\beta}$ is the deviatoric (traceless) stress tensor, $\epsilon^{\alpha\beta}$ is the local strain rate tensor, F represents external forces, and H represents energy sources. Π_{ij} represents the Monaghan numerical viscosity [9,11] used to resolve shocks, accommodate heating along the shock, and resist unphysical material penetration. The material strength model for the solid target uses an elastic-perfectly plastic description of strength [8-10], where the hydrodynamic stress is determined as

$$\sigma_i^{\alpha\beta} = -P_i \delta^{\alpha\beta} + (1-\eta)S_i^{\alpha\beta}, \quad \eta \in [0,1] \tag{6}$$

where η is a material damage indicator, to be discussed later. It should be noted that fully damaged material ($\eta = 1$) is relieved of all stress due to deformation and behaves as a cohesionless fluid

[10,12]. The rubble-pile target is treated in this manner by default. In this elastic-plastic model, the components of the deviatoric stress tensor $S^{\alpha\beta}$ evolve using the following equation based on Hooke's law [8,13]:

$$\frac{DS_i^{\alpha\beta}}{Dt} = 2G_s \left(\epsilon_i^{\alpha\beta} - 3\delta_i^{\alpha\beta} \epsilon_i^{\gamma\gamma} \right) + S_i^{\alpha\gamma} R_i^{\beta\gamma} + R_i^{\alpha\gamma} S_i^{\gamma\beta} \tag{7}$$

where $R^{\alpha\beta}$ is the local rotation rate tensor, G_s is the shear modulus, and the SPH approximation for these terms is given by

$$\epsilon_i^{\alpha\beta} = \frac{1}{2} \sum_{j=1}^{N} \frac{m_j}{\rho_j} \left[(v_j^\alpha - v_i^\alpha) \frac{\partial W(\mathbf{x}_j - \mathbf{x}_i)}{\partial x^\beta} + (v_j^\beta - v_i^\beta) \frac{\partial W(\mathbf{x}_j - \mathbf{x}_i)}{\partial x^\alpha} \right] \tag{8}$$

$$R_i^{\alpha\beta} = \frac{1}{2} \sum_{j=1}^{N} \frac{m_j}{\rho_j} \left[(v_j^\alpha - v_i^\alpha) \frac{\partial W(\mathbf{x}_j - \mathbf{x}_i)}{\partial x^\beta} - (v_j^\beta - v_i^\beta) \frac{\partial W(\mathbf{x}_j - \mathbf{x}_i)}{\partial x^\alpha} \right] \tag{9}$$

To complete this system, we use the following equations governing the change of support radius h [8,9], and the fracture damage ratio η [10]. The latter is limited in accordance with the number of material flaws activated in the structure.

$$\frac{Dh_i}{Dt} = -\frac{1}{n} \frac{h_i}{\rho_i} \frac{D\rho_i}{Dt}, \quad \frac{D}{Dt} \eta^{1/3} = \frac{c_g}{r_s} \tag{10}$$

where c_g is the crack growth rate, here assumed to be 0.4 times the local sound speed [10], and r_s is the radius of the subvolume subject to tensile strain. In the present model, the latter term is estimated by interpolation based on the strain rate tensor of neighbor particles. An equation of state remains to complete the mechanical system. We use the Tillotson equation of state [14] in the solid asteroid and in the aluminum penetrator used to deliver the surface explosive. This is modified to include porosity, and an irreversible crush strength, for the "rubble pile" target [12,15]. We assume a power law distribution for number of implicit flaws in a volume of material with respect to local tensile strain (a Weibull distribution), and assign flaws with specific activation thresholds to each SPH particle [10]. The maximum damage allowed to accumulate in a volume is described by

$$\eta_i^{\max} = \left(\frac{n_i}{n_i^{\mathrm{tot}}} \right)^{1/3}, \quad \epsilon_i = \frac{\sigma_i^t}{(1 - \eta_i)E} \tag{11}$$

where n_i is the number of active flaws ($\epsilon > \epsilon^{\mathrm{act}}$) and n^{tot} is the total number of flaws assigned to a particle, which can vary widely, but is always at least one. Equation (11) also gives the relationship for the local scalar strain, as a function of the maximum tensile stress σ^t, the local damage, and the Youngs modulus E.

Orbit Propagation

Statistics representing the fragmented system are collected and stored as cumulative density functions for the needed variables, similar to those shown in Fig. 1. A representative fragment system of 10,000 to 100,000 fragments is created from these statistics using inverse transform sampling.

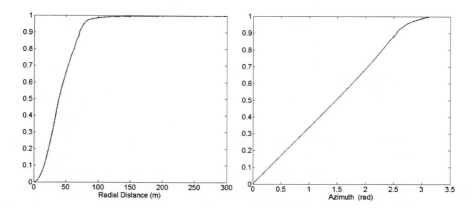

Figure 1. Cumulative Density Functions for Disrupted Asteroid.

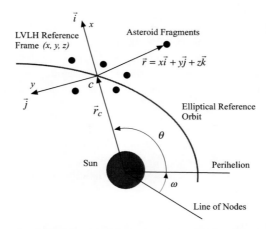

Figure 2. Rotating Local-Vertical-Local-Horizontal (LVLH) Frame.

The debris cloud is given global coordinates in a Local-Vertical-Local-Horizontal (LVLH) reference frame about the center of mass, as shown in Fig. 2. Since the hydrodynamic model is axisymmetric, and has a definite direction of maximum momentum along the axis of symmetry, a desired deflection direction must be chosen. In the present paper, deflections along the 3 LVLH axes are considered: radial ($\pm x$), transverse ($\pm y$), and normal ($\pm z$) axes. These are then integrated to predict an ephemeris for a 48 hour period surrounding the nominal time of impact. Since the LVLH reference frame is computationally beneficial for self-gravity and collision modelling among fragments [5], we use the nonlinear relative equations of motion for this frame to govern fragment trajectories [5,7]:

41

$$\ddot{x}_i = 2\dot{\theta}\left(\dot{y}_i - \frac{\dot{r}_c}{r_c}y_i\right) + \dot{\theta}^2 x_i + \frac{\mu}{r_c^2} - \frac{\mu}{r_d^3}(r_c + x_i) + \frac{\mu_E}{r_{Ei}^3}(x_E - x_i) + F_i^x \qquad (12)$$

$$\ddot{y}_i = -2\dot{\theta}\left(\dot{x}_i + \frac{\dot{r}_c}{r_c}x_i\right) + \dot{\theta}^2 y_i - \frac{\mu}{r_d^3} + \frac{\mu_E}{r_{Ei}^3}(y_E - y_i) + F_i^y \qquad (13)$$

$$\ddot{z}_i = -\frac{\mu}{r_d^3}z_i + \frac{\mu_E}{r_{Ei}^3}(z_E - z_i) + F_i^z \qquad (14)$$

where x, y, z, r_c, and θ are defined as shown in Fig. 2, r_d is the length of the relative coordinate vector, μ and μ_E are gravitational parameters for the sun and the Earth, r_{Ei} is the distance from each fragment to Earth, and (F^x, F^y, F^z) are the combined acceleration components due to 3rd body gravitational terms (solar system major body model [7]), self gravity, and collision corrections. The threading structure for computing the values for self gravity terms is described in [5], while collisions are predicted using a Sort-and-Search algorithm [16], resulting in post-collision changes to position and velocity of fragments. An elastic spherical collision model is assumed for the fragments, with a coefficient of restitution of 0.5.

Uncertainty Analysis

In order to test the response of orbital dispersion with respect to uncertain initial fragment positions and velocities, a Gaussian noise is added to the mapping around the nominal center of mass. A standard deviation of 10% is assumed, resulting in deviations from the hydrodynamic simulations up to $\pm$ 30%. For a given orbit, 1000 random perturbations are integrated to impact, resulting in an average system behavior and a standard deviation representative of the uncertainty due to the initial conditions.

This procedure is completed for a database of 906 orbits chosen to impact at a fixed date. The orbital parameters for the nominal trajectory are sampled from a (a, e, i) space that represents the distribution of known NEOs, as shown in Fig. 3. For each of 6 deflection directions, the Monte Carlo procedure described above results in a characteristic behavior of a disrupted NEO on the range of orbits tested.

DISRUPTION MISSION PROFILES

This section outlines the initial conditions for three method of NEO deflection using nuclear explosive devices. In all cases, a 100 m diameter target asteroid is modeled with an energy source of 100 kt. Thermal emission is omitted from the subsurface and surface explosions due to absorbtion by surrounding material in the time scale of interest.

Subsurface Explosion Setup

For this simulation, the explosive is modeled as a cylindrical energy source buried at a depth of 5 meters. As shown for the solid target in Fig. 4, The blast wave compresses the NEO, reducing it to fragments, and disperses it primarily along the axis of the explosion. The resulting fragment distribution for a case like this has a peak between 20-70 m/s, with a tail of high-speed ejecta like that shown in Fig. 4.

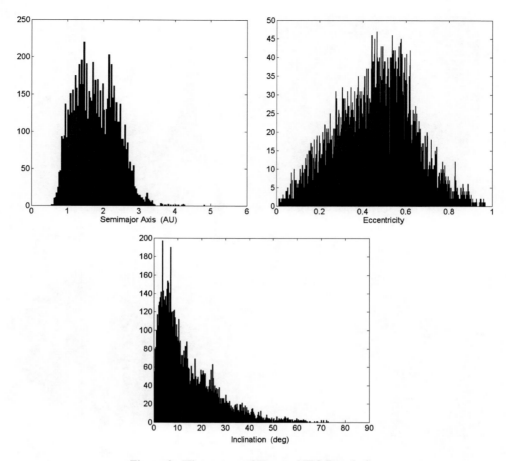

Figure 3. Histograms of Known NEO Population.

Surface Penetrator Model

Two main models for an explosion at the surface are used. One is a static explosion, which results in vastly different systems depending on the composition of the body. For a solid target, cratering and pitting is expected rather than disruption. Even dispersed rubble-pile asteroids have a far lower mean fragment velocity than a similar subsurface system. The second model, shown here, includes an aluminum penetrator impacting the surface at 6.1 km/s. The explosion thermal energy turns the high-mass impactor into a plasma, which burrows into the surface as it releases its energy. Slower dispersion velocity is observed than the subsurface case, but this approach is extremely beneficial from an engineering standpoint, as there is strong coupling between time-to-impact and a reduction in mission fuel cost [17]. The benefit to this method relative to a subsurface explosion is that it does not require a rendezvous, and therefore there are available launch windows for this type of mission right up until immediately before the impact date.

43

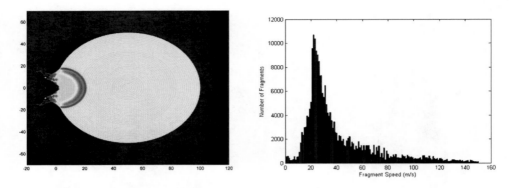

Figure 4. Subsurface Explosion and Resulting Fragment Velocities.

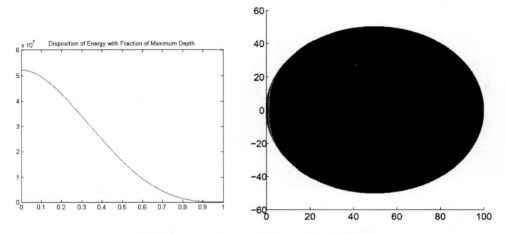

Figure 5. Radial Energy Deposition and Total Deposition Region.

Standoff Energy Deposition

For a standoff blast, additional physics must be considered. An energy deposition strategy is required that does not directly compute X-ray and neutron scattering in the target. For this, a ray-tracing algorithm is used with radial energy deposition at the surface as shown in Fig. 5 for neutrons. This is derived from a Monte Carlo scattering result from TART, a DOE neutron deposition code, in NEO analog materials [18]. A 10% neutron yield is assumed for these simulations, and a maximum deposition depth of 1.5 m to compare to deposition predicted for chondritic materials [19]. The overall deposition region (shown as the logarithm of deposited energy) is also shown in Fig. 5. A modified SPH node representation is created that resembles an ablative modeling grid used in high-energy deposition physics. This distribution is shown in Fig. 6, and has a minimum smoothing scale of 0.1 cm with a maximum local change rate of 10% up to 0.2 m resolution. Also in Fig. 6, the resulting ablation provides an effect similar to that of a rocket, but also disrupts the rubble-pile target completely.

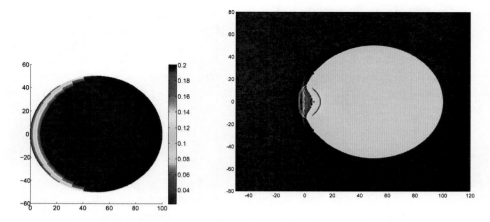

Figure 6. SPH Nodes and Resulting Ablation for Standoff Model.

COMPUTATIONAL APPROACH

This section address the computational approach used to solve the disruption problem. Each state variable update for a fragment is conducted in parallel at each time step. A variety of hardware was available for this project, with a substantial difference in performance. This allowed us to get reasonable estimates on the computational cost of this simulation, in comparison to LINPACK performance numbers. Performance can vary based on the type of arrays used, and the number of threads dedicated to each GPU calculation. These factors are determined by the CUDA Compute Capability (CUDA CC), which is a property of the GPU [20]. These cost estimates are used to determine hardware performance on the various systems. A summary of the hardware used is shown in Table 1 (Note: all CPUs are Intel brand, and all GPUs are NVIDIA brand).

Table 1. Hardware for Benchmark Systems

System	Machine 1	Machine 2	Machine 3	Machine 4	Machine 5
CPU	1x Core2 Q6600	1x Core2 Q6600	1x Xeon X5550	2x Xeon E5520	2x Xeon X5650
CPU Cores	4	4	4	8	12
CPU TPEAK	9.6 GFLOPs	9.6 GFLOPs	12.8 GFLOPs	21.36 GFLOPs	32.04 GFLOPs
GPU	1x 8800GTS	1x GTX470	1x GTX480	4x Tesla c1060	4x Tesla c2050
GPU Cores	112	448	480	960	1792
GPU TPEAK	84 GFLOPs	324 GFLOPs	385 GFLOPs	336 GFLOPs	2060 GFLOPs
CUDA CC	CC 1.0	CC 2.0	CC 2.0	CC 1.3	CC 2.0

Each thread on the GPU calculates the state variable change for one fragment, with the GPU kernel limited to one time step. This is necessary because the positions of the planets and other gravitating bodies must be calculated and transferred to the GPU at each time step. Additionally, the positions of fragments at each integration substep are shared among multiple GPUs and CPU threads. For this reason, the present hydrodynamics model is predominantly bandwidth-limited for small data sets. While grid information is not retained, one of the disadvantages of the SPH hydrocode is that neighboring particles must be calculated at each time step. Our approach in this model is to create a bounding volume for each SPH particle and perform the same Sort and Sweep in parallel as used to detect collisions in the orbital model [16]. We retain the information for neighbors connected by material strength, as well as carrying neighbor information through the correction step of the integrator. This results in a 28% performance improvement over recalculating neighbors at both the prediction and correction steps, while allowing for a variable time step based on the Courant condition [8,9]:

$$\delta t = \min_i \frac{h_i}{c_i} \tag{15}$$

where c is the local sound speed. While the reduction operation to determine the new time step can be done in parallel, all GPU threads must have position information for all particles to determine neighbors. This requirement could be eliminated through clever domain decomposition, but there is a tradeoff between associating a mesh to the model and taking advantage of contiguous memory sections of particles. Load balancing would also require additional communication between GPUs, which has an impact on performance, as PCI-E bandwidth is one of the limiting factors in GPU acceleration [20]. Our memory model for this simulation includes a shared host memory, distributed device memory for each GPU, and data transfers between them handled through explicit array transfer. Each block of compute threads on the GPU takes the data it needs from the global device memory when the kernel reaches its block. This is an important factor, because the varying compute capabilities have different limitations on this block memory, changing the number of threads that may be used in the calculation. Constants are transferred to all GPU memories implicitly using a pointer to the host constant value. While modern dedicated compute GPUs have a high amount of onboard memory, it usually is far less than system memory. Though it may seem advantageous to calculate parameters for every time step before the start of the simulation, the arrays resulting from this approach are quite large. Each model of GPU has a limited number of memory registers available to each computing block of threads [20]. Therefore, the use of several large arrays can actually slow down the simulation in some cases, by lowering the number of threads below the maximum allowed by the architecture. This is addressed in the present code by utilizing asynchronous data transfers and kernel launches to split the work into streams. This allows the CPU to calculate new parameters needed for the next time step while the GPU is updating the current step.

RESULTS

In order to address the effectiveness of different fragmentation methods, we compare the mass remaining on impacting trajectories (including the uncertainty from the Monte Carlo process) against other methods for each orbit. For example, Fig. 7 shows the relative impacting mass for the surface penetrator in both the solid and the rubble-pile targets. On average across the orbits tested, the impacting mass was 10% higher for the solid target compared to the rubble target for deflections in the radial direction. Estimates like this will eventually allow for tabular look-up of performance for various methods without direct computation. It was also found that impacting mass for the solid target was 20% higher than the rubble target in the transverse direction.

No strong correlation was found for the semimajor axis or eccentricity of the NEO orbit with only 15 days of lead time, however, deflections on orbits with high inclination were more effective, as shown in Fig. 8. for the subsurface case. Ejecta velocities for the dynamic surface burst (at 6.1 km/s) were within the 10% assumed noise range compared to a static buried explosive, as shown

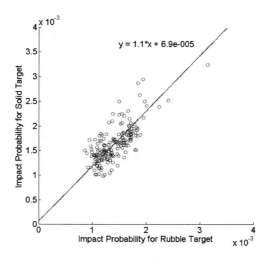

Figure 7. Relative Performance for Surface Impactor.

in Fig. 9. Thus, an emphasis might be placed on hypervelocity intercept and guidance technology rather than a rendezvous mission. One possible interceptor design includes an aluminum impactor followed by an explosive. With both interceptors impacting at 6.1 km/s, the resulting ejecta speed is on average 25% higher than the single surface blast, with a standard deviation of 5.3%. Figure 10 shows the relative velocities for these cases, which results in 20% lower impacting mass on most orbits tested.

Computational Optimization

A single computational node was used to determine optimal distribution of MPI and OpenMP processes across the current worker topology being considered. This system has 2 sockets populated with Intel Xeon X5650 six-core CPUs at 2.66 Ghz. Intel HyperThreading technology is enabled, resulting in 24 logical processors visible to the operating system. Additionally, the default level of OpenMP threading is 24. There are 4 NVIDIA Tesla C2050 GPU cards, each connected on a dedicated PCI-E x16 bus. System RAM is 32 GB, while each GPU has 3 GB GDDR5 for a total GPU work unit of 12 GB (11.2 GB with ECC enabled). Fourteen multiprocessors on each card result in 448 shader cores each, limited to a maximum kernel launch of 1024 threads per thread block. This new "Fermi" GPU architecture has a theoretical peak performance of 515 Mflops in double precision, representing a game-changing leap forward in GPU double precision computing, as shown by real-world results [5].

While grid information does not need to be stored for this model, the drawback is that neighboring particles need to be determined at each time step. Since the integration scheme is a second order predictor-corrector scheme, particle information is needed at both steps. The first change made to the standard scheme was to retain the neighbor ID information for the corrector step. Only the kernel and kernel derivative values at the new neighbor predicted position need to be computed. This reduced time-to-solution by 30.2% compared to a two-stage neighbor finding algorithm. Results for both cases were compared, and while ending state values could be slightly different the distribution remained the same, and the method conserved energy slightly better through the end of the simula-

47

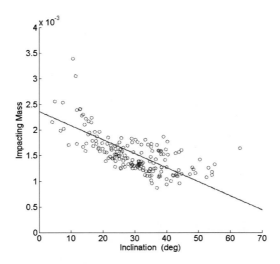

Figure 8. Impacting Mass for Subsurface Explosion on Orbits with Varying Inclination.

tion. A possible beneficial side effect of this approach is the reduction of importance of neighbor changes in a prediction step, which might help damp out numerical instabilities and allow for larger time step changes. This is something to be tested in the future. Also, while brute force computation of neighbor particles was the original approach, a Sort-and-Sweep method reduced this time by 36% for the present target model. This method scales as $N \log N$ rather than N^2 [16].

Neighbor information arrays were stored in a column-major format by particle, allowing stride 1 access to the ID number, kernel value, and kernel derivative values for each neighbor of a particle. Additionally, loop unrolling and inlining for simple functions were implemented, and optimization flags were passed in the build step. For the GPU model, utilizing asynchronous kernel launches to continue computation without synchronization resulted in an 8% performance increase. The theoretical load on each process should be equal, since each has the same number of particles for which a state update needs to be computed. However, in areas of quickly changing density (for example the expanding shock wave), the number of average neighbors for a particle goes up dramatically. This is controlled in 2 ways to aid load balancing. First, the ID assignment scheme works outward in a radial manner, while making sure that mirroring particles on opposite sides of the primary axis are adjacent in memory. Second, the evolution of h strives to keep the number of neighboring particles near the starting value, resulting in an equal computational burden. For the GPU model, a load factor was developed, dividing the minimum time to complete a section between synchronizations by the maximum time. Sampling this load factor allows one to better understand the efficiency of the code section. At a time of 1.2 ms, an example chosen because of the high energy of this point of the simulation, a vertical distribution of particle IDs resulted in a load factor efficiency of around 0.68. The present method has improved this portion to a median of 0.87.

Performance

Pure MPI scalability for up to 12 processes was tested on the present hardware, resulting in near linear scaling and a total parallel speedup of 8.9 for MPI. Including OpenMP in a Hybrid parallel scheme, a total parallel speedup of 11.9 is achieved, showing near perfect expected scalability across

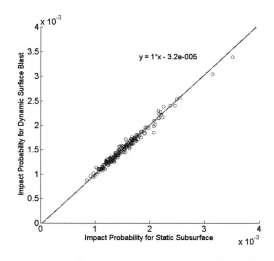

Figure 9. Impacting Mass Comparison for Subsurface and Dynamic Surface Cases.

a single node as shown in Fig. 9. Thus, each additional planned node might add almost 12x speedup for host computation, minus internode communication overhead. As shown in Fig. 9, when the binding option is passed to the Hydra process manager to set 1-2 MPI processes per socket, and an OpenMP thread level of 6 is set, the best performing speedup for the system is obtained. This corresponds to a value of 11.2 for 12 computational threads and 11.9 for 24 computational threads. Performance improvement using ¿ 12 threads is predominantly dependent on the HyperThreading hardware implementation. This is shown to only have an improvement over 12 threads when the shared thread level is 4, 6, 8, or 12. However, good performance with 12 threads among these hybrid schemes was limited to an OpenMP level of 6 and 12. While the default OpenMP maximum thread level for this system is 24, benefits from this technology are implementation dependent, so the preferred setup for future system programming is 1 MPI process per socket with an OpenMP threading level of 6 unless improvement from additional MPI processes can be demonstrated.

GPU acceleration performance for this method is a substantial improvement over a larger CPU-only cluster. Since the threading structure of the GPU is limited to SIMD kernel launches of multiple threads on a multiprocessor, serial performance for comparison is measured on the host CPU. Fig 9 shows then relationship between the number of GPUs used in the state update process and the parallel speedup. At least 1 MPI thread is needed per GPU. In fact, using the currently supported CUDA Fortran toolkit (version 4.0), binding between CPU thread and GPU control requires that additional threading use a shared memory approach such as OpenMP. In a previous test, GPU speedup for this architecture ranges from 50x to 120x for a 50 m diameter target problem. Since the GPU approach works well for data-parallel problems, one would expect that increasing the scale of the problem would yield better performance. In fact, using the current solid target standoff model (3.1M particles) maximum speedup on a single node is increased to 357.9x, as shown in Fig. 9. Since the neighbor search problem is substantially increased, the parallel structure of the GPU is far preferred to the hybrid CPU programming model.

49

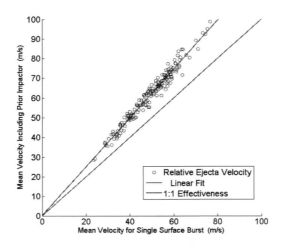

Figure 10. Mean Ejecta Velocity for Single and Double Impactor Cases.

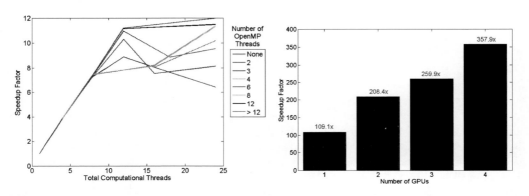

Figure 11. Comparison of Single-Node Performance on CPU and GPU.

CONCLUSION

The present SPH hydrocode suggests that a dynamic model of a hypervelocity surface burst yields results similar in spatial and temporal distribution to a static subsurface explosion. This gives additional launch windows for mission design, limits the fuel needed for a rendezvous burn, and avoids the need to bury the explosive payload. Additionally, the dynamic model should better predict system behavior when addressing high velocity penetrator architectures. This might give an option for realistically determining the limits of such a system for asteroid deflection missions. NEO orbital parameters such as semimajor axis and eccentricity were not found to be important for these time scale, but it was found that inclination was important in determining effectiveness of any given method.

All methods of disruption using a 100 kt nuclear energy source were quite effective for 100 m diameter targets for 15 days lead time, regardless of the orbit considered. Future work should consider larger bodies, a range of source energies, and lead times specific to the available mission time for a given orbit. There was a slight advantage to the two impactor system analyzed compared to a single surface burst, in the form of higher coupled energy and a lower impacting mass on most orbits, including uncertainty.

New HPC technology utilizing GPU acceleration has resulted in orders of magnitude improvement in computational ability. Speedup of the GPU accelerated model compared to serial execution for the both target models has been demonstrated. While the 330,000 particles of the penetrator target are limited mostly by communication bandwidth, the 3.1 million particles in the standoff model are limited by computational speed and memory bandwidth for the threads on the GPU. A substantial speedup improvement, from 53x to 358x, is observed. This shows single node computational performance on the same order as a moderate cluster. The ability to run multiple cases to address statistical system behavior results in simulation being integrated into overall mission design. Mission effectiveness can be estimated in advance of a need for mission design, allowing new architectures and interchangeable components for a universal deflection plan. This paper outlined the development of software and hardware tools to aid the planning of NEO deflection mission design, and the current project strives to identify key technologies for effective implementation. This technology provides a useful reduction in time-to-solution comparable to 30 similar CPU-only nodes (which would cost $4,000 each) in a $14,000 form factor, showing a 8.6x improvement in cost-adjusted performance.

ACKNOWLEDGMENT

This research work was supported by a research grant from the Iowa Space Grant Consortium (ISGC) awarded to the Asteroid Deflection Research Center at Iowa State University. The authors would like to thank Dr. Ramanathan Sugumaran (Director, ISGC) for his support of this research work.

REFERENCES

[1] Boslough, M., "Airburst Warning and Response," IAA-PDC-2166721, *2nd IAA Planetary Defense Conference*, Bucharest, Romania, May 9-12, 2011.

[2] Committee to Review Near-Earth Object Surveys and Hazard Mitigation Strategies, National Research Council, *Defending Planet Earth: Near-Earth Object Surveys and Hazard Mitigation Strategies*, 152 pp, 2010.

[3] Kaplinger, B., and Wie, B., "Parameter Variation In Near-Earth Object Disruption Simulations Using GPU Acceleration," AAS-11-267, *21st AAS/AIAA Spaceflight Mechanics Meeting*, New Orleans, LA, Feb. 13-17, 2011.

[4] Kaplinger, B., Wie, B., and Dearborn, D., "Nuclear Fragmentation/Dispersion Modeling and Simulation of Hazardous Near-Earth Objects," IAA-PDC-2138266, *2nd IAA Planetary Defense Conference*, Bucharest, Romania, May 9-12, 2011.

[5] Kaplinger, B., and Wie, B., "Optimized GPU Simulation of a Disrupted Near-Earth Object Including Self-Gravity," AAS-11-266, *21st AAS/AIAA Spaceflight Mechanics Meeting*, New Orleans, LA, February 13-17, 2011.

[6] Wie, B. and Dearborn, D., "Earth-Impact Modeling and Analysis of a Near-Earth Object Fragmented and Dispersed by Nuclear Subsurface Explosions," AAS 10-137, *20th AAS/AIAA Space Flight Mechanics Meeting*, San Diego, CA, February 15-17, 2010.

[7] Kaplinger, B.D., Wie, B., and Dearborn, D., "Preliminary Results for High-Fidelity Modeling and Simulation of Orbital Dispersion of Asteroids Disrupted by Nuclear Explosives," AIAA-2010-7982, AIAA/AAS Astrodynamics Specialists Conference, Toronto, Ontario, Canada, August 2-5, 2010.

[8] Monaghan, J.J, "Smoothed Particle Hydrodynamics," *Rep. on Prog. in Physics*, vol. 68, pp. 1703-1759, July 2005.

[9] Liu, G.R., and Liu, M.B., *Smoothed Particle Hydrodynamics: A Meshfree Particle Method*, Singapore: World Scientific Publishing, 2003.

[10] Benz, W., and Asphaug, E., "Simulations of Brittle Solids using Smooth Particle Hydrodynamics," *Computer Physics Communications*, vol. 87, pp. 253-265, 1995.

[11] Hiermaier, S., Konke, D., Stilp, A.J., and Thoma, K., "Computational Simulation of the Hypervelocity Impact of Al-Spheres on Thin Plates of Different Materials," *Intl. Journal of Impact Engineering*, vol. 20, pp. 363-374, 1997.

[12] Jutzi, M., Benz, W., and Michel, P., "Numerical Simulations of Impacts Involving Porous Bodies I. Implementing Sub-Resolution Porosity in a 3D SPH Hydrocode," *Icarus*, vol. 198, pp. 242-255, 2008.

[13] Randles, P.W., and Libersky, L.D., "Smoothed Particle Hydrodynamics: Some Recent Improvements and Applications," *Computer Methods in Applied Mechanics and Engineering*, vol. 139, pp. 375-408, 1996.

[14] Tillotson, J.H., "Metallic Equations of State for Hypervelocity Impact," General Atomic Technical Report GA-3216, 1962.

[15] Schuster, S.H., and Isenberg, J. "Equations of State for Geologic Materials," Defense Nuclear Agency Technical Report DNA-2925Z, 1972.

[16] LeGrand, S., "Broad-Phase Collision Detection with CUDA," *GPU Gems 3*, ed. H. Nguyen, Addison-Wesley, 2007.

[17] Wagner, S., and Wie, B., "Analysis and Design of Fictive Post-2029 Apophis Intercept Mission for Nuclear Disruption," AIAA-2010-8375, *AIAA/AAS Astrodynamics Specialists Conference*, Toronto, Ontario, Canada, August 2-5, 2010.

[18] Miles, A.R., "Asteroid Deflection via Standoff Nuclear Explosions," *Asteroid Deflection Research Symposium*, Arlington, VA, October 23-24, 2008.

[19] Plesko, C.S., Weaver, R.P., and Huebner, W.F., "Energy Deposition in Hazard Mitigation by Nuclear Burst: Sensitivity to Energy Source Characteristics, Geometry, and Target Composition," Paper 2588, *42nd Lunar and Planetary Science Conference*, March 711, 2011.

[20] Kirk, D.B. and Hwu, W.W., *Programming Massively Parallel Processors*, Burlington: Morgan Kaufmann, 2010.

DYNAMICS AND STABILITY IN A TRIPLE ASTEROID SYSTEM: APPLICATIONS TO MISSION DESIGN

Julie Bellerose,[*] Keaton J. Burns[†] and Franck Marchis[‡]

We now count two triple asteroid systems in the NEA population. To enable exploration of such systems, we look at the dynamics of triple systems, starting from a two-body and a restricted three body dynamical models. The dynamics of an augmented system is inevitably rich, and we show spacecraft applications for rendezvous and proximity operations at these systems. Finally, we numerically investigate the perturbations and the stability within such systems to show and quantify fate of particles.

INTRODUCTION

Recent discoveries of triple asteroid systems have intrigued the science community, starting with the discovery of the triple system Sylvia.[1] Since then, a number of multi-body systems have been discovered, especially in the Main Belt and Near-Earth Asteroid populations (MBA, NEA). We now count two NEA triple asteroid systems, 2001 SN263 and 1994 CC.[2,3] As current small body missions are tackling multi rendezvous and flyby mission opportunities, multi-asteroid systems now become one of the next interesting small body targets.

Previous works have investigated the dynamics of binary asteroid systems and spacecraft in this environment, showing how the rotational and translational dynamics are coupled, and how energy and mass exchange can occur.[4–6] Feasibility mission concepts have also included some of these systems as potential targets (for instance, LEONARD, ASTEX, Marco Polo R). The dynamics of a n-body system is not new, but increases in complexities as we increase the n number, and makes analytical assessments difficult to obtain. However, with the knowledge that such systems exist, there is a need to understand how to quickly give an assessment of such an environment and the perturbations involved.

In the current work, we look at the dynamics of triple systems, starting from a two-body and a restricted three body dynamical models, where the mass distribution of one of the bodies is taken into account.[5,7] We look at possible regions of stability, or mild instability, and applications to spacecraft missions. We then numerically investigate the importance of an added body mass on the spacecraft dynamics through Monte Carlo simulations, which allow to show and quantify the long-term stability and the fate of particles within such systems.

---

[*]Research scientist, Carnegie Mellon University Silicon Valley, NASA Ames Research Center, MS-202-3, building 202, room 200B, Moffett Field, CA 94035, Member AAS, AIAA.
[†]Research intern, Carl Sagan Center at the SETI Institute, 189 Bernardo Ave., Suite 100, Mountain View, CA 94043
[‡]Planetary Astronomer, Carl Sagan Center at the SETI Institute, 189 Bernardo Ave., Suite 100, Mountain View, CA 94043

DYNAMICAL BACKGROUND AND APPROXIMATIONS

Triple versus Binary System

There has been a number of multi-body system discoveries over the last two decades, starting with binary systems and then triple + systems. Table 1 list the current statistics of binary and triple systems. In this table, the primary and satellite asteroids are referred to as Alpha, Beta and Gamma, with the notation $D_{\alpha,\beta,\gamma}$, $P_{\alpha,\beta,\gamma}$ and d_{system} representing their respective diameter, orbital/spin period, and the separation distance between Alpha and the furthest satellite of the entire system if triple. For the binary cases, the table lists the minimum and maximum cases that have been observed, and averages within the Aten, Apollo, and Amor asteroid groups. For the triple systems, we lists similar parameters for two NEA systems, 2001 SN263 and 1994CC, and three MBA systems, 45 Eugenia, 3749 Balam, and 87 Sylvia.[1,8,9]

Table 1. Statistics of binary and triple asteroid systems. Asterisk indicate average values.

Binary parameters	Range		Average		
	min	max	Aten	Apollo	Amor
D_{α}/D_{β}	1	20	4.4	5.5	3.8
P_{α} (hrs)	2	14	2.8	3.5	2.7
P_{β} (hrs)	5	40	15	20	20
d_{system}/D_{α}	0.8	4.5	1.8	1.8	2.9
Triple parameters	SN263	1994CC	45 Eugenia*	3549 Balam*	87 Sylvia*
D_{α}/D_{β}	3.7	3.7	31	1.2	15.9
D_{α}/D_{γ}	5	6.8	43.4	3	41
P_{α} (hrs)	3.43	2.4	4	N/A	5.1
P_{β} (hrs)	149/15	30	N/A	1464	88
d_{system}/D_{α}	13	19.4	10.7	41	4.7

There is a number of observations that can be made regarding triple systems:

- The Alpha component is large enough to only consider the system itself without external perturbations, as a first approximation, since the system is confined well within the Hill radius of Alpha, and other perturbations such as solar radiation pressure are in the order of 10^{-7} times the Earth gravity.

- In many cases, the gravity of Alpha and Beta can be large enough to approximate the overall gravity field of a triple system as a binary system, having the two-body barycenter between the bodies or within the larger one.

- The NEA triple systems 2001 SN263 and 1994CC have a large primary and smaller secondary satellites, with characteristics similar to binary systems previously studied, such as 1999 KW4.[10,11]

As others have indicated, these observations imply that NEA triple systems likely evolved along the same path as binary systems.[12] Dynamical tools developed for binary systems can be of great help in estimating effects of additional moons and estimating the dynamics to first order for engineering applications.

Underlying Binary System Dynamics

As can be inferred from Table 1, the triple asteroid systems observed to date are composed of two massive bodies, if not only one, having more than 90 % of the total mass. Therefore, since the dynamics are ruled by the mass distribution of a system, we first look at the dynamics of the binary system made of the Alpha and Beta components, and investigate the perturbations from the combination of the Alpha - Gamma pair. Even if the inclination between the satellite orbits and tilt of the asteroids were observed,[12] we did not include these parameters for this first order approximation. In the model, Alpha has its axis perpendicular to the orbital planes of the satellites. In addition, we consider the system to have an ellipsoid-sphere mass distribution. The ellipsoid-sphere system allows the analysis to be simplified by reducing the number of degrees of freedom while keeping interesting dynamics due to the ellipsoidal body properties. In the numerical integration, we let Beta have an ellipsoidal shape with intermediate axes being 95% of its longest axis. In the case where Alpha is observed as being an spheroidal body, having equal equatorial radii, its contribution would be null in the equatorial plane.

For convenience, we re-state equations of motion below,[4] which are computed in the relative frame of the binary, rotating with the ellipsoid Beta. We normalize these equations using the longest axis of the small ellipsoid, called $r_{\alpha,a}$, and the mean orbital motion, $n = \sqrt{(G(M_1 + M_2)/r_{\alpha,a}^3)}$. In this ellipsoid-sphere system rotating frame, the dynamics can be expressed in the form:

$$\ddot{r} + 2\omega \times \dot{r} + \omega \times (\omega \times r) = \frac{\partial U_e}{\partial r}, \tag{1}$$

where r is the position of the spherical mass, ω is the binary orbit rate, and U_e is ellipsoid potential[13] and solved using elliptic integrals methods.[14]

Particle Dynamics

To investigate the dynamics of a particle or spacecraft, or point mass, in this gravitational field, we can express the equations of motion using the same length and time scales,

$$\ddot{\rho} + 2\omega \times \dot{\rho} + \omega \times (\omega \times \rho) = \frac{\partial U_{tot}}{\partial \rho}, \tag{2}$$

where ρ is the position of a particle mass. In this case, the potential U_{tot} is expressed as,

$$U_{tot} = \frac{\nu}{|\rho - (1 - \nu)r|} + (1 - \nu)U_e(\rho + \nu r). \tag{3}$$

If the two asteroids were in equilibrium, the system would allow an integral of motion, the Jacobi integral, which is a measure of the particle energy. The Jacobi constant is expressed as,

$$J = T - V, \tag{4}$$

where V is modified potential,

$$V = -U_{tot} + \frac{1}{2}\omega^2(x^2 + y^2). \tag{5}$$

Of interest are the zero-velocity curves obtained with zero velocity, or $T = 0$, which gives an indication of the allowable region of motion for particles and spacecraft applications. Going through values of J gives rise to the analog Lagrangian points, or equilibrium points. To investigate regions of possible stability in this system, or milder instability, we can map the Jacobi integral and analog Lagrangian points. We give examples of zero-velocity curves in the triple asteroid systems case study section.

CASE STUDIES: 2001 SN263 AND 1994 CC

System Characteristics

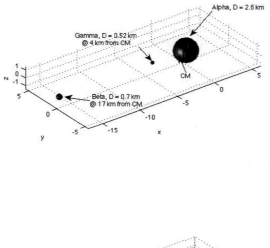

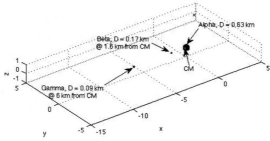

Figure 1. Geometry of the triple asteroid system 2001 SN263 (top) and 1994CC (lower).

SN263 is a triple asteroid system belonging to the Amor group of NEAs. Amors cross the orbit of Mars and graze the orbit of Earth, with a perihelion between 1.017 AU and 1.3 AU, and a semi-major axis larger than 1 AU. Based on a radar orbit fit, the shape of Alpha is that of a top, similar to that of NEA 1999 KW4,[10,11] with a mass of 10 x 10^{12} kg and a diameter of 2.6 km.[2,12] Alpha is spinning at a fairly fast period of 3.43 hours, which contributes to its volume being about 30% smaller than a sphere of the same diameter.. The system's largest moon of about 700 m to 1 km in diameter is the one further away from the system center of mass, referred as Beta. Its orbit is situated about 17 km from Alpha, orbiting in 149 hours and spinning in 14.4 hours. From mutual dynamics computations, we find the Alpha - Beta system to have a bulk density of 1.3 g/cm^3. The intermediate moon, Gamma, orbits 4.5 km away from Alpha, with a period of 16 hours which may be just shy of its own spin period of 15 hours. Gamma is about 500 m in diameter. Figure 1 (top subfigure) shows SN263 geometry.

SN263 is one of the only C-type triple NEA known,[2,3,15] which may contain organics and volatiles materials. From lightcurve observation, Alpha contributes the bulk of SN263 C-type spectrum, while Beta contributes to 13% of the light from SN263 (Gaffey, pers. comm.). Hence, it is assumed to also be C-type. Asteroid types do not influence the dynamics of the system itself, but may impact a robotic mission's operations due to a low albedo and perhaps perhaps being a more porous body.

The other observed triple system, 1994 CC represented in Figure 1 (lower subfigure), is a member of the Apollo group. Apollos are defined as Earth-crossing NEAs with semi-major axes larger than Earth's, but having a perihelion value less than 1.017 AU. The 1994 CC system is of much smaller scale compared to SN263, with its largest asteroid, Alpha, having a diameter of 630 m, four times smaller than SN263 Alpha's diameter, giving a mass of 2.6 x 10^{11} kg. For this system, Beta and Gamma are interchanged compared to SN263. Beta is only 1.7 km away from Alpha and orbits in a synchronous mode with a period of 30 hours. From this dynamics, the system's density would be much higher than that of SN263, possibly as much as 2.2 g/cm^3. Gamma is the distant satellite, being 20 times Alpha radii away, or about 6 km. Due to its small size, 90 m in diameter, its spin period couldn't be resolved in the last ground-based observation.

Table 2 lists both triple systems' physical characteristics. Figure 2 show the orbit of a second moon in the rotating frame of the binary system made of Alpha and Beta, for both SN263 and 1994 CC, top and lower subfigures respectively. Note that the dimensions are in km. Equations 2 were used for the simulation, as first approximation, and fitted with parameters from ground-based observations.[12] Note that Fang et al. have also looked at the long term stability of the system and evolution of these systems, accounting for the full dynamics.[12]

Table 2. Physical parameters of the two NEA triple systems 2001 SN263 and 1999 CC.[2,3]

Characteristics	Alpha$_{SN263}$	Beta$_{SN263}$	Gamma$_{SN263}$	Alpha$_{CC}$	Beta$_{CC}$	Gamma$_{CC}$
Shape	spheroid	irregular	irregular	Spheroid	unknown	unknown
Mass ratio (%)	N/A	2.5	1	N/A	2	1
Diameter (km)	2.8	0.7	0.5	0.63	0.17	0.09
Spin period (hrs)	3.43	14.4	15	2.4	30	unknown
Orbit period (hrs)	149	149	16.3	30	30	200
Orbital radius (km)	N/A	17.5	4.5	N/A	1.7	6.1
Density (g/cm^3)	1.33	1.33	1.33	2.2	2.2	2.2

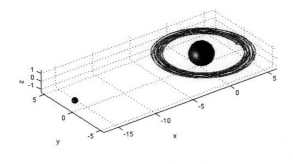

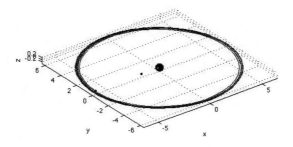

Figure 2. In-plane orbit of a moonlet in the field of a larger binary asteroid made of (top) SN263 Alpha and Beta, with a mass ratio of 0.025, and (lower) 1994CC Alpha and Beta, with mass ratio of 0.02, as seen from the binary rotating frame.

Dynamical Parameters

For the purpose of analyses and operations planning, basic dynamical parameters can be derived to identify the level of accelerations at each component. The net acceleration at the equator (Net eq. g) is obtained by computing the gravity acceleration on a point at the surface of the equatorial region, and subtracting the centripetal acceleration. The most significant difference is for the Alpha bodies, 0.034 cm/s^2 and 0.017 cm/s^2, respectively for 2001 SN263 and 1994CC. At other bodies, the centripetal effect is less than 0.05% of the gravitational acceleration. For Alpha bodies, the pole gravity acceleration will be different than the equatorial acceleration (not taking into account centripetal acceleration). Using two-body dynamics, we can derive escape and surface velocities, as well as resonance altitudes (analogous to Earth's geosynchronous orbits). Finally, the Hill radius indicates the threshold where the asteroid gravity starts to be felt with respect to the Sun, and is a measure of the locations of possible other satellites or debris. These dynamical parameters are listed in Table 3.

Table 3. Dynamical characteristics of the two NEA triple systems 2001 SN263 and 1999 CC.[2,3]

Characteristics	Alpha_{SN263}	Beta_{SN263}	Gamma_{SN263}	Alpha_{CC}	Beta_{CC}	Gamma_{CC}
Net eq. g (cm/s2)	0.0035	0.0125	0.0093	0.0006	0.0052	0.0028
Pole g (cm/s2)	0.026	0.013	0.0097	0.0155	0.0052	0.0029
Escape vel. (cm/s)	98.3	30.2	22.4	33.1	9.4	5.2
Surface vel. (cm/s)	66.2	4.1	3.2	23	0.5	0.3
Resonance alt. (km)	1.35	4.8	0.41	0.41	0.48	0.93
Hill radius (km)	347	101.8	75.7	86.2	24.1	13.2

Figure 3 shows the zero-velocity curves associated with each of the SN263 binary sets: Alpha-Beta and Alpha-Gamma, obtained with Equation 4. The analog Lagrangian points are indicated in the figure for the larger system only for clarity. The L_1 point indicates the limit between the two gravitational fields; particles closer to either Alpha or Beta at that point are more likely to stay in their respective vicinity. Note that due to a low enough mass ratio and a mild ellipsoidal body shape assumed, the L_4 and L_5 regions are stable. We also note that the second moon, Gamma, is well included within the gravity influence of Alpha, as opposed to being close to the L_1 point of the Alpha-Beta system. It is easy to see that an additional moon may have significant effects on the dynamics of the underlying binary system itself, and on particles/spacecraft in the vicinity, which we also show in the later section on numerical results.

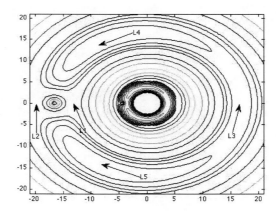

Figure 3. Zero-velocity curves for a binary system made of SN263 Alpha and Beta, with a mass ratio of 0.025, combined with a those of the inner binary Alpha-Gamma.

Figure 4 shows the zero-velocity curves within 1999CC. Note that the larger system is made of Alpha-Gamma in this case, implying slower velocities compared to the inner system.

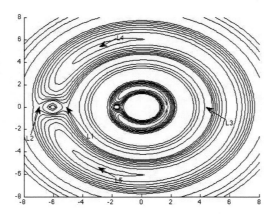

Figure 4. Zero-velocity curves for a binary system made of 1994CC Alpha and Beta, with a mass ratio of 0.02, combined with a those of the inner binary Alpha-Gamma.

Mission Scenarios

The study of particle dynamics is applicable to spacecraft dynamics, as long as the spacecraft is modeled as a point mass. We can find specific orbits that may be more stable, such as the analog equilateral Lagrangian points for a small secondary with mild ellipsoidal shape. However, even if any stable region found to exists may be beneficial for spacecraft station keeping, these regions may involve debris hazards. Operations of a robotic mission are usually designed taking into account both the mission objectives and spacecraft safety. A few options exist when approaching a triple system:

- The spacecraft can follow a non-colliding slow hyperbolic flyby of the asteroid system and/or its components.

- The spacecraft may be able to enter into orbit if the asteroids are large enough, and if the separation distance allows a minimum perturbations from third bodies, i.e. keeping a distance of a few kilometers from other system components at all times.

- The spacecraft can hover near the system or near one of the components, as was done by the Hayabusa mission,[16] as long as fuel expenditure is kept to a minimum (the Hayabusa spacecraft used 10 kg of fuel during a decent rehearsal).

A design concept, Amor, was developed to investigate the nature of the C-type asteroid 2001 SN263.[17] Although the mission itself is not detailed in this paper, we explain how the binary and single asteroid dynamics and tools were used in designing the operations. In the context of a robotic mission, it is necessary to adopt a no-risk approach when performing close surface and system characterization. In order to achieve this, slow hyperbolic flybys were planned for coarse resolution mapping and to determine with better precision the mass of each component. For safety and to achieve best results, the geometry adopted for the flybys was to keep the spacecraft on the sun-side of the entire system, with the components aligned, as much as possible. The hyperbolic flybys insure a no-impact trajectory, while the geometry adopted during the flyby reduce third and fourth body perturbations to a minimum, concentrating the masses in one point in space and time, as shown in Figure 6. To generate this figure, a slow hyperbolic flyby of Beta was simulated using the underlying Alpha - Beta binary asteroid equations of motion. The first slow hyperbolic flyby was to be performed perpendicular to the target Sun line, at a distance at least two times the system diameter to ensure safety.

Applying vis-viva equations at each of the asteroid component of the system, under the flyby geometry condition described, the best flyby conditions were determined in order to obtain 0.1% accuracy on Alpha's mass, and 1% accuracy for Beta and Gamma. Figure 5 indicates where the accuracy in the mass determination stands when obtained from flyby, given a distance and velocity flyby, accounting for 0.1 mm/s measurable accuracy between the start of the maneuver (v_{inf}) and the velocity at close approach. The operations integrated these ideal flyby conditions by including incremental flyby approaches, from 10 to 1 body radius, with a flyby speed between 0.5 and 1 m/s. For the 1994CC system, the required flyby velocity and close approach distance need to be reduced by an order of magnitude. Hence, to achieve 1% accuracy on each Alpha, Beta and Gamma, we require $\sim$ 10 cm/s flyby within 6 km, 3 km and 1 km, at least.

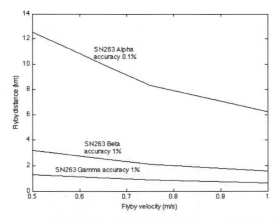

Figure 5. Flyby strategy at 2001 SN263 asteroid components to obtain at least 1% accuracy for determining their mass.

Performing each flyby takes between 10 and 20 hours, not accounting for the downlink and maneuver assessment of the operations. Hence, to account for estimating, planning, and executing each maneuver, the slow hyperbolic flybys were spaced by at least three days. Each asteroid could be encountered weekly. A Beta flyby is the simplest to implement, being further away from the system center of mass, and orbiting in a much longer period. Since Gamma and Alpha are 4.5 km apart with a 16 hrs window, it is difficult to justify passing in between both bodies. Since Alpha is massive, an accurate mass determination can be obtained from a 10 km approach, with a velocity less than 1 m/s to minimize the time near the asteroids and the perturbations from to Gamma. However, due to the relative close distance of Gamma, the mass of Gamma needs to be determined from the mutual dynamics; the flyby approach can only give $\sim$40% accuracy.

Since the mission objective included studying the asteroid composition, landing conditions were evaluated. The spacecraft could enter into orbit around Alpha, performing refined mapping, gravity determination, and landing site selection, prior to land. Landing can also be achieved from a flyby

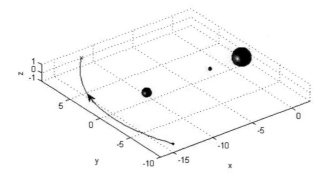

Figure 6. Flyby strategy at a triple asteroid system.

maneuver, where a calculated impulse would brings the spacecraft it close to the surface. As the system dynamics are of rapid scale compared to the communications delays, maneuvering in such an environment can be a challenge. It was accounted that descent and landing rehearsals would be performed to gain experience and knowledge of the system at such close proximity, as was proven by the Hayabusa mission.[16] For the navigation system used on this concept, the physical parameters obtained by the science payload was used to support proximity operations and landing, with surface features acting as landmarks to be tracked and used by an onboard system. The landing sequence uses a fixed axis capture strategy, as sketched in Figure 7. In this figure, the spacecraft approaches from a 6km platform orbit (a), capture the axis to be tracked (b), and then perform a final maneuver (c) to land near the identified site (d).[17]

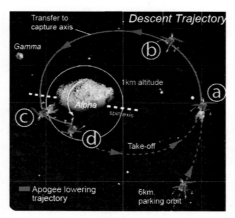

Figure 7. Landing strategy at a triple asteroid system: a) start from a ~6km platform orbit, b) transfer to a safe capture axis guidance, c) maneuver for landing, d) perform science experiment.[17]

NUMERICAL ANALYSES

A Monte-Carlo based n-body simulation was developed to help identify regions of orbital stability around multiple asteroid systems.[18] The simulation includes gravity between asteroid components (which can be modeled as rigid point structures when shape models exist), the spacecraft, and the sun, along with solar radiation pressure on the spacecraft. The adaptive 4/5 Cash-Karp Runge-Kutta method is used to integrate the resulting Newtonian equations of motion of all present bodies.

Defining the z-direction as the targets rotational (when available) or orbital axis, polar stability tests are conducted by uniformly distributing spacecraft positions in the xy plane, with polar velocities normally distributed (with sigma = 1/6) about the Keplerian speed for a circular orbit (to probe a range of eccentricities). Retrograde stability tests are performed similarly, with positions uniformly distributed in the $+xz$ half-plane and normally distributed retrograde velocities. Figure 8 depicts the polar and retrograde initial-position planes with sample orbits to show the geometry used in the numerical simulations plots. Note that in each case, the particle's velocity starts perpendicular to the plane.

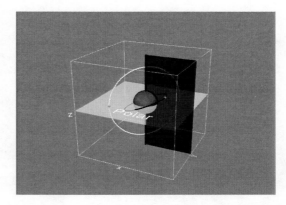

Figure 8. Representation of the polar and retrograde initial-position planes.

The systems are evolved for 20 days, and the spacecrafts orbit is then judged to be stable if it has neither impacted an asteroid component nor strayed further than five times its initial distance from the target component (ejection). Figures 9 to 11 show the results of over 700,000 test orbits around the components of the 2001 SN263 system. Orbits are mapped by their initial positions in the polar (subfigure on the left) or retrograde (subfigure on the right) planes around their target components, and colored by stability time: red/blue dots indicate early impacting/ejecting orbits, fading through yellow/mint for later impacting/ejecting orbits, to green for 20-day stable orbits. A spacecraft of 1200 kg with a 20 m^2 surface area was included in all cases.

The 2001 SN263 maps show complicated stability regions bearing little resemblance to the classical cones of stability seen in other single asteroid systems. In particular, the proximity of the Alpha and Gamma components strongly affects their respective stability maps. In Figure 9, a redder ring is visible at an altitude between 3.25 and 3.75 km from the surface of Alpha, which is Gamma's orbit location. The Gamma stability plot, Figure 11 shows a strong perturbation influence coming from Alpha, as orbits starting further than 1 km away from the surface of Gamma result in impact on Alpha. Note that Alpha is located at (-2.5, -2.9, -0.08) in this figure. In this figure, we can also observe a skewed instability region due to the orbital velocity of the system; orbits get a favorable

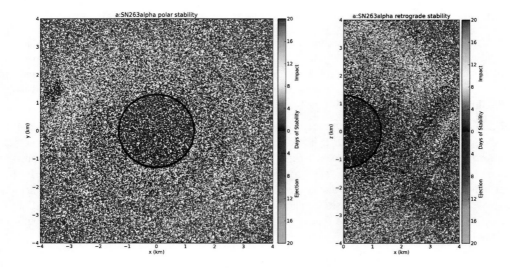

Figure 9. Orbit propagation at Alpha shown in a 1) polar view (left), 2) retrograde plane view (right). The initial positions of stable orbits are indicated in green, impacting orbits in red, and ejecting orbits in blue.

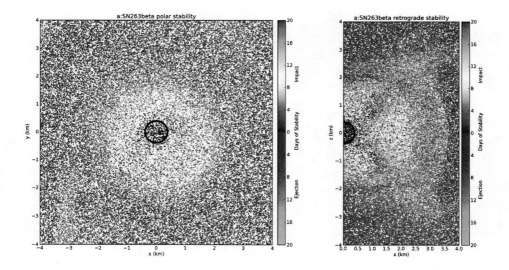

Figure 10. Orbit propagation at Beta shown in a 1) polar view (left), 2) retrograde plane view (right). The initial positions of stable orbits are indicated in green, impacting orbits in red, and ejecting orbits in blue.

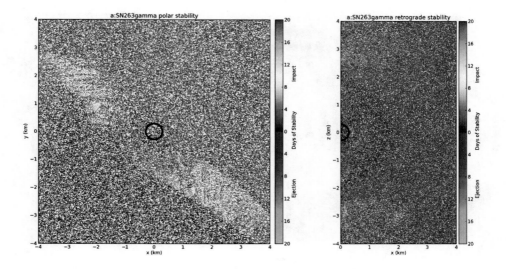

Figure 11. Orbit propagation at Gamma shown in a 1) polar view (left), 2) retrograde plane view (right). The initial positions of stable orbits are indicated in green, impacting orbits in red, and ejecting orbits in blue.

"push" in the leading edge region of Gamma, while particles get slowed down on the other side. On the other end, Beta itself behaves similar to a single asteroid, where a slight cone of stability is visible in its retrograde stability plot, Figure 10. We note that the solar radiation pressure reduces retrograde stability at low inclinations, where the sun is closest to the spacecrafts orbital plane. Figure 12 contains polar (subfigure on the left) and retrograde (subfigure on the right) stability maps computed for Beta without the effects of solar radiation pressure.

We recorded stability statistics in Table 4 for all three components, including the results for Beta without solar radiation effects for better comparison. As expected, more than 60% of the test cases result in escape at satellites Beta and Gamma, whereas more than 95 % cases either orbit or impact Alpha. The stability is reduced by almost 20 % when adding solar radiation pressure.

Debris Applications

The zero-velocity curves represented by Equation 4 and shown in Figures 3 and 4 give a first estimate of the regions of attraction associated with each gravity field. For a system like 2001 SN263, the presence of Gamma may complicate or accelerate particles dynamics. At 1994 CC, Gamma being external to Alpha-Beta brings perturbations at least three order of magnitude smaller than the Alpha or Beta 3rd body perturbations.

For SN263, the numerical simulations discussed above and presented in Figures 9 to 11 and Table 4 gives a better quantification of particles' fate. These results can be compared to earlier work on ejecta within a binary system.[19] We note that the assumptions for this study can be close to the underlying binary system of the NEA triple systems studied here: 1) systems with Alpha less than 10 km in diameter, with a rotation rate faster than the mutual orbit rate, approaching the disruption

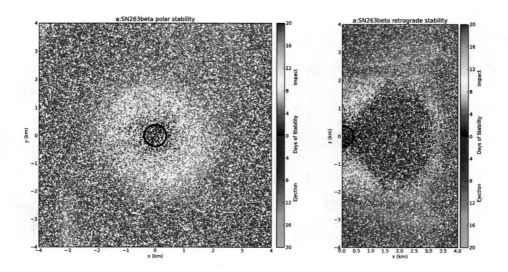

Figure 12. Orbit propagation at Beta without solar radiation pressure shown in a 1) polar view (left), 2) retrograde plane view (right). The initial positions of stable orbits are indicated in green, impacting orbits in red, and ejecting orbits in blue.

Table 4. Spacecraft stability results, for stable, impacting, or escaping orbits, at each component of the triple asteroid system 2001 SN263, including the effect of the solar radiation pressure (SRP).

2001 SN263 system	% stable orbits	% impacting orbits	% escaping orbits
Alpha polar	44.8	50.8	4.2
Alpha retro	42.5	54.2	3.2
Beta polar	0.8	28.7	70.5
Beta retro	5.0	34.2	60.8
Gamma polar	1.7	44.5	53.8
Gamma retro	19.4	10.6	70.0
Beta polar, no SRP	1.1	27.9	71.0
Beta retro, no SRP	23.7	21.1	55.2

limit, 2) the presence of a small elongated ellipsoidal secondary, with an average rotation that is synchronous with the mutual orbit rate. As listed in Table 1, 2001 SN263 and 1994CC potentially fit this description, although some differences exist. SN263 Beta is not locked with Alpha, although seems to be in close resonance with Gamma (both having a spin period near 15 hrs, which for Gamma is in synchronous orbital motion). In the case of 1994CC, Beta has a very low mass ratio while the spin period is undefined.

Results of this study indicated that re-impact of the ejecta was the major outcome, situated within the 20° latitude north and south of Alpha's equator, with a re-impact time scale of tens of hours.[19] An interesting observation was that multiple orbits could be observed for particles being trapped within the secondary gravity field influence. This study revealed the fast-scale nature of small particles' fate within a binary system. The numerical simulations performed for SN263 reach a similar conclusion where re-impact or escape could be observed well within a few days. As future work, we want quantify the possible added perturbations of a non-synchronous Beta rotation spin on debris fields, and compare with the ejecta dynamics of a single asteroid.[20]

CONCLUSION

In this paper, we study triple asteroid systems in the context of spacecraft applications. Approximations to binary systems are outlined using existing analytical tools and results. We then describe a mission scenario and show refined numerical results. Future work involves investigating the effects of different mass distribution, and including the system configuration inclinations and eccentricities. Simulations will also be extended to include other multiple asteroid systems.

ACKNOWLEDGMENT

The authors wish to acknowledge the inputs from KinetX, specifically discussions with David Dunham, Bobby Williams and Jerry Horsewood. Also to be thanked is the Amor mission team and the Mission Design Center staff at NASA Ames Research Center for their valuable input and feedback on the topic. We thank the SETI Institute REU program funded by the National Science Foundation for supporting this research. Dr. Franck Marchis was supported under award number AAG-0807468.

REFERENCES

[1] F. Marchis, P. Descamps, D. Hestroffer, and J. Berthier, "Discovery of the Triple Asteroidal System 87 Sylvia," *Nature*, Vol. 436, 2005, pp. 822–824.

[2] M. Nolan, E. Howell, L. Benner, S. Ostroa, J. Giorgini, M. Busch, L. Carter, R. Anderson, C. Magri, D. Campbell, J.-L. Margot, R. V. Jr., and M. Shepard, "(153591) 2001 SN263," *IAU Circular*, Vol. IAUC 8921, 2008.

[3] M. Brozovic, L. Benner, M. Nolan, E. Howell, C. Magri, J. Giorgini, P. Taylor, J.-L. Margot, M. Busch, M. Shepard, L. Carter, J. Jao, J. v. Brimmer, C. Franck, M. Silva, M. Kodis, D. Kelley, M. Slade, A. Bramson, K. Lawrence, J. Pollock, P. Pravec, D. Reichart, K. Ivarsen, J. Haislip, M. Nysewander, and A. Lacluyze, "(136617) 1994 CC," *IAU Circular*, Vol. IAUC 9053, 2009.

[4] D. Scheeres, "Stability of Relative Equilibria in the Full Two-Body Problem," *Annals of the New York Academy of Sciences*, Vol. 1017, 2004, pp. 81–94.

[5] J. Bellerose and D. Scheeres, "The Restricted Full Three-Body Problem: Application to Binary System 1999 KW4," *Journal of Guidance, Control, and Dynamics*, Vol. 31(1), 2008, pp. 162–171.

[6] E. Fahnestock and D. Scheeres, "Simulation of the Full Two Rigid Body Problem using Polyhedral Mutual Potential and Potential Derivatives Approach," *Celestial Mechanics and Dynamical Astronomy*, Vol. 96(3-4), 2006, pp. 317–339.

[7] D. Scheeres and S. Augenstein, *Spacecraft Motion about Binary Asteroids*, Vol. 116 of *Astrodynamics 2003, Part II, Advances in the Astronautical Sciences Series*, pp. 991–1010. 2003.

[8] F. Marchis, P. Descamps, M. Baek, A. Harris, M. Kaasalainen, J. Berthier, D. Hestroffer, and F. Vachier, "Main Belt Binary Asteroidal Systems with Circular Mutual Orbits," *Icarus*, Vol. 196(1), 2008, pp. 97–118.

[9] F. Marchis, P. Descamps, J. Berthier, D. Hestroffer, F. Vachier, M. Baek, A. Harris, and D. Nesvorn, "Main Belt Binary Asteroidal Systems with Eccentric Mutual Orbits," *Icarus*, Vol. 195(1), 2008, pp. 295–316.

[10] D. Scheeres, E. Fahnestock, S. Ostro, J. Margot, L. Benner, S. Broschart, J. Bellerose, J. Giorgini, M. Nolan, C. Magri, P. Pravec, P. Scheirich, R. Rose, R. Jurgens, E. D. Jong, and S. Suziki, "Dynamical Configuration of Binary Near-Earth Asteroid (66391) 1999 KW4," *Science*, Vol. 314, 2006, pp. 1280–1283.

[11] S. Ostro, J. Margot, L. Benner, J. Giorgini, D. Scheeres, E. Fahnestock, S. Broschart, J. Bellerose, M. Nolan, C. Magri, P. Pravec, P. Scheirich, R. Rose, R. Jurgens, E. D. Jong, and S. Suziki, "Radar Imaging of Binary Near-Earth Asteroid (66391) 1999 KW4," *Science*, Vol. 314, 2006, pp. 1276–1280.

[12] J. Fang, J. L. Margot, M. Brozovic, M. C. Nolan, L. A. M. Benner, and P. A. Taylor, "Orbits of near-Earth asteroid triples 2001 SN263 and 1994 CC: properties, origin, and evolution," *Astronomical Journal*, Vol. 141 (154), 2011.

[13] J. Danby, *Fundamentals of Celestial Mechanics*. VA: Willmann-Bell, second ed., 1992.

[14] B. Flannery, W. Press, S. Teukolsky, and W. Vetterling, *Numerical Recipies in C, The Art of Scientific Computing*. Cambridge University Press, second ed., 1996.

[15] V. Reddy, M. Gaffey, M. Schaal, and D. Takir, "Physical Characterization of First Triplet Near-Earth Asteroid (153591) 2001 SN263," *ACM*, Vol. 8244, 2008.

[16] A. Fujiwara, J. Kawaguchi, D. K. Yeomans, M. Abe, T. Mukai, T. Okada, J. Saito, H. Yano, M. Yoshikawa, D. J. Scheeres, O. Barnouin-Jha, A. F. Cheng, H. Demura, R. W. Gaskell, N. Hirata, H. Ikeda, T. Kominato, H. Miyamoto, A. M. Nakamura, R. Nakamura, S. Sasaki, and K. Uesugi, "The Rubble-Pile Asteroid Itokawa as Observed by Hayabusa," *Science*, Vol. 312, 2006, pp. 1330–1334.

[17] T. Jones, P. Lee, J. Bellerose, R. DeRosee, J. Chartres, J. McCarthy, D. Mayer, P. Bhavsar, G. Mungas, D. Osterman, T. Prettyman, J. Goldsten, D. Lawrence, D. Dunham, J. Horsewood, H. Sanchez, J. Heldmann, P. Smith, B. Williams, E. Fahnestock, M. Gaffey, M. Nolan, P. Thomas, A. Hildebrand, R. Farquhar, G. Benedix, J. Veverka, H. Yano, and R. Elphic, "A Lander to Investigate a C-type Triple Near-Earth Asteroid System: 2001 SN263," *42nd Lunar and Planetary Science Conference*, Vol. 2695, 2011.

[18] K. Burns, F. Marchis, and J. Bellerose, "Orbital Stability of Spacecraft Exploring Multiple Asteroid Systems," *Bulletin of the American Astronomical Society*, Vol. 43, 2011.

[19] E. Fahnestock, D. Durda, K. Houssen, and D. Scheeres, "Surface Impact or Blast Ejecta Behavior in a Small Asteroid System with Application to in-situ Observation," *2010 AAS/AIAA Space Flight Mechanics Meeting*, Vol. AAS 10-248, 2010.

[20] D. Scheeres, D. Durda, and P. Geissler, "The Fate of Asteroid Ejecta," *Asteroid III*, 2002, pp. 162–171.

IMPLEMENTATION OF THE NSTAR THRUSTER TO SUPPORT GRAVITY-TRACTOR OPERATIONS

Dario O. Cersosimo[*]

The NSTAR ion engine model, designed for the DS1 and Dawn missions, is implemented in a gravity-tractor spacecraft to support hovering operations. The model takes under consideration the operational limits of the thruster as well as the Isp profile for varying throttling levels. A gravity-tractor system was modeled and subject to operate under different guidance laws over a variety of asteroid configurations. Our results indicate the importance of an accurate propulsion system model for the gravity-tractor by showing that under certain scenarios, the propellant efficiency of the dynamic hovering laws is improved with respect to the classical inertial hovering.

INTRODUCTION

The gravity-tractor (GT) is an asteroid deflection strategy where a spacecraft uses its own mass to exert a slight gravitational acceleration on a small celestial body over long periods of time.[1] This goal is achieved by applying thrust to keep the spacecraft in an inertial hovering state relative to the center of mass of the asteroid. Due to Newton's law of gravitation, the asteroid will accelerate at a rate proportional to the spacecraft mass and the inverse of the squared distance between the two bodies. The simplest GT scheme consists on a spacecraft with a pair of canted thrusters continuously thrusting to balance the gravitational pull. These thrusters are tilted away from the asteroid to prevent their exhaust plumes from impinging on the surface of the asteroid.

Since its introduction, the GT concept had gained substantial popularity among the planetary defense community and many studies have been done proposing alternative dynamical configurations to improve its efficiency. McInnes,[2] studied the alternative of placing a GT spacecraft in a displaced non-Keplerian orbit with the intention to alleviate the problem of the canted engines that is a key issue for a gravity tractor operating in inertial hovering. This configuration could reduce the thrust demanded by the engines. Wie,[3] elaborates further on the work by McInnes by proposing a constellation of multiple GTs hovering in a pair of displaced non-Keplerian orbits. In the same article, Wie discusses a solar sail alternative to propel a GT during prolonged deflection missions. Fahnestock *et al.,*[4] investigated the coupled dynamics between the GT spacecraft and the asteroid using polyhedral models to analyze the performance for two different GT configurations: a pendulum-shaped and a novel bar-shaped spacecraft, both powered by nuclear electric engines. In their work they point out the effects of the coupled dynamics in the operational performance of the GT. Yeomans *et al.,*[5,6] suggested that a GT mission could be implemented in combination with an impulsive deflection

---

[*]Department of Mechanical and Aerospace Engineering, University of Missouri, E1412 Lafferre Hall, Columbia, Missouri 65211, USA. Phone: 787-565-8958. Email: dario_cersosimo@hotmail.com

system. In this context, a 1-ton GT propelled by solar-electric thrusters is used to fine-tune the deflection maneuver to ensure the new trajectory will not pass through a resonance keyhole, resulting in subsequent collision with Earth several years later. During the towing stage, the GT can serve as a transponder providing precise orbit determination of the target asteroid. In addition, the GT deflection strategy is not sensitive to uncertainties regarding the asteroid surface characteristics, while is gentle gravitational pull is unlikely to cause fragmentation of "rubble-pile" bodies held together by mutual gravity.

We extend further on the GT concept by introducing a novel hovering mode intended to increase the towing merits of the system. For this we shall rely on the observation that most minor celestial bodies in the solar system differ from a spherical shape and can be represented relatively better by an ellipsoidal model.[7] Contrary to the classical GT that hovers in an inertial frame relative to the asteroid center of mass, we consider a hovering spacecraft that is continuously moving towards and away from the asteroid's center of mass. Such motion occurs along the towing vector and is synchronized with the rotation period of the asteroid. The periodic decrement in distance between the centers of mass of the two bodies increases the gravitational pull the GT exerts on the asteroid, consequently increasing its Δv. We refer to this hovering mode as the extended gravity-tractor (xGT).

Maintaining hovering for prolonged periods will require the use of highly efficient propulsion systems. Although the implementation of a low-thrust system to support a GT hovering over a small asteroid has been considered earlier,[3,5,6] no detailed study exist addressing its performance while considering a high fidelity model of an ion thruster and other subsystems. We emphasize on the importance of such study since it could provide the planetary defense community and mission planners with important information regarding the feasibility of a GT mission while paving the road for advanced technical studies on the subject. We consider a GT system equipped with a set of NSTAR thrusters inherited from the technology-demonstrator mission Deep Space 1 and the recent asteroid-chaser spacecraft, Dawn.[8,9] The NSTAR thrusters were designed to be throttled up or down in order to compensate for the varying flux of solar power along the spacecraft's interplanetary cruise; with the throttling sequence taking place at time intervals on the order of several tens of hours. However, its implementation on a GT system could require throttling sequences at shorter time scales. These time scales might be in the order of several minutes or shorter, depending on the hovering environment, which may be driven by factors like the shape and gravity distribution of the asteroid, its spin rate, hovering locus and hovering strategy.

The objective of this work is to examine the performance of the GT and the xGT propelled by a set of NSTAR thrusters. In the process we modeled a simplified GT spacecraft with particular emphasis on the operational constraints of its propulsion system and performed a first-order analysis to examine the Δv merits and fuel penalties due to the xGT versus the classical GT as a function of the asteroid shape and rotation rate.

GRAVITY-TRACTOR MECHANICS

Asteroid Model

Lets begin by assuming that a small Earth-threatening asteroid can be modeled as a solid homogeneous triaxial ellipsoid of semiaxes $a > b > c$, constant density distribution ρ, and gravitational parameter $\mu = \frac{4}{3}\pi G \rho abc$, where $G = 6.6695 \times 10^{-11}$ N·m²/kg² is the universal gravitational constant. The gravitational potential V, of a triaxial ellipsoid at an exterior point is given by Ivory's theorem,[10] resulting in the following expression,

$$V = \frac{3}{4}\mu \int_{\kappa_0}^{\infty} \left(1 - \frac{\xi^2}{a^2 + \kappa} - \frac{\eta^2}{b^2 + \kappa} - \frac{\zeta^2}{c^2 + \kappa}\right) \times \frac{d\kappa}{\sqrt{(a^2 + \kappa)(b^2 + \kappa)(c^2 + \kappa)}}. \tag{1}$$

The solution to Equation (1) is a function of elliptic integrals and it is explicitly derived in MacMillan, 1958.[11] In addition, consider the asteroid is spinning about its principal axis at a rate ω in a direction perpendicular to the towing vector, usually embedded in the orbital plane of the asteroid. This condition allows us to place the GT spacecraft in the equatorial plane of the asteroid.

Hovering Dynamics and Control Scheme

The general guidance law for the GT with respect to an inertial coordinate frame whose origin is at the center of mass of the asteroid is,

$$\ddot{\mathbf{r}} + \frac{\partial V}{\partial \mathbf{r}} = \frac{\mathbf{T}_c}{m}, \tag{2}$$

where m is the mass of the GT, V is the gravitational potential and $\mathbf{T}_c$ is the applied thrust. Inertial hovering is obtained by setting

$$\frac{\mathbf{T}_c}{m} = \frac{\partial V}{\partial \mathbf{r}}. \tag{3}$$

Equation (2) corresponds to the ideal guidance law for the classical GT keeping the GT spacecraft fixed in inertial space.

An alternative guidance law is presented here to maximize the gravitational pull of the GT on the asteroid. Based on the previous assumptions about the asteroid shape and spin, the distance between the two bodies (i.e., asteroid and GT) can be adjusted by guiding the GT motion in synchrony with the asteroid's rotation, as shown in Fig. 1. As seen from a reference frame located at the center of mass of the asteroid whose principal direction $\hat{\mathbf{i}}$ is along the desired towing vector, the GT spacecraft moves towards and away the asteroid as it spins. At a time $t = t_1$ the spacecraft is positioned at a distance $d_1 = a + h$ from the asteroid's center of mass. At a later time $t = t_2$ the attitude of the asteroid changed by angle $\omega(t_2 - t_1) = \pi/2$ and the spacecraft had displaced to a distance $d_2 = h + b$ closer to the center of mass of the asteroid. This dynamical configuration repeats twice for every asteroid's revolution. For our purposes, the amplitude of the translational motion is defined as the difference between the semiaxes a and b (or $d_1 - d_2 = a - b$) though, other regimes could be considered. At time t_1 and t_2 the distance from the surface of the asteroid is set to $h = 80$ meters. The distance h, in addition to the extension of the semimajor axis, determine the hovering farthest position with respect to the center of mass of the asteroid. This dynamical state is what we present in this study as the extended gravity-tractor (xGT), and is defined by the following guidance law,

$$\frac{\mathbf{T}_c}{m} = \frac{\partial V}{\partial \mathbf{r}} - \omega_{GT}^2 \frac{a - b}{2} \cos(\omega_{GT} t) \cos(\lambda)\hat{\mathbf{i}}. \tag{4}$$

The first term on the right balances the gravity acceleration from the asteroid and the second term induces the spacecraft to move in periodic motion along the towing direction $\hat{\mathbf{i}}$, where $\omega_{GT} = 2\omega$ is the angular rate of change of the xGT displacement and λ corresponds to the hovering latitude. Notice that when $\lambda = 90^o$ the translational motion vanish and the GT hovers inertially. In this work we assume $\lambda = 0^o$.

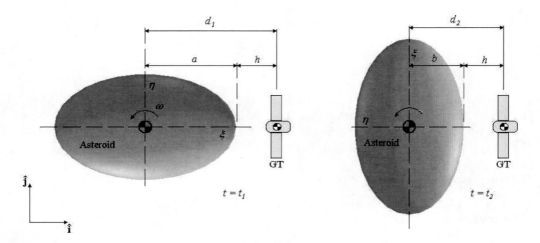

Figure 1. Schematic of the xGT hovering strategy.

To compensate for the action of additional environmental disturbances due to a poor gravity field model, solar wind dynamic pressure, radiation pressure and thruster inaccuracies, a closed-loop term $\mathbf{u}$ can be added into Eqs. (3) and (4). The performance of the GT and xGT is tested under the combined action of a dead-band controller (DB) and a proportional-derivative controller (PD). The DB controller is employed along the $\hat{\mathbf{j}}$-axis of the spacecraft and the PD controller operates on the $\hat{\mathbf{i}}\hat{\mathbf{k}}$-plane.

$$\mathbf{u} = -k_p\left(\mathbf{r} - \mathbf{r}_{ref}\right) - k_d\left(\dot{\mathbf{r}} - \dot{\mathbf{r}}_{ref}\right). \tag{5}$$

The PD controller for the xGT follows the reference state given by,

$$\mathbf{r}_{ref} = \left[a + h - \frac{a-b}{2}(1 - \cos(2\omega t))\cos(\lambda), 0, 0\right]^T, \tag{6}$$

$$\dot{\mathbf{r}}_{ref} = \left[\omega(a-b)\sin(2\omega t)\cos(\lambda), 0, 0\right]^T. \tag{7}$$

The DB controller is used to correct for the disturbances caused by the asteroid rotation along the $\hat{\mathbf{j}}$-axis. The displacement tolerance is 10 m and 10% hysteresis is modeled.

Gravity-Tractor Model

We considered a generic GT spacecraft with an initial mass $m_0 \approx 10^3$ kg, at the beginning of the hovering stage. The propulsion system consist on a set of five NSTAR thrusters with throttling capabilities able to supply a maximum thrust of 92 mN. The engine configuration presented here is based on earlier works by Yeomans *et al.*[5,6] A general spacecraft layout is shown in Fig. 2 with each engine labeled as T_i, where $i = 1, 2, 3, 4, 5$. Thrusters labeled T_1, T_2 and T_3 combine to control the motion in the $\hat{\mathbf{i}}\hat{\mathbf{k}}$-plane whereas thrusters T_4 and T_5 control the dynamics along the $\hat{\mathbf{j}}$-axis. The solar arrays extend along the $\hat{\mathbf{k}}$-axis. The approximated area of the solar array is 30 m^2 if we assume four NSTAR thrusters are operating simultaneously at 1 AU.

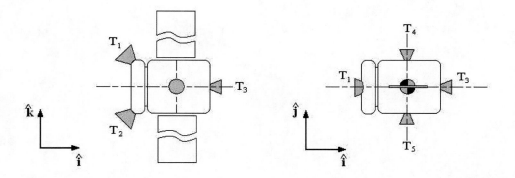

Figure 2. Thrusters layout for the xGT spacecraft.

The amount of thrust supplied by each engine is the vector sum of the required acceleration in the $\hat{\mathbf{i}}$, $\hat{\mathbf{j}}$ and $\hat{\mathbf{k}}$ directions. The canted orientation of thrusters T_1 and T_2 requires the introduction of a mixing algorithm commanding the engines to provide the correct amount of thrust T_i along the desired coordinate. Therefore, given the components of acceleration $a_{\hat{i}}$, $a_{\hat{j}}$ and $a_{\hat{k}}$, the mixing logic for thrusters T_1, T_2 and T_3 is defined as follows:

$$T_1 = \begin{cases} \frac{m|a_{\hat{i}}|}{2\cos\beta} + \frac{m|a_{\hat{k}}|}{\sin\beta}, & \text{if } a_{\hat{i}} > 0 \text{ and } a_{\hat{k}} \leq 0; \\ \frac{m|a_{\hat{k}}|}{\sin\beta|}, & \text{if } a_{\hat{i}} = 0 \text{ and } a_{\hat{k}} \leq 0; \\ 0, & \text{otherwise.} \end{cases} \tag{8a}$$

$$T_2 = \begin{cases} \frac{m|a_{\hat{i}}|}{2\cos\beta} + \frac{m|a_{\hat{k}}|}{\sin\beta}, & \text{if } a_{\hat{i}} > 0 \text{ and } a_{\hat{k}} \geq 0; \\ \frac{m|a_{\hat{k}}|}{\sin\beta|}, & \text{if } a_{\hat{i}} = 0 \text{ and } a_{\hat{k}} \geq 0; \\ 0, & \text{otherwise.} \end{cases} \tag{8b}$$

$$T_3 = \begin{cases} m\,|a_{\hat{i}}| + \frac{m|a_{\hat{k}}|\cos\beta}{\sin\beta}, & \text{if } a_{\hat{i}} < 0 \text{ and } a_{\hat{k}} \neq 0; \\ \frac{m|a_{\hat{k}}|\cos\beta}{\sin\beta}, & \text{if } a_{\hat{i}} = 0 \text{ and } a_{\hat{k}} \neq 0; \\ 0, & \text{otherwise.} \end{cases} \tag{8c}$$

The mixing logic for thrusters T_4 and T_5 is rather simple. These thrusters fire in opposite directions and their firing sequence is evaluated under the following conditions:

$$T_4 = \begin{cases} m \left| a_{\hat{j}} \right|, & \text{if } a_{\hat{j}} < 0; \\ 0, & \text{otherwise.} \end{cases} \tag{9a}$$

$$T_5 = \begin{cases} m \left| a_{\hat{j}} \right|, & \text{if } a_{\hat{j}} > 0; \\ 0, & \text{otherwise.} \end{cases} \tag{9b}$$

Upon determination of the thruster firing mix, we need to evaluate whether the resulting amount of thrust is inside the operational range of the engine. Each thruster is allowed to operate within the range $T_{min} \leq T \leq T_{max}$ where, for the NSTAR thruster, $T_{min} = 0.020$ N and $T_{max} = 0.092$ N. If at a given time the thrust to be applied falls below the 20 mN threshold, then the engine fires at its lower limit and engines in the opposite direction switch-on to compensate for the excess thrust. For all the thrusters the following condition must be satisfied:

$$T_i + \delta a \geq T_{min}, \tag{10}$$

where δa is an additional thrust offset to ensure the commanded thrust is inside the operational range of the thruster. For engines T_1, T_2 and T_3 we have,

$$\delta a_1 \geq T_{min} - T_1, \tag{11a}$$

$$\delta a_2 \geq T_{min} - T_2, \tag{11b}$$

$$\delta a_3 \geq \frac{T_{min} - T_3}{2 \cos \beta}, \tag{11c}$$

where,

$$\delta a = \max \left(\delta a_1, \delta a_2, \delta a_3 \right). \tag{12}$$

The conditions dictated by Eq. (11) guarantee that Eq. (10) is always satisfied for thrusters T_1, T_2 and T_3. The on-off nature of the DB controller along the $\hat{\mathbf{j}}$-axis guaranties that thrusters T_4 and T_5 operate inside limits. These thrusters are set to provide 0.025 N of thrust operating.

NSTAR Thruster Model

The mass flow rate of propellant is determined from the rocket equation i.e.,

$$\dot{m} = \frac{T_{net}}{g_0 I_{sp}}, \tag{13}$$

where $T_{net} = \sum_{i=1}^{5} T_i$ is the total thrust supplied by the five thrusters at a given time and $g_0 = 9.81$ m/s^2 is the acceleration of Earth's gravity at sea level. The I_{sp} values are obtained from the results presented by Brophy et al.,[12] and fitted into a 4th-order polynomial to generate a continuous function of I_{sp} vs. thrust. For each thruster the I_{sp} is approximated by

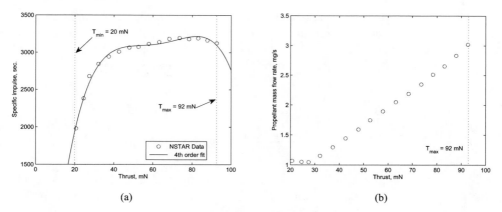

(a) (b)

Figure 3. NSTAR Engine performance plots.

$$I_{sp} = A_0 T^4 + B_0 T^3 + C_0 T^2 + D_0 T + E_0. \tag{14}$$

The coefficients in Eq. (14) are: $A_0 = -4.170 \times 10^8$ sec/N^4, $B_0 = 1.046 \times 10^8$ sec/N^3, $C_0 = -9.628 \times 10^6$ sec/N^2, $D_0 = 3.887 \times 10^5$ sec/N and $E_0 = -2.751 \times 10^3$ seconds; and T is the applied thrust in units of Newtons (N). Equation (14) is plotted in Fig. 3(a) where the hollow circles are the I_{sp} values from the original data and the continuous line represents the 4th-order fit determined by Eq. (14). The propellant mass flow rate is plotted against the applied thrust in Fig. 3(b). The propellant mass rate follows a near linear relation with respect to the applied thrust except near the lower limit threshold T_{min} (Fig. 3(b)).

Engine Canting Angle

The classical gravity-tractor requires the thrusters T_1 and T_2 to be canted to avoid plume impingement on the asteroid. This canting angle is influenced by the asteroid shape and orientation, as well as spacecraft distance from the surface. Earlier studies considered the canting angle to be fixed.[5,6] However, in order to reduce cosine losses we assume that thrusters T_1 and T_2 have gimbals allowing them to adjust their pointing direction for the changing asteroid orientation and spacecraft position. This assumption ensures that at any time engines T_1 and T_2 operate with minimum cosine losses.

From a geometric perspective, the engine minimum canting angle is determined by finding the two vectors tangent to the ellipsoid surface that intersect the center of mass of the GT. Thus, the problem consist on finding the points of tangency $P_s = [x_s, y_s, z_s]$ on the surface of the ellipsoid that belongs to the vectors intersecting at the GT position $P_0 = [x_0, y_0, z_0]$. Finding P_s requires to solve a system of three algebraic equations,

$$A_s x^2 + B_s y^2 + C_s z^2 + D_s xy + E_s xz + F_s yz + G_s = 0, \tag{15a}$$

$$\nabla f(x_s, y_s, z_s) \cdot (\mathbf{r}_s - \mathbf{r}_0) = 0, \tag{15b}$$

$$\mathbf{n}_k \cdot (\mathbf{r}_s - \mathbf{r}_0) = 0. \tag{15c}$$

Generally speaking, Equation (15a) defines an ellipsoidal figure whose coefficients A_s, B_s, C_s, D_s, E_s, F_s and $G_s = -abc$ depend on the dimensions and orientation of the ellipsoid. Equation (15b) corresponds to the planes tangent to the surface of the ellipsoid $f(x, y, z)$, defined in Equation (15a), containing the points P_s and P_0. Equation (15c) is the plane defined by the points P_0, P_s and $P_k = (0, 0, 1)$ such that $\mathbf{n}_k = \overrightarrow{P_0 O} \times \overrightarrow{P_0 P_k}$. Equations (15) are simplified when the spacecraft is constrained to the $\hat{\mathbf{i}}\hat{\mathbf{k}}$-plane, reducing the system (15) into a set of two equations,

$$A_s x_s^2 + C_s z_s^2 + 2E_s x_s z_s + G_s = 0, \tag{16a}$$

$$z_s + \frac{A_s x_s + E_s z_s}{C_s z_s + E_s x_s}(x_s - x_0) = 0, \tag{16b}$$

where Eq. (16a) is the ellipse resulting from the cross sectional cut of the ellipsoid $f(x, y, z)$ in the $\hat{\mathbf{i}}\hat{\mathbf{k}}$-plane, and Eq. (16b) defines a line through P_s and P_0. The solutions to the system in (16) are,

$$x_s = \frac{-G_s \mp \frac{E_s \sqrt{-G_s(G_s + A_s x_0^2)}}{\sqrt{(A_s C_s - E_s^2)}}}{A_s x_0}, \tag{17a}$$

$$z_{s_{1,2}} = \pm \frac{\sqrt{-G_s(G_s + A_s x_0^2)}}{x_0 \sqrt{(A_s C_s - E_s^2)}}. \tag{17b}$$

The angle between the lines formed by the solutions to Eq. (16b) is bisected through the centerline of the spacecraft and added to the plume-half-width ϕ_{phw},

$$\beta = \frac{1}{2}\left(\sin^{-1}\frac{z_{s_1}}{\|\mathbf{r}_0 - \mathbf{r}_{s_1}\|} + \sin^{-1}\frac{z_{s_2}}{\|\mathbf{r}_0 - \mathbf{r}_{s_2}\|}\right) + \phi_{phw}. \tag{18}$$

In practice, a tolerance margin is often considered for irregular shaped bodies.[5,6]

SIMULATION RESULTS AND DISCUSSION

In this section we report on the performance of the GT and the novel xGT in terms of towing merits and propellant penalties for the GT system described above. The numerical simulations were performed using Matlab integrator *ode113* with absolute and relative tolerances of 10^{-8} and 10^{-6}, respectively. The physical parameters for the asteroid model used in these simulations are summarized in Table 1. The configuration parameters of the GT spacecraft are given Table 2.

Our experiment consisted in determining the performance of the GT and xGT in terms of deflection Δv and propellant cost, when subject to operate over bodies of different axial ratios and rotation rates. The task is accomplished by defining a set of ellipsoidal bodies representing an idealized asteroid whose gravitational parameter $\mu = GM$ remains constant for the entire range of body ellipticities. The semiaxes a and b are related by their mutual eccentricity e_{ab} such that,

$$b = a\sqrt{1 - e_{ab}^2}. \tag{19}$$

The semiaxis c is defined to be a fraction of b, say $c = \varepsilon b$, such that $0 < \varepsilon < 1$. It follows that the asteroid's mass M, can be expressed in terms of a and e_{ab},

$$M = \frac{4}{3}\pi\rho a^3 \left(1 - e_{ab}^2\right)\varepsilon. \tag{20}$$

Since mass and density are fixed parameters, we need to find the corresponding major semiaxis a that satisfies Equation (20) i.e.,

$$a = \left(\frac{3M}{4\pi\rho\varepsilon\left(1 - e_{ab}^2\right)}\right)^{1/3}. \tag{21}$$

Equations (19) and (21) were evaluated using axial eccentricity values e_{ab} between 0.05 and 0.90.

Table 1. Asteroid Parameters

Density, kg/m^3	Mass, kg	e_{ab}	ε	Period, hs
2300	2.6×10^{10}	[0.05 - 0.9]	0.75	[2 - 24]

Table 2. GT System Parameters

Initial Mass, kg	Initial position, m	PD Controller Gains, k_p, k_d	DB Controller box, m
1150	$a + 80$	5e-6, 3e-2	±10

The gravitational action by the GT on the asteroid produces an acceleration

$$\dot{v} = \frac{Gm(t)}{r^2}, \tag{22}$$

where r is the distance from the asteroid center of mass and $m(t)$ accounts for the decreasing mass of the spacecraft given by Eq. (13). From Eqs. (13) and (22) the net Δv imparted on the asteroid is estimated as,

$$\Delta v = \frac{Gm_0 I_{sp}g_0}{a_{net}r^2}\left(1 - \exp^{-\frac{a_{net}}{I_{sp}g_0}\Delta t}\right), \tag{23}$$

where $a_{net} = T_{net}/m$. Recall that the second term on the right of Eq. (4) causes the distance between the asteroid and spacecraft to change periodically. Therefore, the Δv on the asteroid due to the xGT is estimated using the average hovering distance over the towing period Δt. Notice that for a fixed hovering distance, the Δv imparted on the asteroid decreases as the propellant is depleted.

Figure 4 shows the Δv exerted on the asteroid after one day of hovering as a function of the asteroid shape. The towing Δv was determined from Eq. (23) and measured along the desired towing direction. From Eq. (21) and the fixed initial altitude h, the increment in the major axis places the GT spacecraft farther from the center of mass of the asteroid, decreasing the gravitational

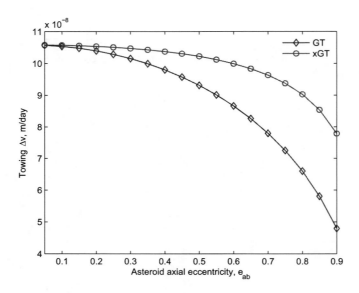

Figure 4. Towing Δv as a function of the asteroid axial eccentricity.

pull. In contrast, the periodic displacement of the xGT reduces the average distance between the two bodies augmenting the Δv on the asteroid. In the most optimistic scenario, the xGT can improve Δv merits by 62% over the GT.

Figure 5(a) shows the daily rate of propellant mass used by a GT operating in the inertial hovering mode for 10 days. The propellant mass is plotted against the asteroid rotation period and the axial eccentricity of a hypothetical ellipsoidal asteroid. These independent parameters i.e., rotation period and axial eccentricity, represent the major environmental factors driving the hovering performance of the GT and xGT. Thus, for a fixed initial altitude h, the axial eccentricity is an indirect measure of the GT distance from the center of mass of the asteroid. The grid is divided into 18×18 elements each representing the propellant daily rate for a single hovering scenario. The contours displayed in Fig. 5(a) indicate that propellant usage has a stronger dependence on the axial eccentricity than on the rotation period. Indeed, depletion rates remain relatively constant when hovering over bodies with small axial eccentricities i.e., $e_{ab} < 0.3$. A sharp increase in propellant rate occurs when the axial eccentricity ranges between 0.3 and 0.6. The propellant consumption rate has its maximum of 0.3 kg/day inside a region bounded by $0.4 < e_{ab} < 0.6$ and rotation periods are longer than 0.2 days (5 hours). Once axial eccentricity becomes greater than 0.6, the propellant mass rate drops to about 0.26 kg/day. Another interesting feature is the faster increase in propellant rate near rotation periods of 0.4 days (≈ 10 hrs) and axial eccentricities $e_{ab} \approx 0.2$. This phenomenon coincides with the locus of a resonance orbit whose period is twice the asteroid rotation. Following the definition given by Broschart,[13] the radius of the first resonant orbit is:

$$r_\omega = \left(\frac{\mu}{\omega^2}\right)^{1/3}. \tag{24}$$

78

Since the initial position of the GT spacecraft is given by

$$r_0 = a + h, \tag{25}$$

we can identify the cases where the initial hovering location falls in the vicinity of the resonance radius by equating $r_0 = r_\omega$, substituting Eq. (21) into Eq. (25) and using the fact that the period $P = 2\pi/\omega$; resulting in:

$$P = n \left[\frac{4\pi^2}{\mu} \left[\left(\frac{3M}{4\pi\rho\varepsilon(1 - e_{ab}^2)} \right)^{1/3} + h \right]^3 \right]^{1/2} \tag{26}$$

The factor n on the right-hand side of Eq. (26) is an integer number representing the ration between the orbital period of the resonance and the rotation period of the asteroid. The resonance region for $n = 2$ is shown in Figs. 5(a) and 5(b).

Figure 5(b) shows the averaged propellant consumption rate for the gravity-tractor operating under the dynamic hovering mode (xGT) given in Eq. (4). Again, the propellant mass rate is plotted against the asteroid axial eccentricity e_{ab} and rotation period. Minimum propellant consumption occurs in the region where the axial eccentricity is less or equal than 0.3 for most rotation periods. The propellant depletion rate displays a sharp increase within a narrow region between $e_{ab} \geq 0.3$ and $e_{ab} < 0.5$ for rotation periods longer than 0.3 days (≈ 7 hours). The effect of the resonance radius can be observed as well near the region of $e_{ab} = 0.2$ and $P = 0.4$ days. Shorter rotation periods influence increased propellant consumption at smaller eccentricities. Beyond $e_{ab} > 0.5$ the increase in propellant consumption is fairly shallow. The propellant mass increases again towards the lower right corner of the map where the axial eccentricities reach 0.9 and the rotation periods are extremely short (≈ 2 hours). Here a void region indicates that the thrust required to support hovering has exceeded the maximum capacity of the thrusters (92 mN). At this point we shall mention that such extreme scenario is unlikely to be found in nature, since rubble pile bodies cannot support the centrifugal forces due to such short rotation periods and extreme axial eccentricities.

The results shown in Fig. 5(b) indicate an increased dependence of the propellant consumption rate with respect to the rotation rate of the asteroid. For those hovering scenarios where the asteroid axial eccentricity e_{ab}, is less than 0.3 and the rotation periods are longer than 0.2 days (5 hours), the amount of propellant depleted between the GT and xGT are fairly similar. A sharp increase in propellant rate is reflected for axial eccentricities between 0.3 and 0.4 and rotation periods longer than 0.3 days (or 7.2 hours). Once the axial eccentricities become larger than 0.5 the increase in propellant expenditures are mild, but the xGT being more efficient in this region.

Figure 6 maps the propellant penalties (in percent) between the GT and xGT strategies for each hovering scenario. Negative values indicate the xGT has used less propellant than the GT under the same scenario, and positive values favor the efficiency of the classical GT in terms of propellant cost. The propellant efficiency of the xGT seems to be favored for all $e_{ab} > 0.3$ with up to 30% in propellant savings within a narrow region bounded by $0.3 < e_{ab} < 0.5$ and rotation periods longer than 0.4 days (10 hours). For eccentricities smaller than 0.3 both, the GT and the xGT appear to perform alike. However the GT appear to be favored within a small region corresponding rotation periods shorter than 0.2 days (approximately less than 5 hours) and axial eccentricities between 0.1 and 0.3.

Figure 7 displays the operation of the lateral thrusters (i.e., T_4 and T_5) for the GT (Fig. 7(a)) and for the xGT (Fig. 7(b)). These thrusters operate in an On-Off basis to control the lateral dynamics

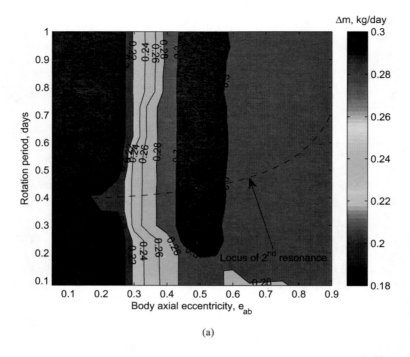

(a)

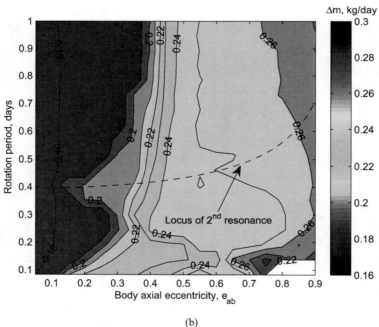

(b)

Figure 5. Propellant consumption rate: (a) GT and (b) xGT.

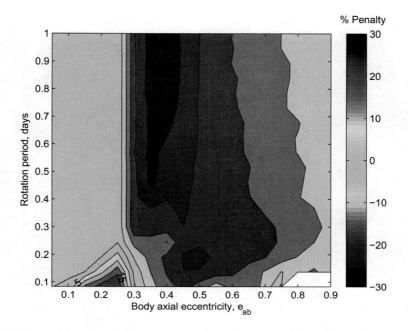

Figure 6. Propellant penalties between the GT and xGT.

of the tractor spacecraft, by activating every time the spacecraft has deviated by 10 m from its prescribed location along the $\hat{\mathbf{j}}$-axis. These results show that the severity of perturbations in the lateral dynamics of the GT are greater when operating over highly prolate bodies whose axial eccentricities are greater than 0.3 for either of the hovering modes. For example, during the 10 days length of the simulation, no lateral corrections were performed when the GT was subject to operate under rotation periods ranging from 0.5 to 1 day and $e_{ab} < 0.2$. However when hovering takes place in the vicinity of a resonance region, the deviations along the $\hat{\mathbf{j}}$-axis are grater. This phenomenon is clearly seen when $e_{ab} = 0.2$ and $P = 0.4$ days. As the rotation periods become shorter ($P < 0.3$ days) the effects of perturbations along the $\hat{\mathbf{j}}$-axis seem to decrease since the plots do not indicate evidence of violation of spatial boundaries along the $\hat{\mathbf{j}}$-axis during the time span of the simulation. Eventually, if the simulations are to be run for longer periods we will observe thruster activity across the entire map.

Figure 8 shows the amplitude variation of the canting angle of thrusters T_1 and T_2. The amplitude variation indicates how much the pointing angle of the thrusters needs to change during one asteroid rotation in order for the plumes to be always tangent to the asteroid's surface, therefore offering the minimum canting angle. For $e_{ab} < 0.7$ the amplitude variation is greater for the GT and does not exceeds 5 degrees. For the classical GT the amplitude of the variation depends only of the axial dimensions and the hovering locus. For the xGT the amplitude of β depends of the body axes, the hovering locus and the amplitude of its translational motion. The amplitude of the canting angle indicates the amount for which the cosine losses can be reduced if a gimbaled system is employed to control the thrusters tilt β rather than leaving it fixed at its maximum value.

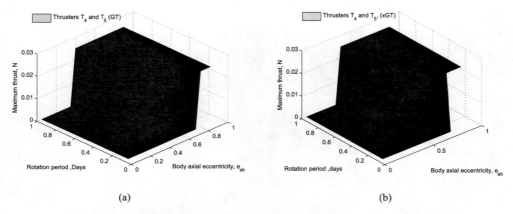

(a)   (b)

Figure 7. Activity of the lateral thrusters (T_4 and T_5): (a) GT and (b) xGT.

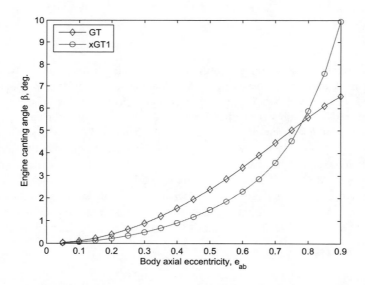

Figure 8. Amplitude variation of the canting angle of thruster T_1 and T_2 over one hovering cycle.

CONCLUSION

We presented a model of a gravity-tractor spacecraft and studied its performance over range of hovering scenarios. These scenarios were based on the asteroid shape and rotation state. We extended on the GT concept by introducing a novel hovering strategy able to improve, in certain cases, the deflection Δv imparted on the asteroid by up to 60% with respect to the classical GT. A realistic model of the NSTAR thruster was implemented on the spacecraft model and the performance of the system was compared between the two hovering strategies: GT and xGT. We found that the propellant efficiency of the xGT was favored with respect to the classical GT with propellant savings of up to 30%. These findings suggest that, under the scenarios considered here and the arbitrary configuration of the GT spacecraft, the xGT may be able to improve asteroid towing merits as well as propellant efficiency relative to the GT. Future works will be focusing on improving the accuracy of the GT model by increasing the detail level of the GT system and its operating environment.

REFERENCES

[1] E. Lu and S. Love, "Gravitational Tractor for Towing Asteroids," *Nature*, Vol. 438, 2005, pp. 177–178.

[2] C. R. McInnes, "Near Earth Object Orbit Modification Using Gravitational Coupling," *Journal of Guidance, Control, and Dynamics*, Vol. 30, May 2007, pp. 870–873, 10.2514/1.25864.

[3] B. Wie, "Dynamics and Control of Gravity Tractor Spacecraft for Asteroid Deflection," *Journal of Guidance, Control, and Dynamics*, Vol. 31, No. 5, 2008, pp. 1413 – 1423, 10.2514/1.32735.

[4] E. G. Fahnestock and D. J. Scheeres, "Dynamic Characterization and Stabilization of Large Gravity-Tractor Designs," *Journal of Guidance, Control, and Dynamics*, Vol. 31, No. 3, 2008, pp. 501–521, 10.2514/1.32554.

[5] D. Yeomans, S. Bhaskaran, S. Broschart, S. Chesey, P. Chodas, M. Jones, and T. Sweetser, "Near-Earth Object (NEO) Analysis of Transponder Tracking and Gravity Tractor Performance," jpl task plan no. 82-120022, Jet Propulsion Laboratory, September 2008.

[6] D. Yeomans, S. Bhaskaran, S. Broschart, S. Chesley, P. Chodas, T. Sweetser, and R. Schweickart, "Deflecting a Hazardous Near-Earth Object," Granada, Spain, 1st IAA Planetary Defense Conference: Protecting Earth From Asteroids, 27-30 April 2009.

[7] D. J. Scheeres, "Dynamics About Uniformly Rotating Triaxial Ellipsoids: Applications to Asteroids," *Icarus*, Vol. 110, 1994, pp. 225–238.

[8] M. D. Rayman, P. Varghese, D. H. Lehman, and L. L. Livesay, "Results from the Deep Space 1 technology validation mission," *Acta Astronautica*, Vol. 47, No. 2-9, 2000, pp. 475 – 487. Space an Integral Part of the Information Age, DOI: 10.1016/S0094-5765(00)00087-4.

[9] M. D. Rayman, T. C. Fraschetti, R. C. A., and C. T. Russell, "Dawn: A mission in development for exploration of main belt asteroids Vesta and Ceres," *Acta Astronautica*, Vol. 58, 2006, pp. 605–616.

[10] J. Ivory, "On the Attractions of Homogeneous Ellipsoids," *Philosophical Transactions of the Royal Society of London*, Vol. 99, 1809, pp. 345–372.

[11] W. D. MacMillan, *The Theory of Potential*. Dover Publications Inc., 1 ed., 1958.

[12] J. R. Brophy, R. Y. Kakuda, J. E. Polk, J. R. Anderson, M. G. Marcucci, D. Brinza, M. D. Henry, K. K. Fujii, K. R. Mantha, J. F. Stocky, J. Sovey, M. Patterson, V. Rawlin, J. Hamley, T. Bond, J. Christensen, H. Cardwell, G. Benson, J. Gallagher, M. Matranga, and D. Bushway, "Ion Propulsion System (NSTAR) DS1 Technology Validation Report," Tech. Rep. JPL Publication 00-10, Jet Propulsion Laboratory, October 2000.

[13] S. B. Broschart and D. J. Scheeres, "Control of Hovering Spacecraft Near Small Bodies: Application to Asteroid 25143 Itokawa," *Journal of Guidance, Control, and Dynamics*, Vol. 28, March 2005, pp. 343–354.

VALIDATION OF A FINITE SPHERE GRAVITATION MODEL WITH APPLICATIONS TO COMET 67P/CHURYUMOV-GERASIMENKO

Paul V. Anderson[*] and Bogdan Udrea[†]

Improved finite element methodology for estimating small body gravitational fields is validated through numeric analyses of asteroid Itokawa. The model implements uniform spherical elements of two sizes to obtain a fill ratio that approximates the asteroid shape model geometry to nearly 100% efficiency. The gravitational model is applied to the geometry of comet 67P/Churyumov-Gerasimenko and employed to analyze orbital dynamics and stability of ESA's *Rosetta* spacecraft during initial stages of the comet mapping and characterization phase in the comet environment.

INTRODUCTION

Finite element methodology provides an alternative technique for approximating the gravitational fields of primitive small bodies (asteroids, comets, planetary satellites) – the irregular geometries of these entities are an immediate consequence of local gravitation too weak to impel spherical shape;[1] accurate estimation of small body attraction is thus a challenging problem in astrodynamics. Finite element schemes attempt to pack the given polyhedral shape model geometry with uniform elements of a predefined density that approximate the asymmetrical mass distribution of the body; the gravity potential of each element is thereby linearly superimposed upon the field point of interest to generate the associated attraction model. Werner and Scheeres[2] derived the gravitation of a constant-density tetrahedron and employed their formulation with a tetrahedral mesh of asteroid Castalia; though this scheme is very accurate in that it optimally models surface geometries, it suffers from computational sluggishness and laborious implementation. Park et. al.[1] developed a finite sphere configuration for asteroid Itokawa that employs the sphere point-mass (*mascon*) potential for improved efficiency and ease of implementation, but with a poor packing density that afflicts the accuracy of the gravitational field model generated. This paper introduces herein an improved *mascon* arrangement that alleviates the packing density issue to offer an optimal combination of field accuracy and computing efficiency.

The finite sphere gravitational model developed within this analysis is furthermore applied to the geometry of comet 67P/Churyumov-Gerasimenko, the targeted body of the European Space Agency (ESA) *Rosetta* mission. Scheduled for cometary rendezvous in May 2014, the Rosetta orbiter will commence global mapping operations within the environment of the nucleus in August 2014[3] – it is therefore within the interests of this study to implement the gravitational model herein presented to provide a preliminary characterization of orbital dynamics in the vicinity of the comet. The stability of polar trajectories in the Sun-terminator plane will be lightly perused, and the viability of each for practical mission implementation during initial stages of the global mapping phase will be assessed. The preliminary results thereby achieved shall serve as the basis for analyses with more complexity and thus demonstrate the flexibility, convenience, and general applicability of this attraction model.

[*]Undergraduate Student (AE), Embry-Riddle Aeronautical University, Daytona Beach, FL, USA; andersp2@my.erau.edu.
[†]Assistant Professor (AE), Embry-Riddle Aeronautical University, Daytona Beach, FL, USA; udreab@erau.edu.

OFFSET SPHERE AND CORRECTION ELEMENT GRAVITATION MODEL

The offset sphere and correction element gravitational model provides an improved finite element methodology for modeling the attraction fields generated by irregularly-shaped small bodies. This model is an extension of the finite sphere configuration developed by Park et. al.,[1] in which the small body geometry is filled with constant-density* spherical elements of a uniform radius; thereafter the finite element approximation of the small body has been constructed, the gravitational potential of each element may be employed to generate the corresponding attraction field. As the acceleration of a spherical point-mass element is computationally efficient and straightforward to implement, finite sphere configurations are advantageous for preliminary orbital and astrodynamics analyses of small bodies. Furthermore, such finite element schemes are preferred over spherical harmonics approaches when the Stokes coefficients are not well-defined or analysis inside the Brillouin sphere is necessary.

Synthesis of Gravitation Model

The accuracy of a finite element approximation is dependent upon how strongly the configuration packs the interior of the small body surface geometry – it is therefore convenient to define a quality metric denoted the *volumetric efficiency*, equivalent to the percent ratio of total encompassing finite element volume to total volume of the examined small body. Expressed for a finite sphere scheme:[†]

$$\eta \equiv \frac{4\pi}{3} R_i^3 N_s \left(\frac{1}{6} \sum_{j \, \in \, facets} \det \left[\mathbf{r}_j^1, \mathbf{r}_j^2, \mathbf{r}_j^3 \right] \right)^{-1} \times 100\% \tag{1}$$

wherein $\mathbf{r}_j^k$ is representative of the kth vertex position vector of the jth surface facet (this formulation of net shape model volume sums the individual volumes spanned by polyhedral elements with vertex coordinates $\mathbf{r}_j^k$ and $\mathbf{0}$, the center of mass of the small body). The offset sphere and correction element gravitation model therefore seeks to achieve an optimal 100% volumetric efficiency for any arbitrary small body geometry to which it is applied – the configuration implements finite spheres of two sizes to densely pack the interior of the examined shape model and thereby provide a highly accurate and computationally efficient means for preliminary approximation of the small body gravitational field.

Implementation of the offset sphere and correction element model begins with the construction of a bounding box of finite sphere elements that completely encompasses the small body shape model geometry (precision polyhedral shape model of the examined small body is assumed to be available). The spherical elements are of user-specified radius and elemental density, arranged within a uniform lattice structure as illustrated within Figure 1(a)-1(b). To augment the packing density of this sphere configuration, a sequence of operations is performed upon the lattice structure to transform it into a hexagonal-close pack (HCP) arrangement, as illustrated within Figure 1(c)-1(d). Note that the HCP arrangement has been mathematically proven the highest-density spherical configuration attainable, regular or irregular;[4] because the density of this packing arrangement never exceeds $\pi / \sqrt{18} \approx 0.74$, spherical correction elements are therefore required to supplement the volumetric efficiency to unity.

---

*Park et. al. note that distinct elemental density values may be individually applied to each fitted sphere for purposes of modeling the internal density distribution of the small body; though this technique may be equivalently applied to the offset sphere and correction element model presented within this study, it is not necessary for the validation of this model.

[†]Reference the Notation section at the end of this document for succinct explanation of all mathematical symbolism.

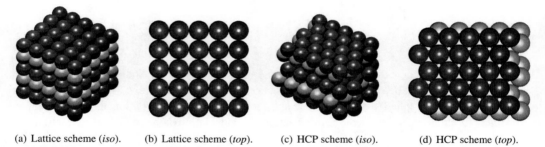

(a) Lattice scheme (*iso*).   (b) Lattice scheme (*top*).   (c) HCP scheme (*iso*).   (d) HCP scheme (*top*).

Figure 1. Sphere packing configurations for finite element approximation of small body geometry.

Spherical correction elements are embedded within the principal HCP arrangement by assembling reference tetrahedrons that span the interstitial vacancies between each cluster of four offset spheres. The correction elements are thus constructed by inscribing a maximum-dimension sphere into each tetrahedron: uncovered space internal to the HCP arrangement is thus minimized, and the volumetric efficiency of the configuration is correspondingly augmented. To establish control over the resultant size of the correction elements, a scaling parameter α is employed to increase the dimensions of the bounding tetrahedrons. For $\alpha = 0$, the centers of the clustered offset spheres provide the vertices of the bounding tetrahedron; for $\alpha = 1$, positions located upon the outer periphery of each offset sphere (symmetrically farthest from the interstitial vacancy of the cluster) form the vertices of the bounding tetrahedron. These correction element configurations are respectively illustrated in Figure 2(a)-2(b) for $\alpha = 0$ and Figure 2(c)-2(d) for $\alpha = 1$. Thereafter the correction elements have been constructed throughout the principal HCP arrangement, the centers of *all* offset spheres and correction elements are numerically tested for position – only those elements that have a center residing within the shape model are retained for the final configuration; spheres that do not satisfy this criterion are eliminated.

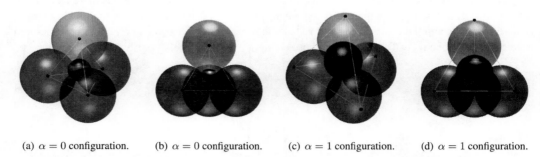

(a) $\alpha = 0$ configuration.   (b) $\alpha = 0$ configuration.   (c) $\alpha = 1$ configuration.   (d) $\alpha = 1$ configuration.

Figure 2. Bounding tetrahedron schemes for construction of the correction elements. As the scaling parameter is increased, the tetrahedrons correspondingly expand such that similarity in their geometry is preserved (tetrahedral edges thus remain parallel).

After the offset sphere and correction element model has been finalized for an arbitrary small body shape model geometry with the methodology outlined above, the density of the correction elements must be modified to conserve the total mass of the utilized shape model; this adjustment is necessary to mitigate the overlapping of the correction elements onto the primary offset spheres, as depicted in Figure 2. Formulated mathematically, this density correction is a statement of conservation of mass:

$$\rho_c \equiv \left[\left(\frac{\rho_s}{6} \sum_{j \in facets} \det \left[\mathbf{r}_j^1, \mathbf{r}_j^2, \mathbf{r}_j^3 \right] \right) - \frac{4\pi}{3} R_i^3 N_s \rho_s \right] \left(\frac{4\pi}{3} \tilde{R}_i^3 N_c \right)^{-1} \tag{2}$$

wherein R_i and $\tilde{R}_i$ denote the corresponding radius and N_s and N_c are the number of fitted elements for the primary offset spheres and auxiliary correction elements, respectively. Thereafter this density correction has been applied, the offset sphere and correction element gravitational model is complete and ready for implementation as the numerical basis for calculation of the small body attraction field.

Application to Asteroid 25143 Itokawa

The offset sphere and correction element model was adapted to polyhedral shape model geometry of the well-studied asteroid 25143 Itokawa with the methodology delineated above for validation of this finite sphere configuration. Implementing low-resolution shape model geometry* comprised of 4285 surface facets, 1775 offset elements with 12-m radius and 3555 correction elements with 7.2-m radius (corresponding to $\alpha = 0.652$) were constructed – collectively, with a net shape model volume of 0.0185 km³, this configuration achieves a volumetric efficiency of 100.02%. Utilizing a principal density[5] of 2.000 g/cm³, the correction element density was adjusted to 2.003 g/cm³ to retain a total mass of 3.69×10^{10} kg (corresponding to a gravitational parameter $\mu \approx 2.46 \times 10^{-9}$ km³/s²). The offset sphere and correction element gravitational model for asteroid Itokawa is illustrated alongside various geometrical constructions of the small body within Figure 3(d). The polyhedral shape model geometry employed in the construction of this configuration is depicted in Figure 3(a)-3(b); a 12-m sphere lattice scheme that achieves a meager 52.31% efficiency is shown in Figure 3(c) for reference.

Gravitational Attraction of Finite Sphere

Employment of the finite sphere model requires implementation of the gravitational potential for each spherical element fitted inside the Itokawa shape geometry; computation of the gravitational acceleration exerted at a field coordinate residing exterior to the surface boundary is therein achieved through differentiation (by manner of the gradient operator) of the effective gravitational potential function at the examined position. Park et al.[1] demonstrate the gravitational potential and generated acceleration, respectively, for the finite sphere element model at a field coordinate designated by $\mathbf{r}$:

$$U_s(\mathbf{r}) = G\rho_s \sum_{i \in N_s} \frac{4\pi}{3} R_i^3 \frac{1}{\| \mathbf{r} - \mathbf{r}_i \|} \tag{3}$$

$$\frac{\partial U_s}{\partial \mathbf{r}} = -G\rho_s \sum_{i \in N_s} \frac{4\pi}{3} R_i^3 \frac{\mathbf{r} - \mathbf{r}_i}{\| \mathbf{r} - \mathbf{r}_i \|^3} \tag{4}$$

wherein R_i and $\mathbf{r}_i$ are representative of the radius and center coordinate vector of the ith spherical element, respectively. Note that the point mass approximation of this model assumes the equivalence of the uniform radius R_i and elemental density $\rho \; \forall \; i \in N_s$. The net gravitational contribution at the field position $\mathbf{r}$ must therefore incorporate the attraction of the offset sphere elements *and* correction sphere elements, the former utilizing user-specified radius and density, and the latter implementing deterministic values of these parameters that are uniquely defined by the configuration of this model.

---

*Asteroid Itokawa shape model may be obtained at: http://darts.isas.jaxa.jp/planet/project/hayabusa/shape.pl?model=past/

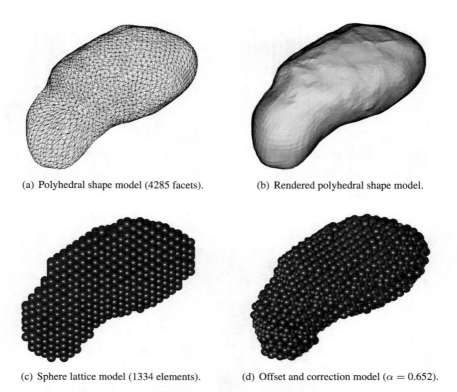

(a) Polyhedral shape model (4285 facets).

(b) Rendered polyhedral shape model.

(c) Sphere lattice model (1334 elements).

(d) Offset and correction model ($\alpha = 0.652$).

Figure 3. **Itokawa offset sphere and correction element gravitation model (1775 *blue* offset elements of 12-m radius; 3555 *red* correction elements of 7.2-m radius) shown with geometrical constructions of the small body. The volumetric efficiencies achieved by the elemental configurations in 3(c) and 3(d) are 52.31% and 100.02%, respectively.**

Gravitational Field Model

The offset sphere and correction element attraction model generated for 1775 fitted finite spheres and 3555 correction elements of 12-m and 7.2-m radii, respectively (corresponding to the elemental densities 2.000 g/cm^3 and 2.003 g/cm^3) is illustrated below in Figure 4; this gravitation model was constructed through an application of Equation 4 to the sphere configuration shown in Figure 3(d). The irregular gravitational attraction exerted near the surface of the asteroid becomes concentrically distributed farther from the center of mass, as anticipated by the preliminary findings of Park et. al.[1]

Comparison with Tetrahedron Model

Validation of the offset sphere and correction element gravitation model is achieved through direct comparison with the tetrahedron formulation implemented by Park et. al.[1] The polyhedral Itokawa shape model considered within this analysis was internally meshed into 6875 tetrahedral elements; these finite tetrahedrons were thereby employed to compute the gravitational attraction of the small body with methodology developed by Werner and Scheeres.[2] As this collective of constant-density tetrahedral elements characterizes the geometry of the small body with perfect volumetric efficiency, the attraction field generated with this configuration is implemented as the *truth model* for this study.

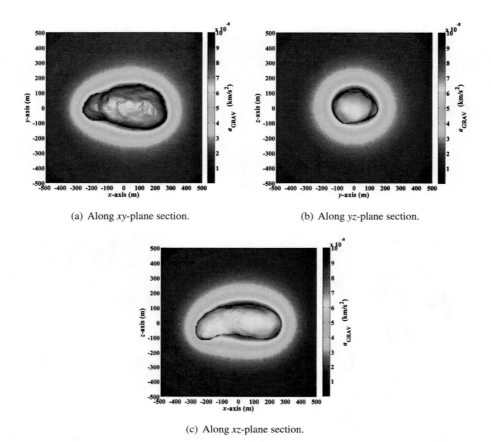

(a) Along xy-plane section.

(b) Along yz-plane section.

(c) Along xz-plane section.

Figure 4. Gravitational field model for Itokawa offset sphere and correction element model (1775 offset elements of 12-m radius and density 2.000 g/cm³; 3555 correction elements of 7.2-m radius and density 2.003 g/cm³). Gravitational attraction increases near the surface and becomes concentrically distributed away from the center of mass.

Comparison of the corresponding acceleration magnitudes is quantified with the error formulation:[1]

$$\lambda(\mathbf{r}) \equiv \frac{\| \, \partial U_t / \partial \mathbf{r} - \partial U_s / \partial \mathbf{r} \, \|}{\| \, \partial U_t / \partial \mathbf{r} \, \|} \times 100\% \qquad (5)$$

wherein $\partial U_t / \partial \mathbf{r}$ and $\partial U_s / \partial \mathbf{r}$ denote the gravitational attraction vectors generated by the tetrahedron and finite sphere configurations, respectively, at the field coordinate designated by $\mathbf{r}$. The volumetric efficiency of the offset sphere and correction element model inherently governs the accuracy of the gravitational field approximation achievable with this arrangement. Furthermore, this finite element scheme deteriorates as the field coordinate approaches the surface of the small body – the increased errors observed within these regions are an immediate consequence of the inadequacy of the sphere configuration in representing geometrically the surface structure of the examined small body shape.*

---

*Park et. al.[1] note that resolution of the surface variation problem may be accomplished by restructuring or applying an

The errors $\lambda(\mathbf{r})$ between the gravitational attraction magnitudes of the offset sphere and correction element model (1775 finite offset spheres of 12-m radius and 2.000 g/cm³ density; 3555 correction elements of 7.2-m radius and 2.003 g/cm³ density) and the tetrahedron model (6875 elements with 2.000 g/cm³ density) are illustrated below within Figure 5. The average field error $\bar{\lambda}(\mathbf{r}) \approx 0.3\%$ is indicative of the validity of this offset sphere and correction element model – as spherical elements are generally easier to implement and tremendously more computationally efficient than tetrahedral elements, this finite sphere configuration offers a convenient alternative to the commonly-employed tetrahedron gravitation scheme. Caution should be exercised for specific applications of this sphere configuration, however: though advantageous for rapid propagation in orbital dynamics and stability analyses, it *must not* serve as a replacement to the tetrahedron model in surface proximity operations.

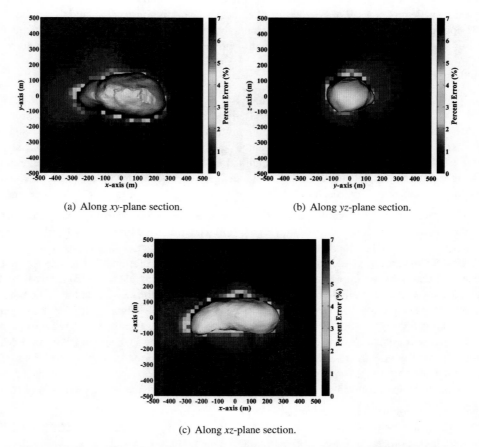

(a) Along *xy*-plane section.

(b) Along *yz*-plane section.

(c) Along *xz*-plane section.

Figure 5.   Comparison of gravitational acceleration magnitudes of offset sphere and correction element model (1775 offset spheres of 12-m radius; 3555 correction spheres of 7.2-m radius) with tetrahedron field model (6875 elements). Enhanced errors near the surface are a consequence of the poor geometric approximation at these positions.

appropriate density correction to the surface-intersecting elements; trivially, letting $R_i \rightarrow 0$ merely inflates computational cost and (rather counter-intuitively) *does not* enhance the volumetric efficiency of the finite sphere configuration presented within this study. For an explanation of this result, reference any text on the *Kepler Conjecture*, such as Hales's overview.[4]

APPLICATION TO COMET 67P/CHURYUMOV-GERASIMENKO

Comet 67P/Churyumov-Gerasimenko (67P/C-G) was selected as the new target body for the ESA *Rosetta* mission in 2003 following cancellation of launch to the original target, comet 46P/Wirtanen, on the basis of favorable orbital geometry for a probe rendezvous.[6] Though observational campaigns and scientific investigations rapidly painted a detailed portrait of the cometary nucleus, its geometry has remained inadequately characterized – a preliminary ellipsoidal representation of the comet has served as the foundation for a polyhedron gravitational field analysis performed by Bertrand et. al.[7] The Rosetta spacecraft was successfully launched on March 2, 2004, and after a circuitous ten-year journey across the solar system, is scheduled for rendezvous with the comet 67P/C-G in May 2014;* it is thus within the interests of this study to provide a more accurate approximation of the cometary attraction field with the offset sphere and correction element gravitational model presented herein. A polyhedral shape model more representative of comet geometry is constructed, and the applied finite sphere configuration is employed to analyze orbital dynamics of the Rosetta orbiter within the initial stages of the planned mapping and characterization phase to occur within the cometary environment.

Modeling of Comet Geometry

The preliminary ellipsoidal shape approximation to the nucleus geometries of the comet 67P/C-G proposed with the analytical formulation of Bertrand et. al.[7] was deemed insufficient for application of the offset sphere and correction element configuration presented within this analysis – polyhedral shape model data that more adequately represented realistic comet geometry were desired to sharpen the results of this study and other scientific examinations of the small body. Applicable methodology was therefore developed to construct the shape model geometry necessary for sufficient gravitational field approximations; this approach is to be further generalized for arbitrary small body geometries.

Cross-sectional geometries of the comet 67P/C-G nucleus (constructed using measurements from the Hubble Space Telescope) shown within Figure 6(a) were imported into the MATLAB workspace and transformed into binary logical matrices – image processing functionality was thereafter applied to each 256×256 pixel cross-sectional image to construct the configuration illustrated in Figure 6(b). Extrusion operations were implemented to generate a three-dimensional binary representation of the comet geometry, and the preliminary polyhedral shape model was thus assembled with the powerful surface meshing capabilities of the MATLAB *iso2mesh* toolbox.† Resultant node coordinates output by the meshing algorithm were thereafter centered about the approximate geometric centroid of the surface mesh; subsequent rotation of the node coordinates placed the shape model within the desired orientation, consistent with the direction of increasing pixel dimension examined within Figure 6(b). Finally, the node coordinates were effectively scaled such that the comet shape model would achieve $21.314 \, \text{km}^3$ in volume, equivalent to that of a 1.72-km-radius sphere (consistent with Lamy et. al.[6]).

The complete polyhedral shape model of comet 67P/C-G employed within this study is comprised of 2000 nodes and 3996 surface facets that collectively encompass a net volume of $21.314 \, \text{km}^3$; the irregular comet geometry achieves moderate axial ratios of $a/b = 1.28$ and $a/c = 1.45$, with overall dimensions of 4.37-km, 3.41-km, and 3.01-km along the body-fixed x-, y-, and z-axes, respectively. Assuming an approximate bulk density of 0.370 g/cm^3 (the upper limit of a predicted density range

---

*For a detailed explanation of the synthesis and objectives of the ESA *Rosetta* mission, reference Glassmeier et. al.[3]

†MATLAB *iso2mesh* toolbox may be downloaded from: http://iso2mesh.sourceforge.net/cgi-bin/index.cgi. Note that modification of the inbuilt functionality provided user-defined control over the maximum allowable node number: 2000 nodes were deemed sufficient, as further increase in this meshing parameter would yield precision surface reconstruction too cumbersome for this analysis – high accuracies should not be attempted with such a largely uncharacterized geometry.

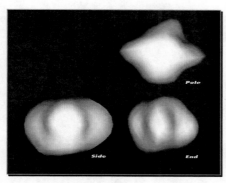

(a) Cross-sectional geometries of comet 67P/C-G.

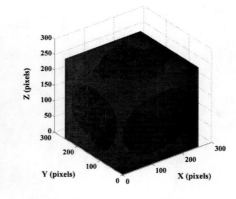

(b) Scheme for 3D binary image construction.

Figure 6. Cross-sectional models of the comet 67P/Churyumov-Gerasimenko nucleus, as created with Hubble Space Telescope measurements (*courtesy of NASA/ESA*) shown with the configuration required for generation of the 3D binary comet model imagery.

for comet 67P/C-G, as noted by Lamy et. al.[6]), the total mass of the comet model is 7.89×10^{12} kg. The cross-sectional geometry of this preliminary shape model is depicted in Figure 7; to the authors' knowledge, this is the most accurate geometric representation of comet 67P/C-G constructed to date.

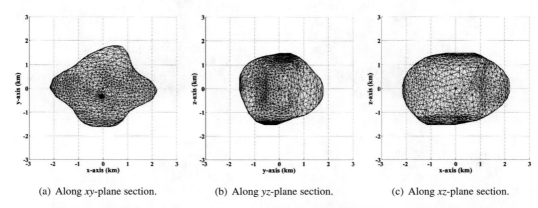

(a) Along *xy*-plane section.　　(b) Along *yz*-plane section.　　(c) Along *xz*-plane section.

Figure 7. Preliminary shape model geometry of comet 67P/Churyumov-Gerasimenko used for gravitational field analyses (approximate geometric centroid depicted as red circle). The shape model consists of 2000 nodes and 3996 surface facets that generate a net shape model volume of 21.314 km³ (equivalent to that of a 1.72-km-radius sphere).

Employing the representative shape model geometry developed for this study, 2036 offset spheres of 120-m radius and 4109 correction elements of 72.6-m radius (corresponding to $\alpha = 0.663$) were constructed for the offset sphere and correction element gravitation model of comet 67P/C-G; with net shape model volume 21.314 km³, this configuration achieves a volumetric efficiency of 100.03%. Using a principal density of 0.370 g/cm³, the correction element density was adjusted to 0.369 g/cm³ to conserve 7.89×10^{12} kg (corresponding to the gravitational parameter $\mu \approx 5.26 \times 10^{-7}$ km^3/s^2). The offset sphere and correction element gravitational model for comet 67P/C-G is shown alongside various geometrical constructions of the small body within Figure 8(d). The polyhedral shape model geometry employed in the construction of this configuration is depicted in Figure 8(a)-8(b); a 120-m sphere lattice scheme that achieves a meager 52.50% efficiency is given in Figure 8(c) for reference.

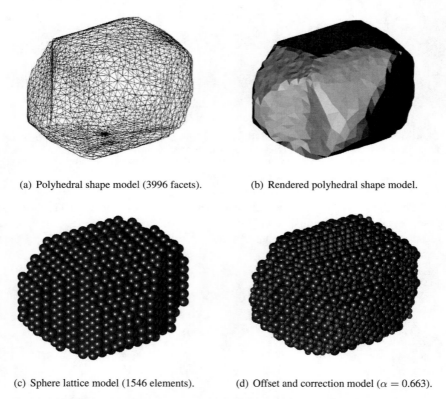

(a) Polyhedral shape model (3996 facets).   (b) Rendered polyhedral shape model.

(c) Sphere lattice model (1546 elements).   (d) Offset and correction model ($\alpha = 0.663$).

Figure 8. Comet 67P/Churyumov-Gerasimenko offset sphere and correction element model (2036 offset spheres of 120-m radius; 4109 correction spheres of 72.6-m radius) with geometrical constructions of the small body. The volumetric efficiencies achieved by the elemental configurations in 8(c) and 8(d) are 52.50% and 100.03%, respectively.

Gravitational Field Model

The offset sphere and correction element attraction model constructed for 2036 fitted finite spheres and 4109 correction elements of 120-m and 72.6-m radii, respectively (corresponding to the element densities 0.370 g/cm^3 and 0.369 g/cm^3) is depicted below within Figure 9; this gravitational model was generated through an application of Equation 4 to the sphere configuration shown in Figure 8(d). The irregular gravitational acceleration exerted near the surface of the comet becomes concentrically distributed farther from the center of mass (the magnitude of the gravitational attraction generated is approximately twice that exerted by asteroid Itokawa); this acceleration field estimation is of utmost significance to the astrodynamics analyses performed at the comet 67P/C-G for the Rosetta mission.

94

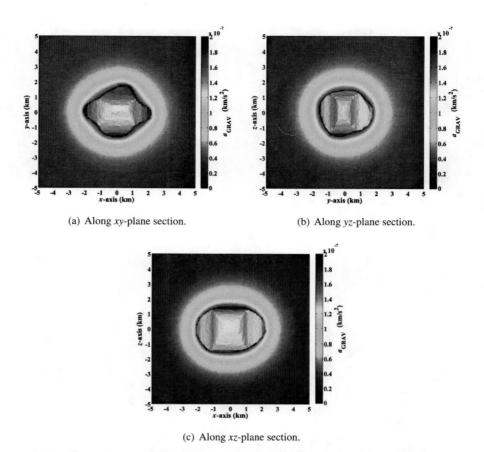

(a) Along *xy*-plane section.

(b) Along *yz*-plane section.

(c) Along *xz*-plane section.

Figure 9. Gravitational field for comet 67P/C-G offset sphere and correction element model (2036 offset elements of 120-m radius and density 0.370 g/cm^3; 4109 correction elements of 72.6-m radius and density 0.369 g/cm^3). Gravitational attraction increases near the surface and becomes concentrically distributed away from the center of mass.

Comparison with Tetrahedron Model

The errors $\lambda(\mathbf{r})$ between the gravitational attraction magnitudes of the offset sphere and correction element model (2036 finite offset spheres of 120-m radius and 0.370 g/cm^3 density; 4109 correction elements of 72.6-m radius and 0.369 g/cm^3 density) and the tetrahedron model (6719 elements with 0.370 g/cm^3 density) of comet 67P/C-G are depicted below within Figure 10. The average field error $\bar{\lambda}(\mathbf{r}) \approx 0.28\%$ is indicative of the validity of this offset sphere and correction element scheme – note that in a manner equivalent to that observed with asteroid Itokawa, this configuration deteriorates in accuracy as the field coordinate approaches the surface of the small body. If higher accuracies within these regions are demanded by analysis, problematic spherical elements immediately adjacent to and within the neighborhood of observed error may be eliminated from the final elemental configuration.

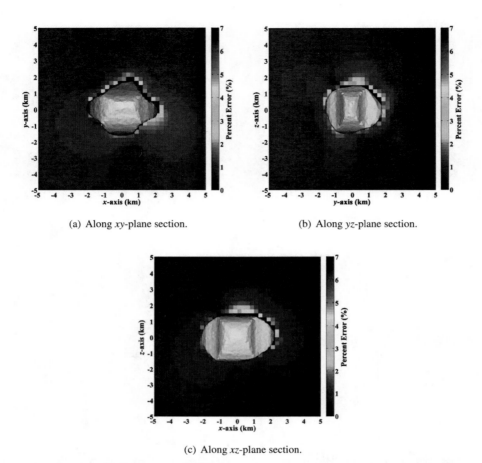

(a) Along xy-plane section.

(b) Along yz-plane section.

(c) Along xz-plane section.

Figure 10. Comparison of gravitation attraction magnitudes of offset sphere and correction element model (2036 offset spheres of 120-m radius; 4109 correction elements of 72.6-m radius) with tetrahedron field model (6719 elements). Enhanced errors near the surface are a consequence of the poor geometric approximation at these positions.

Orbital Dynamics for the *Rosetta* Mission

The global mapping and characterization phase for the Rosetta mission is scheduled to commence on August 22, 2014, following completion of the approximate 30-day far approach trajectory phase, at which radiometric measurements performed by the spacecraft are used to actuate orbital insertion and close approach operations at a distance of 60 comet-radii from the nucleus – a capture maneuver is to be conducted at roughly 25 comet-radii, and resultant polar orbits from 5 to 25 comet-radii will thereafter be implemented for global mapping operations until delivery of the spacecraft's lander on November 10, 2014.[3] During this characterization phase, five potential landing sites will be selected for close observation at a minimum distance of a single comet-radius.[3] It is thereby the objective of this analysis to quantify the orbital behavior and stability of the trajectories traversed by the Rosetta spacecraft during the mapping and characterization phase to occur within the cometary environment.

The implemented dynamical equations of motion governing the Rosetta spacecraft are cast within the body-fixed comet reference frame and therefore incorporate Coriolis and centripetal acceleration terms due to prograde rotation of the cometary nucleus. Casting the formulation of Scheeres et. al.:[8]

$$\ddot{\mathbf{r}} + 2\omega\hat{\mathbf{z}} \times \dot{\mathbf{r}} + \omega^2\hat{\mathbf{z}} \times (\hat{\mathbf{z}} \times \mathbf{r}) = \frac{\partial U_s}{\partial \mathbf{r}} + \mathbf{a}_\odot + \mathbf{a}_{\mathrm{SRP}} \tag{6}$$

wherein $\mathbf{a}_\odot$ is the third-body solar gravitation and $\mathbf{a}_{\mathrm{SRP}}$ is the solar radiation pressure perturbation.[*] The unit vector $\hat{\mathbf{z}}$ positioned along the axis of rotation is assumed parallel with the axis of maximum moment of inertia of the comet shape model (the body-fixed z-axis); uniform principal axis rotation about $\hat{\mathbf{z}}$ with constant counterclockwise angular velocity $\omega = 1.41 \times 10^{-4}$ rad/s (based upon a mean 12.41-h period deduced from light curve analyses[6]) is thereby assumed for the trajectory simulations performed. Note that numerical integration of Equation 6 is conducted within the body-fixed frame; thus, resultant spacecraft state vectors must be transformed to the inertial reference frame (defined as the principal body-fixed axes positioned with null rotation) at each time step for orbital visualization. Heliocentric motion of comet 67P/C-G is furthermore considered within this orbital study; the comet nucleus is assumed to be traversing an elliptical Keplerian orbit with the elements listed in Table 1.[†] Trajectory simulations do not begin at comet perihelion, however: $t = 0$ corresponds to the Rosetta mission phase epoch of interest, wherein generally the true anomaly $\nu \neq 0$ for the cometary nucleus.

Table 1. Comet 67P/C-G Perihelion Elements

Epoch: 28 Feb 2009 10:23:38 UTC

Element	Value	Units
a	3.4649	AU
e	0.6404	–
i	7.0424	deg
Ω	50.1839	deg
ω	12.6982	deg
ν	0.0000	deg

Preliminary computation of the C_{20} coefficient for comet 67P/C-G was performed by propagating a slightly-eccentric polar orbit with a semi-major axis of approximately 5 comet-radii for 30 days of duration – the conducted simulation began at epoch 22 Aug 2014 00:00:00 UTC and included only the gravitational acceleration of the nucleus (i.e. $\mathbf{a}_\odot = \mathbf{a}_{\mathrm{SRP}} = \mathbf{0}$ in Equation 6). Linear regression was thereafter applied to the secular variation observed in the osculating argument of periapsis ω to determine the average recession rate $\dot{\omega}$ of the apse line. The polar orbit implemented in this analysis and the resultant variation in ω are illustrated within Figure 11(a)-11(b), respectively. The observed variation indicated an approximate recession rate of $\dot{\omega} \approx -0.09285$ deg/day $\approx -1.88 \times 10^{-8}$ rad/s; thus, employing this value within the expression for average recession of the argument of periapsis:[9]

$$\dot{\omega} = \frac{3r_0^2\sqrt{\mu}C_{20}}{2(1-e^2)^2a^{7/2}}\left(\frac{5}{2}\sin^2 i - 2\right) \tag{7}$$

---

[*]Trajectories are propagated at a sufficient radius and orientation such that cometary outgassing and jet effects and the influence of the dust tail are considered negligible; gravitation of the nucleus provides the primary forcing in this analysis.

[†]Orbital elements for comet 67P/C-G are drawn from the JPL Small-Body Database at: http://ssd.jpl.nasa.gov/sbdb.cgi

wherein $a = 10.92$ km (approximately 5 comet-radii), $e = 0.1$, $i = 90°$, and $r_0 = 1.72$ km represents the effective sphere radius for the cometary nucleus, the coefficient $C_{20} \approx -0.1454/r_0^2 \approx -0.0492$. Note that use of Equation 7 assumes the nucleus to be of spheroidal geometry with an irregular mass distribution – the normalization radius r_0 therefore bears no physical dynamic significance and may be suppressed from the formulation, such that the coefficient C_{20} therein assumes km^2 dimensions.[6]

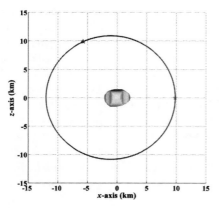
(a) Polar orbit used for C_{20} analysis ($e = 0.1$).

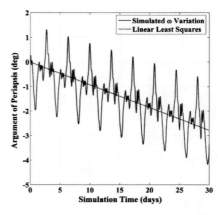
(b) Observed ω variation with regression line.

Figure 11. Configuration for C_{20} analysis of comet 67P/C-G. The implemented polar orbit at 5 comet-radii is depicted with examined secular variations in the argument of periapsis; the computed regression $\dot{\omega} \approx -0.09285$ deg/day implies $C_{20} \approx -0.1454/r_0^2$. Green and red stars illustrated in 11(a) represent initial and final spacecraft positions.

Analysis of the solar radiation pressure perturbation $\mathbf{a}_{SRP}$ was performed by assuming the Rosetta spacecraft to be a flat plate with dry mass of 1180 kg (for purposes of *worst-case* stability analyses) and exposed area 64 m^2 (orbiter parameters from Glassmeier et. al.[3]) with coefficient of reflectivity $c_R = 1.5$. The solar luminosity $L_\odot \approx 3.839 \times 10^{26}$ J/s was implemented for all computations of the solar radiation pressure acceleration imparted on the orbiter. The relevant forcing parameter[8] $\tilde{\beta}$ that quantifies the strength of this perturbation is $\tilde{\beta} = 3.84/B/\mu^{1/3}$, wherein B is the mass-to-area ratio of the examined spacecraft in kg/m^2 and μ is the gravitational parameter of the cometary nucleus in km^3/s^2; for the Rosetta spacecraft, $\tilde{\beta} \sim 28$, indicating that this solar radiation pressure perturbation will be significant in the comet 67P/C-G environment. Note, however, that the strength of the forcing is mitigated by the tremendous distance of the comet 67P/C-G from the Sun for the orbit simulations performed – at comet acquisition on May 22, 2014, the nucleus is at a heliocentric radius of 4.0 AU; upon commencement of the mapping and characterization phase on August 22, 2014, the nucleus is 3.5 AU distant. Figure 12 below illustrates the approximate magnitude of the solar radiation pressure acceleration imparted to the Rosetta spacecraft throughout various phases of the mission from comet acquisition in May 2014 to end of nominal lifespan in December 2015 for two mass approximations: constant dry mass (representative of a *worst-case* scenario), and linearly-decreasing propellant mass. In the case of the former, the maximum acceleration occurs at perihelion passage on August 12, 2015 (447 days following comet 67P/C-G rendezvous) – for the latter, maximum acceleration is achieved 3.8 days after perihelion passage, and is 10.2% lower than that incurred by the constant mass model. The observed offset is due to a propellant depletion rate that is low enough to mitigate the increasing strength of the solar radiation pressure perturbation actuated by enhanced proximities to perihelion.

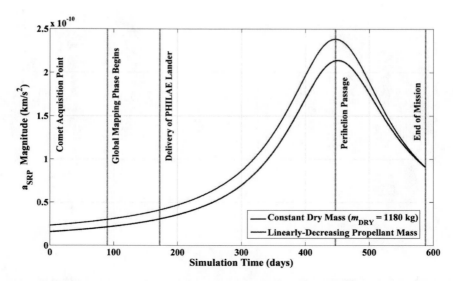

Figure 12. Magnitude of impinging solar radiation pressure acceleration at the comet 67P/C-G for various phases of Rosetta mission for two mass approximations: constant dry mass 1180 kg, and linearly-decreasing mass from 1750 kg (one-third of the initial propellant mass) to dry mass. Perturbation achieves maximum at perihelion passage for constant dry mass; maximum with linearly-decreasing mass occurs 3.8 days after.

Successful global mapping and characterization of the comet 67P/C-G nucleus will require orbital configurations that maintain relatively stable (*bounded*) behavior for the duration of the phase (under cometary gravitation, solar gravitation, and solar radiation pressure, as strictly considered within this study). Trajectories within the 5 to 25 comet-radii regime specified by scheduled mission operations are dominated by cometary gravitation: at the 3.5 AU position at the beginning of the mapping phase (and assuming that the Rosetta orbiter is 5 comet-radii from the nucleus), solar gravitation and solar radiation pressure are approximately 0.0003% and 0.7% of cometary gravitation, respectively, and are thus inconsequential to the stability of the simulated mapping trajectories.[*] This result is readily anticipated, as the radius of the *Hill sphere* (defined as the distance at which solar gravitation equates to the cometary gravitation[8]) at 3.5 AU is $R_{HILL} = d(\mu/3/\mu_\odot)^{1/3} \approx 575$ km (~ 260 comet-radii). Integrated orbital geometries under the complete forcing of Equation 6 for initial semi-major axes of 5 and 10 comet-radii, null eccentricity, and 90° of orbital inclination are illustrated within Figure 13 below (trajectories as viewed from the inertial reference frame with $\Omega_0 = \omega_0 = \nu_0 = 0$); each of the configurations exhibits bounded behavior appropriate for mapping operations of the Rosetta orbiter. The oscillatory characteristic observed in the osculating semi-major axes and eccentricities for each configuration ascertains as to the inherent long-term stability that each maintains: trajectories within this regime do not impact the cometary nucleus nor depart from this environment upon a hyperbolic departure path. As the global mapping and characterization phase is 80 days in length, such initially circular and polar geometries are suitable for the objectives of the Rosetta mission – this preliminary effort has thus demonstrated promising stability in the gravitational environment of comet 67P/C-G.

---

[*]Comet-specific perturbations incorporating outgassing, jets, and the dust tail are more influential than the considered disturbances at low altitudes, but are herein neglected, as the focus of this study is to discern strictly gravitational stability.

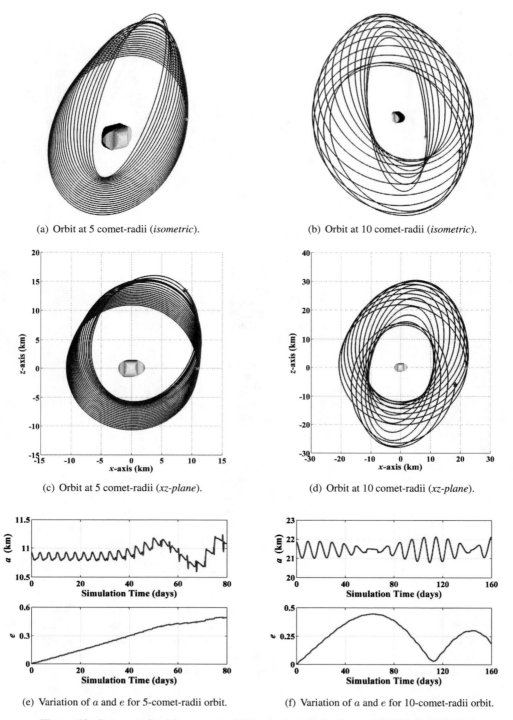

(a) Orbit at 5 comet-radii (*isometric*).

(b) Orbit at 10 comet-radii (*isometric*).

(c) Orbit at 5 comet-radii (*xz-plane*).

(d) Orbit at 10 comet-radii (*xz-plane*).

(e) Variation of a and e for 5-comet-radii orbit.

(f) Variation of a and e for 10-comet-radii orbit.

Figure 13. Integrated orbit geometry in the environment of comet 67P/C-G for initial semi-major axes of 5 and 10 comet-radii, respectively. Propagation was initialized at null eccentricity and polar inclination at epoch of 22 Aug 2014 00:00:00 UTC. Orbits exhibit bounded behavior necessary for mapping operations within the comet vicinity.

CONCLUSION

Refined finite element methodology for the approximation of small body attraction was presented with the offset sphere and correction element gravitational model developed in this study. The model implements uniform sphere elements (*point-masses*) of two sizes—principal offset spheres arranged with the hexagonal-close pack scheme, and subsidiary correction elements inserted into the resulting interstitial vacancies—to obtain a packing density that characterizes the examined geometry with an optimally 100% volumetric efficiency. The configuration was successfully validated with numerical analyses of asteroid Itokawa that demonstrated minimal discrepancy with the tetrahedral truth model: this applicable and highly-efficient sphere model is thus convenient for preliminary orbital dynamics analyses and rapid trajectory propagation in the gravitational environment of primitive small bodies.

The offset sphere and correction element model was thereby applied to the geometry of the comet 67P/Churyumov-Gerasimenko nucleus: a revamped polyhedral shape model more representative of realistic comet 67P/C-G geometries was assembled with image processing techniques, and the offset sphere scheme was employed to characterize the dynamical environment of the cometary nucleus as experienced by the Rosetta spacecraft during the nucleus mapping phase of the mission. Trajectories with null eccentricity and polar inclination as required by mission operations were propagated under simultaneous forcing of comet gravitation, third-body solar gravitation, and solar radiation pressure accelerations: this preliminary study showed that several orbits specified within this mapping regime exhibit bounded stability characteristics that therein render each viable for practical implementation.

ACKNOWLEDGEMENTS

The authors would like to acknowledge Embry-Riddle Aeronautical University, under which the research developed within this document was performed, and presentation thereof at the joint 2011 AAS/AIAA Astrodynamics Specialist Conference in Girdwood, AK, was made financially possible.

NOTATION

Gravitation Model.

η — Volumetric efficiency of finite element configuration, $\eta \in [0, \infty)$

$\mathbf{r}_j^k$ — k^{th} vertex coordinate vector of jth surface facet of shape model

R_i — Uniform radius of ith offset sphere element, equivalent $\forall\, i \in N_s$

ρ_s — Uniform density of ith offset sphere element, equivalent $\forall\, i \in N_s$

N_s — Number of fitted offset spheres of uniform radius R_i and density ρ_s

$\tilde{R}_i$ — Uniform radius of ith correction sphere element, equivalent $\forall\, i \in N_c$

ρ_c — Uniform density of ith correction sphere element, equivalent $\forall\, i \in N_c$

N_c — Number of fitted correction spheres of uniform radius $\tilde{R}_i$ and density ρ_c

G — Universal gravitation constant, $G \approx 6.67428 \times 10^{-20}$ km$^3 \cdot$ kg$^{-1} \cdot$ s^{-2}

$\mathbf{r}_i$ — Center coordinate vector of ith spherical element (*relative to centroid*)

$\mathbf{r}$ — Field coordinate vector, exterior to shape boundary (*relative to centroid*)

U_s — Gravitational potential at field coordinate $\mathbf{r}$, due to spherical configuration

$\partial U_s / \partial \mathbf{r}$ — Gravitational attraction at field coordinate $\mathbf{r}$, due to spherical configuration

$\partial U_t/\partial \mathbf{r}$ Gravitational attraction at field coordinate $\mathbf{r}$, due to tetrahedral configuration

λ Percent error between accelerations $\partial U_t/\partial \mathbf{r}$ and $\partial U_s/\partial \mathbf{r}$ at field coordinate $\mathbf{r}$

Orbital Dynamics.

$\mathbf{r}$ Position vector of spacecraft with respect to rotating body-fixed comet frame

$\dot{\mathbf{r}}$ Velocity vector of spacecraft with respect to rotating body-fixed comet frame

$\ddot{\mathbf{r}}$ Acceleration vector of spacecraft with respect to rotating body-fixed comet frame

ω Constant angular revolution rate of comet 67P/C-G, $\omega \approx 1.406 \times 10^{-4}$ rad/s

$\hat{\mathbf{z}}$ Principal axis of maximum moment of inertia of comet 67P/C-G shape model

$\partial U_s/\partial \mathbf{r}$ Gravitational attraction at spacecraft position $\mathbf{r}$, due to spherical configuration

$\mathbf{a}_\odot$ Perturbing acceleration of third-body solar gravity, $\mu_\odot \approx 1.327 \times 10^{11}$ km^3/s^2

$\mathbf{a}_{\mathrm{SRP}}$ Perturbing acceleration of solar radiation pressure, $L_\odot \approx 3.839 \times 10^{26}$ (N·m)/s

r_0 Effective radius of equivalent volume sphere, $r_0 = 1.72$ km for comet 67P/C-G

μ Gravitational parameter of comet 67P/C-G, $\mu \equiv GM \approx 5.264 \times 10^{-7}$ km^3/s^2

C_{20} Second-degree and zeroth-order gravitational coefficient for comet 67P/C-G

$\tilde{\beta}$ Solar radiation pressure metric, $\tilde{\beta} \equiv 3.84/B/\mu^{1/3}$ with mass-to-area ratio B

R_{HILL} Radius of *Hill sphere*, $R_{\mathrm{HILL}} \equiv d(\mu/3/\mu_\odot)^{1/3}$ with heliocentric distance d

$\{a\ e\ i\ \Omega\ \omega\ \nu\}$ Classical Keplerian orbital elements for spacecraft and comet 67P/C-G orbit

REFERENCES

[1] R. S. Park, R. A. Werner, and S. Bhaskaran, "Estimating Small-Body Gravity Field from Shape Model and Navigation Data," *Journal of Guidance, Control, and Dynamics*, Vol. 33, No. 1, 2010. DOI: 10.2514/1.41585.

[2] R. A. Werner and D. J. Scheeres, "Exterior Gravitation of a Polyhedron Derived and Compared with Harmonic and Mascon Gravitation Representations of Asteroid 4769 Castalia," *Celestial Mechanics and Dynamical Astronomy*, Vol. 65, No. 3, 1997, pp. 313–344.

[3] K. Glassmeier, H. Boehnhardt, D. Koschny, E. Kuhrt, and I. Richter, "The Rosetta Mission: Flying Towards the Origin of the Solar System," *Space Science Reviews*, Vol. 128, No. 1, 2006, pp. 1–21. DOI: 10.1007/s11214-006-9140-8.

[4] T. C. Hales, "An Overview of the Kepler Conjecture," *The Kepler Conjecture*, Cornell University Library, 2 ed., May 2002.

[5] R. Gaskell, O. Barnouin-Jha, D. Scheeres, T. Mukai, N. Hirata, S. Abe, J. Saito, M. Ishiguro, T. Kubota, J. Hashimoto, M. Yoshikawa, K. Shirakawa, and T. Kominato, "Landmark Navigation Studies and Target Characterization in the Hayabusa Encounter with Itokawa," *2006 AIAA/AAS Astrodynamics Specialist Conference and Exhibit*, August 2006. AIAA 2006-6660.

[6] P. L. Lamy, I. Toth, B. J. R. Davidsson, O. Groussin, P. Gutierrez, L. Jorda, M. Kaasalainen, and S. C. Lowry, "A Portrait of the Nucleus of Comet 67P/Churyumov-Gerasimenko," *Space Science Reviews*, Vol. 128, No. 1-4, 2007, pp. 23–66. DOI: 10.1007/s11214-007-9146-x.

[7] R. Bertrand, T. Ceolin, and P. Gaudon, "Rosetta Lander Descending Phase on the Comet 67P/Churyumov-Gerasimenko," tech. rep., European Space Agency, 2004.

[8] D. J. Scheeres, R. Gaskell, S. Abe, O. Barnouin-Jha, T. Hashimoto, J. Kawaguchi, T. Kubota, J. Saito, M. Yoshikawa, N. Hirata, T. Mukai, M. Ishiguro, T. Kominato, K. Shirakawa, and M. Uo, "The Actual Dynamical Environment About Itokawa," *2006 AIAA/AAS Astrodynamics Specialist Conference and Exhibit*, August 2006. AIAA 2006-6661.

[9] H. D. Curtis, *Orbital Mechanics for Engineering Students*. Elsevier Butterworth-Heinemann, 1 ed., 2005.

EARTH-IMPACT PROBABILITY COMPUTATION OF DISRUPTED ASTEROID FRAGMENTS USING GMAT/STK/CODES

Alan Pitz,[*] Christopher Teubert,[*] and Bong Wie[†]

There is a nationally growing interest in the use of a high-energy nuclear disruption/fragmentation option for mitigating the most probable impact threat of near-Earth objects (NEOs) with a short warning time. Consequently, this paper investigates the orbital dispersion and impact probability computation problem of a disrupted/fragmented NEO using several computer programs, called General Mission Analysis Tool (GMAT) developed by NASA, AGI's Satellite Tool Kit (STK), and Jim Baer's Comet/asteroid Orbit Determination and Ephemeris Software (CODES). These tools allow precision orbital simulation studies of many fragmented bodies, with high-fidelity visualizations. Various mathematical models for impact probability computation are examined and compared to JPL's Sentry, which is a highly automated NEO collision monitoring system. For example, we obtained an impact probability of 4.2E-6 for asteroid Apophis on April 13, 2036, which is very close to 4.3E-6 predicted by JPL's Sentry system. Our research effort of exploiting various commercial software such as GMAT, STK, and CODES will result in a robust software system for assessing the consequence of a high-energy nuclear disruption mission for mitigating the impact threat of hazardous NEOs.

INTRODUCTION

Asteroids and comets have collided with the Earth in the past and are predicted to do so in the future. These collisions have a significant role in shaping Earth's biological and geological history, most notably the extinction of the dinosaurs 65 million years ago. Another event is the 1908 Tunguska impact in Siberia, which released an explosion energy equivalent to approximately five to seven megatons of TNT. This explosion had enough power to destroy a 25 km radius of forest. It has been estimated that an impact from the asteroid 99942 Apophis would release approximately 900 megatons of energy, over 130 times the Tunguska event.[1] The results of a collision of this magnitude in a highly populated area would be catastrophic.

This paper is the first step of developing an interface that combines the research efforts in the Asteroid Deflection Research Center with high-fidelity commercial software. The interface is called the Asteroid Mission Design Software Toolbox (AMiDST) to be used for validating and enhancing research in computational astrodynamics using Graphics Processing Units (GPUs), Yarkovsky effect modeling, GN&C algorithms, and nuclear fragmentation modeling. These core research areas will connect through the use of the AMiDST which utilizes JPL's Horizons, CODES, GMAT, STK along with AGI Components, MATLAB, and GMV's CLEON software as illustrated in Figure 1.

---

[*]Research Assistant, Asteroid Deflection Research Center, Iowa State University, 2271 Howe Hall, Room 2355, Ames, IA 50011-2271, alanpitz@gmail.com, teubert@iastate.edu.
[†]Vance Coffman Endowed Chair Professor, Asteroid Deflection Research Center, 2271 Howe Hall, Room 2355, Ames, IA,50011-2271, bongwie@iastate.edu.

The AMiDST is being developed to be used for the design and analysis of real deflection/disruption missions in the future, which will require reliable, high-fidelity, precision orbital modeling and simulations. The commercial software toolbox incorporates all aspects of the mission and creates a foundation for innovation and validation of asteroid missions. Figure 1 depicts the overall research goal while this paper is the first step of developing the AMiDST.

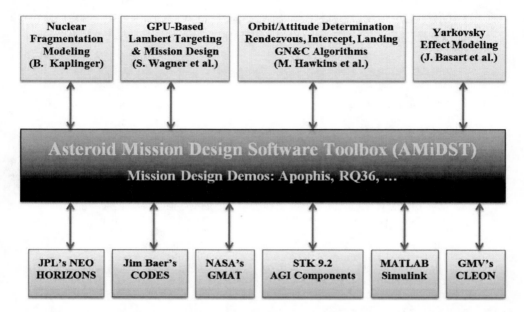

Figure 1. Illustration of the Asteroid Mission Design Software Toolbox (AMiDST).

Given short warning times, high-energy disruption missions, such as delivering a nuclear explosive device to an asteroid, are needed to properly disperse the asteroid fragments from hitting the Earth.[2] Orbital dispersion simulation and analysis results show that fragmenting and dispersing a hazardous NEO could lower the total mass impacting the Earth.[3] This could be beneficial in situations where some impacting mass is inevitable, or where the resulting fragments will be small enough to burn up in Earth's atmosphere.[2] Having an impact probability assessment of such a disruption mission will prove whether Earth is safe from multiple fragments. This paper presents software validation, trajectory analysis, and the implementation of Monte Carlo simulations to find the impact probability of a hazardous NEO. The tools used to find the impact probability can be easily modified to study the consequences of disrupted asteroid fragments from high-energy nuclear disruption missions of Earth-threatening bodies, with short warning time. To accurately estimate the impact probability of disrupted asteroid fragments, commercial mission analysis software are utilized, which include NASA's General Mission Analysis Tool (GMAT), AGI's Satellite Tool Kit (STK), Jim Baer's Comet/asteroid Orbit Determination and Ephemeris Software (CODES), and JPL's Horizons.

There has been a great deal of discussion over the probable impact threat posed by the asteroid Apophis. This possible threat makes Apophis an ideal reference model to study. On April 13, 2029, the asteroid Apophis will have a close-encounter with Earth, in which the asteroid will pass below geostationary orbit.[4] Apophis could pass through a keyhole and impact the Earth on April 13th, 2036. Keyholes are very small regions of the first encounter target-plane causing a resonant return impact with the Earth if an NEO passes through it.[4] Due to the uncertainty in observations, gravitational effects, and other forces, orbit trajectories of small bodies are very difficult to predict in long-term periods. The impact probability of Apophis in 2036 is currently estimated as four in one million, according to JPL's Sentry system.[1]

Apophis was first discovered in 2004. Tables 1 and 2 show the physical parameters and orbital elements respectively of Apophis from JPL's Apophis orbit solution #144. Throughout this study, Apophis is used as a reference asteroid and these orbital elements are used in each simulation. The overall research objective is met but with much difficulty due to the nature of the problem, the software inflexibility, and orbit differences in each software. These differences have been noted and documented, but further investigation of these differences is required.

Table 1. Physical Parameters of Apophis taken from JPL.[1]

Physical Parameters	Value
Rotational Period (hrs)	30.5
Mass (kg)	4.5E10
Diameter (m)	270
Absolute Magnitude H	19.7
Albedo	0.33

Table 2. Orbital elements of Apophis at Epoch 2455800.5 (2011-Aug-27.0) TDB.[1]

Orbital Elements	Value
Semi-Major Axis (AU)	0.92230
Eccentricity	0.19108
Inclination (deg)	3.3319
Ω (deg)	204.4304
ω (deg)	126.4245
M_o (deg)	287.5823

TRAJECTORY ANALYSIS OF APOPHIS USING STK/GMAT/CODES

Introduction

STK is a graphical user interface software for modeling and analyzing several applications including flight paths and logistics, communications, satellites in specific orbits, Earth satellites, defense applications, and more.[5] With high-fidelity visualizations, STK has a multitude of features that trump most physics-based computer programs. A communication interface between STK and MATLAB can be established to utilize functions and script files created in MATLAB while exploiting STK features such as propagators, orbit properties, and post-processing components. Propagators that manage interplanetary missions include the High Precision Orbit Propagator (HPOP) and Astrogator.[5] Astrogator is a highly-versatile component of STK used to study detailed mission scenarios, including the detailed parameterization of the spacecraft subsystems (dry and wet mass, mass flow rates, pressures of fuel tanks, etc.). The high-fidelity visualization that STK provides for conceptual mission design is invaluable to space applications.[5]

GMAT is a space trajectory optimization and mission analysis software developed by NASA, the space community, and the open source community. GMAT's primary goal is to "research, develop, verify, and transfer new technologies in space trajectory optimization and mission design."[7] GMAT is completely open-source allowing for user extension and personalization. MATLAB, minimization, and optimization plug-ins have been released and developers are currently working on a plug-in between GMAT and the MATLAB Orbital Dynamics Toolbox. A built-in scripting language included with GMAT allows for mission creation and modification. The user is able to create their own propagators from a list of integrators and force models. GMAT contains a new but powerful visualization tool for modeling and analyzing mission concepts with emphasis on space missions around Earth or in the Solar System. The Mac and Linux releases of GMAT 2011a are currently in the Alpha stage in the design process while the Windows release is in the Beta.

CODES is a graphical user interface program written by Jim Baer. CODES calculates a variety of small body characteristics such as orbits, optical observations, and physical parameters using a precise n-body numerical integrator. It can use topocentric or geocentric ephemeris based on user-specification or import minor bodies from the Minor Planet Center (MPC) database.[8] Additionally, it allows for linear and non-linear analysis of collisions/near misses between minor planets and major planets. Calculation of the state vector or orbital elements with covariance matrices can be obtained using an n-body simulator accounting for solar radiation pressure, gravity harmonics, and relativistic effects.

JPL's Solar System Dynamics Group provides an on-line ephemeris computation service that provides flexible information about solar system objects. JPL's Horizons has three different access methods; telnet, e-mail, and web-browser. The web interface provides access to a small subset of program functions with an interactive GUI.[9] The system provides access to highly accurate ephemerides for solar system objects including over 560,000+ asteroids and comets, 9 planets, the sun, natural satellites, spacecraft, and more.[9,10] Close-approaches by asteroids and comets to the planets, Ceres, Pallas, and Vesta, can be identified along with the encounter uncertainties and impact probabilities. Orbital uncertainties and covariance matrices can be computed for asteroids and comets. The underlying planet/satellite ephemerides and small-body osculating elements are the same ones used at JPL for radar astronomy, mission planning and spacecraft navigation.[9]

Apophis Orbit Simulation Using STK 9.2

In STK, the HPOP is used to propagate interplanetary trajectories with a solar radiation pressure model, user-specified selection of third-body gravity, object rotation, and high-fidelity visualizations. The HPOP can use several different integrators for numerical analysis. The default integrator for HPOP is the Runge-Kutta-Felhberg (RKF) of order 8 to estimate the local error in the method of order 7. The RKF 7(8) is an integration technique utilizing polynomial functions to approximate the ordinary differential equations.[11] The RKF 7(8) has a variable step size for integration. If the difference between two solutions is outside the bounds of the error tolerance, set by the user, then the solution is estimated again with a decreased step size.[11] Another type of integration scheme that employs a variable step size is the Gragg-Bulirsch-Stoer (GBS) method. This method utilizes rational functions as fitting functions for the Richardson extrapolation instead of polynomial functions.[12] It is also combined with a modified midpoint method which is extremely important in the accuracy of the solution. This method also has a variable step size. Lastly, a Gauss-Jackson (GJ) integration scheme is used to propagate an orbit. The Gauss-Jackson fixed, multi-step predictor-corrector method is widely accepted in numerical integration problems for astrodynamics.[13]

The default minimum and maximum step sizes for both the RKF and the GBS integrator are 1 second and 86400 seconds, respectively. The default error tolerance is 1.0E-13. A change to these default values is listed in Table 3. In order to compare STK to other commercial software, a reasonable compromise was reached for the minimum and maximum step size and error tolerance. For planetary flyby sequences, a minimum step size is most likely used due to the large gravity terms acting on the body. An average speed of an asteroid around the sun is approximately 30 km/s. If the default minimum step size of 1 second is chosen, the distance traveled during one time step is 30 km. Thus if a minimum step size is used during these times, a propagation of 3 meters per step is sufficient. When studying the effects of Earth's gravity on a small asteroid body, a rigorous selection of a step size is important and a 1 second step size is not acceptable. These values listed in the table are used throughout all the STK test cases in this study.

Table 3. Integration parameters in STK 9.2.

Integration Method	Minimum Step-Size (Sec.)	Maximum Step-Size (Sec.)	Error Tolerance
RKF	0.0001	15,000	1.0E-11
GBS			
GJ	15,000	N/A	N/A

The solar radiation pressure model was included based on Apophis's physical parameters such as the slope parameter, albedo, spin rate, size, and mass. The solar radiation pressure model is assumed to be a spherical model with properties reflecting those shown in Table 1. Third-body gravity includes all 9 planets and Earth's moon from ephemeris file DE-421. The Yarkovsky model and relativistic effects were not included in this study.

A comparison is made against the three different integration methods with the same force models. The epoch position and velocity is chosen from JPL's Horizons on January 1, 2029 in the J2000 Ecliptic Coordinate System. STK then propagated the object multiple times, each with a different integration method. The differences are calculated against one another and the results are shown in Table 4. Based on the propagation prior to the close-approach with Earth, it was found that all integrators are able to produce exactly the same results. However one and one-half month later, the Gauss-Jackson integration scheme fails completely due to its fixed step size. If a smaller window of time is to be analyzed with an extremely small step-size, a Gauss-Jackson integrator is as reliable as the other integrators. Since the study of the asteroid is much more than two months, a Gauss-Jackson is not used. Also, from the differences, the Gragg-Bulirsch-Stoer method is nearly identical to the RKF 7(8). This is important in comparing the other mission analysis software since both GMAT and STK have the Gragg-Bulirsch-Stoer method but not the same RKF order method. Due to excessively long computation time, the Gauss-Jackson fixed step-size is not further reduced.

Table 4. Difference between integration schemes in STK at Epoch of January 1, 2029 from Horizons.

	Date	X (km)	Y (km)	Z (km)	$\dot{X}$ (m/s)	$\dot{Y}$ (m/s)	$\dot{Z}$ (m/s)
RKF - GBS	1-Mar-29	0	0	0	0	0	0
	13-Apr-29	9.95E-2	2.67E-2	2.21E-2	1.20E-2	2.0E-3	2.0E-3
	1-Jun-29	0.20	6.84E-4	7.94E-2	0	0	0
RKF - GJ	1-Mar-29	0	0	0	0	0	0
	13-Apr-29	5.77E-2	1.02E-2	1.14E-2	7.00E-3	1.00E-3	1.00E-3
	1-Jun-29	3.63E+6	1.16E+6	5.51E+5	838.12	642.39	81.16
GBS - GJ	1-Mar-29	0	0	0	0	0	0
	13-Apr-29	0.16	3.69E-2	3.35E-2	1.90E-2	3.00E-3	3.00E-3
	1-Jun-29	3.63E+6	1.16E+6	5.51E+5	838.12	642.39	81.16

Apophis Orbit Simulation Using GMAT

GMAT's main strength over other software choices is its versatility. Its scripting ability is easy to use and edit without any knowledge of computer languages. The MATLAB plug-in allows an expansion of the user's ability to personalize each mission. Rather than choosing from a list of possible propagators, the user is able to create his/her own by choosing the propagation settings such as integrator scheme, step size, error tolerance as well as the gravitational bodies, and the non-gravitational forces including drag, solar radiation pressure, and more.

In GMAT there are seven different n-body numerical integrators to choose from. These include the Runge-Kutta 5(6), Runge-Kutta 6(8), Runge-Kutta 8(9), Prince-Dormand 4(5), Prince-Dormand 7(8), Bulirsch-Stoer, and the Adams-Bashforth-Moulton method. Each of these integrators employ variable step sizes and are well tested by the GMAT team. The Runge-Kutta (RK) method, as explained earlier, is a single-step method employing a series of coupled variables to solve differential equations.[14] The Prince-Dormand (PD) method as used in PD 78 and PD 45 is a form of an expanded RK method.

Unfortunately, the Bulirsch-Stoer method could not complete the propagation test within the accuracy limit for long periods of time (more than 7 years). Therefore, this method is considered only as a verification tool but was not used for impact probability simulations. Adams-Bashforth-Moulton, on the other hand is an implicit linear multistep method that iteratively solves the differential equation. The Adams-Moulton integration method is used as a differential corrector for the Adams-Bashforth integration allowing for multistep integration.[15] The Adams-Bashforth-Moulton method also could not complete the propagation within the accuracy limit.

The propagation test comprised of using several different integrators each having the same step sizes and error tolerances. The planetary bodies use ephemeris data from DE-405. Apophis solution #144 is used as the starting conditions listed in Table 2. Each case propagated from August 2011 until April 13, 2036. The 2029 close-approach distance was found as well as the 2036 distance. Table 5 shows the results of the integration test cases.

Each propagator's nominal close-approach distance in 2029 and 2036 is compared to distinguish which integrator performs best. After running each integrator, no difference was seen in the 2029 close-approach. However, after further review of STK and CODES, the Runge-Kutta 8(9) was chosen as the default integrator for simulations. Additionally, after careful evaluation and testing, a maximum step of 15,000 seconds, a minimum step of 1E-4 seconds, and an accuracy of 1E-11 were chosen.

Table 5. Comparison of GMAT Integration Methods using Apophis.

Integration Method	2029 Distance, km	2036 Distance, km	Runtime, sec
RK 89	37,344.48	20,323,355.5	88.92
RK 68	37,344.48	20,323,302.7	50.21
PD 78	37,344.48	20,323,313.9	70.44

Once the integration method is selected, integration parameters can be chosen for the initial step size, accuracy limit, minimum step size, maximum step size, and maximum step attempts. Variable step size calculations change the step size within the bounds set by the minimum and maximum step size variables to achieve the given accuracy limit. If the accuracy is determined to be outside the acceptable range then the integration is repeated with a smaller step size. This is repeated until the accuracy is obtained, the minimum step size is used, or the number of attempts equals the maximum step attempts. If the accuracy cannot be reached, an error is displayed and the program stops. If the accuracy is reached, the integrator moves onto the next step and repeats the process.

GMAT has several different options regarding which gravitational bodies the user wants. Gravitational bodies include the sun, 9 planets, Earth's moon, several large asteroids, and 300 known asteroids. After studying the effects of these bodies it was determined that including all the bodies is not necessary. Many of the smaller bodies have such a small effect on the orbit of an asteroid that they can be neglected. Taking out these bodies improves computation time allowing for more simulations to be run.

For the reference asteroid Apophis, simulations including various heavenly bodies are run to determine at what point their effect becomes negligible. After running these tests, which can be seen in Table 6, the sun, 9 planets, Earth's moon, Ceres, Vesta, Pallas are determined to be the bodies with the largest influence on Apophis. Including other bodies increased the computation time with no significant change in the close-approach distance. Ceres, Vesta and Pallas are added to GMAT by importing their SPICE files, but all the other bodies came built-in with GMAT.

Table 6. Comparison of GMAT Results with Different Gravitational Bodies.

	Sun Only	Sun, Earth, & moon	Sun, 9 Planets, moon, Ceres, Vesta, & Pallas	Sun, 9 Planets, & 300 Asteroids
2029 Distance, km	3,317,819	5,420,063	37,344.5	37,345.1
Runtime, sec	34.94	40.00	45.17	72.12

Another important gravitational force that must be considered for any accurate model is non-spherical gravity. This is accounted for within the integration model with the use of .cof potential files. Gravitational potential files for Venus, Earth, Earth's moon and Mars are built into GMAT, but it also allows for users to add other bodies manually. Repeated tests for the asteroid Apophis revealed that only the Earth's non-spherical gravity has a significant effect. This is possibly because of the 2029 close-approach to the Earth. Future simulations will include Earth as a non-spherical gravitational model.

Other non-gravitational forces can also be included in the propagation. Currently, these include drag and solar radiation pressure (SRP), but the GMAT support team plans on expanding this to include both relativistic and Yarkovsky effects. GMAT includes high-fidelity models, not only for atmospheric drag but also F10.7 drag, and magnetic drag of the Earth. The SRP model can be applied using the albedo, spin rate, size and mass of the asteroid. Both drag and SRP forces are included in the Monte Carlo simulation described later.

Apophis Orbit Simulation Using CODES

CODES is a graphical user interface program used to calculate a variety of information using observations, an N-body numerical integrator, and physical parameters. First, the program asks to designate the type of object, whether it be an asteroid or comet. Afterwards, the user can import a body from the Minor Planet Center (MPC), load in observations, or manually specify an orbit. If observations are chosen the program allows evaluation of the observations and propagates the object with a best-fit orbit using n-body mechanics. These observations can then be compared to positions of known minor planets.

One reason that makes CODES credible is the N-body numerical propagator and force models. The N-body propagator has three options: include all 9 planets and Earth's moon, or the 9 planets, moon, plus Ceres, Pallas, and Vesta, or the 9 Planets, moon, and 300 asteroids.[8] The planetary bodies use ephemeris data from DE-405 while the 300 asteroids use BC-405. Having a rigorous propagator increases computation time and accuracy. The force models include solar radiation pressure, relativistic effects, and gravity harmonics. The numerical integrator utilizes a Dormand-Prince embedded Runge-Kutta 7(8) method.

In this paper, the N-body propagator including the 9 planets, Earth's moon, plus Ceres, Pallas, and Vesta was used for CODES simulation runs. Once the orbit has been propagated, the user can extract the heliocentric ecliptic J2000 orbital elements or state vector at epoch. The orbital elements and state vector can also be propagated to a new epoch with a new covariance matrix. This is important when trying to study an asteroid's orbit further in the future without having to propagate the state vector from the original epoch each time.

Lastly, the collision and/or near miss tool can be used to check for any collisions or near misses to all major planets or Earth. The tool is broken down into a linear and nonlinear analysis. The linear analysis propagates the nominal state vector and covariance matrix to the specified end date. Using N-body mechanics and force models, CODES checks the distance between the object and distance to a solar system body (Sun, planets, and Earth's moon).[8] If the calculated distance is under the specified distance then a near miss is predicted. CODES uses the state vector and covariance matrix to estimate the probability of collision. On the other hand, if the calculated distance is less than the radius of the solar system body, then a collision has occurred and is reported. CODES uses a bisection method that determines the exact date and time of the collision.[8] All of these near misses and collisions are reported in a text file at the end of the simulation.

The nonlinear analysis can also be used. The analysis is primarily used for multiple near misses that result in sensitive orbit trajectories. A nonlinear analysis handles a user-specified number of variant state vectors either distributed normally about the nominal epoch state vector or uniformly along the Line-of-Variations (LOV).[8] The LOV is the major axis of the epoch state vector uncertainty ellipse. Once these state vectors are created, they are then propagated in the same manner as the linear method. If a near miss is found, a Monte Carlo simulation model is created by introducing virtual asteroids to extensively examine the close-approach distance and impact probability.

Unfortunately for our study, the nonlinear analysis, which is required to determine the impact probability of a small body, is not currently setup to handle a specified or imported nominal state vector. Instead, it is required to have both the observations and best-fit orbit with covariance matrix. The nonlinear analysis involves adding normally distributed noise to each observation, calculating the resulting orbit and then propagating it.

Using CODES with a specified orbit from Apophis solution #144 as listed in Table 2, a linear collision analysis was ran. The n-body propagator was chosen as well as the physical parameters were set as shown in Table 1. Table 7 shows the results of the linear analysis simulation. It accurately depicts the close-approach in 2029 with a near miss of 5.97 Earth radii or 38,078 km. Due to the linear analysis and the sensitivity of the close-approach distance in 2029, the near misses, past 2029, should be checked using a nonlinear analysis. All the miss distances are represented in Earth radii.

The original intention of using CODES was to validate the impact probability estimation made

Table 7. Collision/near miss results of a linear analysis for 50 years of Apophis with Epoch on August 27, 2011.

year	mm	dd	hh	mm	secs	Nominal Miss Distance (er)	Impact Probability
2013	01	09	11	42	11.4	2,267.18	0.0
2021	03	06	01	13	43.7	2,642.21	0.0
2029	04	13	21	45	08.9	5.97	0.0
2036	03	26	05	37	38.6	7,859.87	0.0
2037	09	23	01	42	34.2	4,525.3	0.0
2044	07	31	02	52	16.3	2,585.68	0.0

by JPL's Sentry. Once found, the next step is to study the effects of fragments, from a nuclear disruption mission, with an impacting trajectory 15 days prior to impact Earth, and then run a Monte Carlo simulation scenario of the impacting object to determine the impact probability of having multiple fragments hit the Earth. However, due to the inflexibility of CODES, this type of collision assessment cannot be accurately found using a specified orbit with covariance matrix. Future upgrades for CODES, to name a few, include determination of impact on a planet using latitude and longitude, additional asteroid perturbations, Yarkovsky effect, and implementation of JPL's DE-406 planetary ephemeris.

Comparison of Orbit Simulation Results for Apophis

Validation is the first priority to ensure reliable results from the mission analysis software. By testing each software and their respective integrator/propagator using identical initial conditions, validation is achieved. Each program is tested using the same position and velocity vector taken from JPL's Horizons in the J2000 Ecliptic Coordinate System using the same integrator, step size, and error tolerance. Between STK and GMAT a variable step size Gragg-Bulirsch-Stoer integrator scheme is used for propagation. The force models for each are also identical in nature including the solar radiation pressure and third body gravity. JPL's Horizons does not use the same integrator scheme but an Adams-Krogh integrator, named DIVA, with a variable order and variable step size.[10] It contains highly-accurate force and dynamical models used to provide conclusive ephemeris information. For small bodies, JPL's Horizons uses integrated gravitational point-mass equations of motion and can be extended to include solar radiation pressure, Yarkovsky effect, gravity harmonics, and relativistic effects.[10] Although GMAT, STK, and Horizons do not all share the common propagator and properties, similarities can still be drawn among them.

After individual software propagation, the position and velocity vectors are recorded at predefined times. These test cases assess each program's ability to calculate Apophis's close-encounter in 2029 for two months as well as deep-space propagation for several years. There are two types of cases that are used to gather information. Case 1 focuses on the close-approach distance between the asteroid and Earth. The case starts one month prior to the close-approach in 2029 and ends one month after. Case 2 examines the deep-space propagation of the asteroid from one month after the close-approach in 2029 until a possible impact on April 13, 2036. The positions and velocities within each program are recorded and checked against JPL's Horizons.[16] Tables 8 and 9 show the differences in the position and velocity vector components for each case at the specified date.

Case 1 starts with an epoch on March 13, 2029 using position and velocity vectors of Apophis from Horizons. This information is then entered into STK and GMAT. Once propagated, the position and velocity vector on April 13 and May 13 of 2029 are recorded. These differences shown in Tables 8 and 9 show differences between STK and Horizons and GMAT and Horizons. It should be noted that both have a relatively large difference on May 13, however, the difference of both are relatively of equal value. Thus, STK and GMAT match closely with one another for planetary close flybys.

In Case 2, the difference between STK and Horizons is greatly significant and it should be noted as an undesirable difference. Case 2 starts with an epoch date of May 13, 2029 with position and velocity vectors taken from Horizons. After one year of deep-space propagation, the difference between GMAT and Horizons is very small. This implies that the propagation results from GMAT and Horizons are similar for deep space propagation but differ slightly in planetary close flybys. On the other hand, the propagation results from STK and Horizons differ considerably on May 13, 2030. The error between them increases as the propagation continues. A difference of 33,000 km is not acceptable for scientific purposes in the study of accurate impact probability computation.

Table 8. Case 1: Difference Between Horizons and STK/GMAT for Epoch of March 13, 2029.

	Date	X (km)	Y (km)	Z (km)	$\dot{X}$ (m/s)	$\dot{Y}$ (m/s)	$\dot{Z}$ (m/s)
STK	13-Apr-29	11.49	10.42	5.80	0.25	0.13	0.06
	13-May-29	69,138.30	213,142.12	91,981.88	16.01	85.53	32.55
GMAT	13-Apr-29	20.98	6.03	5.29	0.28	0.12	0.06
	13-May-29	68,385.27	213,523.94	89,183.43	15.69	85.75	31.55

Table 9. Case 2: Difference Between Horizons and STK/GMAT for Epoch of May 13, 2029.

	Date	X (km)	Y (km)	Z (km)	$\dot{X}$ (m/s)	$\dot{Y}$ (m/s)	$\dot{Z}$ (m/s)
STK	13-May-30	771.03	4,610.49	175.21	0.76	0.06	0.01
	13-Apr-36	25,000.73	20,351.78	1,105.38	4.71	4.45	0.08
	13-May-36	33,482.19	4,856.95	689.32	1.36	7.15	0.23
GMAT	13-May-30	0.06	27.29	0.42	4.92E-3	1.55E-5	9.19E-5
	13-Apr-36	38.27	39.58	2.03	8.18E-3	1.16E-2	3.22E-4
	13-May-36	52.03	4.37	0.89	2.06E-3	1.52E-2	5.46E-4

Figure 2 shows the radial position differences of Apophis with respect to Horizons using STK and GMAT. STK uses the RK 7(8) method and GMAT uses the RK 8(9) method with identical minimum and maximum step sizes and error tolerances. This comparison uses the same time period as Case 2 along with the same ephemeris data files, DE-421. It is worth noting that there is an increasing sinusoidal difference between STK and GMAT with Horizons for long-term propagation. However, STK shows a much earlier radial position difference which then increases dramatically. GMAT follows a similar trend but with a much smaller difference amplitude for the same propagation time.

Further investigation of this propagation error in STK is conducted using different integrators, variable step sizes, fixed step sizes, higher error tolerances, and planetary ephemeris files. The maximum step size of the Gragg-Bulirsch-Stoer method, is set at 3,750 seconds, one-fourth of the initial maximum step size and the new position vectors are recorded. The difference is taken

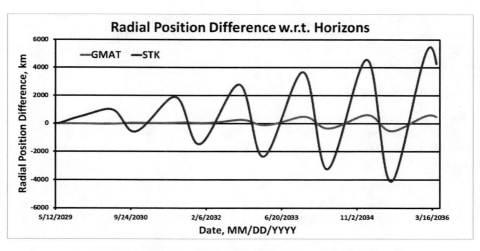

Figure 2. Radial Position Differences of Apophis w.r.t. JPL's Horizons.

from both the GBS methods using different maximum step sizes in STK. The result showed little difference between the new and the old step sizes. Finally, the Gauss-Jackson method was also used in Case 2 with a step size of 60 seconds. On May 13, 2030, the Gauss-Jackson method and GMAT's GBS method resulted in a larger difference than shown in Table 9. Solar radiation pressure model was also turned off in both STK and GMAT. However, the resulting change was a 10-30 km difference from the original orbit in both software. These differences have been noted but examination of the error between the two programs is still continuing. AGI headquarters has heard these differences through customer support and an investigation has begun.

IMPACT PROBABILITY MODELING

Knowledge of an asteroid's position comes from a series of visual, radar and Doppler observations. From these observations a nominal orbit and uncertainty ellipsoid is determined. The uncertainty ellipsoid is the volume inside which the asteroid must exist. The target asteroid's actual position could be anywhere within the uncertainty ellipsoid but statistically it is likely to be at the nominal location. Many methods use a series of Virtual Asteroids (VAs) to determine impacting probabilities. Each VA represents one possible location and orbit of the target asteroid of interest.

One consequence of this positional uncertainty is long-term trajectory propagation error. A probability distribution can then be used to estimate the impact probability (IP) of an asteroid hitting a major body. This impact probability value is important for determining the impact risk of an asteroid to a major body.

Monte Carlo Method

The Monte Carlo (MC) method is widely used for determining impact probability. This method randomly samples a pool of Virtual Asteroids (VAs) from the uncertainty ellipsoid. Since the definite position and orbit of the asteroid is not precisely known, each VA represents a possible position and orbit where the asteroid could exist. Each VA has its own set of six orbital elements which include the semi-major axis, eccentricity, inclination, longitude of the ascending node, argument of periapsis, and mean anomaly angle (a, e, i, Ω, ω, M$_o$). The VAs are propagated until the end date in which the final position is recorded. A statistical tool uses these recorded positions to determine the probability of impact. The MC method, is widely used to simulate unknown, complex physical models such as the orbits of small bodies in the Solar System.

Virtual Asteroid Generation and Propagation

The first step in determining the impact probability using the Monte Carlo method is to create the VAs. A pool of random numbers lying within the interval [0,1] is generated for this purpose. Both GMAT and STK have MATLAB plug-ins allowing for the user to use built-in MATLAB random number generators.

The pool of $6*N$ random numbers is used to sample N VAs from the six-dimensional uncertainty space (a, e, i, Ω, ω, M$_o$). Each orbital element is independently and randomly sampled from a Gaussian distribution as shown in Figure 3.

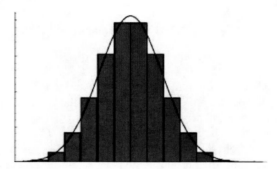

Figure 3.   Example of a Gaussian Distribution.

$$a = \sigma_a \sqrt{2} \left(\text{erf}^{-1} \left(2 * \text{RAND} - 1 \right) + \mu_a \right) \tag{1}$$

The Gaussian distribution of orbital elements is achieved by taking the inverse cumulative distribution function of the random number pool.[17] The inverse cumulative distribution function, as described by Equation 1, is a function of the mean, standard deviation, and the random number sampled from the pool.

This results in the creation of one of the six orbital elements for a VA. Repeating the process five more times defines a VA. Values closer to the mean are favored to create a Gaussian distribution in the pool. This results in a mean and standard deviation equal to the values entered into the MC. In this case the mean and standard deviation are equal to those from Apophis solution #144 as provided in Table 10.[1]

A scatter plot of the virtual asteroids' semi-major axis, eccentricity, and inclination for the Apophis Monte Carlo simulation is provided in Figure 4. Each red dot represents one of the 1000 virtual asteroids created each having its own set of six orbital elements. Each axis shows the variance from the nominal values. The nominal VA is represented by a blue dot located at (0,0,0).

At this point there are some checks that can be done to prevent spurious data. The first of these is a test of the random number generator. The easiest way to do this is to find the mean and standard

Table 10. Orbital elements of Apophis at Epoch 2455800.5 (2011-Aug-27.0) TDB from Apophis Solution #144.[1]

Orbital Elements	Mean Value (μ)	Standard Deviation (σ)
Semi-Major Axis (AU)	0.922300	7.674E-9
Eccentricity	0.191076	3.6429E-8
Inclination (deg)	3.331960	1.5069E-6
Ω (deg)	204.43041	3.0196E-5
ω (deg)	126.42447	3.0819E-5
M_o (deg)	287.5823	3.0636E-5

deviation of all the random numbers generated. For a large pool, the mean and standard deviation values should be approximately equal to 0.5 and 0.34134, respectively. In the case where these values do not match, a new pool of random numbers is generated.

Another method to detect dubious data, is to compare the mean and standard deviation of all the VA's six orbital elements. In this case, they are compared with JPL's Small Body Database Apophis's Orbital Elements.[1] Having too few VAs results in a difference between the calculated and compared mean and standard deviation values.

The pool of VAs are then propagated until they reach perigee in 2036. This is the closest point to the Earth the VAs reach in 2036. Each VA's Cartesian position at perigee is recorded for use in post-processing. Post-processing for determining the impact probability begins once all positions are recorded.

Post-processing

The simplest post-processing method is executed by dividing the number of VAs that hit the Earth, also called Virtual Impactors (VIs), by the total number of VAs used in the calculation. The main limitation of such a method is that the number of VAs required is roughly equal to the inverse of the impact probability.[18] For an asteroid with an impact probability of approximately 1.0E-6, at least one million VAs would be needed in order to validate this claim. This is computationally expensive and difficult to manage; thus, alternative methods have been developed in the literature using an impact probability model of the form:

$$\text{IP} = \iiint\limits_{V_\oplus} \text{PDF}(x, y, z) \, \mathrm{d}x \, \mathrm{d}y \, \mathrm{d}z \tag{2}$$

One such method of decreasing the necessary number of simulations is to use a statistical approximation. The first step in doing this is to find the three-dimensional probability density function (PDF) of the asteroid's close-approach-position. The impact probability of Apophis becomes the integral of the PDF over the volume of the Earth as defined by Equation 2. This expression can then

115

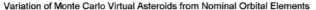

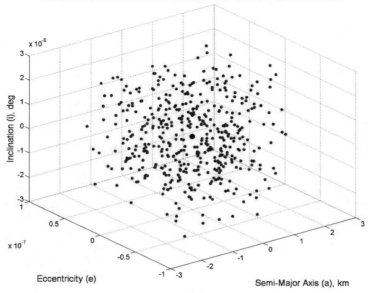

Figure 4. Semi-Major Axis - Eccentricity - Inclination Scatter Plot of VAs created by a Monte Carlo Model.

be simplified by converting it to spherical coordinates, as follows:

$$
\text{IP} = \int_0^{r_\oplus} \text{PDF}(r)\,\mathrm{d}r = \text{CDF}(r_\oplus) - \text{CDF}(0) \tag{3}
$$

$$
= \frac{1}{2}\left[\text{erf}\left(\frac{r_\oplus - \mu}{\sigma\sqrt{2}} \right) - \text{erf}\left(\frac{0 - \mu}{\sigma\sqrt{2}} \right) \right] \tag{4}
$$

where CDF denotes the cumulative density function, μ is the mean distance from the Earth, σ is the standard deviation of the perigee distances from the Earth, and $r_\oplus$ is the radius of the Earth.

This process results in a number between 0 and 1 corresponding to the probability of impact. The MC method must be repeated with various pools of VAs to ensure accuracy. If the difference between the IPs predicted from each run is outside an acceptable range, then this implies that a larger pool of VAs is required. Having a larger pool of VAs increases computation time but results in a more accurate impact prediction.

Impact Probability of Apophis

The most basic application of various software options is finding the asteroid's nominal close-approach distance to the Earth. This value corresponds to the most probable close-approach distance and is of great use in determining how dangerous a potential impactor is to Earth. For Apophis, a comparison of the close-approach distance is made by each software starting with the same initial

116

conditions. The conditions are set to reflect Apophis solution #144 listed in Tables 1 and 2. Starting in August 2011 and propagated to April 13, 2029, the minimum distance was found. Table 11 shows the miss distance of Apophis on April 13, 2029 during its closest approach using JPL's Small Body Database, NEODyS-2, CODES, GMAT and STK. This distance is within geosynchronous orbital altitude and, though it will not hit the Earth, it may pose a danger to Earth's satellites prompting the need for continuous observations.

NEODyS-2 presents information for near-Earth asteroids including orbital elements, physical parameters, a covariance matrix, and a risk table with a convenient Web-based interface. The risk table is calculated using an original software called OrbFit with collaboration with NEODyS/CLOMON2 team and JPL's Sentry team. NEODyS-2 is comparable and similar to JPL's NEO website. NEODyS-2 also includes close-approach tables, ephemeris files, observational data, and possible impact solutions. Table 11 shows the close-approach distance of Apophis in 2029. Figure 5 shows the 2029 close-approach of Apophis generated by GMAT.

Table 11. Nominal Miss Distance of Apophis on April 13, 2029 and Impact Probability in 2036 calculated by each software.

	JPL's Sentry	NEODyS-2	CODES	GMAT	STK
2029 Distance, km	38,067	38,342	38,078	37,859	49,211
Impact Probability	4.3E-6	4.3E-6	-	4.2E-6	-

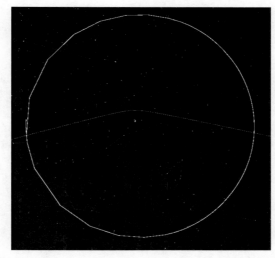

Figure 5. Nominal Trajectory of Apophis with a Close Earth Flyby on April 13, 2029, created by GMAT.

Another use of various software options is determining the impact probability for an asteroid. This impact probability number is important for determining the danger that a specific asteroid poses to Earth. The asteroid Apophis is used here for comparison. In 2036 there is a small chance that Apophis will impact the Earth. This is dependent on the asteroid going through a small 'keyhole' during the 2029 close flyby. Passing through this keyhole results in a 7/5 orbital resonance causing an impact seven years later on April 13, 2036.

The MC simulation is written in GMAT's scripting language. A pool of 6000 random numbers is created using an Inverse Transform Sampling Pseudo-Random Number Generator. The random number distribution is checked and found to have a mean equal to 0.5 and a standard deviation equal to 0.34134. This confirms that the random numbers are evenly distributed.

The pool of 6000 random numbers were then turned into orbital elements creating 1000 VAs. The distribution is confirmed to be equal to the values listed in Table 10.[1] Each set of six orbital elements is assigned to a VA, and the VA is propagated until the 2036 perigee condition. Each state vector is recorded at perigee into a report file. The created report file is then imported into Excel for post-processing. Using built-in Excel functions and Equations 3 and 4, the impact probability is then computed. A comparison of computed impact probabilities from different sources is provided in Table 11. It can be noticed that we obtained an impact probability of 4.2E-6 for asteroid Apophis on April 13, 2036, which is very close to JPL's impact probability value of 4.3E-6.

Impact Probability Concept as Applied to Disrupted Apophis Fragments

If an NEO on an Earth-impacting course can be detected with a mission lead time of at least several years, the challenge becomes mitigating its threat. When the time to impact exceeds a decade, the velocity perturbation needed to alter the orbit is small ($\approx$ 2 cm/s).[3] When the time to impact is short, the necessary velocity change may become very large, and the use of a nuclear subsurface explosion may become inevitable.[3] A common concern for such a powerful nuclear option is the risk that the deflection or disruption mission could result in fragmentation of the NEO, which could rather substantially increase the damage upon its Earth impact. Therefore, it is important to develop a computational tool to determine the impact probability of the disrupted fragments from a nuclear subsurface disruption mission.

A conservative estimation of the impacting mass for a worst-case mission scenario with a lead time of 15 days before impact is studied for a nuclear subsurface explosion with a shallow burial ($<$ 5 m) for a test case of Apophis in Refs. 2 and 3. At detonation, the energy source region expands, creating a shock that propagates through the body resulting in fragmentation and dispersal. The mass-averaged speed of the fragments after 6 seconds was near 50 m/s with a peak near 30 m/s.[2] As a result only 0.2% of the initial mass resulted in impacting the Earth if the explosion direction is aligned along the inward or outward direction of the orbit, i.e., perpendicular to NEO's orbital flight direction.[3] Such a sideways push is known to be optimal when a target NEO is in the last orbit before the impact. Obviously, the impact mass can be further reduced by increasing the intercept-to-impact time or by increasing the energy level of nuclear explosives (i.e., higher yields).[3]

A simulation of a nuclear disruption mission of a fictitious Earth-impacting Apophis trajectory is considered. Furthermore, the impact probability of the orbital dispersal fragments from this nuclear disruption mission 15 days before impact is extensively examined. Table 12 displays the modified state vector of an Earth-impacting Apophis at an Epoch date of March 29, 2036 in the J2000 Ecliptic Coordinate System. This sample test case is used as a reference which demonstrates the development of the AMiDST.

Table 12. Modified State Vector of Apophis at Epoch of March 29, 2036, in a Collision Course with Earth on April 13, 2036.

X (km)	Y (km)	Z (km)	$\dot{X}$ (km/s)	$\dot{Y}$ (km/s)	$\dot{Z}$ (km/s)
-155,168,152.5446	-23,546,881.5797	-1,508,530.2557	9.7751	-28.1744	1.1376

The fragmentation model consists of an impulsive velocity perturbation which is applied to each fragment. Typically, velocity perturbations of fragments from disrupted asteroids are non-Gaussian with a tail of high-velocity ejecta. However in this sample test case, the magnitude of the velocity perturbations is assumed to form a Gaussian distribution sampled randomly, with a mean value of 50 m/s and a standard deviation of 10 m/s. The velocity perturbation direction is sampled to favor directions perpendicular to Apophis's velocity vector. For simplicity, the velocity perturbation directions are set in the spherical coordinate system, with the origin at the asteroid's body and the x-axis along the velocity vector. By using the same Gaussian Monte Carlo method, the right ascension is sampled with a mean value and standard deviation of 90° and 45°, respectively. The declination is then sampled between 0° and 360°, randomly. This process is repeated to create N fragments each having a random velocity magnitude and direction.

STK and GMAT are used to carry out the calculations of this disruption model. STK was chosen for the illustration of this study due to its superior visualization tools and Astrogator feature. Due to the short time frame of this simulation and little deep space propagation, STK's performance for this simulation study is not affected by the discrepancies noted earlier.

A sample test case of delivering a nuclear explosive device (NED) to a fictitious Apophis impact is simulated and the results are illustrated in Figures 6-9. The simulation starts with the interception by a spacecraft carrying a NED to the threatening asteroid Apophis as depicted in Figure 6. The spacecraft intercepts Apophis on March 29, 2036, 15 days before the fictitious impact with Earth on April 13, 2036.

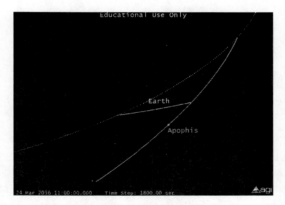

Figure 6. Nuclear Disruption Mission for the Fictitious Impact of Apophis on April 13, 2036.

A dispersion cloud of fragments is created to simulate the consequence of a nuclear disruption of Apophis.[2] This cloud is created by imposing a velocity perturbation individually on each fragment. In this visual sequence of events only 50 fragments were considered. The resulting orbital dispersion forms a debris cloud as shown in Figure 7.

Each fragment is then propagated until April 30, 2036 using the Astrogator feature in STK. Figure 8 shows these fragments being propagated as they approach Earth. If a fragment reaches an altitude of 120 km above the Earth, it is assumed that the fragment has impacted Earth. This conservative model results in a safe estimation of the impact probability. Figure 9 shows the debris cloud after Earth passes through. The debris cloud is then broken due to Earth's gravity and each fragment's miss distance is recorded to be analyzed in post-processing.

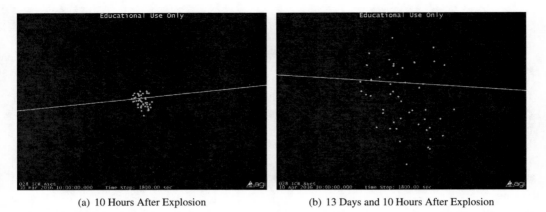

(a) 10 Hours After Explosion (b) 13 Days and 10 Hours After Explosion

Figure 7. Orbital Dispersion of Fragments after Nuclear Explosion of Apophis.

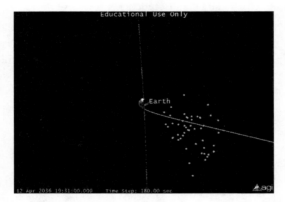

Figure 8. Debris Cloud Approaching the Earth. The size of each fragment shown here is not to scale.

The same sample model is used as reference to find the impact probability of 2000 fragments instead of 50. The recorded miss distances are used to estimate the Gaussian probability density function of the fragments' potential location in three-dimensional space. Integrating over the volume of the Earth solves for the probability of impact for each fragment. Table 13 shows the results of this sample test case, which is in agreement with the results of Refs. 2 and 3.

Table 13. Statistical Results of Nuclear Disruption of Apophis Using 2000 Fragments.

Mission Analysis Software	Mean Miss Distance (km)	Standard Deviation (km)	Impact Probability
STK	47,549	14,328	1.6E-3
GMAT	47,123	14,474	9.0E-4

This simple model was used to demonstrate the AMiDST's initial capabilities of finding the impact probability of disrupted fragments resulting from a nuclear disruption mission. The impact probability analysis of the disrupted asteroid fragments under a variety of fragmentation conditions will be needed when planning a nuclear disruption mission. This application can encompass multi-

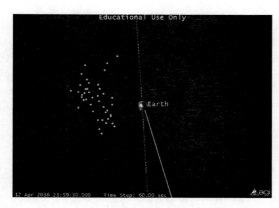

Figure 9. Orbital Dispersion of Fragments After Passing through the Earth Target Plane.

ple intercepting dates, NED sizing, and impacting trajectories, to determine an optimal solution for a disruption mission.

A more realistic fragmentation model will replace the simple model used in this paper as future research is undertaken by incorporating the study result described in Ref. 19. The next step for AMiDST is to develop the capability to enter in various statistics resulting from a nuclear fragmentation simulation using an advanced hydrodynamic code to generate N fragments in an orbital dispersion cloud. This will allow an accurate representation of the impact probability of a worst-case scenario for nuclear disruption missions.

Summary

Future research efforts include a more accurate nuclear fragmentation model and extending the applications to the asteroid 1999 RQ36. The nuclear fragmentation model is under current research efforts of the Asteroid Deflection Research Center in collaboration with the Lawrence Livermore National Laboratory. The asteroid RQ36 is NASA's new target for an unmanned spacecraft to collect samples and return them to Earth. RQ36 is an asteroid with a diameter of approximately 560 meters and an estimated impact probability of 2.8E-04 on September 2182.[19] This high impact probability makes it a potential target for a deflection mission.

CONCLUSION

In this study STK, GMAT, CODES, and JPL's Horizons have been exploited to find the close-approach distance of a reference asteroid Apophis, calculate the impact probability of the asteroid, and extend the simulation to handle a fragmentation model to study the consequences of high-energy nuclear disruption missions. The impact probability computation process has been setup through the use of a Monte Carlo method. Through post-processing, the use of a statistical model can estimate the impact probability of one body or a fragmented body. The ultimate goal of this research is the development of an interface that integrates the research efforts in the Asteroid Deflection Research Center with commercial astrodynamics software to be used by practicing engineers and researchers for real mission planning and design.

ACKNOWLEDGMENT

This research work was supported by a research grant from the Iowa Space Grant Consortium (ISGC) awarded to the Asteroid Deflection Research Center at Iowa State University. The authors would like to thank the undergraduate research assistants Mike Kurtz, Scott Drake, and Tanner Munson working at the ADRC for their supportive research efforts. Technical advices from the AGI and GMAT Support Teams, Jim Baer (currently an aerospace doctoral graduate student at James Cook University in Queensland, Australia) and Jon Giorgini at JPL are greatly appreciated.

REFERENCES

[1] Solar System Dynamics Group, "NASA's Near-Earth Object Program," Last Updated: 2011. neo.jpl.nasa.gov

[2] B. Kaplinger, B. Wie, and D. Dearborn, "Preliminary Results for High-Fidelity Modeling and Simulation of Orbital Dispersion of Asteroids Disrupted by Nuclear Explosives," AIAA 2010-7982, AIAA/AAS Astrodynamics Specialist Conference, 2010.

[3] B. Wie, and D. Dearborn, "Earth-Impact Modeling and Analysis of a Near-Earth Object Fragmented and Dispersed by Nuclear Subsurface Explosions,"AAS 10-137, AAS/AIAA Space Flight Mechanics Meeting, 2010.

[4] J. Giorgini, L. Benner, S. Ostro, M. Nolan, and M. Busch, "Predicting the Earth Encounters of (99942) Apophis," ICARUS 193, 2008.

[5] AGI, "STK - Analytical Graphics Inc.," 2011. agi.com/products/applications/stk

[6] GMAT Design Team, "General Mission Analysis Tool (GMAT)," gmat.gsfc.nasa.gov/index.html

[7] GMAT Design Team, "General Mission Analysis Tool (GMAT) Mission and Vision Statement," 2007.

[8] J. Baer, "Comet/asteroid Orbit Determination and Ephemeris Software User's Manual," 2007. home.earthlink.net/ jimbaer1

[9] JPL Solar System Dynamics Group, "Horizons (Version 3.36)," 2010.

[10] F. T. Krogh, "Issues in the Design of a Multistep Code," Annals of Numerical Mathematics 1, 1994.

[11] Wolfram Research Inc, "Mathematica Documentation 5.2: Explicit Runge Kutta," 2011. reference.wolfram.com

[12] S. Shanbhag, "Bulirsch-Stoer Method," 2009. people.sc.fsu.edu/ sshanbhag/BulirschStoer.pdf

[13] M. M. Berry and L. M. Healy,"Implementation of Gauss-Jackson Integration for Orbit Propagation," Astronautical Sciences, Vol. 52, No. 3, 2004, pp. 331-357.

[14] GMAT Development Team,"General Mission Analysis Tool (GMAT) Mathematical Specifications–DRAFT," reference manual.

[15] Mathematics Source Library C & ASM, "Adams-Bashforth and Adams-Moulton Methods," 2004. mymathlib.webtrellis.net/diffeq/adams

[16] JPL, "Solar System Dynamics Group, Horizons System," Last Updated: 2011. ssd.jpl.nasa.gov/?horizons

[17] Wolfram Research Inc., "Distribution Function," 2011. mathworld.wolfram.com/DistributionFunction.html

[18] A. Milani, S. Chesley, P. Chodas, and G. Valsecchi, "Asteroid Close Approaches Analysis and Potential Impact Detection," *Asteroids 3,* 2002, pp. 55-69.

[19] Near-Earth Object Program,"101955 1999 RQ36 Earth Impact Risk Summry," 2010. neo.jpl.nasa.gov/risk/a101955.html

[20] B. Kaplinger, and B. Wie, "Comparison of Fragmentation/Dispersion Models for Asteroid Nuclear Disruption Mission Design," AAS 11 - 403, AAS/AIAA Astrodynamics Specialist Conference, 2011.

THE PROBABILITY OF ASTEROID-EARTH COLLISIONS BY WAY OF THE POSITIONAL UNCERTAINTY ELLIPSOID

Christopher J. Polito[*] and David B. Spencer[†]

An alternative to the conventional method for determining impact probability by an asteroid is presented that utilizes the positional uncertainty ellipsoid. This method is used commonly for Earth-orbiting satellite collision probability. In the scaling up process, the gravitational influence of one of the bodies in the collision is taken into account, namely that of the Earth. The restricted three-body problem is sufficient to provide a backdrop for the probability analysis, while making sure to note that the results are only hypothetical given a simplified dynamic model. Uncertainty is represented mathematically by the covariance matrix and is propagated into the future. Encounter regions are defined as regions along the nominal trajectory of the asteroid where the propagated uncertainty encloses the Earth. Probability is calculated by a triple integral of the probability density function (pdf) over the volume swept out by the Earth through the encounter region. The trend in probability calculated vs. initial uncertainty is investigated, and it is found that higher probabilities result from initial uncertainties that are tighter in the radial, in-track and out-of-plane directions.

INTRODUCTION

As a natural disaster, impact by an asteroid is the only event that can, in theory, be averted. The process to deflect an asteroid from a collision course takes a significant amount of lead-time. The first step in this process is discovery of the asteroid itself and then the determination that it will impact the Earth with high probability. There are automated systems in place today that scan the catalogue of known Near Earth Asteroids (NEAs) and calculate their probabilities of impact in the far future. These systems, known as Sentry at the Jet Propulsion Laboratory (JPL) and CLOMON2 at the University of Pisa, Italy are independent and both use a variation of the method of Line of Variations (LOV). For a discussion on the LOV see Milani et al. (2005a,b).

The LOV is not the only method available for determining probability of impact. In the field of Earth orbiting satellite collision probability determination, probabilities are calculated without using the LOV. It is possible to scale up the analysis in Earth orbit to examine the collision between two objects, now, that are the Earth itself and an asteroid. In the scaling process, the central focus is moved from the Earth to the Sun and the disparity in mass of the two objects in question is taken into account by including the gravitational influence of the Earth on the asteroid. The result is the restricted three-body problem. While this dynamic model is simplified, it is sufficient

---

[*] Graduate Research Assistant, Department of Aerospace Engineering, The Pennsylvania State University, 229 Hammond Bldg., University Park, PA 16802.
[†] Associate Professor, Department of Aerospace Engineering, The Pennsylvania State University, 229 Hammond Bldg., University Park, PA 16802. Senior Member, AAS; Associate Fellow, AIAA.

to perform the probability analysis. It is intended that this model be replaced by a more sophisticated model in the future.

The methods for determining probability of collision in Earth orbit use positional uncertainty ellipsoids that surround each object. The ellipsoidal uncertainty is the 3σ surface (where σ is one standard deviation) of a three-dimensional Gaussian probability density function (pdf) that is represented mathematically by the covariance matrix. Specifically, the pdf can be thought of as a function of one variable—the covariance matrix.

Uncertainty changes as the asteroid is propagated into the future. In order to find how the uncertainty deforms in the future, the State Transition Matrix (STM) is calculated simultaneously along with the nominal trajectory. The propagation of uncertainty is then achieved by a transformation of the STM onto the covariance matrix. The total solution is then embodied by the deformed uncertainty whose center at each time step is the nominal solution at that time (Polito 2011).

The probability of impact is not desired at all times along the solution. Rather an encounter region is defined that appears in the solution only a small finite number of times. The total solution is propagated to the encounter region, which is a finite region along the nominal solution. The probability of impact is then the integration of the pdf over the volume swept out by the Earth through the encounter region. This process, because the pdf is not constant during the encounter, is discussed further.

Through a Monte Carlo simulation, the trend in initial uncertainty vs. total probability is examined. Results are given for 100 runs of the simulation for two cases. The remainder of this paper presents the equations of motion for the nominal three-body problem as well as the equations to solve for the STM. Next, we discuss sources of uncertainty, reasons it is necessary to propagate it in the future, the mathematical representation of uncertainty, and the method for uncertainty propagation. The paper continues with a discussion of the encounter region and, along with the Appendix, gives the process by which they are found in all cases. We also discuss the integration of the time varying pdf through the encounter, and describes the Monte Carlo simulation and presents results of two cases: an example of a fictitious asteroid on a collision course with Earth and a hypothetical case based on a real asteroid. The paper then explains the results by a simple example and discusses the limitations of the method, as well as drawing conclusions on what was found.

DYNAMICS

The requirements of the dynamic model are that it provides the nominal trajectory of the asteroid and the STM for uncertainty propagation. It should be able to produce these two results with stability for a long enough time span into the future (e.g. 30 years). It should be simple in extent and easy to employ. It is not required to be especially accurate as, at this stage, can be only a backdrop for the probability analysis. A more sophisticated dynamic model is suggested in the future work.

The problem is as follows. An asteroid is free to move in three-dimensional space subject to the gravitational influence of two massive bodies, each of which is under mutual gravitation. The problem is "restricted," in that the asteroid does not reciprocate gravitationally.

The equations of motion are presented for the Circular Restricted Three-Body Problem (CR3BP) as well as the equations used to solve for the STM.

Equations of Motion

CR3BP is often formulated in a frame that rotates with the two unequally massive bodies. As seen in Figure 1, the x-axis is the line connecting those bodies, pointing from the center of mass of the system in the direction of the more massive of the two. The z-axis is parallel to the angular velocity of the system and the y-axis completes the right-handed system.

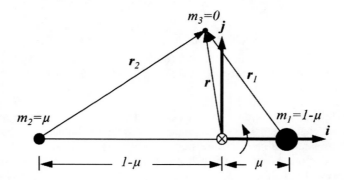

Figure 1: The arrangement of the bodies in the rotating frame of CR3BP

The mass ratio is the mass of the less massive body normalized by the sum of the masses of the two bodies, $m_2 = \mu$. This leads to the mass of the more massive body to be, $m_1 = 1 - \mu$. The distance between the bodies is normalized to one and the origin is at the center of mass of the system. This leads to the distance from the origin of the massive bodies to be: $x_1 = \mu$ and $x_2 = 1 - \mu$. In this normalization process, the mean motion is unity. Further, the distance from each massive body to the asteroid is given by:

$$r_1 = \left[(x-\mu)^2 + y^2 + z^2 \right]^{\frac{1}{2}} \tag{1}$$

$$r_2 = \left[(x+1-\mu)^2 + y^2 + z^2 \right]^{\frac{1}{2}} \tag{2}$$

The equations of motion of the asteroid are found by equating the inertial acceleration felt by the rotating frame with the gravitational influence of both massive bodies. The equations (Wiesel 1989) are:

$$\ddot{x} = 2\dot{y} + x - \frac{(1-\mu)(x-\mu)}{r_1^3} - \frac{\mu(x+1-\mu)}{r_2^3}$$

$$\ddot{y} = -2\dot{x} + y - \frac{(1-\mu)y}{r_1^3} - \frac{\mu y}{r_2^3} \tag{3}$$

$$\ddot{z} = -\frac{(1-\mu)z}{r_1^3} - \frac{\mu z}{r_2^3}$$

These equations are highly non-linear. Many attempts were made in the 100 years following their formulation to solve them analytically. They were ultimately shown to be unsolvable in closed form (Wiesel, 1989). Today, methods to solve them numerically are prevalent.

State Transition Matrix

The nominal solution is not the only result of the dynamic model necessary. The State Transition Matrix (STM) must also be found. The STM is found by solving the following differential equation given by Howell (1983), among others,

$$\frac{d\Phi(t,t_0)}{dt} = A(t)\Phi(t,t_0) \tag{4}$$

where $\Phi(t_0,t_0) = I$ and A is the Jacobian of the reduced-order version of Eq. (3). Equation (3) is appended by Eq. (4) element by element and the resulting 42 equations are solved simultaneously. Polito (2011) gives more detail on the numerical solution of these equations.

UNCERTAINTY

Uncertainty manifests itself in the solution of the asteroid's orbit in several forms. There are observational inaccuracies inherent in any techniques to observe the asteroid, both in imperfect equipment and in computational noise. More significantly, because the orbit is determined practically from a finite set of observations, it is possible to fit multiple orbits to the data. These types of uncertainty are present initially.

Uncertainty is accumulated in the future propagation of the asteroid because, first of all, the dynamic model is an approximation to reality. It is impossible for the mathematical model to represent reality perfectly and impractical even to use the most sophisticated models, so approximations are made to an initially imperfect model. This is not to say that the dynamic models are not close, but uncertainty must be taken into account that includes the unknown, true trajectory.

Because the uncertainty accumulates over the course of the solution, it must be propagated forward from its initial values subject to the dynamics. This is accomplished by a linear transformation of the STM on the covariance matrix.

Covariance Matrix

The covariance matrix represents the uncertainty ellipsoid mathematically. What is known is the size and orientation of the initial uncertainty ellipsoid. What is meant by size are the lengths of the principal semi-major axes of the ellipsoid and what is meant by orientation is the three orthogonal vectors that are the principal axes. The inverse of the square of the lengths of the principal axes are the eigenvalues of the covariance matrix and the three principal axes are the eigenvectors. If E is the diagonal matrix of eigenvalues and V is the matrix with the eigenvectors as its columns, then the initial covariance matrix, P_0, is given by,

$$P_0 = VEV^{-1} \tag{5}$$

and because V is orthogonal, P_0 is symmetric.

This is the inverse of the covariance matrix as it is conventionally defined and could be more appropriately called the information matrix. It is defined as the inverse to avoid taking the inverse of this matrix later, which can cause computational problems.

Propagation

As stated above, the uncertainty at any future time is found by a linear transformation of the STM on the covariance matrix as given by Der and Danchick (1996), among others.

$$P(t) = \Phi(t,t_0)P_0\Phi^T(t,t_0) \tag{6}$$

Because there is an assumption of linearity with Eq. (6), it can fail in certain circumstances. It is sometimes necessary to propagate the uncertainty non-linearly.

ENCOUNTER REGION

Encounter regions are necessary because the probability of impact is not desired over the entire solution. Instead, only when the probability is known to be highest is a calculation actually performed. The probability is highest when the Earth is within a certain distance of the nominal solution. It is found that this distance is best defined not in an absolute sense, but rather a distance based on the uncertainty, or 3σ. This translates to the definition of the encounter region being: any region along the orbit of the asteroid where the Earth intersects the uncertainty ellipsoid.

For the scales involved in the asteroid-Earth-Sun system, it is sufficient to treat the Earth as a point in most cases. For that, the times of the encounter regions are given when the following condition is met:

$$r'(t)^T P^{-1}(t) r'(t) < 1 \tag{7}$$

where $r'(t)$ is the relative Earth vector from the center of the ellipsoid to the center of the Earth.

In cases where the nominal solution makes a very close approach, it is necessary to take into account the size of the Earth. Details on this solution process are found in the Appendix.

PROBABILITY CALCULATION

The pdf is a function of the covariance matrix:

$$f(x, y, z) = \sqrt{\frac{9}{(2\pi)^3 |P|}} \exp\left[-\frac{9}{2}\begin{bmatrix} x & y & z \end{bmatrix} P^{-1} \begin{bmatrix} x \\ y \\ z \end{bmatrix}\right] \tag{8}$$

Because P is the 3σ covariance matrix, it must be multiplied by 3^2 so the proper pdf is obtained, which is a function of the 1σ covariance matrix.

Probability is then the triple integral of $f(x,y,z)$ over the volume of the Earth (Chan 2004). This gives a set of probabilities for each encounter. Each event during the encounter (the instantaneous times during the encounter) is mutually exclusive because collision can only occur once. Probability theory calls for a sum of probabilities of mutually exclusive events to obtain the total probability. This is incorrect in this case because increasing the resolution of the numerical results should not affect the total probability. To obtain the total probability for the encounter, Polito (2011) integrates again over time. This quadruple integral is what is meant by integration of the pdf over the volume swept out by the Earth.

RESULTS

This section describes the Monte Carlo simulation used to produce the initial uncertainty and presents the results of two cases: a fictitious asteroid on a collision course with the Earth and a hypothetical case based on a real asteroid.

Monte Carlo Simulation

True uncertainty is obtained from observations and the techniques used to obtain the orbit. This paper, instead, varies the initial uncertainty according to a Monte Carlo simulation and examines the effect it has on the resulting total probabilities.

The initial uncertainty is aligned with the initial velocity vector and the size is varied. Each principal axis, in-track, normal, and out-of-plane, is given a range of values from which a random length is chosen for each of the 100 runs of the simulation.

For three non-overlapping ranges, four values are needed. The sequence,

$$a_{k+1} = \frac{a_k}{e}, \; k = 1, 2, 3 \tag{9}$$

gives these four values. The ranges for the uncertainty are then,

$$
\begin{array}{lcr}
a_2 < & \text{in} - \text{track} & < a_1 \\
a_3 < & \text{normal} & < a_2 \\
a_4 < & \text{out} - \text{of} - \text{plane} & < a_3
\end{array}
\tag{10}
$$

For each case, a_1 and e are specified.

Impact Example

For the impact scenario, the asteroid is propagated for only two days. A longer time span would not be more revealing. The range values are $a_1 = 10^{-4}$ and $e = 2$. Figure 2 shows the encounter along with the principal axes of the uncertainty at each time step. The weak direction stays aligned with the velocity vector only because the encounter takes place close to t_0. Shortly after the encounter, the uncertainty is seen to deviate from the local velocity vector.

The probabilities calculated from the Monte Carlo simulation are shown in Figure 3. Each dot represents a run of the simulation and the resulting total probability of the encounter. The position of the dot is indicative of the size of the initial uncertainty and the shade of the dot conveys the relative magnitude of the probability. All values are normalized: each direction of initial uncertainty by the range from which it was randomly selected and the probability by the maximum and minimum probabilities over 100 runs. Higher probabilities are darker while lower probabilities are light gray; the background color is outside the gray scale of the dots.

As can be seen in Figure 3, there is a trend in probability along the normal vs. in-track initial uncertainties. Higher probabilities tend to occur when the in-track is lower in its range. When the in-track is high, lower probabilities tend to occur when the uncertainty in the normal direction is also high in its range. A similarly subtle trend occurs on the left side: when the in-track is low, the dots become slightly grayer when one moves towards greater normal uncertainty.

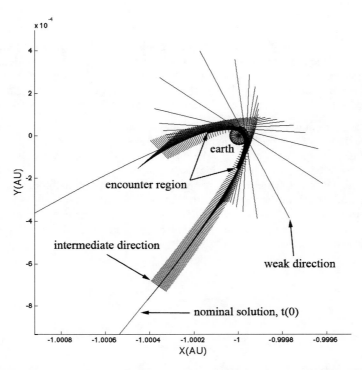

Figure 2: A fictitious asteroid on a collision course with Earth. This figure shows the principal axes of the uncertainty along several time steps around the encounter (wide swath) superimposed onto the nominal solution (thin line). The point at which the uncertainty begins to deviate is shortly after the encounter.

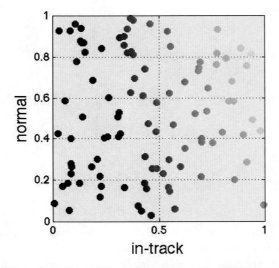

Figure 3: The trend in probability of the impact example. Higher probabilities tend to occur closer to the origin of the normal vs. in-track space

129

Hypothetical

The hypothetical case is based on the asteroid Apophis. By this, it is meant that the initial position and velocity of the nominal solution is that of Apophis. The dynamic model is not accurate enough to be considered the true trajectory of Apophis' nominal solution, but for the purposes of this analysis, it is sufficient. The initial conditions are used for ease of finding a solution in the three-body problem that has long term activity near the Earth.

With these initial conditions, the equations of motion of the three-body problem are integrated and linearized to obtain the nominal solution of the hypothetical case and the STM. Running the Monte Carlo simulation produces the size of the initial uncertainty. Along with the information about its orientation from the initial local velocity vector, the initial covariance matrix can be constructed. The covariance matrix is propagated forward in time by the linear transformation of the STM and, at each time step, the check is made whether the Earth is inside the current uncertainty ellipsoid. When this check is positive, the time step is saved. These saved time steps over the entire solution make up the encounters. The encounters of the hypothetical case for a typical run of the simulation are shown in Figure 4.

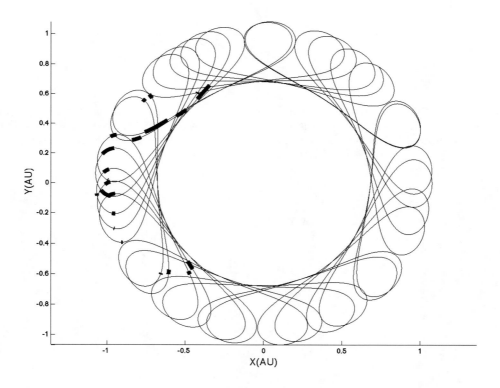

Figure 4: The nominal solution of CR3BP with initial conditions of Apophis over 30 years (CR3BP is a simplified dynamic model so that this is not the true nominal trajectory of Apophis). The rotating frame causes the orbit to be shaped as a series of loops that advance in a circle. The Sun is near the origin and the Earth is near (-1,0). The thick portions of the orbit are a typical set of encounter regions.

Now, each encounter is considered. Taking an individual encounter, the pdf's at each time step through the encounter are integrated using the current covariance matrix. The result is a set of probabilities for the encounter. This set of probabilities is a function of time, which is then integrated to produce the total probability for the encounter. This process is repeated for each encounter. One run of the simulation results in a set of total probabilities, one for each encounter.

Running the simulation 100 times for the hypothetical case, that is 100 different initial covariance matrices, results in 2274 total probabilities. What is found is that despite the initial uncertainty being a uniform random sample along a given range, there is a finite set of encounters to which all or some of the runs adhere.

Table 1 is a list of encounters of the hypothetical case by date and their frequency in the 100 runs. The encounters are those that are distinct by 15 days, but the list is not exhaustive. The date of all the encounters varies for each covariance matrix to the resolution of the numerical orbital solution, but the encounters are still distinct over the long term.

Table 1: Frequency of Encounters. These are some of the encounters of the hypothetical case that are distinct by fifteen days. The date for the encounter is only an identifier; it does not indicate a higher probability of impact by the asteroid Apophis.

Encounter			Frequency
Month	Day	Year	
11	1	2010	25
9	6	2011	90
1	14	2012	100
4	11	2017	100
7	12	2017	29
6	2	2035	100
10	20	2035	100
8	28	2039	100
12	31	2039	100
2	21	2040	30
4	10	2040	100

With 2274 data points over a variety of initial uncertainties, it is desired to understand the trend in total probability calculated. There is no trend in probability across all the encounters, rather, each encounter individually has a trend. In general, higher probabilities are correlated with initial uncertainties that are tighter in all three directions, or more certain. Figure 5 shows the probabilities of a typical encounter. The plot is three-dimensional with each axis corresponding to a direction of the initial uncertainty. The scales of the axes are the normalized ranges of the respective direction. Higher probabilities are near the origin, where the uncertainty is tighter.

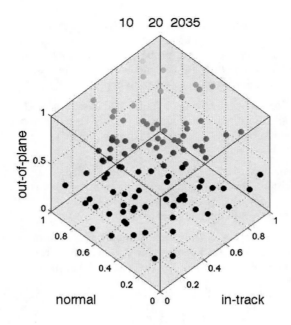

Figure 5: The trend in probability of the hypothetical case for the encounter on 10/20/2035 is from higher to lower as the uncertainty grows in all three directions.

Polito (2011) identifies two categories of encounters for the hypothetical case. The other being those that trend in the same way as above but only in normal vs. in-track. These two categories are only slightly different from one another, the first category is more stringent its requirements and in the majority of all the encounters. The second category can be thought of as the exception, but the conclusions for both categories are the same. Figure 5 is an encounter in the first category. Figure 3 is an example of the second category.

CONCLUSIONS

The primary contribution of this paper is to present an alternative approach to impact probability calculations for asteroids with regard to the Earth. The uncertainty inherent in the orbit of any asteroid, along with its mathematical representation and dynamic propagation was discussed earlier. The encounter regions in which the probability is appreciable acts as locations along the nominal solution where probability calculation takes place. The results of the simulation in its entirety and the trend in the data aims to explain this trend by a simple example and show how it is a limiting case for the size of the uncertainty used for the simulations. The limitations of these methods are discussed and recommendations for work in the future that could address these issues are made.

Explanation of trend

The encounters are, for the most part, the same for each run of the simulation as seen in Table 1, and the distance from the Earth is the same for each calculation of probability in all the runs for a given encounter. The dynamics are the same for each run of the simulation, so that the uncertainty is propagated equally from run to run. There is a one to one relationship between the uncertainty during the encounter and the initial uncertainty. The initial uncertainty is the only variable in this problem. So for two unequal uncertainties for the same encounter, where the uncertainty is described by standard deviations in three-dimensional space (the covariance matrix), the probabilities calculated will be unequal.

Two one-dimensional probability density functions with differing standard deviations are shown in Figure 6. The solid pdf has a lower standard deviation and the vertical lines are 3σ. Clearly, the solid pdf will integrate to a higher probability if the domain of integration is within the range where the solid pdf is greater than the dashed pdf. This range is found by equating the two pdf's and solving for the distance from the mean. This distance is given by (Polito, 2011):

$$s = n\sigma\sqrt{\frac{2\ln\sqrt{n}}{n^2 - 1}} \tag{11}$$

where n is the multiplicative factor difference of the standard deviations, greater than one, and σ is the lower standard deviation. For Figure 6, from Eq. (11), $s = 0.334$.

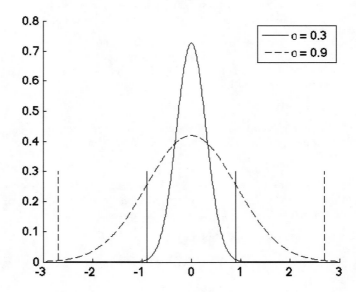

Figure 6: Two probability density functions of differing standard deviations. Note how the lesser standard deviation has a higher pdf near the mean.

When the Earth is within this distance, s, a lower uncertainty will integrate to a higher probability. It is found that this requirement is easily met by the values of uncertainty chosen for this Monte Carlo simulation and subsequent propagation. For example, the 3σ uncertainty can grow to be as large as 300 AU. With $n = e = 2$, the value for s is approximately 48 AU, while the Earth can be only at most 2 AU away from the asteroid during any encounter. This is why tighter uncertainties produce higher probabilities: at the distance the Earth is from the nominal solution during the encounter (the mean of the pdf) the pdf for the tighter uncertainty is greater than for larger uncertainty.

Limitations and Recommendations

Higher probabilities are desired for any analysis of impact to avoid a false sense of security. Also, with advances in observational and analytical techniques to determine asteroid orbits, the positions will be known with greater accuracy. It seems that the trend found here is optimistic then, that probabilities will tend to become more conservative in the future. As uncertainties drop substantially and the distance to the Earth remains constant, the distance s will be surpassed, leading to a reversal of the trend found here. However, smaller uncertainties that would cause this reversal are not compatible with these methods directly. The large uncertainties are desired because when the uncertainty is small initially, it does not grow enough over time to cause encounter regions except during very close approaches. With no encounter regions, the probability calculation cannot proceed.

Here it is seen that the dynamic model is very important. Without an accurate dynamic model, asteroids that make very close approaches cannot be flagged and this method cannot be used with realistic uncertainties. With an accurate dynamic model and realistic uncertainties, the trend found here would persist for asteroids that make a very close approach.

Alternatively, the linear assumption with which the uncertainty is propagated can be abandoned and replaced by non-linear propagation. This would lead to a faster growth of uncertainty over time, in which case a small initial uncertainty could still lead to encounters far in the future.

The goal of work in the future is to refine these methods so that they produce probabilities comparable to current automated methods. By using a more accurate dynamic model and realistic uncertainties, with the recommendations given here, these methods can be used as an alternative to current impact probability determination.

Acknowledgements

We would like to thank Dr. Ken Chan at the Aerospace Corporation for his work on satellite collision probability that greatly influenced and contributed to this work.

Appendix: Earth with Extent

The problem is to determine when two ellipsoids intersect. The two ellipsoids are the uncertainty ellipsoid and the Earth (the Earth is an ellipsoid with three equal principal axes). Alfano and Greer (2003) and Chan (2002) develop the technique to do this.

The surface of an ellipsoid can be described by:

$$XTST^T X^T = 0 \qquad \text{(A-1)}$$

where

$$X = \begin{bmatrix} x & y & z & 1 \end{bmatrix} \qquad \text{(A-2)}$$

$$T = \begin{bmatrix} 1 & 0 & 0 & 0 \\ 0 & 1 & 0 & 0 \\ 0 & 0 & 1 & 0 \\ -x_0 & -y_0 & -z_0 & 1 \end{bmatrix} \qquad \text{(A-3)}$$

$$S = \begin{bmatrix} C_{11} & C_{12} & C_{13} & 0 \\ C_{21} & C_{22} & C_{23} & 0 \\ C_{31} & C_{32} & C_{33} & 0 \\ 0 & 0 & 0 & -1 \end{bmatrix} \qquad \text{(A-4)}$$

where $\begin{bmatrix} x_0 & y_0 & z_0 \end{bmatrix}$ is the center of the ellipsoid and C_{ij} are the elements of the inverse of the covariance matrix.

The two ellipsoids are then

$$XAX^T = 0 \tag{A-5}$$

$$XBX^T = 0 \tag{A-6}$$

By subtracting Eq. (A-6) from a scaled Eq. (A-5): $X(\lambda A - B)X^T = 0$, the problem becomes an eigenvalue problem. To get it in the recognizable form, left multiply the inner matrix by AA^{-1}.

$$XA(\lambda I - A^{-1}B)X^T = 0 \tag{A-7}$$

As explained by Alfano and Greer (2003) and Chan (2002), two of the eigenvalues of $A^{-1}B$ are indicative of the state of intersection of the two ellipsoids described by A and B. This is extended by Polito (2011) so that when any of the four eigenvalues are complex conjugates, the ellipsoids are overlapping, when all four are positive, they are overlapping, when any two are negative and equal they are touching, when any two are negative and unequal, they are separate.

With this check on the eigenvalues of $A^{-1}B$, the regions along the orbit of the asteroid when the instantaneous uncertainty ellipsoid and the sphere of the Earth intersect can be determined. This works whether A or B is the Earth.

References

Alfano, S., Greer, M., 2003. Determining if Two Solid Ellipsoids Intersect. Journal of Guidance, Control and Dynamics, 26, 106–110.

Chan, F.K., 2002. A Simple Mathematical Approach for Determining Intersection of Quadratic Surfaces. Advances in Astronautical Sciences, 109, 785–801.

Chan, F.K., 2008. Spacecraft Collision Probability. The Aerospace Press, El Segundo, CA.

Der, G., Danchick, R., 1996. Analytic and Numerical Error Covariance Matrix Propagation (for spacecraft in earth orbital environments), in: Astrodynamics Conference, San Diego, CA, July 29-31, pp. 854–878.

Howell, K., 1983. Three-Dimensional, Periodic Halo Orbits in the Restricted Three-Body Problem. Ph.D. dissertation, Stanford University.

Milani, A., Chesley, S.R., Sansaturio, M.E., Tommei, G., Vasecchi, G.B., 2005a. Nonlinear Impact Monitoring: Line of Variation Searches for Impactors. Icarus 173, 362–384.

Milani, A., Sansaturio, M.E., Tommei, G., Arratia, O., Chesley, S.R., 2005b. Multiple Solutions for Asteroid Orbits: Computational Procedure and Applications. Astronomy and Astrophysics 431, 729–746.

Polito, C., 2011. The Effect of Variable Initial Uncertainty on the Probability of Asteroid-Earth Collisions. Master of Science thesis, Department of Aerospace Engineering, The Pennsylvania State University.

Wiesel, W.E., 1989. Spacecraft Dynamics. pp. 278-281, McGraw-Hill. 2nd edition.

ORBITAL DEBRIS I

SESSION 2

Chair: Dr. Thomas Starchville
                                         The Aerospace Corporation

100-YEAR LOW EARTH ORBIT DEBRIS POPULATION MODEL

Alan B. Jenkin,[*] Marlon E. Sorge,[†] Glenn E. Peterson,[‡]
John P. McVey[§] and Bernard B. Yoo[**]

This paper presents a process to generate discrete future low Earth orbit debris populations for input to space system performance simulations. This process has several features that are different from previously developed debris prediction models, including use of the IMPACT breakup model and logarithmic down-sampling. Results show that the debris population caused by the current tracked population will grow even without future launches. Intact objects were ranked in terms of their potential to result in debris creation. Results preliminarily indicate that large numbers of collisions between large and small untracked objects may generate significant amounts of debris.

INTRODUCTION

In response to the dramatic increase of the cataloged low Earth orbit (LEO) population (caused primarily by collision events) since early 2007, the United States Air Force (USAF) developmental planning and architectures group (SMC/XRD) initiated a study to assess the effect of an increasing debris population on the performance of future U.S. military space systems. To support this effort, The Aerospace Corporation was tasked to develop a process to generate discrete future LEO debris populations for input to space system simulations. This process is functionally similar to debris environment prediction models that have been previously developed by other national and international organizations, such as LEGEND,[1] IDES/DELTA,[2, 3, 4] SDM,[5] and DAMAGE[6], but most of the detailed steps and components were developed independently. A feature of this model that is different from previous models is the use of the IMPACT breakup model. This permits accounting for the effect of the masses of both objects on the mass and spread velocity distributions of the resulting fragments. This feature in-turn makes it possible to rank objects in terms of their debris generation potential, thereby identifying potential candidates for active removal. Another new feature is the use of logarithmic down-sampling. This feature combined with use of IMPACT makes it possible to model collisions involving small untracked de-

---

[*] Senior Engineering Specialist, Astrodynamics Department, The Aerospace Corporation, P.O. Box 92957, Los Angeles, CA 90009-2957, Associate Fellow AIAA, Member AAS.
[†] Senior Project Engineer, Space Innovation Directorate, The Aerospace Corporation, 2155 Louisiana Blvd., NE, Suite 5000, Albuquerque, NM, 87110-5425, Senior member AIAA, Member Directed Energy Professional Society.
[‡] Senior Engineering Specialist, Astrodynamics Department, The Aerospace Corporation, P.O. Box 92957, Los Angeles, CA 90009-2957, Member AIAA, Member AAS.
[§] Engineering Specialist, Astrodynamics Department, The Aerospace Corporation, P.O. Box 92957, Los Angeles, CA 90009-2957.
[**] Engineering Specialist, Astrodynamics Department, The Aerospace Corporation, P.O. Box 92957, Los Angeles, CA 90009-2957.

bris. This paper presents the process methodology, future population prediction results, and classes of intact objects that could be candidates for active removal.

OVERALL METHODOLOGY

The debris model generation process consists of the following steps.

Step 1. The initial population of objects is determined using a recent unclassified catalog of resident space objects. To generate the 1-5 cm and 5-10 cm populations, a mass-law relation is used to extrapolate the catalog population (> 10 cm) down to the lower size regions.

Step 2. A population of future launched objects is generated by repeating recent past launch activity.

Step 3. Initial and future launched objects are propagated using the mean element propagator MEANPROP to determine mean element trajectories for 100 years beyond the start epoch.

Step 4. Monte Carlo ensembles of statistical collisions are generated using an orbit trace crossing method. (Collisions involving the initial 5 – 10 cm and 1 – 5 cm populations were not modeled in this study due to limited scope).

Step 5. Debris cloud fragments are generated using the breakup modeling code IMPACT. IMPACT accounts for the effect of the mass of both objects on the mass and velocity distribution of the resulting fragments. Hence, for example, the fragment cloud resulting from a collision between a large intact object with a 10 cm debris fragment will be different from the fragment cloud resulting from a collision between two large intact objects with the same collision geometry.

Step 6. The debris fragment set is down-sampled to a smaller, weighted population.

Step 7. The down-sampled and weighted debris fragments are propagated using the mean element propagator MEANPROP to determine mean element trajectories for 100 years beyond the start epoch.

Steps 4-7 can be repeated to feed the new generation of debris back into the previous population to produce the next generation of debris. The use of logarithmic down-sampling permits efficient modeling of debris down to 1 cm, facilitating feedback of small debris to the collisional process. Other than a few exceptions, only results through the first generation of debris are shown in this paper. Detailed results including subsequent generations of debris will be presented in a future paper.

The final model consisted of a discrete population of objects over the next 100 years in the form of two-line element sets (TLEs). From this population, spatial densities can be determined and the effect on satellites can be assessed via follow-on simulations.

The process flow is illustrated in Figures 1 and 2.

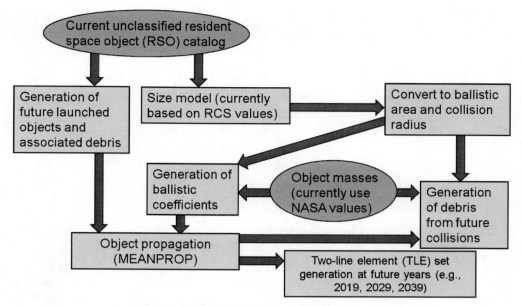

Figure 1. Debris Model Generation Process.

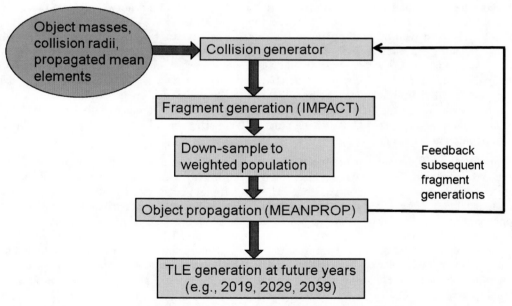

Figure 2. Generation of Debris from Future Collisions.

POPULATION NOMENCLATURE

The following nomenclature was used to represent the various populations included in the study.

CT: Current tracked population: from the unclassified resident space object (RSO) catalog of July 9, 2009.

FL: Future launched objects (all intact and trackable).

CT vs. CT 1st generation debris: Debris from CT vs. CT collisions (hence 1st generation of debris).

FL vs. CT 1st generation debris: Debris from FL vs. CT collisions.

FL vs. FL 1st generation debris: Debris from FL vs. FL collisions.

CT 5 - 10 cm debris: Current 5 – 10 cm debris (untracked, not included in CT).

CT 1 - 5 cm debris: Current 1 – 5 cm debris (untracked, not included in CT).

STARTING POPULATIONS

The starting population for the model was divided into three categories of objects based upon size: >10 cm (CT), 5-10 cm, and 1-5 cm. The >10 cm category represents those orbiting objects that are currently reliably observed by the Space Surveillance Network (SSN) and contained in the public Resident Space Object (RSO) catalog. The >10 cm starting population was therefore based upon two-line element sets from the USSTRATCOM unclassified catalog of resident space objects when the debris study began in June of 2009. The 5-10 cm category represents those objects that could conceivably be observed with an improved SSN. The 1-5 cm population is unlikely to be observed with currently planned tracking improvements, but might be observable with future technology towards the end of the 100-year simulation duration. Debris of this size is likely to be catastrophic to a space vehicle should a collision occur. A mass-law relation was used to extrapolate the current >10 cm population down to the smaller size regimes with additional spreading in the orbit elements being allocated to simulate the greater influence of collision/fragmentation events on smaller objects. The resulting starting number of objects was 13004 for the >10 cm population, 48200 objects in the 5-10 cm size region, and 307235 objects in the 1-5 cm population.

Figure 3 shows the number of objects for each of the three groups as a function of mean altitude and inclination. The >10 cm population has been further divided into large intact objects (satellites and rocket bodies) and large debris. The top left plot shows that the currently existing intact tracked population is not smoothly distributed in space. Instead, the distribution has very tight concentrations of objects consistent with current operational practice. In essence, the same orbits are used time and again. The >10 cm debris is much more spread out in the altitude direction than the intact population as would be expected from decay. The >5 cm and >1 cm debris continue this trend. As the population size decreases, the particles from collision and fragmentation events become more spread out due to the greater influence of collision and fragmentation energies on the initial spread, and, as time evolves, greater susceptibility to drag.

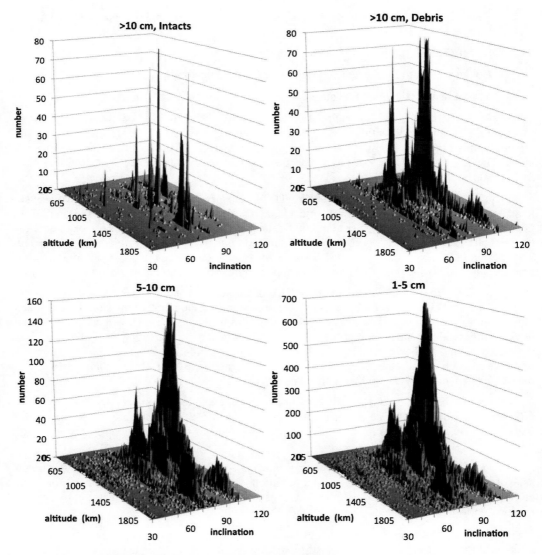

Figure 3. Distribution in Orbit Elements of the Simulation Starting Population.

MODELING OF FUTURE LAUNCHED OBJECTS

The Future Launch Model (FLM) was developed to provide a plausible input of future launch objects for LEO debris population forecasting studies. FLM takes a selection of launches from a user-selected historical launch period, and repeats them to fill a user-selected future launch period. The FLM process can be broken down into the following steps:

1. Select historical launch objects from the USSTRATCOM unclassified Satcat (Satellite Catalog)

2. Select TLEs for all historical launch objects

3. Convert TLEs to Earth Centered Inertial (ECI) state vectors

4. Repeat historical launch ECI state vectors over the future launch period

For this study, the historical launch period was 1999-07-09 to 2009-07-08. This launch period was the most recent period with sufficient data at the time of the study. The selection of this time period implies a business as usual assumption, based on the actual launches from the previous ten years. The future launch period into which these launches were projected was 2009-07-09 to 2109-07-08.

A database query is made on the USSTRATCOM unclassified Satcat database. The query selects Satcat objects from the desired historical launch period. Interplanetary objects are excluded. Objects with perigee height greater than 2000 km are excluded. Debris objects are excluded. International Space Station (ISS) and Space Transportation System (STS) objects are excluded. The ISS and STS objects are excluded because we assume they are actively monitored and maneuvered to avoid collisions. This leaves unmanned payload and rocket body objects.

The next step in the FLM is to query the TLE database and obtain orbit information from the USSTRATCOM TLE for each object. The objective is to find the nominal mission orbit for each object. In order to filter out pre-mission orbits and orbit maneuvers, TLEs with epochs less than 60 days after the launch date are ignored. The first TLE occurring at least 60 days after launch is selected to represent the object's orbit. This 60 day cutoff period is assumed to produce a representative mission orbit. No attempt is made to identify and adjust for objects that continue pre-mission maneuvering beyond 60 days after launch.

A second effect of the 60 day TLE cutoff period is to exclude any objects that reenter within 60 days after launch. As a consequence, there may be a slight underestimate in collisions with objects that are very close to reentry. This expediency reduces computation and processing burden.

Once the TLEs are selected, they are converted to ECI state vectors representing the initial state of each object. Simplified General Perturbations (SGP4) propagation is used to perform this conversion. To add randomness to the in-plane positions, each object is propagated forward by a random, uniformly distributed, fraction of one orbit period.

The previous processes produce a set of epochs and ECI state vectors describing the launches in the historical launch period. This set of representative launches and launch epochs is repeated, with appropriate epoch offsets, to fill the future launch period. Thus the schedule of future launches is modeled as a continuously repeating replica of the selected historical launch period.

For this study, all objects were left on their initial orbits to decay under natural atmospheric drag. No post-mission disposal was modeled. This includes Iridium and Globalstar satellites. Disposal was not modeled in this study in order to quantify the risk that disposal mitigates.

Figure 4 shows the cumulative number of historical launched intact objects vs. time along with the cumulative number of projected future launches from the model. As can be seen from the slope of the curve, the modeled future launch rate is representative of recent launch rates and is lower than the higher launch rate that prevailed from 1970 through 1990.

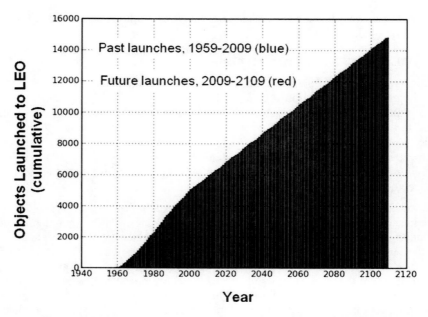

Figure 4. Historical and Projected Future Cumulative Launches to LEO.

COLLISION GENERATION METHODOLOGY

An orbit trace crossing method was used to generate future random collisions. For each pair of objects, all orbit trace crossings (OTCs) during the simulation time interval were determined. MEANPROP propagation results were used to account for evolution of the orbits. At each OTC, the collision probability (p_C) at each crossing was computed, assuming that the in-track positions of the two objects are not known (too far in the future to accurately predict). If a uniform random variate drawn from the interval [0,1] is $\leq p_C$, then a collision is recorded in an output file. This process is repeated in Monte Carlo fashion to generate a broad range of collision scenarios. For this study, 100 Monte Carlo groups of collisions were generated. A 1000 Monte Carlo test case run yielded a similar distribution of collisions as the 100 Monte Carlo case. The final output file with all Monte Carlo groups of collisions is then sent to IMPACT for fragment generation. Relative to traditional spatial density-based methods, this method is convenient in that it latently retains the correlation between spatial density and relative velocity, thereby accurately modeling collision rates (i.e., fluxes) and relative collision velocities used in fragment generation.

The object sizes have a strong influence on the number of collisions, and the object masses have a strong influence on the amount of debris generated by collisions. For this study, RSO catalog radar cross sections (RCS) were used to estimate object sizes. For each cataloged object, a time series of RCS values was first time-averaged. The NASA Size Estimation Model (SEM) was then used to convert the time-averaged RCS values to object size. Through further trial and error, it was found that a scale factor of 1.64 had to be applied across all objects to yield collision rates that were not grossly inconsistent with the actual number of collision over the historical time period of spaceflight. For the results presented in this study, object masses were obtained from the NASA database of object masses. Since this study was performed, an independent database of

145

sizes and masses has been developed at The Aerospace Corporation for the intact objects and some of the debris population.

COLLISION DEBRIS GENERATION MODELING

The debris created from projected collision events were modeled using The Aerospace Corporation fragmentation model IMPACT.[7] IMPACT is a semi-analytic model combining empirical distributions for fragment masses, velocities, and sizes from space-based events and ground-based tests with enforcement of mass, energy, and momentum conservation. Collision characteristics generated from the collision generation code are input into the fragmentation model which generates the resulting debris distributions for fragments of 1 cm and greater. The debris distributions' characteristics represent effects of the masses of the colliding objects, and the collision geometries and energies.

A number of collisions, typically between small objects, often debris, and large intact objects, have insufficient energy to completely fragment the larger object. These partial breakups are modeled assuming that part of the larger object will fragment similarly to a complete fragmentation, while the remaining portion of the larger object will remain intact. The amount of fragmented mass from the larger object scales with the relative kinetic energy of the smaller object. The mass distribution of the fragments is similar to a typical complete fragmentation event as observed by Yasaka.[8] There is a considerable amount of uncertainty in determining the amount of mass to be fragmented by a partial fragmentation. A number of tests have been conducted for much smaller impactors and some results exist for larger impactors that resulted in complete fragmentation of the target, but little data is available for intermediate-sized $1 - 10$ cm impactors. This represents an area of future research.

LONG-TERM PROPAGATION ANALYSIS AND DOWN-SAMPLING

The Aerospace Corporation's long-term orbit propagation and control tool MEANPROP was used to generate mean orbital element histories (up to 100 years) from initial state vectors and epochs. To model natural orbital evolution, MEANPROP calls the Semi-Analytic Orbit Propagator (SAOP[9]), a program developed by the Charles Stark Draper Laboratory. The perturbation force model includes Sun and Moon gravity, solar radiation pressure, an Earth Geopotential Model (EGM96) 16 x 16 Earth gravity model, and the Mass Spectrometer Incoherent Scatter Extended model (MSISE-90) atmosphere model. For the atmosphere model, the solar flux parameter F10.7 and the geomagnetic index Ap values used were the 50th percentile monthly predictions published by the NASA Marshall Space Flight Center in July 2009. These predictions are based on NOAA measurement data, and the last 11-year solar cycle pattern is repeated from the end of the predictions to year 2109.

The amount of fragments generated by IMPACT for all collisions in 100 Monte Carlo cases is typically too large to post-process. This is especially the case when fragments down to 1 cm are to be retained. This problem is typically addressed by down-sampling to a smaller, weighted population. However, this is complicated by the fact that the resulting distribution of fragments in mass and size is nonlinear. The $5 - 10$ cm group contains approximately $3 - 4$ times more objects than the > 10 cm group, and the $1 - 5$ cm group contains an order of magnitude more objects than the $5 - 10$ cm group. To address this distribution non-linearity, a logarithmic down-sampling algorithm was developed. This method brings the number of fragments down to a more practical level, but the resulting mass and size distribution better represents the original population than linear down-sampling would. A uniform linear down-sampling is performed in log mass space. A non-uniform weighting across the resulting fragment population is applied based on local mapping of the down-sampling interval in log-mass space back to mass space. As the mass decreases,

146

the weighting factors increase. The weighting factors are then used in any subsequent post-processing of the fragment population, such as the generation of future collisions involving these fragments and the generation of density and flux plots.

The fragments from all 100 Monte Carlo cases are sorted by mass from largest to smallest. When the file sizes of these 100 Monte Carlo groups grow too large, the operating system or physical memory will limit the amount of fragments that can be sorted. In this case, the complete set of fragments in all 100 Monte Carlo cases is divided into 10 groups of 10 Monte Carlo cases to perform the mass sorting. To facilitate propagation with MEANPROP, the 10 groups are filtered to remove fragments that are on ballistic or hyperbolic trajectories. The criterion to accept a fragment for propagation requires a semi-major axis less than 60,000 km, an eccentricity less than .9999, and a perigee altitude greater than 120 km. The filtered fragment list is then logarithmically down-sampled on each of the 10 groups to produce 1,000 weighted representative fragments. These 10 groups of 1,000 down-sampled cases are combined to provide the average population of 10,000 weighted fragments. The weighting is adjusted so this represents a single average Monte Carlo case. These 10,000 cases are propagated in MEANPROP for 100 years past their start epoch. The resulting propagated cases are then used with their weighting factors to generate TLE's of populations at desired future time points, and they can also be fed back into the collision process to determine the next generation of debris.

SIMULATION RESULTS

Figure 5 shows collisions between CT objects ("CT vs. CT") from all 100 Monte Carlo scenarios that were generated. Each symbol (diamond) represents a collision and shows the epoch (x-axis) and altitude (y-axis) of occurrence. The mean number of collisions was 16.9, and the standard deviation was 5.6. Figure 6 shows results for Monte Carlo Case 2 only, which is a typical scenario. The plots show that the majority of collisions occur in two altitude bands: one from 500 to 1200 km, and the other from 1400 to 1700 km.

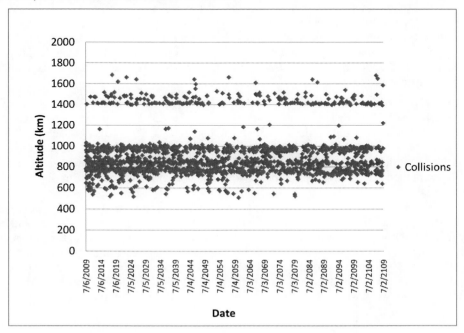

Figure 5. CT vs. CT Collisions from all 100 Monte Carlo Cases.

147

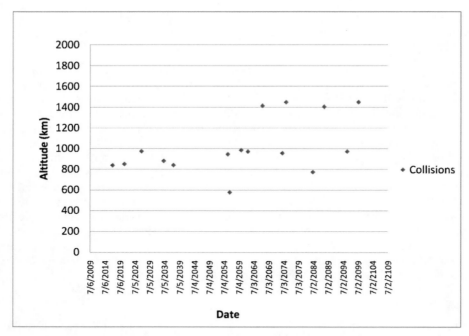

Figure 6. CT vs. CT Collisions from Monte Carlo Case 2.

Figure 7 shows the cumulative number of collisions between all objects in the combined CT and FL populations over time, averaged over the 100 Monte Carlo cases. As can be seen, the number of CT vs. CT collisions per unit time (i.e., the slope of the curve) decreases with time due to the gradual reduction of that population caused by atmospheric decay. However, the addition of the FL population causes the total number of collisions per unit time to increase. Initially, most FL objects that collide do so with a CT object. Then, later in the 100-year interval, the number of FL vs. FL collisions increases.

Figure 8 shows the total number of objects on orbit in a given year during the 100-year interval in the combined CT and FL population as well as the 1st generation debris populations larger than 10 cm that resulted from collisions within the combined CT and FL populations. Figure 9 shows the total number of objects on orbit in a given year in the initial 5-10 cm population as well as the 1st generation debris populations in the 5-10 cm size range that resulted from collisions within the combined CT and FL populations. Figure 10 shows the total number of objects on orbit in a given year in the initial 1-5 cm population as well as the 1st generation debris populations in the 1-5 cm size range that resulted from collisions within the combined CT and FL populations. Figures 8-10 are stacked to show the contributions of the various populations. The plots show clearly that the debris population will grow even without future launches, in agreement with the findings of Liou and Johnson[10] and Lewis et al.[6] They also show that slightly more than half of the population at 100 years is caused by collisions involving future launched objects. As a caveat, it should be remembered that these plots show the average result and do not show the Monte Carlo variation. Future work will carry Monte Carlo variations through multiple generations.

Figure 11 shows the total number of objects on orbit in a given year in the initial 1-5 cm population as well as the 1st and 2nd generation debris populations in the 1-5 cm group that resulted from collisions within the combined CT and FL populations. This plot is significant in that it indicates that the 2nd generation debris comprises 50% of the total 1-5 cm population. While the number of 1st generation debris fragments larger than 10 cm after 100 years is comparable to the total number of CT and FL objects, those fragments are much smaller than the CT and FL objects, and therefore they can generate neither as many collisions nor as much debris per collision as the CT vs. FL collisions. Therefore, the large amount of 2nd generation debris in the 1-5 cm size range cannot all be originating from collisions between 1st generation debris larger than 10 cm and CT or FL objects. There must be debris originating from another source. In this case, it is the large number of collisions occurring between small 1st generation debris in the 1-5 cm and 5-10 cm groups with the large objects in the CT and FL populations. This also implies that there may be large numbers of collisions between the initial small populations in the 1-5 cm and 5-10 cm groups with large objects in the CT and FL populations that collectively generate large amounts of debris. This study did not extend to the simulation of those collisions, but they will be considered in future work.

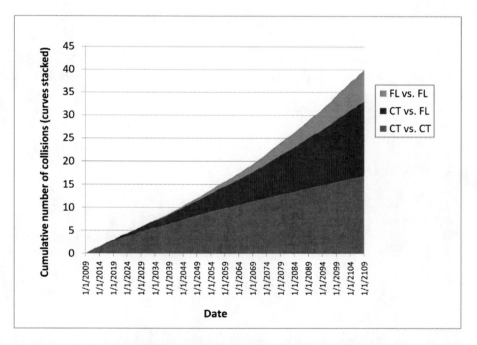

Figure 7. Cumulative Number of Collisions Between All Objects in the Combined CT and FL Populations, Averaged over 100 Monte Carlo Cases, vs. Time.

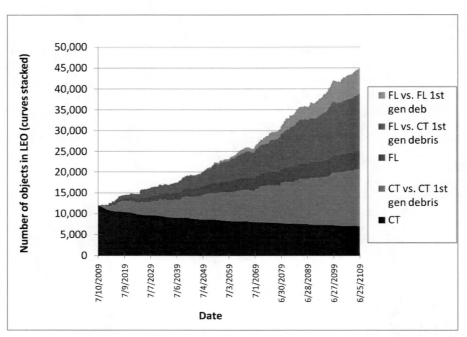

Figure 8. Number of > 10 cm Objects in the CT, FL, and CT+FL 1st Generation Debris Populations vs. Time.

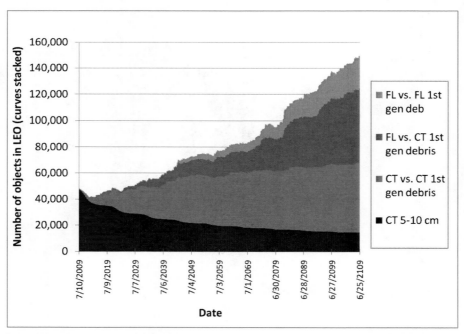

Figure 9. Number of 5-10 cm Objects in the CT and CT+FL 1st Generation Debris Populations vs. Time.

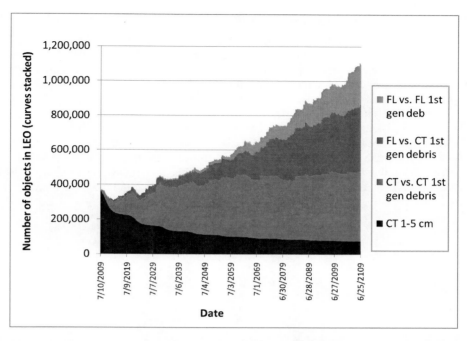

Figure 10. Number of 1-5 cm Objects in the CT and CT+FL 1st Generation Debris Populations vs. Time.

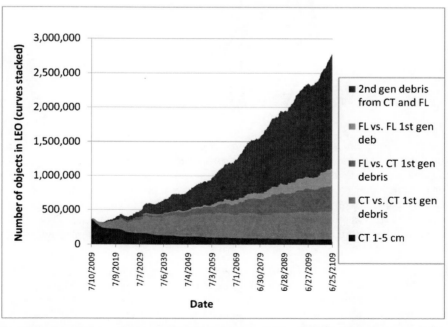

Figure 11. Number of 1-5 cm Objects in the CT and CT+FL 1st and 2nd Generation Debris Populations vs. Time.

COLLISION AND COLLISION DEBRIS DISTRIBUTION CHARACTERISTICS

The collisions resulting from interactions between the currently tracked and future launch populations generate what is called the first generation debris. The characteristics of these collisions and the resulting debris reveal the major sources of the self-perpetuating growth in the debris environment. Figure 12 shows the distribution of collisions by colliding object mass for all first generation debris-creating collisions involving greater than 10 cm objects. The colliding objects are divided into four categories: debris (Deb), intact objects less massive that Iridium satellites (< Irid), Iridium satellites (Irid), and intact objects more massive that Iridium (> Irid). It can be seen that more than 99% of the collisions involved at least one intact object. 72% of the collisions involved an object with a mass greater than Iridium with slightly less than half of these collisions being with a piece of debris. The frequency of the large intact versus debris collisions is related to the combination of the large area of the massive object and the large number of debris objects.

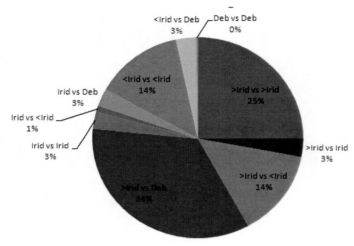

Figure 12. Distribution of Collisions that Create 1ˢᵗ Generation Debris by Parent Object Type.

Figure 13 shows the distribution of debris fragments from the same set of collisions, again segregated by colliding object mass. The disproportionate effect of collisions involving two objects more massive than Iridium can be seen in that 52% of the debris resulted from these collisions whereas they only represent 25% of the total number of collisions. 78% of the debris is generated by collisions involving only intact objects with most of the remaining debris being generated by collisions between debris and the largest intact objects. This illustrates the importance of intact objects, and large intact objects in particular, in the growth of the future debris environment.

Figure 14 shows a similar set of information to that in Figure 13 except for the 1-5 cm fragments. In the case of these smaller fragments the dominance of the large intact objects in debris production is even greater than with the 10 cm and larger debris. 87% of the 1-5 cm first generation debris is created from collisions involving intact objects only, with 59 % of the total debris coming from large intact versus large intact collisions. The debris from collisions involving currently tracked debris are almost all created through collisions with large intact objects. Other collisions involving debris provide a negligible contribution to the population.

152

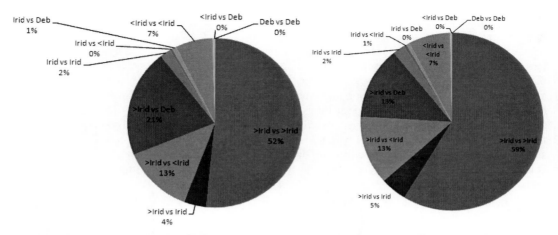

**Figure 13. Distribution of Greater than 10 cm
1st Generation Debris by Source Collision.**

**Figure 14. Distribution of 1-5 cm 1st
Generation Debris by Source Collision.**

Using the information on which specific individual objects were involved in the future projected collisions and the amount of debris resulting from those collisions, a combined parameter can be generated for each object reflecting both the probability of collision and severity of the results. The probability-severity parameter is the total number of debris fragments ≥ 1 cm generated by all of the collisions from all of the Monte Carlo runs involving each object. Figure 15 shows the top 100 objects based on the probability-severity parameter for the currently tracked objects versus currently tracked objects collisions. Although the exact location in the list will change for any particular object within another set of Monte Carlo runs, the overall results are similar.

Several points are noticeable from Figure 15. One is that the probability-severity chart is dominated by large upper stages with a significant portion of them being Russian or Soviet in origin. The second is that there is a gradual roll-off in the impact each object has to the first generation debris population, meaning that the effect of removing objects on the reduction in first generation debris accumulates slowly. Removal of all of the top 100 objects would only have the cumulative effect of reducing the first generation ≥ 1 cm debris population after 100 year by ~ 50%.

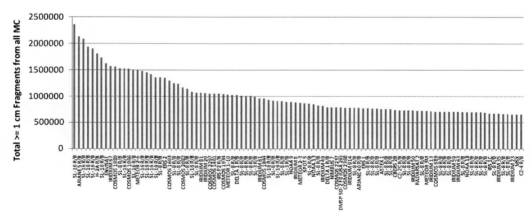

Figure 15. Collision Probability-Severity Top 100 Objects.

153

A preliminary consideration of second generation debris was made. Second generation debris is debris produced in collisions involving first generation debris as one or both of the colliding objects. As Figure 16 illustrates most of the second generation debris is created by collisions with large intact objects (87%). Figure 17 shows the division of second generation debris by the size of the first generation debris that was involved in its creation. The second generation debris is approximately evenly split between being created by first generation debris above and below the trackable, 10 cm, size. This suggests that collisions between sub-trackable debris and intact objects may not be negligible in their contributions to the future debris environment, although they may be generally unobservable with current tracking systems. The overall contribution of the sub-trackable debris to future growth is highly dependent on the amount of debris produced in collisions between 1- 10 cm debris and intact objects, emphasizing the importance of better understanding these events.

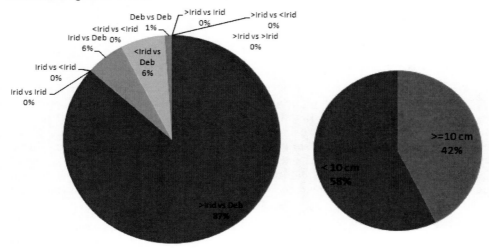

Figure 16. Distribution of Greater Than 10 cm 2nd Generation Debris by Source Collision.

Figure 17. Distribution of Greater Than 10 cm 2nd Generation Debris by Source 1st Generation Debris Size.

154

SPATIAL DENSITY RESULTS

During the collision generation process, each discrete piece of debris retained from the down sampling is propagated from the time of its creation to the end of the 100-year simulation duration. Similarly, each starting current population object and future launch object is propagated for the same time span. At one-year intervals, the propagated states of each object are saved. This forms the basis of the discrete catalogs representing the debris environment at distinct snapshots in time. The spatial density is computed from these yearly discrete catalogs. Each object is propagated through one orbital period with its spatial location (altitude and declination) and velocity saved into a spatial bin that is 10 km in altitude and approximately 1 deg in declination. The spatial density is then simply found from the number of objects that pass through a given spatial bin normalized to account for the volume of the bin and the time spent in the bin.

Figures 18-20 show the growth in the spatial density as derived from the model as a function of time and altitude (results have been averaged over the declination). For the three population sizes, there are observable peaks in LEO at distinct altitudes. The most dominant is around the 700-850 km altitude band; this is where most Sun-synchronous satellites reside along with the Iridium constellation and residual objects from the Fengyun-1C event. The growth of the objects in time is most pronounced in this altitude region as well. There is a second distinct peak at a slightly higher altitude of 950-1000 km; the Russian Parus constellation lies here. A third peak exists at the high LEO altitude of near 1400 km where Globalstar constellation and the Russian Strela-1 & Strela-3 satellites reside.

The assessment of the effect of this future debris population on spacecraft mission utility and launch accessibility is presented in a separate paper.[11]

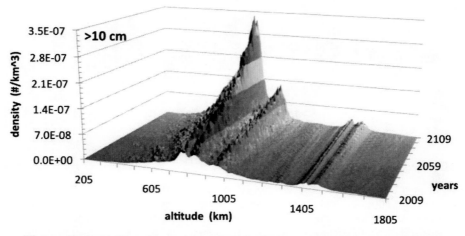

Figure 18. Spatial Density as a Function of Altitude and Date for >10 cm Objects.

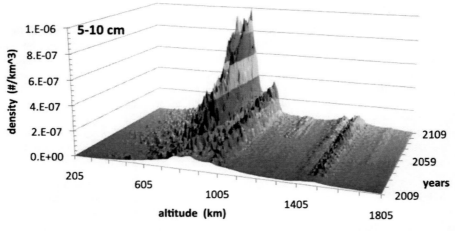

Figure 19. Spatial Density as a Function of Altitude and Date for 5-10 cm Objects.

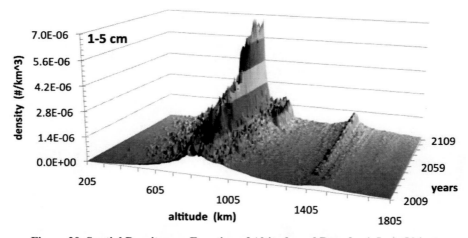

Figure 20. Spatial Density as a Function of Altitude and Date for 1-5 cm Objects.

CONCLUSION

An independent process has been developed to generate discrete future LEO debris populations for use in simulations of future space system performance. Current results show that the debris population caused by the current tracked population will grow even without future launches. This confirms results from previous studies by Liou and Johnson and Lewis et al. Collisions involving future launched objects contribute more than 50% of the total 1st generation debris after 100 years. The creation of 1st generation debris is dominated by intact vs. intact collisions, because intact objects contain much more mass than do fragments. Intact objects were ranked in terms of their potential to result in debris creation. It was found that a large number of intact objects would have to be removed to significantly reduce the amount of future debris. Removal of 100 intact objects would yield approximately a 50% reduction of 1st generation debris resulting from collision sbetween objects in the current tracked population. The total 1st generation debris population resulting from collisions between both the current tracked population and the future

156

launched population would be reduced by 25%. Finally, results preliminarily indicate that large numbers of collisions between large and small untracked objects may generate significant amounts of debris.

ACKNOWLEDGMENTS

This work reflects research conducted under U.S. Air Force Space and Missile Systems Center Contract FA8802-09-C-0001. The authors wish to thank several individuals for their support of this work and assistance in preparing this paper. Technical committee members Spencer Campbell, Steve Hast and Richard Gong provided technical review of the paper. Richard Gong provided internal programmatic support for this work. Program support for conference attendance was provided by Darryl Sutton, Mark Oleksak, Hai Nguyen, Bart Lundblad, John Berg, Ranwa Haddad, Charlie Griffice, and Mary Ellen Vojtek. Nicholas Johnson of the NASA Orbital Debris Program Office supplied the NASA table of object masses. The Aerospace Corporation's Office of Technical Relations and Capt. Monica Jordan of the Department of the Air Force, SMC/XRD, provided publication clearance review.

REFERENCES

[1] J.-C. Liou, "LEGEND – A Three-Dimensional LEO-to-GEO Debris Evolutionary Model," Advances in Space Research 34 (2004) 981-986.

[2] R. Walker, S. Hauptmann, R. Crowther, H. Stokes, and A. Cant, "Introducing IDES: Characterizing the Orbital Debris Environment in the Past, Present, and Future," American Astronautical Society, AAS Paper 96-113, Feb. 1996.

[3] C. Martin, P.H. Stokes, R. Walker, et al., "The Long-Term Evolution of the Debris Environment in High Earth Orbit Including the Effectiveness of Mitigation Measures," Space Debris 2001 Science and Technology Series vol. 105, J. Bendisch, Editor, American Astronautical Society, pp. 141–154.

[4] S. Flegel et al., "The MASTER-2009 Space Debris Environment Model," Proceedings of the Fifth European Conference on Space Debris, Darmstadt, Germany, March 30 – April 2 2009 (ESA SP-672, July 2009).

[5] A. Rossi, L. Anselmo, C. Pardini, R. Jehn, "The New Space Debris Mitigation (SDM 4.0) Long Term Evolution Code," Proceedings of the Fifth European Conference on Space Debris, Darmstadt, Germany, 30 March - 2 April 2009, (ESA SP-672, 2009).

[6] H.G. Lewis, G.G. Swinerd, R.J. Newland, A. Saunders, "Active Removal Study for On-Orbit Debris Using DAMAGE," Proceedings of the Fifth European Conference on Space Debris, Darmstadt, Germany, March 30 – April 2 2009 (ESA SP-672, July 2009).

[7] M.E. Sorge, "Satellite Fragmentation Modeling with IMPACT," Paper No. AIAA-2008-6265, AIAA/AAS Astrodynamics Specialist Conference, Honolulu, Hawaii, August 18-21, 2008.

[8] T.Yasaka, T. Hanada, H. Hirayama, "Low-Velocity Projectile Impact on Spacecraft." *Acta Astronautica*. Vol. 47, No. 10, pp 763-770, 2000.

[9] W.D. McClain, "A Recursively Formulated First-Order Semianalytic Artificial Satellite Theory Based on the Generalized Method of Averaging," Computer Sciences Corporation, CSC/TR-77/6010, Greenbelt, MD, November 1977.

[10] J.-C. Liou, N.L. Johnson, "Instability of the Present LEO Satellite Population," Advances in Space Research 41 (2008) 1046-1053.

[11] G.E. Peterson, "Effect of Future Space Debris on Mission Utility and Launch Accessibility," paper no. AAS 11-414, AAS/AIAA Astrodynamics Specialist Conference, Girdwood, Alaska, July 31 - August 4, 2011.

ANALYZING THE CRITERIA FOR A STABLE ENVIRONMENT

B. Bastida Virgili[*] and H. Krag[*]

The number of human made objects in space has not stopped increasing since the beginning of spaceflight. Latest model predictions show that the population has already reached a point, where the number of objects would increase even without further human interaction. This also means that current mitigation measures are insufficient to stop this growth. In this study, with the help of an environment prediction model, we will investigate the drivers for the instability and propose solutions to achieve the stability based on a reformulation of the mitigation measures and on active removal missions.

INTRODUCTION

The number of human made objects in space has undergone a steady increase since the beginning of spaceflight. The fear that the future environment growth might be dominated by collisions, rather than by launches and explosions, was expressed already decades ago. In response to this, the IADC (Inter-Agency Space Debris Coordination Committee) formulated a set of mitigation requirements that were issued in 2002.[1] These requirements aimed at a limitation of the growth rate rather than at a reduction of the object population below the current numbers.

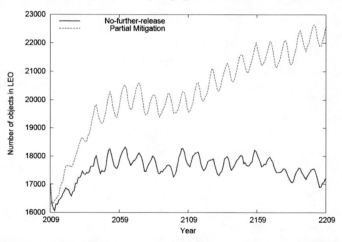

Figure 1. Future evolution of the number of objects in LEO in a no-further-release scenario and in a Partial Mitigation scenario with 90% accomplishment of mitigation measures.

[*] ESA Space Debris Office. ESA/ESOC. Robert-Bosch-Str. 5. 64293 Darmstadt. Germany.

As shown in recent studies done with different environment prediction tools from different agencies, even the current environment will grow in the case of no further mission deployments (i.e. a "no further release scenario"), as can be seen in Figure 1. [2, 3, 4] This kind of instability indicates that the existing and currently proposed mitigation measures are not sufficient to stop the increase of the collision rate even when they are strictly implemented.

To stabilize the environment, the idea of actively removing objects from space has been raised.[5] Active debris removal (ADR) implies robotic missions with the capability to interact with passive spacecraft or rocket bodies in order to reduce their remaining orbital lifetime. Some studies suggest that 5 objects should be removed every year in order to stop the growth of the environment.[3] Obviously, such efforts are only acceptable if all mitigation measures proposed by IADC are strictly followed. The analysis of optimal environment remediation strategies has just begun and the different mitigation measures and removal strategies need to be carefully weighted for effective results. Furthermore the selection of the deployment orbit and the nature of the top-ranking removal targets needs to be optimized.[2] A precondition for such analyze is, however, a good understanding of the sensitivity of the environment to the initial population of intact objects, the allowed orbital lifetime and the initial population of fragments.

In this study, we will use DELTA (Debris Environment Long-Term Analysis), the ESA environment prediction model. It will allow us to analyze initial populations corresponding to different historical epochs to determine at what stage key milestones were reached and what are the conditions in which collision fragment generation rate supersedes the decay rate.

Further we will evaluate the available means to obtain stability based on the current environment. This includes the rate of application of active removal measures, reduced launch rates, as well as the effect of mitigation measures and post-mission orbital lifetimes. The major goal of this paper is to conclude on the major responsible factors for the environment instability and to propose a set of optimized mitigation requirements in combination with potential active removal measures.

DELTA (Debris Environment Long-Term Analysis)

The tool used in the study is the ESA Debris Environment Long-Term Analysis (DELTA) software, developed by QinetiQ. DELTA is a three-dimensional, semi-deterministic model, which in its entirety allows a user to investigate the evolution of the space debris environment and the associated mission collision risks in the low, medium and geosynchronous Earth orbit regions over the future. DELTA is able to examine the long-term effects of different future traffic profiles and debris mitigation measures, such as passivation and disposal at end-of-life. It has been modified to add the active debris removal capabilities. The current version is v3.1.

DELTA uses an initial population and a future traffic model as input and forecasts all objects larger than 1 mm in size. The population is described by representative objects, predicted with a fast analytical orbit propagator which takes into account the main perturbation forces. The high fidelity of the DELTA model is ensured by using a set of detailed future traffic models for launch, explosion and solid rocket motor firing. They are each based on the historical activity over the eight preceding years (2001-2009). The collision event prediction is done by using a target centered approach, developed to stochastically predict impacts for large target objects (mass higher than 50 kg) within the DELTA population.[6,7,8] The fragmentation model used is based on the EVOLVE 4.0 break-up model.[9]

The sensitivity of the environment's evolution to the solar flux has been analyzed, since a higher solar flux causes a faster natural reentry of objects leading to a different conclusion on the stability of the environment. For this study, the future solar flux was predicted based on an analysis of the last 10 solar cycles.

NO-FURTHER-RELEASE SCENARIO IN HISTORICAL EPOCHS

In order to evaluate the sensitivity of the environment evolution as a function of the composition of the initial population, we have used DELTA to simulate the evolution of the population starting from different historical epochs. The selected prediction time span is 200 years for any of the scenarios. In order to be able to compare and quantify the effect of the initial population in the environment, we have selected a no-further-release scenario for these simulations. A no-further-release scenario is an ideal situation where no more objects are added in space (which means no new launches and no explosions of objects already in space), so that only the collisions between objects can cause an increase. The initial populations at historical epochs are extracted from the MASTER 2009 (Meteoroid and Space Debris Terrestrial Environment Reference Model) historical model populations. We have selected as epochs the 1st of May of 1969, 1979, 1989, 1999, 2005 and 2009. For each of the scenarios, 40 Monte-Carlo runs have been performed.

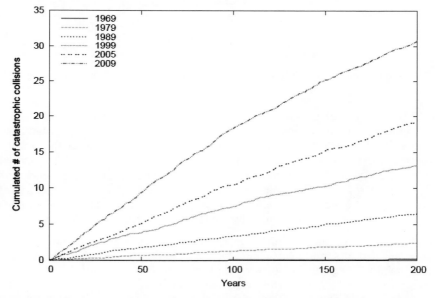

Figure 2. Cumulated number of catastrophic collisions over time for "no-further release" scenarios starting from different historical populations

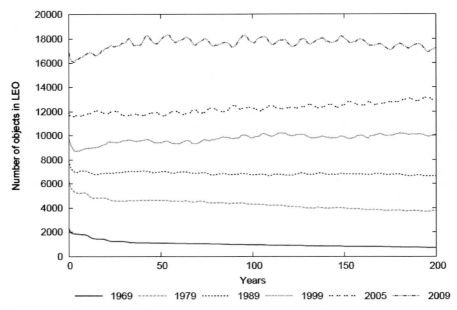

Figure 3. Number of objects in LEO over time for "no-further release" scenarios starting from different historical populations

Figure 2 shows the average number of detected catastrophic collisions (over 40 MC runs) as function of time for each of the initial populations. A catastrophic collision occurs when the kinetic energy is large enough to cause the complete destruction of the objects involved in the collision, thus generating a cloud of new fragments. The threshold between catastrophic and non-catastrophic collisions has been determined empirically at an EMR (energy-to-mass ratio) of 40 J/g (of the target mass). [10,11] Therefore, the initial population contains only objects above 10 cm of diameter, since those are the ones able to cause a catastrophic collision and because 10 cm is the limiting size for the tracking of objects by the US Space Surveillance Network.

Figure 3 shows the evolution of the population in LEO for each of the initial populations. It can be observed that at some point in time between 1989 and 1999 the population exceeds a threshold of stability, where the population will keep increasing by itself due to the collisions. It should be noted that the averaged results of Monte Carlo runs do not necessarily indicate the most likely future scenario. A statistical evaluation of the Monte Carlo runs needs to be performed in order to refine the analysis as shown in the following.

Maximum Number of Intact Objects Allowed in Space

All the newly generated fragments in space originate from an intact body, through a collision or an explosion. Therefore we can consider that the real driver for the evolution of the population is the number of intact objects (payloads and rocket bodies) that are in space at a given epoch. A large cross-section yields a higher collision probability, and the mass is the driver for the number of fragments generated in a collision or explosion. Large and massive objects are, thus, the prime focus for environment remediation.

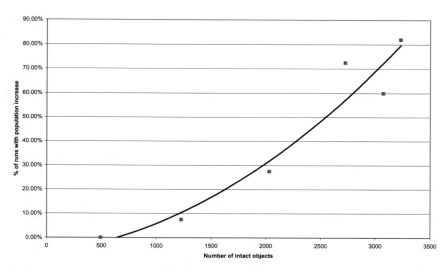

Figure 4. Percentage of runs with population increase as a function of the number of intact objects at the initial epoch (+ 5 years)

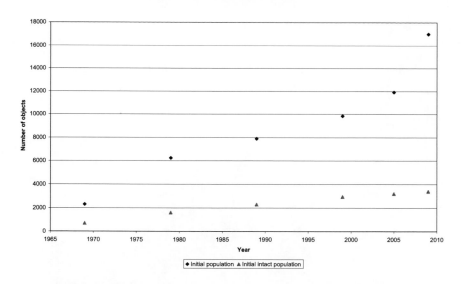

Figure 5. Initial population and initial intact population at different historical epochs

We have calculated the percentage of MC runs which lead to a population increase after 200 years as a function of the number of intact objects after 5 years of simulation (in order to avoid the effect of the fast decays of the first years that can be observed in Figure 3). The results and the fitting in a second order polynomial function can be observed in Figure 4. In view of the results, we can affirm that the probability that the population will be larger in 200 years than today increases linearly to the number of intact objects. A 50% probability would then represent a kind of tip-over scenario after which an increase is more likely than a decrease. Such a threshold of stability is reached at a little more than 2500 intact objects. This corresponds to a situation that was

163

reached between 1989 (~2050 objects) and 1999 (~2750 objects), as can be seen in Figure 5. The natural forces cause a decay of around 30% of the intacts in the 200 years of simulation, and this percentage is almost constant and independent of the initial population. However, this rate has to be used with caution, because we observe a faster decay during the first years of the simulations. In addition, the objects in the upper region of LEO are in orbits where the atmospheric drag is almost inexistent, and there may be a remainder population which will not decay by natural means.

THREE METHODS TO ACHIEVE A DESIRED NUMBER OF INTACTS

The previous section dealt with an ideal scenario of no-further-release. However, as we can not stop space activities completely, and with the current number of intact objects (~3300 in 2009) already above the threshold, some measures need to be taken to reach stability. In Figure 1 we presented the results of a partial mitigation scenario where no more explosions were occurring in space and with a lifetime limitation of 25 years implemented with 90% of success. The scenario follows a launch profile based on the last 8 years (2001-2009). There the increase of the population is already 35% (with 20% for the intacts). This re-confirms that the current proposed mitigation measures are not sufficient to stop the growth. However, we have simulated also a business-as-usual scenario, where no mitigation measures are applied and explosions continue to happen. In this scenario the population follows an exponential growth and reaches 250,000 objects in 200 years, while the number of intacts approaches 10,000.

We can think of three possible methods to reduce the number of intact objects in the future in order to achieve stability: modify the launch rate, change the orbit lifetime limitation, and perform active debris removal. In the next sub-sections we analyze the effect of each of the methods and we show the need for a combination of all of them to obtain the desired result.

Launch Rate

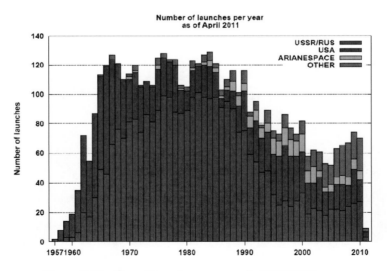

Figure 6. Number of launches per year (ref DISCOS)

Looking at the history of launches in Figure 6, some kind of steady state is observed in the number of launches per year in the last few years. The launch profile currently used in DELTA is based on the launches of the years 2001 to 2009. Each of the Monte-Carlo run simulates a different launch scenario, but on average we observe 72 launches per year, with half of them inserting objects into LEO (2 or more objects are inserted with every launch). The average decay rate of 0.15% per year supposes the natural removal of 5 intacts (based on the 3300 intacts of 2009). This means that the current launch rate combined with natural decay increases the number of intacts to at least 67 objects per year.

If we were trying to stabilize the number of objects at the current numbers, then we would have to decrease the launch rate to 2.5 launches in LEO (a reduction of 93%). If the objective was to reach the 2500 objects in 200 years, we would be required to insert only 4 new objects per year, which means stopping almost completely the launches (reduction of 94%). It is therefore clear that this measure has to be combined with others in order to be effective.

Lifetime Limitation

The IADC mitigation guidelines states that for the objects intersecting the LEO region, 25 years is a reasonable and appropriate lifetime limit.[1] For satellites, this rule is to be implemented after the end-of-life, while for rocket bodies it should be implemented immediately after insertion. However, as seen in Figure 1, this rule is not sufficient to stabilize the environment.

If we consider an ideal case with 100% success on the implementation of the de-orbiting rule and an average of 8 years lifetime for the satellites, then, with the current launch rate, we would have a constant population of 1200 satellites in orbit (36 satellites per year x 33 years in orbit). This number is to be added to the 900 rocket bodies used to insert the satellites (36 launches per year x 25 years in orbit, although some may decay faster). Hence, we have a constant population of 2100 intact objects (decaying within 25 years after EOL) added to the current 3300 (which are naturally decaying at 0.15% per year, reaching 2300 in 200 years). In case that the success of the implementation is not of 100%, more objects will be left in space. It is clear that the desired threshold cannot be reached with these orbital lifetimes.

Table 1. Constant number of intacts in LEO as function of lifetime

Lifetime (years)	Satellites	Rocket bodies	Total
5	468	180	648
10	648	360	1008
15	828	540	1368
20	1008	720	1728
25	1188	900	2088

In Table 1 we have computed the constant population of intacts according to different lifetimes (always considering 8 years of operation for the satellites and 36 launches in LEO per year). We observe that every 5 years of lifetime reduction leads to 360 objects ((36+36) x 5) less in space. But even with a 5 years lifetime limit, the overall population would be above the desired threshold of 2500 in 200 years (and even so in 100 years). Therefore, it is necessary to combine this measure with the others to stabilize the environment.

Active Debris Removal

Active debris removal (ADR) is being proposed more and more often as the only way of controlling the environment. An ADR mission should try to bring the intact satellites and rocket bodies to an orbit compliant with the 25 years rule, or target it into a controlled re-entry. A lot of technical aspects, such as where to deploy these type of missions, how to select the best candidates for removal, and the capability of removing more than one object per mission, were studied in other papers.[2,3,4]

The number of objects per year to be removed if ADR would be the only measure is too big to assume that it could be realised. Nevertheless we shall demonstrate that with ADR the population can be stabilized, even if we continue to launch.

Combination of mitigation and remediation measures

As seen in the previous sub-sections, none of the measures is able to stabilize the environment on its own. Even worse, in the no-further-release scenario with the 2009 population, we have 2300 intact objects remaining after 200 years, which would mean that only 200 of the newly inserted objects would be allowed to remain in orbit at that time if no ADR is done. If we try to reach the intact population threshold before 200 years, we definitively need ADR.

In case that the lifetime limitation is applied with 100% success, the ADR would have to remove only objects which are already in LEO to reach a given threshold in the specified time. If the success rate is not 100%, the extra objects left on space will also have to be removed by ADR.

Table 2. Combination of the different measures to stabilize the environment

Success rate of mitigation measures	Lifetime limitation (years)	Number of launches in LEO	Years to reach threshold	Number of objects in 100/200 years	ADR need (objects/year)
100%	25	36	100	4443	19.4
100%	10	36	100	3633	11.3
100%	25	18	100	3624	11.2
100%	10	18	100	3219	7.2
100%	25	54	100	5262	27.6
100%	10	54	100	4047	15.5
100%	25	36	200	3948	7.2
100%	10	36	200	3138	3.2
100%	25	18	200	3129	3.1
100%	10	18	200	2724	1.1
100%	25	54	200	4767	11.3
100%	10	54	200	3552	5.3
90%	25	36	100	4549	20.5
90%	10	36	100	3820	13.2
90%	25	18	100	3677	11.8
90%	10	18	100	3313	8.1
90%	25	54	100	5421	29.2
90%	10	54	100	4328	18.3
90%	25	36	200	4324	9.1
90%	10	36	200	3595	5.5
90%	25	18	200	3317	4.1
90%	10	18	200	2953	2.3
90%	25	54	200	5331	14.2
90%	10	54	200	4238	8.7

In Table 2 we have combined the different measures and calculated the expected number of intact objects after 100 or 200 years, plus the ADR rate necessary to achieve the 2500 intacts at that time. We have supposed that every launch into LEO inserts a single satellite, and that only half of the rocket bodies stay in orbit for the lifetime limit (we consider that the other half decays immediately). In case of a success rate under 100%, we consider also that 1.5 objects remain in orbit, for a period of half of the span time selected.

The results of Table 2 show that even in the best mitigation (an ideal scenario reducing the launches to a half of the current rate and applying a 100% mitigation success with a remaining orbit lifetime of 10 years), at least one object will have to be actively removed. In a more realistic situation (the one of Figure 1, with 90% success of the 25 years lifetime rule with the current launch rate), we will need to remove 20 objects per year if we want to reach the threshold of 2500 objects in 100 years, or 9 objects per year if we want to reach it in 200 years. Some of these theoretical results have been simulated with DELTA to proof their validity.

SIMULATION RESULTS

Launch Rate in Partial Mitigation Scenario

Using as reference the partial mitigation scenario shown in Figure 1, with 90% success of the de-orbiting in 25 years (with the current launch rate), we have studied 3 possible cases of modification of the launch rate combined with the lifetime limitation of 25 years with 90% success. One case considers a constant decrease to half of the current launch rate for the next 200 years starting in 2009. The other 2 cases consider an increase of the launch rate, but with a slight difference. One considers a fixed increase of 50% of the current launches as of 2009, while the other uses a linear increase of 1% every year starting in 2009 until reaching a 70% increase in 2079 (remaining stable for the rest of the simulation).

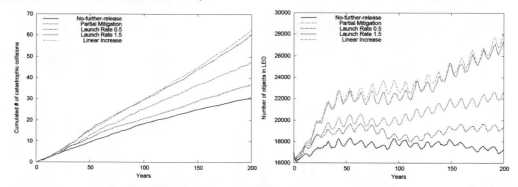

Figure 7. (a) Cumulated number of catastrophic collisions and (b) number of objects in LEO for the different launch rate cases

Figure 7 shows the results of the DELTA simulations for the analyzed cases, as well as for the 2 reference scenarios (no-further-release, and partial mitigation with the current launch rate). We can observe the effects of the different launch rates and note that a relative increase of 50% in the launch rate causes more than 50% relative increase of the population (due to a higher number of catastrophic collisions). The comparison between the 2 scenarios with traffic increase shows that what counts for the evolution of the environment is the number of intact objects in the environment at each moment in time.

167

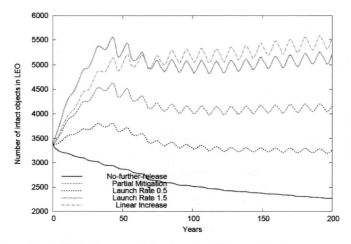

Figure 8. Number of intact objects for the different launch rate cases

In Figure 8 we can observe the evolution of the number of intacts for the different launch rate cases. The results after 200 years compare well with those theoretically calculated (see Table 2). However, the theoretical results after 100 years are always higher than in the simulations, because the decay rate is not constant throughout the time span (faster at the beginning, slower at the end), and this effect can be observed for all curves.

Lifetime Limitation (Partial Mitigation Scenario)

The lifetime limitation modification effects have been studied independently of the other 2 measures. We have simulated 5, 10 and 20 years lifetimes with 90% implementation success rate, and compared the results with our partial mitigation scenario (where the 25 year lifetime rule has been applied).

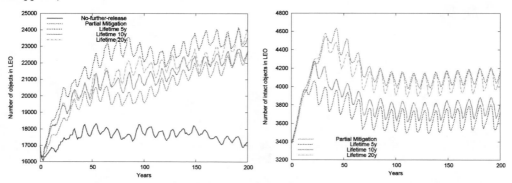

Figure 9. (a) Number of objects and (b) number of intact objects in LEO

In Figure 9 we can notice that the number of intact objects follows the trend as proposed in Table 1 and 2, but with different numbers. We see a smaller difference than expected in the number of intact objects between the different lifetimes. However, in the global number of objects we do not see an improvement for any of the lifetimes limitations, with all having similar rates of increase. This is a situation that we have already predicted theoretically, since all of the cases stay far from the 2500 threshold.

Active Debris Removal in Partial Mitigation Scenario

As proven in the previous section, the only possible way to achieve stability while continuing space activities is to perform ADR. The technical and political aspects that need to be solved to realize such missions are not of interest for this study. The approach taken here supposes that the ADR missions start in 2010 and that every mission instantaneously takes out of the population a certain number of objects per year (5 or 10 in the following simulations). The selection of the objects to be removed is limited to dead satellites and rocket bodies which have not been de-orbited according to the lifetime limitation rules. The selection criterion is the mass (objects with bigger mass are removed first). We have constrained the ADR to objects below 1300 km of altitude (which is also the limit between de-orbiting and re-orbiting in LEO).

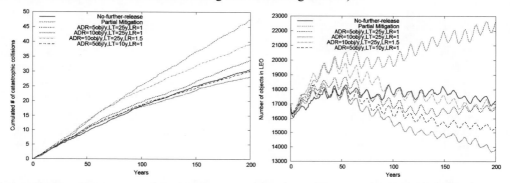

Figure 10. (a) Cumulated number of catastrophic collisions and (b) number of objects in LEO for the different scenarios with active debris removal as well as the two reference cases (no-further release and partial mitigation). ADR: number of objects removed per year, LT: lifetime limitation (with 90% success of implementation), LR: launch rate (with respect to current one).

Figure 10 shows that ADR is able to reduce the number of collisions, and therefore to bring the number of objects in LEO below the level of the no-further-release scenario and in some of the cases, even below the initial population, so that it can be said that the environment is stabilized. However, it is important to remember that ADR has to be combined with the execution of the de-orbiting rules. The simulated scenarios and the level of ADR were selected based on Table 2.

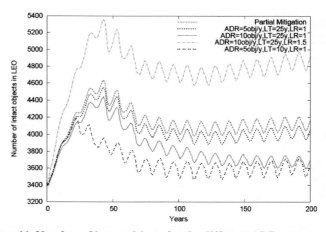

Figure 11. Number of intact objects for the different ADR rate cases

In Figure 11 we observe that we don't reach the expected number of intact objects at the end of the simulation (around 2500). Moreover, we are still far from it and with an increase as compared to the initial intact population. The reason for it may be explained partially by the limiting of the ADR altitude to 1300 km, which causes a fixed population, slowly increasing due to the not completely successful de-orbit and re-orbit, remaining in a region where the air drag has small impact and the objects take more than 200 years to decay. Other reasons may be found in the assumptions used to compute Table 2, which used a simple and general law for all the orbital regimes in LEO. However, as seen in Figure 10, where ADR is combined with the mitigation measures, we are able to stabilize the population, even in the case of an increase in the launch rate. The effect of removing the bigger masses from the space environment reduces significantly the number of objects created by collisions, thus decreasing the risk for the objects remaining in space.

CONCLUSION

The propagation of historical populations in a no-further-release scenario indicates a clear correlation between the number of intact objects in LEO and the stability of the environment. A threshold of 2500 intacts can be therefore determined and used as an upper limit if we want to regain stability in the future. This threshold was surpassed between 1989 and 1999.

Three possible methods (modifying the launch rate, modifying the lifetime limitations, and introducing active debris removal) can be used to achieve the desired goal, but only the combination of all of them is effective. Trying to use the methods independently of each other does not stabilize the population below the desired threshold.

Performing ADR is also necessary, if we want to achieve stability while using space as a resource in a similar way as we do today. As can be derived from the historical populations, the longer we wait to start applying the mitigation measures successfully and to perform ADR, the more difficult it will be to reach the desired population threshold, because more intact objects will remain in space. The removal of 5 to 10 objects per year (depending on the future evolution of the launch rate and on the implementation of the mitigation measures) seems to be sufficient to stabilize the environment.

The simulation results have proven (with small differences) that the theoretical analysis performed matches computer models of the long-term environment evolution.

The ADR of objects, with the biggest masses to be removed first, has a huge and positive impact on the stabilization of the environment, where that the mass of the intact objects in orbit is a stronger driver than their number.

Further analysis has to be done to study the relation between the masses and the number of objects, as well as considering the ADR in the higher regions of LEO (above 1300 km).

REFERENCES

[1] IADC. "IADC Space Debris Mitigation Guidelines". 2002.

[2] B. Bastida Virgili, H. Krag. "Strategies for Active Removal in LEO." *Proceedings of the 5th European Conference on Space Debris.* 2009

[3] J.-C. Liou. "An active debris removal parametric study for LEO environment remediation." *J.Adv.Space Res.* 2011. doi:10.1016/j.asr.2011.02.003

[4] H. Lewis et al. "The Space Debris Environment: Future Evolution". *CEAS 2009 European Air and Space Conference, Manchester, UK.* 26 - 29 Oct 2009

[5] J.-C. Liou, N.L. Johnson "A sensitivity study of the effectiveness of active debris removal in LEO". *Acta Astronautica 64, pp 236-243.* 2009

[6] R. Walker, C.E. Martin et al. "Analysis of the effectiveness of space debris mitigation measures using the Delta model". *Adv. Space Res. Vol. 28, No. 9, pp 1437-1445.* 2001

[7] C.Martin, R.Walker, H.Klinkrad. "The sensitivity of the ESA DELTA model". *Adv. Space Res. Vol. 34, pp 969-974.* 2004

[8] R. Walker, C.E. Martin. "Cost-effective and robust mitigation of space debris in Low Earth Orbit". *Adv. Space Res. Vol. 34, pp 1233-1240.* 2004

[9] N. L. Johnson et al. "NASA's new breakup model of evolve 4.0". *Adv. Space Res. Vol. 28 No. 9, pp 1377-1384.* 2001

[10] T.D. Bess. "Mass distribution of orbiting man-made space debris". *NASA technical Note D-8108.* 1975.

[11] D.S. McKnight. "Determination of breakup initial conditions". *AIAA 91-0299. 29th Aerospace Sciences Meeting.* 1991

AUTOMATED BALLISTIC COEFFICIENT ESTIMATION TECHNIQUE TO ANALYZE THE DEBRIS FROM THE COSMOS-2251 AND IRIDIUM-33 COLLISION

John P. McVey[*] and Chia-Chun Chao[†]

The collision of the Cosmos-2251 and Iridium-33 satellites generated thousands of debris fragments. A ballistic coefficient estimation technique was developed to analyze these fragments and to extract information about the debris clouds for use in fragmentation models and other analyses. In order to characterize debris clouds, an automated estimation process was developed. The resulting ballistic coefficient estimate distributions from these debris clouds are distinctly different from each other and could yield information about the characteristics of the collision, which will aid in the determination of the characteristics of future collisions.

INTRODUCTION

The collision between the Cosmos-2251 and Iridium-33 satellites resulted in the generation of orbital debris clouds containing large numbers of fragments that pose a danger to operating satellites. The Space Surveillance Network (SSN) can track only a small fraction of the potentially hazardous debris from such an event. The unobservable debris must be modeled to determine the most probable distribution of fragment sizes and velocities in order to assess both the short-term and long-term risks to satellites. The Aerospace Corporation IMPACT fragmentation model[1] was developed to model orbital altitude explosions and hypervelocity collisions, generating debris fragment mass, size, and spreading velocity distributions. Distributions of spreading velocity, ballistic coefficients (area to mass ratio multiplied by drag coefficient) Eq. (1), and size information from actual collision and explosion events are used to calibrate this model along with ground test data.

$$B = C_d A/M \tag{1}$$

Estimating ballistic coefficients involves a large amount of manual interaction making it very labor-intensive. In order to characterize debris clouds, such as the Cosmos/Iridium event, thousands of fragments must be analyzed, requiring the automation of this process. To determine ballistic coefficients, a two-line-element (TLE) history for each fragment is required as this provides

---

[*] Engineering Specialist, Astrodynamics Department, The Aerospace Corporation,
   El Segundo, CA 90245, Tel. (310) 336-2354, Fax (310) 336-2831, email: John.P.McVey@aero.org

[†] Senior Engineering Specialist (Retired), Astrodynamics Department, AIAA Associate Fellow,
   Tel. (310) 336-4295, Fax (310) 336-2831, email: Chia-Chun.Chao@aero.org

the details of the fragment's orbital evolution. The effects of atmospheric drag imparted on each of the debris pieces presents itself in the change of semi-major axis and eccentricity over weeks to months. From these perturbations, the ballistic coefficient can be estimated by fitting the predicted trajectory to the daily TLE data as observations over the fit span. These estimated ballistic coefficients have residual errors associated with the fitting process due to unknowns in the solar radiation pressure modeling, the attitude of the object, atmospheric density model errors, and errors in the TLE sets. The method of ballistic coefficient estimation has been used in previous studies examining satellite breakup debris[7][8], and drag coefficient for satellite calibration spheres[2][6]. This study differs from those by using newer atmospheric models, upgraded force modeling, numerical propagation and instantaneous state vectors, and a different method for assigning the fit span. The previous studies also estimated tens to a few hundred objects, where this study will focus on a few calibration spheres (BLITS, ANDE-2, ODERACS-1, 2) and the Cosmos/Iridium collision with well over a thousand fragments. By comparing the ballistic coefficient estimates and actual dimensions and mass from the calibration spheres, it can be determined how well the automated estimation process performed. This automated process is then used to determine the ballistic coefficient distributions for Cosmos/Iridium collision debris. The ballistic coefficient distributions were produced for both debris clouds and show distinct differences between the two satellite breakups.

METHODOLOGY

Introduction

The process of obtaining a ballistic coefficient for each object consists of two steps. The first step is to convert a set of temporally sequential TLE data to Cartesian components of position and velocity in an Earth-Centered Inertial (ECI) frame at or near the epoch that are treated as observables. The second step fits these observables using an upper diagonal (UD) batch filter to differentially correct (DC) the initial velocity components and ballistic coefficient. Reasons for limiting the estimation to only four parameters are to increase processing speed, favor using the TLE position components over the less accurate velocity components[15], and avoid a high correlation problem if position and velocity are estimated. This least squares process will produce a ballistic coefficient estimate along with the radial, in-track, and cross-track (RIC) residual error components associated with it. In order to characterize debris clouds, hundreds to thousands of fragments must be analyzed, requiring the automation of this process. The Aerospace Corporation tool ADOBE (Automated Debris Orbit Ballistic coefficient Estimator) was developed to automatically obtain estimates for the ballistic coefficients of large groups of LEO debris fragments over any sufficiently long period of time for which TLE data is available. ADOBE is a script that controls the sequential runs of two core programs TLE2EPH and FIT-TLE. These core programs perform the functions of step one and two respectively. The following sub-sections provide more detail of this automated estimation process.

Step 1: Converting TLE Histories into Ephemeris Files

The TLE2EPH program converts a TLE data file containing one or more TLE sets for a single object into an ECI position and velocity ephemeris data file. The accuracy of the ephemeris computed from the TLE depends mainly on the quality and frequency of the skin tracking data. A state vector is calculated using Simplified General Perturbations (SGP4) for each TLE at its epoch. Additional evenly spaced ephemeris points are generated with the heritage version of SGP4[12] and propagated over one orbit revolution to capture the dynamics of the orbit. A control input allows the user to set the number of points around each orbit. This will add more observations to the ephemeris file used in the fitting algorithm.

174

Step 2: Estimating Ballistic Coefficients

The FIT-TLE program performs the differential corrections to estimate the initial velocity components and ballistic coefficient such that the residual RIC position error of the fit trajectory relative to the TLE ephemeris is minimized. The orbital data from the ephemeris is propagated and the partial derivatives are computed by finite difference using a Runge-Kutta 7/8th (RK78) numerical integrator in a sequential mode. An efficient UD batch square root information filter (SRIF), developed by Bierman[3], is used to process the stable least squares solutions. The force models used in the propagation include: 8x8 EGM96 Earth gravity model, lunisolar gravity attractions, solar radiation pressure and atmospheric drag. Two state-of-the-art atmospheric density models, Mass Spectrometer Incoherent Scatter 2000 (MSIS 2000)[4] and Jacchia-Bowman 2008 (JB2008)[5], were used to account for atmospheric drag. Figure 1 is a simple flow diagram of the FIT-TLE program.

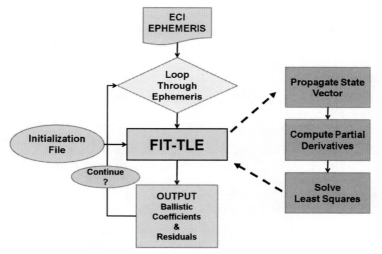

Figure 1. FIT-TLE flow diagram

FIT-TLE uses an input file that contains controls for the a-priori ballistic coefficient and covariance, force model selections, and length of time to fit the span of data (i.e., fit span). Choosing the correct initial parameters in the input file is problematic, and a single run of the differential corrections process will not necessarily produce the most accurate fit. Accuracy can be improved by using the estimated parameters of the first fit as the a-priori guess for a subsequent fit. This process can be continued until the estimated values converge. The check on convergence is depicted in Figure 1 by the continue statement. Once convergence is achieved, the final estimates and residuals are output by the program.

Automating the Estimation Process using ADOBE

ADOBE manages the sequential runs of TLE2EPH and FIT-TLE in order to generate a large set of ballistic coefficient estimates to a specified tolerance. In order to run this automated process, with a group of TLE sets of any size, three input files control the settings for the two core programs and ADOBE. The input file controlling TLE2EPH requires the user to select the number of ephemeris points to be generated around each TLE epoch point. ADOBE will then repeatedly run TLE2EPH to convert all the TLE data sets into the equivalent ephemeris files. Also, there is an option to automatically split up TLE files where time gaps in the data are larger than a specified number of days. The input file controlling the fitting algorithm is where the a-priori values, fit span timing for non-automated runs, and force model parameters are set. ADOBE will automatically control the timing of the fit spans and continue processing until it has reached the end of the ephemeris file. The ADOBE input file controls the overall automation of the two core programs in a series of four loops. The looping procedures are illustrated in Figure 2 from the outermost loop to the innermost loop sequentially. Each loop is described below:

1. TLE Loop – The outermost loop iterates over all of the TLE ephemeris files. This includes any TLE files that were split because of data gaps in the TLE files.

2. Epoch Loop – This loop iterates over the fit epoch start time, incrementing by the number of days in the previous fit span. There are two modes:

   a. User specifies the initial epoch and the maximum number of days (within the TLE data set).

   b. The runs will cover the time span of the individual TLE ephemeris.

3. Fit Span Loop – This loop iterates while gradually increasing the fit span until a specified ballistic coefficient covariance threshold is met, or the maximum fit time span has elapsed.

4. Differential Corrections (DC) Convergence Loop – The innermost loop iterates in an attempt to get a converged ballistic coefficient fit for the current epoch and fit span. This is the same convergence loop described earlier in Figure 1.

All the ADOBE statistical information about the individual fits for each fragment are summarized and include all the ballistic coefficient estimates, associated residuals, quality of convergence, and the standard deviations of all of the fits for each TLE data set. ADOBE obtains a weighted average ballistic coefficient for a TLE object by combining the converged individual ballistic coefficient estimates after completion of each Epoch Loop.

For efficiency, multiple runs of ADOBE are performed simultaneously with each run covering a subset of the TLE files to be processed. This distributed computation using a 64-node server cluster can take a few days to a couple of weeks depending on the amount of data to process. The runs are initiated and managed by a script that uses as many processors as possible, and combines the various output files when the runs are completed.

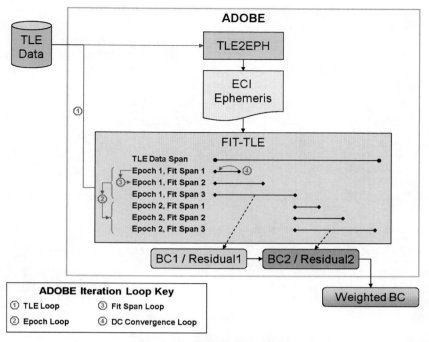

Figure 2. ADOBE flow diagram

CALIBRATION ANALYSIS USING SPHERICAL SATELLITES

To validate the resulting ballistic coefficient estimates from ADOBE, spherical satellites were chosen and run through this process to determine the program's performance. These satellites were selected because they fit a set of four criteria to reduce as many uncertainties in the estimation as possible. The first criterion was that the satellite be a simple geometric shape with known physical dimensions and mass. The second criterion was the satellite must be passive with no orbital maneuvering. The third criterion was that the TLE data set for the satellite needed to be continuous with at least a few months of observations. The final criterion was that the satellite needed to be low enough in altitude to be affected by atmospheric drag[8]. There were nine spherical satellites chosen that meet these criteria and will be used in this calibration analysis. The following is a listing of the satellites and properties:

BLITS (Ball Lens In The Space) – A spherical nano-satellite retro-reflector developed by FSUE IPIE in accordance with the Federal Space Program of Russia[9]. The orbital and physical parameters are listed in Table 1.

Table 1. BLITS Orbital and Physical Parameters

Name	Launch Date	Altitude (km)	Inclination (deg)	Spherical Diameter (cm)	Mass (kg)
Blits	Sept. 17, 2009	~830	98.77	17.032	7.53

ANDE-2 (Atmospheric Neutral Density Experiment) – The mission consists of two spherical micro-satellites, Castor and Pollux, developed by the Naval Research Laboratory[10][11]. The orbital and physical parameters for each satellite are listed in Table 2.

Table 2. ANDE-2 Orbital and Physical Parameters

Name	Launch Date	Altitude (km)	Inclination (deg)	Spherical Diameter (in.)	Mass (kg)
Castor	July 30, 2009	~350	51.6	19	47.5
Pollux	July 30, 2009	~350	51.6	19	27.4

ODERACS-1, 2 (Orbital Debris Radar Calibration Spheres) – These two NASA missions deployed a total of 12 objects. The ODERACS-1 mission deployed six calibration spheres in February, 1994. The ODERACS-2 mission deployed three more calibration spheres and 3 dipole objects in February, 1995[2]. Only six of the nine calibration spheres had enough orbital data to use in this calibration analysis. The orbital and physical parameters for the spherical satellites labeled A, B, E, F, 2A, and 2B are listed in Table 3.

Table 3. ODERACS-1, 2 Orbital and Physical Parameters

Name	Launch Date	Altitude (km)	Inclination (deg)	Spherical Diameter (in.)	Mass (kg)
Oderac A	Feb. 9, 1994	~350	51.6	4	1.48
Oderac B	Feb. 9, 1994	~350	51.6	4	1.48
Oderac E	Feb. 9, 1994	~350	51.6	6	5.00
Oderac F	Feb. 9, 1994	~350	51.6	6	5.00
Oderac 2A	Feb. 3, 1995	~350	51.6	6	5.00
Oderac 2B	Feb. 3, 1995	~350	51.6	4	1.48

Weighting and Averaging Statistics Definitions

The definitions of the following tables of ballistic coefficient statistics are described below:

Weighted Average Ballistic Coefficient (Wgt Avg BC) - The dot product of the individual ballistic coefficients multiplied by the normalized weighting vector. The weighting vector is the mean of the root sum square of the residuals divided by the ith residual. This assigns higher weights to the ballistic coefficients with lower residual values and vise versa.

Hypothetical Ballistic Coefficient (Hypothetical BC) – This is a best guess of the ballistic coefficient using the physical area and mass of the object, and a typical drag coefficient of 2.2[14].

Weighted Average Drag Coefficient (Wgt Avg C_d) – The weighted average ballistic coefficient divided by the physical area-to-mass ratio of the object.

Average Ballistic Coefficient (Average BC) – This is an unweighted average of the ballistic coefficients excluding the estimates that failed to converge.

Ballistic Coefficient Standard Deviation (BC StdDev) – This is the standard deviation of the ballistic coefficients excluding the estimates that failed to converge.

Ballistic Coefficient Percent Difference (BC percent difference) – This is the percent difference between the weighted average ballistic coefficient and the hypothetical ballistic coefficient.

BLITS Ballistic Coefficient Estimation Results

The BLITS satellite was deployed from a Soyuz 2-1b rocket in September 2009. This nanosatellite is a spherical glass retro-reflector designed for laser ranging experiments[9]. This sphere was ideal for validating the ballistic coefficient estimation because of its shape, its ~800 km altitude regime, and continuous TLE data set. ADOBE was used to estimate the ballistic coefficients using JB2008 and MSIS00 atmospheric models. Figure 3 depicts the resulting individual estimates of the ballistic coefficients along with the residual error components over the TLE data span. The residuals of each of these estimates were very low and consistent with the level of accuracy of the TLE data[13]. The low residual values indicate good fits to the ballistic coefficients. The ballistic coefficient statistics, in Table 4, provide a means to compare consistency and accuracy of the fits. The ballistic coefficient percent difference was about one percent, which is very low, but the difference could be a little higher if you assume a higher hypothetical drag coefficient for this altitude[6]. Three data points in Figure 3 that are bad fits are marked with red "X", and are not used in the weighting calculation. Comparing the two atmospheric model cases side-by-side, there is very little difference between them. The BLITS sphere experiences a relatively low drag environment and has a stable orbit with just enough decay to provide a good quality orbit estimate. This bodes well for the ballistic coefficient estimation of the Cosmos/Iridium debris that is roughly at the same altitude and occurs in this same time frame.

Table 4. BLITS Ballistic Coefficient Estimation Statistics

Name	Atmo. Model	Wgt Avg BC (m²/kg)	Wgt Avg C_d	Average BC (m²/kg)	BC StdDev (m²/kg)	BC Percent Difference
Blits	JB2008	**0.0070**	**2.3043**	0.007332	0.0061	1.16
Blits	MSIS00	**0.0065**	**2.1519**	0.006873	0.0055	0.55
Name	Atmo. Model	Hypothetical BC (m²/kg)	Hypothetical C_d	Avg Radial Res (km)	Avg In-track Res (km)	Avg CrossTrack Res (km)
Blits	JB2008	0.0067	2.2000	0.2555	0.9085	0.5965
Blits	MSIS00	0.0067	2.2000	0.2559	0.9101	0.5961

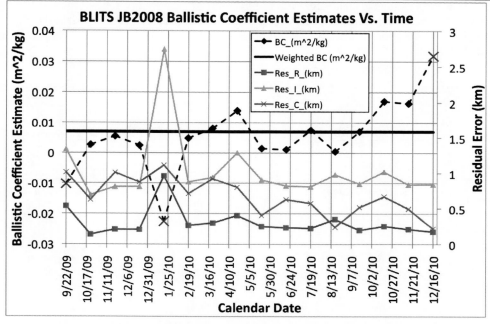

Figure 3. BLITS Ballistic Coefficient Estimation Summary

ANDE-2 Ballistic Coefficient Estimation Results

The ANDE-2 satellites, Castor and Pollux, were identical in size, but had different masses. Both spheres were launched from the Space Shuttle STS-127 at an altitude of ~350 km on the same day. These spheres were chosen for estimation because of their shape, altitude regime, and continuous TLE data set. ADOBE was used to estimate their ballistic coefficients for the length of their orbital lifetimes. Figures 4 and 5 depict the individual ballistic coefficient estimates for the Castor sphere using JB2008 and MSIS00 atmospheric density models respectively. The residuals were low overall with the exception of the last couple of months before reentry. Two possible sources of error could be a changing drag coefficient with altitude near reentry, and the quality of TLE data. The ballistic coefficient estimates have a slight upward trend for the first eight months, and then flatten out closer to reentry. Comparing the estimates between the choices of atmospheric model, JB2008 had lower residuals and the ballistic coefficients were clustered more tightly together than the MSIS00. The percent difference in Table 5 shows that the Castor sphere compares very well to the hypothetical value of six percent or less. The hypothetical drag coefficient is comparable, but not exact for a LEO satellite in this altitude regime[14]. The average

179

residual errors and ballistic coefficient standard deviation are low, which gives confidence that this is a reasonable fit.

Figures 6 and 7 depict the individual ballistic coefficient estimates for the Pollux sphere using JB2008 and MSIS00 respectively. The residual error components are relatively low for the first six months, and grow larger as the satellite nears reentry. This residual growth could be due in part to a rapid orbital decay and to poor TLE data quality. The ballistic coefficient estimates have an upward trend similar to Castor's estimates, but with a sharper rise near reentry. Comparing the estimates made using the two atmospheric models, JB2008 performed better than MSIS00. The percent difference for the Pollux sphere is less than 6% and 11% for the two atmospheric models respectively. The JB2008 model provided a better weighted average drag coefficient that was closer to Castor's estimates than MSIS00. The overall fit of the Pollux sphere was good for the JB2008 case with residual errors still very low. The MSIS00 case had much higher residuals near reentry, but it was a good fit with 11% error as compared to the hypothetical value, and could use further fine-tuning.

Table 5. ANDE-2 Ballistic Coefficient Estimation Statistics

Name	Atmo. Model	Wgt Avg BC (m²/kg)	Wgt Avg C$_d$	Average BC (m²/kg)	BC StdDev (m²/kg)	BC Percent Difference
Castor	JB2008	0.007254	1.8817	0.0074	0.0009	3.90
Castor	MSIS00	0.006668	1.7297	0.0070	0.0016	5.98
Pollux	JB2008	0.01171	1.7567	0.0122	0.0014	5.60
Pollux	MSIS00	0.009475	1.4214	0.0103	0.0020	10.75
Name	Atmo. Model	Hypothetical BC (m²/kg)	Hypothetical C$_d$	Avg Radial Res (km)	Avg In-track Res (km)	Avg CrossTrack Res (km)
Castor	JB2008	0.0085	2.2000	0.1915	0.8200	0.2856
Castor	MSIS00	0.0085	2.2000	0.2051	0.9537	0.2974
Pollux	JB2008	0.0147	2.2000	0.3750	1.6188	0.4007
Pollux	MSIS00	0.0147	2.2000	0.3742	1.6309	0.4342

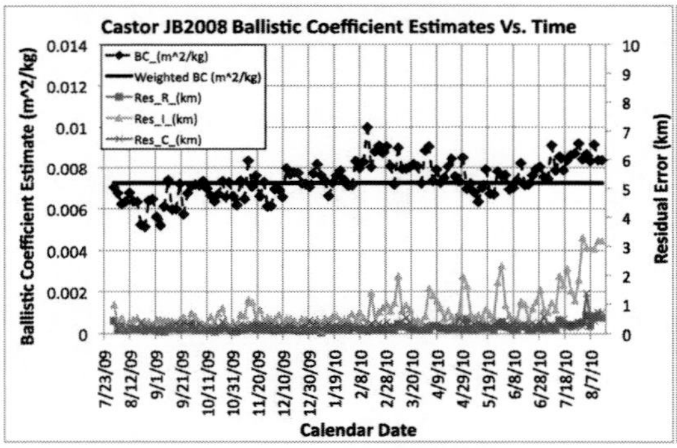

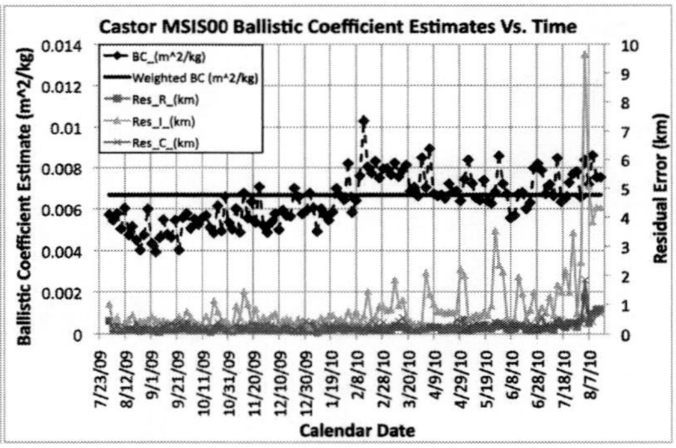

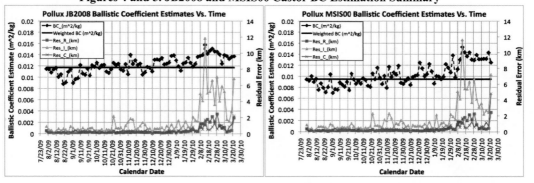

Figures 4 and 5. JB2008 and MSIS00 Castor BC Estimation Summary

Figures 6 and 7. JB2008 and MSIS00 Pollux BC Estimation Summary

ODERACS-1, 2 Ballistic Coefficient Estimation Results

The ODERACS-1 satellites (A – F) were deployed by the Space Shuttle (STS-60) in February 1994. The following year, ODERACS-2 satellites (2A-2F) were deployed by the Space Shuttle (STS-63) in February 1995[2]. Only six of the ODERACS satellites for missions 1 and 2 (A, B, E, F, 2A, and 2B) were chosen to process their ballistic coefficient estimates through ADOBE. These satellites were selected because of their simple shape and altitude regime, and they were in orbit during a different part of the solar cycle than the previous spheres. These runs only use the MSIS00 atmospheric model because the solar flux indices for JB2008 do not cover 1994-1996. Figures 8 and 9 show the individual ballistic coefficient estimates for the ODERACS satellites A and 2A. The spheres B, E, and F had similar profiles to A, and 2B was similar to 2A; the estimation statistics are shown in Table 6. The residual errors were low overall, but a little higher when compared to the ANDE-2 spheres. Some of the possible error could be attributed to a changing drag coefficient, and the quality of TLE data for the first two months. The ballistic coefficient estimates for ODERACS-1 satellites (A, B, E, and F) have a downward trend and tend to decrease their rate of change near reentry. The estimates for ODERACS-2 satellites (2A, and 2B) have an initial downward trend for a month after deployment and then remain nearly constant for the remaining time. The percent difference in Table 6 is shown to be very low (~3% or less) for all six spheres. The ballistic coefficient fits were good for all six ODERACS satellites, and the residual errors were comparable to the ANDE-2 spheres for the same ~350 km altitude regime.

Table 6. ODERACS-1, 2 Ballistic Coefficient Estimation Statistics

Name	Atmo. Model	Wgt Avg BC (m²/kg)	Wgt Avg C_d	Average BC (m²/kg)	BC StdDev (m²/kg)	BC Percent Difference
Oderac A	MSIS00	0.0130	2.3675	0.0132	0.0027	1.83
Oderac B	MSIS00	0.0132	2.4155	0.0130	0.0020	2.33
Oderac E	MSIS00	0.0090	2.4646	0.0089	0.0013	2.84
Oderac F	MSIS00	0.0091	2.4832	0.0091	0.0017	3.02
Oderac 2A	MSIS00	0.0075	2.0623	0.0075	0.0013	1.62
Oderac 2B	MSIS00	0.0122	2.2347	0.0119	0.0022	0.39

Name	Atmo. Model	Hypothetical BC (m²/kg)	Hypothetical C_d	Avg Radial Res (km)	Avg In-track Res (km)	Avg CrossTrack Res (km)
Oderac A	MSIS00	0.0120	2.2000	0.4721	1.6744	0.3872
Oderac B	MSIS00	0.0120	2.2000	0.4022	1.5407	0.3625
Oderac E	MSIS00	0.0080	2.2000	0.3968	1.9282	0.4061
Oderac F	MSIS00	0.0080	2.2000	0.2844	1.3468	0.3496
Oderac 2A	MSIS00	0.0080	2.2000	0.2903	1.1859	0.3644
Oderac 2B	MSIS00	0.0120	2.2000	0.4210	2.0086	0.4702

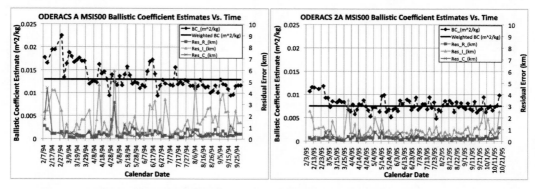

Figures 8 and 9. ODERACS A and 2A BC Estimation Summary

Calibration Analysis Conclusion

This calibration analysis yielded accurate fits for all nine satellites when the sources of error were taken into account. The BLITS sphere had low residual errors, and the weighted average ballistic coefficient was close to the hypothetical value, which provides confidence in the fits. The ANDE-2 spheres had a larger percent difference to a hypothetical ballistic coefficient than BLITS and ODERACS, but a 6% error for the JB2008 cases is considered a good fit. The six ODERACS satellites performed very well overall. The residual errors were low and comparable to the ANDE-2 spheres. The percent difference in the ballistic coefficient was ~3% or less for all six spheres, which indicates good fit estimates. Comparable accuracy can be expected for additional runs in the ~800 and ~350 km altitude ranges. As such, these results can provide a measure of confidence in the Cosmos and Iridium analysis presented in the next section.

COSMOS/IRIDIUM BALLISTIC COEFFICIENT RESULTS

The Cosmos-Iridium collision occurred at ~780 km altitude with both satellites in near-circular orbits with inclinations of 74 and 86 degrees respectively. The Cosmos-2251 and Iridium-33 satellites had masses of approximately 900 kg and 550 kg, respectively, prior to the event. Post-collision debris clouds developed for each satellite along the original bodies' orbits. Each cloud contained debris with a significant spread in apogees and perigees. Both the spread in apogees and perigees and the large number of fragments presented challenges for executing the estimation process. The cataloged TLE data used in the estimation process spanned eleven months starting at the beginning of 2010. The number of debris pieces on orbit, as of May 2010, for Cosmos and Iridium are 1267 and 521 respectively[16]. The TLE data was fairly continuous throughout, and most ballistic coefficient estimates converged to the specified covariance tolerance providing acceptable ballistic coefficient estimates. The Cosmos and Iridium ballistic coefficient estimates are plotted in Figures 10 and 11, respectively. The blue curves shown in the figures represent the weighted average ballistic coefficient estimate for each fragment sorted from smallest to largest ballistic coefficient value. The orange dots represent the average root sum square (RSS) residual error corresponding to each estimate. The Cosmos satellite generated more than twice the number of trackable debris as Iridium. The majority of Cosmos ballistic coefficient estimates were between 0.01 - 1 (m^2/kg). Only half of the Iridium debris ballistic coefficient estimates were below 1 (m^2/kg).

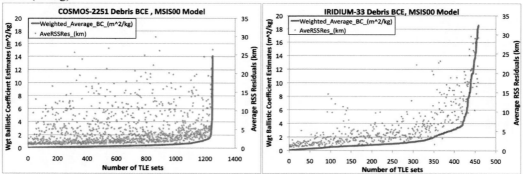

Figures 10 and 11. MSIS00 Cosmos-2251 and Iridium-33 Debris BC Estimates

The distribution of RSS residuals in Figure 12 shows the percentage of residuals below a given threshold for both Cosmos and Iridium. The general trend is that Cosmos has lower residual values as a percentage than Iridium. The ballistic coefficient estimations performed reasonably well with ~80% of the residuals less than 10 km.

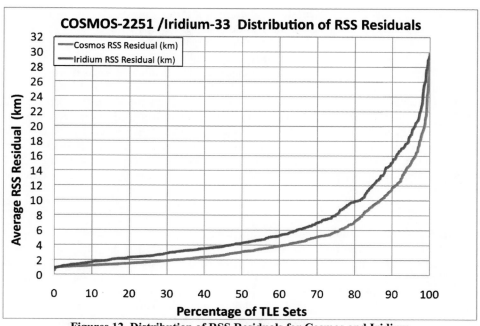

Figures 12. Distribution of RSS Residuals for Cosmos and Iridium

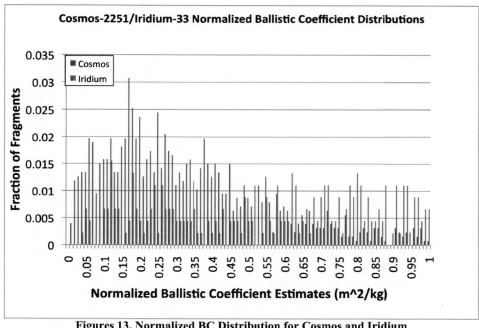

Figures 13. Normalized BC Distribution for Cosmos and Iridium

183

The normalized ballistic coefficient distribution, in Figure 13, shows a comparison of the Cosmos and Iridium debris. The normalization was done using the total number of fragments in each cloud to put both ballistic coefficient estimates on a scale from zero to one. The Cosmos debris has a much higher concentration of fragments toward smaller ballistic coefficients, with gradually decreasing numbers as the ballistic coefficients increase. The Iridium debris is more concentrated toward the higher end, but more distributed throughout its range than Cosmos. Since the estimates were found to be reasonably accurate, the two debris clouds show the characteristics of the collision itself. This suggests possible differences in types of materials used to construct the two objects or other physical characteristics of the debris. The lighter materials used in the construction of the more modern Iridium satellite such as carbon fiber will have higher area-to-mass ratios than the aluminum which makes up most of the Cosmos satellites. Although, it would be difficult to tell the exact material properties by this method, it would show differences in the types of objects that collided.

CONCLUSIONS

This study has described an automated technique to estimate ballistic coefficients for a large number of LEO objects. The program ADOBE was developed to perform this estimation given sequential sets of TLE data. ADOBE is a script that controls the sequential runs of two other core programs TLE2EPH and FIT-TLE in a series of four loops. The TLE2EPH program performs the conversion of TLE data into ephemeris files of position and velocity, and FIT-TLE executes the least squares fitting algorithm. To validate the resulting ballistic coefficient estimates from ADOBE, a calibration analysis was performed using TLE data from spherical satellites. The TLE data from the BLITS, ANDE-2, and ODERACS-1 and 2 satellites were processed through ADOBE. The resulting ballistic coefficient estimates were analyzed, and found to provide reasonably accurate fits for all calibration spheres. This calibration provided a level of confidence that ADOBE could provide comparable accuracy for the Cosmos and Iridium collision that generated thousands of debris objects. The ballistic coefficient estimates from the Cosmos/Iridium collision were computed using ADOBE. The ballistic coefficient and residual distributions were created from the resulting estimates. The RSS residual distribution showed that Cosmos had lower residuals overall compared to Iridium. The normalized ballistic coefficient distribution compared the two debris cloud estimates on the same scale. These distributions from the Cosmos and Iridium have a distinctly different pattern from each other. These patterns could yield information about the characteristics of the debris from each of the satellites. By looking at many different known collisions and explosions, a database of patterns could be used to determine the evolution of satellite breakup events in the future.

ACKNOWLEDGMENTS

This work was funded by an internal research and development project led by Marlon Sorge of The Aerospace Corporation (Aerospace). The authors would like to thank Glenn Peterson, Steve Bandel, and Marlon Sorge for their contribution, and review of this paper. Special thanks are also due to Brian Hansen, an Aerospace colleague, for his effort in development of the special tool (ADOBE), and for his contribution to this project and review of this paper.

Special permission was granted by U.S. Strategic Command to publish derived results from two-line element sets presented in this paper.

REFERENCES

1. Sorge, M. E., "Satellite Fragmentation Modeling with IMPACT," Paper No. AIAA-2008-6265, AIAA/AAS Astrodynamics Specialist Conference, Honolulu, Hawaii, August 18-21, 2008.

2. Chao, C. C., Gunning, G. R., Moe, K., Chastain, S. H., and Settecerri, T. J., "An Evaluation of Jacchia 71 and MSIS90 Atmosphere Models with NASA ODERACS Decay Data", *Journal of the Astronautical Sciences*, Vol. 45, No. 2, April-June 1997.

3. Bierman, G. J., *Factorization Methods for Discrete Sequential Estimation,* Academic Press, New York, 1977.

4. Picone, J. M., Hedin, A. E., Drob, D. P. and Aikin, A. C., "NRLMSISE-00 Empirical Model of the Atmosphere: Statistical Comparison and Scientific Issues," *Journal of Geophysical Research*, Vol. 107, No. A12, 1468, doi:10.1029/2002JA009430, 2002.

5. Bowman, B. R., "A New Empirical Thermospheric Density Model JB2008 Using New Solar and Geomagnetic Indices", Paper No. AIAA-2008-6438, AIAA/AAS Astrodynamics Specialist Conference, Honolulu, Hawaii, August 18-21, 2008.

6. Pardini, C., Anselmo, L., "Comparison and Accuracy Assessment of Semi-Empirical Atmosphere Models through the Orbital Decay of Spherical Satellites", Paper No. AAS 99-384, AAS/AIAA Astrodynamics Specialist Conference, Girdwood, Alaska, August 16-19, 1999.

7. Glover, R. A., Hoots, F. R., France, R. G., "Ballistic Coefficient Estimation for Satellite Breakup Debris: Calibration Analysis", Paper No. AIAA-88-4241, AIAA/AAS Astrodynamics Conference, Minneapolis, Minnesota, August 15-17, 1998.

8. Glover, R. A., "Final Report for Characterization of Satellite Breakup Debris", December 1998.

9. BLITS, International Laser Ranging Service (ILRS), http://ilrs.gsfc.nasa.gov/satellite_missions/list_of_satellites/blit_general.html, 2011

10. ANDE2, International Laser Ranging Service (ILRS), http://ilrs.gsfc.nasa.gov/satellite_missions/list_of_satellites/anda_general.html, 2011

11. Nicholas, A. C., Finne, T., Davis, M. A., Kessel, R., "Atmospheric Neutral Density Experiment (ANDE-2) Flight Hardware Details", http://ilrs.gsfc.nasa.gov/docs/anderr_hw.pdf, 2007.

12. Hoots, F. R., Roehrich R. L., "Models for Propagation of NORAD Elements Sets", Spacetrack Report No. 3, Project Spacetrack, Aerospace Defense Command, United States Air Force, Colorado Springs, Colorado, USA, December 1980.

13. Kaya, D., Snow, D., "Element Set Prediction Accuracy Assessment", Paper No. AAS 99-425, AAS/AIAA Astrodynamics Specialist Conference, Girdwood, Alaska, August 16-19, 1999.

14. Moe, K., Moe, M. M., "Gas-surface interactions and satellite drag coefficients", *Planetary and Space Science*, 53, 793-801, 2005.

15. Peterson G. E., "Effect of Large Velocity Covariance on Collision Probability Computation", Paper No. AAS-03-552, Astrodynamics Specialist Conference, Big Sky, Montana, August, 2003.

16. Johnson N. L., Liou J. C., "Orbital Debris Quarterly News", NASA, Vol. 14, Issue 3, July 2010.

DETERMINATION OF ORBIT CROSS-TAG EVENTS AND MANEUVERS WITH ORBIT DETECTIVE

Daniel L. Oltrogge[*] and Sal Alfano[†]

Track misassociation, cross-tag and orbit maneuver events can often be detected using a low-pass filter based upon pre- and post-event statistics accumulation. In this paper, we examine the implementation of such a filter in the Orbit Detective tool, and we apply the filter to the Galaxy 15 mission to determine cross-tag frequency of occurrence. Maneuver detection and calibration using such a low-pass filter are also discussed.

INTRODUCTION

The space operations community depends daily upon Non-Cooperative Tracking (NCT) data (e.g., radars and optical sensors). NCTs are the only tracking data source for debris objects, and they generally provide very functional information and services.

Certain orbit regimes offer a challenge to the NCT community. As shown in Figure 1, the GEO belt is very crowded, and satellite flybys are a common occurrence. Radar and optical sensors can have difficulty associating observations with the correct object during flyby periods, resulting in track misassociation or "cross-tag" conditions.

GEO Belt, 10 August 2010

Figure 1. GEO Belt Population as of 10 August 2010 (www.CelesTrak.com)

[*] Senior Research Astrodynamicist, AGI's Center for Space Standards and Innovation, 7150 Campus Drive, Suite 260, Colorado Springs, CO 80920.
[†] Senior Research Astrodynamicist, AGI's Center for Space Standards and Innovation, 7150 Campus Drive, Suite 260, Colorado Springs, CO 80920.

Although NCTs are the only reliable source for debris positional and metric data, it is essential for space operators to characterize the performance of such NCT data on an on-going basis. To help characterize this performance, AGI's Center for Space Standards and Innovation (CSSI) has created the "Orbit Detective" tool. This effort was undertaken on behalf of the Space Data Association (SDA), a non-profit association that brings together satellite operators who value the controlled, reliable, and efficient data-sharing that is critical to the safety and integrity of the space environment and the RF spectrum. The SDA was founded by Inmarsat, Intelsat and SES — three leading global satellite communications companies. By collecting definitive SDA Member RF, CA, ephemeris data, and points-of-contact information in the SDA's Space Data Center (SDC) analysis repository, Space Situational Awareness and threat mitigation analyses can now be completed to levels of previously unachievable accuracy and realism.

TRACK MISASSOCIATION AND CROSS-TAGGING

Track misassociation occurs when some or all NCT observations are tagged to the wrong satellites. When **all** observations incorporated into an orbit determination solution are misassociated, the resultant orbit solution can be labeled as a "cross-tag" event; in this case, the orbit solution can be accurate, but it is for the wrong object. Typically, track misassociation events can have large impacts on the accuracy of resultant orbit solutions for both Resident Space Objects (RSOs) during a transit of two satellites. The situation is often further aggravated because the most likely time for track misassociation to occur is during flyby events, which is precisely when satellite owner/operators require the most accuracy. Unfortunately, the application of a higher-accuracy orbit propagation scheme (e.g. numerical integration instead of semi-analytic theory) does not significantly help reduce such track misassociation events.

Note that track misassociation is not a result of using low-quality space surveillance hardware or employing unknowledgeable space analysts; rather, it is a direct result of the NCT method, which lacks active ranging and telemetry-based tracking.

ORBIT MANEUVER DETECTION AND CALIBRATION

The detection and removal of misassociated or cross-tagged orbital data permits the remaining orbital state vectors and/or ephemerides to be used to detect potential maneuvers and determine overall NCT orbit solution and prediction accuracy. As with track misassociation occurrences, NCTs are typically unaware of RSO maneuvers and can easily fit orbit solutions through the maneuver, resulting in degraded orbit estimation accuracy. This is especially prevalent among a number of GEO satellites that use low-thrust, long-duration burns to accomplish stationkeeping. Again, the use of higher-accuracy orbit propagation schemes does not reduce orbit solution degradation due to fitting through satellite maneuver events.

ANALYSIS OF TIME SEQUENCES OF ORBIT DATA VIA "ORBIT DETECTIVE"

In order to examine track misassociation, cross-tag and maneuver effects, a low-pass filter approach was implemented in the "Orbit Detective" tool. This basic approach is shown in Figure 2. By propagating both forward and backward from the epochs of a sequence of ephemerides or orbit solution states, distribution statistics may be generated for each orbit solution epoch. By examining median and percentile values at each epoch, an assessment can be made whether: (a) the orbit solution state in question is outside of the population bounds, either by more than a user-selectable 'N'-percentile value or (if assuming a normal error distribution) and 'N'-sigma value, indicating a potential track misassociation or cross-tag event; or (b) the orbit solution is within the bounds of the pre- or post-event statistics, but outside of the other statistics, indicating a potential maneuver.

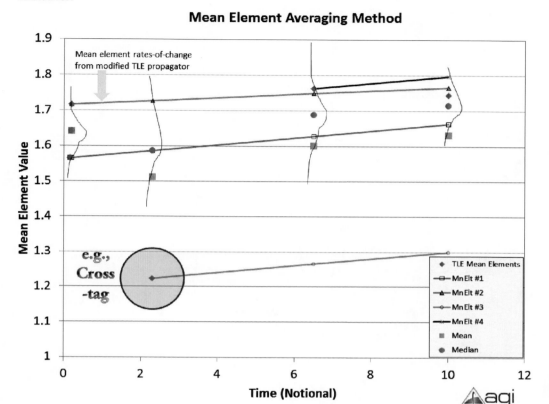

Figure 2. Time Sequence of Orbit Solutions Propagated to Epochs of Bounding Cases

APPLICATION OF "ORBIT DETECTIVE" TO GALAXY-15 CASE

As a test case, we now apply this low-pass filter approach to the Galaxy 15 mission to determine track misassociation and cross-tag frequency of occurrence. Two-Line Element (TLE) data from the CelesTrak site[1] is used exclusively for all TLE data products in this paper. A likely solar flare-induced Galaxy-15 satellite anomaly, which occurred on 5 April 2010, yielded a satellite that was unable to maneuver or respond to commands yet was able to continue to broadcast. Because the Galaxy-15 satellite hosts a GPS Wide Area Augmentation System (WAAS) transponder, the operations team was able to maintain very precise orbit solutions for Galaxy-15. This Galaxy-15 anomaly is a very good test case for track misassociation investigations because (a) an eastward drift was initiated due to the lack of stationkeeping; (b) the location of the satellite is precisely known by the operator but not in the public catalog; and (c) no maneuvers occurred. Control of Galaxy-15 by the ground operations team was reestablished on 23 December 2010.

Examination of classical orbital elements for the year 2010 (Figure 3 - Figure 7) shows the 8.5-month anomaly period. The difference in the signature of the classical orbit elements is readily apparent during this period. In addition to this signature difference, discrete step functions in the orbit elements may be observed.

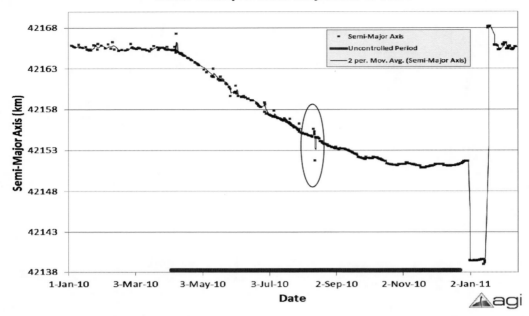

Figure 3. RSO Semi-Major Axis Versus Time in 2010

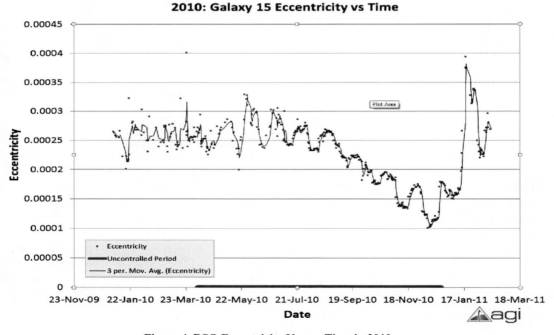

Figure 4. RSO Eccentricity Versus Time in 2010

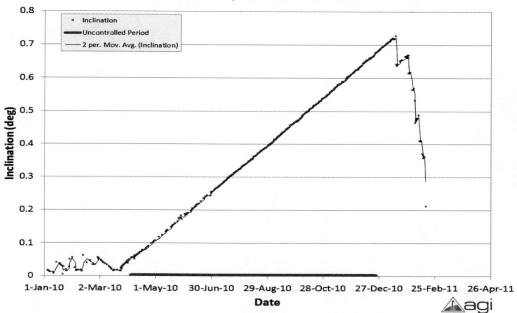

Figure 5. RSO Inclination Versus Time in 2010

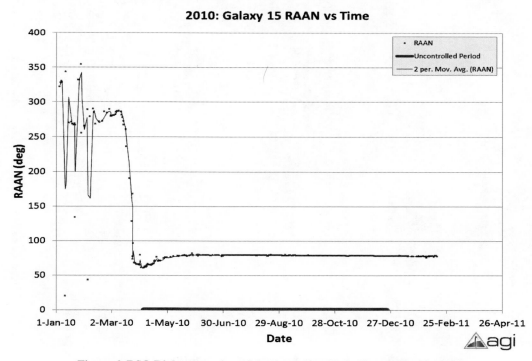

Figure 6. RSO Right Ascension of the Ascending Node Versus Time in 2010

191

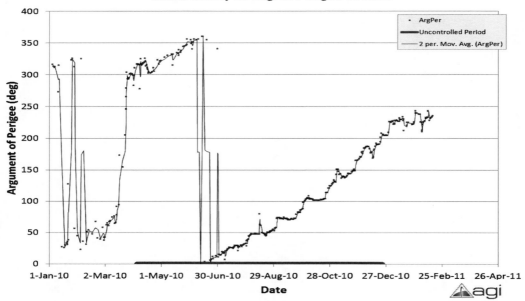

Figure 7. RSO Argument of Perigee Versus Time in 2010

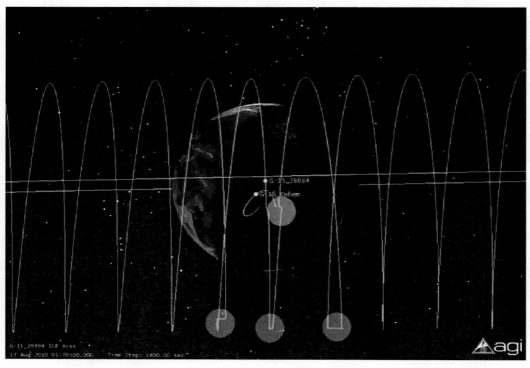

Figure 8. Galaxy-15 and Galaxy-18 Earth-Relative Paths During Flyby Encounter

192

Note the ellipse-encompassed step function in semi-major axis that occurred for multiple TLE vectors on approximately 13 Aug 2010. Examination of Earth-relative orbit paths during this time period reveals that these TLE step functions occurred at the approximate time of Galaxy-15's flyby of Galaxy 18, as shown in Figure 8. The figure also shows distinct step functions in the Earth-relative orbit paths for Galaxy-15 during this period.

The "scallop" pattern shown in Figure 8, coupled with what seems likely to be track misassociation problems, indicates that observations taken by NCT sensors are not taken at times that are designed to avoid track misassociation problems. An NCT should predict upcoming transit or "flyby" events occur and prioritize tasking/observation times which avoid the immediate transit event. Taking Galaxy-18 observations when Galaxy-18 is most to the north or most to the south from Galaxy-15 would likely minimize such track misassociation and/or cross-tagging events. Yet it is not clear that such prioritization can be accommodated in the "contributing and collaborating sensors" framework that comprises, for example, the US Space Surveillance Network.

Using a 2.5σ filter mentioned above with recursive excision, such step functions in the orbit elements may be either removed or replaced by new elements produced by the low-pass filter distribution statistics. Note that while the current low-pass filter employs symmetric standard deviation limits about the mean value, we have not as yet demonstrated that the distribution is actually symmetric. In the future, a simple replacement of the selected 2.5σ value with equivalent percentile values (+2.5σ corresponding to a percentile of 98.76% and -2.5σ a percentile of 1.24%) will remove any assumptions on skewness, kertosis, etc. that the current approach makes.

That said, it appears that the applied 2.5σ filter worked very well in identifying and replacing equinoctial element outliers as shown in Figure 9. The figure shows that this approach identifies time periods when orbit element inconsistencies have occurred. Again, this is a non-maneuvering satellite, so any observed inconsistencies are solely caused by NCT tracking methods and susceptibilities. An interesting statistic from this figure is that out of 348 Galaxy-15 TLEs obtained during the uncontrolled period, 52 of them (15%) were found to contain track misassociations, cross-tags or equivalent data inconsistencies. Such inconsistencies cause overall accuracy degradation in predicted positional knowledge.

AGI is currently working on an automated approach to studying each one of these potential track misassociation or cross-tag periods. For now, a somewhat manual procedure using the STK deck access tool for Galaxy-15 was employed to determine when major GEO flyby events occurred. The results are shown in Figure 10. As is evident, the potential track misassociation or cross-tag periods are strikingly similar to the detected flyby event times.

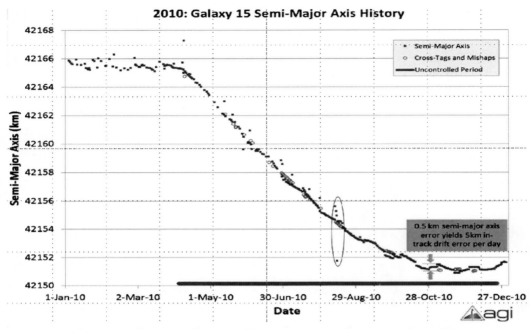

Figure 9. Orbit Element Replacement Using Orbit Detective Low-Pass Filter

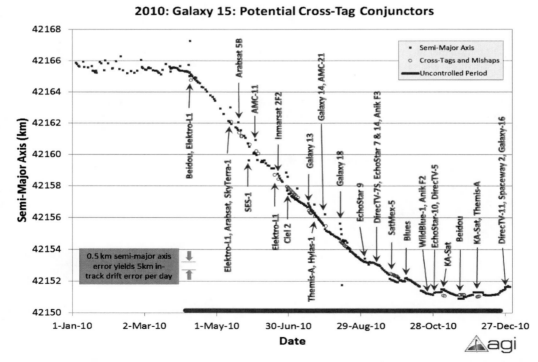

Figure 10. Correlation of Potential Track Misassociation or Cross-tag Events with Galaxy-15 Flybys

APPLICATION OF FILTER TO ENTIRE GEO POPULATION

Upon completion of the Galaxy-15 analysis, the same low-pass filter was applied to the remaining GEO regime RSOs. Distributions of the percentage of TLEs that showed such data inconsistencies were generated as a function of orbital period, longitude, and orbit update frequency.

CORRELATION OF POTENTIAL TRACK MISASSOCIATION WITH ORBIT PERIOD

It was anticipated that objects that are nearly, but not quite, rotating at Earth's rotation rate would experience more track misassociation data inconsistencies, because the relative drift could lead to frequent observation association problems. However, as shown in Figure 11 - Figure 13, there is not a strong correlation, and for a given percent cross-tagging/degradation, super-sync and sub-sync orbits are equally likely to experience that percentage.

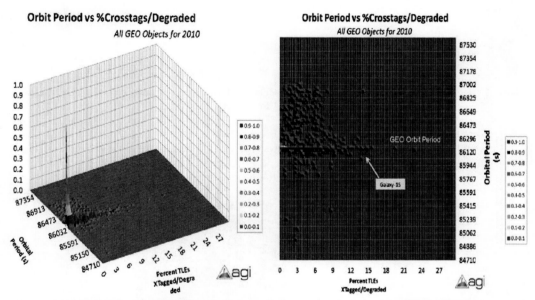

Figure 11. Distribution of Potential Track Misassociation/Cross-tag Percentage versus Orbital Period (3D)

Figure 12. Distribution of Potential Track Misassociation/Cross-tag Percentage versus Orbital Period

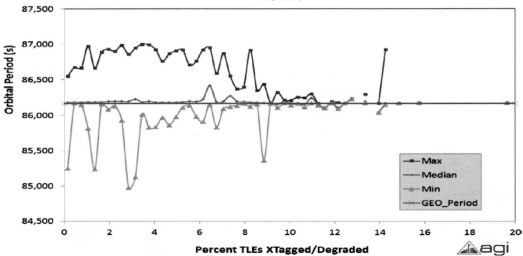

Figure 13. Distribution of Potential Track Misassociation/Cross-tag Percentage versus TLE Update Frequency

The correlation between GEO longitude and percent cross-tagging/degradation are examined next. Factors that may lead to such a correlation include the longitudinal distribution of NCT sensor placement, GEO longitude population, and GEO gravitational stability points. Figure 14 and Figure 15 show such a correlation to gravitational stability point location.

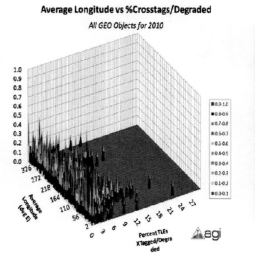

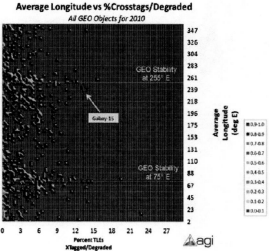

Figure 14. Distribution of Potential Track Misassociation/Cross-tag Percentage versus TLE Update Frequency (3D)

Figure 15. Distribution of Potential Track Misassociation/Cross-tag Percentage versus TLE Update Frequency

196

It was also thought that perhaps those objects that were tracked at a higher frequency (based upon their TLE update or publication frequency) might be less susceptible to cross-tagging. But as shown in Figure 14 through Figure 18, frequently-tracked objects are just as susceptible to potential track misassociation events.

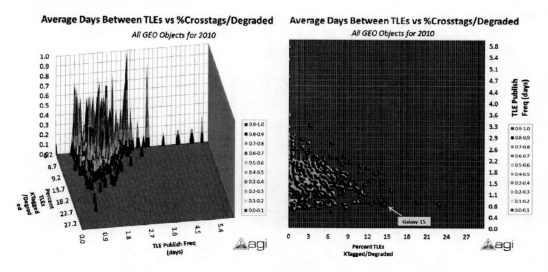

Figure 16. Distribution of Potential Track Misassociation/Cross-tag Percentage versus TLE Update Frequency (3D)

Figure 17. Distribution of Potential Track Misassociation/Cross-tag Percentage versus TLE Update Frequency

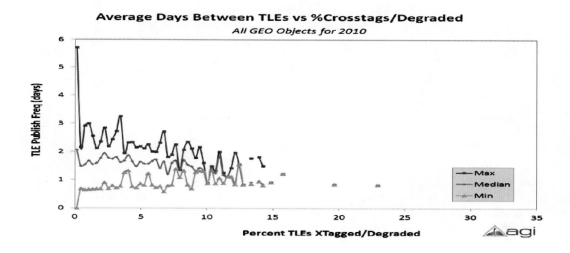

Figure 18. Distribution of Potential Track Misassociation/Cross-tag Percentage versus TLE Update Frequency

INCORPORATION OF MANEUVER DETECTION

Once outlier NCT has been removed from the orbital time history, our next step will be to incorporate maneuver detection into the Orbit Detective tool. Details of this capability are presented at this conference in a separate session[2]. A sample output from the maneuver detection capability is shown in Figure 19. The figure shows the maneuver optimization topology for a sample in-track maneuver, as well as the detected maneuver conditions shown by the red star.

The performance and capabilities of this tool are detailed in Ref. 2.

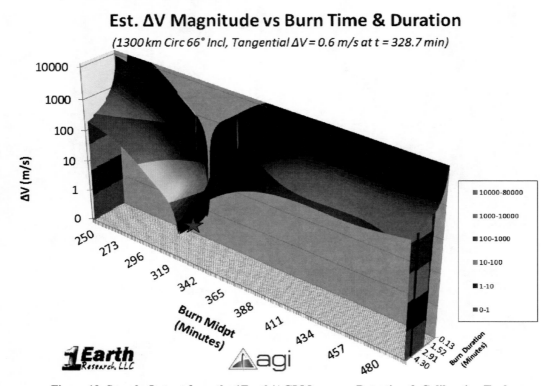

Figure 19. Sample Output from the 1Earth/AGI Maneuver Detection & Calibration Tool

CONCLUSIONS

A low-pass orbit elements filter method has been shown to be an effective approach to identifying potential cross-tagged or similarly-degraded orbit solution accuracy events. The cross-tags can be identified by rapid short-term spikes in orbital elements, which return rapidly to 'nominal' values after the event. Maneuver events can be similarly identified, but with orbital elements taking a step-function in time.

FUTURE WORK

Additional work is planned to apply these low-pass filtering techniques to the RSO catalog on an on-going basis. The current standard deviation-based low-pass filter will also be modified to rely on percentile filtering limits to remove any assumptions on distribution symmetry or Gaussian distribution. Following that, it is planned to incorporate an on-going maneuver detection capability into the Orbit Detective tool.

ACKNOWLEDGMENTS

The authors wish to thank CSSI technical experts for their insightful comments and review of this paper.

REFERENCES

[1] CelesTrak site, www.CelesTrak.com

[2] Oltrogge, D.L., "Maneuver Event Detection and Reconstruction Using Body-Centric Acceleration/Jerk Optimization," AAS 11-578, August 2011 AIAA/AAS Astrodynamics Specialist Conference, Girdwood, AK.

EFFECT OF FUTURE SPACE DEBRIS ON MISSION UTILITY AND LAUNCH ACCESSIBILITY

Glenn E. Peterson[*]

Future growth of space debris in Low Earth Orbit will have an effect on two aspects of space operations: on-orbit mission utility and launch accessibility. Using a newly developed model, these two aspects are examined for three size regimes of debris: >10 cm (current tracking capability), 5-10 cm (upgraded tracking system), and 1-5 cm (potentially destructive to vehicle). Results show that as the debris environment grows, the number of actions (i.e., extra requests for tracking, maneuvers, etc.) at the examined orbit regime may be large enough to affect mission operations as will the potential amount of launch window closures.

INTRODUCTION

The Fengyun-1C event and Iridium-33/Cosmos-2251 collision have increased the LEO debris population. After these events, the USAF Space and Missile Systems Center (SMC/XRD) tasked The Aerospace Corporation to develop a process to generate discrete future LEO debris populations for input to SMC simulations. The details of this model are presented in another paper at this conference[1] while some of the consequences of the debris growth are examined here.

At least three areas are influenced by the growth in the debris environment: overall mission cost, operations, and accessibility. The first of these issues, cost, was addressed by a DARPA funded study[2] performed by The Aerospace Corporation using an early version of the debris model. This study examined three types of satellite constellations (government, commercial, and assembly-line commercial) deployed at the expected worst altitude of 850 km in 2010, 2020, and 2030, and found that cost increases due to reliability issues when operating in the projected debris field would be on the order of 3-18%. The second issue, effect of future debris on mission operations, was addressed in the SMC study[3] also using the early version of the debris model and found that improvements to tracking update frequency and tracking quality were shown to be effective in reducing the number of potentially dangerous conjunctions. The current research updates some of the mission utility issues using the latest version of the model (going out for 100 years) and addresses the issue of accessibility to space as measured by the orbital debris impact on launch window closures.

---

[*] Senior Engineering Specialist, Astrodynamics Department, The Aerospace Corporation, P.O. Box 92957, Los Angeles, CA 90009-2957, Associate Fellow AIAA, Member AAS.

100-YEAR LEO MODEL

The 100-year projection of the LEO debris environment is detailed elsewhere in this conference[1], but a summary of the method and results is warranted here, in so far as it influences the current study. The model discretely determines collisions between individual objects. This discretization allows for the identification of those objects that are statistically likely to contribute the most to the growth in the debris population, thus providing potential target objects for either active debris removal campaigns or increased tracking to enable more efficient collision avoidance of these objects. Analysis of the model results found that collisions between large objects (both in terms of size and mass) were dominant contributors to the future debris environment.

The starting point of the model simulation consists of four populations: current catalog when the original study started in June of 2009, discrete representations of the current 5-10 cm and 1-5 cm populations, and a future launch population generated from a repetition of the previous 10 years of launch activity (1999-2009). The three size regimes were selected to represent various space surveillance scenarios: the >10 cm population is the population observable by current tracking systems; the 5-10 cm population represents what could be observable with a future improved space surveillance system; the 1-5 cm population cannot be tracked with foreseeable improvements to space surveillance technology and so cannot be responded to in an operational manner, but is still potentially catastrophic to spacecraft. The current catalog consists of only those objects large enough to be reliably tracked (>10 cm in size). To generate the smaller 5-10 cm and 1-5 cm populations, a mass-law relation was used to extrapolate the current >10 cm population down to the smaller size regimes. The future launch population was assumed to be those objects deliberately placed into orbit and so are consequently of the size >10 cm.

These four populations were propagated into the future for 100 years (with additional future launch objects being added every year). The statistical likelihood of collisions between the propagated objects was determined through an orbit trace crossing method that identifies orbits that intersect each other. The probability that a collision occurs is determined by the likelihood that each object is at the crossing point at the same time. A random draw on the probability determines if the collision actually occurs. The generated collisions are then input into the hypervelocity code IMPACT, which computes the corresponding discrete debris fields. An average debris environment is generated from 100 Monte Carlo variations on the random draw of the collision probabilities.

The orbits of the newly created debris objects are propagated out from the time of their creation to the end of the 100-year time frame. With this methodology, discrete catalogs representative of the average debris environment at any desired time can be created. The debris objects from the collisions were categorized into three groups: debris from collisions between the current population and itself, debris from the future launch population against itself, and debris from the collisions between the future and current populations.

Figure 1 shows the resulting spatial density as derived from the discrete catalogs for the three size bins at three snapshots in time: 2009, 2059, and 2109. In general, the density is expected to increase noticeably over the next 100 years with the growth mostly occurring in the out-years. Peaks occur in the heavily populated low LEO region (~700-900 km) where Sun-synchronous satellites, and Iridium and Orbcomm constellations reside, at ~900-1000 km where the Russian Parus satellites inhabit, and at high LEO (~1400 km) where the Globalstar constellation and Russian Strela satellites lie. The orbit examined in this study was chosen to be near-circular at 850 km altitude to be consistent with the previous cost analysis[2] and is denoted by the dotted line on the plots.

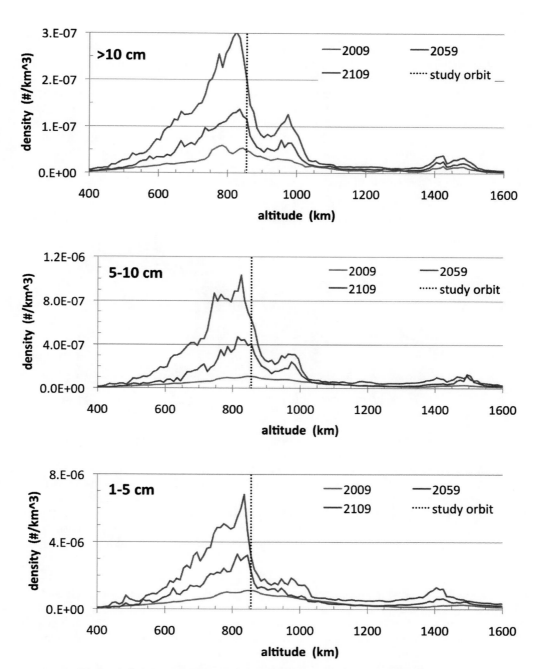

Figure 1. Spatial density from discrete catalogs as a function of altitude.

Figure 2 shows the growth in the spatial density for an 850 km altitude orbit over the next 100 years in one year intervals for objects in the >10 cm size regime. Each of the categories is depicted separately with the results being presented in a stacked plot format. For the >10 cm population, the current population slowly decays while the future launch population slowly adds to the population. At this altitude, the main contributors to the debris growth are collisions between currently orbiting objects and collisions between current and future launch objects; collisions between future objects has a much smaller net effect. Over the next 100 years, the >10 cm debris environment is expected to increase by roughly a factor of 4. The results indicate that the projected debris environment is already in a state of self-generation and will grow even if there is no future launch activity (or equivalently, perfect collision avoidance and complete removal at end-of-life). This confirms previous studies performed by others[4].

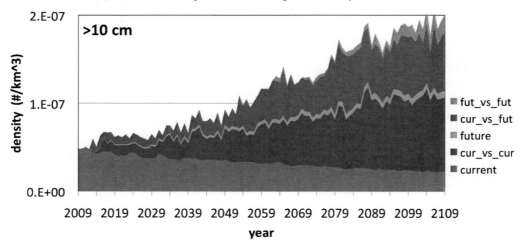

Figure 2. Temporal growth in >10 cm density for 850 km altitude orbit broken into categories.

Figures 3 and 4 show the growth in the spatial density for objects in the two smaller size regimes. For these sizes, there is assumed to be no deliberate addition of objects by the space community and so no future launch population exists, but debris from collisions involving the >10 cm future launch objects still contributes to the growth in the density. For the current objects in the 1-5 and 5-10 cm sizes, the decay that was observed for the >10 cm objects is even more pronounced until by the end of the 100 years, their presence has been reduced by over an order of magnitude.

The debris from collisions is completely dominated by the current-on-current collisions up until around 2050, after which time the remaining current-on-current population stabilizes for the 5-10 cm objects, and slowly decays for the 1-5 cm objects. However, the debris from current-on-future collisions, while quiet early on, begins to grow at around the same time. For the remainder of the 100 years, the debris from collisions involving future launches becomes almost as large an effect as the current-on-current debris. Overall, the spatial density will continually increase over the next 100 years for all three of the size regimes. It should be emphasized that these results apply to an 850 km altitude orbit; the behavior at other altitudes may be different.

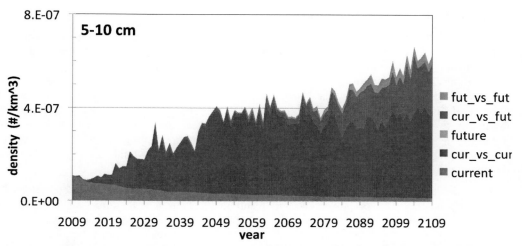

Figure 3. Temporal growth in 5-10 cm density for 850 km altitude orbit broken into categories.

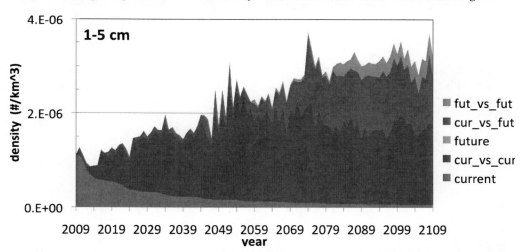

Figure 4. Temporal growth in 1-5 cm density for 850 km altitude orbit broken into categories.

The collision avoidance (COLA) analysis that follows uses the discrete catalogs from the model at one-year intervals for the 100-year time span to generate a multitude of individual close approaches and associated probabilities of collision. For the mission utility analysis, the satellite's orbit was near circular at 850 km with a Sun-synchronous inclination; for the launch accessibility analysis, a satellite was launched into the same 850 km orbit. When computing the probability of collision, the size (collision radius) of the two objects is required; as part of the model development process, a database of sizes for currently orbiting objects was created. This information was used for the current and future populations. The primary satellite collision radius was assumed to be the average of LEO satellites from this database (2.38 m). The debris objects are small in comparison to the satellite size and so they were assigned an average collision radius commensurate with the bin to which they belonged.

MISSION UTILITY METHODOLOGY

The on-orbit part of the COLA analysis utilizes the numerical "chi-plot" method[5,6] wherein a fictitious satellite constellation is placed into orbit and compared against the predicted debris environment. The chi-plot methodology is summarized in Figure 5. First, a large number of discrete individual conjunctions and associated probabilities of collision are generated between the desired operational orbit and the background catalog using the Collision Vision software[7]. In the case of Figure 5, the operational orbit was at 850 km altitude, and the background catalog is the public two-line element set catalog at the epoch of the model simulation in June of 2009. Summing the probabilities over all of the individual conjunctions and normalizing to a one-year time span yields the latent probability of collision that the satellite would face (for the example, the latent probability is $\sim 4.2 \times 10^{-4}$ per year).

Once the latent probability is computed and a desired reduction in mission risk is selected, a threshold probability is computed that will result in the chosen reduction. This is performed numerically, and for each discrete threshold probability, every conjunction that has a probability larger than the threshold is reduced in probability to the threshold value with a new total probability corresponding to that threshold being computed (solid curve in Figure 5). The example in Figure 5 depicts a 50% reduction (reducing the overall mission probability to 2.1×10^{-4} per year), which will require an individual conjunction probability threshold of 9.5×10^{-7}.

The metric of measure for the mission utility analysis will be how often the threshold probability is violated thereby requiring some type of response on the part of operators (i.e., these realistically do not have to be satellite maneuvers, but could be additional tracking). Therefore, at the same time that the total probability for each possible threshold is computed, the number of violations of the threshold is monitored (dashed curve). For the example, there were ~ 119 violations of the 9.5×10^{-7} threshold per year for a single satellite at 850 km.

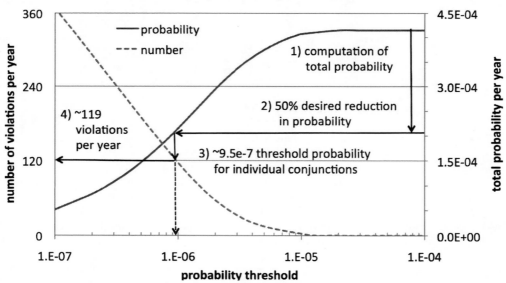

Figure 5: Sample chi-plot using the current (June, 2009) public catalog for an 850 km orbit with GP orbit accuracies

Crucial to the computation of the number of violations is the quality of the data being used, that is, how well the on-orbit objects are tracked. For purposes of this study, three types of data quality will be considered. The term "GP" refers to General Perturbations (i.e., SGP4 theory) and is the baseline level of error as determined from analysis of the public two-line elements sets[8]. This process determines an error ellipsoid in the along-track, cross-track, and normal-to-the-orbit coordinate system for each object in the catalog, and therefore each object has its own time-varying ellipsoid. The average GP error at epoch resulting from this process for the LEO objects examined here is 1.68 km along-track, 0.28 km cross-track, and 0.46 km normal. There are slight growth terms in the cross-track and the normal directions, but the growth is dominated by the along-track component of ~0.45 km/day. This GP level of error was used in Figure 5.

Two other levels of error will also be considered. The first, labeled "SP", will simulate the accuracy of the catalog as if a numerical Special Perturbations technique was used in the orbit estimation process; SP will be assumed to be three times more accurate than GP (each object's ellipsoid was scaled down by a factor of 3). The other, "HP" ("High Precision"), is a further factor of three improvement over SP and is assumed to represent the level of orbit accuracy possible through a future tracking system. Figure 6 depicts the same satellite at the same altitude with the same background population as in Figure 5, but assuming SP level of tracking. Notice that the latent total probability is approximately the same as in Figure 5, but that the curve has shifted and the threshold probability corresponding to a 50% reduction in probability is now just over an order of magnitude larger than the GP accuracy case (1.0×10^{-5} vs. 9.5×10^{-7}) while the number of violations is just over an order of magnitude lower than in the GP case (~11 per year vs. ~119). In general, the more accurate the orbit knowledge, the higher the threshold and the fewer number of violations will occur for the same level of reduction in overall mission risk.

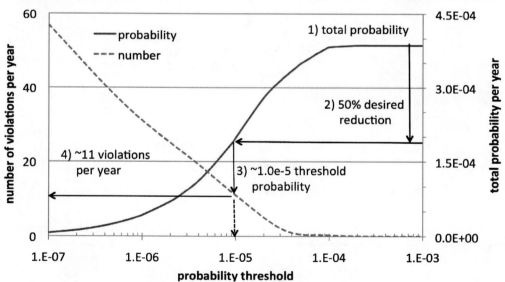

Figure 6: Sample chi-plot using the current (June, 2009) public catalog for an 850 km orbit with SP orbit accuracies

MISSION UTILITY RESULTS

Figure 7 shows the total collision probability as a function of time. There are 9 curves, one for each combination of tracking accuracy and secondary object size. Results for the two sizes of debris objects that are operationally actionable are shown: >10 cm (currently tracked) and >5 cm (tracked with improved system), along with the non-actionable >1 cm (untracked but dangerous). Although the 1-5 cm population is assumed to be too small to be actionable in this study, the risk for that population is included here for purposes of comparison. Note that the results from each population are shown *cumulatively*; in other words, the >5 cm risk shows the probability of collision for those particles in the 5-10 cm range plus the risk from the >10 cm population; similarly, the >1 cm curves contain the 1-5 cm, 5-10 cm, and >10 cm probability. This is reflective of actual operations: if the particles down to 5 cm are observed with an improved tracking system, the probability a satellite faces would be the sum of the 5-10 cm and >10 cm particles. During the analysis process, the populations were treated separately, but in the following plots are shown cumulatively. In Figure 7, the 9 curves can be seen to group into 3 very similar sets based upon object size (>1 cm on top, >5 cm in the middle, >10 cm at the bottom). This is not unexpected as the latent risk that a satellite faces due to a given debris population should be independent of the tracking accuracy and solely dependent on the flux. The probability for all three size populations increased by close to an order of magnitude after 100 years with the >1 cm and >5 cm probability being fairly consistently greater than the >10 cm probability by average factors of 20 and 3.7 respectively.

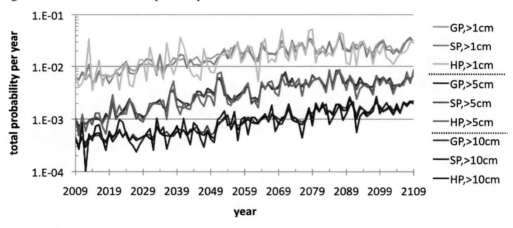

Figure 7: Cumulative total collision probability for the satellite at 850 km altitude

Figure 8 shows the threshold probability for a 50% reduction in the total probability as a function of time. Recall that in Figure 7, there were 3 sets of 3 curves grouped by secondary object size. In Figure 8, there are also 3 sets of 3 curves, but here the grouping is by tracking accuracy (HP on top, SP in the middle, GP at the bottom). The thresholds are changing roughly by an order of magnitude for every factor of 3 improvement in the accuracy. The threshold does not show a strong dependency on the object size or on time, although there is variation about the mean. This variation is driven predominantly by the individual variation in the secondary object error ellipsoids. Since the secondary object size is a direct substitute for the flux, then this lack of dependency of the threshold probability on secondary object size implies that once a desired percentage of reduction is set, the choice of threshold is not a function of the flux environment.

208

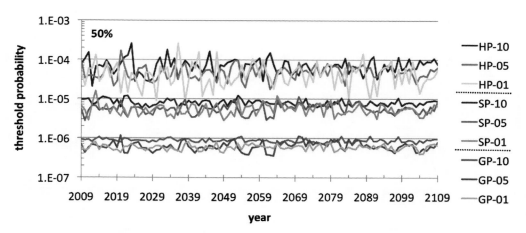

Figure 8: Threshold probability for 50% reduction at 850 km altitude

Figure 9 shows the number of violations that occur for the three size regimes (>10 cm, >5 cm, and >1cm) for the three tracking accuracies for a 50% reduction in total probability. Unlike the latent probability, which depends on flux but not tracking accuracy, and the threshold, which depends on tracking accuracy but not flux, the number of violations depends on both. At the current time with current GP tracking accuracy (first point in the top curve on the top plot), a violation occurs roughly once every three days, and remains at a similar level for the next several decades (taking approximately 40 years to double). However, as the debris accumulates over a longer period of time, the number of actions grows and will be between one-to-two per day by the end of the century.

As tracking capabilities improve so that smaller objects are placed into the catalog, the number of violations correspondingly increases. For the >5 cm population, the number of violations is approximately 2.9 times the >10 cm population while the >1 cm is averages 22 times the >10 cm population. These ratios are fairly consistent regardless of the tracking accuracy. For the >5 population, the number of violations could reach 4-5 per day by the end of 100 years and almost 30 per day for the >1cm objects. This increase is offset by potential improvements to tracking quality with about an order of magnitude decrease for every factor of 3 improvement to quality. For example, the number of violations for the >1 cm objects would drop from ~30 per day for GP quality data to ~3 per day if SP accuracies are assumed, and from ~3 per day to ~1 every 3 days if HP accuracy is achieved.

These results have significant implications for future tracking and confirm the results of the previous study that examined 30-year projections of the debris environment[3]. If a future proposed tracking system is able to pick up smaller particles without producing better observations, then the number of violations will significantly impact mission operations. But moderate increases in quality will noticeably improve the situation. Note also that the specific numerical results shown here apply to a single average-sized satellite. When operating a large satellite, a constellation of satellites, or when monitoring the LEO environment as a whole, the number of violations will increase accordingly and could become excessive at a much earlier date.

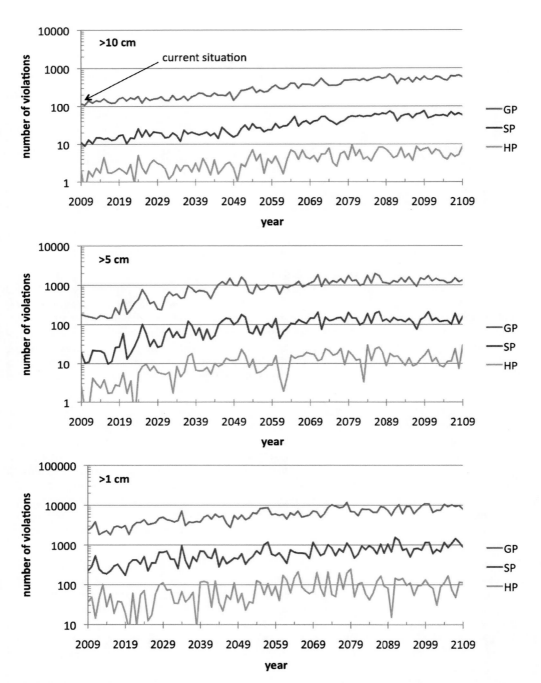

Figure 9. Predicted number of actions per year for a single satellite at 850 km for 50% reduction in total probability of collision.

210

LAUNCH ACCESSIBILITY ANALYSIS

The issue of launch accessibility due to debris is separate from mission utility. In mission utility analysis, a satellite is on orbit for years and the goal is reduction of the overall probability that the satellite faces during its mission. Therefore, the satellite's operators need to be concerned about every conjunction that violates the threshold probability. However, in launch operations, there is a launch window that contains multiple launch opportunities and each launch opportunity may have multiple conjunctions occurring along its trajectory. Since it is relatively inexpensive and low-risk to wait for the next opportunity in the window, any single conjunction that exceeds a chosen threshold will close out the opportunity regardless of how many violating conjunctions occur. For example, if the threshold is 1×10^{-7}, then regardless of whether there are one, two, three or more individual conjunctions with probabilities larger than 1×10^{-7}, then that launch opportunity is closed. All conjunctions occurring during that opportunity are then eliminated from further consideration. The metric in this analysis is the likelihood that a given launch opportunity will be closed due to various probabilistic criteria. Since the number of opportunities will vary according to the mission, the effectiveness of a chosen threshold is determined by how much the average probability per opportunity is decreased. The trade-off in the mission utility analysis was between the reduction in the total probability and the number of violations operators would have to deal with. The trade-off in the launch accessibility analysis is between the reduction in the average probability per opportunity and the likelihood of closure.

Therefore, while the mission utility and launch accessibility analyses are different in concept, the launch accessibility analysis utilizes a chi-plot methodology similar to the mission utility analysis where the launch vehicle trajectory and associated uncertainties are compared to the background catalog to determine potentially dangerous conjunctions[6]. Consistent with the earlier mission utility analysis, the launch trajectory used here consists of a simulated launch to a Sun-synchronous 850 km altitude orbit. The spacecraft and upper stage are stacked together and treated as a single object until spacecraft separation. After separation, the two components are treated as distinct objects with separate trajectories and separate sizes (spacecraft COLA radius of 2.38 m to be consistent with the mission utility analysis and an upper stage size of 6.5 m). The spacecraft enters its 850 km near-circular orbit with the upper stage being left in a slightly lower orbit commensurate with current launch vehicle separation velocities (~1.7 m/s). The simulation duration of the launch trajectory is from launch through one orbital period after spacecraft separation (approximately two hours from launch). The uncertainty used for the launch trajectory is a constant ellipsoid based upon launch injection 3-sigma accuracies of ± 5 km in the radial direction, ± 100 km in the along-track direction, and ± 5 km in the orbit normal direction. The mission profile, upper stage size, separation velocity, and injection accuracies are based upon an average of publicly reported values for existing launch systems and is not meant to be reflective of any particular system[9,10,11].

For the full analysis, the launch trajectory is compared against the model background at yearly intervals for a 1-day launch window with individual launch opportunities at the top of each minute (total of 1441 opportunities per window). The goal is to determine the percentage of those 1441 opportunities that are closed out for three thresholds: 1×10^{-5}, 1×10^{-6}, and 1×10^{-7}. These thresholds were chosen to reflect current operational practices. The Aerospace Corporation reports window closeouts above a 1×10^{-7} probability when performing launch COLA operations while the US government AFI 91-217 standards document establishes mandatory closeouts at 1×10^{-5} for unmanned objects and 1×10^{-6} for manned.

Figure 10 shows the chi-plot modified for the launch problem. Like the mission utility chi-plot example of Figure 5, this case uses the current >10 cm catalog for the background environment. Since launch windows vary with mission, the desired reduction is to take place in the average probability of collision per launch opportunity within the launch window; the average probability replaces the total probability of the mission utility analysis on the right hand axis. On the left hand axis, the percentage of the launch opportunities that are closed replaces the number of violations. In Figure 10, a 1×10^{-6} threshold (that is, closing all launch opportunities that have a single probability greater than 1×10^{-6}) would yield a 54% reduction in the average probability and close 14% of the launch opportunities. The AFI 91-217 threshold of 1×10^{-5} would only reduce the average probability by ~4% and close out only 0.2% of the opportunities; the reporting threshold of 1×10^{-7} would close 65% of the opportunities while reducing the risk by 95%. It is apparent that selecting a threshold that is too low will close out a high percentage of the launch window while selecting a threshold that is too high will not have an appreciable result on reducing the average probability per opportunity.

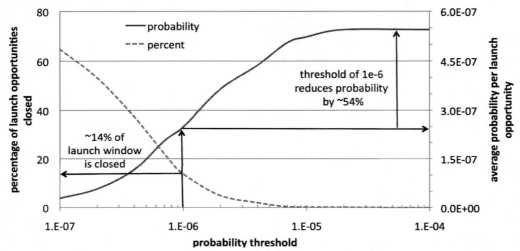

Figure 10. Sample chi-plot using the current (June, 2009) public catalog for launch to an 850 km Sun-synchronous orbit.

Figure 11 shows the latent average probability of collision per launch opportunity for the simulated launch for the three secondary object size regimes: >1 cm, >5 cm, and >10 cm as a function of time. Similar to the total probability of the mission utility analysis (Figure 7), the average probability increases with time. The >5 cm probability starts out at approximately twice the level of the >10 cm probability, but at the end of the 100 years, is about three times as high. Similarly, the >1 cm probability starts out at ~20 times the >10 cm probability, but grows faster as expected due to the increase in small particles from fresh collisions. Similar to what was observed in Figure 7 for the mission utility analysis, the tracking accuracy on the secondary background objects has negligible influence on the average probability of collision the launch vehicle components face.

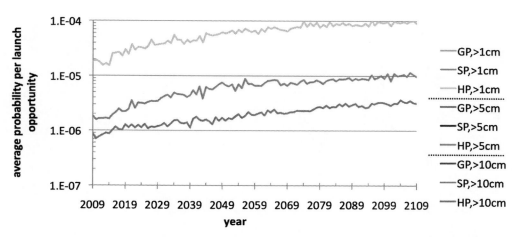

Figure 11. Average probability per launch opportunity for simulated launch to 850 km altitude.

Figure 12 shows the percentage of launch window closures for the examined size regimes. The first thing to note is that the tracking accuracy on the secondary background objects is not influential on the solutions. Improvements to tracking accuracy will not impact launch accessibility simply because the along-track uncertainty in the launch vehicle trajectory is so much larger than orbital accuracies. This is unlikely to change significantly in the future as launch vehicle uncertainties are driven by factors outside of easy control without significant investment in the development of new technology that does not necessarily serve the primary purpose of launch vehicles (i.e., placing a satellite into its desired orbit).

When examining the top plot (threshold of 1×10^{-5}), it is apparent that establishing too high of a threshold will result in very few window closeouts, and thus result in the launch COLA process not having any appreciable effect on reducing the overall average risk. But having a threshold that is too low (bottom plot with threshold of 1×10^{-7}) will result in a situation where, while the overall average risk is significantly reduced, too many launch opportunities are closed. For a threshold of 1×10^{-6}, the larger size regimes (>10 cm and >5 cm) result in significant but manageable closures for the foreseeable future while the >1 cm population will close out the entire window within a few decades. The current operational procedure of reporting all closeouts to 1×10^{-7} is acceptable for the short term, but in the long term will have to change. This was seen directly in the chi-plot example of Figure 10 as well, but now can be seen to become worse in the future. If an improved tracking system became available, then the expected debris growth will close out entire windows within a few decades from now if the reporting threshold is still being used. Therefore, relying on a fixed threshold value rather than one based upon the desired level of overall probability reduction could be problematic; threshold determination should be based upon the characteristics of the tracking system and the desired amount of overall reduction.

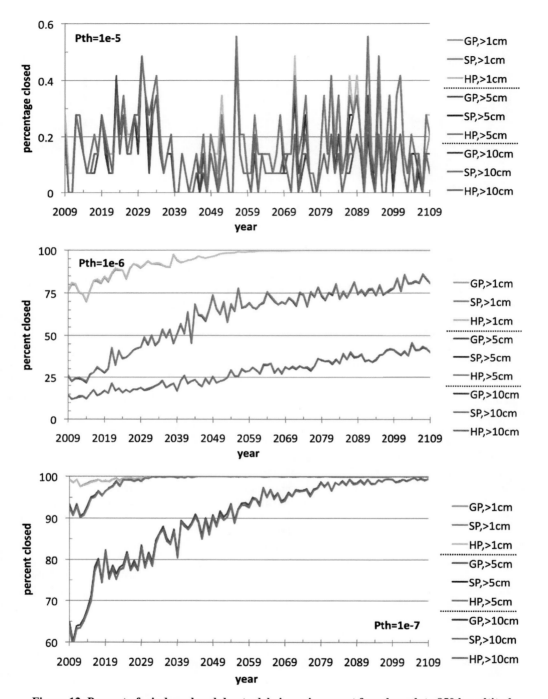

Figure 12. Percent of window closed due to debris environment for a launch to 850 km altitude.

CONCLUSIONS

The projected growth in the debris environment will have a significant impact on future satellite operations. The probability of collision to on-orbit satellites will increase by roughly an order of magnitude after 100 years. The required operational response for collision avoidance (COLA) with tracked objects will similarly increase, but this could be addressed by improvement in tracking accuracy. At certain altitudes within LEO, and depending upon the level of protection desired for a given satellite system, the direct probability or the COLA action frequency might not be acceptable. Other means of reducing the impact of orbital debris such as improved compliance with disposal requirements, debris removal, increased spacecraft survivability, or constraining missions to operate in regions of LEO with lower debris density may be necessary to mitigate the probability posed by the projected growth in debris.

In launch accessibility, establishing a threshold that the launch vehicle trajectory accuracy does not warrant will result in a situation where very few launch opportunities are closed and hence there is very little reduction of the average risk. Establishing a threshold too low, however, results in the opposite situation where too many launch opportunities are closed. Just as in the mission utility analysis, balance must be maintained between a low enough threshold that a significant reduction in average probability is obtained without closing too much of the window and not having so high of a threshold that the results do not add value to safety process.

REFERENCES

[1] A. B. Jenkin, M. E. Sorge, G. E. Peterson, J. P. McVey, B. B. Yoo, "100-Year Low Earth Orbit Debris Population Model," *AAS 11-410,* AAS/AIAA Astrodynamics Specialist Conference, Girdwood, Alaska, August, 2011.

[2] W. Ailor, J. Womack, G. E. Peterson, E. Murrell, N. Lao, "Effects of Space Debris on the Cost of Space Operations," 61st International Astronautical Conference, September 27, 2010, Prague, Czech Republic.

[3] D. Sibert, D. Borgeson, G. E. Peterson, A. B. Jenkin, M. E. Sorge, "Operational Impact of Improved Space Tracking on Collision Avoidance in the Future LEO Space Debris Environment," Advanced Maui Optical and Space Surveillance Technologies Conference, Maui, Hawaii, September 14-17, 2010.

[4] J.-C. Liou, "NASA's Long-term Debris Environment and Active Debris Removal Modeling Activities," Government Roundtable on Orbital Debris, International Conference on Space Debris Removal, December 7-9, 2009, Chantilly, Va.

[5] A. B. Jenkin, G. E. Peterson, "Collision Risk Management for Geosynchronous Spacecraft," *COSPAR02-A-00286,* 34th COSPAR Scientific Assembly, World Space Congress, Houston, Texas, October, 2002.

[6] A. B. Jenkin, "Effect of Data Quality on the Feasibility of Collision Risk Management," *Journal of Spacecraft and Rockets,* Vol. 41, July-August, 2004, pp. 677-683.

[7] R. G. Gist, D. L. Oltrogge, "Collision Vision: Covariance Modeling and Intersection Detection for Spacecraft Situational Awareness," AAS 99-351, AAS/AIAA Astrodynamics Specialist Conference, Girdwood, Alaska, July, 1999.

[8] G. E. Peterson, R.G. Gist, D. L. Oltrogge, "Covariance Generation for Space Objects using Public Data," *AAS 01-113,* 11th AAS/AIAA Space Flight Mechanics Meeting, Santa Barbara, CA, February, 2001.

[9] SpaceX Space Exploration Technologies, "Falcon 9 Launch Vehicle Payload User's Guide, Rev 1," SCM 2008-010, Rev. 1, 2008.

[10] United Launch Alliance, "Delta IV Payload Planners Guide," 06H0233, September, 2007.

[11] Lockheed Martin Corporation, "Lockheed Atlas Launch System Mission Planners Guide," CLSB-0409-1109, Rev 10a, January, 2007.

EFFECTS ON ORBIT DECAY
DUE TO CO$_2$ GROWTH IN THE ATMOSPHERE

C. C. "George" Chao,[*] Bernard B. Yoo[†] and Richard Walterscheid[‡]

This paper presents the results of a study of the effects on orbit decay due to the gradual increase in carbon dioxide (CO$_2$) in the atmosphere. In this study, we assume three types of estimates of CO$_2$ growth: (1) simple linear growth of 1.7% per decade, (2) three-stage linear model by Walterscheid, and (3) composite model of 2.9% per decade for solar minimum and 0.8% per decade for solar maximum. Based on the above models for CO$_2$ growth, effects on orbit lifetime of LEO spacecraft were estimated using a semi-analytic orbit propagation tool, LIFETIME. Orbit lifetime can increase from 5% to as large as 67% depending on initial orbit altitude, ballistic coefficient and launch date. The Inter-Agency Space Debris Coordination Committee (IADC) requires that a LEO spacecraft must reserve adequate fuel to lower the perigee at end of life for natural reentry due to atmosphere drag decay within 25 years. Thus, the significantly increased orbit lifetime will result in increased fuel requirement for ensuring the natural decay time of an active LEO spacecraft within 25 years at end of life.

INTRODUCTION

Due to the increase in atmospheric carbon dioxide (CO$_2$), the thermosphere will cool down and as a consequence the upper atmosphere density will gradually decrease. This was first shown in idealized calculations by Roble and Dichenson[1]. Since then observations and predictions with thermospheric circulation models confirm the phenomena[2,3,4,5]. The effects of CO$_2$ growth on orbit decay were first reported by Lewis[6], et al. in 2005 based on a linear model, 3 to 5% per decade in atmosphere density decrease rate, following Emmert et al. (2004)[3]. Their results suggest that orbital lifetimes can be extended by up to 24%, depending on altitude and solar activity. Their estimated average increases in debris population on 1 May 2101 are 30% for objects > 1 cm and 10% for objects >10 cm. Later in 2007, Oltrogge and Chao[7] in a simple simulation with a linear rate of 1.7% per decade in atmosphere density decrease concluded that the lifetime of a circular orbit at 800 km altitude with a pre-calculated ballistic coefficient is slightly less than 25 years due to drag decay without CO$_2$ growth. However, with the above assumed density decrease (1.7% per decade), the lifetime of the orbit increased by 7% and exceeded the 25-year orbit decay time requirement recommended by the Inter-Agency Space Debris Coordination Committee (IADC).

---

[*] Senior Engineering Specialist (Retired), Astrodynamics Dept., The Aerospace Corporation, 310 336-4295
[†] Engineering Specialist, Astrodynamics Dept., The Aerospace Corporation, 310 336-8574
[‡] Distinguished Scientist, Space Science Applications Laboratory, The Aerospace Corporation, 310 336-7352

Two studies by Marcos, et al.[8] and Qian, et al.[9] indicate that the average trends in atmosphere density decrease caused by CO_2 growth at 350 km and 450 km are 2.2% per decade and 2.9% per decade for solar minimum conditions, while at solar maximum, they are 0.7% per decade and 0.8% per decade, respectively. In a recent study, The Aerospace Corporation derived a three-stage linear model[10] for CO_2 growth based on observations of 27 space objects over four decades starting in 1961. Accurate predictions of both long-term (25-year) and short-term orbit decay required by space debris disposal call for an up-to-date analysis of the CO_2 effects based on more accurate estimates of CO_2 growth. This analysis also examines the impacts of CO_2 effects on fuel requirements for end-of-life disposal and orbit sustenance of LEO satellites.

ASSUMPTIONS

In this study, we assume the following three types of estimates for atmosphere density decrease induced by CO_2 growth.

- Simple linear change in atmosphere density of -1.7% per decade[6]
- Three-stage linear model by Walterscheid: -2% per decade below 200 km; -2 to -4 % linear between 200 km and 700 km; -4% per decade above 700 km
- Composite model of -2.9% per decade for solar minimum and -0.8 % for solar maximum

The first and third models of the above three models apply to all altitudes. The composite model is approximated by a simple sinusoidal function with 11-year cycle. The two peaks of the density rates equal to -2.9% and -0.8% per decade. Two atmosphere density models (Jacchia 71 and MSIS2000) are used with a 50th percentile of an 11-year solar cycle data file (Fig. 1). The data file was statistically determined from the daily measurements of solar flux index, F10.7, and geomagnetic index, Ap, in the past 6 cycles (longer than 64 years). The Aerospace Corporation semi-analytical orbit propagation tool, LIFETIME[11] is modified to simulate the density decrease caused by the above three types of CO_2 growth. The starting date for the CO_2 growth is assumed to be January 1, 1980.

SEMI-ANALYTIC PROGRAM FOR ORBIT PROPAGATION -- LIFETIME

The formulation of the semi-analytic theory used in LIFETIME was based on the work of Liu and Alford[12]. The averaged equations of motion including J_2, J_3, J_2^2, J_4, lunisolar gravity and solar radiation pressure are integrated with a step size of one orbit or larger. The atmospheric drag effects are integrated over each orbit using the Gaussian quadrature method. The short-period variations due to J_2 are recovered for computing the atmospheric density at the true altitude corrected for the Earth oblateness. This compact semi-analytical formulation has significantly improved the computational efficiency with desired accuracy as compared with numerical integration. LIFETIME computes the solar flux and geomagnetic index (F10.7 and Ap) from a built-in table of the 11-year cycle (Figure 1). The table repeats as needed by the orbit propagation. A user can select one of the three levels of percentiles (95%, 50% and 5%).

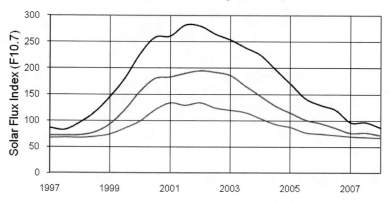

Solar Flux of one cycle assumed in LIFETIME 6.1
(blue=95%, red=50%, green=5%)

Figure 1 Statistically determined solar flux variations of a 11-year cycle

LIFETIME has been a major orbit analysis tool at The Aerospace Corporation for the past two decades for estimating orbit decay lifetime and stationkeeping fuel requirements. The precision of long-term orbit propagation has been periodically verified against numerical integration programs, such as TRACE[13]. TRACE is the trajectory analysis and orbit determination program developed and maintained by The Aerospace Corporation. The orbit propagator is a ninth-order Gauss-Jackson method with a Runge-Kutta starter. Table 1 shows the most recent comparison between the latest version (6.1) of LIFETIME and TRACE. The common epoch and initial orbital elements assumed in the comparison tests are, respectively, 2010/3/3/0., 100 deg (right ascension of ascending node), 200 deg (argument of perigee) and 30 deg (mean anomaly).

The values of ballistic coefficients, B, shown in Table 1 (column 1) are in m^2/kg following AIAA Astrodynamics Standards (B=CdA/M). Early conventions use the inverse of B for ballistic coefficients.

Table 1 Comparison of orbit lifetime computed by TRACE and LIFETIME 6.1

Mean Altitude Deg	Inclination	TRACE Days	LIFETIME Days	Difference days	Difference %
300 km (B=0.035 m^2/kg)	30	9.82	9.930	-0.11	1.1
400 km (B=0.070 m^2/kg)	40	40.035	40.22	-0.185	0.46
500 km (B=0.105 m^2/kg)	50	180.70	180.61	0.09	0.05
600 km (B=0.140 m^2/kg)	60	612.09	608.82	3.27	0.53

MSIS90 density model with constant F10.7 =150 and Ap =15 , 3rd body and solar radiation pressure

ORBIT SELECTION

A large population of LEO satellites reside in so-called sun-synchronous orbits, such as DMSP, NPOESS, and TOPEX missions. Therefore, for this analysis, the reference orbit is a sun-synchronous, circular orbit with a 6 am local time at ascending node. Based on this reference orbit, the epoch, initial altitude, and ballistic coefficient were varied.

Initial altitudes of 350 km to 850 km, in steps of 50 km, were selected. 350 km is representative of typical minimum operational orbit altitudes, including that of the International Space Station (ISS). 850 km is a representative altitude for sun-synchronous weather satellites. The selected orbits were simulated for the 2010, 2020, and 2030 epochs. 2010 is representative of satellites (and debris) in orbit at present. 2020 is representative of space missions in development at present, assuming a ten year lead time before launch. 2030 is a future projection.

Three sets of ballistic coefficients, 0.01, 0.03 and 0.09 m^2/kg, were simulated. This range of ballistic coefficient values is representative of many operational and non-operational man-made space objects. The object with a ballistic coefficient of 0.01 m^2/kg is representative of the ISS, while the value of 0.03 m^2/kg is representative of LEO weather satellites. The relatively large ballistic coefficient of 0.09 m^2/kg is assumed for a debris piece broken off from a spacecraft. Actual values of ballistic coefficients of debris pieces may be significantly larger than 0.09 m^2/kg depending on material and size of the debris piece. The corresponding lifetime will be considerably shorter and thus less important in the effect due to CO_2 growth (see results in the following section).

RESULTS OF ORBIT LIFETIME ESTIMATION

Long-term orbit lifetime estimations based on the above selected orbits and ballistic coefficients were generated using LIFETIME 6.1 with and without CO_2 growth. The three models of the CO_2 effect on atmospheric density discussed earlier were used. The primary purpose of this analysis is to estimate the increase in orbit lifetime from the 25-year decay guideline. Therefore, all the LIFETIME propagations are confined to no longer than 50 years. Furthermore, the above three models may no longer be valid beyond 2080, or 50 years after the last starting epoch in 2030.

Figs. 2-4 show the results from Model 1. Figs. 5-7 show the results from Model 2. Figs. 8-10 show the results from Model 3. Omitted data points represent cases when the orbit lifetime exceeded 50 years.

Fig. 11 illustrates how a delay into the next solar cycle causes the largest lifetime increases.

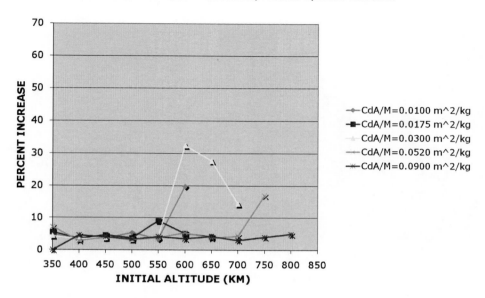

LIFETIME PERCENT INCREASE, MODEL 1, 2010 LAUNCH

Figure 2   Percentage increase in estimated lifetime due to CO_2 growth with 2010 launch (-1.7%/decade model)

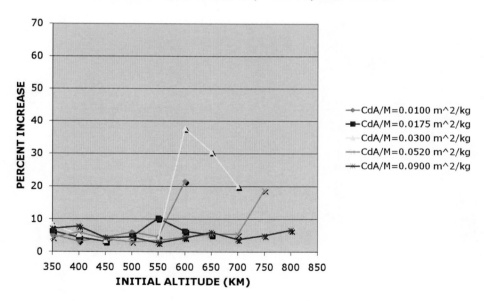

LIFETIME PERCENT INCREASE, MODEL 1, 2020 LAUNCH

Figure 3   Percentage increase in estimated lifetime due to CO_2 growth with 2020 launch (-1.7%/decade model)

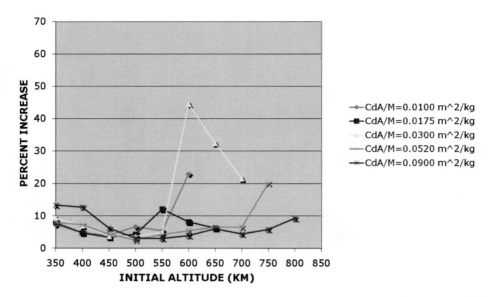

Figure 4 Percentage increase in estimated lifetime due to CO_2 growth with 2030 launch (-1.7%/decade model)

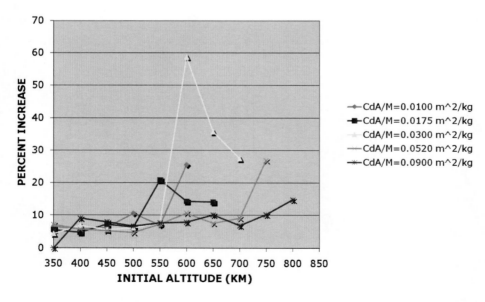

Figure 5 Percentage increase in estimated lifetime due to CO_2 growth with 2010 launch (3-stage model)

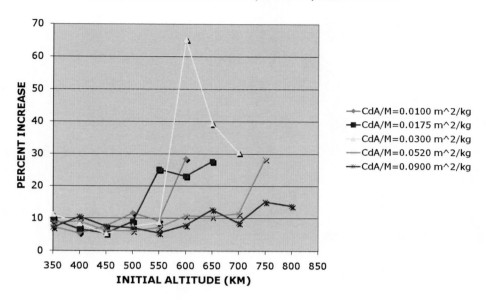

LIFETIME PERCENT INCREASE, MODEL 2, 2020 LAUNCH

Figure 6 Percentage increase in estimated lifetime due to CO_2 growth with 2020 launch (3-stage model)

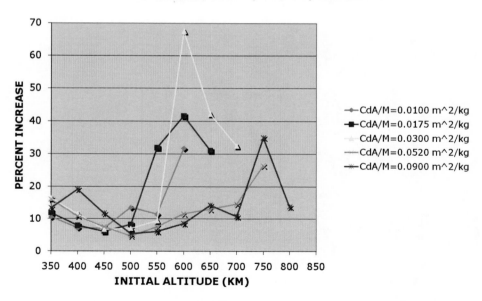

LIFETIME PERCENT INCREASE, MODEL 2, 2030 LAUNCH

Figure 7 Percentage increase in estimated lifetime due to CO_2 growth with 2030 launch (3-stage model)

223

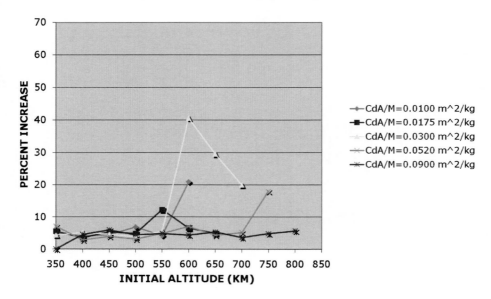

LIFETIME PERCENT INCREASE, MODEL 3, 2010 LAUNCH

Figure 8   Percentage increase in estimated lifetime due to CO_2 growth with 2010 launch (Solar cycle composite model)

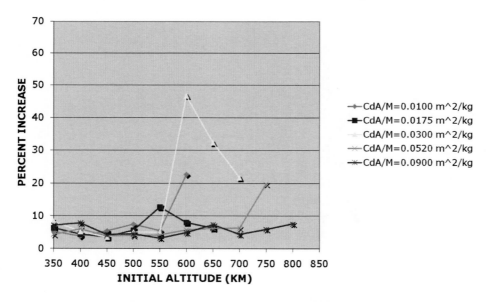

LIFETIME PERCENT INCREASE, MODEL 3, 2020 LAUNCH

Figure 9   Percentage increase in estimated lifetime due to CO_2 growth with 2020 launch (Solar cycle composite model)

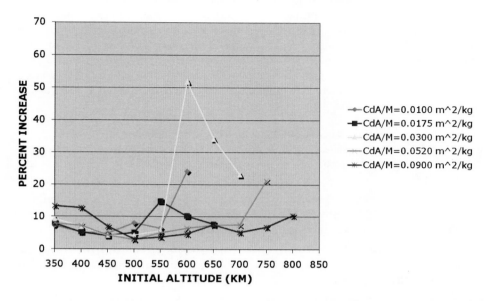

Figure 10   Percentage increase in estimated lifetime due to CO_2 growth with 2030 launch (Solar cycle composite model)

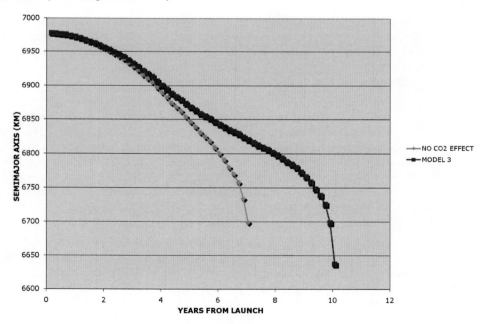

Figure 11   Decay history for 2020 launch, 600 km initial altitude, CdA/M=0.0300 m²/kg. The shape of the curve suggests the large increase is due to orbit decay delayed to next solar cycle.

Results from all three models share the following general characteristics:

- The longer the lifetime of the orbit without CO_2 effects, the larger the lifetime increase
- largest increases seem to occur in the 550 km to 750 km altitude range, the rapid decrease higher than 600 to 750 km is due to the truncation of lifetime at 50 years, therefore the results shown in the plots become meaningless when the altitude is higher than 600 km for CDAM less than 0.05 m^2/kg and higher than 750 km for larger values of CDAM
- 2030 launches show larger increase at all altitudes compared to 2010 and 2020 launches due to the accumulated density decrease

The largest lifetime increases range from 32% to 67%, depending on initial lifetime, CO_2 growth model and launch year. Later launch years produce larger increases, due to declining density. Model 2 (3-stage model) produces larger increases than Models 1 and 3, due to higher density reduction rates.

Note that the largest increase in lifetime may go higher than 67% if the 50-year orbit propagation limit is removed in LIFETIME. For cases with lifetime longer than 20 years, the relative phasing with the 11-year solar cycle can cause significant variations in lifetime.

For orbits with altitude below 550 km, most lifetime increases are less than 10%, but increase with later launch date. For 2030 launches, there is an increasing lifetime trend at the lower altitudes (350 km to 450 km) compared to 2010 and 2020 launches.

IMPACT ON FUEL REQUIREMENTS

The gradual decrease in atmospheric density due to CO_2 growth will have two kinds of impacts on fuel requirements for LEO satellites. The negative impact is that additional fuel is required in order to ensure the 25-year decay time at end of life. The positive impact will be the reduced fuel requirements for sustaining a LEO mission altitude. These two kinds of impacts on fuel requirements are illustrated by the following two examples.

For a typical sun-synchronous satellite at 800 km altitude with a ballistic coefficient of 0.035 m^2/kg, the estimated orbit disposal fuel requirement to ensure 25-year decay lifetime is 83 lbs, assuming a 3,500 lb spacecraft with an Isp of 230 seconds. Results of several LIFETIME runs indicate an 11-lb fuel increase due to CO_2 growth (3-stage model) when the end-of-life de-orbit maneuver takes place in March of 2011. The corresponding increases in fuel requirements for end-of-life maneuvers in March 2021 and March 2031 are 14 lbs and 16 lbs, respectively. The above example suggests that the CO_2 growth may require additional 13% to 19% fuel for end-of-life orbit disposal. The percentage increase may be considerably higher if the initial mission orbit is lower than 800 km.

For the positive impact, we use International Space Station (ISS) as an example. The estimated average ballistic coefficient (C_DA/M) is 0.0097 m^2/kg with a total mass of 417300 kg. At an average altitude of 355 km, the fuel requirements per ten years with and without the CO_2 growth are determined from LIFETIME and plotted in Figure 12. The differences in drag makeup fuel requirements per decade among the three decades are due to the relative location of the peak of the 11-year solar flux cycles during each of the 10-year duration. The 3-stage Walterschied model (model 2) for CO_2 growth gives the largest reduction in fuel requirement.

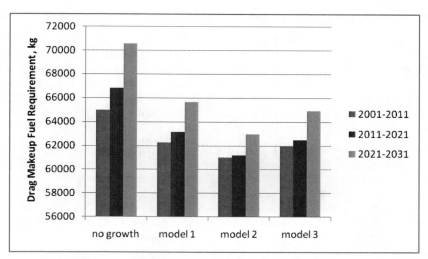

Figure 12 Estimated total drag makeup fuel required for maintaining ISS for the three decades from 2001 to 2031 with and without CO_2 growth

Figure 13 gives the net reductions in ISS fuel requirements for drag makeup for the three decades (2001 to 2031) with simulated CO_2 growth. The largest reduction is little over 10% or 7500 kg for the decade of 2021to 2031 with the 3-stage model. Even with the most conservative assumption (1.7% per decade by model 1), the fuel reduction can range from 4.3% to 7.6 %. In general, the saving in fuel cost may be significant, the benefit is out-weighted by the more pronounced increase in fuel requirements for end-of-life de-orbit for all LEO satellites and the increased collision risks at LEO altitude.

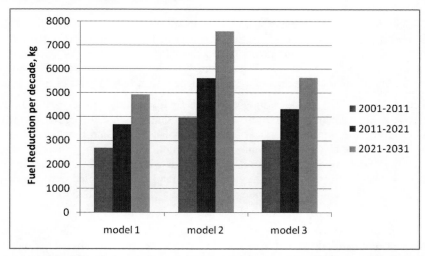

Figure 13 Estimated reductions in ISS drag makeup fuel requirements for the three decades from 2001 to 2031 with CO_2 growth

CONSIDERATIONS FOR IADC AND LEO MISSION ANALYSTS

The results of this study are in general agreement with the 2005 study by Lewis, et al.[6] Both studies are based on the assumption of linear growth of CO_2 in the future decades. Any change in the rate of growth will affect the results of orbit lifetime predictions. It is therefore recommended that IADC revises the LEO debris disposal standards or guidelines periodically in order to include any changes in atmosphere density on orbit lifetime estimation. It is also recommended that LEO mission designers and analysts should consider allocating additional fuel for ensuring the orbit decay within 25 years after end of life.

Considerations were also made for the uncertainties of orbit lifetime prediction due to solar flux (F10.7) and geomagnetic index (A_p) variations. For example, the lifetime of a typical sun-synchronous orbit with a initial altitude of 672 km and a ballistic coefficient of 0.035 m^2/kg is 21.8 years for a 50th percentile solar flux. The corresponding lifetimes for the 95th and 5th percentiles are, respectively, 3.2 years and 76.4 years. Table 2 shows a comparison of variations of orbit decay lifetimes of two sample orbits, one at 697.5 km altitude and one at 672 km. Both orbits are near circular with 51.6 deg inclination. The common epoch is June 1, 2011, 17:53:0.0 (UT). The atmosphere density model used in LIFETIME is MSIS2000.

Table 2 Orbit decay lifetimes in years from epoch (for 697.5 km orbit/for 672 km orbit)

CO_2 growth model	5th Percentile	50th Percentile	95th Percentile	Random Draw
No CO_2 growth	109.9/76.4	31.4/21.8	6.9/3.2	24.6/17.2
Simple linear	131.8/87.3	33.3/22.6	9.6/3.4	27.9/21.0
3-stage growth	198.6/107.1	35.0/23.6	10.4/3.8	32.8/22.1

The 10% to 67% increases in lifetime due to CO_2 growth are well within the above range, between 5th and 95th percentiles. However, the lifetime increase due to CO_2 growth is deterministic while the uncertainties due to solar flux and geomagnetic index fluctuations are probabilistic. It is unlikely that the daily values of the solar flux or geomagnetic index will remain in the 95th or 5th percentile longer than one 11-year cycle, let alone 25 years (more than two 11-year cycles).

As discussed in Reference 7, a random draw approach for predicting future solar flux and geomagnetic index is a different option to consider. Rather than attempt to predict a 'mean' curve, which would ignore the highly non-linear aspects of solar storms and quiet periods, the suggested approach is to utilize historical $F_{10.7}$ and A_p (geomagnetic) data directly, thereby retaining the wide variability and non-linearity of the data. Note that we already have more than five solar cycles of data to choose from. Processing of this data maps each coupled and correlated triad of datum ($F_{10.7}$, $F_{10.7}$ Bar, and A_p) into a single solar cycle range of 10.82546 years (3954 days).

After implementing this historical data, mapped into a single solar cycle, we then use random draws upon the number of data triads available on any day within the single solar cycle. Since we have accumulated daily data since the February 14, 1947[7], on any given day within the 3954-day solar cycle we have at least five data triads to choose from. It is important that the random draw retains the integrity of each data triad, since $F_{10.7}$, $F_{10.7}$ Bar and A_p are interrelated. It is interesting to note that the estimated lifetimes of the two sample orbits using the random draw method match reasonably well with that computed by the 50th percentile for all the cases with or without the CO_2 growth (Table 2).

CONCLUSIONS

Based on three different models for CO_2 growth, effects on orbit lifetime of LEO spacecraft were estimated using a semi-analytic orbit propagation tool, LIFETIME. Orbit lifetime can increase from 5% to as large as 67% depending on initial orbit altitude, ballistic coefficient and launch date. The Inter-Agency Space Debris Coordination Committee (IADC) requires that a spacecraft must reserve adequate fuel to lower the perigee at end of life for natural reentry due to atmosphere drag decay within 25 years. Thus, the significantly increased orbit lifetime will result in increased fuel requirement for ensuring the natural decay time of an active LEO spacecraft within 25 years at end of life. An example using a typical sun-synchronous orbit at 800 km altitude shows an increase in fuel requirement of 13 to 19% depending on starting year. Furthermore, the delayed reentry of a LEO spacecraft or debris object will increase the population density in the LEO region and thus increase the collision risks of future launches and LEO satellites.

On the positive side, the atmosphere density decrease due to CO_2 growth results in reductions in ISS fuel requirements for drag makeup. The largest reduction is little over 10% for the decade of 2021to 2031 with the 3-stage model. Even with the most conservative assumption (1.7% per decade by model 1), the fuel reduction can range from 4.3% to 7.6%. In general, the saving in fuel cost may be significant, the benefit is out-weighted by the more pronounced increase in fuel requirements for end-of-life de-orbit for all the LEO satellites and the increased collision risks at LEO altitude.

ACKNOWLEDGEMENTS

This work reflects research conducted under U.S. Air Force Space and Missile Systems Center (SMC) Contract FA8802-09-C-0001 and sponsored by Mr. Thomas Huynh of SMC/ENE. Special thanks are due to colleagues of The Aerospace Corporation, John Cox, Alan Jenkin and Glenn Peterson, for their review and comments of this paper.

REFERENCES

1. Roble, R.G., and R.E. Dickinson (1989), "How will changes in carbon dioxide and methane modify the mean structure of the mesosphere and thermosphere?", *Geophys. Res. Lett.*, 16(12), 1441-1444.
2. Emmert, J.T., J.M. Picone, J.L. Lean, and S.H. Knowles (2004a), "Global change in the thermosphere: Compelling evidence of a secular decrease in density", *J. Geophysi. Res.*, 109, A02301, doi:10.1029/2003JA010176.
3. Emmert, J.T., J.M. Picone, J.L. Lean, and S.H. Knowles (2004b), Correction to "Global change in the thermosphere: Compelling evidence of a secular decrease in density", *J. Geophysi. Res.*, 109, A04307, doi:10.1029/2004JA010462.
4. National Oceanic and Atmospheric Administration (NOAA 2010), Global Monitoring Division, *Trends in Carbon Dioxide*, http://www.esrl.noaa.gov/gmd/ccgg/trends
5. Picone, J.M., A.E. Hedin, D.P. Drob, and A.C. Aikin (2002), "NRLMSISE-00 empirical model of the atmosphere: Statistical comparisons and scientific issues", *J. Geophys. Res.*, 107(A12), 1468, doi:10.1029/2002JA009430.
6. Lewis, H. G., G. G. Swinerd, C. S. Ellis, and C. E. Martin, "Response of the Space Debris Environment to Greenhouse Cooling," *Proceedings of the Fourth European Conference on Space Debris*, Darmstadt, Germany, 18-20 April 2005 (ESA SP-587, August 2005).

7. Oltrogge, D. L., and C. C. Chao, "Standardized Approaches for Estimating Orbit Lifetime after End-of-Life," AAS Paper 07-261, *Proceedings of the AAS/AIAA Astrodynamics Specialist Conference* held in Mackinac, Michigan, August 19-23, 2007.

8. Marcos, F. A., J. O. Wise, M. J. Kendra, N. J. Grossbard, and B. R. Bowman, "Detection of a long-term decrease in thermospheric neutral density," *Geophys. Res. Lett.*, 32, L04103, doi:10.1029/2004gl021269.

9. Qian, L., R. G. Roble, S. C. Solomon, and T. J. Kane (2006), "Calculated and observed climate change in the thermosphere, and a prediction for solar cycle 24", *Geophys. Res. Lett.*, 33, L23705, doi:10.1029/2006GL027185.

10. Chao, C. C., R. Walterscheid, and B. B. Yoo, "Modeling the Effect of Thermospheric Changes on Satellite Orbit Lifetime," *Crosslink*, The Aerospace Corporation magazine of advances in aerospace technology, Summer 2011 Vol. 12 No.1.

11. Chao, C. C. and M. H. Platt, "An Accurate and Efficient Tool for Orbit Lifetime Predictions," AAS Paper 91-134, *Proceedings of the AAS/AIAA Spacecraft Mechanics Meeting*, Houston, TX, 11-13 February 1991.

12. Liu, J. J. F., and R. L. Alford, "Semianalytic Theory for a Close-Earth Artificial Satellite," Journal of Guidance and Control, Vol. 3, No. 4, July-August 1980.

13. Downs, W. D. III, et al., "TRACE Trajectory Analysis and Orbit Determination Program, Vol. VII: Usage Guide," The Aerospace Corporation Report SAMSO-TR-71-141, 31 May 1974.

GETTING TO KNOW OUR SPACE POPULATION FROM THE PUBLIC CATALOG

Daniel L. Oltrogge[*] and T.S. Kelso[*]

Our space population continues to increase as satellites are launched and de-bris-producing catastrophic events occur. For operators and policy makers, a periodic examination of the publicly available space population is useful. In this paper, bivariate distributions and visualizations of orbital elements and simple spatial density metrics clearly delineate regions of higher collision risk. For the highest risk region, benefits obtained by application of ISO orbital de-bris mitigation standards are discussed. Application of concentric spherical zone "Ring Shells" governed in latitude by object maximum latitude distribution helps provide a more realistic spatial density and collision probability picture compared with previous analyses.

INTRODUCTION

The space population continues to increase at an unsteady rate, averaging roughly 300 new Resident Space Objects (RSOs) per year according to publicly-available, historical Non-Cooperative Tracking (NCT) data. As shown in Figure 1, this RSO increase has experienced

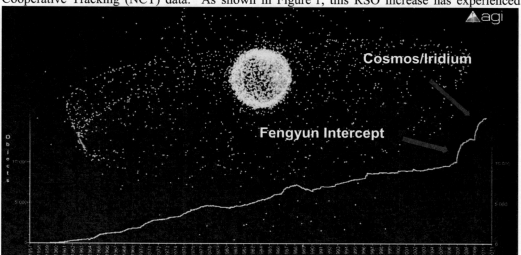

Figure 1. Evolution of the Resident Space Population from 1957 to Present

[*] Senior Research Astrodynamicist, AGI's Center for Space Standards and Innovation, 7150 Campus Drive, Suite 260, Colorado Springs, CO 80920.

growth spurts due to catastrophic debris-creating events such as the Iridium/Cosmos collision in 2007 and the Fengyun ASAT intercept in 2008.

This fresh examination of the space population was undertaken on behalf of the Space Data Association Ltd. (SDA), a non-profit organization that brings together satellite operators who value the controlled, reliable and efficient data-sharing that is critical to the safety and integrity of the space environment and the Radio Frequency (RF) spectrum. The SDA was founded by Inmarsat, Intelsat and SES — three of the leading global satellite communications companies. By collecting and analyzing definitive SDA Member RF, Conjunction Assessment (CA), ephemeris data, the SDA's Space Data Center (SDC) is able to perform Space Situational Awareness and threat mitigation analyses with previously unachievable accuracy. Currently, the SDA membership spans both GEO and LEO regimes, with over sixty percent of GEO satellites operated by SDA members.

DATA SOURCES

The space population was characterized using on-orbit (i.e., non-decayed) RSOs, based upon the 22 February 2011 Satellite Catalog maintained at www.CelesTrak.com. A variety of single and bivariate distributions were then taken of the data, including:

- Perigee Versus Apogee Altitude Distribution
- Maximum Latitude Versus Altitude Distribution
- Origination Year Versus Altitude Distribution
- Spatial Density Versus Altitude Distribution
- Eccentricity Versus Altitude Distribution
- RCS Versus Altitude Distribution
- Inclination Versus Altitude Distribution
- Collision Probability Versus Perigee and Apogee Altitudes

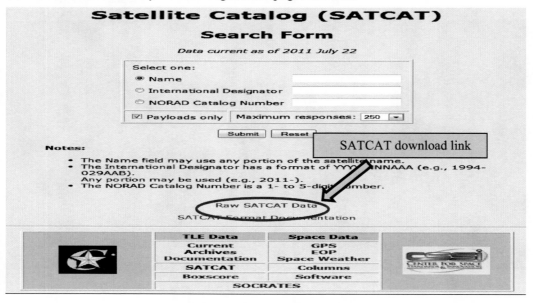

Figure 2. CelesTrak SATCAT download link

232

SPACE POPULATION DISTRIBUTION BY ALTITUDE

By accumulating the distribution in satellite perigee and apogee altitudes, the entire space population can be categorized. The resulting perigee-vs-apogee distribution for the public space population is shown in Figure 3 and Figure 4.

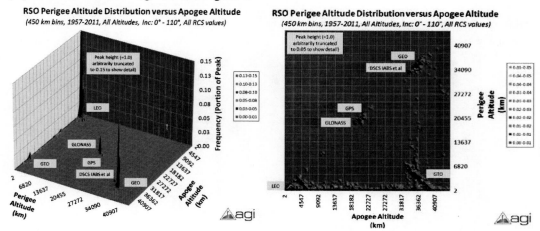

Figure 3. Space Population Perigee-vs-Apogee Distribution (3D)

Figure 4. Space Population Perigee-vs-Apogee Distribution (2D)

Altitude Distribution Statistics

It is also of interest to examine the minimum, median and maximum perigee altitude values as a function of apogee altitude, as shown in Figure 5.

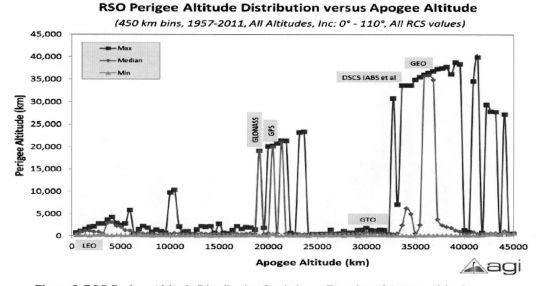

Figure 5. RSO Perigee Altitude Distribution Statistics as Function of Apogee Altitude

LEO ALTITUDE DISTRIBUTION STATISTICS

The Low-Earth Orbit (LEO) regime (altitude ranging from 0 to 2000 km) is characterized as shown in Figure 6 and Figure 7. In these views, the circular orbits (along the diagonal line, which defines a circular orbit) ranging from 450 to 1000 km are more heavily populated. Additionally, the Iridium and Fenyun 1C catastrophic debris-creating events can be clearly seen as bands of RSOs running along fixed apogee and perigee lines.

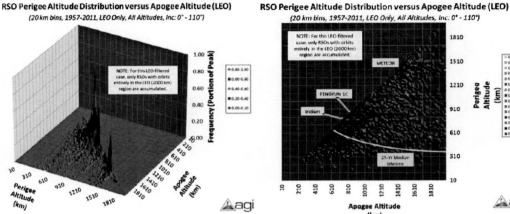

Figure 6. LEO Space Population Perigee-vs-Apogee Distribution (3D)

Figure 7. LEO Space Population Perigee-vs-Apogee Distribution (2D)

Figure 7 and Figure 8 show an enlarged view of the LEO regime, focusing upon the most highly populated regions. As was the case in Figure 7, the ISO Standard 25-year median orbit lifetime curve has been inserted corresponding to a ballistic coefficient[1] of $\beta = 181.6 cm^2 / kg$. The figure shows that the preponderance of LEO RSO population will remain on orbit for a very long time.

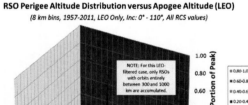

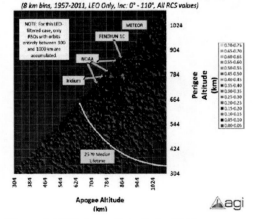

Figure 8. LEO Space Population Perigee-vs-Apogee Distribution (Zoom-in, 3D)

Figure 9. LEO Space Population Perigee-vs-Apogee Distribution (Zoom-in, 2D)

MEO ALTITUDE DISTRIBUTION STATISTICS

As Figure 4 showed, the Middle-Earth Orbit (MEO) regime is sparsely populated except for the GLONASS and GPS constellations. Accordingly, we focus our MEO examination on these two orbits as shown in Figure 10 and Figure 11. The GLONASS constellation is observed to be more tightly controlled in a circular orbit than the control in the GPS system.

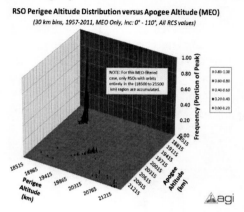

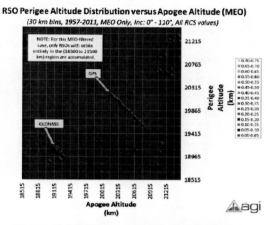

Figure 10. MEO Space Population Perigee-vs-Apogee Distribution (Zoom-in, 3D)

Figure 11. MEO Space Population Perigee-vs-Apogee Distribution (Zoom-in, 2D)

GEO ALTITUDE DISTRIBUTION STATISTICS

The Geosynchronous Earth Orbit (GEO) population distribution is shown in Figure 12 and Figure 13. In these plots, the large spike of GEO satellites is evident. A small spike of DSCS Integrated Apogee Boost Systems (IABS) and similar objects are seen below GEO altitude; these upper stages raised the satellite's orbit nearly to GEO and allowed the satellite to complete the ascent to its orbital station.

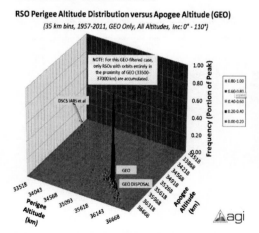

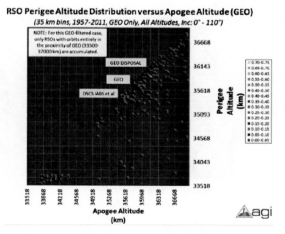

Figure 12. GEO Space Population Perigee-vs-Apogee Distribution (3D)

Figure 13. GEO Space Population Perigee-vs-Apogee Distribution (2D)

235

ORIGINATION YEAR DISTRIBUTION STATISTICS

One metric retained in the Space Object catalog is the origination year for the satellite or debris object of interest. This metric can be misleading: it is not the year that the object originated in space, but rather the year that the object was first deployed in space. Fragments that stemmed from a catastrophic debris-causing event (e.g. Fengyun-1C) are assigned the date of the Fengyun-1C deployment in space, as opposed to the actual debris-causing intercept.

It is interesting to observe the development of the various orbital regimes in Figure 14 and Figure 15. The year of occupancy for a given circular orbit can plainly be seen, in addition to the upper stages and boosters required to place the satellite in those circular orbits.

Major fragmentation events can be observed in Figure 16 and Figure 17, as attributable to Cosmos 2251 (launched in 1993) & Iridium (1997) collision and Fengyun Intercept events.

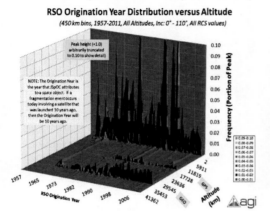

Figure 14. RSO Origination Year vs Altitude (3D)

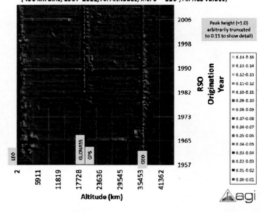

Figure 15. RSO Origination Year vs Altitude (2D)

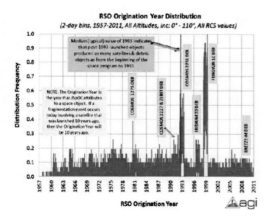

Figure 16. RSO Origination Year

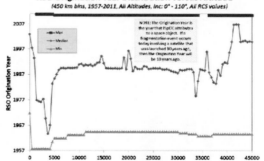

Figure 17. RSO Origination Year Distribution Statistics

236

CATALOG INTRODUCTION YEAR DISTRIBUTION STATISTICS

A more interesting and representative distribution is that of the Space Object catalog introduction date for each fragment. This is the year that the object was first introduced into the public space catalog. Fragments that stemmed from a catastrophic debris-causing event (e.g. Fengyun-1C) are assigned to the actual debris-causing intercept time.

The evolution of the various orbital regimes is shown in Figure 18 and Figure 19. The year of occupancy for a given circular orbit can plainly be seen, in addition to the upper stages and boosters required to place the satellite in those circular orbits. The dominant introduction of debris from major fragmentation events (2007 Fengyun-1C intercept and 2009 Cosmos 2251/Iridium 33 collision) can be observed. These debris events are also prominent features in Figure 20 and Figure 21.

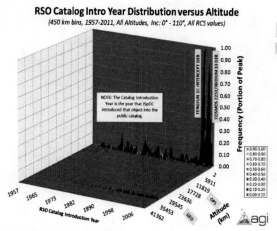

Figure 18. RSO Catalog Intro Year vs Altitude (3D)

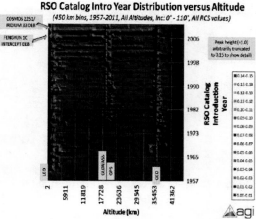

Figure 19. RSO Catalog Intro Year vs Altitude (2D)

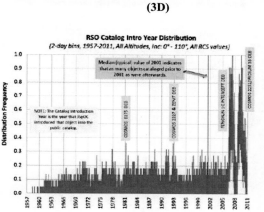

Figure 20. RSO Catalog Intro Year

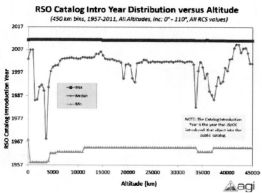

Figure 21. RSO Catalog Intro Year Distribution Statistics

237

ECCENTRICITY DISTRIBUTION STATISTICS

Eccentricity distributions readily separate circular orbits from both transfer & operational elliptical orbits, as shown in Figure 22 and Figure 23. Overall eccentricity distribution and related statistics are shown in Figure 24 and Figure 25.

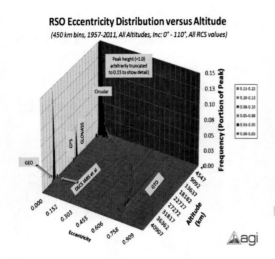

Figure 22. RSO Eccentricity Distribution (3D)

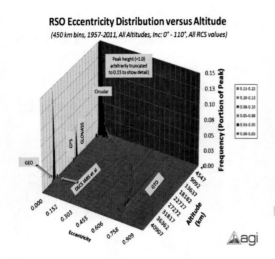

Figure 23. RSO Eccentricity Distribution (2D)

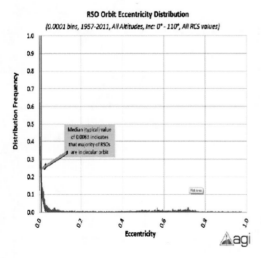

Figure 24. RSO Eccentricity Distribution

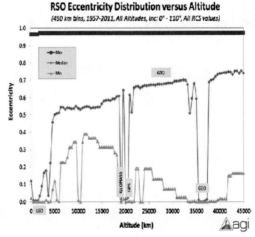

Figure 25. RSO Eccentricity Distribution Statistics

INCLINATION DISTRIBUTION STATISTICS

Inclination distributions readily differentiate between various constellations and launch site transfer orbits, as shown in.Figure 26 and Figure 27. Overall eccentricity distribution and related statistics are shown in Figure 28 and Figure 29.

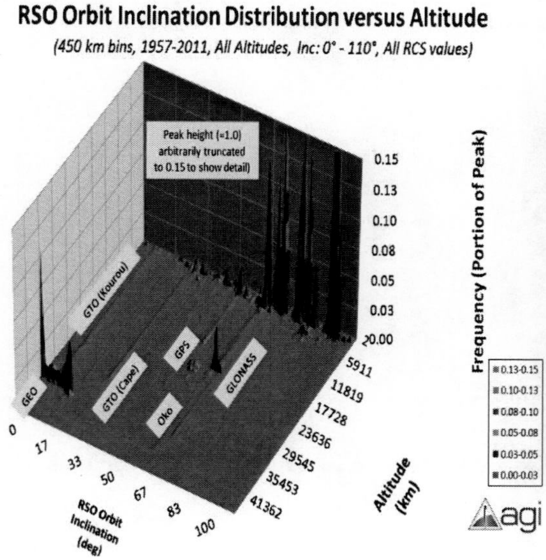

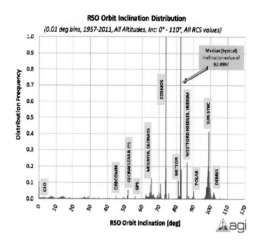

Figure 26. RSO Inclination Distribution (3D)

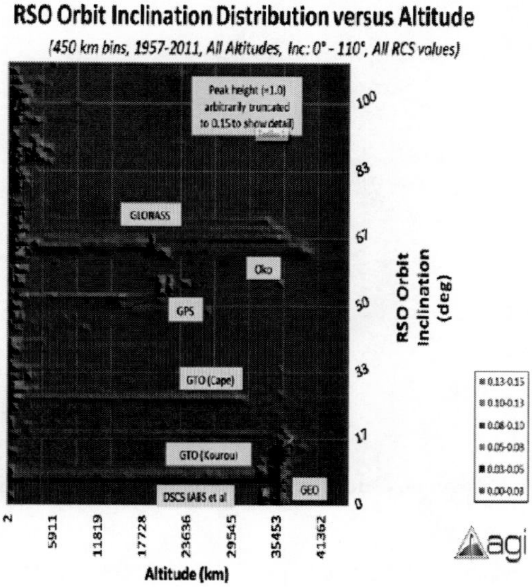

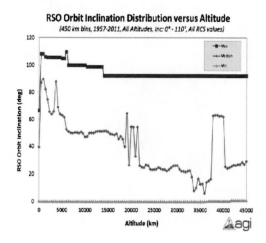

Figure 27. RSO Inclination Distribution (2D)

Figure 28. RSO Inclination Distribution

Figure 29. RSO Inclination Distribution Statistics

PERCENT OF SATELLITES THAT ARE OPERATIONAL

Using satellite operational status code from CelesTrak (Figure 32), the distribution in percent of Resident Space Objects that are operational can be determined (Figure 33). The chart is cropped at 0.15 so more detail can be shown. While debris dominates the percent of objects at LEO, while operational satellites comprise as much as thirty percent in the GEO regime.

SATCAT Operational Status

Operational Status	Descriptions
+	Operational
-	Nonoperational
P	Partially Operational
B	Backup/Standby
S	Spare
X	Extended Mission
D	Decayed
?	Unknown

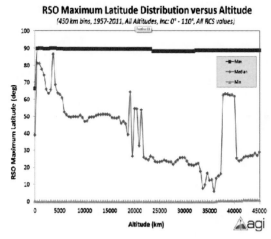

Figure 30. Operational Status Legend   **Figure 31. RSO Percent Operational Distribution**

MAXIMUM LATITUDE DISTRIBUTION STATISTICS

Maximum latitude distribution (Figure 30) and median value (Figure 31) provide a method to define "Ring Shells" for typical satellite spatial density calculations. We will use the median value of maximum latitude as a function of altitude in the next section.

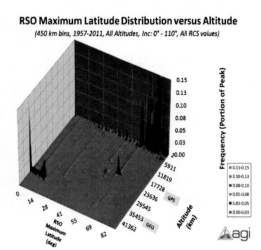

Figure 32. Maximum Latitude Distribution   **Figure 33. Maximum Latitude Distribution (1D)**

SPACE POPULATION SPATIAL DENSITY DISTRIBUTION STATISTICS

Spatial density has often been used to define the number of RSOs per unit volume as a function of altitude. This computation is performed by "flying" each satellite through concentric shells, and accumulating the portion of each orbit that flies through a given shell. After the entire space population is accumulated, the analyst can simply divide the number of objects contained within a concentric shell by the volume of the shell to yield spatial density at that shell's altitude, as shown in Figure 34.

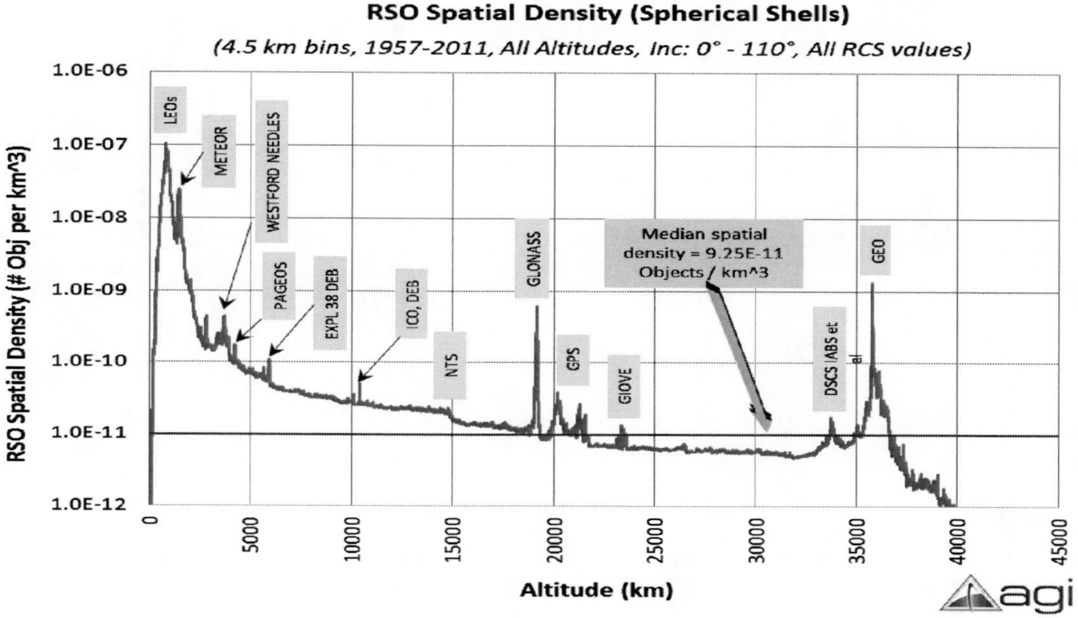

Figure 34. RSO Spatial Density Using Spherical Shells

The spatial density plot allows the user to readily identify various constituents of the space population, as the identification tabs show. The user can also see that the spatial density of the GEO population is several orders of magnitude below that of the LEO population.

However, by revisiting Figure 30 and Figure 31, we can see that the underlying assumption of spherical shells is flawed. Whereas in the LEO regime it is very common to get high orbit inclinations (yielding high maximum latitudes), it is rare to get high maximum latitudes in the GEO regime. Generalizing this observation, we see that dividing the population by a spherical shell volume is therefore misleading, because the objects don't really occupy the entire shell.

A more realistic approach is to adopt a "Ring Shell," defined to be a ring bounded by the upper and lower spherical zones spanning the latitude range between ± (maximum latitude). The result is shown in Figure 35. We can now observe that spatial density is actually slightly higher in the GEO regime than it is in LEO.

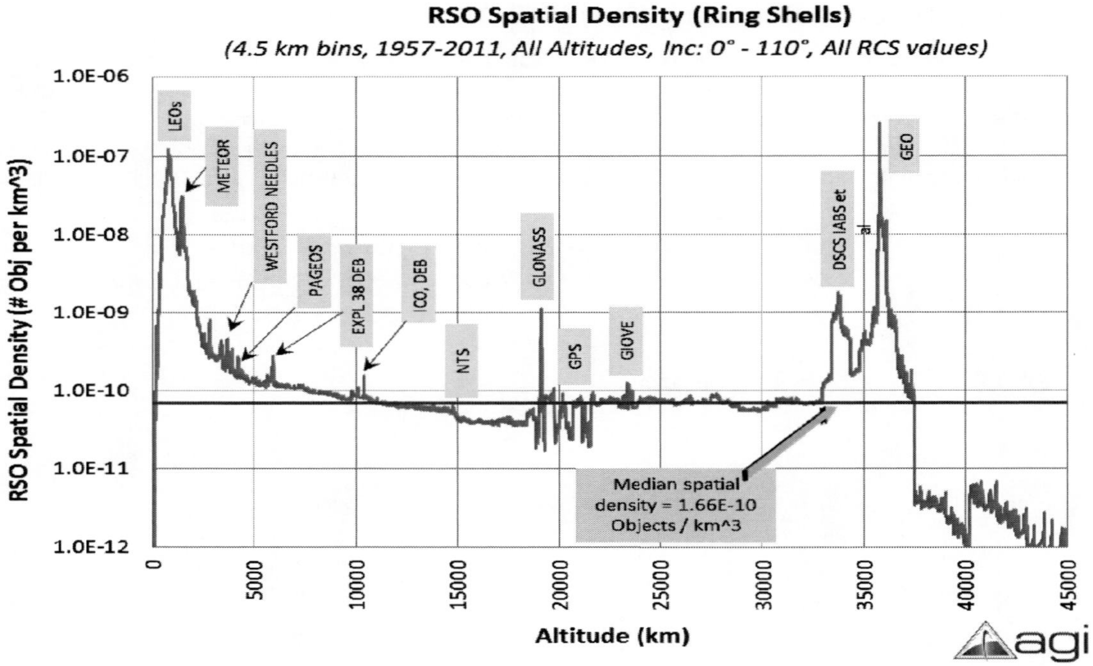

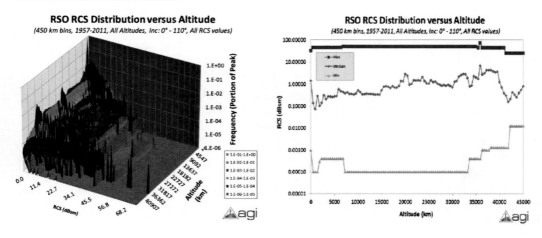

Figure 35. RSO Spatial Density Using Ring Shells

RADAR CROSS SECTION DISTRIBUTION STATISTICS

As shown in Figure 36 and Figure 37, Radar Cross Section (RCS) distribution exhibits a fairly uniform trend, with slight emphasis on tracking larger objects at GEO altitudes (as expected). Note in Figure 37 that a median RCS value has been obtained as a function of altitude; this profile will be used in the next section.

Figure 36. RSO RCS Distribution (3D)   Figure 37. RSO RCS Versus Altitude

242

COLLISION PROBABILITY DISTRIBUTION STATISTICS

By making additional assumptions and adopting the "Ring Shell" spatial density profile, we can now determine collision probability on an annual basis. The required simplifying assumptions are that: (1) the portion of time a primary object spends flying through each "Ring Shell" is dictated only by its flight path angle and altitude; (2) objects are randomly distributed throughout each ring; (3) objects that are flying entirely within the shell (e.g., GEO orbits) will transit the entire population.

It is the third assumption which is the most questionable, in that one could perform standard GEO stationkeeping maneuvers to ensure that one's GEO object does not fly past all the other GEO objects. Assumption #3 (above) is more valid for GEO debris collision probability estimations.

However, for the remainder of other RSOs, the above assumptions are considered to be fairly valid. Our goal is to obtain reasonably accurate average collision probability values from which overall observations can be made.

The results are shown in Figure 38 and Figure 39. An obvious result is that even though we concluded that GEO spatial density was higher than that of LEO, the resultant collision probability at GEO is more than an order of magnitude lower than that of LEO. This occurs because GEO objects only have one orbit per day, whereas LEO objects can have more than 15 orbits per day.

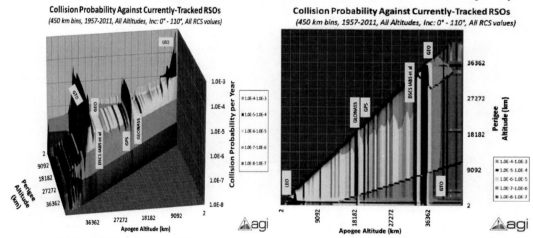

Figure 38. Space Population Perigee-vs-Apogee Distribution (3D)

Figure 39. Space Population Perigee-vs-Apogee Distribution (2D)

ORBIT DISTRIBUTION STATISTICS FACILITATE HYPOTHETICAL CATALOGS

Hypothetical space object catalogs that are significantly larger than our current public-tracked space population allow the space analyst to assess network loading, sensor availability, and model sensor resolution as a function of assigned object sizes. In order of increasing sophistication (and, perhaps, realism), the three principal ways of developing such a catalog are to:

(1) Examine the existing space population distribution (spanning orbital elements) and simply introduce additional (smaller) debris objects that are consistent with that population;

243

(2) Adopt a debris model (such as Master) and use a "splash plate" analysis[2] or a gridded cell population to create a complete catalog (either starting with the null set or the existing catalog) that is consistent with that model;

(3) Retain the large space objects currently in the catalog, gather up all known information on all known breakups and explosions (NASA debris digest, etc.), and then run a program such as DEBBIE to model each collision and explosion. Each event will provide several dials/knobs that one could control to provide an overall catalog (after incorporating rapid orbital decay estimation, as DEBBIE does) that matches the desired catalog size.

The statistical distributions shown in this paper easily permit the construction of large hypothetical catalogs consistent with method (1) listed above. To build this catalog, the mean motion (n) distribution (revs/day) is constructed as a function of orbit altitude, across all orbits in the current TLE catalog. Simultaneously, distributions in {"Ecc","Inc","RAAN","w","BStar"} are collected as a function of the mean motion bins (i.e. dependent distributions as a function of the independent "n" distribution. The use of 1000 bins for all variables appeared to work well.

Then, random draws of percentile (0% - 100%) of the mean motion distribution were accomplished, which in turn identified the dependent variable distributions for the other orbital elements that were also randomly drawn upon for that identified mean motion bin. In doing so, representative random draws of the orbit population distribution are achieved that reflect where space objects actually are instead of arbitrarily selection. Mean anomaly was simply selected based upon random draw from 0 to 360 deg.

We recognize that the distribution of very small particles is not likely to match that of larger ones, but we feel that it probably matches them much better than it does a uniform distribution. Note that BStar may also be randomized outside of the current catalog's distribution, since small fragments typically will have different BStar terms by nature of being small.

Current limitation on single catalog size is 99,999 objects, since the current NORAD ID is limited to only 5 characters. Such a catalog has been produced and could be made freely available via www.CelesTrak.com. The authors also suggest that by replacing the current integer SSC scheme with an equivalent 5-character hexadecimal representation, catalog sizes containing as many as 1048575 RSOs (FFFFFh) could be realized.

CONCLUSIONS

The orbital characteristics of our current public space population have been explored. New approaches of computing spatial density and collision probability have been employed. It is felt that the resulting products more accurately portray conditions in space, facilitating a better understanding of relative collision risk as a function of orbit regime, date and orbital characteristics.

FUTURE WORK

Since the space environment is ever-changing, it is proposed that these types of studies be periodically updated to maintain currency. Improvements in space surveillance technology may lead to dramatic evolution of knowledge of our space population, which may require "unscheduled" updates in addition to our regular analysis frequency.

ACKNOWLEDGMENTS

The authors wish to thank AGI's CSSI technical experts for their insightful comments and review of this paper.

REFERENCES

[1] Finkleman, D. and Oltrogge, D.L., "Twenty-five Years, more or less: Interpretation of the LEO Debris Mitigation 25-Year Post-Mission Lifetime Guideline", AIAA/AAS Astrodynamics Specialist Conference, Toronto, CA 2010, 14 Aug. 2010.

[2] Vance, L. and Mense, Allan, "Updated Value Analysis for Orbital Debris Removal: The Business Case", Raytheon, IAC-10.A6.2.12, 27 Sept. 2010.

LASER TRACKING OF SPACE DEBRIS FOR PRECISION ORBIT DETERMINATION

Craig Smith,[*] Yue Gao, Jizhang Sang, Ben Greene

The relatively high levels of uncertainty in orbit predictions available from the current space surveillance and tracking systems has been established as the primary cause of the failure to predict (and avoid) the recent space crash between an active (Iridium) telecommunications satellite and a large debris object (a defunct Cosmos spacecraft). The most effective solution to this problem is by making significantly higher accuracy observations of satellite orbits.

Incorporating laser tracking systems into the existing network offers an alternative approach to radars that could potentially provide high-precision orbit updates for critical objects. EOS laser tracking systems use a short pulse laser range finder system and have already demonstrated the basic ability to track small space objects (< 10 cm diameter), and determine their location in space to within a few meters.

This paper describes the laser tracking systems and provide some results from the tracking demonstrations and precision orbit determinations. Also described are some upgrades that are currently being undertaken to extend the performance of the system and provide full automation of the tracking station operations.

INTRODUCTION

The use of orbital space over the past 50 years has led to a growing hazard to navigation due to the risk of collision with space debris. Various NASA and ESA studies estimate that there are between 200,000-600,000 uncontrolled objects of 1cm diameter or greater in Low Earth Orbits (LEO). Each of these debris objects is capable of causing catastrophic damage should a collision occur with an active satellite. The US North American Aerospace Defence (NORAD) system uses a suite of radars to track a number of the larger debris objects and orbit predictions generated from these tracks are used to assess likely conjunctions (collisions) between space objects. If feasible, active satellites maneuver to avoid potential collisions.

The recent Chinese ASAT demonstration significantly added to the number of debris objects, which are now approaching the saturation limits of current space surveillance assets. Further-

---

[*] EOS Space Systems Pty Limited, EOS House, Mt Stromlo Observatory, Cotter Road, (Locked Bag 5000), Weston Creek, ACT, 2611, Australia

more, the failure to predict the recent collision between an active Iridium satellite and a large debris object (Cosmos) has shown that the orbits predictions generated from current radar data alone do not provide sufficient accuracy to reliably predict collisions. Certainly a means to improve the accuracy of satellite and debris orbit predictions is required if future collisions are to be predicted and the loss of critical defense assets avoided.

Furthermore, developments in space technologies in developing nations has meant that there are now capabilities for proximity operations and maneuvers [potentially unfriendly] occurring between critical space assets and space craft of potential adversaries. Many of these operations are undetectable or without sufficient resolution to evaluate the nature of the operation using existing SSA capabilities alone.

Over the past 20 years, Electro Optic Systems (EOS) has developed techniques using active laser tracking to provide extremely accurate (~1m) measurements of space debris locations and propagation of satellite orbits to significantly enhance the accuracy of orbit predictions and satellite conjunctions. This ability to accurately track debris objects with lasers was presented to US and Australian Defence Forces during two demonstrations (RazorView in 2004 and NEOT in 2005).

The accuracy of this tracking capability provides a potential capability to significantly improve orbit determination accuracy from important objects, reducing risk of accidental or deliberate collisions or other interference with operational satellites.

In its current configuration the laser tracking system takes an indirect radar cue, in the form of a NORAD generated two-line-element (TLE) orbit. However, the accuracy of orbit prediction from the radar TLE is not sufficient to allow the precision laser tracker to find the target (due to the narrow pencil beam of the laser) and so an additional acquisition system is employed. The acquisition system in use is a visible wide field camera, which provides excellent search and guidance capabilities, but its operation is limited to terminator conditions, when debris objects remain sun-illuminated in a dark sky. The laser tracking system itself does not have the same constraints and can track objects day or night, provided the target can be located under the laser boresight.

It is proposed that rather than taking indirect radar cues (from a TLE) the laser tracking system could be provided with direct cueing from a space surveillance radar. Real-time provision of angles, ranges and range rates from the radar should provide a much better hand-off to the laser tracker making day/night laser tracking of radar cued objects feasible. The integration of radar and laser tracker combines the strengths of each system (volume search of radar and precision track of laser), while using complementary capabilities to negate respective limitations.

ACTIVE E/O (LASER) SPACE DEBRIS TRACKING

System Overview

EOS has developed passive and active electro-optic (E/O) techniques for the tracking and precision orbit determination of satellites and space debris. The laser tracking system uses a visible light acquisition/targeting system and an infrared laser tracking system to track objects smaller than 10 cm in diameter, with unprecedented accuracy (<1m ranging). To accomplish this EOS has developed a number of technologies including telescopes, lasers, timing systems, combined by a layer of systems integration and control that makes it possible to deliver and detect energy in a precise way.

Critical components of the system include:

(i)   An acquisition system capable of detecting small debris objects and guiding them onto the laser bore-sight for ranging.

(ii)   A telescope and enclosure to provide accurate and stable beam delivery.

(iii)   A high power laser generating precisely controlled pulses of energy that are directed to the target by the beam delivery system.

(iv)   A detection and timing system able to detect single photons returning from the target and measure the time travel to pico-second accuracy.

(v)   Orbital determination software to generate accurate orbits.

The EOS Space Debris tracking system was successfully proven in formal demonstrations of capability (Project RazorView) in June-August 2004. The laser tracking prototype system developed at the EOS Space Research Centre located at Mt Stromlo is pictured below.

Figure 1. EOS Space Research Centre, as configured for the RazorView demonstration.

System Architecture

The debris tracking system is constructed from five basic sub-systems shown schematically in Figure 1.

1.   Target Acquisition System (TAS)
2.   Beam Locking System (BLS)
3.   High Energy Laser (HEL)
4.   Beam Delivery System (BDS)
5.   Ranging Transceiver System (RTS)

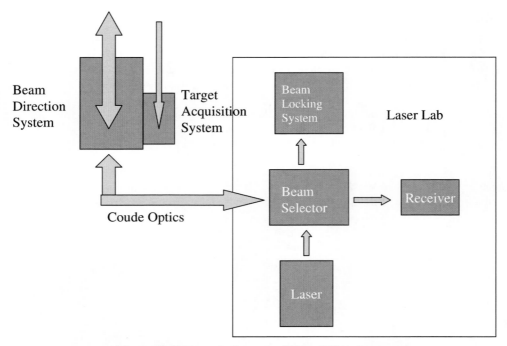

Figure 2. Schematic Layout of RazorView System

Each of the sub-systems in the Debris Tracking System is described separately below.

Target Acquisition System (TAS)

The TAS is used to detect a target and centre the target in the Beam Locking System field of view (FOV). The TAS uses a 35cm diameter f/0.75, wide field telescope and high sensitivity CCD capable of detecting moving debris objects fainter than 16-17 visual magnitudes, even against the strong Canberra sky background.. The camera optical design provides excellent image quality over a wide field for this very fast optical beam.

Beam Locking System (BLS)

The BLS is a high sensitivity CCD at the end of the 1.8m telescope Coudé path. This camera locks the visible target to the laser bore sight to sub-arcsecond accuracy. This camera is able to easily detect all targets seen in the TAS, having the advantage of a 1.8m diameter collecting area, but has a narrow field of view of ~2 arcminutes diameter on the sky. This camera drives the telescope and fast steering mirror servo loops.

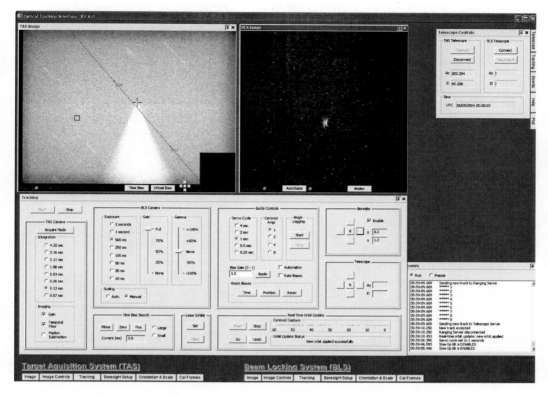

Figure 3. Typical screen showing TAS and BLS working in co-operation.

Upon initial acquisition the TAS has control of the telescope tracking servo system, until the target appear in the BLS FOV. At this point the TAS hands-off to the BLS for fine guiding and beam locking. A typical TAS display is shown in Figure 3.

The BLS also feeds angle data to the Real-Time Orbit (RTO) Engine. This system takes angles data from the BLS and re-computes the target orbit in real time, providing more stable target tracking and more lock time with the BLS. The real time orbit update system uses various orbital solution algorithms to determine the track of the satellite and provide an initial distance estimate to the ranging system.

High Energy Laser (HEL)

The HEL is the main ladar ranging laser. The HEL is an actively Q-switched, diode pumped Nd:YAG laser operating at 1.064um and providing 100W average power with 5ns pulses at 100 Hz.

The laser system is completely diode pumped with the design was based on a single frequency master oscillator, followed by multi-stage pre-amplifiers and multi-channel power amplifiers. The laser system also incorporates a number of advanced solid state laser technologies, such as phase conjugate mirror (Stimulated Brillouin Scattering cell), and imaging relays for high energy pulse lasers.

251

Diode pumping from the oscillator to the amplifiers improves the electro/optical conversion efficiency by an order of magnitude compared with conventional flashlamp pumped systems. The key challenge for developing high average power solid state lasers is the correction of thermal-mechanical distortions, including thermal lensing, mechanical stress, depolarization, and possible fractures in the solid state laser gain medium caused by the waste heat deposited into the laser gain medium by optical pumping. Again, compared with conventional flashlamp pumped lasers, the diode pumping produces much less heat, allowing the system to operate at high repetition rate and still maintain good beam quality, and beam pointing stability. Beam quality and stability are critical requirements for the system is to deliver the energy efficiently to the target. This laser provides beam quality of x1.2 Diffraction Limited and a beam pointing stability of less than 1 arc-second at 100 Hz.

The laser operation is fully automated under software control, and needs minimal maintenance. The laser typically used every night for 6 months or more before any maintenance or alignment is required.

Beam Delivery System (BDS)

From the HEL, the beam is expanded up and then conveyed by the Coude optics to the beam delivery telescope. This is a 1.8m high performance telescope in Mersenne (beam expander) configuration, installed in a 9m co-rotating IceStorm enclosure. The BDS system is configured to provide optimum throughput, using proprietary coatings, high laser damage resistance, minimal degradation of beam quality and high performance tracking capability for LEO targets.

The beam director telescopes are capable of providing absolute pointing of ~1.5 arcsec rms, anywhere on the sky and provide tracking (beam pointing stability) to better than 50milli-arcseconds rms over any 10 second period. The optical system is capable of providing 85nm rms wavefronts, though beam projection is limited by atmospheric turbulence. The beam quality degradation by the atmosphere is minimized by careful control of the thermal environment, as any differences between the temperature of the telescope optics and the air can lead to thermal plumes causing air turbulence. The telescope and enclosure minimize these effects by ensuring that air is able to flow through the enclosure and across the telescope. The enclosure is insulated to minimize day time heating and all of the telescope optics are light-weighted to ensure they are able to track the ambient temperature.

Ranging Transceiver System (RTS)

The RTS provides transmit and receive multiplexing, as well as time of flight measurements for the ranging pulses. The timing system provides timing accuracy of ~10 pico-seconds rms. The detectors are able to detect a single return photon from each laser pulse.

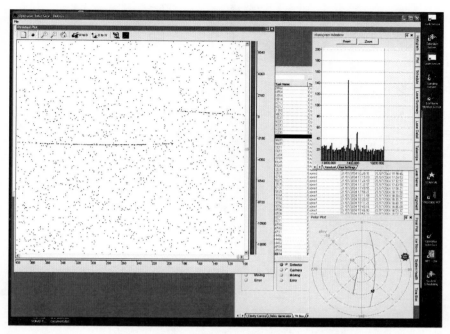

Figure 4. Typical track output from RTS. Other screens in thus view show the target trajectoryand telescope position (polar plot) and the range residual histogram.

A typical ranging display is shown in Figure 4. The ranging screen (upper left in Figure 4) shows the detected photon returns. Each dot represents a single photon detection of the target with ~1m range accuracy. The random dots are largely thermal noise in the detector, but the target track is a clear trace through the center of the frame. The axis are time on the abscissa (with 0 or current epoch at the lower right corner). The vertical axis shows the range residual, which plots the difference between measured and predicted range to the target measured in pico-seconds. The discontinuity in the trace shows where a real time orbit update has been completed and it is clear that the range residual is much closer to zero after the update, indicating a significantly improved orbit prediction.

The window behind the ranging screen shows the system autonomous scheduling (behind in upper right).

TRACKING ACCURACY

The absolute accuracy of the tracking system is measured by tracking Geodetic satellites that are also tracked by the world wide Satellite Laser Ranging (SLR) network that tracks objects to mm precision and provides reference orbits for Geodetic Satellites. EOS SLR stations also contribute data to this network.

In this case the Geodetic satellite LAGEOS was tracked and the differences between the range and alt/az positions as determined by the Debris Laser Tracking system compared with published orbits for LAGEOS (which are typically accurate to a few centimeters) were recorded (Fig 5 below).

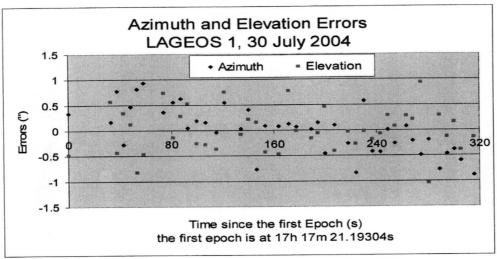

RMS Angular Error ~1.5 arcsec

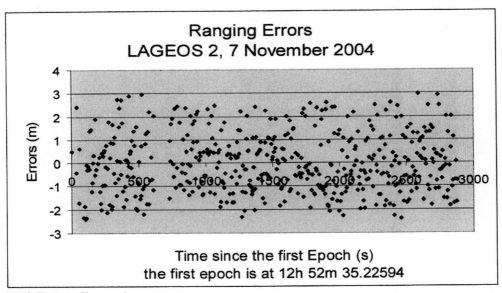

RMS Range Error ~1m

Figure 5. This figure shows the differences between the positions of Lageos as measured by the Debris tracking system compared with Lageos published orbit.

254

AUTOMATING LASER TRACKING

The capability to track debris objects with laser ranging techniques has been well proven. However, there remain a number of operational constraints that need to be addressed in order to transition to an operational capability. The operational constraints were that:

- the original demonstrations were not fully automated and had an operator in the control loop;

- the system's operations were restricted to the terminator periods (an hour or so before dawn and an hour or so after dusk where the ground site is in the dark but the satellite is still in the sun);

- limitations on emissions from high power lasers (eg the US Laser Clearing House).

Recently, EOS has been funded by the Australian Department of Innovation, Industry, Science and Research (DIISR) to help address some of the current operational limitations. The specific goals of this project are to provide an automated, user-ready capability available to support Australian and worldwide space surveillance needs. In particular, the project will develop and demonstrate fully remote, automated operation of a high performance tracking station for provision of responsive high-accuracy orbit determination. This will include the capability to provide scheduling of the Mt. Stromlo tracking system based on tasking instructions, laser emissions restrictions limitations and external cueing; and provide automated processing of the tracks to facilitate near-real-time delivery of observations. The current system will have improved optical performance permitting higher sensitivity observations;

Automation of Laser Tracking Systems

The original demonstrations of active tracking capabilities included an operator to control the system. This was considered essential at the time by all parties to ensure laser safety, correct identification of the target before laser illumination and responsiveness to variable conditions. However, an operational systems needs to operate 24/7 unattended for maximum efficiency and cost benefit. EOS proposes to add full automation to the existing debris tracking capability at Mt Stromlo. EOS has significant experience with autonomous systems such as the Satellite Laser Ranging (SLR) system constructed for GeoScience Australia (GA) and maintained and operated on GA's behalf. This is a completely autonomous system providing precision satellite tracking data to GA.

To achieve robust automated operation for a non-cooperative debris tracking system (compared with a cooperative SLR tracking system) it is necessary to generally improve the system sensitivity and then implement a major software upgrade that provides automated operation as well as the necessary safety and sensor input to the control systems that provide "robust" automation in all the various possible operating environments and modes. Upgrades will include increasing laser transmit power, power transmission efficiency, increased detector sensitivity, aircraft, cloud and weather monitors and well as system health and safety monitoring.

Terminator Constraints on the Acquisition System

As not previously the current debris tracking system uses a visible light acquisition system to guide debris targets under the laser boresight. This acquisition system is sensitive, fast and efficient, but is limited to terminator conditions (after sunset and before sunrise) where the shy background is dark but the orbital object remains sun-illuminated. The terminator periods typically provide around 4 hours per day (less for lower altitude object) of suitable tracking conditions for mid-latitude sites. Part of the upgrade program is to develop alternative cueing methods to allow the acquisition of objects outside of the terminator constraints.

One proposed technique is what we call "orbit bootstrapping" whereby a track of a debris object using the laser tracking system during terminator provides sufficient accuracy that we are then able to propagate the orbit forward for 24 hours and then re-acquire the object without resorting to the visual acquisition system (ie outside terminator). Provided the object is tracked daily should then be possible to maintain this level or orbit accuracy without the acquisition system.

Another technique to be explored is using an IR camera system to provide the initial acquisition system.

Finally it is planned to investigate the ability of a direct hand-off from a radar acquisition to the E/O tracker to provide precision orbit determination.

Limitations on Laser Emissions

Laser tracking systems with sufficient power to track non-compliant space debris objects can also represent a hazard to active satellites (with optical sensors) should the beam accidently strike an active satellite rather than debris target. Considering the very narrow beam of the laser tracking systems (~20 micro-radians) the probability of this is extremely low, but not negligible. In the US the Laser Clearing House monitors and limits such emissions. In order for an active E/O system to become a useful and responsive contributor to Space Situational Awareness, without threatening existing satellites, a real-time ability to determine the proximity of non-intended objects is needed. Such a system could evaluate the risk and limit emissions in real time.

EOS has been developing high-fidelity models of the known Earth/LEO space environment that are able to propagate all known satellite and debris orbits with high precision and in real-time. It is proposed to develop this system to provide automated laser emissions control to minimize the risk of accidental laser illumination of non-target space objects.

CONCLUSION

The ability to track space objects with high precision using E/O laser tracking techniques has been demonstrated. EOS is now working to transition this capability from a proof of principle experiment to an operationally useful capability. This will primarily involve automating all systems, including emissions safety and developing alternative cueing techniques to help remove terminator constraints on the acquisition and tracking of debris objects.

MITIGATING POTENTIAL ORBIT DEBRIS: THE DEORBIT OF A COMMERCIAL SPACECRAFT

Timothy Craychee[*] and Shannon Sturtevant[†]

In the spring of 2011, a commercial spacecraft (SSC Object #27838) performed a final maneuver that sent the spacecraft into Earth's lower atmosphere resulting in a reentry event that began over the southern Pacific Ocean. While it is not known if any spacecraft debris survived reentry, the design of the final orbit was such that potentially surviving debris would impact within a "safe zone" in the Pacific Ocean. The purpose of this paper is to report the deorbit trajectory design and implementation, which includes accommodating constraints and limitations of a vehicle whose design and mission never included a controlled deorbit.

INTRODUCTION

In 2010, a decision was made to perform a controlled reentry of a polar orbiting commercial satellite SSN #27838. This decision was prompted by the fact that the satellite's primary mission terminated in 2007 and the ground system being used to maintain contact with the vehicle was slated to be decommissioned. Instead of abandoning a functioning and commandable satellite in an orbit that would take years to naturally decay, posing an ongoing conjunction threat to other space objects and potentially exacerbating the increasing density of objects in the space environment, a decision was made to command a controlled deorbit of the satellite. However, it is significant to note that there was no mission or regulatory requirement to perform a controlled deorbit and the vehicle was not designed to support such an activity. Thus, there were many ground and space system limitations and constraints that needed to be accommodated as part of the successful execution of this controlled reentry. These factors, along with other requirements and guidelines, influenced the overall trajectory design and implementation. This paper presents both the original deorbit design as well as its evolution throughout execution.

INITIAL DEORBIT DESIGN

With the spacecraft nominal mission ending in March of 2007, the spacecraft continued to orbit without any maintenance maneuvers. This left the vehicle in a slightly decayed orbit from that of its original mission. The orbital parameters incorporated into the original deorbit design were obtained from a two-line element from CelesTrak[1] and are illustrated in Table 1.

---

[*] Senior Aerospace Engineer, Space Group, Applied Defense Solutions, 8171 Maple Lawn Blvd Fulton MD 20759
[†] Senior Mission Analyst, Independent, 3560 Otis St, Wheat Ridge, CO 80033.

Table 1. Initial Kozai-Izsak Mean Elements Derived from TLE

Elements	Initial Design State
Epoch (UTCG)	1/5/2011 12:00
Mean_Semimajor_Axis (km)	6808.404112
Mean_Eccentricity	0.001124
Mean_Inclination (deg)	97.034
Mean_RAAN (deg)	53.003
Mean_Argument_of_Perigee (deg)	83.149
Mean_True_Anomaly (deg)	6.351

Because initial orbit parameters identified the vehicle at an altitude above the International Space Station (ISS), the deorbit was designed to have two phases, referred to as Phase 1 and Phase 2 from here forward. Phase 1 was designed to lower the spacecraft to an approximately circular orbit with a mean radius below that of the ISS. Phase 2 followed and was designed to lower the periapsis altitude such that a reentry occurred with a specific impact location in the Pacific Ocean (detailed below).

The design utilized six burn activities for Phase 1 and five burn activities for Phase 2. Two days were incorporated between each maneuver to allow time for telemetry collection and analysis, burn calibration, and updates to future maneuver plans.

The two phase approach was a conservative strategy designed so that if, due to some unknown factor, any of the maneuver activities happened to be the last, the spacecraft would not be an immediate threat to another space object, with utmost attention given to the manned ISS. Once the design was finalized, the proposed deorbit plan was then submitted to regulatory agencies for government approval, which it received. The following sections provide more detail on each phase as designed.

Phase 1 Design

The Phase 1 design consisted of six burn activities. The first two were test activities including a checkout with a zero second burn duration and a 30 second calibration maneuver. The intention of the zero second maneuver was to test the command load generation procedure as well as to ensure that the spacecraft behavior matched simulation results. The calibration burn was designed to validate and finalize assumptions in models being used for maneuver planning, specifically those associated with the propulsion model. The remaining four activities were the primary burns used to lower the entire spacecraft orbit below that of the ISS, each with a 300 second burn duration. The reasons for implementing this approach were twofold:

- Minimize the time the spacecraft spends in an ISS crossing orbit.

- Adhere to an onboard constraint limiting maximum burn duration to 300 seconds.

Since the spacecraft's orbital radius would necessarily cross the ISS orbit no matter the deorbit strategy, the decision was made to lower the entire orbital radius below that of the ISS. This ensured that at the end of Phase 1 the spacecraft would no longer have the potential to conjunct with the ISS. However, an early-identified operational constraint required multiple burns to achieve this goal. In the earliest examination of the feasibility of a controlled deorbit of this vehicle, an onboard constraint was identified that limited the maximum commandable burn duration to 300 seconds. Therefore, circularization below the ISS required a four burn sequence following the two test activities of Phase 1.

The Phase 1 design is illustrated in Figure 1 and Figure 2. Figure 1 is a comparison of the orbit radii of the spacecraft and the ISS. Included in the figure are the four 300 second maneuvers that complete Phase 1. Upon completion of the third maneuver in the figure, the spacecraft and the ISS orbital radii overlap until the following maneuver, after which the orbital radii would no longer overlap.

Since the Phase 1 design included an overlap between the spacecraft and the ISS, the design utilized the synodic period between the two objects as a constraint. The synodic period is defined as the relative orbit period between the spacecraft and ISS. The first three maneuvers of Figure 1 increased the synodic period to over 100 days when the orbital radii overlap would occur (see Figure 2). This would allow for ample reaction time if an anomaly were to occur.

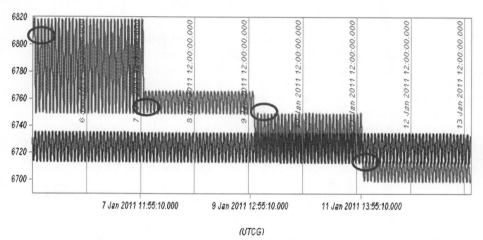

Figure 1. Phase 1 Design: Spacecraft (red) and ISS (blue) Orbit Radii in km

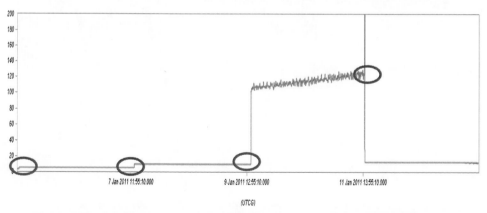

Figure 2. Phase 1 Design: Synodic Period between Spacecraft and ISS in days

Phase 2 Design

The Phase 2 design utilized five maneuvers to lower the orbit periapsis to reentry and also to align the impact area to the desired location, described in detail below. NASA-STD 8719.14[2] was only used as a guideline for the Phase 2 design. The standard states:

> "If the amount of debris surviving reentry exceeds the requirement, then either the ground impact point is modified by a post mission disposal maneuver or measures are taken to reduce the amount of debris surviving reentry. Options to consider include:
>
> a. Performing a controlled reentry. Maneuver the structure at EOM to a reentry trajectory with an effective perigee altitude no higher than 50 km to control the location of the reentry and ground impact points (see Section 4.6)."

Since a survivability analysis had not been performed, the trajectory was conservatively designed to lower the periapsis altitude to 50 km where a controlled reentry event would occur due to the drag force induced by Earth's atmosphere.

Phase 2 was still mostly designed to work within the confines of the 300-second burn duration limit however it was assumed that the onboard constraint would be increased prior to the final maneuver. The flight dynamics team was committed to revising the onboard limit so that the departure periapsis for the final burn could be maximized. This was desired to reduce risk associated with attitude control at low perigee altitudes. In addition, unlike Phase 1, Phase 2 maneuvers were designed to target specific post-maneuver periapsis altitudes that incrementally stepped the vehicle toward reentry. Targeting altitudes allowed flexibility in the overall deorbit design such that perturbations and uncertainties during operations could be easily absorbed by burn duration, which would be allowed to vary in subsequent maneuver planning. The design also allowed for the spacecraft state and heath to be evaluated in stages as it dipped deeper into the Earth's atmosphere. Maneuver timing was also a significant component of Phase 2 since the timing of the first maneuver was used to rotate the line of apsides to set the desired impact location, which also affected the burn durations required by the following maneuvers. The effect of the Phase 2 maneuvers on the orbital radius of the spacecraft can be seen in Figure 3.

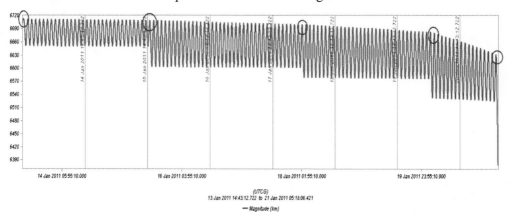

Figure 3. Phase 2 Design: Spacecraft Orbit Radius in km

A complete list of the Phase 1 and Phase 2 primary maneuvers as designed is shown in Table 2.

Table 2. Deorbit Design Maneuver Summary (Excluding Checkout and Calibration)

Maneuver Number	Start Time (UTCG)	Stop Time (UTCG)	Duration (sec)	Delta V (m/sec)	Fuel Used (kg)
1	1/5/2011 12:42	1/5/2011 12:47	300	15.553715	2.027
2	1/7/2011 13:22	1/7/2011 13:27	300	15.074523	1.954
3	1/9/2011 14:32	1/9/2011 14:37	300	14.645088	1.889
4	1/11/2011 14:37	1/11/2011 14:42	300	14.257949	1.83
5	1/13/2011 15:14	1/13/2011 15:19	300	13.907042	1.776
6	1/15/2011 15:32	1/15/2011 15:37	300	13.587404	1.727
7	1/18/2011 2:04	1/18/2011 2:07	150	6.68247	0.846
8	1/20/2011 3:21	1/20/2011 3:26	298.503	13.092829	1.652
9	1/21/2011 4:28	1/21/2011 4:40	671.34	28.542039	3.574
		Totals:	2919.843	135.343058	17.274

Preliminarily Identified Contingencies

As part of the design phase, preliminary contingencies were identified along with steps necessary to address them if possible. Those contingencies were:

- The inability to perform maneuvers
- Loss of X-Band communications capability
- Loss of spacecraft attitude control (tumble event)

In the event that the spacecraft was unable to perform subsequent maneuvers, the flight dynamics team imposed planning requirements to ensure risk to other spacecraft was minimized. The first requirement was to screen each maneuver plan for conjunctions up to four days following execution. If a conjunction of concern was identified, the maneuver plan would be adjusted to mitigate the event. . In addition, as explained above, Phase 1 was designed to minimize the conjunction threat to the ISS.

Early involvement with spacecraft operations preceding the deorbit identified a possible communication vulnerability. The spacecraft had two forms of communicating with the ground, an X-Band antenna (primary) and a UHF antenna (secondary). Occasionally, the X-Band communications would be lost and the spacecraft would switch to the UHF antenna. Experience showed that X-band could be recovered fairly quickly; however, steps were taken to improve the efficiency of the UHF downlink ensuring that the majority of the data needed would be available.

Lastly, loss of attitude control during the deorbit was identified as a possibility. The spacecraft's attitude control system included torque rods and four reaction wheels, one on each primary axis and one askew to all three axes. In the event that one or more of these wheels became saturated due to high torques on the vehicle, such as those expected in the increasing atmospheric drag environment of Phase 2, the spacecraft could succumb to an unrecoverable tumble. If this were to happen, deorbit operations would cease. The flight dynamics team identified two strategies to address this issue. The first involved analyzing the utility of a low-drag flight profile during times when the spacecraft would encounter the highest drag environment. Early analysis showed that implementing the low drag profile increased the ability of the vehicle to retain control throughout the high drag periods. The second, mentioned above, was to revise the onboard burn duration limit to maximize the departure periapsis for the final burn.

REENTRY REQUIREMENTS AND IMPACT AREA SELECTION

In order to perform a controlled deorbit, the location of the reentry and ground impact points had to be selected. Again, the NASA-STD 8719.14[2] was used for guidance. The standard states:

> "For controlled reentry, the selected trajectory shall ensure that no surviving debris impact with a kinetic energy greater than 15 joules is closer than 370 km from foreign landmasses, or is within 50 km from the continental U.S., territories of the U.S., and the permanent ice pack of Antarctica (Requirement 56627)."

Based on analysis, there are three zones that meet these criteria in the Atlantic, Pacific, and Indian Oceans. Of these three, the Pacific Ocean zone is the largest. Figure 4 depicts the allowable impact zone used for planning this activity with boundaries at least 700 km from the nearest land mass, exceeding the NASA-STD 8719.14[2] requirements.

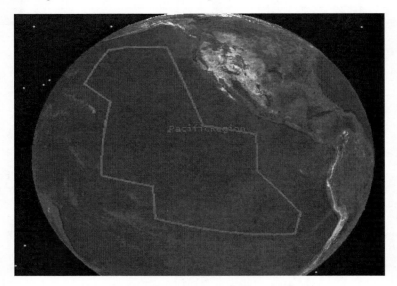

Figure 4. Allowable Pacific Impact Region

Since a break-up analysis was not performed, the flight dynamics team conducted a monte carlo analysis of potentially surviving debris in order to predict the impact location. This analysis examined the effects of maneuver execution errors and breakup uncertainties on the final maneuver burn duration and impact location. The maneuver execution errors were modeled as perturbations in terms of thrust efficiency as well as pointing errors. The monte carlo perturbs individual maneuvers while still performing the remaining maneuvers to determine if the trajectory goals are still met.

The monte carlo utilizes Gaussian distributions for the maneuver magnitude error (thrust efficiency) and maneuver direction, where the three sigma value is six percent and one degree respectively. Additionally, the monte carlo modeled break-up uncertainties as a function of ballistic coefficient.

The monte carlo executed 1000 cases with all 1000 cases impacting within the allowable area shown in Figure 4. The precise impact location of each case is shown in Figure 5. The latitude and longitude values were then analyzed to determine the footprint of the 3-sigma impact ellipsoid[3]. The size of the footprint is determined using Equation 1 and Equation 2. In the equations the parameter "A" varies from 0 to 2π in steps of five degrees as depicted in Figure 5.   The resulting ellipse has a semi-major axis of 761 km and a semi-minor axis of 721 km and encompasses all Phase 1 and 2 activities.

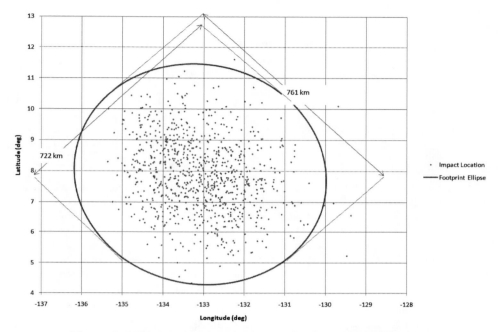

Figure 5. Monte Carlo Impact Locations and 3-sigma Ellipsoid

$Ellipse_{Lat} =$
$Latitude_{Mean} + Latitude_{StdDev} * Cos(A) * Cos(Clock\ Angle) - Longitude_{StdDev} *$
$Sin(A) * Sin(Clock\ Angle)$

1

$Ellipse_{Lon} = Longitude_{Mean} + Latitude_{StdDev} * Cos(A) * Sin(Clock\ Angle) -$
$Longitude_{StdDev} * Sin(A) * Sin(Clock\ Angle)$

2

MANEUVER OPERATIONS

The following sections detail the actual execution of the deorbit including changes to the trajectory design and challenges encountered along the way.

Phase 1 Execution

Phase 1 consisted of seven maneuver activities, one more than in the design. The difference was the addition of a collision avoidance (COLA) maneuver following the checkout and calibration activities. Another change from design was that the four primary burns were changed from 300 seconds in duration to 296 seconds. With a better understanding of vehicle commanding, Equation 3 was used to determine the maximum commandable burn duration related to the 300 second burn duration constraint. The results of these maneuvers are shown in Table 3.

$Max\ Commandable\ Burn\ Duration =$
$(Max\ Burn\ Duration\ Constraint) - (Max\ Burn\ Duration\ Constraint) * (2\%\ margin) +$
$(2\ Second\ Automatic\ Cuoff\ Delay)$

$$3$$

Table 3. Phase 1 Maneuver Results

Maneuver	Ignition Time (UTCG)	Burn Duration (sec)	Fuel Usage (kg)	Maneuver Goal	Periapsis Alt. (km)	Apoapsis Alt. (km)	Thrust Eff. (%)	Total Fuel Remaining (kg)
Initial State	-----------------------	--------	----------	-----------	421.9619479	439.1203476	--------	23.837
Calibration Burn	22 Dec 2010 12:52:34.200	30.34775	0.1895	Lower Perigee	416.7681586	439.1076402	93.3	23.6475
COLA Mnvr	02 Jan 2011 06:50:32.887	30.01675	0.186699	Lower Perigee	411.598784	438.78833	94.6	23.460801
Maneuver 1	05 Jan 2011 12:27:50.361	287.705	1.8034532	Lower Perigee	363.0832021	438.311241	92.09	21.657348
Maneuver 2	07 Jan 2011 13:05:49.722	287.7125	1.7469524	Lower Apogee	363.3818341	390.5161209	92.164	19.910395
Maneuver 3	09 Jan 2011 14:15:51.466	286.3125	1.6858694	Lower Apogee	343.7927444	364.0438907	91.727	18.224526
Maneuver 4	11 Jan 2011 17:18:25.000	--------	----------	Lower Apogee	-----------	-----------	--------	-----------

The checkout and calibration activities performed exactly as expected based on documentation obtained through research. The maneuver planning was done such that mismodeled parameters could be accounted for and revised quickly without significant impact to the overall de-orbit plan. As part of this design, the calibration maneuver plan assumed a 100% efficiency to ensure that the maneuver was not being biased during the planning stages, even though documentation suggested that the efficiency would approximately be 93%. Actual post-burn calibration, detailed below, resulted in an efficiency of 93.3% verifying the documentation. Calibrated efficiency values were then used for subsequent planning as illustrated in Table 3.

The COLA maneuver was performed to avoid a piece of Delta-1 debris, SSN 9617. The flight dynamics team used this maneuver to contribute to the deorbit efforts and matched the burn duration to that of the calibration burn. This resulted in a larger than required COLA maneuver but allowed the flight dynamics team to verify the thruster efficiency value of 93.3% obtained from the calibration maneuver.

Figure 6 shows the affects of the calibration and COLA maneuvers. Both maneuvers occurred at apoapsis, lowering periapsis.

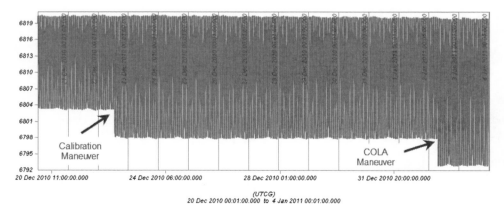

Figure 6. Orbit Radius Change Due to Calibration & COLA Maneuvers

The four primary maneuvers of Phase 1 continued to lower the spacecraft, via a series of apoapsis and periapsis maneuvers, to an orbital radius below that of the ISS. Two of the four maneuvers, conducted specifically at periapsis, lowered the orbital radius such that once the maneuver had completed, the pre-maneuver periapsis location became the post-maneuver apoapsis location. Figure 7 illustrates this.

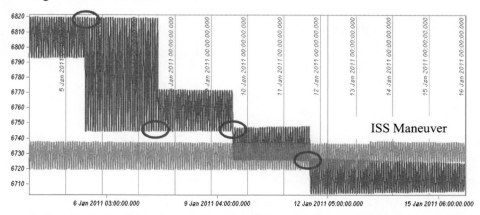

Figure 7. Phase 1 Execution: Spacecraft (red) and ISS (blue) Orbit Radii in km

As per the design the second to last maneuver of Phase 1 put the spacecraft into an orbit with a radius that overlapped that of the ISS. This maneuver increased the synodic period from approximately 10 to 150 days (Figure 8), well over the design goal of 100 days.

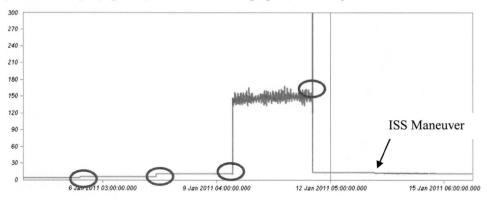

Figure 8. Phase 1 Execution: Synodic Period between Spacecraft and ISS in days

For Phase 1 the main difference between the design and the actual maneuvers was due to maneuver performance. The design utilized a performance value of 100%, which was expected to change based on performance data. Following execution, the maneuver spacing allowed the actual maneuvers to be analyzed. Analysis results revealed a performance of about 92-93% due to thruster off pulsing. This was accounted for by updating the trajectory plan along the way to ensure that the final burn of Phase 1 would successfully lower the spacecraft below the ISS. In addition, a scheduled maneuver that boosted the ISS orbit contributed to successful completion of Phase 1.

Phase 2 Revision

The design of Phase 2 consisted of a total of five maneuvers, approximately two days apart, with the final maneuver lowering the periapsis from 150 km to 50 km. Using the maneuver performance values derived during the execution of Phase 1 along with enhanced understanding of the vehicle capabilities gained from additional research and analysis during the Phase 1 activity, the Phase 2 execution changed significantly from the design. There were four major items that arose during the activity that needed resolution before initiating the execution of Phase 2:

- Adjusting the onboard maximum burn duration constraint
- Determining the maximum burn duration for which the spacecraft could maintain attitude control
- Identifying the trajectory of the final maneuver including:
  - minimum altitude of the last maneuver based on the ability of the spacecraft to maintain attitude control through low altitude perigees
  - post-final-maneuver periapsis altitude
- Revising the impact location after changing above items

Adjusting the Onboard Maximum Burn Duration Constraint

Investigations during the activity revealed that the onboard maximum burn duration limit could be adjusted via a flight parameter upload. The limit of 300 seconds did not impact the operations of Phase 1 but if left unchecked, limited the options available in Phase 2. Therefore, so as not to impose an artificial constraint on the activity, a decision was made to perform a parameter upload changing the constraint from 300 to 2400 seconds, the maximum burn duration the thruster hardware could support as stated by the vendor. This parameter change led to the first changes to the Phase 2 design. It was decided to increase the duration of the first burn of Phase 2 to 350 seconds to validate the onboard change. Assuming validation, it was then decided to use a large enough burn duration so that the second burn would reduce the periapsis to 200 km. This altitude was chosen to be a checkout location where telemetry would be collected and analyzed. These changes also reduced the number of burns required to complete Phase 2 by one.

Determining the Maximum Controllable Burn Duration

Based on telemetry analysis during Phase 1, it became apparent that attitude control during burns longer than 300 seconds may be a concern. During a maneuver, the spacecraft controlled pitch and roll (about the X and Y) body axis via thruster off-pulsing but utilized the reaction wheels for yaw control about the body-Z axis. Telemetry showed that when the thrusters fired, the Z axis reaction wheel speed grew in magnitude from its nominal steady state value as exemplified in Figure 9.

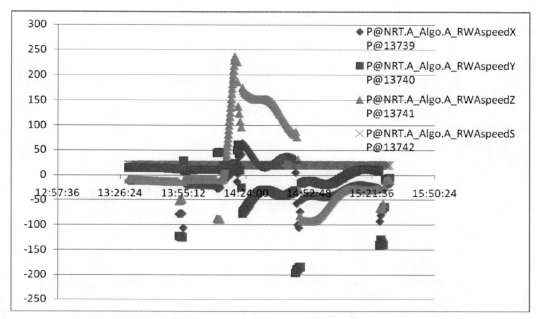

Figure 9. Deorbit Maneuver 3 Reaction Wheel Speeds (rad/s)

Examination of the data showed the Z-wheel speed grew almost linearly during each maneuver. The assumption of linear growth was applied to all available maneuver data to calculate an average growth rate shown in Table 4. In addition, a time lag appeared in the data, where the Z-wheel-speed growth extended beyond the commanded maneuver duration requiring the use of a burn duration multiplier of 1.05. Therefore the Z- wheel-speed growth rate and the change in Z-wheel speed over a maneuver could be determined by Equation 4 and Equation 5.

Table 4. Z-Wheel-Speed Growth During Maneuvers

Maneuver Number	Start Time	Stop Time	Duration (sec)	Starting Z Axis Value (rad/s)	Stopping Z Axis Value (rad/s)	Change in Wheel Speed (rad/s)	Growth Rate ((rad/s)/s)
1	12:27:46	12:32:56	310	-8.89	253.953	262.843	0.847
2	13:06:16	13:11:26	310	-9.171	258.922	268.09388	0.8648
3	14:13:36	13:18:46	310	-8.3125	236.234	244.5465	0.788
					Average:	258.49446	0.8332667

$$Wheel\ Growth\ Rate = (Change\ in\ Wheel\ Speed)/Duration \qquad 4$$

$$Z\ Wheel\ Final\ Speed = \\ (Burn\ Duration * Burn\ Duration\ Multiplier) * (Wheel\ Growth\ Rate) + \\ Z\ Wheel\ Starting\ Speed \qquad 5$$

The reason this was a concern is that Z-wheel speeds projected over maneuvers longer than 300 seconds approached hardware limitations of the reaction wheels. In an attempt to improve this situation, an investigation began into the possibility of changing onboard reaction-wheel-speed limits as well as using the skew-wheel to bias the initial steady state value of the Z-wheel to allow for more growth.

Figure 10 shows the maximum possible reaction wheel speed as a function of power and temperature of the reaction wheel assembly. Based on the observed temperature and power levels of the vehicle, a conclusion was made that the wheels could achieve approximately 450 rad/s before saturation. Thus, in an attempt to leverage the maximum capacity of the reaction wheels, conservative onboard safety limits where adjusted to accommodate the demanding use.

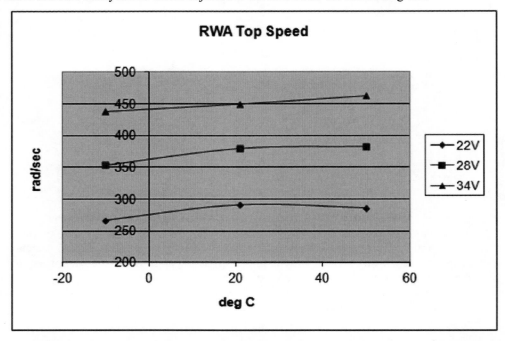

Figure 10. Reaction Wheel Unit Test Data: Top Wheel Speed Based on Battery Voltage and Temperature

In addition to the onboard limit adjustments the skew reaction wheel was used to bias the steady state Z-wheel speed. The skew wheel was commandable and could be used to inflict a torque on the spacecraft that the remaining three wheels were required to counter to maintain a zero momentum system. The orientation of the reactions wheels (see Figure 11) showed that, if the skew wheel was commanded to a positive value, the Z-wheel reacted in the opposite direction.

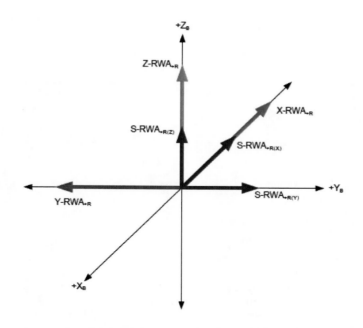

RWA	Z_R Vector Orientation in B-frame		
	X_B Component	Y_B Component	Z_B Component
X-RWA	-0.999989359	-0.004464100	-0.001168534
Y-RWA	-0.000392899	-0.999967302	-0.008079991
Z-RWA	-0.000028102	-0.007335945	0.999973110
S-RWA	-0.608913450	0.612375690	0.504269651

Figure 11. Reaction Wheel Directions and Components

Utilizing the Z-wheel growth rate, the estimated maximum achievable wheel speed, and the skew wheel bias, a burn duration that corresponded to wheel saturation could be calculated, which was used as the maximum commandable duration with reliable attitude control. The following equations and assumptions were used:

- Maximum commandable skew wheel speed: 375 rad/s (conservatism included)
  - This value is the maximum speed expected during nominal operation and was chosen to be conservative; the intention was to rely on nonstandard performance from only the Z-wheel.
- Maximum achievable Z wheel speed: 450 rad/s (conservatism included)
- The final burn does not need the 1.05 multiplier
  - After the final burn the vehicle's attitude stability is no longer a concern.

$$Z\ Wheel\ Starting\ Speed = -Skew\ Wheel\ Speed * 0.504269651$$

$$Z\ Wheel\ Starting\ Speed = -375\left(\frac{rad}{s}\right) * 0.504269651 = -189.10\frac{rad}{s}$$

$$Delta\ Wheel\ Speed = Max\ Achievable\ Wheel\ Speed - Z\ Wheel\ Starting\ Speed$$

$$Delta\ Wheel\ Speed = 450(\tfrac{rad}{s}) - (-189.10(\tfrac{rad}{s})) = 639.10\ (\tfrac{rad}{s})$$

$$Maximum\ Burn\ Duration = \frac{Delta\ Wheel\ Speed}{Wheel\ Growth\ Rate * Burn\ Duration\ Multiplier}$$

$$Maximum\ Burn\ Duration\ (no\ multipler) = \frac{639.10\left(\tfrac{rad}{s}\right)}{0.8332667\tfrac{rad}{s}} = 766.981\ sec$$

It was decided that the maximum burn duration value would be rounded down to 750 seconds to be conservative.

Identifying the Trajectory of the Final Maneuver

Once the maximum controllable burn duration had been determined, the remaining trajectory constraints were the departure altitude (i.e. the periapsis altitude of the orbit prior to the maneuver) and the impact location. The initial deorbit design had the fifth and final maneuver of Phase 2 lower the periapsis from 150 km to 50 km to meet objectives. This occurred two days after the fourth maneuver. However, based on a better understanding of the limitations of the attitude control system, concerns also began to arise related to the spacecraft's ability to counter the torque resulting from the high-atmospheric-density, low-periapsis portion of the orbit. To better understand the vehicle capabilities, the spacecraft manufacturer ran a simulation to estimate the likelihood of the spacecraft being able to survive the perigee pass of an orbit with a 300 km apoapsis and 150 km periapsis. Simulation results of 100 runs gave the spacecraft an 85% chance of maintaining control through this period of time. Thus, a choice was made to reduce the amount of time that would occur between the final two maneuvers from two orbits to two days. This reduced the time that the spacecraft would spend in the highest drag environment it would experience before reentry. In addition, it was clearly desirable to raise the departure altitude above 150 km by as much as possible. The maximum controllable burn duration remained a significant constraint but a decision was made to allow the final periapsis altitude to vary. The 50 km target periapsis was an ideal value but past experience allowed the flight dynamics team to be comfortable with a value of 70 km. This resulted in a variety of trajectory options that were examined (see Table 5). The options varied the duration and the periapsis departure altitude of the final maneuver. The resulting impact point (latitude and longitude) as well as final periapsis altitude were then evaluated.

Table 5. List of Design Cases for Phase 2

Case Name	Departure Altitude (km)	Burn Duration (sec)	Impact Latitude (deg)	Impact Longitude (deg)	Final Perigee Altitude (km)	Notes
Current Nominal	150	801	7.829	-136.534	50.002	
D150B800	150	800	7.898	-136.547	50.108	Most Desired - Lowest Depart, Longest Burn Duration
D150B750	150	750	11.688	-137.250	55.746	Desirable - Lowest Depart, Long Burn Duration
D150B700	150	700	16.091	-138.082	61.479	Desirable - Lowest Depart
D150B600	150	600	27.900	-140.470	73.217	Undesirable - Low Depart, High Per Alt
D160B800	160	800	14.592	-137.851	59.578	Desirable - Low Depart, Longest Burn Duration
D160B750	160	750	19.415	-138.783	65.249	Desirable - Low Depart, Long Burn Duration
D160B700	160	700	25.311	-139.976	71.017	Desirable - Low Depart
~~D160B600~~	~~160~~	~~600~~	~~43.861~~	~~-144.494~~	~~82.827~~	~~Unfeasible - Too High Per Alt~~
D170B800	170	800	23.147	-139.583	69.023	Desirable - Longest Burn Duration
D170B750	170	750	29.899	-141.016	74.728	Undesirable - High Per Alt
~~D170B700~~	~~170~~	~~700~~	~~39.103~~	~~-143.226~~	~~80.530~~	~~Unfeasible - Too High Per Alt~~
~~D170B600~~	~~170~~	~~600~~	~~81.612~~	~~94.002~~	~~92.411~~	~~Unfeasible - Too High Per Alt, Impact Outside Potential Zone~~

Three of the final trajectory options were eliminated immediately as infeasible; all three yielded final periapsis altitudes that had the potential to skip off the Earth's atmosphere resulting in an uncontrolled and unpredictable reentry. The remaining options were then evaluated against the flight dynamics team's increased understanding of the vehicle and assessment of the various risks involved for each case. Ultimately, case D160B750 was chosen from Table 5 as the option that provided the best chance of a successful deorbit while considering the spacecraft constraints.

Revising the Impact Location

Once the intended maneuver plans for Phase 2 had been adjusted, an additional monte carlo run occurred to create a new impact footprint, shown in Figure 12. The completion of Phase 1 and the reduction in the number of maneuvers to be used in Phase 2 resulted in a more elliptical footprint than the original. The updated monte carlo run yielded a tighter grouping of the impact points due to the reduction in the overall perturbations and the time that the perturbations had to propagate out.

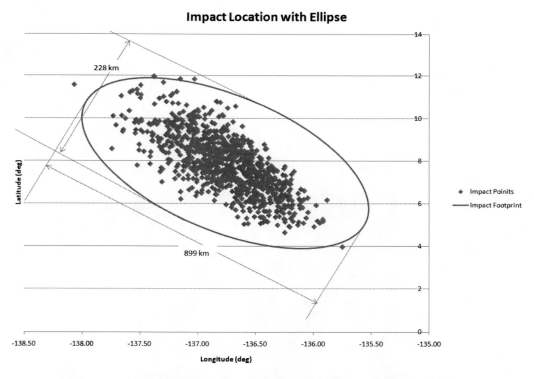

Figure 12. Updated Monte Carlo Impact Locations and 3-Sigma Ellipsoid

Phase 2 Execution

The maneuver results for Phase 2 are shown in Table 6. The first maneuver of Phase 2 ("Maneuver 5") was used to rotate the line of apsides to set the impact location and ensure that the remaining maneuvers were at their optimal location (centered at or near apoapsis). The rotation is illustrated in Figure 13 where there is a change in both periapsis altitude and periapsis altitude, thus rotating the respective locations.

Table 6. Phase 2 Maneuvers Results

Maneuver	Ignition Time (UTCG)	Burn Duration (sec)	Fuel Usage (kg)	Maneuver Goal	Periapsis Alt. (km)	Apoapsis Alt. (km)	Thrust Eff. (%)	Total Fuel Remaining (kg)
Maneuver 5	05 Mar 2011 15:28:03.000	350.2925	1.9470371	Lower Perigee	261.9827754	319.6708421	95.03	14.632963
Maneuver 6	10 Mar 2011 00:17:36.020	--------	2.2469003	Lower Perigee	200.1981534	310.0616746	94.9	12.386063
Maneuver 7	13 Mar 2011 02:21:37.000	--------	----------	Lower Perigee	----------	----------	--------	----------
Maneuver 8	13 Mar 2011 05:15:50.000	--------	----------	Lower Perigee	----------	----------	--------	----------

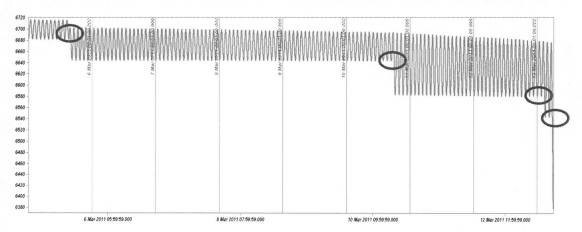

Figure 13. Phase 2 Execution: Spacecraft Orbit Radius in km

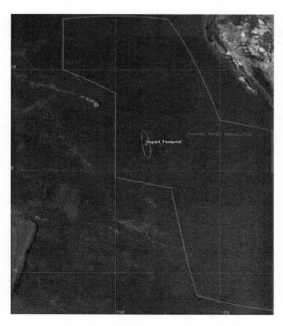

Figure 14. Impact Footprint Location

272

The final maneuver executed on 13 Mar 2011 05:15:50 UTCG and the estimated impact location was centered approximately 3000 miles southeast of the main island of Hawaii (see Figure 14). Telemetry was evaluated throughout Phase 2 and showed the vehicle was healthy and maintaining control prior to Maneuver 8, which led the flight dynamics team to believe that the last maneuver executed successfully. Ultimate confirmation came from JSpOC via Spacetrack where the final satellite TLE released on 14 March listed the object as "Decayed 2011-03-13".

Maneuver Calibration Evaluation

After each maneuver with sufficient data, a calibration occurred to solve for values characterizing actual thrust efficiency and pointing accuracy. These values were then used as input for the next maneuver (data was not available following the final maneuver of Phase 1 and the last two maneuvers of Phase 2). The maneuver calibration process utilized a differential corrector method to solve across the maneuver.

The process allows the differential corrector to solve for thrust efficiency and pointing error using the best known information prior to start of the maneuver (updated orbit state, tank pressure), during the maneuver (spacecraft attitude, thruster pulsing, burn duration) and post maneuver (post maneuver orbit state computed from OD). The resulting thrust efficiency and pointing values indicate how closely the maneuver performed compared to the plan and also serve as updates to subsequent maneuver planning.

Table 7, Table 8, Table 9 show the planned and calibrated (actual) values along with the difference between the two. The largest difference occurred for the calibration maneuver. This was due to the limited knowledge regarding the thrusters and their performance before on-orbit data was available. Following the initial calibration, the largest difference occurred for "Maneuver 5" in the tables. The likely cause of this was the longer burn duration where the inefficiencies at the beginning and end of the burn were not as apparent, an effect that was accounted for in the planning of subsequent maneuvers with longer durations.

Table 7. Planned Maneuver Values

Maneuver	Ignition Time (UTCG)	Burn Duration (sec)	Fuel Usage (kg)	Maneuver Goal	Periapsis Alt. (km)	Apoapsis Alt. (km)	Thrust Eff. (%)	Total Fuel Remaining (kg)
Initial State	------------------------	--------	----------	-----------	421.9619479	439.1203476	--------	23.837
Calibration Burn	22 Dec 2010 12:52:34.200	30	0.2062	Lower Perigee	416.3307226	439.0911573	100	23.6308
COLA Mnvr	02 Jan 2011 06:50:32.887	30	0.1884846	Lower Perigee	411.5500685	438.7883065	93.3	23.442315
Maneuver 1	05 Jan 2011 12:27:50.361	296	1.8267387	Lower Perigee	362.4524025	438.3112546	93.3	21.615577
Maneuver 2	07 Jan 2011 13:05:49.722	296	1.7410338	Lower Apogee	363.3822987	390.6765728	92	19.874543
Maneuver 3	09 Jan 2011 14:15:51.466	296	1.6860007	Lower Apogee	343.6878575	364.0669521	92	18.188542
Maneuver 4	11 Jan 2011 17:18:25.000	296	1.6414156	Lower Apogee	319.7440074	342.931244	92	16.547127
Maneuver 5	05 Mar 2011 15:28:03.000	350	1.8861408	Lower Perigee	263.572505	319.6983342	92	14.693859
Maneuver 6	10 Mar 2011 00:17:36.020	418	2.2492243	Lower Perigee	200.0421115	309.9677742	95	12.383776
Maneuver 7	13 Mar 2011 02:21:37.000	264	1.3810163	Lower Perigee	159.9683788	294.689391	95	11.005084
Maneuver 8	13 Mar 2011 05:15:50.000	750	3.6970219	Lower Perigee	64.20942792	292.3669949	93	7.3080781

Table 8. Calibrated Maneuver Values

Maneuver	Ignition Time (UTCG)	Burn Duration (sec)	Fuel Usage (kg)	Maneuver Goal	Periapsis Alt. (km)	Apoapsis Alt. (km)	Thrust Eff. (%)	Total Fuel Remaining (kg)
Initial State	------------------------	--------	----------	-----------	421.9619479	439.1203476	--------	23.837
Calibration Burn	22 Dec 2010 12:52:34.200	30.34775	0.1895	Lower Perigee	416.7681586	439.1076402	93.3	23.6475
COLA Mnvr	02 Jan 2011 06:50:32.887	30.01675	0.186699	Lower Perigee	411.598784	438.78833	94.6	23.460801
Maneuver 1	05 Jan 2011 12:27:50.361	287.705	1.8034532	Lower Perigee	363.0832021	438.311241	92.09	21.657348
Maneuver 2	07 Jan 2011 13:05:49.722	287.7125	1.7469524	Lower Apogee	363.3818341	390.5161209	92.164	19.910395
Maneuver 3	09 Jan 2011 14:15:51.466	286.3125	1.6858694	Lower Apogee	343.7927444	364.0438907	91.727	18.224526
Maneuver 4	11 Jan 2011 17:18:25.000	--------	----------	Lower Apogee	-----------	-----------	--------	-----------
Maneuver 5	05 Mar 2011 15:28:03.000	350.2925	1.9470371	Lower Perigee	261.9827754	319.6708421	95.03	14.632963
Maneuver 6	10 Mar 2011 00:17:36.020	--------	2.2469003	Lower Perigee	200.1981534	310.0616746	94.9	12.386063
Maneuver 7	13 Mar 2011 02:21:37.000	--------	----------	Lower Perigee	-----------	-----------	--------	-----------
Maneuver 8	13 Mar 2011 05:15:50.000	--------	----------	Lower Perigee	-----------	-----------	--------	-----------

Table 9. Planned vs. Calibration Delta Values

Maneuver	Ignition Time (UTCG)	Burn Duration (sec)	Fuel Usage (kg)	Maneuver Goal	Periapsis Alt. (km)	Apoapsis Alt. (km)	Thrust Eff. (%)	Total Fuel Remaining (kg)
Initial State	------------------------	--------	----------	-----------	0	0	--------	0
Calibration Burn	22 Dec 2010 12:52:34.200	0.34775	-0.0167	Lower Perigee	0.437435957	0.016482866	-6.7	0.0167
COLA Mnvr	02 Jan 2011 06:50:32.887	0.01675	-0.0017856	Lower Perigee	0.048715505	2.35267E-05	1.3	0.0017856
Maneuver 1	05 Jan 2011 12:27:50.361	-8.295	-0.0232855	Lower Perigee	0.630799574	-1.362E-05	-1.21	0.0232855
Maneuver 2	07 Jan 2011 13:05:49.722	-8.2875	0.0059186	Lower Apogee	-0.00046465	-0.1604519	0.1638	-0.0059186
Maneuver 3	09 Jan 2011 14:15:51.466	-9.6875	-0.0001313	Lower Apogee	0.104886969	-0.02306144	-0.2734	0.0001313
Maneuver 4	11 Jan 2011 17:18:25.000	--------	----------	Lower Apogee	-----------	-----------	--------	-----------
Maneuver 5	05 Mar 2011 15:28:03.000	0.2925	0.0608963	Lower Perigee	-1.58972957	-0.02749209	3.03	-0.0608963
Maneuver 6	10 Mar 2011 00:17:36.020	--------	-0.002324	Lower Perigee	0.156041982	0.093900355	-0.0999	0.002324
Maneuver 7	13 Mar 2011 02:21:37.000	--------	----------	Lower Perigee	-----------	-----------	--------	-----------
Maneuver 8	13 Mar 2011 05:15:50.000	--------	----------	Lower Perigee	-----------	-----------	--------	-----------

ACKNOWLEDGMENTS

The authors of this paper would like to thank the following people for their dedication, commitment and creativity in the successful deorbit. Mike Bashioum, Sandy Pitzak, David Sipple, Sean LevTov, Mike Mahoney, John Carrico, John Earp, Travis Schrift, Hank Grabowski, Carlos Niederstrasser, Kevin MacMillian, Sudeep Singh, Rob Bowlin, Dave Ward and the countless others.

REFERENCES

[1] T.S Kelso. "CelesTrack" http://celestrack.com/, Dec 19, 2010.

[2] "Process for Limiting Orbital Debris", NASA-STD 8719.4, 23 July 2009.

[3] Ellipse" Wikipedia, http://en.wikipedia.org/wiki/Ellipse, 19 December 2010.

SATELLITE COLLISION PROBABILITY COMPUTATION FOR LONG TERM ENCOUNTERS

J. C. Dolado,[*] P. Legendre,[†] R. Garmier,[‡] B. Revelin,[§] and X. Pena[**]

With the significant increase in the number of satellite constellations and GEO objects, long-term encounters become common. Such geometries are characterized by a curvilinear relative motion and important position and velocity uncertainties. We first determine the relative velocity limits between the linear and non-linear encounters and the limits between negligible or not negligible velocity uncertainties. We then propose an algorithm combining a Monte Carlo and an importance sampling method to compute the collision probability for the curvilinear domain. We finally apply this algorithm to various encounters to demonstrate its efficiency in terms of accuracy and computation time.

INTRODUCTION

With the significant increase in the number of satellite constellations and the over-population of the geostationary arc, long-term dangerous conjunctions between two satellites or between an operational satellite and a debris, become more and more common. By long-term encounter, we mean a geometrical situation where both objects spend a significant fraction of their orbital period in the vicinity of each other.

These long-term encounters are to oppose to the well-studied short-term encounters.

For short-term encounters, the relative velocity is in the order of km/s and the close approach duration is very brief. One can assume the velocity uncertainties negligible and the relative motion can be considered as rectilinear. With these approximations, one can show that the conjunction risk assessment can be managed without loss of generality, projecting the position uncertainties for both objects on the collision plane.

For long-term encounters, the previous assumptions are not any more valid as we must take into account the curvilinear relative motion with important position and velocity uncertainties.

Methods[1, 2, 3] commonly presented in literature for computing the probability of collision for long-term encounters, are based on more or less complicated segmentations of the long encounter on a finite number of short ones, in which the hypotheses commonly used for short term encoun-

---

[*] Spaceflight Dynamics Engineer, CNES, 18 avenue Edouard Belin 31401 Toulouse France. E-mail address: Juan-carlos.doladoperez@cnes.fr, Tel.:+33 5 61 27 45 41; fax: +33 5 61 28 18 55
[†] Applied Mathematics Senior Specialist, CEMAES, 9 route de Damiatte 81500 Fiac France.
[‡] Spaceflight Dynamics Engineer, CS-SI, 5 rue Brindejonc des moulinais BP 15872, 31506 Toulouse France.
[§] Spaceflight Dynamics Engineer, CS-SI, 5 rue Brindejonc des moulinais BP 15872, 31506 Toulouse France.
[**] Spaceflight Dynamics Engineer, CNES, 18 avenue Edouard Belin 31401 Toulouse France.

ters are applied (i.e. the relative motion can be considered as linear at the time of closest approach, and the velocities uncertainties can be neglected).

In this context, we focused our efforts on the development of a new probability computation method that could be applied for long term encounters taking into account the curvilinear relative motion as well as the position and velocity uncertainties.

On the first section, we present the approach followed in order to determine the relative velocity limits between the linear and non-linear encounters as well as the limits between negligible or not negligible velocity uncertainties. To do so, we analyze, from a geometrical point of view, a group of LEO and GEO real and simulated conjunctions with relative velocities ranging from 1 m/s to 2000 m/s, and we developed a criterion to tune the limits between the different domains.

On the second section, we present an empirical approach to compute the probability of collision for the non-linear relative velocity domain (this method, as it is not based on geometrical assumptions, is indeed valid for all relative velocities). Such an approach is a Monte Carlo method coupled with importance sampling techniques, in order to significantly reduce the number of samples without a significant loss on the accuracy of the computed probability. The optimization of the number of Monte Carlo samplings is of key importance, as the number of samples to compute a collision probability of 10^{-N} with a standard deviation of $10^{-(N+1)}$ must be at least of 10^{N+2}.

Importance sampling is a generalization of Monte Carlo method based on a weighting function of the trials. On a practical point of view, it allows us to modify the probability density function from which the samples are going to be extracted. The new probability density function allows to optimize the sampling process in order to maximize the number of simulated conjunctions with a relative distance smaller than the security volume (i.e. smaller than the hard body radius), thus the number of samples required to reach the same level of uncertainty decreases considerably. In our paper we present the analysis that we have done on the best choice of the probability density function.

On the last section, we present a series of numerical results obtained with a software tool implementing importance sampling techniques. This software has been developed during our study and has been tested with short and long terms real and simulated conjunctions, in order to demonstrate the validity and computational performance of our method. With the developed tool, we are able to compute probabilities in 10^{-4} with a 10^{-5} accuracy with 2000 trials. A basic Monte Carlo would require 10^6 shootings to achieve an equivalent accuracy.

LINEAR VS NON-LINEAR RELATIVE VELOCITY LIMIT EVALUATION

The relative trajectory of two objects orbiting around a body is curvilinear. Nevertheless, depending on the relative distance and on relative velocity we can split the general case on two particular cases:

In one side the conjunctions taking place at high relative velocity. The relative velocity at the TCA is in the order of several kilometers per second therefore the conjunction will take place during several milliseconds. At the vicinity of the TCA the relative motion will evolve on a linear manner, the velocity uncertainty could be neglected and the collision risk will be driven by the position uncertainty.

In the other side the conjunctions taking place at low relative velocity. The relative velocity at the TCA is in the order of several meters per second therefore the conjunction may last for a non-negligible fraction of the orbital period. During the period of time that the two objects will stay close one from the other, the relative motion could not be considered rectilinear and the position uncertainty as well as the velocity uncertainty must to be taken into account for the collision risk assessment.

The main objective of this section is to present the limits between linear and non-linear relative motion. To do so, initially we present some of the conjunction geometries that have been used to perform this analysis. Secondly we analyze the relative motion between the primary and the secondary objects on a deterministic manner and finally we introduce the position and velocity errors to define the limits between linear and non-linear relative motion.

Study Cases

At this point of the study, the limit between low and high relative velocity is not yet known. Therefore the conjunctions selected to carry out this study, cover a relative velocity domain going from several meters per second to several kilometers per second. Those conjunctions have been selected either from existing publications, from the CNES operational conjunction assessment database or from simulated conjunctions.[1,4]

Table 1. Sub-set Of Selected Conjunctions

Primary Object	Secondary Object	Type	Distance at TCA (m)	Relative velocity at TCA (m/s)
McKinley's [1]	McKinley's [1]	Real Case	10.0	0.99
Spot 5 (27421)	Debris (13574)	Real Case	181.6	2027.0
Jason (26997)	Topex (22076)	Real Case	519.7	11.38

Table 2. Primary and Secondary orbital elements at TCA

Conjunction	ID Norad	a [m]	e	i [°]	w [°]	Ω [°]	M [°]
McKinley	-	7077000	0	98	90,85	220,35	-0,85
	-	7078869,6	0,000267	98	90	220,35	0
Spot5 / Debris	27421	7191580,27	0,002779	98,68	92,66	330,97	178,7
	13574	7220719,35	0,001406	98,72	242,18	315,11	26,69
Jason / Topex	26997	7707343,83	0,001094	66,02	87,71	189,99	-178,39
	22076	7707250,31	0,001167	66,02	90,27	190,09	178,99

Conjunction Geometry Analysis

The main objective is to analyze the evolution in time of the geometry of conjunction. In order to do so, we are going to propagate numerically the orbit of the primary and secondary object during an orbital period centered at the TCA. The orbital period is the one of the primary object. The forces model implemented on the numerical propagation for LEO orbit is different than the one implemented for GEO. For the objects presented on table 1, the considered forces are: 4x4 order Earth potential (GRIM5 model) and Drag (DTM 2000 model). The considered orbital elements for the primary and secondary object are presented on table 2.

Table 3. Characteristics Of Primary and Secondary Objects

	Mass (kg)	Surface (m2)	Drag Coefficient Cd
Primary Objet	1000	47.95	2.2
Secondary Objet	1000	8.3	2.2

For each propagated conjunction we are going to analyze the evolution in time of the following parameters: Relative distance, relative velocity norm, angle between the relative velocity at time t and the relative velocity at TCA and the norm of the difference between the relative velocity at time t and relative velocity at TCA.

The Evolution in time of those parameters will allow us to identify non-linear effects on the primary – secondary objects' relative motion.

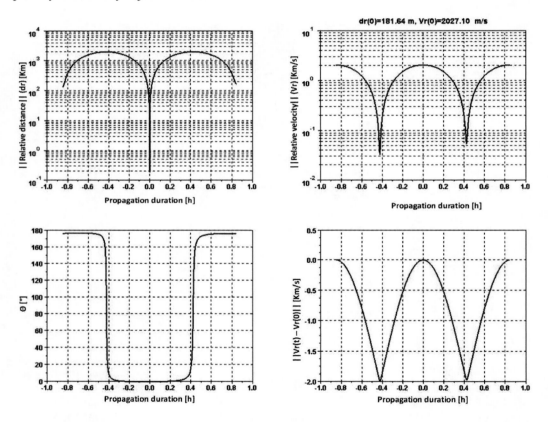

Figure 1. Evolution in time of the relative distance norm (upper left), relative velocity norm (upper right), angle between relative velocity at TCA and velocity at t (lower left) and norm of the difference between relative velocity at TCA and relative velocity at t (lower right) for SPOT5 vs. #13574 conjunction case.

As can be seen in Figure 1, the conjunction between SPOT5 and the debris of ID NORAD 13574 has a clear linear behavior. For a conjunction with a relative velocity at TCA of 2027.10 m/s, the relative distance centered at the time of closest approach varies very sharply which means that both objects spends a very short period of time one close from the other. Also centered at TCA, the norm of the relative velocity is quite constant compared to the relative velocity at TCA, the angle between the relatives velocities is equal to zero and the difference between the relative velocities in negligible compared to the relative velocity at TCA.

Accordingly with the evolution in time of the parameters presented above, we can consider for the SPOT5 vs. #13574 conjunction case that at the surroundings of the TCA, the relative motion is linear, the position errors remains constant and the velocity errors can be neglected.

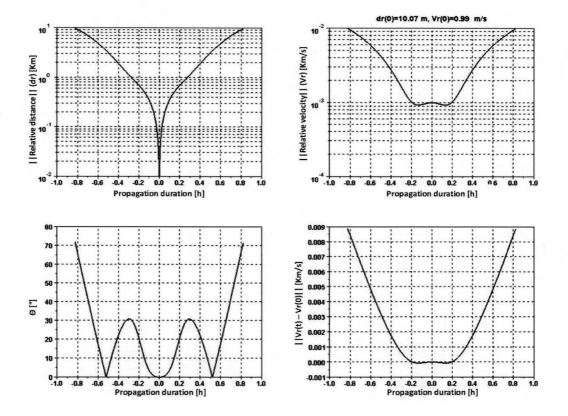

Figure 2. Evolution in time of the relative distance norm (upper left), relative velocity norm (upper right), angle between relative velocity at TCA and velocity at t (lower left) and norm of the difference between relative velocity at TCA and relative velocity at t (lower right) for McKinley[1] conjunction case.

The conjunction presented in Figure 2 is to oppose to what has been presented in Figure 1. For McKinley's[1] conjunction case, we show that the evolution of the relative distance centered at TCA varies softer than for the previous case. This means that both objects spend a non-negligible amount of time one close from the other. In addition to this, we show that centered at TCA neither the evolution of relative velocity with time nor the difference between the relative velocities are negligible compared with the relative velocity at TCA. We also show that the angle between the relative velocities has a significant variation around the TCA.

In consequence, for this type of conjunction, both objects could spend a significant fraction of their orbital period one close from the other. The conjunction cannot be considered as linear, the orbital errors must to be propagated during the conjunction time and the position errors as well as the velocity errors must to be taken into account to properly asses the conjunction risk.

Taking Into Account Orbital Errors To Define The Limit Between Linear And Non-linear Relative Motion

The introduction of the orbital errors to the study of the conjunction geometry analysis has a double purpose. In one side we intend to determine the period of time, centered at TCA, that has to be considered in order to conclude if a conjunction is linear or not. In the other side we aim to analyze the effect that the velocity errors have on the assessment of a conjunction risk.

In order to carry out this study, we consider that the position and velocity errors of the primary and secondary object can be modeled by a Gaussian law.

To determine the period of time, centered at TCA, to analyze if the conjunction is linear or not, we have taken advantage of the collision plane definition. The collision plane is centered on the primary object and normal to the relative velocity vector. In consequence, the time during which the secondary object will be close to the primary object will depend on the orbital error of both objects along the relative velocity direction.

$$\Delta T = \left[-\frac{3\sigma_Z}{V_{rel}^{ref}}, \frac{3\sigma_Z}{V_{rel}^{ref}} \right] \tag{1}$$

The sampling process has been performed using a covariance matrix expressed in equinoctial parameters an modeled by a Gaussian law. The covariance matrices of the primary and secondary objects are summed and assigned to the secondary object. Following a Monte Carlo approach, we have performed 1000 trials. For each of them we have recomputed the TCA, as well as the angle between the relative velocity of the reference conjunction (cf. Table 2) and the relative velocity at the new TCA.

Table 4. 1σ Standard deviation for Topex / Jason Conjunction case

Conjunction	σa [m]	σex	σey	σhx	σhy	$\sigma(\omega+\Omega+v)$ [rad]
Topex / Jason	0,67	1,38E-05	9,70E-06	1,15E-05	1,67E-05	4,41E-05

Table 5. Topex / Jason Correlation Matrix

Topex / Jason Correlation Matrix					
1,00	-0,24	-0,11	0,06	0,15	-0,98
-0,24	1,00	0,53	0,18	-0,86	0,21
-0,11	0,53	1,00	0,84	-0,68	0,17
0,06	0,18	0,84	1,00	-0,39	0,04
0,15	-0,86	-0,68	-0,39	1,00	-0,13
-0,98	0,21	0,17	0,04	-0,13	1,00

The numerical values shown in tables 4 and 5 have been used to define the covariance matrices applied for the computation of the results shown in Figures 3 and 4.

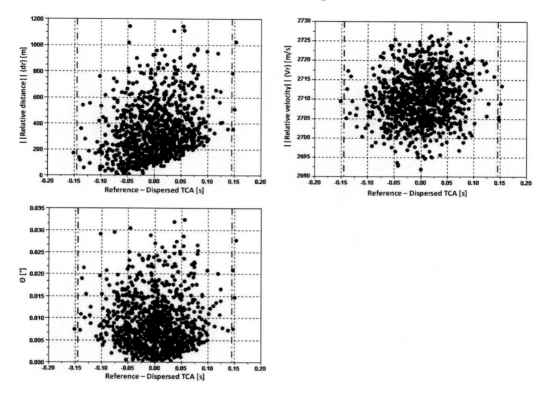

Figure 3. Comparison of relative distance (upper left), relative velocity (upper right) and relative velocity angle (lower left) at TCA between SPOT5 vs. #13574 reference (cf. Table 2) and dispersed conjunction. On x axis, we represent the difference in date between the reference and the dispersed TCA. The red slashed lines represent the interval from Equation (1). The red star accounts for the reference conjunction.

When orbital errors are taken into account the hypothesis stated in the previous paragraph are confirmed. This is, for SPOT5 vs. #13574 conjunction, we show that the period during which we have to evaluate the nature of the relative motion is very brief (i.e. 0.3 seconds). During the evaluation period, we show that the position errors have an important effect on the conjunction analysis, nevertheless the velocity errors can be neglected in comparison with the reference's relative velocity. Concerning the angle between relative velocities, we show that its variation is in the order of [0, 0.035°].

On the other side, regarding McKinley's[1] conjunction (cf. Figure 4) we show that the period of analysis is in the order of half an hour. This means that the two objects will be one close from the other during an important fraction of the orbital period. We show that the position errors are still important and that the relative velocity errors are in the order of magnitude of the reference relative velocity, consequently the velocity errors must to be taken into account to evaluate the conjunction risk. Regarding the angle between relative velocities, we show that it varies from 0° to 40°, therefore the relative motion is clearly non-linear.

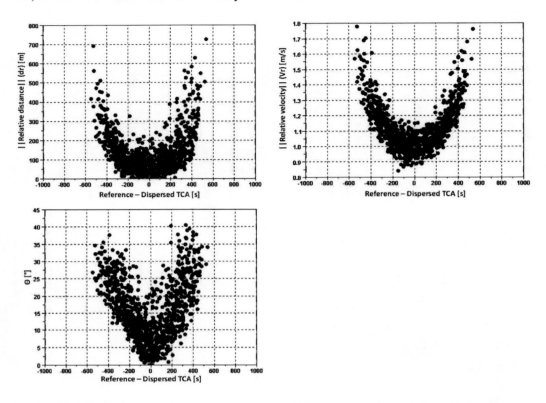

Figure 4. Comparison of relative distance (upper left), relative velocity (upper right) and relative velocity angle (lower left) at TCA for McKinley's[1] reference (cf. Table 2) and dispersed conjunction. On x axis, we represent the difference in date between the reference and the dispersed TCA. The red slashed lines represent the interval from Equation (1). The red star accounts for the reference conjunction.

Computation of a Collision Probability

The last measurable parameter that we have decided to use in order to split the velocity domain in linear and non-linear relative motion is the probability of collision.

In order to do so, we have defined three types of conjunction's relative distances. The first relative distance (d_{min}) has been computed using a Monte Carlo Sampling. In consequence it is the relative distance of reference, as no hypothesis have been taken into account for its computation.

The second relative distance (d_1) is computed considering that at TCA the relative motion is linear, the position errors are constant and the velocity errors can be neglected.

$$d_1 = \left\| \delta\vec{P} - \left(\delta\vec{P} \cdot \vec{C}_3 \right) \cdot \vec{C}_3 \right\| \tag{2}$$

Where $\delta\vec{P}$ is the relative position vector expressed on the collision plane reference frame $\{\vec{C}_1, \vec{C}_2, \vec{C}_3\}$.

The third relative distance (d_2) is computed considering that at TCA the relative motion is linear and the position and velocity errors are constant and not negligible.

$$d_2 = \left\| \delta\vec{P} - \frac{(\delta\vec{P} \cdot \delta\vec{V})}{\|\delta\vec{V}\|^2} \delta\vec{V} \right\| \qquad (3)$$

Where $\delta\vec{V}$ is the velocity error vector expressed in the collision-plane reference frame.

Rich bibliography[7] exists on the computation of a probability of collision for a linear relative motion conjunction.

The common approach is to integrate the primary / secondary relative position's probability density function over a circle whose radius is the summation of the hard body radius of both objects.

This probability density function is commonly modeled by a Gaussian law, thus the probability of collision, once projected on the collision plane, can be expressed as:

$$P_a(s) = \iint_D \mathcal{N}(\vec{X} + \vec{d} + \vec{\mu}_p - \vec{\mu}_s, \Sigma_p + \Sigma_s) dS \qquad (4)$$

Where dS is a differential of surface, D is the diameter of the security volume projected on the collision plane, μ_p and Σ_p are the mean and the covariance of the primary object on the collision plane, μ_s and Σ_s are the mean and the covariance of the secondary object on the collision plane, $\mathcal{N}$ is a 2 dimensions Gaussian law and d is the relative distance vector expressed on the collision plane.

Considering that the probability density function is constant over the integration surface, Equation (4) can be simplified in:

$$P_a(s) = \pi s^2 \mathcal{N}(\vec{d} + \vec{\mu}_p - \vec{\mu}_s, \Sigma_p + \Sigma_s) \qquad (5)$$

In order to conclude about the limit between linear and non-linear conjunction, we have decided to proceed via a Monte-Carlo approach. We have performed 10 Monte Carlo samplings of 1000 trials each, using each of the covariance matrices presented in Table 6. Then for each sample we have computed the three relative distances presented above and the probability of collision with d_{min} using a Monte Carlo approach and with d_1 and d_2 using Equation (5). Tables 7, 8 and 9 summarizes the mean collision probability and the 1σ standard deviation for McKinley[1], Jason vs. Topex and SPOT5 vs. #13574 conjunctions respectively.

Table 6. 1σ Standard deviation at TCA expressed on the collision plane

Conjunction	Covariance Matrix	σx [m]	σy [m]	σz [m]	σVx [m/s]	σVy [m/s]	σVz [m/s]
McKinley	I	79,183	120,807	973,511	1,051	0,145	0,084
	II	36,716	75,624	651,082	0,721	0,05	0,039
	III	27,433	30,936	445,312	0,48	0,082	0,029
Jason / Topex	I	1054,205	81,964	135,38	0,072	0,968	0,295
	II	706,594	63,606	106,259	0,058	0,645	0,116
	III	482,603	40,126	68,369	0,034	0,445	0,136
SPOT5 / #13574	I	918,87	59,142	208,3	0,052	0,955	0,135
	II	676,552	59,481	102,694	0,065	0,688	0,076
	III	377,853	30,132	111,525	0,029	0,392	0,036

Table 7. Probabilities of collision for McKinley's Conjunction case (0.99 m/s)

Covariance Matrix	Probability dmin		Probability d1		Probability d2	
	Mean Probability	Standard deviation	Mean Probability	Standard deviation	Mean Probability	Standard deviation
I	0,0051	0,0022	0,0212	0,0034	0,0050	0,0020
II	0,0164	0,0047	0,0699	0,0082	0,0164	0,0045
III	0,0602	0,0079	0,2382	0,0098	0,0601	0,0079

Table 8. Probabilities of collision for Topex vs. Jason Conjunction (11 m/s)

Covariance Matrix	Probability dmin		Probability d1		Probability d2	
	Mean Probability	Standard deviation	Mean Probability	Standard deviation	Mean Probability	Standard deviation
I	0,0227	0,0053	0,0224	0,0053	0,0227	0,0053
II	0,0149	0,0048	0,0149	0,0047	0,0149	0,0048
III	0,0055	0,0017	0,0056	0,0019	0,0055	0,0017

Table 9. Probabilities of collision for SPOT5 vs. #13574 Conjunction (2027 m/s)

Covariance Matrix	Probability dmin		Probability d1		Probability d2	
	Mean Probability	Standard deviation	Mean Probability	Standard deviation	Mean Probability	Standard deviation
I	0,0173	0,0034	0,0173	0,0034	0,0173	0,0034
II	0,0189	0,0051	0,0189	0,0051	0,0189	0,0051
III	0,0235	0,0043	0,0235	0,0043	0,0235	0,0043

In order to have a better knowledge of the velocity domain between 1 and 5 m/s, we have simulated from Jason vs. Topex conjunction at 11 m/s three new conjunctions with relative velocities of 2, 5 and 10 m/s. Figure 5 shows the evolution of the mean squared error of d_1 and d_2 taking d_{min} as reference, as a function of the security threshold.

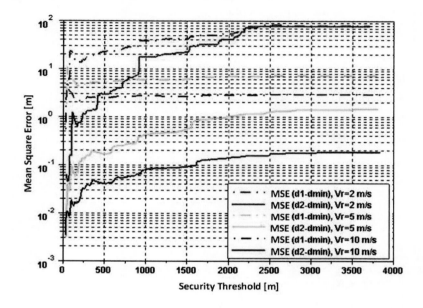

Figure 5. Mean Square Errors for d1 and d2 distances for 2, 5 and 10 m/s relative velocity conjunctions. The covariance matrix considered for this particular figure is of type II (cf. Table 6)

From previous results we can conclude:

✓ For relative velocities between 1 and 5 m/s, even if from Table 7 one may conclude that Pdmin ≈ Pd2 ≠ Pd1, Figure 5 shows that the relative movement is not linear. In consequence, a general method (e.g. Monte-Carlo) must be applied to assess this type of conjunction.

✓ For relative velocities between 5 and 10 m/s Pdmin ≈ Pd2 ≠ Pd1. The conjunction can be considered as linear and the position errors as well as the velocity errors must to be taken into account to evaluate the conjunction risk.

✓ For relative velocities higher than 10 m/s Pdmin ≈ Pd1 ≈ Pd2. At TCA the conjunction can be considered as linear, the position errors are constant and the velocity errors can be neglected

COMPUTATION OF AN EMPIRICAL PROBABILITY

As presented in the previous section, the collision probability evaluation of conjunctions with relative velocities higher than 5 m/s can be done in a time efficient and relative simple manner. For conjunctions with relative velocities between 1 and 5 m/s we have shown that the position and velocity errors must to be taken into account to properly evaluate the risk. We have also shown that, covariance matrices cannot be considered as constant during the conjunction period.

It is important to notice, that the conjunctions with relative velocities lower than 1 m/s are out of the scope of our study.

A simple approach to compute the probability of collision for a non-linear conjunction is to use a Monte Carlo method. Such a method does not take any hypothesis concerning neither the relative motion nor the evolution of the orbital error. In consequence, the Monte Carlo method gives us a correct probability of collision for all the considered ranges of velocities. The only parameter to be correctly tuned is the number of trials to be done in order to guarantee a good confidence in our results.

Monte Carlo method

We assume that the uncertainties on position and velocity of a space object are distributed according to a normal law $g = \mathcal{N}(\vec{M}_{pv}, \Sigma_{pv})$ where $\vec{M}_{pv}$ and Σ_{pv} are the mean vector and covariance matrix in position and velocities.

Let us write the mean vector $\vec{M}_{pv}$ by

$$\vec{M}_{pv} = \begin{pmatrix} \vec{M}_p \\ \vec{M}_v \end{pmatrix} \tag{6}$$

Where

✓ $\vec{M}_p$ is the position mean vector,

✓ $\vec{M}_v$ is the velocity mean vector.

By the same way, we can write the covariance matrix in position and velocity by:

$$\Sigma_{pv} = \begin{pmatrix} \Sigma_p & C_{p,v} \\ {}^t C_{p,v} & \Sigma_v \end{pmatrix} \tag{7}$$

Where

✓ Σ_p is the position covariance matrix

✓ Σ_v is the velocity covariance matrix

✓ $C_{p,v}$ is a matrix taking into account the correlation between the position and velocity components.

For each trial, we randomly disperse the initial position velocity vectors of the chaser and the target according to their respective covariance matrices. We then propagate numerically the two trajectories over a period of time necessary to reach the conjunction. We then search the dangerous conjunctions (i.e. conjunctions with a close approach distance lower than a security threshold s). The collision probability is then equal to the number of trials presenting a dangerous conjunction divided by the total number of trials:

$$P_c^{MC}(s) = \frac{\sum\limits_{i=1}^{N} \chi_s(\vec{e}_i)}{N} \tag{8}$$

✓ s is the security threshold. In our case, s is the summation of the radius of the smallest sphere enclosing the chaser and the one enclosing the target.

✓ N is the number of Monte Carlo trials.

✓ $\vec{e}_i$ is the dispersion added to the original position and velocity of the target and chaser for the ith trials.

✓ $$\begin{cases} \chi_s(\vec{e}_i)=1 & \text{if the miss-distance of the } i^{th} \text{ trial is lower or equal than s} \\ \\ \chi_s(\vec{e}_i)=0 & \text{Otherwise} \end{cases} \qquad (9)$$

The variance of the collision probability is:

$$\text{var}(P_c^{MC}(s))=\frac{P_c^{MC}(s)}{N}(1-P_c^{MC}(s)) \qquad (10)$$

To reach a standard deviation of the Monte Carlo probability ten times smaller than the computed probability, one shall realize a number of trials N given by:

$$N=\text{floor}\left(\frac{100}{P_c^{MC}(s)}\right) \qquad (11)$$

As a figure of merit, CNES for the conjunction risk daily assessment uses a 10^{-4} probability threshold. If we would like to detect a 10^{-4} probability with a standard deviation of 10^{-5}, we would need to realize 10^6 trials. Such a number of trials would be dramatic in terms of CPU run-time.

It is important to know that the covariance matrix from which we perform the trials, comes from the summation of the target's and chaser's covariance matrices. By this approach we consider the trajectory of the target as fully known (i.e. we do not perform any trial on the primary object). On the other hand, the trajectory of the chaser is dispersed according to the combined covariances of target and chaser. We then decrease by almost two the number of trajectories to propagate. We numerically check that this assumption is acceptable by computing the MSE on the miss-distance and comparing collision probabilities computed either through combination and disjunction of the covariance matrices.

Importance Sampling method

For the daily collision risk assessment, we usually have a very large set of small probabilities to compute. Of course, most of them are smaller than the probability threshold. For instance, CNES computes a collision probability for all conjunction with a miss distance lower than 10 km, being the security threshold used to compute the collision probability is in the order of ten meters. The lack of efficiency of the Monte Carlo method comes from the fact that we realize the trials around the chaser's position when we want to compute the number of trials entering the security volume centered at the primary object.

There exists a generalization of the Monte Carlo method, so called importance sampling method, which allows the user to define the probability density function as well as the position and velocity uncertainties to use when performing the trials.

Lets $g=\mathcal{N}(\vec{M}_{pv},\Sigma_{pv})$ be the normal law used to realize the classical Monte Carlo trials.

For importance sampling, the collision probability is obtained through:

$$P_c^h(r)=\frac{\sum_{i=1}^{N} q_i.\omega_i}{N} \qquad (12)$$

Where:

$$\checkmark \quad \begin{cases} q_i = 1 & \text{if the miss-distance of the i}^{th} \text{ trial is lower or equal than s} \\ \\ q_i = 0 & \text{Otherwise} \end{cases} \quad (13)$$

$\checkmark \quad \omega_i = \dfrac{g(\vec{e}_i)}{h(\vec{e}_i)}$ is a weight $\hfill (14)$

$\checkmark$ h is the probability density function that should fulfill:

$$q_i g(\vec{e}) = 0 \Rightarrow h(\vec{e}) = 0 \quad (15)$$

The variance of this probability can be written as:

$$\text{var}(P_c^h(r)) = \frac{1}{N}\left(\sum_{i=1}^{N} \frac{q_i \omega_i^2}{N} - \left(\sum_{i=1}^{N} \frac{q_i \omega_i}{N} \right)^2 \right) \quad (16)$$

We should notice that if g=h, the weights are equals to one and we are in the case of the classical Monte Carlo.

On the other hand, if we improperly choose the h function, one may have weights larger than one, which will degrade the quality of the results.

We propose to use a normal law for h. So for this function, we have to choose the value of the mean vector and a covariance matrix.

According to the first paragraph of this section, the choice of the mean vector is direct: it shall be the miss-distance between the target and chaser to ensure trials around the target position.

The choice of a covariance matrix is trickier: we look for trials with miss-distance inside the security volume. A first guess could be to consider a diagonal covariance in position depending on the security threshold. This point will be investigated later on the section.

For the moment let us consider that we have chosen a mean vector equal to the miss-distance, vector $\vec{d}$, and a covariance matrix in position Σ_p^*. At this point we must choose the velocity errors necessary for the Monte Carlo method.

We propose to determine the velocity components by a two steps procedure:

1. Position trials: We first realize trials for the position components according to the $h = \mathcal{N}(\vec{d}, \Sigma_p^*)$ probability density function. For N trials, we obtain for the chaser position the set of initial dispersed positions $\{\vec{P}_1, ..., \vec{P}_N\}$

2. We then compute trials on velocity knowing the given position $\vec{P}_i$: one can show that the velocity errors knowing $\vec{P}_i$ are distributed along a normal law $\mathcal{N}$ characterized by :[8]

   $\checkmark$ A velocity mean vector $E\left(\vec{V}|\vec{P}_i\right) = C_{P,V}^T \Sigma_p^{-1} \vec{P}_i$

   $\checkmark$ A covariance matrix $\Sigma\left(\vec{V}|\vec{P}_i\right) = \Sigma_V - C_{P,V}^T \Sigma_p^{-1} C_{P,V}$

So for each position of the set $\{\vec{P}_1,...,\vec{P}_N\}$, we can compute the velocity mean vector and the covariance matrix for a given Pi. By this two-steps procedure, we are able to compute N pairs of correlated position and velocity vectors.

In order to keep the velocity error characteristics unchanged, the trials on Pi are computed using the Σ_p^* covariance matrix while the velocity covariance matrix remains unchanged.

After a few algebraic manipulations, one can show that $\omega_i = \dfrac{g(\vec{e}_i)}{h(\vec{e}_i)} = \dfrac{\mathcal{N}(\vec{e}_i, 0, \Sigma_p)}{\mathcal{N}(\vec{e}_i, \vec{d}, \Sigma_p^*)}$.

For the choice of Σ_p^*, we tried different solutions. An acceptable covariance matrix (expressed in the conjunction frame) is:

$$\Sigma_p^* = \begin{pmatrix} \dfrac{s^2}{9} & 0 & 0 \\ 0 & \dfrac{s^2}{9} & 0 \\ 0 & 0 & \sigma_{C3}^2 \end{pmatrix} \tag{17}$$

Where s is the probability threshold and σ_{C3} is the standard deviation of the component out of the collision plane.

We defined the third diagonal component of Σ_p^* matrix different from the two others because of the relative movement of the two objects. A moving sphere will generate a cylinder. This is true for short-term encounters and an acceptable hypothesis for the long-term encounter cases that we have simulated. For quite low relative velocity encounters, the definition of the Σ_p^* matrix may be reviewed.

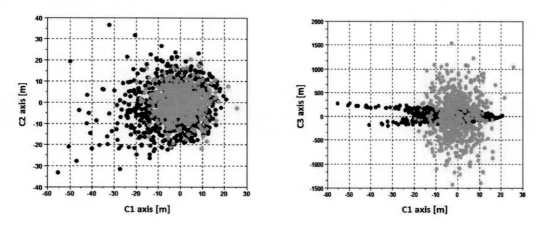

Figure 6. Comparison between Monte-Carlo Sampling (black dots) and importance sampling using a Σ_p^* type position's covariance matrix (green points) for McKinley's[1] conjunction. The Monte-Carlo sampling has been performed with a type III covariance Matrix (cf. table 6)

289

The Monte-Carlo samples shown on figure 6 (i.e. black dots), correspond to the N samples out of 100 000 whose had its distance at TCA lower than the security threshold. The distribution of the Monte-Carlo samples on the collision plane shows the effect that the velocity errors have on the relative movement. We show by the comparison between the Monte-Carlo and the importance sampling trials, performed with a Σ_p^* type position's covariance matrix, that due to those velocity errors the choice of the probability density function for the importance sampling technique is not a trivial matter. On the next section, we propose a dynamic method to optimize the choice of the importance sampling probability density function.

Table 10. McKinley's[1] conjunction probabilities of collision (20 m security threshold)

Covariance Matrix	Reference Probability	Importance Sampling $h = \mathcal{N}(\vec{d},\Sigma_p)$ (10 000 trials)		Importance Sampling $h=\mathcal{N}(\vec{d},\Sigma_p^*)$ (1000 trials)	
	MC, 100 000	Probability	Standard Deviation	Probability	Standard Deviation
I	4,610E-03	4,872E-03	6,751E-04	2,778E-03	1,043E-03
II	1,496E-02	1,528E-02	1,149E-03	1,191E-02	3,032E-03
III	6,033E-02	6,163E-02	2,216E-03	5,827E-02	9,152E-03

With table 10 we show that importance sampling with $h=\mathcal{N}(\vec{d},\Sigma_p^*)$ probability density function is not an optimal choice. In fact, when the velocity errors can be neglected or are not very important, this type of importance sampling will be quite efficient. As the reader might notice, to solve such a type of conjunction, we can use more run-time efficient methods than importance sampling.

Improved algorithm

When one ignores something, the best approach is to ask to someone who knows. The classical Monte Carlo algorithm can teach us how to choose the mean vector and the covariance matrix of h.

Let us imagine that we will have no limitation on CPU run-time and by hence we could perform any number of Monte Carlo trials we want. Following this approach we could search all trials with a miss-distance lower than S, the security threshold. For this set of selected trials, we consider the initial chaser positions dispersed by the Monte Carlo (i.e. before propagation). After propagation of each dispersed positions up to the time of closest approach, one just needs to compute the mean vector and covariance positions from the propagated conjunctions cloud. Following this approach we can compute an optimal mean vector and covariance matrix to use for h.

One can think that the presented approach is foolish because we could directly compute the collision probability after performing the Monte Carlo trials.

We propose to consider two security thresholds S and s with S>>s. Let $h_{opt}(S)$ and $h_{opt}(s)$ be the two optimal h functions (i.e. each one having its own mean vector and covariance matrix).

Then as S>>s, we have $h_{opt}(s) \subset h_{opt}(S)$. If a miss-distance is lower than s, then it is automatically lower than S.

We propose to use this property to choose the parameters of h:

1. We first realize N_1 Monte Carlo trials and search for the closest miss-distances. We sort them and select M of them ($M \leq N_1$). The largest mean distance of the M points gives the security threshold S. If S>>s, we derived from the Monte Carlo data the mean vector and mean covariance matrix for position corresponding to $h_{opt}(S)$.

2. We realize the importance sampling method with N_2 trials by using the mean vector and covariance matrix in position determined in step 1 and we compute for the security threshold s the collision probability and its standard deviation according to the two steps procedure.

This method needs to be tuned. We have to search for N_1 and N_2 the number of trials for the Monte Carlo and importance sampling method and M the number of Monte Carlo trials selected to compute the h parameters.

After performing several simulations to tune this method, we conclude that choosing $M=1/3$ N_1 and $N_1 = N_2$ provides quite acceptable results.

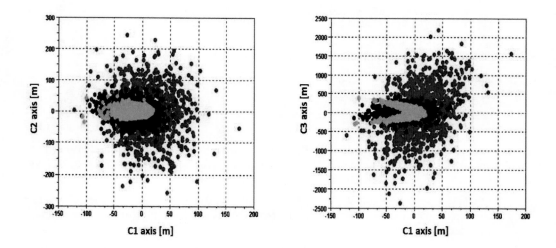

Figure 7. Comparison between Monte-Carlo Sampling (red dots), Monte-Carlo samples inside the security threshold (green point) and importance sampling computed from a sub-set of the Monte Carlo Samples (black dots), for McKinley's[1] conjunction. The Monte-Carlo sampling has been performed with a type II covariance Matrix (cf. table 6)

On figure 7 we show that the dynamic computation of a probability density function to perform the importance sampling, gives us a cloud of samples in coherence of what we call the optimal cloud (i.e. green dots on Figure 7). As the reader may notice, this cloud is much less dispersed than the one computed by the standard Monte-Carlo method. As shown on Table 11, the probability of collision computed with this approach, is very much in accordance with a 10^5 trials Monte-Carlo's probability of collision, which is used as reference.

Table 11. McKinley's[1] conjunction probabilities of collision (20 m security threshold)

Covariance Matrix	Reference Probability	Importance Sampling $h = \mathcal{N}(\vec{d}, \Sigma_p)$ (10 000 trials)		Importance Sampling $h = \mathcal{N}(\vec{d}, \Sigma_{\vec{p}})$ (1000 trials)		MC (1000 trials) + Importance sampling $h = \mathcal{N}(\vec{d} + \vec{\mu}_{opt}, \Sigma_p^{opt})$ (1000 trials)	
	MC, 100 000	Probability	Standard Deviation	Probability	Standard Deviation	Probability	Standard Deviation
I	4,610E-03	4,872E-03	6,751E-04	2,778E-03	1,043E-03	4,968E-03	6,846E-04
II	1,496E-02	1,528E-02	1,149E-03	1,191E-02	3,032E-03	1,599E-02	1,146E-03
III	6,033E-02	6,163E-02	2,216E-03	5,827E-02	9,152E-03	6,218E-02	2,539E-03

CONCLUSION

On this paper we have assessed on an innovative manner, as regards of the overall existing publications, the non-linear collision risk assessment topic.

On the first section we have widely exposed a geometric as well as a probabilistic analysis aiming to define the barrier within the linear and non linear conjunctions.

The main conclusions of this section are:

✓ For relative velocities between 1 and 5 m/s $P_{dmin} \neq P_{d1} \neq P_{d2}$. The conjunction can not be considered as linear, the position and the velocity errors are not constant and they must to be taken into account to evaluate the conjunction risk.

✓ For relative velocities between 5 and 10 m/s Pdmin ≈ Pd2 ≠ Pd1. The conjunction can be considered as linear and the position errors as well as the velocity errors must to be taken into account to evaluate the conjunction risk.

✓ For relative velocities higher than 10 m/s Pdmin ≈ Pd1 ≈ Pd2. At TCA the conjunction can be considered as linear, the position errors are constant and the velocity errors can be neglected

These boundaries, especially, the one between 5 and 10 m/s are depending on the covariance matrices used. If the velocity errors were smaller, the 5/10 m/s boundary may go closer to the 1/5 m/ boundaries.

On the second section of this paper we have presented an empirical method to compute the collision probability for conjunctions' relative velocities higher than 1 m/s. Such empirical method is based on a Monte-Carlo sampling coupled with an importance sampling method.

After developing the mathematic basis of such a method we have presented two approaches for the selection of the probability density function to be used for the importance sampling. One of those approaches consists on a dynamic probability density function selection. This dynamic approach allows us to use an importance sampling that will be close from the optimal one.

We show that using such quasi-optimal importance sampling approach, we considerably decrease the necessary number of trials without making any assumptions on the way to realize them.

NOTATION

TCA	Time of Closest Approach

Collision Plane   Plane defined at TCA. This plane is centered on the primary object and defined by $\{\vec{C}_1, \vec{C}_2, \vec{C}_3\}$ axis, being $\vec{C}_3$ normal to the plane

$$\vec{C}_3 \qquad \frac{\vec{V}_{deb} - \vec{V}_{sat}}{\left\| \vec{V}_{deb} - \vec{V}_{sat} \right\|}$$

$$\vec{C}_2 \qquad \frac{\vec{V}_{sat} \wedge \vec{V}_{deb}}{\left\| \vec{V}_{sat} - \vec{V}_{deb} \right\|}$$

$$\vec{C}_1 \qquad \frac{\vec{C}_2 \wedge \vec{C}_3}{\left\| \vec{C}_2 - \vec{C}_3 \right\|}$$

σ_z — Standard deviation along the $\vec{C}_3$ axis resulting from the addition of the primary and secondary orbital errors at the TCA on the collision plane.

V_{rel}^{ref} — Relative velocity's norm at TCA before dispersing the position and velocity vectors of the primary and secondary object

a — Semi-major axis

e — Eccentricity

i — inclination

ω — Argument of the perigee

Ω — Right ascension of the ascending node

ν — True anomaly

Equinoctial parameters
$$\left[a, e_x = e\cos(\omega + \Omega), e_y = \sin(\omega + \Omega), h_x = \tan\left(\frac{i}{2}\right)\cos(\Omega), h_y = \tan\left(\frac{i}{2}\right)\sin(\Omega), \right.$$
$$\left. \Omega + \omega + \upsilon \right]$$

[1] D. McKinley, "Development of a nonlinear probability of collision tool for the earth observing system". AIAA-2006-6295.

[2] Russell P. Patera., "Collision Probability for Larger Bodies Having Non-Linear Relative Motion". AAS-05-309 2005

[3] Salvatore Alfano, "Addressing Nonlinear Relative Motion for Spacecraft Collision Probability". AIAA 2006

[4] A. Jenkin, "Probability Concepts for GEO Collision Risk Assessment," Proceedings of 5th European Conference on Space Debris, p. 8 (ESA, Noordwijk, 2009)

[5] D.A. Danielson, C.P. Sagovac, B. Neta and L.W. Early, "Semi analytical satellite theory" Technical report, NPS-MA-95-002, Monterey CA, Naval Post Graduate School

[6] B. D. Ripley, "Stochastic Simulation", 1987, Wiley & Sons

[7] Salvatore Alfano, "Review of Conjunction Probability Methods for Short-Term Encounters". AAS 07-148

[8] Eric D. Kolaczyk, "Statistical Analysis of Network Data: Methods and Models". Springer Series in Statistics, 2009

DYNAMICAL SYSTEMS THEORY

SESSION 3

Chair:
John Sims
Jet Propulsion Laboratory

The following papers were not available for publication:

AAS 11-422
(Paper Withdrawn)

AAS 11-429
(Paper Withdrawn)

A NEW LOOK AT THE PLANAR DYNAMICS OF LIBRATION-ORBIT COUPLING FOR SPACECRAFT

Jay W. McMahon[*] and Daniel J. Scheeres[†]

In this paper, the planar dynamics of libration-orbit coupling for a spacecraft in orbit about a spherical Earth are examined. The coupled equations, up to second order moments of inertia of the satellite, are derived from first principles. The integrals of motion available in the system are used to reduce the system to a 2 degree-of-freedom relative representation in the radial distance and libration angle of the spacecraft. The conservation of energy is used to derive zero-velocity curves which can be used to bound the libration angles of the spacecraft. Analytical relationships for the maximum libration amplitude based on initial conditions at a zero libration angle are derived. The usage of these analytical relationships are illustrated through simulation of the Space Shuttle in low-Earth orbit. Importantly, the analytical relationships are shown to be able to predict the eccentricity where the libration can be circulate.

INTRODUCTION

The problem of coupling between the orbit of a finite body and its attitude motion have been studied since Lagrange. In the restricted (spacecraft) case, where the orbiting body is miniscule compared to the primary body, this problem is of studied under the name gravity gradient.[1] The main assumption in the gravity gradient problem is that the orbit remains Keplerian, and is not perturbed by the finite body of the spacecraft whether it is attitude motion is quiescent or excited.

The majority of the analytical results in the gravity gradient problem are concerned with the case when the spacecraft is in a circular orbit. In this case, since the radius is considered constant, there is no coupling from the orbit on the attitude motion. The in-plane attitude motion behaves exactly like a pendulum; therefore the dynamics are integrable using elliptic integrals.[1,2] In the circular orbit case, the total attitude motion can be restricted by the energy as was shown by Auelmann[3] and Pringle.[4]

When the orbit is allowed to be non-circular, analytical results are more difficult to determine. This is because even in the case when no effect on the orbital motion is considered, the attitude equation is now a forced non-linear differential equation. Much of the research into elliptical orbits revolves around near-circular orbits. In this case, perturbation methods can be used to try and infer information about the motion of the system.[2] If the method of successive approximations is used, the attitude motion can be resolved as a Mathieu equation,[1] which allows certain claims to be made. Mohan[5] used the method of averaging to determine the coupled effects on the attitude and translational motion.

Recent work has considered the full two-body problem,[6,7,8,9,10] largely motivated by the binary asteroid problem where the coupling is non-trivial. However these studies often result in complicated expressions that don't answer simple questions about the attitude motion.

In this paper, we analyze the planar problem where the spacecraft librates only in the orbital plane. Euler's equations[11] tell us that to second order moments of inertia, the in-plane motion is uncoupled from the out-of-plane motion as long as the out-of-plane modes are non excited. The assumption of second order moments of inertia is appropriate considering the very small coupling in this case; higher orders can be investigated,[12] however for the majority of spacecraft this will make little to no difference on finite precisions computers.

[*]PhD. Candidate, Aerospace Engineering Sciences, University of Colorado at Boulder, 429 UCB, Boulder, CO, 80309

[†]A. Richard Seebass Endowed Chair Professor, Aerospace Engineering Sciences, University of Colorado at Boulder, 429 UCB, Boulder, CO, 80309

This study is motivated by two question. First, can we determine the maximum libration amplitude without integrating the equations of motion given some initial conditions? Second, as the nominal Keplerian becomes elliptical, at what eccentricity is the forcing strong enough so that bounded libration is not possible? These questions are answered through both analytical derivation, and proof of concept with numerical examples based on the Space Shuttle in orbit at ISS altitudes.

SYSTEM DYNAMICS

The system under consideration in this paper is the planar dynamics of a spacecraft in orbit about a spherical planet. The spacecraft's mass distribution is represented up to second order using the principle moments of inertia. The fact that the spacecraft has a finite body creates a coupling between the orbit and attitude motion of the spacecraft. In this section, we derive the equations of motion for the fully coupled system, and use the integrals of motion available to reduce the dimensionality of the system. These results are compared to the classical equations of motion where the spacecraft's attitude motion is influenced by the orbital motion, but the orbit remains purely Keplerian.

Coupled System

The fully coupled system incorporates all coupling up to the second order moments-of-inertia of the spacecraft between both the orbit and the attitude motion. Equations of motion are derived and simplified using available integrals, and the linearized equations of motion are also derived.

Equations of Motion In general, we begin with the planar full two-body problem where both bodies are finite, but constrained to have their individual rotation poles perpendicular to the mutual orbit plane. This situation is illustrated in Fig. 1 with the angles of interest and radius defined.

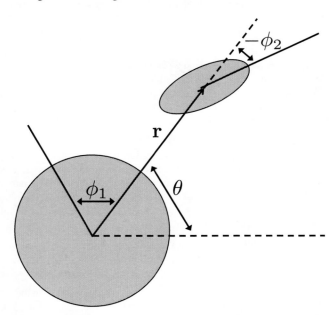

Figure 1. Definition of the system angles and relative radial vector.

Scheeres[13] showed that in this case, the potential energy using a second order expansion in the moments of inertia is,

$$V(r, \phi_1, \phi_2) = -\frac{GM_1M_2}{r}\left\{1 + \frac{1}{2r^2}\left[\mathrm{Tr}\,(\bar{\mathbf{I}}_1) + \mathrm{Tr}\,(\bar{\mathbf{I}}_2) - \frac{3}{2}\left(\bar{I}_{1_x} + \bar{I}_{1_y}\right.\right.\right.$$
$$\left.\left.\left. - \left(\bar{I}_{1_y} - \bar{I}_{1_x}\right)\cos 2\phi_1 + \bar{I}_{2_x} + \bar{I}_{2_y} - \left(\bar{I}_{2_y} - \bar{I}_{2_x}\right)\cos 2\phi_2\right)\right]\right\}$$

(1)

where $\bar{\mathbf{I}}_i$ is the mass normalized (signified by the bar) inertia dyad of body i, and the subscripts on the non-bold versions indicate a principle moment of inertia. G is the gravitational constant, M_i the mass of body i, Tr() indicates the trace of the dyad.

In the case of a spherical primary, which means that $\bar{I}_{1_x} = \bar{I}_{1_y} = \bar{I}_{1_z}$, and therefore the potential simplifies to,

$$V(r, \phi_2) = -\frac{GM_1M_2}{r}\left\{1 + \frac{1}{2r^2}\left[-\frac{1}{2}\bar{I}_{2_x} - \frac{1}{2}\bar{I}_{2_y} + \bar{I}_{2_z} + \frac{3}{2}\left(\bar{I}_{2_y} - \bar{I}_{2_x}\right)\cos 2\phi_2\right]\right\}$$

(2)

Note that the spherical symmetry causes the potential energy to be independent of the primary's orientation, as represented in the planar problem by ϕ_1.

The kinetic energy using a second order expansion in the moments of inertia is,

$$T = \frac{1}{2}I_{1_z}\dot{\theta}_1^2 + \frac{1}{2}I_{2_z}\dot{\phi}_2^2 + \frac{1}{2}m\dot{r}^2 + \frac{1}{2}\left(I_{2_z} + mr^2\right)\dot{\theta}^2 + I_{2_z}\dot{\phi}_2\dot{\theta}$$

(3)

where $\dot{\theta}_1 = \dot{\phi}_1 + \dot{\theta}$.

The reduced mass is defined as,

$$m = \frac{M_1M_2}{M_1 + M_2} \simeq M_2$$

(4)

where the approximate relationship comes from the fact that for our problem of interest here, $M_2 \ll M_1$.

We define the general moment of inertia as,

$$I_z(r) = I_{2_z} + mr^2$$

(5)

The Lagrangian, $L = T - V$ for this system is,

$$L = \frac{1}{2}I_{1_z}\left(\dot{\theta} + \dot{\phi}_1\right)^2 + \frac{1}{2}I_{2_z}\dot{\phi}_2^2 + \frac{1}{2}m\dot{r}^2 + \frac{1}{2}\left(I_{2_z} + mr^2\right)\dot{\theta}^2 + I_{2_z}\dot{\phi}_2\dot{\theta} - V(r, \phi_2)$$

(6)

Using Lagrange's equations with out any external forces,

$$\frac{\mathrm{d}}{\mathrm{d}t}\left(\frac{\partial L}{\partial \dot{q}_i}\right) = \frac{\partial L}{\partial q_i}$$

(7)

the equations of motion for this system with the coordinates r, θ, ϕ_1, and ϕ_2 are,

$$\ddot{r} = \dot{\theta}^2 r - \frac{1}{m}\frac{\partial V}{\partial r}$$

(8)

$$\ddot{\phi}_1 = -\left(1 + \frac{mr^2}{I_{1z}}\right)\frac{1}{mr^2}\frac{\partial V}{\partial \phi_1} - \frac{1}{mr^2}\frac{\partial V}{\partial \phi_2} + 2\frac{\dot{r}\dot{\theta}}{r}$$

(9)

$$\ddot{\phi}_2 = -\left(1 + \frac{mr^2}{I_{2z}}\right)\frac{1}{mr^2}\frac{\partial V}{\partial \phi_2} - \frac{1}{mr^2}\frac{\partial V}{\partial \phi_1} + 2\frac{\dot{r}\dot{\theta}}{r}$$

(10)

$$\ddot{\theta} = \frac{1}{mr^2}\frac{\partial V}{\partial \phi_1} + \frac{1}{mr^2}\frac{\partial V}{\partial \phi_2} - 2\frac{\dot{r}\dot{\theta}}{r}$$

(11)

However, the potential is not a function of ϕ_1 so that

$$\frac{\partial V}{\partial \phi_1} = 0 \tag{12}$$

and the equations of motion for the angles become,

$$\ddot{\phi}_1 = -\frac{1}{mr^2}\frac{\partial V}{\partial \phi_2} + 2\frac{\dot{r}\dot{\theta}}{r} \tag{13}$$

$$\ddot{\phi}_2 = -\left(1 + \frac{mr^2}{I_{2_z}}\right)\frac{1}{mr^2}\frac{\partial V}{\partial \phi_2} + 2\frac{\dot{r}\dot{\theta}}{r} \tag{14}$$

$$\ddot{\theta} = \frac{1}{mr^2}\frac{\partial V}{\partial \phi_2} - 2\frac{\dot{r}\dot{\theta}}{r} \tag{15}$$

The partials of the potential are,

$$\frac{\partial V}{\partial r} = \frac{\mu m}{r^2}\left\{1 + \frac{3}{2r^2}\left[-\frac{1}{2}\overline{I}_{2_x} - \frac{1}{2}\overline{I}_{2_y} + \overline{I}_{2_z} + \frac{3}{2}\left(\overline{I}_{2_y} - \overline{I}_{2_x}\right)\cos 2\phi_2\right]\right\} \tag{16}$$

$$\frac{\partial V}{\partial \phi_2} = \frac{3}{2}\frac{\mu m}{r^3}\left(\overline{I}_{2_y} - \overline{I}_{2_x}\right)\sin(2\phi_2) \tag{17}$$

where the approximation $\mu = G(M_1 + M_2) \simeq GM_1$ has been used.

Integrals of Motion In the current problem there are three integrals of motion. The first is the total energy of the system, which is shown to be the Jacobi integral of this system since it is time invariant,

$$h = \dot{\mathbf{q}} \cdot \frac{\partial L}{\partial \dot{\mathbf{q}}} - L = T + V \tag{18}$$

The second integral of motion is the total angular momentum of the system. This is found because the coordinate θ is ignorable, meaning that $\mathrm{d}/\mathrm{dt}(\partial L/\partial \dot{\theta}) = 0$, so the integral is written as,

$$\begin{aligned} K_{tot} &= \frac{\partial V}{\partial \dot{\theta}} \\ &= I_z(r)\dot{\theta} + I_{2_z}\dot{\phi}_2 + I_{1_z}\dot{\theta}_1 \end{aligned} \tag{19}$$

The third integral is found by combining Eqs. (13) and (15), so we find that

$$\ddot{\theta}_1 = \ddot{\phi}_1 + \ddot{\theta} = 0 \tag{20}$$

Therefore the inertial angular velocity of the primary, $\dot{\theta}_1$, is an integral of motion. This implies that the terms in the kinetic energy and angular momentum expressions which depend only on $\dot{\theta}_1$ are also conserved. This fact makes intuitive sense as a primary that is symmetric about the spin axis can't have any gravitational torques exerted on it from the secondary since the center of mass and the center of gravity (in the secondary's gravity field) are at the same location in the primary.

Using this fact, we will redefine the kinetic energy from Eq. (3) as,

$$T = T_1 + \frac{1}{2}I_{2_z}\dot{\phi}_2^2 + \frac{1}{2}m\dot{r}^2 + \frac{1}{2}I_z\dot{\theta}^2 + I_{2_z}\dot{\phi}_2\dot{\theta} \tag{21}$$

where $T_1 = (1/2)I_{1_z}\dot{\theta}_1^2$ is the kinetic energy of the primary, which is constant. Likewise, we can define the free angular momentum from Eq. (22) to be,

$$K = K_{tot} - K_1 = I_z(r)\dot{\theta} + I_{2_z}\dot{\phi}_2 \tag{22}$$

300

where $K_1 = I_{1_z}\dot\theta_1$ is the angular momentum of the primary, which is constant. This relationship between the free angular momentum and the orbit angular velocity will allow us to eliminate $\dot\theta$ from the system. Solving Eq. (22) for the angular velocity gives,

$$\dot\theta = \frac{K - I_{2_z}\dot\phi_2}{I_z(r)} \tag{23}$$

Substituting Eq. (23) into Eq. (21) allows us to write the kinetic energy as,

$$T = T_1 + \frac{1}{2}\frac{K^2}{I_z} + \frac{1}{2}m\dot r^2 + \frac{1}{2}\frac{I_{2_z}mr^2\dot\phi_2^2}{I_z} \tag{24}$$

so that the total energy of the system can be written as,

$$h = T_1 + \frac{1}{2}\frac{K^2}{I_z} + \frac{1}{2}m\dot r^2 + \frac{1}{2}\frac{I_{2_z}mr^2\dot\phi_2^2}{I_z} + V(r,\phi_2) \tag{25}$$

or alternatively the free energy of the system can be written as,

$$E = h - T_1 = \frac{1}{2}\frac{K^2}{I_z} + \frac{1}{2}m\dot r^2 + \frac{1}{2}\frac{I_{2_z}mr^2\dot\phi_2^2}{I_z} + V(r,\phi_2) \tag{26}$$

It is interesting to note that the description of the free energy of the system does not require any knowledge about the primary spin state as neither ϕ_1 or $\dot\phi_1$ appear anywhere in Eq. (26).

We can now reduce the order of the system by using the facts that ϕ_1 is ignorable, and that through the conservation of angular momentum we can remove any dependence on θ using Eq. (23). Therefore, the system is reduced to 2 degrees-of-freedom, and the equations of motion are

$$\ddot r = \frac{(K - I_{2_z}\dot\phi_2)^2 r}{I_z^2} - \frac{1}{m}\frac{\partial V}{\partial r} \tag{27}$$

$$\ddot\phi_2 = -\left(1 + \frac{mr^2}{I_{2_z}}\right)\frac{1}{mr^2}\frac{\partial V}{\partial\phi_2} + 2\frac{\dot r(K - I_{2_z}\dot\phi_2)}{rI_z} \tag{28}$$

These coordinates describe the relative motion of the spacecraft and Earth. If they are represented in a frame that is fixed to the spacecraft body, they are in fact polar coordinates. This frame is pictured in Fig. 2.

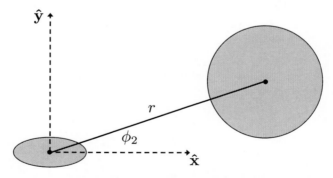

Figure 2. Definition of the secondary fixed relative frame.

This frame rotates with the orbit, so that if there is no libration of the spacecraft ($\phi_2(t) = 0$), the Earth location will be fixed. When the spacecraft is librating, the Earth will appear to move relative to the secondary due to the libration, as well as changing the separation distance as energy is traded between the orbit and the libration.

301

Linearized System Dynamics While the motion of the dynamical system will always lie on or within a zero-velocity curve for a given free energy and angular momentum, the system need not necessarily explore the entire region. In this section, we analyze the manifolds around the equilibrium points and the presence of periodic orbits which will influence the behavior of a system within its zero-velocity curve bounded region.

This analysis require us to determine the dynamic matrix,

$$A = \frac{\partial \mathbf{f}(\mathbf{q}, \dot{\mathbf{q}})}{\partial [\mathbf{q}, \dot{\mathbf{q}}]} \tag{29}$$

where $\mathbf{q} = \begin{bmatrix} r & \theta & \phi_1 & \phi_2 \end{bmatrix}$.

The dynamical matrix is a 4x4 matrix with the form,

$$A = \begin{bmatrix} 0 & 0 & 1 & 0 \\ 0 & 0 & 0 & 1 \\ \frac{\partial \ddot{r}}{\partial r} & \frac{\partial \ddot{r}}{\partial \phi_2} & 0 & \frac{\partial \ddot{r}}{\partial \dot{\phi}_2} \\ \frac{\partial \ddot{\phi}_2}{\partial r} & \frac{\partial \ddot{\phi}_2}{\partial \phi_2} & \frac{\partial \ddot{\phi}_2}{\partial \dot{r}} & \frac{\partial \ddot{\phi}_2}{\partial \dot{\phi}_2} \end{bmatrix} \tag{30}$$

The partials are,

$$\frac{\partial \ddot{r}}{\partial r} = \frac{1}{I_z^2} \left[K^2 - 2KI_{2_z}\dot{\phi}_2 + I_{2_z}^2 \dot{\phi}_2^2 \right] - \frac{1}{m}\frac{\partial^2 V}{\partial r^2}$$
$$- \frac{r}{I_z^4} \left[\left(4I_{2_z}mr + 4m^2r^3 \right) \left(K^2 - 2KI_{2_z}\dot{\phi}_2 + I_{2_z}^2 \dot{\phi}_2^2 \right) \right] \tag{31}$$

$$\frac{\partial \ddot{r}}{\partial \phi_2} = -\frac{1}{m}\frac{\partial^2 V}{\partial r \partial \phi_2} \tag{32}$$

$$\frac{\partial \ddot{r}}{\partial \dot{\phi}_2} = \frac{2r}{I_z^2} \left[-KI_{2_z} + I_{2_z}^2 \dot{\phi}_2 \right] \tag{33}$$

$$\frac{\partial \ddot{\phi}_2}{\partial r} = \frac{2}{mr^3}\frac{\partial V}{\partial \phi_2} - \left(1 + \frac{mr^2}{I_{2_z}} \right) \frac{1}{mr^2}\frac{\partial^2 V}{\partial r \partial \phi_2} - \frac{2\dot{r}}{r^2 I_z^2} \left[\left(K - I_{2_z}\dot{\phi}_2 \right) \left(I_{2_z} + 3mr^2 \right) \right] \tag{34}$$

$$\frac{\partial \ddot{\phi}_2}{\partial \phi_2} = -\left(\frac{1}{mr^2} + \frac{1}{I_{2_z}} \right) \frac{\partial^2 V}{\partial \phi_2^2} \tag{35}$$

$$\frac{\partial \ddot{\phi}_2}{\partial \dot{r}} = \frac{2}{rI_z} \left(K - I_{2_z}\dot{\phi}_2 \right) \tag{36}$$

$$\frac{\partial \ddot{\phi}_2}{\partial \dot{\phi}_2} = -\frac{2I_{2_z}\dot{r}}{rI_z} \tag{37}$$

And the second partials of the potential are given by,

$$\frac{\partial^2 V}{\partial r^2} = -\frac{2\mu m}{r^3} \left\{ 1 + \frac{3}{r^2} \left[-\frac{1}{2}\bar{I}_{2_x} - \frac{1}{2}\bar{I}_{2_y} + \bar{I}_{2_z} + \frac{3}{2} \left(\bar{I}_{2_y} - \bar{I}_{2_x} \right) \cos 2\phi_2 \right] \right\} \tag{38}$$

$$\frac{\partial^2 V}{\partial \phi_2^2} = \frac{3\mu m}{r^3} \left(\bar{I}_{2_y} - \bar{I}_{2_x} \right) \cos 2\phi_2 \tag{39}$$

$$\frac{\partial^2 V}{\partial r \partial \phi_2} = -\frac{9\mu m}{2r^4} \left(\bar{I}_{2_y} - \bar{I}_{2_x} \right) \sin 2\phi_2 \tag{40}$$

Classical Semi-Coupled Equations

Classically, the spacecraft libration case is analyzed by assuming the orbital elements are constant so that the time history of r (and $\ddot{\theta}$) are known *a priori*. By making this assumption that the finite spacecraft body has no effect on the orbital motion relative to the Earth, the librational equation of motion is written as[1,2]

$$I_{2_z}\ddot{\phi}_2 + 3\frac{\mu}{r^3}\left(I_{2_y} - I_{2_x}\right)\sin(2\phi_2) = I_{2_z}\ddot{\theta} \tag{41}$$

This equation of motion can be easily derived by substituting Eq. (15) into Eq. (14). In this case, as was mentioned above, the orbital motion is purely Keplerian so that Eq.(23) does not apply, and therefore $\dot{\phi}_2$ has no effect on $\dot{\theta}$.

EQUILIBRIUM CONDITIONS

In this section, we derive the conditions for finding point of relative equilibrium between the two bodies. If the spacecraft is placed at these points, the relative states will be constant. We also derive the conditions for investigating the stability of these relative equilibrium points.

Determination of Equilibrium Points

Following Scheeres,[13] we find the equilibrium points by searching for places where the variations in energy are stationary at a constant value of angular momentum. In other words, we find when the following conditions hold:

$$\frac{\partial E}{\partial r} = \frac{\partial E}{\partial \dot{r}} = \frac{\partial E}{\partial \phi_2} = \frac{\partial E}{\partial \dot{\phi}_2} = 0 \tag{42}$$

at a given value of K, as seen in Eq. (26).

The following relationships are found,

$$\frac{\partial E}{\partial \dot{r}} = m\dot{r} \tag{43}$$

$$\frac{\partial E}{\partial \dot{\phi}_2} = \frac{I_{2_z}mr^2\dot{\phi}_2}{I_z} \tag{44}$$

$$\frac{\partial E}{\partial \phi_2} = \frac{3}{2}\frac{\mu m}{r^3}\left(\overline{I}_{2_y} - \overline{I}_{2_x}\right)\sin(2\phi_2) \tag{45}$$

which when combined with the stationarity conditions imply, respectively, that $\dot{r} = 0$, $\dot{\phi}_2 = 0$, and $\phi_2 = 0$, $\pm\pi/2$, or π. Using these conditions, we can evaluate the partial with respect to r to be,

$$\frac{\partial E}{\partial r} = -mr\frac{K^2}{I_z^2} + \frac{\mu m}{r^2}\left[1 + \frac{3}{2}\frac{C_2^\pm}{r^2}\right] \tag{46}$$

where

$$C_2^\pm = \begin{cases} -2\overline{I}_{2_x} + \overline{I}_{2_y} + \overline{I}_{2_z} & \text{if } \phi_2 = 0, \pi \\ \overline{I}_{2_x} - 2\overline{I}_{2_y} + \overline{I}_{2_z} & \text{if } \phi_2 = \pm\pi/2 \end{cases} \tag{47}$$

Now, applying the condition for stationarity with respect to r gives,

$$\begin{aligned} r^6 &- \frac{K^2}{m^2\mu}r^5 + \left[\frac{2I_{2_z}}{m} + \frac{3}{2}C_2^\pm\right]r^4 \\ &+ \left[\frac{I_{2_z}^2}{m^2} + \frac{3I_{2_z}}{m}C_2^\pm\right]r^2 + \frac{3}{2}\frac{I_{2_z}^2}{m^2}C_2^\pm = 0 \end{aligned} \tag{48}$$

303

Equilibrium Point Stability

The stability of the equilibrium points can be investigate by linearizing the dynamics around the equilibrium point and analyzing the eigenvalues of the dynamics matrix. Recall that the equilibrium points must occur at $\dot{r} = 0$, $\dot{\phi}_2 = 0$, and $\phi_2 = 0, \pm\pi/2$, or π. Therefore the partials for the dynamic matrix are greatly reduced to become,

$$\frac{\partial \ddot{r}}{\partial r} = \frac{K^2}{I_z^2} - \frac{1}{I_z^4} \left[\left(4I_{2_z} m r_{eq} + 4m^2 r_{eq}^3 \right) K^2 r_{eq} \right] - \frac{1}{m} \left(\frac{\partial^2 V}{\partial r^2} \right)_{eq} \tag{49}$$

$$\frac{\partial \ddot{r}}{\partial \phi_2} = -\frac{1}{m} \left(\frac{\partial^2 V}{\partial r \partial \phi_2} \right)_{eq} \tag{50}$$

$$\frac{\partial \ddot{r}}{\partial \dot{\phi}_2} = -\frac{2 r_{eq} K}{I_z^2} \tag{51}$$

$$\frac{\partial \ddot{\phi}_2}{\partial r} = \frac{2}{m r_{eq}^3} \left(\frac{\partial V}{\partial \phi_2} \right)_{eq} - \left(1 + \frac{m r_{eq}^2}{I_{2_z}} \right) \frac{1}{m r_{eq}^2} \left(\frac{\partial^2 V}{\partial r \partial \phi_2} \right)_{eq} \tag{52}$$

$$\frac{\partial \ddot{\phi}_2}{\partial \phi_2} = -\left(\frac{1}{m r_{eq}^2} + \frac{1}{I_{2_z}} \right) \left(\frac{\partial^2 V}{\partial \phi_2^2} \right)_{eq} \tag{53}$$

$$\frac{\partial \ddot{\phi}_2}{\partial \dot{r}} = \frac{2K}{r_{eq} I_z} \tag{54}$$

$$\frac{\partial \ddot{\phi}_2}{\partial \dot{\phi}_2} = 0 \tag{55}$$

Where the equilibrium point distance is indicated by r_{eq}.

The second partials of the potential evaluated at the equilibrium points depend on the value of ϕ_2. In the case where $\phi_2 = 0$ or π, the equations are,

$$\frac{\partial^2 V}{\partial r^2} = -\frac{2\mu m}{r_{eq}^3} \left\{ 1 + \frac{3}{r_{eq}^2} \left[-\frac{1}{2}\bar{I}_{2_x} - \frac{1}{2}\bar{I}_{2_y} + \bar{I}_{2_z} + \frac{3}{2} \left(\bar{I}_{2_y} - \bar{I}_{2_x} \right) \right] \right\} \tag{56}$$

$$\frac{\partial^2 V}{\partial \phi_2^2} = \frac{3\mu m}{r_{eq}^3} \left(\bar{I}_{2_y} - \bar{I}_{2_x} \right) \tag{57}$$

$$\frac{\partial^2 V}{\partial r \partial \phi_2} = 0 \tag{58}$$

In the case where $\phi_2 = \pm\pi/2$, the equations are,

$$\frac{\partial^2 V}{\partial r^2} = -\frac{2\mu m}{r_{eq}^3} \left\{ 1 + \frac{3}{r_{eq}^2} \left[-\frac{1}{2}\bar{I}_{2_x} - \frac{1}{2}\bar{I}_{2_y} + \bar{I}_{2_z} - \frac{3}{2} \left(\bar{I}_{2_y} - \bar{I}_{2_x} \right) \right] \right\} \tag{59}$$

$$\frac{\partial^2 V}{\partial \phi_2^2} = -\frac{3\mu m}{r_{eq}^3} \left(\bar{I}_{2_y} - \bar{I}_{2_x} \right) \tag{60}$$

$$\frac{\partial^2 V}{\partial r \partial \phi_2} = 0 \tag{61}$$

304

Given that the linearized system near the equilibrium point is simplified significantly, we can find the eigenvalues of the system analytically. The dynamics matrix around the equilibrium points has the form,

$$A = \begin{bmatrix} 0 & 0 & 1 & 0 \\ 0 & 0 & 0 & 1 \\ P & 0 & 0 & Q \\ 0 & R & S & 0 \end{bmatrix} \tag{62}$$

where the non-zero partials ($\frac{\partial \ddot{r}}{\partial r}$, $\frac{\partial \ddot{r}}{\partial \phi_2}$, $\frac{\partial \ddot{\phi}_2}{\partial \ddot{r}}$, and $\frac{\partial \ddot{\phi}_2}{\partial \phi_2}$) have been represented by simpler variable expressions (P, Q, R, and S). The characteristic equation for this matrix is simply,

$$\lambda^4 - (P + R + QS)\lambda^2 + PR = 0 \tag{63}$$

The roots of this equation are,

$$\lambda^2 = \frac{P + R + QS \pm \sqrt{(P + R + QS)^2 - 4PR}}{2} \tag{64}$$

The determination of the eigenvalues can easily be carried out numerically on a case-by-case basis to determine the dynamical behavior around the equilibrium point.

The eigenvectors can also be computed analytically by writing the eigenvalue problem as,

$$\left[\lambda I - A \right] \mathbf{v} = 0 \tag{65}$$

where the eigenvector is $\mathbf{v} = [v_1 \quad v_2 \quad v_3 \quad v_4]^T$. The four equations that result are,

$$\lambda v_1 - v_3 = 0 \tag{66}$$

$$\lambda v_2 - v_4 = 0 \tag{67}$$

$$-Pv_1 + \lambda v_3 - Qv_4 = 0 \tag{68}$$

$$-Rv_2 = Sv_3 + \lambda v_4 = 0 \tag{69}$$

The eigenvector can be computed from these relationships to be

$$\mathbf{v} = \begin{bmatrix} 1 \\ \sigma \\ \lambda \\ \sigma\lambda \end{bmatrix} \tag{70}$$

where

$$\sigma = \frac{\lambda^2 - P}{Q\lambda} \tag{71}$$

Note that for this system, the stable equilibrium point (located at $\phi = 0°$) has two sets of complex eigenvalues with zero real parts, and the unstable equilibrium point (located at $\phi = 90°$) has one pair of stable/unstable real eigenvalues and a set of complex eigenvalues with zero real parts.

ZERO VELOCITY CURVES

Recalling the relationship for the free energy of the system, Eq. (26), we can rearrange this to read,

$$E - \frac{1}{2}\frac{K^2}{I_z} - V(r, \phi_2) = \frac{1}{2}m\dot{r}^2 + \frac{1}{2}\frac{I_{2_z}mr^2\dot{\phi}_2^2}{I_z} \tag{72}$$

305

We note that the right hand side of Eq. (72) is always positive, therefore we can state the relationship for a zero-velocity curve (ZVC),

$$E - \frac{1}{2}\frac{K^2}{I_z} - V(r, \phi_2) \geq 0 \tag{73}$$

or equivalently,

$$E \geq \frac{1}{2}\frac{K^2}{I_z} + V(r, \phi_2) \tag{74}$$

Eqs. (73) and (74) give a relationship that restricts the limits of the motion of the primary and secondary relative to one another. In fact, since θ and $\dot{\theta}$ are not present in these relationships at all, this directly places limits on the relative separation distance and the secondary libration angle. These ZVCs are easy to visualize in the secondary fixed frame, as shown in Fig. 2, since they depend only on r and ϕ_2.

Eq. (74) is a powerful relationship that can be used to bound the extents of the relative motion of the two bodies. A given system will have some area in the $r - \phi_2$ space which it can reside in based upon the free angular momentum and energy. In fact, given a value for the free angular momentum of the system, the entire phase space can be mapped with varying energy levels determined by Eq. (74). For a given value of free energy for the system, there will be some area to which the primary is constrained to reside. Note that due to the fact that this relationship is an inequality, the primary can be anywhere inside the free energy level, not only on the surface. Therefore this relationship clearly doesn't solve the equations of motion to tell us what the state is at any given time, but it does tell us absolutely that the state is always inside the area bounded by that free energy.

LIMITS ON LIBRATIONAL AMPLITUDE

The zero-velocity curves derived in the previous section are a good first test to determine the extents of possible motion in the rotating frame. If the energy is less than that of the unstable equilibrium point, then we can use the ZVC to limit the librational motion. However, if the energy is greater than that of the unstable equilibrium, the ZVC will be open in the librational direction, meaning that no information about the librational motion can be obtained. In this section we show that by intelligently analyzing the components of the system energy, a relationship can be determined which limits the maximum libration amplitude based on the initial libration rate.

To motivate this idea, first we recognize that the current problem is effectively that of two harmonic oscillators, the orbit and the libration, which are coupled together. We can write the free energy of the system using Eqs. (2), (3) and (21) as,

$$E = V + T - T_1 = mE_{Kep} + E_\phi + E_{coup} \tag{75}$$

where E_{Kep} is the Keplerian specific energy, E_ϕ is the librational energy (identical to a pendulum), and E_{coup} is the "coupling" energy. The first two energies are the energy in each of our harmonic oscillators and are given by the standard relationships

$$E_{Kep} = -\frac{\mu}{r} + \frac{1}{2}\dot{r}^2 + \frac{1}{2}r^2\dot{\theta}^2 \tag{76}$$

$$E_\phi = \frac{1}{2}I_{2_z}\dot{\phi}_2^2 + \frac{3\mu m}{2r^3}\left(\overline{I}_{2_y} - \overline{I}_{2_x}\right)\sin^2\phi_2 \tag{77}$$

Recalling the trigonometric relationship

$$\frac{1}{2}\cos 2\phi_2 = \frac{1}{2} - \sin^2\phi_2 \tag{78}$$

allows us to determine the coupling energy from Eq. (75), using Eqs. (76) and (77) as

$$E_{coup} = -\frac{\mu m}{2r^3}C_2^+ + \frac{1}{2}I_{2_z}\dot{\theta}^2 + I_{2_z}\dot{\theta}\dot{\phi}_2 \tag{79}$$

where C_2^+ was defined in Eq. (47).

306

Circular Orbit

Classical analysis of a librating spacecraft in a circular orbit looks at the two harmonic oscillators as uncoupled systems. Therefore the coupling energy is ignored, which means that the assumption is either a) the coupling energy is zero, or b) the coupling energy is constant. These assumptions are improper, as this energy is not insignificant, and clearly changes with the librational state.

A more applicable assumption for the case of a spacecraft in orbit about a large body is that the coupling is one-way. In effect, the radial dynamics are unaffected by the librational motion, and the relationship between r and $\dot{r}$ are preserved in Keplerian fashion. The rotational motion is affected however; the orbit rate is not purely Keplerian due to the the the conservation of angular momentum in Eq. (23), and the librational motion clearly varies.

Under these assumptions, we will remove $\dot{\theta}$ from the energy equations by using Eq. (23). Then, we separate the energy into two terms, those that depend only on r and $\dot{r}$, and are considered constant, and those that depend on the librational states ϕ_2 and $\dot{\phi}_2$. This allows us to write,

$$\Delta E_{lib} = E + \frac{m\mu}{r} - \frac{1}{2}m\dot{r}^2 + \frac{\mu m}{2r^3}C_2^+ - \frac{1}{2}\frac{K^2}{I_z} \tag{80}$$

which is considered a constant for this system. The remainder of the energy terms which depend on libration are then equal to this value,

$$\Delta E_{lib} = \frac{I_{2_z}mr^2\dot{\phi}_2^2}{2I_z} + \frac{3\mu m}{2r^3}\left(\bar{I}_{2_y} - \bar{I}_{2_x}\right)\sin^2\phi_2 \tag{81}$$

Eq. (81) can be used to determine the maximum libration angle ($\phi_{2,max}$) for a given initial libration rate ($\dot{\phi}_{2,0}$) and radius value. Effectively, we set

$$\Delta E_{lib}(r, \phi_2 = 0, \dot{\phi}_{2,0}) = \Delta E_{lib}(r, \phi_{2,max}, \dot{\phi}_2 = 0) \tag{82}$$

which gives the relationship

$$\frac{I_{2_z}mr^2\dot{\phi}_{2,0}^2}{2I_z} = \frac{3\mu m}{2r^3}\left(\bar{I}_{2_y} - \bar{I}_{2_x}\right)\sin^2\phi_{2,max} \tag{83}$$

It is interesting to compare Eq. (83) to the classical gravity gradient result with no coupling energy considered. In that case, the left hand side is simply $1/2I_{2_z}\dot{\phi}_{2,0}^2$. In the case where the system is dominated by the orbit, $mr^2 \gg I_{2_z}$, and therefore $I_z \to mr^2$. Making this substitution into Eq. (83) simplifies it to the classical result.

Eq. (83) is a key result, which has two main applications. First, a certain initial libration rate and radius can be tested to determine the maximum reachable libration amplitude. Second, the maximum amplitude can be set to $90°$, and then the maximum initial libration rate above which libration will occur can be found. In other words, the equation

$$\dot{\phi}_{2,0}^2 = \frac{3\mu I_z}{I_{2_z}r^5}\left(\bar{I}_{2_y} - \bar{I}_{2_x}\right) \tag{84}$$

gives the limiting libration rate, above which the spacecraft will circulate, and below which the libration will be bounded. Recall that the value of $\dot{\phi}_2$ is limited by the energy at a given radius through Eqs. (80) and (81), so that it may or may not be possible for the value computed from Eq. (84) to be achievable in a given system.

Near Circular Orbit

In reality, even very weakly coupled systems will cause the orbit to be non-Keplerian, and thus r and $\dot{r}$ will vary from their Keplerian values and thus affect the energy. To investigate this situation without resorting to numerical integration of the equations of motion, we take the variation of the system energy with respect to r and $\dot{r}$.

Starting from Eqs. (76), (77), and (79), we find the variations in the energies to second order in δr and $\delta \dot{r}$ to be given by,

$$\delta E_{kep} = \dot{r}\delta\dot{r} + \frac{1}{2}\delta\dot{r}^2 + \left[\frac{\mu}{r^2} + r\dot{\theta}^2 + \frac{2mr^3\dot{\theta}^2}{I_z}\right]\delta r$$
$$+ \left[-\frac{\mu}{r^3} + \frac{1}{2}\dot{\theta}^2 + \frac{5mr^2\dot{\theta}^2}{I_z} + \frac{6m^2r^4\dot{\theta}^2}{I_z^2}\right]\delta r^2 \tag{85}$$

$$\delta E_\phi = \frac{3\mu m}{2r^3}\left(\overline{I}_{2_y} - \overline{I}_{2_x}\right)\sin^2\phi_2\left[-3\frac{\delta r}{r} + 6\frac{\delta r^2}{r^2}\right] \tag{86}$$

$$\delta E_{coup} = \left[\frac{3\mu m}{2r^4}C_2^+ + \frac{2mrI_{2_z}\dot{\theta}}{I_z}\left(\dot{\theta} + \dot{\phi}_2\right)\right]\delta r$$
$$+ \left[-\frac{3\mu m}{2r^5}C_2^+ + \frac{I_{2_z}\dot{\theta}^2}{I_z}\left(m + \frac{2m^2r^2}{I_z}\right) + \frac{I_{2_z}\dot{\theta}\dot{\phi}_2}{I_z}\left(m + \frac{4m^2r^2}{I_z}\right)\right]\delta r^2 \tag{87}$$

In these equations, the values of $\dot{\theta}$ and I_z are determined at the nominal radius, r; these equations account for their variations with respect to r.

To analyze the system, we first note that ΔE_{lib} remains constant, as defined in Eq. (80). However, Eq. (81) becomes,

$$\Delta E_{lib} = \frac{I_{2_z}mr^2\dot{\phi}_2^2}{2I_z} + \frac{3\mu m}{2r^3}\left(\overline{I}_{2_y} - \overline{I}_{2_x}\right)\sin^2\phi_2 + \delta E_{kep} + \delta E_\phi + \delta E_{coup} \tag{88}$$

First, we compute the value of ΔE_{lib} from Eq. (80) at our initial testing radius, usually taken to be r_{eq} since that point has the most energy available for the velocities. Our view is to use the variations only when looking at $\phi_{2,max}$; therefore we first look at Eq. (81), setting $\phi_2 = 0$, and determine what value of $\dot{\phi}_2$ can be achieved. Then, we use Eq. (88) to find $\phi_{2,max}$ for a variety of δr and $\delta \dot{r}$ values.

The application of Eq. (88) is of particular importance when trying to determine the exact value of $\dot{\phi}_{2,0}$ which will lead to libration, as the value determined from Eq. (84) will be slightly high due to the fact that no variation in r was allowed. Here, by considering the variations in radius and radial velocity, we can determine when these variations free up more energy to increase $\phi_{2,max}$. Looking only at the first variations for the maximum libration angle, we use the relationship

$$\Delta E_{lib} = \frac{3\mu m}{2r^3}\left(\overline{I}_{2_y} - \overline{I}_{2_x}\right)\sin^2\phi_{2,max}\left[1 - 3\frac{\delta r}{r}\right] + \left[\frac{\mu}{r^2} + \frac{3rK^2}{I_z^2} + \frac{3\mu m}{2r^4}C_2^+\right]\delta r \tag{89}$$

where the fact that we are looking at a circular orbit, so that $\dot{r} = 0$, has been used. The dominant terms relating to the variation are $3rK^2/I_z^2$ and μ/r^2, which tells us that to first order, if $\delta r < 0$, $\phi_{2,max}$ is increased, and vice versa.

In order to find the limiting $\dot{\phi}_{2,0}$, you must solve Eq. (89) for $\phi_{2,max} = 90°$, given some maximum variation that can be deduced from the ZVC of the previous section. Then Eq. (81) can be used to find at what values of r and $\dot{\phi}_{2,0}$ the value of ΔE_{lib} can be achieved.

Elliptical Orbit

In the case of an elliptical orbit, the assumption made in previous sections that the radius is constant, and therefore all energy terms that depend only on the radius are constant, is clearly not true. However, due to the fact that this system is weakly coupled, we can still make the assumption that the Keplerian energy is constant. In this case, we write the excess librational energy as

$$\Delta E_{lib} = E + \frac{m\mu}{r} - \frac{1}{2}m\dot{r}^2 - \frac{1}{2}\frac{K^2}{I_z} \tag{90}$$

and we assume that this value is constant over the orbit. The remaining energy terms form the companion expression

$$\Delta E_{lib} = \frac{I_{2_z}mr^2\dot{\phi}_2^2}{2I_z} + \frac{3\mu m}{2r^3}\left(\overline{I}_{2_y} - \overline{I}_{2_x}\right)\sin^2\phi_2 - \frac{\mu m}{2r^3}C_2^+ \tag{91}$$

Analysis of a librating spacecraft in an eccentric orbit first requires computation of the excess librational energy from Eq. (90). Given this value, Eq. (91) can be used in two ways. First, in order to determine the initial conditions for a simulation of the system, the equation can be solved for $\dot{\phi}_2$ at a given r and ϕ_2. Second, we can rearrange the equation to solve for the maximum libration angle by setting $\dot{\phi}_2 = 0$

$$\sin^2\phi_{2,max} = \frac{2r^3}{3\mu m\left(\overline{I}_{2_y} - \overline{I}_{2_x}\right)}\left[\Delta E_{lib} + \frac{\mu m}{2r^3}C_2^+\right] \tag{92}$$

It is important to note that this computed maximum libration angle holds for the entire trajectory. In other words, for the system with the given energy, E, and angular momentum, K, starting at some point on an elliptical orbit (chosen by true anomaly which gives r and $\dot{r}$), the initial libration rate is determined from the total energy and the maximum reachable libration angle is given as computed above. It is important to note, however, that there is technically some amount of coupling which changes the orbit energy by small amounts. This can be analyzed using the variations in Eqs. (85) - (87), if desired. The main outcome of ignoring that coupling is that the computed maximum libration angle will be slightly below the actual maximum libration amplitude.

OSCULATING ORBITAL ELEMENTS

In this section, we discuss how the osculating values of semi-major axis and eccentricity can change for a system with a given amount of free energy and free angular momentum. This is of particular interest due to the recognized relationship between the eccentricity of an orbit and the librational motion. By deriving these relationships, we can gain a deeper understanding of the coupling between the orbit and the librational motion.

Let us consider a zero velocity curve with the free energy, E, and the free angular momentum, K. When the inequality in Eq. (73) is precisely equal to zero, we know that $\dot{r} = 0$ and $\dot{\phi}_2 = 0$; all of the free kinetic energy in the system has been transferred to the radius and libration amplitude. At any point inside the zero velocity curve(s) defined by E, the inequality will be greater than zero as there is an excess of energy, ΔE. This situation is depicted in the cartoon shown in Figure 3. Returning to Eq. (72), it is clear that in this case, the left hand side is greater than zero, and therefore either $|\dot{r}| > 0$, $|\dot{\phi}_2| > 0$, or some combination of the two.

$$\Delta E(r, \phi_2) = E - \frac{1}{2}\frac{K^2}{I_z} - V(r, \phi_2) = \frac{1}{2}m\dot{r}^2 + \frac{1}{2}\frac{I_{2_z}mr^2\dot{\phi}_2^2}{I_z} \tag{93}$$

The Keplerian orbit energy at any point can be written as,

$$E^K = \frac{1}{2}v^2 - \frac{\mu}{r} = \frac{1}{2}r^2\dot{\theta}^2 + \frac{1}{2}\dot{r}^2 - \frac{\mu}{r} \tag{94}$$

The Keplerian angular momentum can be written as,

$$H^K = |\mathbf{r} \times \mathbf{v}| = r^2\dot{\theta} \tag{95}$$

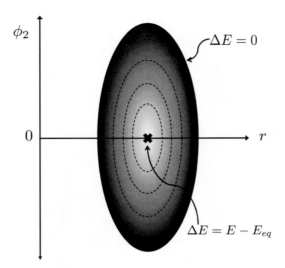

ϕ_2

$\Delta E = 0$

0

r

$\Delta E = E - E_{eq}$

Figure 3. The zero-velocity curve for the given energy, E, has zero excess energy, as shown. Moving in toward the equilibrium point increases ΔE until reaching the equilibrium point (marked by the x), where the excess energy is at a maximum. Intervening zero-velocity curves are drawn with dotted lines.

where $\dot\theta$ was defined in Eq. (23).

Then the osculating semi-major axis and eccentricity can be computed in terms of the energy and angular momentum as,

$$a = \frac{-\mu}{2E^K} \tag{96}$$

$$e^2 = 1 + \frac{2E^K H^{K2}}{\mu^2} \tag{97}$$

The free energy from Eq. (72) is apportioned between the radial and librational velcoties. The split in the energy will be determined by the factor κ, which determines what percentage of the excess energy goes into the radial velocity. The scale factor is therefore bounded such that

$$0 \le \kappa \le 1 \tag{98}$$

This means that the radial velocity and ellipsoid rotation rate are defined as,

$$\dot r^2 = \frac{2\kappa\Delta E}{m} \tag{99}$$

$$\dot\phi_2 = \pm\sqrt{\frac{2(1-\kappa)\Delta E I_z}{I_{2_z} m r^2}} \tag{100}$$

Using these definitions, the Keplerian energy then becomes,

$$E^K = \frac{r^2}{2I_z^2}\left(K^2 \mp 2K\sqrt{\frac{2(1-\kappa)\Delta E I_z I_{2_z}}{mr^2}} + \frac{2(1-\kappa)\Delta E I_z I_{2_z}}{mr^2}\right) + \frac{\kappa\Delta E}{m} - \frac{\mu}{r} \tag{101}$$

310

And the Keplerian angular momentum is,

$$H^K = \left(K \mp \sqrt{\frac{2(1 - \kappa)\Delta E I_z I_{2_z}}{mr^2}} \right) \frac{r^2}{I_z} \tag{102}$$

Note that in the special case where the system is exactly on a zero-velocity curve, or equivalently the energy is precisely equal to the stable equilibrium point energy, the excess energy is zero. In this case, the expressions simplify greatly to become,

$$E^K = \frac{K^2}{2I_z^2} r^2 - \frac{\mu}{r} \tag{103}$$

$$H^K = \frac{K}{I_z} r^2 \tag{104}$$

It is important to realize that e and a are only a function of r on a ZVC because the Keplerian determination of the energy and angular momentum ignores the attitude of the secondary, and there is no excess energy by definition. It is also interesting to note that if we want to recover the Keplerian system, we simply let $I_{2_z} \to 0$ in Eqs. (103) and (104), which recovers the Keplerian relationships with $\dot{r} = 0$.

SPACE SHUTTLE SIMULATIONS

To illustrate the results of this paper, we will present results for the Space Shuttle in low-Earth orbit. The required Space Shuttle properties are given in Table 1. The nominal system parameters are set by choosing $r = 6758$ km, which is roughly the current ISS radius, and setting the libration rate, $\dot{\phi}_2 = 0$. The angular momentum of the system is then set by using Eq. (23) with the orbit rate assumed to be from a circular orbit,

$$\dot{\theta} = \sqrt{\frac{\mu}{r^3}} \tag{105}$$

Once the angular momentum is obtained, the equilibrium points and their associated energies can be found using Eqs. (26) and (48).

Table 1. Space shuttle properties used for simulation, obtained from Reference 14.

Property	Value
m_2	83,000 kg
I_{2_x}	1,029,066 kg-m^2
I_{2_y}	7,816,290 kg-m^2
I_{2_z}	8,015,596 kg-m^2

The analysis of this system starts by drawing ZVCs using Eq. (73) for varying values of free energy, E. The result for the nominal system is shown in Fig. 4. The fact that the system is very weakly coupled can be seen by noticing that the energy at the unstable equilibrium point only allows for a maximum radial deviation from the stable equilibrium point of roughly 15 m. The ZVCs indicate that if the free energy on one of the intervening levels, the libration can be strictly bound, although it will be shown momentarily that the actual maximum libration amplitude depends on the initial conditions.

Fig. 5 shows three different trajectories starting at $r = r_{eq}$ inside the first ZVC from Fig. 4. By adjusting the initial conditions, completely different trajectories can be realized. If all excess energy is put into $\dot{\phi}_2$ ($\kappa = 0$), the maximum libration amplitude can be reached. Note that although that trajectory is initialized with $\dot{r} = 0$, the coupling does allow for some motion in the radial direction. The opposite case, when all

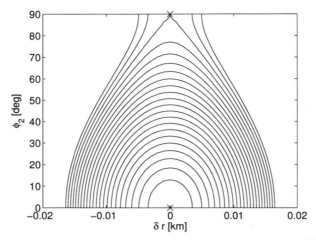

Figure 4. Nominal case zero-velocity curves. The stable equilibrium point is at 6757.999 km, while the angular momentum, computed with $r = 6758$ km, is $K = 4.309 \times 10^9$ kg-m²/s. Each curve is increased by 5% of the energy difference between the stable and unstable equilibrium points.

excess energy is apportioned to the radial velocity ($\kappa = 1$), allows the system to explore the full extent in the radial direction, but almost no libration occurs. Finally the intermediate case shows what would be a more generally occurring case.

Fig. 6 shows the interesting fact that when the energy is high enough so that the ZVC is open, this does not mean that all trajectories will circulate. Here, if 90% of the excess energy is given to $\dot{\phi}_2$, the trajectory circulates, however when only 70% is apportioned, the libration amplitude is bounded. The dotted line shows that the equations computed previously to predict the maximum libration amplitude are quite accurate for this case; it should be noted that the max amplitude computed for the circulating case correctly predicted that the amplitude was unbound.

In order to gain a more full understanding of the initial conditions that lead to libration, Fig. 7 illustrates the mapping of circulating trajectories to their initial conditions at $\phi_2 = 0$. The limiting circulating trajectories are those that barely make it; $\dot{\phi}_2 = 0$ at $\phi_2 = 90°$. These are the trajectories that map to the lowest values of $\dot{\phi}_2$ at $\phi_2 = 0$. The analytical prediction of this bound, computed using Eq. (83), doesn't perfectly predict the lower bound of $\dot{\phi}_2$, however it is very close. To find the exact bound, one would have to iterate between the value of r and $\dot{\phi}_2$, as that line was computed at $r = r_{eq}$.

Fig. 7 gives a good idea of what initial conditions will lead to circulation, however the numerical mapping, which goes slightly below the analytical prediction, have only been computed for direct crossings. In other words, we've only propagated directly back from 90° to 0, without searching for trajectories that may start outside those initial conditions and wander into a circulating state. In order to check this, all of the trajectories were continuously propagated back in time from Fig. 7 until they circulated crossed $|\phi_2| > 90°$. The results are shown in Fig. 8. In all cases, the trajectories crossed $\phi_2 = 0$ very close to the analytical limit. The longest any of these trajectories stayed bound was for roughly 100 orbits. This implies that the analytical bound is a very good approximation of what initial conditions will circulate.

To this point, the cases that have been analyzed have been near-circular, so the question of at what eccentricity the libration becomes unstable is still unexplored. However, we have the tools to investigate this situation. We keep the same nominal angular momentum, meaning the equilibrium point stays in the same location and at the same energy. In order to investigate different eccentricities, the energy required to reach periapse and apoapsis at $\phi_2 = 0$ is determined, and the maximum value is chosen. Then, this energy and

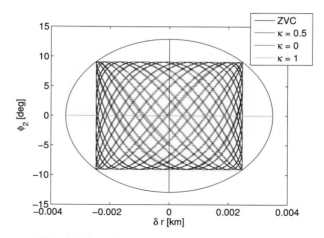

Figure 5. Three different trajectories for the nominal case with energy 5% **of the way to the unstable equilibrium energy.**

nominal Keplerian orbit is used to determine ΔE_{lib} at each reachable r and $\dot{r}^2$ pair, in other words at each true anomaly (ν). The results of this study are shown in Figs. 9 and 10; ν stops at $180°$ as the relationship is symmetric about this point.

Fig. 9 shows the maximum libration amplitude for different eccentricity orbits, when the initial values of r and $\dot{r}$ are determined by selecting a true anomaly, and $\phi_2 = \dot{\phi}_2 = 0$. If the eccentricity is less than 1×10^{-4} the libration is bounded for any initial condition. For larger eccentricities, the initial conditions must be nearer to periapsis in order for the libration to remain bounded. It should be noted again that each eccentricity line is at a different energy level, but they all have the same angular momentum value.

In order to illustrate the validity of these relationships, four different simulations indicated on Fig. 9 with circles were simulated for 500 orbits. These trajectories are plotted in Fig. 10. It is clear that the bounds are accurately predicting the librational motion, and the unbounded case does circulate immediately.

CONCLUSION

In this paper, the planar dynamics of libration-orbit coupling for a spacecraft in orbit about a spherical Earth have been examined. The goal of this study was to answer two questions concerning the transition from a bounded librational attitude motion, to unbounded circulation: can we determine the maximum libration amplitude without integrating the equations of motion given some initial conditions, and as the nominal Keplerian becomes elliptical, at what eccentricity is the forcing strong enough so that bounded libration is not possible. These questions were answered by analyzing the fully coupled system. Taking advantage of the conservation of energy and angular momentum in the system, the effects of the orbital motion on the attitude motion were characterized. By properly analyzing these relationships, we were able to determine analytical conditions to answer the previous questions. The analytical equations were proven to be good answers through numerical examples.

Future work on this problem consists of two main thrusts. First, we wish to explore the (un)stability of the system when the angular momentum and/or energy are changed due to external forces. This has important implications for considering the effects of energy damping and external forces such as drag and solar radiation pressure. Second, the methods explored here should be extended to out-of-plane motion to determine limits on the total attitude deviation in any orbit.

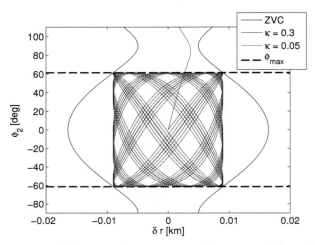

Figure 6. **Two different trajectories for the nominal case with energy** 10% **above the unstable equilibrium energy. The dotted horizontal line indicates the computed** $\phi_{2,max} = 61.34°$ **from Eq. (83) for the** $\kappa = 0.3$ **trajectory.**

REFERENCES

[1] P. C. Hughes, *Spacecraft Attitude Dynamics.* Dover Publications, 2004.

[2] V. V. Beletskii, *Motion of an Artificial Satellite About its Center of Mass.* Israel Program for Scientific Translations, 1966.

[3] R. R. Auelmann, "Regions of Libration for a Symmetrical Satellite," *AIAA Journal*, Vol. 1, No. 6, 1963, pp. 1445–1447.

[4] R. Pringle, "Bounds on the Librations of a Symmetrical Satellite," *AIAA Journal*, Vol. 2, No. 5, 1963, pp. 908–912.

[5] S. N. Mohan, J. V. Breakwell, and B. O. Lange, "Interaction Between Attitude Libration and Orbital Motion of a Rigid Body in a Near Keplerian Orbit of Low Eccentricity," *Celestial Mechanics*, Vol. 5, 1972, pp. 157–173.

[6] L. Wang, P. Krishnaprasad, and J. Maddocks, "Hamiltonian Dynamics of a Rigid Body in a Central Gravitational Field," *Celestial Mechanics and Dynamical Astronomy*, Vol. 50, 1991, pp. 349–386.

[7] A. J. Maciejewski, "Reduction, Relative Equilbria and Potential in the Two Rigid Bodies Problem," *Celestial Mechanics and Dynamical Astronomy*, Vol. 63, 1995, pp. 1–28.

[8] W.-S. Koon *et al.*, "Geometric Mechanics and the Dynamics of Asteroid Pairs," *Astrodynamics, Space Missions, and Chaos* (E. Belbruno, D. Folta, and P. Gurfil, eds.), Vol. 1017, pp. 11–38, Annals of the New York Academy of Science, 2004.

[9] H. Cendra and J. E. Marsden, "Geometric Mechanics and the Dynamics of Asteroid Pairs," *Dynamical Systems*, Vol. 20, No. 1, 2005, pp. 3–21.

[10] D. J. Scheeres, "Stability in the Full Two Body Problem," *Celestial Mechanics and Dynamical Astronomy*, Vol. 83, 2002, pp. 155–169.

[11] H. Schaub and J. Junkins, *Analytical Mechanics of Space Systems.* AIAA Education, AIAA, 2nd ed., 2009.

[12] G. B. Sincarsin and P. C. Hughes, "Gravitational Orbit-Attitude Coupling for Very Large Spacecraft," *Celestial Mechanics*, Vol. 31, 1983, pp. 143–161.

[13] D. J. Scheeres, "Stability of the planar full 2-body problem," *Celestial Mechanics and Dynamical Astronomy*, Vol. 104, 2009, pp. 103–128.

[14] H. W. Stone and R. W. Powell, "Entry Dynamics of Space Shuttle Orbiter With Lateral-Directional Stability and Control Uncertainties at Supersonic and Hypersonic Speeds," Tech. Rep. 1011, NASA, December 1977.

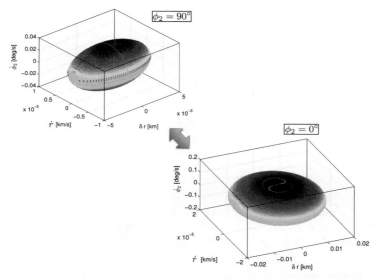

Figure 7. **Initial condition ellipsoids at $\phi_2 = 0$ and $90°$. Each ellipsoid represents the admissible states at a given ϕ_2 for the case when the energy 10% above the unstable equilibrium energy, as in Fig. 6. Each dot on the $\phi_2 = 90°$ ellipsoid corresponds to a similarly colored dot on the $\phi_2 = 0$ ellipsoid. Clearly all of the circulating trajectories map to initial conditions at $\phi_2 = 90°$ with higher allowable values of $\dot{\phi}_2$.**

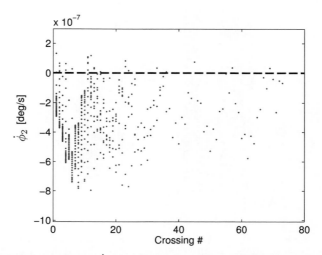

Figure 8. **Absolute values of $\dot{\phi}_2$ (with respect to the analytical prediction of 0.10379 deg/s) as back-propagated trajectories cross $\phi_2 = 0$. Red dots indicate crossings in the positive direction, blue are negative crossings. The minimum difference from Fig. 7 is 1.34×10^{-7} deg/s.**

315

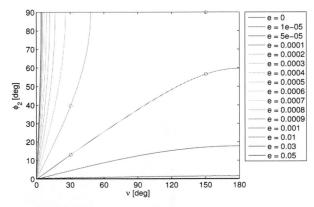

Figure 9. Maximum libration amplitudes at different points on a Keplerian orbit computed with ΔE_{lib} from Eq. (81) with $\dot{\phi}_2 = 0$. When $e = 0$, maximum libration amplitude at apoapsis is only $0.34°$ and at $e = 1 \times 10^{-5}$, the amplitude can reach $1.65°$ at apoapsis. The unstable eccentricity is between $e = 1 \times 10^{-4}$ and $e = 2 \times 10^{-4}$. For all eccentricities, there are some initial conditions that stay bounded; e.g. for $e = 0.05$, the libration amplitude is bounded for $\nu < 0.0125°$.

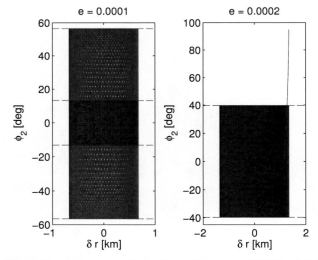

Figure 10. Four trajectories chosen from Fig. 9, integrated for 500 orbits. The circulating trajectory was stopped upon passing $\dot{\phi}_2 = 95°$. These numerical integrations prove the validity of the relationships shown in Fig. 9.

316

APPLICATIONS OF TRAJECTORIES IN THE VICINITY OF SUN-EARTH L₃ FOR A SOLAR OBSERVATION MISSION

Jonathan F. C. Herman,[*] Kathryn E. Davis,[†] George H. Born[‡] and Ron Noomen[§]

This research investigates the feasibility of the L_3 region of the Sun-Earth system as the target for a solar observation mission that aims to observe the far side of the Sun as well as the higher (possibly polar) latitudes of the Sun. A grid search of the L_3 region is performed to locate families of periodic orbits, and the most promising results are identified. The possibility of using three-body dynamics for a transfer trajectory is briefly considered. Furthermore, the applicability of three-body dynamics for this region is discussed as well as the importance of other perturbations known to be present. Keeping the nature of the actual dynamics of this region in mind, the most interesting feasible orbits for a solar observation mission are identified.

INTRODUCTION

In recent years, scientific interest of the Sun has been increasing as solar behavior has shown unexpected deviations from otherwise periodic behavior that has been observed for centuries. Other reasons for increased interest are the effect of the Sun on global climate change and the concern that violent solar behavior (such as solar flares or coronal mass ejections) may pose a threat to a civilization that is progressively more reliant on electronics, providing limited historical experience of its vulnerability. Finally, full observational coverage of the Sun would allow for more timely predictions of spacecraft that will be hit by a solar storm. This is especially applicable for spacecraft traveling outside of the Earth-Moon system as these vehicles may be on the far side of the Sun, and of increased importance for any spacecraft transporting humans.

While the quality and amount of acquired data of current observation methods greatly exceeds that of even a few decades ago, there are still improvements to be made. Among desired observations are coverage of the polar or high-latitude regions of the Sun which, to date, has only been achieved by the Ulysses spacecraft.[1] In addition to this, coverage of the far side of the Sun (as seen from Earth) is also desired, a goal that is currently being fulfilled by the STEREO mission.[2] However, both of the STEREO spacecraft will move to the near side of the Sun again in a few years, and there will be no way to gather information concerning events on the far side of the Sun. No replacement missions are currently planned to observe this region.

The following research aims to combine the goals of far side and higher latitude/polar coverage by looking at the feasibility of placing an observatory in the vicinity of the Sun-Earth libration point L_3 with an orbit that has a sizable component out of the ecliptic plane. Such a spacecraft could

---

[*]Graduate Research Assistant, Delft University of Technology, The Netherlands

[†]Research Associate, The Colorado Center for Astrodynamics Research, University of Colorado, Boulder, CO 80309.

[‡]Director, The Colorado Center for Astrodynamics Research, University of Colorado, Boulder, CO 80309.

[§]Assistant Professor, Delft University of Technology, The Netherlands

be considered as complementary to an observatory like SOHO, which resides near the Sun-Earth L_1 libration point (but is restricted to motion close to the ecliptic).[3] Due to the region of interest coinciding with one of the libration points, the applicability of three-body dynamics in this region is evaluated in this paper.

THE CIRCULAR RESTRICTED THREE-BODY PROBLEM

As is common in the Circular Restricted Three-Body Problem (CR3BP), a reference frame is utilized that rotates with the two massive (primary) bodies about the system barycenter. In addition,

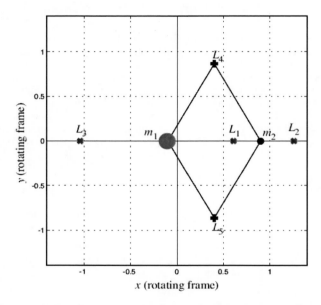

Figure 1. Rotating reference frame with the five libration points.[4]

positions and velocities are normalized with the total distance between the primaries and the orbital velocity of the smaller primary around the system barycenter, respectively. A graphical representation of the CR3BP is shown in Figure 1. The five resulting libration points are also shown (a derivation of the location of these libration points is not presented here, but can be found in many texts such as Reference 5). This reference frame results in a system with the following equations of motion:

$$X = (x, y, z, \dot{x}, \dot{y}, \dot{z}) \quad ; \quad \dot{X} = (\dot{x}, \dot{y}, \dot{z}, \ddot{x}, \ddot{y}, \ddot{z}) \tag{1}$$

$$\ddot{x} = x + 2\dot{y} - (1 - \mu)\frac{x + \mu}{r_1^3} - \mu\frac{x - (1 - \mu)}{r_2^3}$$

$$\ddot{y} = y - 2\dot{x} - (1 - \mu)\frac{y}{r_1^3} - \mu\frac{y}{r_2^3} \tag{2}$$

$$\ddot{z} = -(1 - \mu)\frac{z}{r_1^3} - \mu\frac{z}{r_2^3}$$

318

$$r_1 = \sqrt{(x+\mu)^2 + y^2 + z^2} \quad ; \quad r_2 = \sqrt{(x+\mu-1)^2 + y^2 + z^2} \tag{3}$$

$$\mu = \frac{m_2}{m_1 + m_2} \tag{4}$$

Where X is the state vector, $\dot{X}$ is the time derivative of the state at any given time, m_1 and m_2 are the mass of the larger and smaller primary, respectively, and r_1 and r_2 are the distances to the larger and smaller primaries, respectively.

In addition to the equations of motion, it is often useful to propagate the State Transition Matrix (STM), $\Phi(t, t_0)$, which provides a linearized approximation of changes in the final state at some epoch t as a function of changes in the initial state at some epoch t_0. The initial condition of the STM is $\Phi(t_0, t_0) = I(6, 6)$; a 6x6 identity matrix. The STM can be obtained along with the state by integrating its time derivative, also known as the State Propagation Matrix (SPM), $\overline{F}$. The SPM can be calculated as follows:

$$\overline{F} = \begin{bmatrix} \overline{0} & \overline{I} \\ \overline{\Omega} & \overline{A} \end{bmatrix} \tag{5}$$

Where $\overline{0}$ is a 3x3 zero-matrix, $\overline{I}$ is a 3x3 identity matrix and $\overline{A}$ is identified as follows

$$\overline{A} = \begin{bmatrix} 0 & 2 & 0 \\ -2 & 0 & 0 \\ 0 & 0 & 0 \end{bmatrix} \tag{6}$$

Finally the matrix $\overline{\Omega}$ gives the second partial derivatives of Ω with respect to the coordinates x, y and z, where Ω, the zero-energy formulation of the Jacobi integral, is given by:

$$\Omega = \frac{1}{2}(x^2 + y^2) + \frac{1-\mu}{r_1} + \frac{\mu}{r_2} + \frac{1}{2}\mu(1-\mu) \tag{7}$$

Integration of these equations is done with a Runge-Kutta-Fehlberg (RKF) 7(8) method, which is a 7th order integration method with 8th order stepsize control to ensure the accuracy meets a specified tolerance (for this research, a tolerance of 10^{-15} is used).[6]

For a more thorough and exhaustive discussion of the derivation and equations of the CR3BP, the reader is directed to Reference 4.

Orbital stability and orbit manifolds

Using $\Phi(T + t_0; t_0)$, the STM for a full revolution of a periodic orbit (where T is the orbital period), the stability of an orbit can be determined. This particular representation of the STM is also known as the Monodromy matrix, M, and its eigenvalues are used for determining the stability of the orbit. The 6x6 Monodromy matrix has six eigenvalues. If any of these eigenvalues has a real component whose absolute magnitude is greater than 1, the orbit is asymptotically unstable. If all real components of the eigenvalues have an absolute value smaller than or equal to 1, the orbit is (asymptotically) stable. Using such eigenvalues for unstable periodic orbits, stable and unstable manifolds can be created that enable a spacecraft to travel to or from these orbits for a very low ΔV (or in some cases even free transfers).

For a more thorough discussion of stability in the three-body problem or generating manifolds, the reader is again referred to Reference 4 as a useful guide.

APPLICABILITY IN THE L$_3$ REGION

Although L$_3$ is one of the collinear libration points, there is a fundamental difference that sets it apart from the collinear libration points L$_1$ and L$_2$. As can be seen in Figure 1, all libration points are at a similar distance from the larger primary and are thus equally affected by it. However, L$_1$ and L$_2$ are exceptional in the sense that they are much closer to the smaller primary than any of the other libration points. Naturally, this means that L$_3$ is significantly less affected by the smaller primary than the other collinear libration points (this also holds for L$_4$/L$_5$ to a large degree). Essentially, this means that the orbits near L$_3$ approach two-body orbits as the value of the mass ratio μ goes down. Depending on the mass ratio of the system, the effect of the smaller primary on the L$_3$ region may or may not be ignored altogether (for acceptable approximations), as will be shown later. While this is straightforward enough in a qualitative sense, this research uses a three-body model to get a quantitative sense of the importance of three-body dynamics in the L$_3$ region for the Sun-Earth system, with a brief discussion of other systems.

Other perturbations

It is worth mentioning that in the Sun-Earth system, which has a relatively small value of μ, there are other forces in the solar system that will be significant in the L$_3$ region, most notably the gravity of Venus and Jupiter, and solar radiation pressure. For some geometries, these forces may even be more significant than the attraction of the Earth. Simple computations were performed to analyze these additional perturbations. It may be said that none of the additional perturbations are significant enough that they are a decisive factor in the feasibility of these orbits. That is to say, if an orbit is desirable in the CR3BP in terms of coverage, stability, or another characteristic, it also possesses similar characteristics in a system which includes additional perturbations, and hence still is a desirable orbit. Since this study focuses on three-body orbits, additional perturbations are not considered for this part of the research in order to maintain generality. Although the Sun-Earth system is under consideration, analogs of some of the presented orbits can be found in other systems with different mass parameters (over a certain range). In such systems, additional perturbations may be very different in nature or magnitude.

ORBITS IN THE VICINITY OF L$_3$

This section discusses the orbits studied for this research. In order to acquire as many relevant orbits as possible, a grid search was performed over the ranges given in Table 1. Initial conditions were of the form $X = (x, 0, z, 0, \dot{y}, 0)$, in an attempt to focus on orbits that have sufficient separation from the solar disk as seen from Earth (indicated by the z component). The parameter N specifies half the amount of crossings a periodic orbit has with the XZ-plane. For a halo orbit, for example, N = 1, as it has two crossings with the XZ plane. For a figure 8 orbit N = 2, and so on. As N increases, so does the complexity of the periodic orbits. For z, only positive values were used because of the well-known symmetry about the XY-plane in the CR3BP. The ranges and step-sizes for this grid were chosen based on a number of searches on smaller grids; it represents a good balance between computational effort and resulting unique periodic orbits. All discussed orbits are presented in the Sun-Earth system ($\mu \approx 3.04 \cdot 10^{-6}$), unless specifically mentioned otherwise. The values given in Table 1 are in units of non-dimensional position and velocity, with the origin at the barycenter.

Table 1. Grid used for searching periodic orbits

Parameter	Minimum	Maximum	Stepsize
x	-2.29	-0.2	0.07
z	0	0.6	0.03
$\dot{y}$	-0.6	0.6	0.03
N	1	4	1

For all following plots, orbits will be shown in a non-dimensional rotating reference frame. Like Figure 1, the barycenter is at the origin, but in the Sun-Earth system that coincides closely with the center of the Sun (larger primary), which will thus appear to be at the origin in the subsequent plots. L$_3$ is represented by the black dot at $x \approx -1$. The Earth, although not plotted, is positioned at $x \approx 1$. It should be noted that the plotted size of the Sun is greatly exaggerated, for easier recognition.

Constraints for realistic observation orbits

No hard constraints for feasibility are set for a target orbit in the initial grid search to avoid precluding orbits that are on the edge of feasibility, but may also offer significant benefits. Of course certain practical constraints arise for a mission that intends to observe the far side of the Sun as well as the higher latitudes. For example, it is desirable that the satellite spends as much time as possible on the far side of the Sun. For similarly obvious reasons, out-of-plane motion (with respect to the ecliptic) is desirable for coverage of the solar poles, or at the least higher latitudes of the Sun (the rotation axis of the Sun will be assumed perpendicular to the ecliptic). In addition, energy levels of target orbits must be deemed realistic with current technologies. While no precise limit for orbital energy is set, orbits requiring a ΔV of 20 km/s are clearly not viable candidates. Finally, orbits are required to spend as little time as possible directly behind the Sun, as seen from the Earth, or travel too close to the Sun, both of which would hinder communication. Whenever the spacecraft is within 5 degrees of the solar disk, communication is assumed impossible.[7]

Unfortunately, many of the orbits found in the grid search are not practical (when keeping the above constraints in mind) for solar observation purposes, in many cases due to energy levels that are not feasible for spacecraft in the foreseeable future. However, some of these orbits are discussed briefly as they may be interesting for other purposes or for study in other systems (such as the Earth-Moon system, which has much more accessible energy levels than the Sun-Earth system).

Orbits of general interest

A large amount of orbits resulted from the grid search that were not of real value for a solar observation mission; an exhaustive discussion of which would span much more than is necessary or appropriate for this paper. However, it is interesting to point out two results from the evolution of the system. The first of these is the Halo family at L_3, since Halo orbits have been frequently applied for L_1 and L_2, in some cases for solar observation missions. However, generally speaking, the Halo family at L_3 is of no practical use for a solar observation mission, as some examples in Figure 2 illustrate.

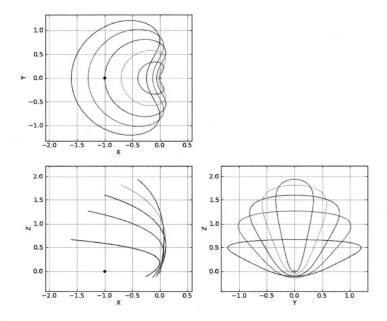

Figure 2. The Halo family at L_3

Halo orbits at L_3 have far greater amplitudes than their L_1/L_2 counterparts. Observe that certain orbits in Figure 2 have z-amplitudes that approach 2.0 non-dimensional units (practically 2 AU). The energy levels of these orbits are entirely inaccessible for current technology. In addition, they all make very close passes to the Sun, in many cases closer than the orbital distance of Mercury (0.2 AU or even less). This is such a diverse environment over the course of each orbit that it would significantly complicate the design of any spacecraft. While interesting, the L_3 Halo family appears currently to be of no practical use.

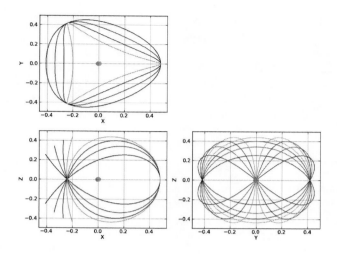

Figure 3. A family of possible future use for thorough and detailed coverage of the Solar surface

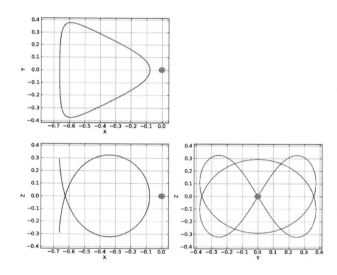

Figure 4. A single orbit from the same family as the one presented in Figure 3, evolved to a mass ratio of $\mu \approx 0.4$

Another interesting result is the orbit family shown in Figure 3. The energy levels for this orbit are also out of reach for current technology, although they could be placed at the orbital distance of Mercury or Venus in an attempt to inject into these orbits through a fly-by maneuver and make them more accessible. If, at some point, it is deemed interesting to have (near-)continuous coverage of the entire Sun (including both poles at the same time), a constellation of solar observers could be spread along one of the orbits of this family and provide such coverage. The smaller distance to the Sun would be beneficial not just from a power standpoint (assuming solar panels are used), but would also allow an increased resolution for observation of the solar surface. An actual application for this orbit is unlikely in any foreseeable future though, but if mankind ever builds a system of meteorological satellites for our nearest star, an orbit like the one shown here may prove to be useful due to its very constant geometry with respect to the Earth. One final interesting aspect is that when the orbit is evolved to higher mass ratios, it will effectively become an orbit about L_3 (i.e. no crossings of the y axis with $x > 0$), as the plot in Figure 4 shows for a mass ratio of $\mu \approx 0.4$

Realistic observation orbits

The orbits presented in the previous section, interesting as they may be, suffer from severe practical constraints. Either they display behavior that is simply not desirable for a solar observation mission, or they are impossible for spacecraft injection with foreseeable technology (or both). The only interesting target orbit that satisfies the objective of continuous far-side solar observation and higher latitude coverage (at acceptable energy levels) is the vertical family, an example of which is shown in Figure 5.

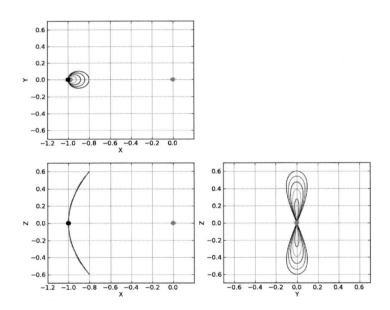

Figure 5. The smaller examples of the vertical family at L_3

Depending on the energy level considered feasible (thus, available ΔV), the out-of-plane component of this orbit can be scaled to fit an acceptable balance between ΔV and observable solar latitudes. For example, if the higher-latitude observations are considered significantly less important than far side solar observation, or if the cost for the out-of-plane motion is simply too high, the target orbit could have as little out-of-plane motion as the completely planar Lyapunov orbits,

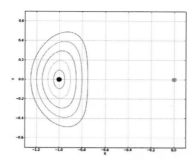

Figure 6. **The smaller examples of the Lyapunov family at L_3 for similar energy values as the vertical family**

examples of which are shown in Figure 6 (in this case only the XY-projection is shown, as little information is added about the motion of planar orbits in the other projections). The orbital period for all orbits in either family is approximately one year, which means the most significant downside of these orbits is that there are two extended periods for each revolution where the satellite is behind the Sun (or too close to it) to allow communication with Earth. For the shown vertical orbits, this ranges from approximately 30 days for the largest orbit to approximately 80 days for the smallest orbit (and as smaller orbits were plotted, an increasing segment of the orbit would be hidden for communication purposes, until it was completely hidden). For the planar orbits, a similar behavior applies. Clearly, a satellite in one of these orbits would be unable to communicate directly with Earth for significant periods of time. This behavior may be avoided though, as will be discussed in subsequent paragraphs.

USING THREE-BODY DYNAMICS FOR A TRANSFER TO L_3

In this section, possible connections between the L_3 region and the Earth will be discussed for the Sun-Earth system. The manifolds of L_3 orbits, as well as the manifolds of L_1/L_2 orbits will be analyzed.

Connection using L_3 manifolds

Due to the small influence of the Earth on orbits in the vicinity of L_3, even the unstable periodic orbits are only slightly unstable. In addition to this, the invariant manifolds of some (but not all) L_3 orbits display horseshoe behavior for the Sun-Earth system.[8] While some of these manifolds come close to the Earth (and conceivably might be used for a transfer), they are very 'slow' manifolds, requiring a large amount of time (on the order of a thousand years) for a transfer from the Earth to L_3. Manifolds that do not display horseshoe behavior (such as those of the L_3 Halo family) but rather propagate around the entire system will still keep a significant distance from the Earth while doing so. In addition, their energy levels are inaccessible and their transfer times are, like other L_3 orbit manifolds, on the order of a thousand years. Obviously, the L_3 manifolds are not a practical means of transfer.

Connection using L_1/L_2 manifolds

In the past, some research has investigated the connection from manifolds of orbits around L_1/L_2 to an orbit at L_3.[9, 10] Since the energy levels of L_1/L_2 orbits are not (or just barely, in the case of some large planar orbits) open for L_3, these manifold transfers require a ΔV upon departure and arrival. Unlike transfers between L_1 and L_2 orbits (which are much closer in energy level), there appear to be no free transfers between L_1/L_2 and L_3. However, transfers can be designed and will offer a much more reasonable flight time (on the order of 10 years) than a transfer through an L_3 manifold. Nonetheless, with the energy levels not matching particularly well with the target orbits, these manifold transfers also do not appear to be the most convenient option for a transfer.

CHARACTERISTICS OF THE L_3 REGION

In this section, characteristics of the L_3 region arising from the weak three-body dynamics that are observed in the Sun-Earth system are discussed, and in what way this may be used advantageously when designing an orbit in this region. The extent to which this may hold in other three-body systems is also discussed.

Shifting of periodic orbits

Although a number of periodic three-body orbits were presented, most of them appear to be impractical (or with foreseeable technology even impossible) for solar observation missions. They may be more feasible (for different purposes) in other three-body systems, such as the Earth-Moon system, but for a solar observation mission, realistic options are restricted to the simplest orbits discussed, namely Lyapunov and Vertical orbits. These orbits are favorable, except for the fact that they make two passes (per orbit) behind the Sun, hindering communication. However, some advantage can be taken from the nature of the L_3 region. Since it is a region that is subjected only to minor perturbations (from both the Earth and other causes), orbits that are not strictly periodic can be made periodic at minimal costs in ΔV (or alternatively, a drift can be accepted that is small on the timescale of a typical observation mission). The most practical example of this is shifting an orbit to a more favorable position, for example by rotating the orbits in the Vertical family from Figure 5 around the z-axis to a position where they never pass behind the Sun, as shown in Figure 7. This is a purely geometrical rotation of the state vector. If these orbits are propagated for 10 revolutions (approximately 10 years) in the CR3BP, the final mismatch will be of order 10^{-5} for position and 10^{-3} for velocity (non-dimensional coordinates). While small, such a mismatch does not meet the requirement of periodicity, an acceptable mismatch for which would be 10^{-8} (or less).[11] The mismatch for the shifted orbit corresponds to a mismatch on the order of 1500 km and 30 m/s for the Sun-Earth system. The mismatch after a certain period could be reduced further by altering the state vector elements to take into account the new position (and thus new force distribution along the orbit), although the orbit will never be completely periodic. Such a correction is not done here to illustrate the insignificance of the drift even when the altered position is ignored. Taking other perturbations (such as gravity of planets or SRP) into account will increase both mismatches by approximately an order of magnitude. Such mismatches can be corrected throughout the mission, but in fact it may be considered more favorable to accept the drift as it will not significantly alter the position of the spacecraft with respect to the Earth (and as such the observations). The YZ projection for a 10 year propagation for the largest orbit from Figure 7 is shown in Figure 8 (perturbations of the other planets are included in this propagation), illustrating the insignificance of the drift.

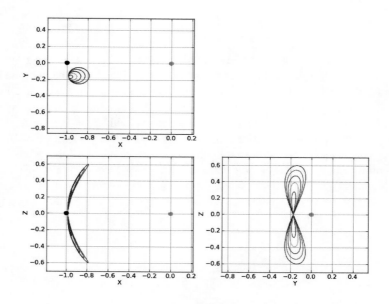

Figure 7. Example of shifting vertical orbits (10 degree counter-clockwise rotation)

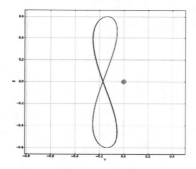

Figure 8. Illustration of (the effective absence of) drift in a 10 year propagation of a shifted orbit with perturbations included in the model

A similar shift can be made for the Lyapunov orbits. A 10 revolution (approximately 10 year) propagation for these orbits produces similar results as for the vertical orbits.

These shifts are convenient, as they allow greater flexibility in choosing a target orbit. It may be noted that much larger shifts than shown can be made, while still having drifts that are not significantly greater than discussed here. However, the possibility of these rotations illustrates the limited effect of three-body dynamics in this region. This is discussed in more detail in a following section.

327

Asymmetric orbits

Another advantage of the weak three-body dynamics of the L_3 region is that it allows a little more creativity with target orbits. Orbits that do not exhibit periodicity in the three-body problem can still be used for periods typical for spacecraft mission lifetimes, either with small corrections or a small drift. An example is the orbit shown in Figure 9, plotted for a single revolution. This orbit was initially created roughly by hand, then converged on with a single shooter. The position mismatch after a single revolution can be reduced to zero, but a velocity mismatch of 10^{-5} (30 cm/s in the Sun-Earth system) will remain illustrating the non-periodic nature of this orbit. Placing such an asymmetric orbit centered on L_3 can further reduce this error by an order of magnitude. Other shapes can be produced relatively easily. While these orbits are not periodic, they are close enough to periodicity to be feasible (from a periodicity standpoint, other constraints may still apply).

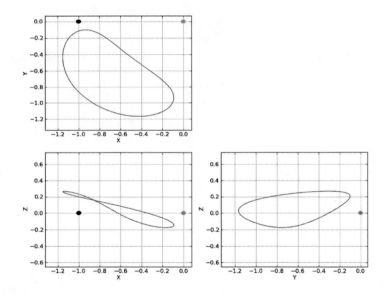

Figure 9. Example of a non-periodic three-body orbit that may be used in a low mass ratio system

Essentially, a satellite operating in this region is formation flying with the Earth (it can be said that neither the Earth nor the satellite affect each other's orbit in a significant way). It may be interesting to evaluate applications of techniques used for the design of formation flying missions to design orbits at L_3 that are not periodic in a three-body sense, but still have acceptable drifts. For the current research this is not pursued. The target orbits presented earlier can be scaled to satisfy any requirement expected for the observation mission under consideration, so there is no current need for more complicated orbits that may be created with alternative techniques.

Applications to other systems

While the previous discussions applies to the Sun-Earth system, similar behavior may be seen in systems with a higher μ value. For comparison, the Earth-Moon system is briefly considered, as it has a very high mass ratio ($\mu \approx 0.0125$) when comparing it with most other systems in the solar system. As an example, an orbit equivalent to the vertical orbit rotated and propagated as shown in Figure 8 was evaluated in the Earth-Moon system. After a single revolution (instead of 10), the mismatch in position and velocity are already of orders 10^{-2} and 10^{-1} respectively (on the order of 4000 km and 100 m/s in the Earth-Moon system). After 10 revolutions the orbit is not in any way recognizable, and would completely drift away unless corrective maneuvers were applied. The distances and velocities used to normalize the Earth-Moon system are smaller, providing some balance for such maneuvers, but since the period of the Earth-Moon system is approximately a month rather than a year this does not change much in the long run (the mismatches build up much quicker). It would appear that for mass ratios in this range, three-body effects are much more pronounced in the vicinity of L_3, to the point where rotations as discussed above are not practical. Similar problems apply for trying to maintain asymmetric non-periodic three-body orbits. A quick calculation for ($\mu \approx 10^{-4}$) systems shows that a 10 degree shift would still produce an acceptable drift for a few revolutions, but it too sees a significant drift after 10 revolutions.

Two-body / three-body approximation

As discussed at the beginning of this paper, the influence of the Earth on the L_3 region is minimal. This can be illustrated perhaps no more clearly than the behavior of the presented shifted orbits and asymmetric orbits. Although these are not actual periodic three-body orbits, their motion is very close to being periodic due to the small influence of the Earth in this region. The effects of other planets and solar radiation pressure distort these orbits further but not to a degree that such orbits cannot be used for a spacecraft mission.

In essence, orbits in the vicinity of L_3 can, to a high degree of accuracy, be described as two-body orbits for preliminary mission design. This is true in the Sun-Earth system, but in the Earth-Moon system such a simplification is arguable. To find a precise limit for the mass ratio where the L_3 region should be considered as a three-body or two-body region is difficult. As a (very) rough indication, it appears that for $\mu \approx 10^{-4}$ a two-body approximation is adequate for short time periods, but not far above this mass ratio such a simplification becomes a poor estimate altogether. For determining if the approximation is adequate, the rough criterion used was the presence of a significant change (of the order 10^{-3} or higher) in the state after a single revolution. It can be said in general that as μ decreases the time in which trajectories can be propagated as two-body trajectories without drift increases. For the μ value of the Sun-Earth system a two-body approximation will give at least a very decent initial guess for the actual orbit, and can be considered acceptable for preliminary mission design.

CONCLUSIONS

A number of conclusions can be drawn. For a solar observation mission, it appears that orbits in the vicinity of Sun-Earth L_3 are feasible. While no truly periodic three-body orbit was found that seems practical for such a mission (either their energy level is inaccessible, or they spend too much time out of communication range), opportunities are created by the (near) two-body nature of this region. Due to this nature, there is more flexibility in selecting an orbit, making this region a feasible position for a solar observatory. Further research is required to investigate the feasibility of a transfer to such an orbit.

More general conclusions are that for mass ratios similar to (or lower than) that of the Sun-Earth system, it appears that the L_3 region can be regarded as a two-body region, meaning the gravitational attraction of the Earth can be ignored entirely for a good approximation of the actual orbit. However, for higher mass ratios, such an approximation would provide results that poorly agree with the actual motion. The mass ratio where this transition occurs is low enough that a number of real examples are known where a two-body approximation produces significant errors, such as the Earth-Moon system. A precise mass ratio marking the boundary for using a two-body or three-body approximation was not pursued, but as a rough estimate a value of $\mu \approx 10^{-4}$ could be used. However, such a limit was never the focus of this research, and this value is a very rough indication.

Further work

Regarding Sun-Earth L_3, further interesting work could restrict itself to a two-body approximation of the region (certainly for preliminary design, with perturbations added at a later stage). It may be interesting to study which orbits are actually within reach using present-day technology, by studying a full transfer from the Earth to a target orbit like those presented here. Such a study would determine if far-side observation can be effectively combined with higher-latitude/polar coverage for an actual mission. If other mission purposes are envisioned for Sun-Earth L_3 (or other systems with low mass ratios) that have requirements that can not be satisfied by the orbits discussed, it may be interesting to look into the application of techniques typically used for formation flying (or other two-body relative motion techniques). In any system where a two-body approach is acceptable for the L_3 region, the spacecraft is essentially formation flying with the smaller 'massive' body (in this case the Earth), therefore such techniques may be useful in designing more unusual orbits that fit the need of the mission objective being considered. The rotated or asymmetric orbits presented here are simple examples of such possibilities for low μ systems.

Further interesting work for the case of L_3 in general would be to further explore at what mass ratio three-body effects become important in this region (effects that are noticeable to a significant degree within a single revolution of the system, for example). It may also be interesting to study the behavior of orbits and manifolds in systems with high mass ratios, such as the Earth-Moon system or (perhaps more interestingly) the Pluto-Charon binary system, possibly with a mission design aspect in mind. Alternatively, L_3 orbits and their manifolds could be examined more closely in any system to examine their role in particle motion within that system. Although the dynamics are weak, the region is relatively stable and once an object is captured in an orbit it can remain there for a very long time (even when including additional perturbations).

ACKNOWLEDGMENTS

The authors would like to thank Jon Sims, Al Cangahuala and Heinz Stoewer for the opportunity to test the ideas developed throughout this research in (certainly for this field) the most challenging environment of all: the mission analysis groups of the Jet Propulsion Laboratory. This being the first elaborate experience with performing research for the first author, the help and comments of Jon Sims, Dan Grebow, Jeff Parker, Rodney Anderson, Stefano Campagnola and Aline Zimmer greatly helped in giving this research a better sense of direction at a time when a number of different paths presented themselves.

Finally, the first author would like to thank the Colorado Center for Astrodynamics Research for its extensive and continued support of this research, as well as Dutch Space for its innovative and dedicated support of Dutch students in exploring the world of spaceflight.

REFERENCES

[1] NASA, "Ulysses Official Website," http://ulysses.jpl.nasa.gov/, last accessed 15/11/2010.

[2] NASA, "Stereo Official Website," http://stereo.gsfc.nasa.gov/, last accessed 15/11/2010.

[3] NASA, "SOHO Official Website," http://sohowww.nascom.nasa.gov/, last accessed 15/11/2010.

[4] W. Koon, M. Lo, J. Marsden, and S. Ross, *Dynamical Systems, the Three-Body Problem and Space Mission Design*. CalTech, 2006. http://www.cds.caltech.edu/ koon/book/KoLoMaRo_DMissionBk.pdf.

[5] V. Szebehely, *Theory of Orbits: The Restricted Problem of Three Bodies*. Academic, New York, 1967.

[6] E. Fehlberg, "Classical Fifth-, Sixth-, Seventh- and Eight-Order Runge-Kutta Formulas with Stepsize Control," Tech. Rep. NASA TR R-287, NASA Marshall Space Flight Center, 1968.

[7] H. Franz, P. Sharer, K. Ogilvie, and M. Desch, "WIND nominal mission performance and extended mission design," *Journal of the Astronautical Sciences*, Vol. 49, No. 1, 2001, pp. 145–167.

[8] E. Barrabes and M. Olle, "Invariant manifolds of L_3 and horseshoe motion in the restricted three-body problem," *Nonlinearity*, Vol. 19, Sept. 2006, pp. 2065–2089.

[9] X. Hou, J. Tang, and L. Liu, "Transfer to the Collinear Libration Point L3 in the SunEarth+Moon System," Tech. Rep. 20080012700, NASA, 2007.

[10] M. Tantardini, E. Fantino, Y. Ren, P. Pergola, G. Gmez, and J. Masdemont, "Spacecraft trajectories to the L_3 point of the Sun-Earth three-body problem," *Celestial Mechanics and Dynamical Astronomy*, Vol. 108, No. 3, 2010, pp. 215–232.

[11] K. C. Howell, "Three-Dimensional Periodic Halo Orbits," *Celestial Mechanics*, Vol. 32, Jan. 1984, pp. 53–+.

331

AAS 11-423

COMPARISON OF LOW-ENERGY LUNAR TRANSFER TRAJECTORIES TO INVARIANT MANIFOLDS

Rodney L. Anderson[*] and Jeffrey S. Parker[*]

In this study, transfer trajectories from the Earth to the Moon that encounter the Moon at various flight path angles are examined, and lunar approach trajectories are compared to the invariant manifolds of selected unstable orbits in the circular restricted three-body problem. Previous work focused on lunar impact and landing trajectories encountering the Moon normal to the surface, and this research extends the problem with different flight path angles in three dimensions. The lunar landing geometry for a range of Jacobi constants are computed, and approaches to the Moon via invariant manifolds from unstable orbits are analyzed for different energy levels.

INTRODUCTION

The design of Earth-Moon transfer trajectories is a problem with a rich heritage that has been approached with a wide variety of techniques. These techniques in combination with ever-changing mission requirements have produced an even greater number of possible trajectories ranging from the direct trajectories of Apollo[1] to more indirect trajectories making heavy use of multi-body dynamics. In addition to transfers to lunar orbit or the lunar surface, many previous conceptual mission designs have included the use of libration point orbits in the three-body problem for use in transfer to the Moon or to achieve operational orbits around the Moon. Now, the first mission to operationally fly on a lunar libration orbit, ARTEMIS,[2,3] has successfully demonstrated the feasibility of lunar libration orbit trajectories, and the two planned GRAIL[4–6] spacecraft will follow low-energy trajectories as part of their mission. With the increased use of these types of trajectories in mission design, it becomes important to examine the possible connections between unstable libration orbits and other locations of importance such as the lunar surface. Often the trajectories of interest are not those that travel directly to the unstable orbits, rather they are guided by the invariant manifolds of the unstable three-body orbits. Using the invariant manifolds as guides for potential trajectories provides mission designers a method for reducing the complications involved with design in this highly nonlinear dynamical environment. This work seeks to place low-energy lunar transfers to the surface in context with these invariant manifolds to enable mission designers to more easily develop trajectories in this multi-body environment.

Some framework and understanding already exists in regard to the relationship between invariant manifolds of unstable orbits and the Moon. Much of the work to design low-energy trajectories from the Earth to the Moon has focused on the use of libration point orbits along with their stable and unstable manifolds.[7–10] Koon, Lo, Marsden, and Ross examined this problem for the planar case,[11] and Parker studied approach cases to lunar libration orbits using invariant manifolds in his dissertation.[12] Baoyin and McInnes analyzed some specific cases of transfers from libration points and planar Lyapunov orbits to the lunar surface.[13] In particular, they searched for the Jacobi constant that would provide complete coverage of the lunar surface by the invariant manifolds of the selected Lyapunov orbit. Kirchbach et al.[14] looked at the characteristics of the invariant manifolds of a Lyapunov orbit as they intersected the surface of Europa in the context of the escape problem. Alessi, Gómez, and Masdemont[15] examined the locations of the Moon reachable by

[*]Member of Technical Staff, Jet Propulsion Laboratory, California Institute of Technology, 4800 Oak Grove Drive, M/S 301-121, Pasadena, CA 91109

the stable manifolds of a range of halo orbits and square Lissajous orbits. They computed the intersections of these invariant manifolds with the surface of the Moon with the expectation that they could be used for astronauts to escape to a libration point orbit if necessary.

In this work, we explore unstable orbits along with their invariant manifolds and examine the computed lunar approach trajectories within the context of the resulting invariant manifold pathways. It has been known since Conley's research[16] that libration orbits act as a gateway through which transiting trajectories must pass for certain energies. The specific details of how these transiting trajectories behave as they approach the Moon relative to the invariant manifolds are of interest here. A focus of this study is the exploration of the practical aspects and implications of this knowledge in the Earth-Moon system for mission design applications. In our previous work,[17] we examined Earth-Moon ballistic transfer trajectories to the lunar surface with trajectories impacting the Moon at varying angles for the planar case and normal to the surface for collision orbits[18, 19] in the three-dimensional case. These results for trajectories encountering the Moon normal to the surface were obtained using techniques previously implemented in Anderson and Lo.[20] This analysis is extended here to examine three-dimensional cases with additional flight path angles at the lunar surface. Next, the invariant manifolds of selected unstable orbits in the circular restricted three-body problem (CRTBP) are computed for different Jacobi constants, and their approach characteristics at the Moon are analyzed. These invariant manifolds are then compared to the previously computed trajectories and used to provide a context for these lunar approach trajectories.

MODELS

The analyses in this study are carried out within both the CRTBP and the ephemeris problem. The CRTBP generally provides a good approximation to the ephemeris problem, and a variety of tools and symmetries exist within this problem that make it convenient for initial analysis. While trajectories similar to those that exist within the CRTBP generally exist within the ephemeris problem, the CRTBP does not necessarily capture all those trajectories that exist in the ephemeris problem as the result of perturbations of additional bodies.[17] The ephemeris model is therefore used in the analysis to include these additional trajectories that are especially important in the low-energy regime.

Circular Restricted Three-Body Problem

Many of the trajectories and periodic orbits used in this analysis are computed in the CRTBP.[21] In this model, a larger body (the primary) and a smaller body (the secondary) are assumed to rotate about their center of mass in circular orbits, and the motion of a third infinitesimal mass is modeled in this system. The equations of motion are formulated in a rotating frame where the x axis is aligned with the position of the primary and secondary, and the positive x axis direction is defined in the direction from the primary to the secondary. Dimensionless quantities are used so that the primary has mass $1 - \mu$, and the secondary has mass μ. The value for μ is defined by $\mu = m_2/(m_1 + m_2)$ where m_1 is the mass of the primary, and m_2 is the mass of the secondary. The distance between the primary and the secondary, the mean motion, and the gravitational constant are all unity. The primary is located at $x_1 = -\mu$, and the secondary is located at $x_2 = 1 - \mu$. The equations of motion in the rotating frame may be written as

$$\ddot{x} - 2\dot{y} = \frac{\partial \Omega}{\partial x}$$
$$\ddot{y} + 2\dot{x} = \frac{\partial \Omega}{\partial y} \tag{1}$$
$$\ddot{z} = \frac{\partial \Omega}{\partial z}$$

where

$$\Omega = \frac{x^2 + y^2}{2} + \frac{(1 - \mu)}{r_1} + \frac{\mu}{r_2} \tag{2}$$

and

$$r_1 = \sqrt{(x - x_1)^2 + y^2 + z^2}$$
$$r_2 = \sqrt{(x - x_2)^2 + y^2 + z^2}. \tag{3}$$

A constant of motion referred to as the Jacobi constant is defined by

$$C = x^2 + y^2 + \frac{2(1 - \mu)}{r_1} + \frac{2\mu}{r_2} - \dot{x}^2 - \dot{y}^2 - \dot{z}^2. \tag{4}$$

For particular values of the Jacobi constant, certain regions, known as forbidden regions, exist where the infinitesimal mass may not travel. Five equilibrium points, referred to as Lagrange points, exist in the CRTBP. The two Lagrange points primarily used in this study are L_1 and L_2 where L_1 exists on the line between the primary and the secondary, and L_2 is on the far side of the secondary from the primary. Various types of unstable periodic orbits, several of which are computed in this study, are known to exist around these points. A useful symmetry is also known to exist in the CRTBP which extends the results of this analysis to other trajectories. Using this symmetry, it is known that if $(x, y, z, \dot{x}, \dot{y}, \dot{z}, t)$ is a solution in the CRTBP, then $(x, -y, z, -\dot{x}, \dot{y}, -\dot{z}, -t)$ is also a solution. Given this information, if a trajectory is reflected about the x-z plane, a valid trajectory may then be obtained by traveling reverse in time. Approach trajectories to the Moon may then be computed from departure trajectories and vice versa. An additional symmetry that will be useful to reduce the amount of computations required for some of the spatial analyses in the CRTBP also exists. For this symmetry, if $(x, y, z, \dot{x}, \dot{y}, \dot{z}, t)$ is known to exist, then $(x, y, -z, \dot{x}, \dot{y}, -\dot{z}, t)$ is also a solution. See Miele[22] or Szebehely[21] for more detailed information on these symmetries. The constants used in this model and the rest of the analysis are listed in Table 1. Several useful Jacobi constants, including those computed at the Earth-Moon Lagrange points, are listed here to place the results presented later in the paper in context.

$$C_{L_1} = 3.1883411054012485$$
$$C_{L_2} = 3.1721604503998044$$
$$C_{L_3} = 3.0121471493422489 \tag{5}$$
$$C_{L_4}, C_{L_5} = 2.9879970524275450$$
$$C_{Avg(L_1,L_2)} = (C_{L_1} + C_{L_2})/2 = 3.1802507779005262$$

Table 1. Constants used in the CRTBP and this analysis.

Quantity	Value
GM_{Earth} (km^3/s^2)	398600.43623333969
GM_{Moon} (km^3/s^2)	4902.80007622774
μ	0.012150584270572
Radius$_{Earth}$ (km)	6378.14
Radius$_{Moon}$ (km)	1737.40
Period$_{Moon}$ (sec.)	2360591.5104

Invariant Manifolds

Invariant manifolds of unstable orbits play an integral role in many trajectory options for transfers to the lunar surface, and their computation is essential for the comparisons described in this work. They may be computed for a variety of different orbit types, but the focus here is on computing the stable (W^s) and unstable (W^u) invariant manifolds of libration point orbits about the L_1 and L_2 libration points including Lyapunov and halo orbits. It is well known that these libration orbits act as a gateway through which trajectories transiting between different regions in the low-energy regime in the CRTBP must pass.[16] It is therefore expected that they will serve as guides to further understand these transiting trajectories.

Stable (unstable) manifolds of an unstable periodic orbit may be described as those trajectories that approach the selected orbit as time approaches ∞ $(-\infty)$. They are computed by integrating the state transition matrix for one complete period of the orbit (called the monodromy matrix) and examining the stability characteristics of this matrix. The local unstable (stable) direction may be computed from the eigenvector of the eigenvalue with a magnitude greater (less) than one. The stable (unstable) manifolds may be globalized by taking offsets of approximately 10^{-6} in the direction of the desired eigenvector for each point along the orbit and integrating backward (forward) for a selected period of time.[23]

Ephemeris Model

While the CRTBP is conceptually useful for understanding trajectories in three-body systems and it provides an accurate tool for the initial design of trajectories, the design of real-world trajectories eventually must incorporate accurate information about the position of all bodies from the ephemeris model. For this investigation, the precise orbital characteristics of the Moon are taken into account as well as perturbations from the Sun. The Moon's orbit varies from the assumptions of the CRTBP in that its mean inclination relative to the ecliptic is 5.145396° , and its mean eccentricity is 0.05490.[24] The inclusion of the Sun in combination with the Moon's inclination relative to the ecliptic causes the problem to become non-planar. The Moon's mean distance from the Earth is approximately 3.844×10^5 km, and it varies from about 363296.44 km to 405503.56 km.[24] The specific ephemeris model chosen for use in this study is the JPL DE421 Planetary and Lunar Ephemerides.[25] More detailed information on lunar constants and the geometry related to the JPL Lunar Ephemeris 403 may be found by referring to Roncoli.[26] For this analysis, only the Sun, Earth, and Moon are included in the integrations, and each of these bodies are modeled as point masses.

PLANAR ANALYSIS

In our previous work, lunar impact trajectories encountering the lunar surface at a variety of flight path angles were examined to determine their origin given a 200 day integration backward in time. A chaotic set of points were computed that generally formed in bands based on the origin of the trajectory with some structure observed in each band. Results were plotted for different Jacobi constants using the coordinates α

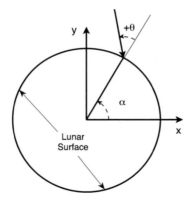

Figure 1. Diagram showing location and orientation of velocity vector as it intersects the lunar surface. The xy axes shown here are centered on the Moon in the same orientation as the axes in the rotating frame.

and θ as illustrated in Figure 1. The variable α corresponds to the location of the impacting trajectory on the surface of the Moon, and θ corresponds to the angle of the impacting trajectory with 0° being normal to the surface. Trajectories with different combinations of α and θ are integrated backward in time for 200 days and color coded gray to indicate a lunar origin in this time period, blue to indicate an Earth origin, and white to indicate no intersections with the primaries. The structure observed in these points is examined in the following plots by comparison with the invariant manifolds of planar Lyapunov orbits to determine whether the invariant manifolds may act as a guide for mission design to understand the behavior of these impactor trajectories. Two sample Lyapunov orbits found in Anderson and Parker[17] are replotted here in Figure 2. The Jacobi constants for these orbits were chosen so that the invariant manifolds of the Lyapunov orbits just graze the surface of the Moon. The Jacobi constants where the Lyapunov orbits cover the surface of the Moon were computed by Baoyin and McInnes[13] as approximately $C = 3.12185282430647$ for an L_1 Lyapunov orbit and $C = 3.09762627497867$ for an L_2 Lyapunov orbit. Kirchbach et al.[14] compared the invariant manifolds of an

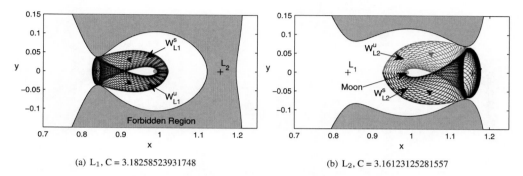

(a) L_1, $C = 3.18258523931748$ (b) L_2, $C = 3.16123125281557$

Figure 2.   Manifolds of libration orbits computed for Jacobi constants where the manifolds are tangent to the surface of the Moon.

L_1 Lyapunov orbit using this technique for trajectories escaping from Europa in the Jupiter-Europa system for a single value of Jacobi constant. They confirmed for this case that the invariant manifolds act as a boundary between the escape and non-escape cases as expected from Conley's theory. It is natural to question whether the invariant manifolds also act as boundaries between those trajectories originating from different bodies or elsewhere, and this question is explored here. Specifically, the same technique is used to examine impact trajectories using the invariant manifolds of both the L_1 and L_2 Lyapunov orbits in the Earth-Moon system over a wide range of Jacobi constants. The insights gleaned from this planar analysis are then used to aid in understanding the more complicated spatial problem.

In order to obtain an overview of the variation of the invariant manifold's intersections with the surface of the Moon, the Lyapunov orbits and their corresponding unstable manifolds were computed for a larger range of Jacobi constants in the CRTBP. A selected subset of the plots for several Jacobi constants are shown in Figure 3. One of the initial questions to be answered in computing the invariant manifolds is related to how long the integration duration should be. For mission design purposes, the approach from the Lyapunov orbit should typically be less than the duration of 200 days allowed for transfers from the Earth to the Moon. However, sufficient time should be allowed for the invariant manifolds to intersect the surface of the Moon and result in useful structure. A series of analyses were used with different integration times ranging from 50 to 200 days, and plots with sufficient structure were chosen for each Jacobi constant. The selected time duration for the integration of the invariant manifolds is noted for each plot with the most common duration being 25 dimensionless time units or approximately 109 days. Note that the longer integration times often showed more of the points of the invariant manifolds around additional structures not necessary for the current analysis, but filling these points in densely would require significantly more computational effort. In each case, the background points indicating the origin of the trajectory were all integrated for 200 days.

Examining the results in Figure 3, it is apparent that the manifolds are influential in dividing types of motion of the trajectory into different categories. The trajectories coming in to impact the lunar surface from other regions at C_{L_2} and $C_{Avg(L_1,L_2)}$ are bounded by the invariant manifolds of the L_1 Lyapunov orbit. This is similar to the results seen in Kirchbach et al. When both the L_1 and L_2 Lyapunov orbit invariant manifolds are shown for lower Jacobi constants, it is apparent again that they play a significant role in dividing the regimes of motion. In several cases, the invariant manifolds of the L_1 orbit bound one side of the lunar origin trajectories, and the invariant manifolds of the L_2 orbit bound the other side of these trajectories in the plot.

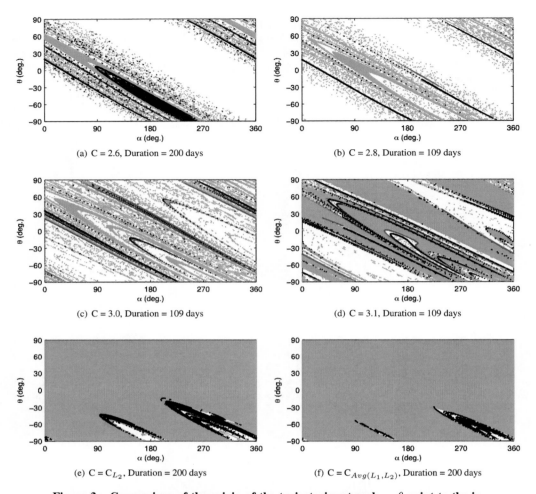

(a) C = 2.6, Duration = 200 days

(b) C = 2.8, Duration = 109 days

(c) C = 3.0, Duration = 109 days

(d) C = 3.1, Duration = 109 days

(e) $C = C_{L_2}$, Duration = 200 days

(f) $C = C_{Avg(L_1, L_2)}$, Duration = 200 days

Figure 3. Comparison of the origin of the trajectories at each α, θ point to the invariant manifolds of the L_1 and L_2 Lyapunov orbits. Gray indicates the trajectory originated at the Moon and blue that it originated at the Earth. Red points are the intersection of the L_1 unstable manifold with the Moon, and orange corresponds to the L_2 unstable manifold.

For the C = 2.6 case, the invariant manifolds of the L_1 orbit segregate the most predominate set of Earth-origin trajectories from the rest. It is apparent from this result that the invariant manifolds play a significant role in transfers between bodies. More specifically, the invariant manifolds form a boundary between the trajectories originating at the Earth and those originating at the Moon. It should be noted that these invariant manifold points only show up when the integration time is increased to approximately 200 days. It is also interesting that although the manifolds form boundaries in the plots, they do not always strictly separate the points coming from different origins. This has to do in part with the length of time that the trajectories and manifolds are integrated and the particular region of interest. One of the reasons for this will be discussed next.

Some of the characteristics of these boundaries and the way in which trajectories follow the invariant manifolds in position space may be further explored by examining some cases involving specific trajectories

338

in more detail. One interesting case occurs for C = 3.1 in Figure 3(d) where the trajectories transition from lunar origin trajectories to trajectories with no origin over the 200 day time span while crossing the line formed by the L_2 Lyapunov orbit unstable manifold. They then transition back while crossing the L_2 manifold again. A particular case may be taken by moving across α from 130° to 180° while holding $\theta = -3°$. Selected trajectories computed along this line are shown in Figure 4. For this case, the selected L_2 manifold trajectories bound most of the trajectories originating elsewhere (shown here as black), while the lunar-origin trajectories lie on either side of the manifolds at the initiation of the backward integration. The invariant manifold trajectories act as a boundary between the trajectory types as they circle around the Earth twice in the rotating frame until the trajectories traveling backward in time approach the Moon once again. At

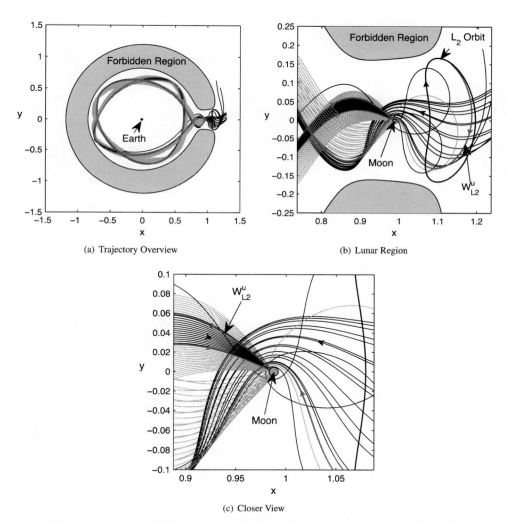

(a) Trajectory Overview

(b) Lunar Region

(c) Closer View

Figure 4. Comparison of selected trajectories plotted in position space for the C = 3.1 case to unstable manifold trajectories of the L_2 Lyapunov orbit. The trajectories are selected from the line at $\theta = -3°$ with $130° < \alpha < 180°$. The two trajectories on $\mathbf{W}_{L_2}^u$ are the ones intersecting nearest the selected line.

this point, the invariant manifolds approach the L_2 Lyapunov orbit, the lunar-origin trajectories encounter the Moon, and the other trajectories generally travel through the L_2 gateway and away from the Moon. One exception to this is a trajectory lying just outside of the guiding invariant manifold trajectories. Given its location it might be expected that it would be a lunar origin trajectory, however, it passes just above the surface of the Moon, spends some time in the neighborhood of the Moon, and returns to the interior region. This behavior is worth describing in more detail. The invariant manifolds are guiding the trajectories, and indeed only those trajectories starting between the manifolds could originate through the L_2 gateway. The trajectory of interest was forced to remain in the vicinity of the Moon, but here, the important independent parameter of the Moon's radius comes into play. If the Moon possessed a larger radius, this trajectory would have originated at the Moon. If the Moon's radius were smaller, other trajectories would be observed that failed to originate at the Moon. This indicates that the invariant manifolds can guide the trajectories and keep them in a region where they are likely to impact a body, but impact may not always occur depending on the constraint of the body's radius. This behavior leads to some fuzziness in the boundaries observed in the previous plot. It can also be seen that if the trajectories are integrated long enough they are likely to return to encounter the Moon at an earlier time. Once these exterior trajectories return, other structures may be observed indicating that additional dynamical structures may be at play in the trajectories' behavior.

An additional case was selected to analyze the effects of two different manifolds on the trajectories, and the results are given in Figure 5. For this case, selected trajectories were taken from the bend indicated in the inset of Figure 5(a). Single trajectories from the invariant manifold of both the L_1 and L_2 Lyapunov orbits were taken from the bends in the curves. Trajectories selected from the lunar-origin trajectories and just outside this region were then integrated and plotted as shown in Figure 5. This case is more complicated than the previous case, but the guiding effect of the invariant manifolds may still be observed. For this case, the integration for the lunar impacting trajectories is started as shown in the inset of Figure 5(b), and as the integration progresses, the trajectories travel once around the Earth in the rotating frame. As the trajectories approach the Moon, the trajectories between the manifolds are found to originate at the Moon. Those on the other side of the L_1 Lyapunov orbit travel through the L_1 gateway into the interior region, and those

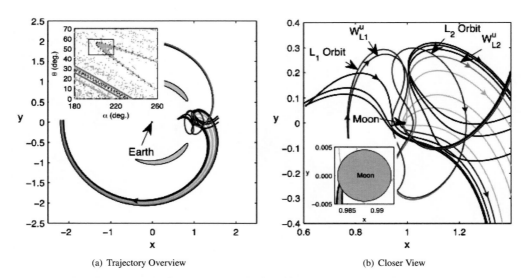

(a) Trajectory Overview   (b) Closer View

Figure 5. Comparison of trajectories on the unstable manifolds of the L_1 and L_2 Lyapunov orbits to selected trajectories impacting the Moon for C = 3.0. The points used to compute the trajectories were taken from the box in the inset of (a). They included a trajectory from each manifold on the bend of the curve and points selected by hand between the manifolds (that originate at the Moon) and just outside the manifolds.

340

on the other side of the L_2 Lyapunov orbit travel through the L_2 gateway to the exterior region. Again, the trajectories that originate at the Moon would be affected by the radius of the Moon, but the invariant manifolds generally guide the trajectories to where they have a greater chance of an encounter with the Moon.

In general the dynamics are more complicated and difficult to analyze in position space than in the lunar surface intersection plots. It is clear, however, from this two-dimensional analysis that the invariant manifolds are influential in guiding the Earth and Moon-origin trajectories from their respective origins. These results imply that similar mechanisms may be at work in the three-dimensional problem, and this topic is the focus of the remainder of this study.

THREE-DIMENSIONAL ANALYSIS

The planar CRTBP provides a convenient framework in which to understand and visualize the relationship between invariant manifolds and lunar approach trajectories, but the design of real-world equivalent trajectories often requires a landing at either higher or lower latitudes. Indeed, many of the recently proposed landing sites at the Moon are at northern or southern latitudes,[27] and one of the locations that is currently a focus for a lunar lander is more southern latitudes in the Aitken Basin. In this analysis, lunar landing trajectories are analyzed over the three-dimensional surface of the Moon, and the approach geometry of the trajectories in three dimensions is analyzed. The approach trajectories following the invariant manifolds of various spatial libration point orbits are then compared to these lunar landing trajectories.

Earth-Moon Landing Geometry

The landing geometry of trajectories traveling from the Earth to the Moon is of particular importance for mission design. In our previous paper[17] we analyzed trajectories encountering the Moon normal to the surface to determine whether these trajectories originated at the Earth within the previous 200 days. Given this elevation angle constraint, only some locations of the Moon's surface were found to be accessible from the Earth. For this analysis, trajectories were allowed to approach each point on the lunar surface from all directions. These directions were specified relative to the surface at each point. The azimuth angle (Ω) is measured clockwise from north where north is the lunar orbit's north pole, rather than the Moon's north pole to be consistent with the results from the CRTBP. The elevation angle (ϕ) is measured positive above the Moon's surface with a trajectory encountering the Moon's surface normal to the surface having an elevation angle of $90°$. (Note that this is different from θ used for the planar case, but it was chosen to be more consistent with typical mission design parameters.) While the previous analysis was ideal for impactors, the trajectories computed here are applicable for a wide range of mission types traveling to the lunar surface. Additional parameters for each trajectory related to the original characteristics relative to the Earth may be computed as in our previous paper, but the focus here is on characterizing the approach geometry. For the following analysis the trajectories were computed over the surface of the Moon using $1°$ increments in α and β. The same definition is used for α that is used in the planar problem in Figure 1. β is measured like latitude and is positive above the x-y plane. Two different grids were used for the azimuth and elevation angles. In each case, the elevation angle was varied in even increments, and the steps taken in azimuth angle were specified initially for an elevation angle of $0°$. The number of azimuth points were then decreased with $\cos(\phi)$ so that the number of points decreased with elevation angle. Both a fine grid and a coarser grid were used in this analysis. For the fine grid case, $1°$ increments were taken at $0°$ elevation for Ω, and $1°$ increments were used for elevation. For the coarser grid, $10°$ increments were used for Ω at $0°$ elevation, and $3°$ increments were used for elevation. This coarser grid was found to provide a good approximation that conveyed the overall trends of the fine grid, while allowing for a more reasonable computation time. Even with this coarser grid, computing trajectories over the entire surface in the ephemeris problem for each Jacobi constant required approximately seven days running in parallel on 40 processors. Unless otherwise stated, this coarser grid is the one used throughout the analysis.

As an initial step in the analysis, the set of trajectories were computed in the CRTBP for a Jacobi constant of 2.6. The trajectories were computed for both the fine grid and the coarser grid. A comparison of the maximum and minimum elevation angles resulting in trajectories that originate at the Earth is shown in Figure 6. Using the symmetry about the xy plane mentioned earlier, it can be seen that the northern and southern latitudes

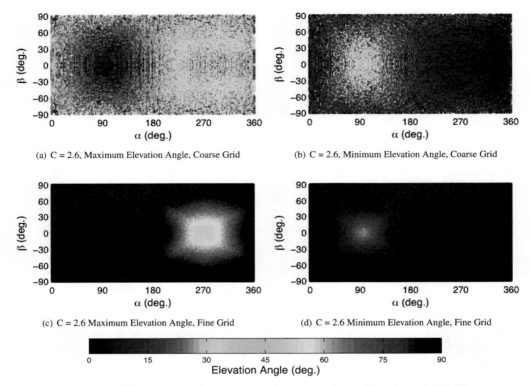

(a) C = 2.6, Maximum Elevation Angle, Coarse Grid

(b) C = 2.6, Minimum Elevation Angle, Coarse Grid

(c) C = 2.6 Maximum Elevation Angle, Fine Grid

(d) C = 2.6 Minimum Elevation Angle, Fine Grid

Elevation Angle (deg.)

Figure 6. Maximum and minimum elevation angles for trajectories originating at the Earth and encountering the Moon at each point on the surface. These cases are computed in the CRTBP for C = 2.6. Results from two different grids (in elevation and azimuth angle) are shown.

will be reflected for the elevation plots in the CRTBP. Note that the azimuth angles would need to account for the reflection if they are plotted, and although similar results would be expected in the ephemeris problem, the variations in the ephemeris require that the northern and southern quadrants be computed independently. Using this symmetry the values computed for the northern and southern hemispheres were reflected in Figure 6 to save computation time. By comparing the plots, it can be seen that, as might be expected, the finer grid captures more trajectories at higher and lower elevation angles that originate at the Earth, however, the overall trends in the data remain the same for both grids. In each case the range of elevation angles from minimum to maximum is shifted higher near $\alpha = 90°$ and lower near $\alpha = 270°$. Referring back to Figure 1, the $90°$ direction corresponds to the leading edge of the Moon, and the $270°$ direction to the trailing edge. The coarser grid is used in the remainder of this analysis, so it should be remembered that details in the plots may change with a finer grid, but the overall trends can still be observed.

An analysis of trajectories for a Jacobi constant of C = 2.8 confirmed our earlier result for trajectories encountering the Moon normal to the surface of the Moon that no Earth return trajectories were found for this Jacobi constant or higher ones in the CRTBP. However, it is expected that Earth-origin trajectories with velocities consistent with higher Jacobi constants in the CRTBP will exist in the ephemeris problem because these trajectories may use the Sun's perturbations to travel from the Earth to the Moon. Those higher Jacobi constants, especially those approaching the values near C_{L_1} and C_{L_2} are especially relevant for the computation of the invariant manifolds of libration point orbits which is useful for the comparison later in this study. The elevation angle range results are shown in Figure 7 for Jacobi constants ranging from C = 2.6 to 3.1 in

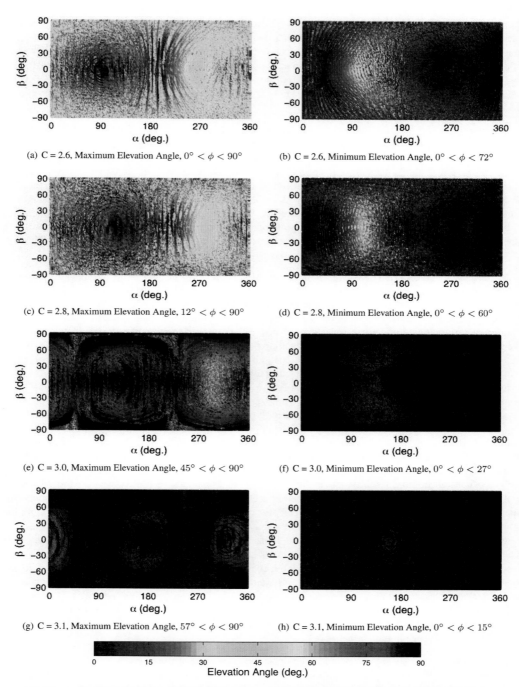

(a) C = 2.6, Maximum Elevation Angle, $0° < \phi < 90°$

(b) C = 2.6, Minimum Elevation Angle, $0° < \phi < 72°$

(c) C = 2.8, Maximum Elevation Angle, $12° < \phi < 90°$

(d) C = 2.8, Minimum Elevation Angle, $0° < \phi < 60°$

(e) C = 3.0, Maximum Elevation Angle, $45° < \phi < 90°$

(f) C = 3.0, Minimum Elevation Angle, $0° < \phi < 27°$

(g) C = 3.1, Maximum Elevation Angle, $57° < \phi < 90°$

(h) C = 3.1, Minimum Elevation Angle, $0° < \phi < 15°$

Elevation Angle (deg.)

Figure 7. The minimum and maximum elevation angles of trajectories originating at the Earth for each point on the lunar surface. These trajectories are computed in the Earth-Moon ephemeris system including the Sun's perturbations.

343

the ephemeris problem. Note that, as in our previous paper,[17] the Jacobi constant for the ephemeris plots is used as a shorthand for a particular set of velocities computed around the Moon in the CRTBP. These same velocities are attached to the Moon in the ephemeris problem referenced to the instantaneous orbital plane of the Moon's orbit around the Earth. The symmetry used to simplify the computations in the CRTBP is no longer present for the ephemeris problem, and trajectories were directly computed for the entire plot. Once the trajectory is integrated backward from the Moon, the Jacobi constant of the trajectory will vary in both the Earth-Moon and Sun-Earth systems.

Comparing the results from Figure 6 for the Jacobi constant case of 2.6 in the CRTBP and the ephemeris problem results reveals that they are quite similar. The maximum and minimum elevation values still occur at approximately the same locations on the surface for each case. However, several new bands of high elevation angle cases occur for the ephemeris case near $\alpha = 180°$ for the maximum elevation angle case and from approximately $\alpha = 290°$ to $360°$. Additional bands also seem to exist for the minimum elevation angle case, especially for high and low latitudes. It is natural to expect from past work that these bands may represent trajectory options that exist as a result of the Sun's influence, and it is interesting that these types of bands remain up through C = 2.8. An interesting topic planned for future study is to determine how these characteristics vary with a finer grid. However, the comparison performed here is with the same grid in each case, indicating that these additional trajectories exist.

As the Jacobi constant increases even more as seen in Figures 7(e) through 7(h), the range of elevation angles for lunar landing at each point seems to increase even more. The location of the peaks also seems to shift, and for the maximum elevation angle plots, the peaks move to the right or eastward with increasing Jacobi constant. When a Jacobi constant of 3.1 is reached, the maximum elevation angle for points containing a trajectory originating at the Earth never drops below $57°$, and the minimum elevation angle for the same points never goes over $15°$. It is important to mention that although the points look dense across the surface in the plots, this is because of the size of the plot and the points used for plotting. There are individual points on the surface where no Earth-origin trajectory exists for this grid, but there are always nearby points where such a trajectory exists. For real-world mission design, a small ΔV can be used to target slightly different points, and the surface of the Moon is covered in practice for mission design purposes. It has also been found for particular points that if a much finer grid is used, typically some Earth-origin trajectories are found, and these points will be included in future studies. The points with no Earth-origin trajectories for this grid are not included in the elevation angle ranges listed in the plots. These results for higher Jacobi constants agree generally with the normal trajectory cases seen in our previous work.[17] The additional range of geometries available for landing at these energies appears to be a result of the increasingly chaotic nature of the system as the Jacobi constant approaches the values at the L_1 and L_2 libration points. In other words, the trajectories are more able to take advantage of chaos to arrive at different elevation and azimuth angles. This also indicates that these Jacobi constants are of particular interest for comparison with the invariant manifolds of libration orbits. One interesting statistic to examine with a fixed grid is the maximum number of trajectories at a particular point that originate at the Earth. Although this number is generally quite low, there are some points where it peaks. The maximum number of trajectories at a particular point is listed in Table 2 for different Jacobi constants. The higher values are found for a Jacobi constant of 2.6 and 3.1. The C = 2.6 results include more direct trajectories that still exist in the CRTBP and do not require the Sun's influence, and the C = 3.1 results include those trajectories that are heavily influenced by the Sun. The total number of Earth-origin trajectories follows the same trend. These numbers are a function of the grid that is being used and can be refined by using a denser grid, however they do align with the results from the trajectories computed normal to the lunar surface seen in our earlier work.

Because the trajectories are computed in the ephemeris problem for the cases just discussed, the results will naturally vary with the initial epoch of the integration. A sample of the results was computed for four different epochs around the Moon's orbit (with the time intervals each at approximately one-quarter of the Moon's orbit) to determine how they might vary with the initial epoch. Representative results for a Jacobi constant of 2.8 are shown in Figure 8. The salient features of the plots remain generally the same for each epoch in that the maximum values still occur near $\alpha = 90°$ and the minimum values occur near $\alpha = 270°$. The January 7 and 21 cases have more locations with higher elevation angles, especially near $\alpha = 270°$,

Table 2. Maximum number of Earth-origin trajectories at a single point on the lunar surface for a fixed grid including the corresponding location and the total number of Earth-origin trajectories for various values of Jacobi constant.

Jacobi Constant	Maximum at a Point	Location (α, β)	Total Number
2.6	27	(193°, -36°)	290,672
2.8	16	(213°, -18°)	114,684
3.0	14	(225°, -11°)	162,061
3.1	36	(192°, 7°)	298,621

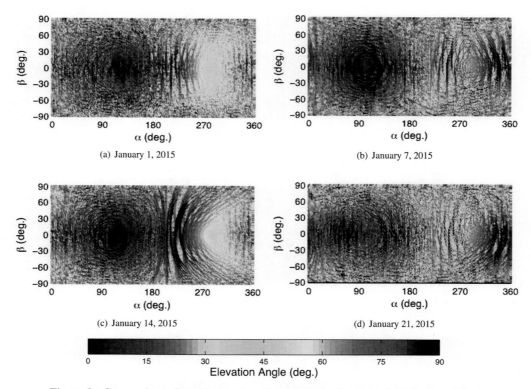

(a) January 1, 2015

(b) January 7, 2015

(c) January 14, 2015

(d) January 21, 2015

Figure 8. Comparison of maximum elevation angle results around the lunar orbit at seven day intervals for C = 2.8.

mixed in with lower elevation angle points. These two cases appear better positioned to take advantage of the Sun-Earth libration point dynamics, which could increase the range of elevation angles that may be obtained for approaching the Moon. Overall though, given this comparison, it is expected that the results from this study may be extrapolated to other epochs without drastically changing the outcome.

Another important aspect of the approach for mission design is, of course, the azimuth angle of the trajectory. Plotting this information in a global sense is difficult, but a sample of the types of results obtained for each Jacobi constant may be visualized in Figure 9 for a subset of the points. The azimuth angles are plotted for each point on a grid computed at 30° intervals in both α and β. For these plots, the fine grid was used at each point on the surface which of course produced more trajectory options. The orientation of the lines

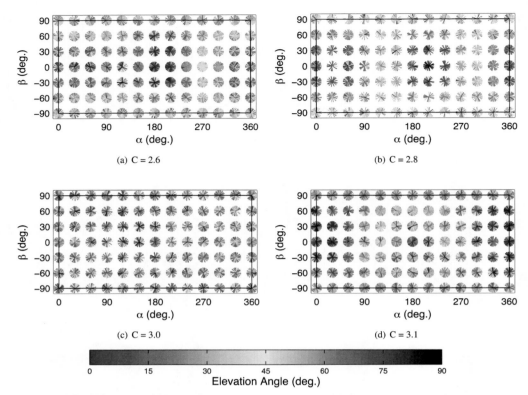

Figure 9. Azimuth angles at points on a 30° grid on the lunar surface. The plotted lines at each gridpoint are oriented in the proper azimuth direction for each individual trajectory. The color corresponds to the elevation angle of that trajectory.

centered on each point indicates the azimuth angle, and the color is used to designate the corresponding elevation angle of each trajectory. Note that the ±90° cases used azimuths that were rotated differently at each elevation as a result of the transformation used to compute them. So the specific results differ, but they generally show similar trends. It is interesting that there are definite regions where the majority of Earth-origin trajectories appear to have similar elevation angles. In each case though, there are often just a few high or low trajectories that result in the extremes seen in the elevation angles plots. This fact is worth keeping in mind for mission design since a particular elevation angle may be available in combination with only a few azimuth angles. In general it appears that higher elevation options are more available as the Jacobi constant increases, although there are typically at least a few low elevation angle options at each point. The combinations of available elevation and azimuth angles are evaluated in more detail for C = 3.1 in the following comparison with invariant manifolds, which will help explain the features seen in these plots a little more directly. In general, these plots can provide a broad overview of the available trajectory options.

Invariant Manifold Analysis

The invariant manifolds of libration orbits in the planar problem were found to provide general boundaries to different regimes of motion in the planar CRTBP. It is expected that similar types of behavior exist in phase space for the three-dimensional problem. However, with the increase in the dimension of the problem, the visualization of the invariant manifolds compared to the Earth-Moon landing trajectories becomes drastically more difficult. Spatial comparisons are therefore made using the intersection geometry of the invariant manifolds of libration orbits with the Moon and by looking in detail at specific landing locations on the Moon. For this comparison, halo orbits computed within the CRTBP are used, and a rough comparison with the ephemeris results is performed. This technique ensures that the velocities at specific points on the Moon are the same for each case. It has also been found that over the short integration times used for the invariant manifolds to travel from the halo orbit to the Moon, the Sun should have little time to perturb the trajectory, and it should remain similar to those computed in the ephemeris problem. The transfers to the halo orbits from the Earth are not analyzed here because techniques for performing these transfers using the Sun's influence are summarized in Parker's dissertation.[12] More detailed analysis in the ephemeris problem will be performed in the future.

As a first step in the comparison, the lunar landing geometry of the invariant manifolds of various halo orbits is analyzed. Alessi, Gómez, and Masdemont[15] examined similar trajectories for escaping the surface of the Moon to various halo orbits and summarized the areas on the Moon from which such escape trajectories are possible. We are concerned here with a combination of the landing location along with the landing geometry, therefore, a similar technique as that used in Figure 9 is employed here. In subsequent figures, the intersections of the unstable manifolds of the L_1 halo orbits are indicated by a red point, and the intersections for the L_2 halo orbits are orange points. The azimuth angle and the elevation angle are indicated by the direction and the color of the line segments, respectively.

The results for a halo orbit at C = 3.1 are shown in Figure 10. It can be immediately seen that for this energy, the L_1 halo orbit manifolds generally fall on the leading edge of the Moon in its orbit, and the L_2 halo orbit manifolds fall on the trailing edge of the Moon. As expected, the intersections of the northern and southern halo orbits are reflected about $\beta = 0$. The elevation angles are somewhat lower for the L_1 halo orbits than the L_2 halo orbits. All together, the unstable manifolds provide relatively broad coverage of much of the lunar surface, although significant regions are still not intersected by the manifolds. This may be remedied by examining the manifolds at additional energies. The unstable manifold intersections with the Moon can change significantly with the Jacobi constant as can be seen for the intersections plotted with a Jacobi constant of 3.08 in Figure 11. The intersections for the L_1 case have divided into two different regions, and the L_2 intersection case has grown tighter together. It should be reiterated that the unstable manifold intersections can increase if larger time intervals are used for the integration, and these plots focus on short-duration trajectories. The unstable manifold intersections also change even more as energy continues to change, but these energies appear to provide some of the most direct transfers.

This analysis shows that the unstable manifolds of halo orbits can provide broad coverage for landing at various points on the Moon, although not with the nearly complete coverage found from the previous results. It is also interesting to explore the relationship between the unstable manifolds and these Earth-origin trajectories from the general analysis. A similar examination to the one made for the planar problem would be desired, but the nature of the three-dimensional problem makes this drastically more complex. One possible method for performing this comparison is to examine the origin of the trajectories coming from all azimuth and elevation angles at each point that the unstable manifolds intersect the surface of the Moon. In this case, only one unstable manifold intersection is plotted for each location on the Moon relative to the trajectories coming in from all angles, but it still allows this point to be placed in context of the dynamics indicated by the source of each trajectory.

An initial comparison with this technique was made in Figure 12 using points from the L_2 northern halo orbit at C = 3.1 since the unstable manifold intersections move across a broad portion of the Moon, and we are interested in trajectories that may travel through the L_2 gateway to be influenced by the Sun. The results are plotted with each plot corresponding to one of the unstable manifold intersections with Moon. For these plots a fine grid stepping in one degree increments in both azimuth and elevation angle was used. Although the unstable manifold points are computed in the CRTBP, and the remaining points are computed in the ephemeris, the results are intriguing. The unstable manifold points in each case often lie on the boundary of the Earth-origin and lunar-origin trajectories. The primary set of Earth-origin trajectories appear to form a line or circle as the position is moved across the surface of the Moon, and comparing these results to Figure 9(d) sheds some light on why elevation angles are grouped together in that plot. In all cases, the unstable manifold

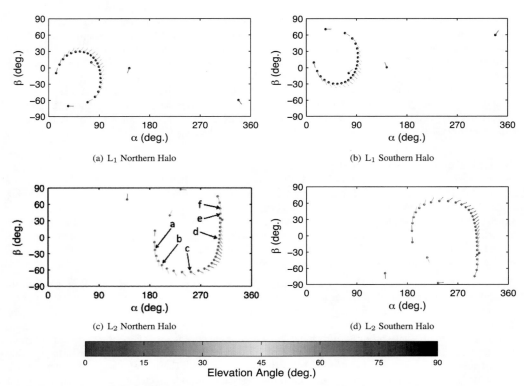

(a) L_1 Northern Halo

(b) L_1 Southern Halo

(c) L_2 Northern Halo

(d) L_2 Southern Halo

Figure 10. Unstable manifold intersections of the specified orbits with the Moon for C = 3.1. The labels in (c) are used to designate the plots in Figure 12.

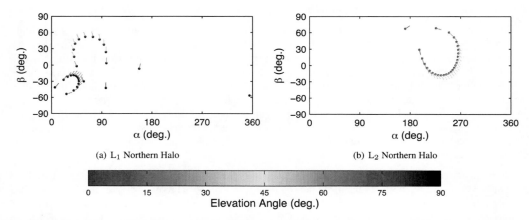

(a) L_1 Northern Halo

(b) L_2 Northern Halo

Figure 11. Unstable manifold intersections of the specified orbits with the Moon for C = 3.08.

point lies between this main set of Earth-origin trajectories and the larger band of lunar-origin trajectories. Although there is no line of unstable manifold points to separate the regimes of motion as in the planar problem, the unstable manifold still appears to lie on the general boundary between the two trajectory types. The fact that such a relationship exists in the dynamics is an argument that the CRTBP unstable manifolds are a good approximation over short times to the unstable manifolds found in the ephemeris, but more work is needed to verify this statement.

Finally, it is interesting to examine several trajectories plotted in position space corresponding to the lunar surface intersections. Several trajectories selected from either side of the unstable manifold intersection in Figure 12(b) are plotted in Figure 13. Here it can be seen that the Earth-origin trajectories do indeed travel through the Earth-Moon L_2 gateway during the transfer while the lunar-origin trajectories do not. Remember that the L_2 manifold is computed in the CRTBP, but it provides a guideline as to how the manifolds would behave in the ephemeris problem. If the Earth-origin trajectories are followed further to their source, it can be seen that they approach the L_1 region of the Sun-Earth system and then either encounter the Earth directly or use phasing orbits to do so. It appears that this set of trajectories is following the invariant manifold pathways connecting the Sun-Earth and Earth-Moon libration orbit invariant manifolds found in Koon, Lo, Marsden and Ross,[11] Parker and Lo,[8] and Parker.[12] It also appears that the main band of Earth-origin trajectories follows this route, and that similar pathways may be targeted from each selected point on the Moon.

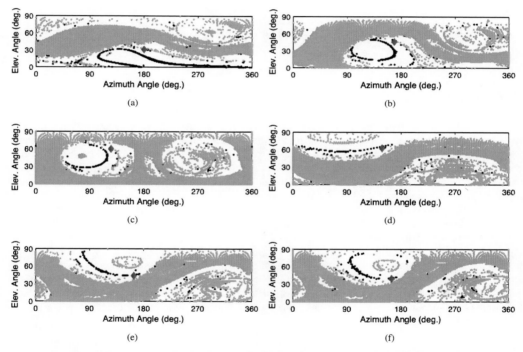

(a)

(b)

(c)

(d)

(e)

(f)

Figure 12. The origin of trajectories plotted for various azimuth and elevation angles computed for several intersection points of the L_2 northern halo unstable manifolds (indicated by the orange diamond) with the lunar surface. Each subfigure corresponds to the associated point as labeled in Figure 10(c). (C = 3.1)

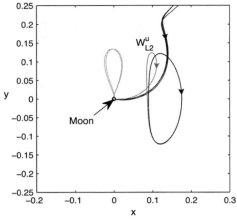

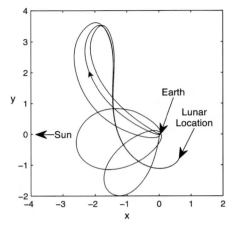

(a) Comparison in Earth-Moon Frame

(b) Earth-Origin Trajectories in Sun-Earth Frame

Figure 13. Comparison of the selected Earth-origin, lunar-origin and invariant manifold trajectories in the Earth-Moon and Sun-Earth rotating frames. The L_2 unstable manifold trajectory is superimposed on the plot because it is computed in the CRTBP.

CONCLUSIONS

The characteristics of Earth and lunar-origin trajectories encountering the lunar surface at different elevation angles have been quantified and compared to the invariant manifolds of libration orbits in both the planar and three-dimensional problem. In the planar problem, the unstable manifolds of Lyapunov orbits were shown to generally bound the different regimes of motion between the trajectories with different origins. The boundaries were explored, and it was shown that some points may cross the boundary as a result of factors such as the radius of the Moon and the chosen integration time. A wide range of elevation angles were shown to be available for landing at different points on the Moon for different Jacobi constants in the three-dimensional problem with higher elevation angles generally available on the leading edge of the Moon and lower elevation angles possible on the trailing edge. The invariant manifolds of halo orbits were shown to provide coverage of specific areas spread over a large portion of the Moon's surface with small changes in Jacobi constant allowing a wider coverage. The particular approach of the unstable manifolds of the L_2 northern halo orbit was found to lie generally on the boundary between the set of Earth-origin trajectories and a band of lunar-origin trajectories. The Earth-origin trajectories from a particular sample appear to transit through the Earth-Moon L_2 gateway and travel near the Sun-Earth L_1 libration point region on their journey from the Earth.

FUTURE WORK

The results from this study bring up many possible avenues for future work. A more refined grid in the ephemeris problem will likely allow a more detailed analysis of the possible connections between the Earth and the Moon. Different integration times for the different trajectories can be explored in addition to examining different epochs for the initial epoch in the integration. The halo orbits generated in the CRTBP for the comparison can also be generated in the ephemeris problem for a more detailed comparison. Finally, additional mission design parameters can be generated to aid in selecting particular trajectories for specific missions, and Earth departure characteristics can be generated.

ACKNOWLEDGEMENTS

The authors would like to thank Ted Sweetser for his support and for making this work possible. They would also like to thank Roby Wilson and Damon Landau for their helpful comments and reviews of this work.

The research presented in this paper has been carried out at the Jet Propulsion Laboratory, California Institute of Technology, under a contract with the National Aeronautics and Space Administration.

REFERENCES

[1] Mission Evaluation Team, "Apollo 11 Mission Report," Tech. Rep. NASA SP-238, National Aeronautics and Space Administration, 1971.

[2] S. B. Broschart, M.-K. J. Chung, S. J. Hatch, J. H. Ma, T. H. Sweetser, S. S. Weinstein-Weiss, and V. Angelopoulos, "Preliminary Trajectory Design for the ARTEMIS Lunar Mission," *Advances in the Astronautical Sciences, Astrodynamics* (A. V. Rao, T. A. Lovell, F. K. Chan, and L. A. Cangahuala, Eds.), Vol. 135, Part II, Pittsburgh, Pennsylvania, American Astronautical Society, Univelt Inc., 2009, pp. 1329–1344.

[3] M. Woodard, D. Folta, and D. Woodfork, "ARTEMIS: The First Mission to Lunar Libration Orbits," *21st International Symposium on Space Flight Dynamics*, Toulouse, France, Centre National d'Études Spatiales, September 28 - October 2 2009.

[4] R. B. Roncoli and K. K. Fujii, "Mission Design Overview for the Gravity Recovery and Interior Laboratory (GRAIL) Mission," *AIAA/AAS Astrodynamics Specialist Conference*, No. AIAA 2010-8383, Toronto, Ontario, Canada, August 2-5 2010.

[5] M. J. Chung, S. J. Hatch, J. A. Kangas, S. M. Long, R. B. Roncoli, and T. H. Sweetser, "Trans-Lunar Cruise Trajectory Design of GRAIL (Gravity Recovery and Interior Laboratory) Mission," *AIAA Guidance, Navigation and Control Conference*, No. AIAA 2010-8384, Toronto, Ontario, Canada, August 2–5 2010.

[6] S. J. Hatch, R. B. Roncoli, and T. H. Sweetser, "GRAIL Trajectory Design: Lunar Orbit Insertion through Science," *AIAA/AAS Astrodynamics Specialist Conference*, No. AIAA-2010-8385, Toronto, Ontario, Canada, August 2–5 2010.

[7] M. W. Lo and M.-K. J. Chung, "Lunar Sample Return via the Interplanetary Superhighway," *AIAA/AAS Astrodynamics Specialist Meeting*, No. Paper AIAA 2002-4718, Monterey, California, 2002.

[8] J. S. Parker and M. W. Lo, "Shoot the Moon 3D," *Advances in the Astronautical Sciences, Astrodynamics* (B. G. Williams, L. A. D'Amario, K. C. Howell, and F. R. Hoots, Eds.), Vol. 123, Part III, Lake Tahoe, California, American Astronautical Society, Univelt Inc., 2005, pp. 2067–2086.

[9] J. S. Parker, "Families of Low-Energy Lunar Halo Transfers," *Advances in the Astronautical Sciences, Spaceflight Mechanics* (S. R. Vadali, L. A. Cangahuala, J. Paul W. Schumacher, and J. J. Guzman, Eds.), Vol. 124, Part I, Tampa, Florida, American Astronautical Society, Univelt Inc., 2006, pp. 483–502.

[10] M. Ozimek and K. Howell, "Low-Thrust Transfers in the Earth-Moon System Including Applications to Libration Point Orbits," *Journal of Guidance, Control, and Dynamics*, Vol. 33, March-April 2010, pp. 533–549.

[11] W. S. Koon, M. W. Lo, J. E. Marsden, and S. D. Ross, "Shoot the Moon," *AAS/AIAA Astrodynamics Specialist Conference*, No. AAS 00-166, Clearwater, Florida, January 23-26 2000.

[12] J. S. Parker, *Low-Energy Ballistic Lunar Transfers*. PhD Dissertation, University of Colorado at Boulder, Boulder, Colorado, 2007.

[13] H. Baoyin and C. R. McInnes, "Trajectories to and from the Lagrange Points and the Primary Body Surfaces," *Journal of Guidance, Control, and Dynamics*, Vol. 29, July-August 2006, pp. 998–1003.

[14] C. Von Kirchbach, H. Zheng, J. Aristoff, J. Kavanagh, B. F. Villac, and M. W. Lo, "Trajectories Leaving a Sphere in the Restricted Three Body Problem," *Advances in the Astronautical Sciences, Spaceflight Mechanics* (D. A. Vallado, M. J. Gabor, and P. N. Desai, Eds.), Vol. 120, Part II, Copper Mountain, Colorado, American Astronautical Society, Univelt Inc., 2005, pp. 1875–1902.

[15] E. M. Alessi, G. Gómez, and J. J. Masdemont, "Leaving the Moon by Means of Invariant Manifolds of Libration Point Orbits," *Communications in Nonlinear Science and Numerical Simulation*, Vol. 14, December 2009, pp. 4153–4167.

[16] C. Conley, "Low Energy Transit Orbits in the Restricted Three-Body Problem," *SIAM Journal of Applied Mathematics*, Vol. 16, 1968, pp. 732–746.

[17] R. L. Anderson and J. S. Parker, "A Survey of Ballistic Transfers to the Lunar Surface," *21st AAS/AIAA Space Flight Mechanics Meeting*, No. AAS 11-278, New Orleans, Louisiana, February 13-17 2011.

[18] R. W. Easton, "Regularization of Vector Fields by Surgery," *Journal of Differential Equations*, Vol. 10, 1971, pp. 92–99.

[19] R. McGehee, "Triple Collision in the Collinear Three-Body Problem," *Inventiones Mathematicae*, Vol. 27, 1974, pp. 191–227.

[20] R. L. Anderson and M. W. Lo, "Virtual Exploration by Computing Global Families of Trajectories with Supercomputers," *Advances in the Astronautical Sciences, Spaceflight Mechanics* (D. A. Vallado, M. J. Gabor, and P. N. Desai, Eds.), Vol. 120, Part II, Copper Mountain, Colorado, American Astronautical Society, Univelt Inc., 2005, pp. 1855–1874.

[21] V. Szebehely, *Theory of Orbits: The Restricted Problem of Three Bodies*. New York: Academic Press, 1967, pp. 7-41.

[22] A. Miele, "Theorem of Image Trajectories in the Earth-Moon Space," *Astronautica Acta*, Vol. 6, No. 51, 1960, pp. 225–232.

[23] G. Gómez, A. Jorba, J. Masdemont, and C. Simó, "Study of the Transfer from the Earth to a Halo Orbit Around the Equilibrium Point L_1," *Celestial Mechanics and Dynamical Astronomy*, Vol. 56, August 1993, pp. 541–562.

[24] P. K. Seidelmann, Ed., *Explanatory Supplement to the Astronomical Almanac*. Sausalito, California: University Science Books, 1992.

[25] W. M. Folkner, J. G. Williams, and D. H. Boggs, "The Planetary and Lunar Ephemeris DE421," Interoffice Memo IOM 343R-08-003, Jet Propulsion Laboratory, March 31 2008.

[26] R. B. Roncoli, "Lunar Constants and Models Document," Tech. Rep. JPL D-32296, Jet Propulsion Laboratory, September 23 2005.

[27] "NASA's Exploration Systems Architecture Study," Tech. Rep. NASA-TM-2005-214062, National Aeronautics and Space Administration, November 2005.

ESTIMATION STRATEGIES FOR DYNAMICAL SYSTEMS WITH EQUALITY CONSTRAINTS

Julie J. Parish[*] and John E. Hurtado[†]

Constrained dynamical systems are common in spacecraft and aerospace robotics. For the class of systems subject to equality constraints, monitoring constraint violation is useful for determining the more appropriate dynamical model of the system. In this paper, two strategies for sequentially estimating the states and constraint are presented with examples. The first method constructs the constraint estimate and variance from the linearized constraint relationship and state estimates, whereas the second method directly estimates both the constraint and variance. The constraint variance is then used to calculate uncertainty bounds for determining constraint violation and subsequently selecting the appropriate system model.

INTRODUCTION

Sometimes a dynamical system subject to a constraint is configured or undergoes motion such that the constraint is not held for some period of time, often unintentionally. For example, a tether connecting two spacecraft may fail. For intervals where the constraint is not held, a different dynamical model of the system may be more appropriate. In order to determine whether a constraint is violated, a qualitative measure of the constraint and an associated confidence bound is needed. Furthermore, this measure must be updated frequently to monitor changes in the system associated with a constraint violation. In this paper, a sequential estimate of the constraint itself is the measure employed. Two methods for estimating the constraint are presented: first, construction of the constraint using state estimates and second, estimation of the constraint via the Kalman Filter framework.

The Dynamic Model

In this paper, it is assumed that the dynamical system can be represented in the following form, shown in Einstein index notation:[1,2]

$$\dot{x}_i = f_i(x_i, u_i, t) \tag{1}$$

$$\phi_j(x_i, t) = 0 \tag{2}$$

Here, f_i is a function of the $i = 1 \ldots n$ states x_i, ϕ_j are the $j = 1 \ldots m$ constraints written in Pfaffian form, and u_i are the control inputs acting on the system.

---

[*]Ph.D. Student, Department of Aerospace Engineering, Texas A&M University, H.R. Bright Building, Rm. 701, Ross Street - TAMU 3141, College Station TX 77843-3141.
[†]Associate Professor, Department of Aerospace Engineering, Texas A&M University, H.R. Bright Building, Rm. 701, Ross Street - TAMU 3141, College Station TX 77843-3141.

Continuous-Discrete Extended Kalman Filter

Several formulations of the Kalman filter exist; here, an estimation algorithm for nonlinear systems modeled with differential equations and discrete measurements is utilized called the Continuous-Discrete Extended Kalman Filter (CDEKF). The details of developing this estimator can be found in Ref. 1. Let $\tilde{\boldsymbol{y}}_k$ be the measurement vector, $\hat{\boldsymbol{x}}$ be the state estimate vector, and $\tilde{\boldsymbol{x}}$ be the error between the state estimates and true states. Unbiased Gaussian measurement noise, $\boldsymbol{v}_k$, and process noise, $\boldsymbol{w}(t)$, is assumed with respective covariance matrices R_k and $Q(t)$. Initializing with state estimate $\hat{\boldsymbol{x}}(t_0) = \hat{\boldsymbol{x}}_0$ and state covariance matrix $P_0 = E\{\tilde{\boldsymbol{x}}(t_0)\tilde{\boldsymbol{x}}^T(t_0)\}$, the following estimation algorithm can be utilized.

System Model

$$\dot{\boldsymbol{x}}(t) = \boldsymbol{f}(\boldsymbol{x}(t), \boldsymbol{u}(t), t) + G(t)\boldsymbol{w}(t) \tag{3}$$

Measurement Model

$$\tilde{\boldsymbol{y}}_k = \boldsymbol{h}_k(\boldsymbol{x}_k) + \boldsymbol{v}_k \tag{4}$$

Gain Equation

$$K_k = P_k^- H_k^T(\hat{\boldsymbol{x}}_k^-) \left[H_k(\hat{\boldsymbol{x}}_k^-) P_k^- H_k^T(\hat{\boldsymbol{x}}_k^-) + R_k \right]^{-1} \tag{5}$$

State Estimate Update

$$\hat{\boldsymbol{x}}_k^+ = \hat{\boldsymbol{x}}_k^- + K_k[\tilde{\boldsymbol{y}} - \boldsymbol{h}(\hat{\boldsymbol{x}}_k^-)] \tag{6}$$

State Covariance Matrix Update

$$P_k^+ = [I - K_k H_k(\hat{\boldsymbol{x}}_k^-)]P_k^- \tag{7}$$

State Estimate Propagation Equation

$$\dot{\hat{\boldsymbol{x}}} = \boldsymbol{f}(\hat{\boldsymbol{x}}(t), \boldsymbol{u}(t), t) \tag{8}$$

State Covariance Matrix Propagation Equation

$$\dot{P}(t) = F(\hat{\boldsymbol{x}}(t), t)P(t) + P(t)F^T(\hat{\boldsymbol{x}}(t), t) + G(t)Q(t)G^T(t) \tag{9}$$

Here, the measurement and state matrices, $H_k(\hat{\boldsymbol{x}}_k^-)$ and $F(\hat{\boldsymbol{x}}(t), t)$, matrices are defined as follows.

$$H_k(\hat{\boldsymbol{x}}_k^-) = \left.\frac{\partial \boldsymbol{h}}{\partial \boldsymbol{x}}\right|_{\hat{\boldsymbol{x}}_k^-} \quad ; \quad F(\hat{\boldsymbol{x}}(t), t) = \left.\frac{\partial \boldsymbol{f}}{\partial \boldsymbol{x}}\right|_{\hat{\boldsymbol{x}}(t)} \tag{10}$$

METHODOLOGY

Two approaches for estimating the constraint and associated variance are investigated. Recall that ϕ represents either a holonomic or a nonholonomic (scleronomic) constraint and $\boldsymbol{x}$ represents the state vector of generalized coordinates and velocities. Each of the proposed approaches use the current estimates of the states to construct an "estimate" or a "measurement" for ϕ.

$$\hat{\phi} = \phi(\hat{\boldsymbol{x}}) \tag{11}$$

The two methods vary, however, in how this value is utilized and how the associated variance is constructed.

354

Method 1: Construct Constraint and Variance

The first estimation strategy utilizes the property that expectation, $E\{x\}$, is a linear operator.[1]

$$E\{ax_1 + bx_2\} = aE\{x_1\} + bE\{x_2\} \tag{12}$$

Here, a and b are not functions of the states and are usually constant coefficients. The constraint error covariance is based on the constraint error, which is the difference between the true value of the constraint, ϕ_t, and the estimated value, $\hat{\phi}$.

$$\tilde{\phi} = \hat{\phi} - \phi_t \tag{13}$$

Note that if the constraint is held, the estimate for ϕ_t should equal zero (within some confidence bound associated with the constraint error covariance). For a constraint linear in the states, $\phi = a_i x_i$, the variance associated with this bound can be constructed in the following manner with $i \neq j$.

$$
\begin{aligned}
\sigma_\phi^2 = E\{\tilde{\phi}^2\} &= a_i^2 E\{\tilde{x}_i^2\} + 2a_i a_j E\{\tilde{x}_i \tilde{x}_j\} \\
&= a_i^2 \sigma_i^2 + 2a_i a_j \sigma_{ij}
\end{aligned}
\tag{14}
$$

Here, a_i represents the coefficient of x_i, σ_i^2 is the variance associated with x_i, and σ_{ij} is the covariance associated with x_i and x_j. These values can be extracted from the state error covariance matrix. For a nonlinear constraint, this relationship can be approximated by first linearizing the constraint estimate about the true value of the constraint ($\phi_t = \phi(\boldsymbol{q}_t)$).

$$
\begin{aligned}
\tilde{\phi} &\approx \phi \Big|_{\boldsymbol{x}_t} + \frac{\partial \phi}{\partial x_i}\Big|_{\boldsymbol{x}_t} (\hat{x}_i - x_{i_t}) + \dots \\
&\approx \phi_t + \frac{\partial \phi}{\partial x_i}\Big|_{\hat{\boldsymbol{x}}} (\tilde{x}_i) + \dots
\end{aligned}
\tag{15}
$$

The constraint error can then be approximated.

$$\tilde{\phi} \approx \hat{\phi} - \phi_t = \frac{\partial \phi}{\partial x_i}\Big|_{\hat{\boldsymbol{x}}} \tilde{x}_i \tag{16}$$

An approximation for the constraint error variance can then be constructed in a similar manner as for linear constraints.

$$
\begin{aligned}
\sigma_\phi^2 = E\{\tilde{\phi}\} &\approx E\left\{ \left[\frac{\partial \phi}{\partial x_i}\right]_{\hat{\boldsymbol{x}}}^2 \tilde{x}_i^2 + 2\left[\frac{\partial \phi}{\partial x_i}\frac{\partial \phi}{\partial x_j}\right]_{\hat{\boldsymbol{x}}} \tilde{x}_i \tilde{x}_j \right\} \\
&\approx \left[\frac{\partial \phi}{\partial x_i}\right]_{\hat{\boldsymbol{x}}}^2 E\{\tilde{x}_i^2\} + 2\left[\frac{\partial \phi}{\partial x_i}\frac{\partial \phi}{\partial x_j}\right]_{\hat{\boldsymbol{x}}} E\{\tilde{x}_i \tilde{x}_j\} \\
&\approx \left[\frac{\partial \phi}{\partial x_i}\right]_{\hat{\boldsymbol{x}}}^2 \sigma_i^2 + 2\left[\frac{\partial \phi}{\partial x_i}\frac{\partial \phi}{\partial x_j}\right]_{\hat{\boldsymbol{x}}} \sigma_{ij}
\end{aligned}
\tag{17}
$$

In this approach, both $\hat{\phi}$ and σ_ϕ^2 are constructed in the propagation/prediction step of the CDEKF using the values $\hat{\boldsymbol{x}} = \hat{\boldsymbol{x}}_k^+$ from the most recent update step. The logic employed for both methods is later described. Note that the variance terms along the diagonal, σ_i^2, tend to dominate the state error covariance matrix.

Method 2: Estimate Constraint and Variance

A second approach for estimating both the constraint and variance is to append ϕ to the state vector within the Kalman Filter framework. The computational complexity of this approach can be reduced by building a secondary constraint filter that essentially runs parallel to the state filter and uses the state estimates to construct constraint "measurements," $y_{m_\phi}(t_k) = \hat{\phi}(\boldsymbol{x}_k^-)$. Within the CDEKF framework, the following matrices subsequently result.

$$H_{\phi_k} = 1 \quad ; \quad F_\phi = 0 \tag{18}$$

The constraint measurement covariance matrix, R_{k_ϕ}, is constructed using Eq. 17, and $Q_\phi(t) > 0$ is tuned to provide a small perturbation to the covariance matrix propagation via process noise. To propagate the constraint estimate itself in the "prediction" step of the Kalman Filter, the time derivative of the constraint is employed.

$$\dot{\phi} = \frac{\partial \phi}{\partial x_i} \dot{x}_i \tag{19}$$

The remaining equations of the CDEKF can be applied for the constraint as written. Unlike in Method 1, though, the constraint "measurements" are constructed in the update/correction step.

Employing the Constraint Variance

The constraint variance provides a measure of the uncertainty of the constraint estimate. Taking the square root of the variance provides the $1 - \sigma$ bound for the constraint estimate. By assuming that the "truth" value for the constraint is equal to zero, constraint violation can be detected when the constraint estimate leaves the $1 - \sigma$, $2 - \sigma$, $3 - \sigma$, etc. bound, as determined most appropriate by the user.

Given two potential system models, $\dot{\boldsymbol{q}}_c = \boldsymbol{f}_c(\boldsymbol{q}, t)$ and $\dot{\boldsymbol{q}}_u = \boldsymbol{f}_u(\boldsymbol{q}, t)$, where c and u indicate "constrained" or "unconstrained," the uncertainty bound can then be combined with conditional logic to allow the estimation algorithm to autonomously choose the more appropriate dynamic model for the system.

If $|\hat{\phi}_k| > \sigma_{\phi_k}$,
$\qquad \dot{\boldsymbol{q}}_u = \boldsymbol{f}_u(\boldsymbol{q}, t)$
Else
$\qquad \dot{\boldsymbol{q}}_c = \boldsymbol{f}_c(\boldsymbol{q}, t)$
End

Here the $1 - \sigma$ bound is used. Note that, for systems subject to more than one constraint, both approaches can be modified to accommodate multiple constraints using vector notation. The most difficult accommodation is the logic employed to switch between candidate system models.

SIMULATION RESULTS

Two candidate systems are simulated using each of the two proposed methods. The first system is a two-dimensional disk rolling without slip along a straight, horizontal surface. The linear constraint associated with this system is violated when the wheel begins to slip for a specified time interval. Example 2 consists of a planar pendulum with an obstacle in the right-hand plane. The simulation results from the first two examples indicate that Method 1 is both more effective and less computationally expensive. An additional, more complex example is simulated using only Method 1. This final example is a tethered satellite system orbiting the Earth.

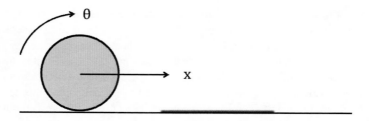

Figure 1. Rolling Disk Illustration.

Example 1: Rolling Disk

In this section, the simulation results for a disk of radius R and mass m rolling initially without slip, and for some time with slip, are presented. Figure 1 illustrates this system. The states for this system are the displacement, x, translational velocity, $\dot{x}$, disk angle, θ, and disk angular velocity, $\dot{\theta}$.

If the constraint $\phi = \dot{x} - R\dot{\theta}$ is held, the dynamics of this system can be described with Model 1.

$$\dot{q} = \begin{bmatrix} \dot{\theta} \\ \ddot{\theta} \\ \dot{x} \\ \ddot{x} \end{bmatrix} = \begin{bmatrix} 0 & 1 & 0 & 0 \\ 0 & 0 & 0 & 0 \\ 0 & 0 & 0 & 1 \\ 0 & 0 & 0 & 0 \end{bmatrix} \begin{bmatrix} \theta \\ \dot{\theta} \\ x \\ \dot{x} \end{bmatrix} + \begin{bmatrix} 0 \\ 1/Rm \\ 0 \\ 1/m \end{bmatrix} [u] \tag{20}$$

However, if the constraint is violated and the disk begins to slide rather than roll without slip, the more appropriate model is Model 2.

$$\dot{q} = \begin{bmatrix} \dot{\theta} \\ \ddot{\theta} \\ \dot{x} \\ \ddot{x} \end{bmatrix} = \begin{bmatrix} 0 & 1 & 0 & 0 \\ 0 & 0 & 0 & 0 \\ 0 & 0 & 0 & 1 \\ 0 & 0 & 0 & 0 \end{bmatrix} \begin{bmatrix} \theta \\ \dot{\theta} \\ x \\ \dot{x} \end{bmatrix} + \begin{bmatrix} 0 \\ 0 \\ 0 \\ 1/m \end{bmatrix} [u] + \begin{bmatrix} 0 \\ 0 \\ 0 \\ 1/m \end{bmatrix} [-\mu mg] \tag{21}$$

For the following simulations, $R = m = 1$, $g = 10$, $u = 2$ and $\mu = .1$f for the time interval $0 < t < 10$. The measurements are the configuration coordinates x and θ, and are constructed with measurement error $\sigma_{y_m} = 2$, which is not insignificant. The measurement covariance matrix is $R_k = \sigma_{y_m}^2 I$ where I is a 2×2 identity matrix. The process noise covariance matrix is a 4×4 diagonal matrix with entries $[0.0025, 0.5, 0.0025, 0.5]$, and the states are initialized with 10% error.

The true system experiences slip between $t = 1$ and $t = 5$. At $t = 3$, $u = 0$ until the constraint is again held. Also note that, although this constraint is holonomic and can be integrated, the constraint is used "as-is" with velocity-level states that are estimated (i.e., not measured directly). Integration of this constraint with respect to time requires initial conditions at time t_0.

$$\int_{t_0}^{t} (\dot{x}(\tau) - R\dot{\theta}(\tau))d\tau = [x(t) - R\theta(t)] - [x(t_0) - R\theta(t_0)] \tag{22}$$

Here t_0 refers to the point where the constraint is initially engaged, which may occur at several points in the time interval. Thus, using the velocity-level constraint with instantaneous state estimates is more easily facilitated in the estimation framework.

357

The simulations show that both methods are able to track the constraint violation, albeit with some delay, as shown in Figs. 2 and 3. The time delay is likely related to the uncertainty bound, as the non-zero constraint estimate must pass this bound for constraint violation to be detected with a set level of certainty. Note that, in order for Method 2 to perform comparably to Method 1, a very large amount of process noise, i.e. $Q_\phi = 15$, must be applied to the constraint covariance propagation equation. Typically, process noise is increased to accommodate modeling errors and to drive the CDEKF to more heavily weight the measurements. Here, the large amount of process noise indicates that driving Method 2 to behave "more like" Method 1 increases its effectiveness.

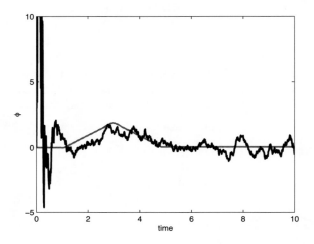

Figure 2. Example 1: True and Estimated Constraint Value Using Method 1.

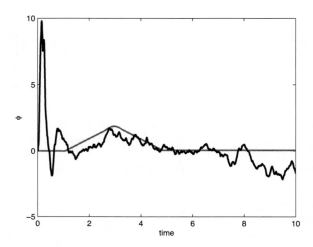

Figure 3. Example 1: True and Estimated Constraint Value Using Method 2.

Figures 4-5 show that the constraint estimate leaves the $1 - \sigma$ error bound in the "slip" region and Model 2 is successfully implemented. With Method 2, however, the constraint estimate drifts and Model 2 is incorrectly applied when the constraint is not violated. Even though only position-level states are sensed, all four states are well-tracked with Method 1. Method 2 tracks effectively until Model 2 is incorrectly employed late in the time interval. The state estimate errors for both methods are shown in Figs. 6-7. Note that the estimates and errors are solid black lines, whereas the truth and error bounds are shown in gray or dashed lines.

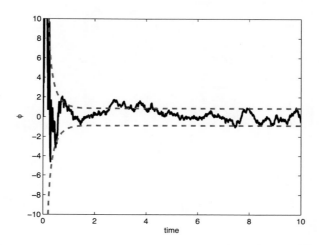

Figure 4. Example 1: Constraint Estimate with $1 - \sigma$ Error Bounds Using Method 1.

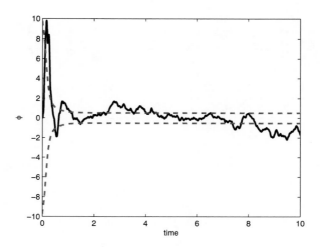

Figure 5. Example 1: Constraint Estimate with $1 - \sigma$ Error Bounds Using Method 2.

359

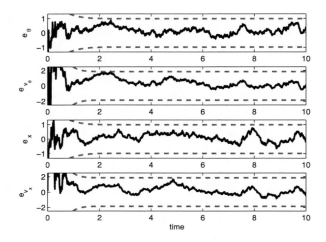

Figure 6. Example 1: State Estimate Error with $3 - \sigma$ Error Bounds Using Method 1.

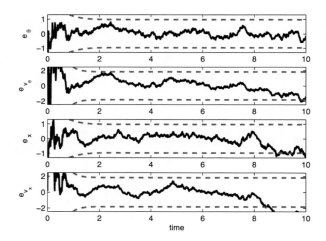

Figure 7. Example 1: State Estimate Error with $3 - \sigma$ Error Bounds Using Method 2.

Example 2: Asymmetric Pendulum

The second constrained system example is a variation of the classic pendulum moving in the plane under the influence of gravity. In this version, an obstacle of a semicircle is placed in the right-hand plane, as shown in Fig. 8.

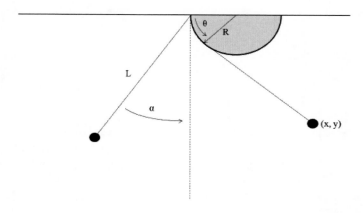

Figure 8. Asymmetric Pendulum Illustration.

The kinematics for each half-plane are different, so the dynamics of this system must be modeled separately for each side. First, the right-hand side is considered. The pendulum position in the right-half plane can be described with the following vector.

$$r = (R - R\cos\theta + (L - R\theta)\sin\theta)\,\hat{\imath} + (-R\sin\theta - (L - R\theta)\cos\theta)\,\hat{\jmath}$$
$$= x\hat{\imath} + y\hat{\jmath} \tag{23}$$

Equating the terms along the horizontal and vertical axes results in two holonomic constraints.

$$\phi_1 = x - R + R\cos\theta - (L - R\theta)\sin\theta = 0$$
$$\phi_2 = y + R\sin\theta + (L - R\theta)\cos\theta = 0 \tag{24}$$

Solving for the Lagrange multipliers results in the following equations of motion.[3,4]

$$\ddot{x} = -(L - R\theta)\dot{\theta}^2\sin\theta - g\sin\theta\cos\theta$$
$$\ddot{y} = (L - R\theta)\dot{\theta}^2\cos\theta - g\sin^2\theta$$
$$\ddot{\theta} = \frac{1}{L - R\theta}\left(R\dot{\theta}^2 - g\sin\theta\right) \tag{25}$$

In the left-hand plane, the position vector is as follows.

$$r = L\sin\alpha\hat{\imath} - L\cos\alpha\hat{\jmath}$$
$$= x\hat{\imath} + y\hat{\jmath} \tag{26}$$

361

Again equating the terms along the $\hat{i}$ and $\hat{j}$ axes yields two different holonomic constraints for the left-hand plane.

$$\phi_1 = x - L\sin\alpha = 0$$
$$\phi_2 = y + L\cos\alpha = 0 \tag{27}$$

These constraints can be combined into a single constraint: $x^2 + y^2 = L^2$. Applying Lagrange's equations for constrained systems, the governing equations for the left-hand side result.

$$\ddot{x} = -\frac{x}{L^2}\left(\dot{x}^2 + \dot{y}^2\right) + \frac{gxy}{L^2}$$
$$\ddot{y} = -\frac{y}{L^2}\left(\dot{x}^2 + \dot{y}^2\right) - \frac{gx^2}{L^2}$$
$$\ddot{\alpha} = \frac{-g\sin\alpha}{L} \tag{28}$$

Note that, as the two angles θ and α approach zero, the two dynamical models converge to the same equations with $\alpha = \theta$. For the simulations, this property is utilized to simplify the transition between models. Thus $\theta = \alpha$ for $\theta < 0$ in the forthcoming plots. One additional consideration is nature of the term $(L - R\theta)$, which dominates the expressions for the constraint and constraint variance. When the pendulum first enters the left-half plane and constraint violation has not yet been detected, θ becomes negative and a consequence is $(L - R\theta) > L$, which is physically impossible for this system. Thus, in implementation, $(L - R|\theta|)$ is used to compute the values for the constraint and constraint variance for both methods.

For these numerical results, $R = 1$, $L = 3$, and $g = 10$. The initial position and velocity estimates are constructed using the constraints with $\theta(t_0) = \pi/3$ rad and $\dot{\theta}(t_0) = 1.5$ rad/s. A small amount of error, 5%, is applied to allow the configuration coordinates to remain nearly "constraint compatible", but still be imperfect guesses. The two measurement sources are only the x and y coordinates, but all six states are filtered. The initial state estimate covariance matrix is $P_k(t_0) = 50I$, where I is the identity matrix, and the process error covariance matrix is a diagonal matrix with entries $\text{diag}(Q) = [0.0025, 0.1, 0.05, 0.01, 0.05, 0.01]$. The measurement error for both states is $\sigma_{y_m} = 0.05$, and R_k is constructed as in Example 1.

For this example, two constraints are being considered. The logic employed to account for multiple constraints is modified accordingly with L and R indicating the left- and right-hand side models.

$|\hat{\phi}_k| = \text{mean}([|\hat{\phi}_{1k}|, |\hat{\phi}_{1k}|])$
$\sigma_{\phi_k} = \text{mean}([\sigma_{\phi_{1k}}, \sigma_{\phi_{1k}}])$
If $|\hat{\phi}_k| > \sigma_{\phi_k}$,
$\qquad \dot{q}_L = f_L(q, t)$
Else
$\qquad \dot{q}_R = f_R(q, t)$
End

The simulation results in Figs. 9-18 show that both Method 1 and Method 2 can successfully switch between the two models and effectively filter the six states. Through significant process noise tuning effort, the performance of Method 2 can be increased to be nearly comparable to that of Method 1. Note that Method 2 is again found to be very sensitive to the values of the process noise chosen for Q_{ϕ_1} and Q_{ϕ_2}. Here, each is equal to one. The combination of (1) less computational complexity and (2) less sensitivity to process noise recommends Method 1 as a more advantageous approach to constraint monitoring in the CDEKF estimation framework than Method 2. For the remaining example (of greater complexity), Method 1 alone is applied.

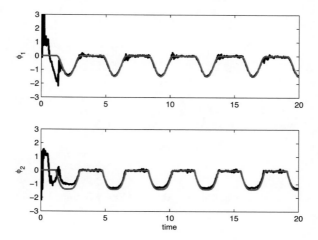

Figure 9. Example 2: True and Estimated Constraint Value Using Method 1.

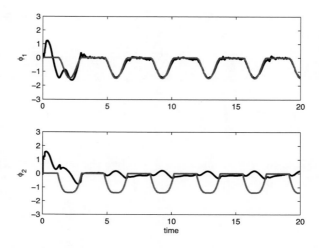

Figure 10. Example 2: True and Estimated Constraint Value Using Method 2.

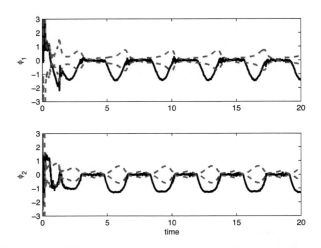

Figure 11. Example 2: Constraint Estimate with $1 - \sigma$ Error Bounds Using Method 1.

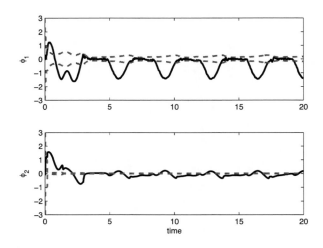

Figure 12. Example 2: Constraint Estimate with $1 - \sigma$ Error Bounds Using Method 2.

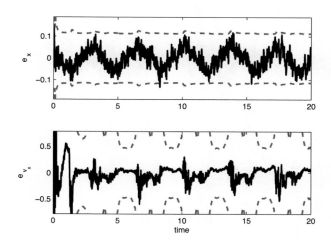

Figure 13. Example 2: x **State Estimate Error with** $3 - \sigma$ **Error Bounds Using Method 1.**

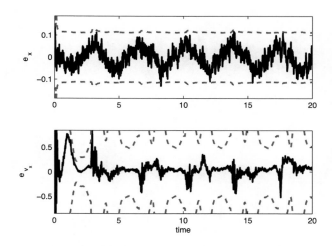

Figure 14. Example 2: x **State Estimate Error with** $3 - \sigma$ **Error Bounds Using Method 2.**

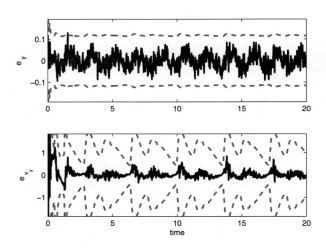

Figure 15. Example 2: y **State Estimate Error with** $3 - \sigma$ **Error Bounds Using Method 1.**

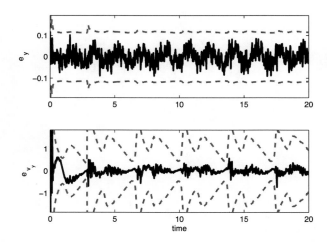

Figure 16. Example 2: y **State Estimate Error with** $3 - \sigma$ **Error Bounds Using Method 2.**

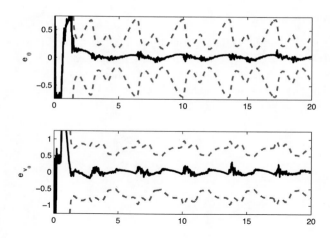

Figure 17. Example 2: θ State Estimate Error with $3 - \sigma$ Error Bounds Using Method 1.

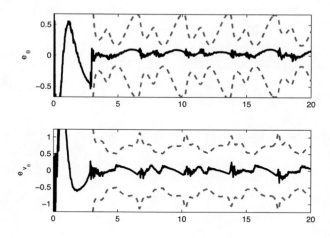

Figure 18. Example 2: θ State Estimate Error with $3 - \sigma$ Error Bounds Using Method 2.

Example 3: Tethered Satellite System

For a more complex example with a nonlinear constraint, a tethered satellite system is investigated. This system consists of two satellites orbiting the Earth that are connected by a tether. Here, the tether is modeled as a massless, rigid rod of length L and gravitational effects other than that of the Earth are neglected. The polar coordinates used to describe the kinematics of the two satellites are shown in Fig. 19.

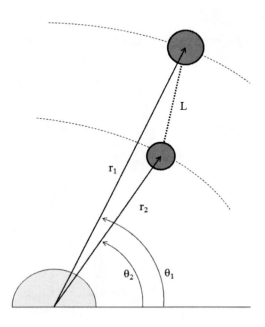

Figure 19. Tethered Satellite System Illustration.

For each of the $i = 1, 2$ satellites, the position, velocity, and acceleration can be described using these polar coordinates.

$$\boldsymbol{r}_i = r_i \hat{\boldsymbol{e}}_{r_i}$$
$$\dot{\boldsymbol{r}}_i = \dot{r}_i \hat{\boldsymbol{e}}_{r_i} + r_i \dot{\theta}_i \hat{\boldsymbol{e}}_{\theta_i}$$
$$\ddot{\boldsymbol{r}}_i = \left(\ddot{r}_i - r_i \dot{\theta}_i^2 \right) \hat{\boldsymbol{e}}_{r_i} + \left(r_i \ddot{\theta}_i + 2 \dot{r}_i \dot{\theta}_i \right) \hat{\boldsymbol{e}}_{\theta_i} \tag{29}$$

The tether alters the satellite system motion according to the following nonlinear holonomic constraint.

$$\phi = r_1^2 + r_2^2 - 2 r_1 r_2 \cos(\theta_1 - \theta_2) - L^2 = 0 \tag{30}$$

The associated constraint influence matrix can be written with $\theta_{ij} = \theta_i - \theta_j$.

$$C = \begin{bmatrix} r_1 - r_2 \cos \theta_{12} \\ r_1 r_2 \sin \theta_{12} \\ r_2 - r_1 \cos \theta_{12} \\ -r_1 r_2 \sin \theta_{12} \end{bmatrix} \tag{31}$$

368

Using Lagrange's equations (with Newton's law of gravitation to construct the potential energy) yields the equations of motion.

$$\ddot{r}_1 = r_1 \dot{\theta}_1^2 - \frac{Gm_E}{m_1 r_1^2} + \frac{C_{11}}{m_1} \lambda_1$$

$$\ddot{\theta}_1 = -2\frac{\dot{r}_1 \dot{\theta}_1}{r_1} + \frac{C_{21}}{m_1 r_1^2} \lambda_1$$

$$\ddot{r}_2 = r_2 \dot{\theta}_2^2 - \frac{Gm_E}{m_2 r_2^2} + \frac{C_{31}}{m_2} \lambda_1$$

$$\ddot{\theta}_2 = -2\frac{\dot{r}_2 \dot{\theta}_2}{r_2} + \frac{C_{41}}{m_2 r_2^2} \lambda_1 \qquad (32)$$

As before, one can find solutions for the Lagrange multipliers as a function of the states.

$$\begin{aligned}
\lambda_1 = &- \frac{m_1 m_2}{L^2(m_1 + m_2)} \left(r_1^2 \dot{\theta}_1^2 + r_2^2 \dot{\theta}_2^2 + \dot{r}_1^2 + \dot{r}_2^2 \right. \\
&\left. - 2(r_1 \dot{\theta}_1 r_2 \dot{\theta}_2 + \dot{r}_1 \dot{r}_2) \cos \theta_{12} + 2(r_1 \dot{\theta}_1 \dot{r}_2 - r_2 \dot{\theta}_2 \dot{r}_1) \sin \theta_{12} \right) \\
&+ \frac{Gm_E m_1 m_2}{L^2(m_1 + m_2) r_1^2 r_2^2} \left(r_1^2 (r_2 - r_1 \cos \theta_{12}) + r_2^2 (r_1 - r_2 \cos \theta_{12}) \right) \qquad (33)
\end{aligned}$$

For this system, the unconstrained equations of motion equal the constrained equations of motion with $\lambda = 0$.

In simulation, the tethered satellite system is released, in a constraint-compatible configuration, at perigee. The parameters chosen for this study are outlined in Table 1.

Table 1. Tethered Satellite System Parameter Values.

Parameter	Value
c	10^4
G	6.67300×10^{-20} km^3/kg/s^2
m_{Earth}	5.9722×10^{24} kg
r_{Earth}	6371 km
L	5 km
m_1	500 kg
m_2	5 kg
$r_1(t_0)$	8376 km
$r_2(t_0)$	8371 km
$\theta_i(t_0)$	0 rad
$\dot{r}_i$	0 km/s
$\dot{\theta}_i$	8.238×10^{-4} rad/s

The orbit of the satellite system is monitored for time 0s $< t <$ 1500s, and the tether breaks at time $t = 500$s. The four configuration-level states (r_i, θ_i) are sensed, and all eight (configuration and velocity) states are estimated. The measurement noise covariance matrix is constructed as before with $\sigma_{y_m} = [1, .0001, 1, .0001]$, and the diagonal elements of the process noise covariance matrix are $Q = 10^{-10} \times \text{diag}[400, 400, 500, 0.04, 400, 400, 500, 0.04]$. The initial state covariance matrix is $P_k(t_0) = 100I$, and the state estimates are initialized with approximately 5% error. Note that the difference in magnitudes between the radial and angular measures for this system required a scaling factor, c, to efficiently integrate the equations in the state estimate propagation equation of the CDEKF.

The plots in Figs. 20-21 show that implementation of Method 1 constraint monitoring is effective for switching models for this system, but that there is some time delay in switching models as the constraint estimate moves out of the uncertainty bound.

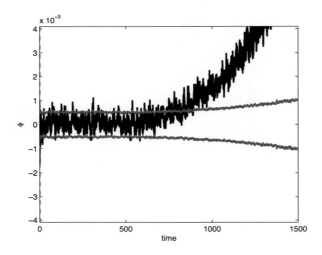

Figure 20. Example 4: Constraint Estimate with $1 - \sigma$ Error Bounds.

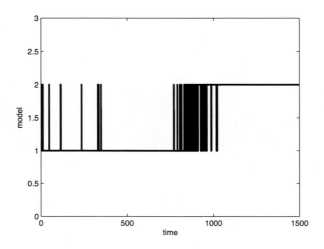

Figure 21. Example 4: Model Time History

370

For this example, a $1.5 - \sigma$ uncertainty bound is selected due to a small bias in the constraint estimate, which is apparent in Fig. 20. A similar and potentially related bias is reflected in the θ_i estimate errors; this bias reflects the angular difference θ_{ij} that appears throughout the system model equations of motion (i.e., the angles do not appear independently). The bias is therefore likely a consequence of the coordinate choice for the system model and not a reflection on the proposed method or the CDEKF. The state errors for these simulations are bounded by approximately .5km and .1km/s for the radial coordinates and velocities, and 3×10^{-4}rad and 1×10^{-5}rad/s for the angular coordinates and velocities. These errors stay consistently within the $3 - \sigma$ error bounds.

CONCLUSIONS

The general strategy presented in this paper is useful in design of a constrained system that can autonomously monitor its constrained motion, detect constraint violation, and make estimation and control decisions accordingly. Each of the two strategies outlined are shown to successfully detect constraint violation with respect to an associated confidence bound and automatically select the dynamical model that better reflects the unconstrained motion. In order to detect constraint violation with some degree of certainty, a measure is needed to bound the estimate of the constraint value. Here, the measure selected is the variance associated with the constraint estimate. This measure can be approximated by linearizing the constraint about the "true" constraint value and then evaluating the partial derivative coefficients with the estimated state values. Using this linearized constraint relationship, the linear property of the expectation operator can be utilized to approximate the variance associated with the constraint. It is then up to the user to impose switching logic that accounts for the certainty of constraint violation via the constant coefficient (i.e., 1-, 2-, 3-, etc.) of the constraint σ_ϕ bound.

The plots and analysis from the numerical results show that the two methods presented can be successfully implemented in the CDEKF. These simulations also indicate that Method 1 is the more advantageous approach due to the additional complexity and sensitivity to process noise of Method 2. Through several examples, this approach is shown to work for both holonomic and nonholonomic constraints, as well as for multiple constraints. Overall, this method allows multi-model (constrained and unconstrained) estimation for systems subject to broken constraints.

REFERENCES

[1] J. Crassidis and J. Junkins, *Optimal Estimation of Dynamic Systems*. Boca Raton, FL: Chapman & Hall\CRC Press, 2004.
[2] W. M. Lai, D. Rubin, and E. Krempl, *Introduction to Continuum Mechanics*. Burlington, MA: Butterworth-Heinemann, third ed., 1999.
[3] A. Laulusa and O. Bauchau, "Review of Classical Approaches for Constraint Enforcement in Multibody Systems," *Journal of Computational and Nonlinear Dynamics*, Vol. 3, No. 1, Jan. 2008, pp. 011004: 1–8.
[4] J. Parish and J. Hurtado, "State Estimation for Constrained Systems with Redundant Coordinates," *AIAA Guidance, Navigation, and Control Conference*, Portland, Oregon, 8-11 August 2011.

371

FLYBYS IN THE PLANAR, CIRCULAR, RESTRICTED, THREE-BODY PROBLEM

Stefano Campagnola,[*] Paul Skerritt[†] and Ryan P. Russell[‡]

This paper presents an analysis of gravity assisted flybys in the planar, circular, restricted three-body problem that is inspired by the Keplerian map and by the Tisserand-Poincaré graph. The Flyby map is defined and used to give new insight on the flyby dynamics and on the accuracy of the linked-conics model. The first main result of this work is using the Flyby map to extend the functionality of the Tisserand graph to low energies beyond the validity of linked conics. Two families of flybys are identified: Type I (direct) flybys and Type II (retrograde) flybys. The second main result of this work is showing that Type I flybys exist at all energies and are more efficient than Type II flybys, when both exist. The third main result of this work is an example trajectory that consists of Type I flybys only, all outside the linked-conics domain of applicability. The trajectory is computed with the patched-cr3bp, and connects an initial orbit around Jupiter intersecting the Callisto orbit, to a 200-km circular orbit around Europa. The trajectory saves up to 30% in Δv (endgame and orbit insertion) compared to the current baseline for Europa orbiters computed in patched conics, without any significant increase to the time of flight nor the radiation dose.

INTRODUCTION

Gravity assisted flybys are important mechanisms in celestial mechanics. They are also a common and powerful tool in the design of space mission trajectories. Yet even in the case of planar motion, their dynamics still warrant further study, especially when considering the gravity of more than one body at a time.

The linked-conics (or zero-sphere-of-influence, patched-conics) model provides the simplest model for a flyby: the minor body rotates the relative velocity vector v_∞ by a bending angle δ, which depends on the altitude of the closest approach. The model is only valid for Keplerian orbits around the major body that intersects the minor body orbit. The model is less and less accurate in the "low-energy" regimes as the $\|v_\infty\|$ decreases. A higher-fidelity approach to model flybys uses the planar, circular, restricted, three-body problem (pcr3bp), where the analysis involves a high-dimensional solution space, which is explored mainly by numerical integration. The design of multiple-flyby trajectories typically consists of finding sets of initial conditions that are scanned[1,2] or guessed and corrected through shooting methods.[3–5] In space mission design, these trajectories include small impulsive maneuvers (if any) to target the best initial conditions for the next flyby. In existing literature,[1,4,6] the design of multiple-flyby trajectories in the cr3bp is limited to quasi-ballistic, long time-of-flight transfers. This analysis is very sensitive to the initial conditions, and an exploration of the full solution space is often impossible.

An original attempt to simplify the analysis and design of flybys in the planar, circular, restricted three-body problem is the Keplerian map,[7] which relies on (1) approximating the motion of the spacecraft as Keplerian, and (2) integrating the perturbations along the unperturbed trajectory. The Keplerian elements before the flyby are mapped into the Keplerian elements after the flyby using a quadrature formula. The map

---

[*]Postdoctoral Scholar, Outer Planet Mission Analysis Group, Jet Propulsion Laboratory, California Institute of Technology, 4800 Oak Grove Drive , Pasadena, CA 91109, stefano.campagnola@jpl.nasa.gov

[†]Ph.D. Candidate, Physics Department, California Institute of Technology, 1200 E. California Blvd, Pasadena, CA, 91125, skerritt@caltech.edu

[‡]Assistant Professor, The University of Texas at Austin, Department of Aerospace Engineering and Engineering Mechanics, 1 University Station, C0600, Austin, TX 78712-0235, ryan.russell@utexas.edu

gives insight into the chaotic structure of the solution space, however it is reasonably accurate only for very low three-body energies.[5]

Another attempt to extend the simplicity of the linked-conics approach to the three-body problem is the T-P graph,[2] a Poincaré section with Tisserand level-sets that partly overlaps the Tisserand graph. The T-P graph gives insight on the dynamics of multiple flyby trajectories and can be used to define target conditions that otherwise are unknown. However the T-P graph cannot be used to predict the effects of a single flyby, as done by the Tisserand graph.

The three-body flyby analysis performed in this paper is new and is inspired by the Keplerian map and by the T-P graph. The analysis gives new insight on the flyby dynamics and on the accuracy of the linked-conics model. The analysis also suggests a simple way to design multiple flyby trajectories on the T-P graph, which will be presented in a follow-up paper. The method has already been implemented to compute endgame scenarios for NASA's Europa orbiter options and for ESA's Jupiter Ganymede Orbiter.

The first main result of the paper is the definition of the Flyby map, a discrete map similar to the Keplerian map. The Flyby map is computed by numerical integration and can be applied to any set of initial three-body energies and semi-major axes, with the exclusion of the minor-body semi-major axis. The second main result of the paper is the identification, through the Flyby map, of two families of flybys (Type I and II). The first family exists at any energy, while the second family only appears at high energies, where the third body can access the both sides of the minor body. The analysis in this work bridges the low-energy regime, where Type I flybys are approximated by the Keplerian map, and the linked-conics regime, where Type I and Type II flybys are approximated by direct and retrograde gravity assists, respectively. We also show that Type I flybys are more efficient than Type II flybys, explaining why trajectories with direct gravity assists have sometimes been proven preferable, when computed in a real-ephemeris model.[2]

BACKGROUND

This section summarizes the state-of-the art approaches for the analysis and the design of flybys. The first part describes the linked-conics approach, while the second part describes the circular, restricted, three-body problem approach. Only planar flybys (i.e. in the minor-body orbital plane) are considered in this work. All variables are non-dimensionalized using the scaling factors $(\tilde{M} + \tilde{m})^*$ for the mass, $\tilde{a}_m$ for the length, and $\sqrt{(\tilde{a}_m^3/\tilde{G}(\tilde{M} + \tilde{m})}$ for the time.

Flybys in the linked-conics model on the Tisserand graph

In the linked-conics model, the spacecraft and the minor body move on two intersecting Keplerian orbits around the major body. A flyby occurs if both the spacecraft and the minor body are at the same intersection at the same time. The flyby is modeled as an instantaneous rotation of the v_∞ vector by an angle δ

$$\sin \frac{\delta}{2} = \frac{Gm}{Gm + v_\infty^2(r_m + H)}, \quad H > H_{min} \tag{1}$$

where the gravity-assist altitude h is a free parameter. If α_A is the pump angle (between the minor body velocity and the v_∞ vector[8,9]) before the flyby, the pump angle after the flyby is

$$\alpha_B \in [\alpha_{Bmin}, \alpha_{Bmax}] \tag{2}$$

where

$$\alpha_{Bmin} = \max(0, \alpha_A - \delta), \quad \alpha_{Bmax} = \min(\pi, \alpha_A + \delta). \tag{3}$$

The post-flyby semi-major axis and eccentricity are function of the pump angle (see APPENDIX A)

---

*The mathematical symbols are explained in the notation section at the end of the paper.

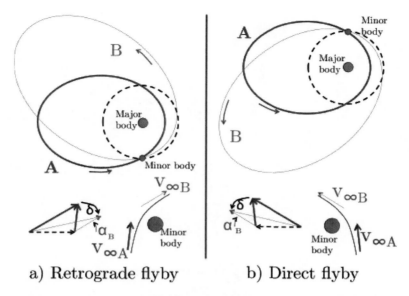

a) Retrograde flyby   b) Direct flyby

Figure 1. Two symmetrical flyby geometries in the linked-conics model

$$a_B = \frac{1}{1 - 2v_\infty \cos\alpha_B - v_\infty^2}$$

$$e_B = \sqrt{1 + (v_\infty^2 + 2v_\infty \cos\alpha - 1)(1 + v_\infty \cos\alpha)^2} \tag{4}$$

Figure 1 shows two symmetrical flyby geometries in the inertial frame. The thick line is the pre-flyby orbit of the spacecraft; the thin line is the post-flyby orbit. The orbit of the minor orbit is represented with a dash line. In Figure 1a, the flyby occurs on the incoming leg of the spacecraft's orbit and is modeled by a direct hyperbola with close approach altitude h relative to the minor body. In Figure 1b, the flyby occurs on the outgoing leg of the spacecraft orbit and is modeled by a retrograde hyperbola with the same close approach altitude h relative to the minor body. The post-gravity-assist conditions are the same in terms of eccentricity and semi-major axis, because the pump angle α_B is the same in both cases.

A common graphical tool to design gravity-assist trajectories is the Tisserand graph,[10, 11] a two-dimensional graph with two Keplerian elements on the axes ($r_p - Period$ or $r_a - r_p$). Every point on the graph corresponds to a spacecraft orbit crossing the minor body orbit. Tisserand graphs include v_∞ level sets, and a gravity assist is represented by a jump within the same level set. The length of the jump depends on $\alpha_B - \alpha_A$, and therefore on δ and on the gravity assist altitude. The maximum jump occurs for $\alpha_B = \alpha_{Bmax}$ (maximum a_B) and $\alpha_B = \alpha_{Bmin}$ (minimum a_B). Figure 2 shows the Tisserand graph with the v_∞ level sets and the set of orbits with the $3 : 2$ resonance with the period of the minor body (line with slope -1). Flybys map all the points on the 3:2 line to the thick curve on the right or on the left, depending on whether the gravity assist is used to increase or reduce the period. Note that, although they occurr at different intersection, both the direct and the retrograde gravity assists in Figure 1 result in the same change in orbital elements, so they cannot be distinguished in the Tisserand graph. However, some recent work (motivation for the current study) showed that retrograde and direct gravity assists perform differently when they are computed in the circular three-body problem.[2]

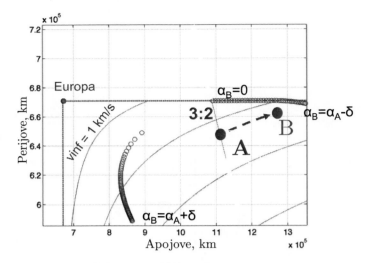

Figure 2. Flyby in the Tisserand graph

The planar, circular, restricted, three-body problem

The circular, restricted, three-body problem (cr3bp) is a more accurate model to study flybys. The motion of the spacecraft is described in a rotating frame, centered at the barycenter of the major and minor bodies. The equations of motion for the spacecraft are

$$\begin{cases} \ddot{X} - 2\dot{Y} &= \frac{\partial\Omega}{\partial X} \\ \ddot{Y} + 2\dot{X} &= \frac{\partial\Omega}{\partial Y} \end{cases} \tag{5}$$

$$\Omega(X,Y,Z) \equiv \frac{1}{2}\left(X^2 + Y^2\right) + \frac{1-\mu}{R_1} + \frac{\mu}{R_2} + \frac{1}{2}\left(1-\mu\right)\mu \tag{6}$$

where $R_1 = \sqrt{(X+\mu)^2 + Y^2}$ and $R_2 = \sqrt{(X+\mu-1)^2 + Y^2}$ are the distances to the primaries, and $\mu = \frac{m}{m+M}$ is the mass parameter. The system of Eq. (5) has one integral of motion,[12,13] the Jacobi constant:

$$J = 2\Omega - \left(\dot{X}^2 + \dot{Y}^2\right) = \left(X^2 + Y^2\right) + 2\frac{1-\mu}{R_1} + 2\frac{\mu}{R_2} + \left(1-\mu\right)\mu - \left(\dot{X} + \dot{Y}\right) \tag{7}$$

which is beneficial for a variety of uses including the definition of valid regions of motion. Far from the minor body, the Jacobi constant is approximated by the Tisserand parameter[14]

$$\begin{aligned} J \approx T &= \frac{1}{a} + 2\sqrt{a\left(1-e^2\right)} = \\ &= \frac{2}{r_a + r_p} + 2\sqrt{\frac{2r_a r_p}{r_a + r_p}} \end{aligned} \tag{8}$$

which can be expressed as function of the v_∞[2,15]

$$T = 3 - v_\infty^2 \tag{9}$$

The Jacobi constant is a measure of the energy of the third body: a high J corresponds to a low energy, a low J corresponds to a high energy (and high v_∞). In this paper, the word energy refers to the spacecraft energy

376

in the three-body problem, while the spacecraft energy in the two-body problem is referred to as Keplerian energy.

The system of Eq. (5) has five equilibrium points, the Lagrangian points $L_i, i = 1, \ldots, 5$. L_1 and L_2 are near the boundaries of Hill's sphere of influence,[13] centered at the minor body and with radius

$$R_{Hill} = \sqrt[3]{\frac{\mu}{3(1 - \mu)}} \tag{10}$$

Poincaré maps and T-P graphs Poincaré maps are powerful tools in dynamical system theory as they transform a continuous problem into a discrete problem with lower dimensionality. A Poincaré map is a discrete map between two Poincaré sections, which are two surfaces of section in phase space transversal to the flow. Poincaré maps are typically used to study periodic orbits and their stability, and to visualize chaotic regions in the phase space. More generally, Poincaré sections simply define boundary conditions for the flow, and the Poincaré map is a tool used to gain insight into the general dynamics on a lower dimension space.[16] Villac and Scheeres,[17] for example, defined a Poincaré map between a section close to L_2 and a section at the closest approach to the minor body, and used it to study the condition for escape in the Hill's problem.

In a previous work, we placed a Poincaré section on the negative x-axis of the rotating frame of the cr3bp to study trajectories that naturally jump between resonances. In that work, the Poincaré section was enhanced by Tisserand level sets and by period level sets, thus defining the T-P (Tisserand-Poincaré) graph. The T-P graph can be considered as an extension of the Tisserand graph to the three-body problem, because the Tisserand levels are also v_∞ level sets (see Eq. 9) (in regions where v_∞ is defined).

Keplerian map The study of flybys in the cr3bp is more challenging than in the linked-conics model. The minor body is always perturbing the Keplerian motion of the spacecraft, so a flyby has no clear boundary conditions. Also, there are no closed form solutions (with the exception of series solutions) for the change of Keplerian elements over a finite time interval. To overcome some of these difficulties, Ross and Scheeres[7] defined a Keplerian map for elliptical orbits with low energies ($J > J_{L2}$)*. The Keplerian map provides the change in Keplerian energy at each crossing of a single Poincaré section placed at pericenter. The map approximates the minor-body effects on the spacecraft semi-major axis using the *energy kick function*, which is normalized and computed once by quadrature. The Keplerian map has interesting properties: it is fast to compute and qualitatively models the dynamics well. However it is applicable only to low energies $J > J_{L2}$, and its accuracy decreases for initial semi-major axis far from the one used to compute the energy-kick function.[3,5]

FLYBY MAP

The Flyby map introduced in this paper is a new approach to explain the dynamics of flybys in the three-body problem for a wide range of energies and semi-major axes. It is inspired by both the Keplerian map and the T-P graph. The Flyby map is a map between two three-dimensional Poincaré sections in the four-dimensional phase space parametrized by the coordinates (a, T, λ, f), where λ is the longitude of the pericenter (if $a > 1$) or of the apocenter (if $a < 1$) in the rotating frame. The map is computed with numerical integration of Eq. 5; the Poincaré sections define the boundary conditions for the integration and are placed close to an apsidal point, and far from the minor body. This section defines (1) the parametrization of the phase space and the coordinate transformation to and from Cartesian coordinates, and (2) the definition of the Poincaré sections in the (a, T, λ, f) space. Finally, (3) the Flyby map algorithm is given, and (4) applied iteratively to model multiple-revolution trajectories.

(a, T, λ, f) Coordinates

A full exploration of the flyby in the pcr3bp requires exploring a five dimensional space: four parameters to define the initial conditions, and one parameter to define the transfer time. A proper choice of coordinates however can be used to reduce the problem dimensionality and to define meaningful boundary conditions

---

*Keplerian maps were first introduced to study the motion of comets in near-parabolic orbits[18,19]

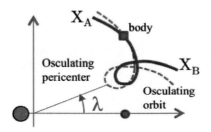

Figure 3. Definition of λ for $a > 1$

(i.e., Poincaré sections). In this paper we introduce the coordinates a, T, f, λ, where f is the true anomaly and λ is the longitude of the apsis of reference in the rotating frame. The apsis of reference $\overline{f}$ is defined as

$$\overline{f} = \begin{cases} 0 & \text{if} \quad a > 1 \\ \pi & \text{if} \quad a < 1 \end{cases} \tag{11}$$

that is, $\overline{f}$ is the pericenter when $a > 1$, while $\overline{f}$ is the apocenter when $a < 1$. For instance, for a point with semi-major axis $a > 1$, λ is the traditional argument of pericenter ω, measured from the minor body at the time of the pericenter passage.

Another equivalent interpretation for λ is explained in Figure 3, which shows the spacecraft trajectory in the rotating frame. At any given time, the spacecraft state defines an osculating Keplerian orbit, which is plotted with a dash line. λ is the angular distance between the $x-$axis and the location of the osculating pericenter. It is emphasized that λ is associated to the osculating Keplerian elements and therefore will change depending on the specific spacecraft state.

The coordinate chart φ maps the direct elliptical domain $\mathcal{E}$ in the rotating frame (APPENDIX B) to the coordinates (a, T, f, λ)

$$\varphi : \mathcal{E} \longrightarrow [(0,1) \times \mathbb{R}_+ \times (-\pi, \pi) \times (0, 2\pi)] \cup [(1, \infty) \times \mathbb{R}_+ \times (-\pi, \pi) \times (-\pi, \pi)]$$
$$\left(X, Y, \dot{X}, \dot{Y}\right) \longmapsto (a, T, \lambda, f)$$

The algorithm for φ and for its inverse φ^{-1} are explained in APPENDIX B. The appendix also proves the following symmetry property

$$(a, T, \lambda, \overline{f} + \alpha) = \varphi\left(X, Y, \dot{X}, \dot{Y}\right) \iff (a, T, -\lambda, \overline{f} - \alpha) = \varphi\left(X, -Y, -\dot{X}, \dot{Y}\right), \; \forall \alpha \in (0, \pi). \tag{12}$$

The coordinate transformation is not defined for $a = 1$; however, the change of coordinates is applied only at the Poincaré sections where $a \neq 1$.

Poincaré sections

Two Poincaré sections are used to define the boundary conditions for the numerical integration of the map. The first section Σ_A is defined in local coordinates by the conditions

$$\Sigma_A \equiv \{(a_A, T_A, \lambda_A) \mid a_A \neq 1, , R_2(a_A, T_A, \lambda_A, f_A^*) > R_{2min}\} \tag{13}$$

with

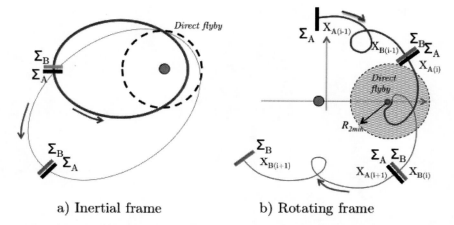

a) Inertial frame   b) Rotating frame

Figure 4. **A trajectory with multiple crossings of the Poincaré sections, (a) in the inertial frame, (b) in the rotating frame. In practical applications, the Flyby map is numerically computed only between $A(i)$ and $B(i)$, while it is approximated by the identity map in the rest of the trajectory.**

$$f_A^* = \begin{cases} -\pi + \epsilon & \text{if} \quad a_A > 1 \\ \epsilon & \text{if} \quad a_A < 1 \end{cases} \tag{14}$$

where $\epsilon > 0$ is an arbitrarily small value, and $R_{2min} = 5R_{Hill}$ in this paper. The section is the set of apocenters (when $a > 1$) or pericenters (when $a < 1$) far from the minor body; more precisely, it is the set of points following the apsis by an arbitrarily small angle ϵ, and farther than R_{2min} from the minor body.

The second section Σ_B is defined as

$$\Sigma_B \equiv \{(a_B, T_B, \lambda_B) \mid a_B \neq 1, , R_2(a_B, T_B, \lambda_B, f_B^*) > R_{2min}\} \tag{15}$$

with

$$f_B^* = \begin{cases} \pi - \epsilon & \text{if} \quad a_B > 1 \\ 2\pi - \epsilon & \text{if} \quad a_B < 1 \end{cases} \tag{16}$$

the only difference from Σ_A being the true anomaly f_B^*, which shortly *precedes* the apocenters (when $a > 1$) or pericenters (when $a < 1$). The introduction of the parameter $\epsilon > 0$ in the definition of Σ_B is necessary to keep $f_B^* \in U$. Because both sections are far from the minor body, the spacecraft motion there is well approximated by a Keplerian orbit with $\dot{f} \neq 0$, so that the flow is transversal to the sections. Figure 4 shows an example trajectory in the inertial and rotating reference frames, and the locations of the sections.

Flyby map: definition, algorithm and properties

The Flyby map is defined as the map between a point in Σ_A and the first crossing of Σ_B along its flow. In local coordinates $F : \Sigma_A \to \Sigma_B$ can be written as

$$(a_B, T_B, \lambda_B) = F(a_A, T_A, \lambda_A)$$

When the third body is very far from the minor body (i.e. when no fly-by occurs), the map is approximated by the identity map. Only when the spacecraft flys by the minor body (as in the central arc of Figure 4), the Flyby map is computed numerically in three steps

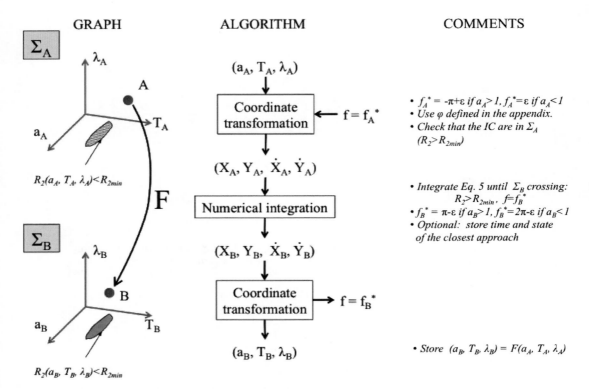

GRAPH	ALGORITHM	COMMENTS

Figure 5. Flyby map

1. Given the initial condition (a_A, T_A, λ_A) on Σ_A, the initial state in the rotating frame is computed using φ^{-1} (APPENDIX B)

$$\left(X_A, Y_A, \dot{X}_A, \dot{Y}_A\right) = \varphi^{-1}(a_A, T_A, \lambda_A, f_A^*)$$

2. The initial conditions are integrated numerically using Eq. 5 until $R_2 > 5R_{Hill}$ and $f = f_B^*$

3. The final Cartesian coordinates are mapped to the section Σ_B

$$(a_B, T_B, \lambda_B, f_B^*) = \varphi \left(X_B, Y_B, \dot{X}_B, \dot{Y}_B\right)$$

Figure 5 shows a schematic representation of the map, and the algorithm used to compute it. The map has some important properties: first, because the initial and final point are far from the minor body, the initial and final Tisserand are approximately equal. This allows a reduction of the problem dimension and thus $T = T_A \approx T_B$ can be considered as a parameter. Also, for a purely Keplerian motion (for $\mu \to 0$) the map is the identity. So the changes in a and λ are only due to the minor body. The compute cost is higher than that required by the Keplerian map, however the domain of applicability is much wider, and the map is as accurate as the integration method used.

Finally due to the time symmetry of the cr3bp

$$t, X, Y, \dot{X}, \dot{Y} \to -t, X, -Y, -\dot{X}, \dot{Y}$$

and to the property of φ Eq.(12), the inverse map F^{-1} is easily obtained from F by changing the sign of λ_A and λ_B. In particular, if

$$F^{-1}(a', T', \lambda') = (a'', T'', \lambda'')$$

then a'', T'', λ'' are obtained from

$$(a'', T'', -\lambda'') = F(a', T', -\lambda').$$

Equivalently,

$$F^{-1} = \Theta \circ F \circ \Theta \qquad (17)$$

where

$$\Theta(a, T, \lambda) = (a, T, -\lambda).$$

Successive crossings

In this paper, trajectories in the cr3bp are divided into arcs connecting consecutive crossings at either section, as shown in Figure 4. Each point $A(i)$ is mapped to $B(i)$ using F, while each $B(i)$ is mapped to $A(i + 1)$ by simply subtracting the osculating period from $\lambda_{B(i)}$. The iterate from $A(i)$ to $A(i + 1)$ is then computed as

$$
\begin{aligned}
(a_A, T_A, \lambda_A)^{(i)} &\rightarrow (a_B, T_B, \lambda_B)^{(i)} = F\left((a_A, T_A, \lambda_A)^{(i)}\right) \rightarrow \\
&\rightarrow (a_A, T_A, \lambda_A)^{(i+1)} = (a_B, T_B, \lambda_B + 2\pi\left(1 - \sqrt{a_B^3}\right))^{(i)} \qquad (18)
\end{aligned}
$$

Note that when the spacecraft is far from the minor body $F \approx$ Identity, and the numerical integration can be avoided for large portions of the trajectory.

DIRECT AND RETROGRADE FLYBYS IN THE PCR3BP

We now use the Flyby map to study flybys in the pcr3bp. Although the Flyby map can be applied for any initial values (except for $a \neq 1$), the third body dynamics for $a \approx 1$ and for very low energies is mainly chaotic and dominated by periodic orbits and their manifolds.[20] In this very low energy regime, the spacecraft is often temporarily captured, and an analysis of these families of orbits with the Flyby map, although possible, is not the purpose of this paper.

As a representative example, in this section the Flyby map is applied on a subsection of Σ_A with constant a_A

$$a_A = (3/2)^{2/3},$$

which is the set of initial orbits in a 3:2 resonance with the minor body's orbital period. Also we consider

$$\mu = 2.527766 \,\mathrm{x} 10^{-5},$$

corresponding to the mass parameter of the Jupiter-Europa-spacecraft cr3bp. For any given T, we apply the map to a set of λ_A and store

$$(a_B, T, \lambda_B) = F((3/2)^{3/2}, T, \lambda_A)$$

The flyby dynamics are then analyzed graphing a_B versus λ_A, with T acting as parameter.

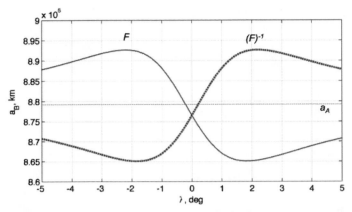

Figure 6. Using F, the semi-major axis a_B is plotted as function of λ_A, for $T_A = T_B = J_{L1}$. The initial semi-major axis a_A is also shown. The dash line shows the range of the inverse function F^{-1}.

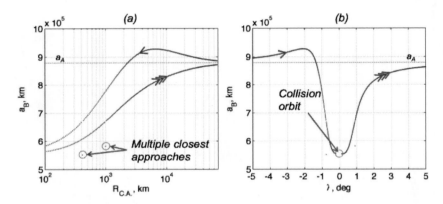

Figure 7. Semi-major axis a_B as function of R_{CA} and λ_A, for $T_A = T_B = \bar{T}$

The thick line in Figure 6 shows a_B as function of λ_A at a very low energy $T = T_A = T_B = 3.0036678286$, corresponding to the Jacobi constant at L_1. Each point on the graph represents a flyby. In all these flybys, the third-body velocity relative to the minor body defines a direct orbit at closest approach. Such flybys are called "direct", or "Type I" flybys. The function $a_B(\lambda_A)$ is very similar to the *Keplerian energy kick function* used to compute the Keplerian map:[7] both functions have one maximum and one minimum, although the energy kick function is odd. Figure 6 also shows the graph of the inverse function F^{-1}

$$F^{-1}((3/2)^{2/3}, T, \lambda)$$

with a dash line. The graph of the inverse function is the symmetric of F with respect to $\lambda_A = 0$, as predicted by Eq. 17.

As the energy increases, the radius of the closest approach decreases. $T = \bar{T}$ is defined as the Tisserand value for which there is one specific $\lambda_A = \bar{\lambda}$ which results in $R_{CA} = 0$ (indicating a collision orbit). Figure 7b shows $a_B(\lambda_A)$ for $T = \bar{T}$. The collision trajectory occurs at $\bar{\lambda} \approx 0°$, and is shown as a missing dot in the graph. For each flyby, Figure 7a shows a_B against the closest approach distance. The figure also highlights

382

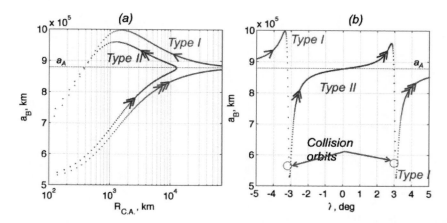

Figure 8. Semi-major axis a_B as function of R_{CA} and λ_A, for $v_\infty = 2$ km/s (where defined).

two points that do not belong to the family. For these values of λ_A, the third body loops twice around the minor body in a temporary capture before escaping again to cross Σ_B.

For higher energies ($T < \bar{T}$), there are two values of $\lambda_A = \bar{\lambda}_i$, $i = 1, 2$, for which $R_{CA} = 0$. The flybys with initial λ_A between $\bar{\lambda}_1$ and $\bar{\lambda}_2$ belong to a different family, called Type II. During a Type II flyby, the spacecraft velocity relative to the minor body defines a retrograde orbit at closest approach. Figure 8 shows the semi-major axis a_B as function of λ_A and of $R_{C.A.}$ for $T = 2.978935$, corresponding to $v_\infty = 2$ km/s (where v_∞ is defined). In the figure, type I and Type II flybys are separated by the collision orbits at $\lambda \approx \pm 3^\circ$. At these energy levels, the spacecraft osculating pericenter at A is below Europa's orbit and the linked-conics model can also be used. We then introduce the minimum-altitude constraint

$$H_{C.A.} > H_{min} = 100 \, km \tag{19}$$

to compare the change in post-flyby semi-major axis a_B obtained with the Flyby map and with Eq.4.

Figure 9 is the same as Figure 8, except that the flybys violating Eq. 19 are removed from the graph. The figure shows that the linked-conics model underestimates a_B in case of direct flybys, and overestimates a_B in case of retrograde flybys. The figure also shows that Type I flybys (direct) are more efficient than Type II flybys (retrograde).

EXAMPLE APPLICATION FOR A JUPITER MOON TOUR

By computing the minimum and maximum a_B for different values of T, the T-P graph can be equipped with the same quantitative information available in the Tisserand graph. Figure 10 shows the T-P graph with the minimum and maximum (r_p, r_a) that can be achieved with a flyby from a 3:2 resonance. The curves are computed by (1) applying F to a given T and different λ_A; (2) finding the extrema and their corresponding (r_a, r_p) for each family; (3) repeating (1) and (2) for different values of T. Minimum- and maximum-(r_p, r_a) curves in the linked-conics model are computed using Eq. 4 (as shown on the Tisserand graph on Figure 2), and plotted again here for comparison. The graph shows that even at high perijoves, a flyby of Europa can provide a significant change to the spacecraft Keplerian energy. In this same region, impulsive maneuvers are very efficient in reducing the spacecraft Jacobi constant, because the Tisserand level-sets are closer to each other than in the linked-conics regime.

Starting from these considerations, a new design approach has been developed to design trajectories in these low-energy regions of the T-P graph, using the Flyby map. The method relies on an innovative tech-

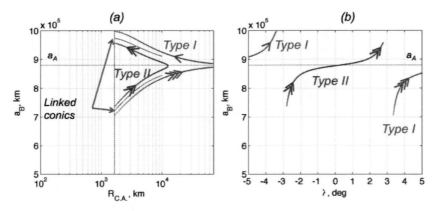

Figure 9. Semi-major axis a_B as function of R_{CA} and λ_A, for $v_\infty = 2$ km/s (where defined), and a minimum-altitude constraint.

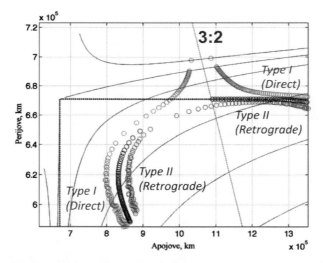

Figure 10. T-P graph with the Type I and Type II families. The circles represents the boundaries of the reachable trajectories starting with the initial conditions on the 3:2 resonance line.

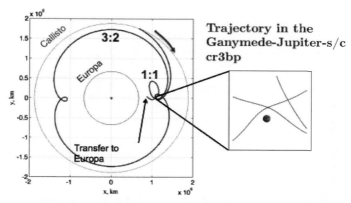

Figure 11. Trajectory from Callisto to Europa in the Ganymede-Jupiter-spacecraft pcr3bp using Type I flybys.

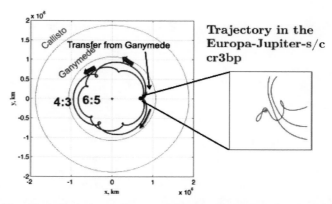

Figure 12. Trajectory from Ganymede to Europa orbit insertion in the Europa-Jupiter-spacecraft pcr3bp using Tisserand-leveraging transfers.

nique, called Tisserand-leveraging maneuver*, which is the low-energy equivalent of the v_∞-leveraging maneuver.[22-24] The Tisserand-leveraging maneuvers and the design method will be presented in a follow-up paper, but an example trajectory is presented here to illustrate the potential savings when using Type I flybys and the Flyby map.

The example trajectory starts with an orbit around Jupiter with $v_\infty \approx 2\ km/s$ relative to Callisto, ends with the Europa orbit insertion, and uses low-energy flybys at Ganymede and Tisserand-leveraging transfers at Europa. The trajectory is split into two parts. The first part (shown in Figure 11) is computed in the Ganymede-Jupiter-spacecraft pcr3bp and includes three Ganymede flybys linked by 3:2 and 1:1 resonant orbit. The second part (shown in Figure 12) is computed in the Europa-Jupiter-spacecraft pcr3bp and includes two Europa flybys and the Europa orbit insertion, linked by a 4:3 and a 6:5 resonant orbits and two maneuvers at the apojoves. We assume that the initial epoch is chosen to solve the phasing constraint in the Ganymede-to-Europa transfer.

The radiation dose and the transfer time are very similar to the current baseline for the Jupiter Europa Orbiter (two months from Callisto to Europa orbit insertion[25]) but the total Δv is reduced from $\approx 850\ m/s$

---

*In some recent works,[21] Tisserand-leveraging maneuvers appears in low-energy trajectories as a result of the numerical optimization.

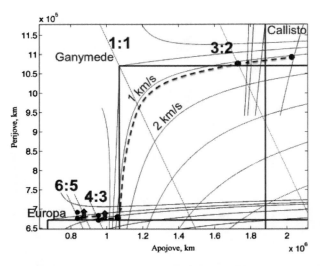

Figure 13. Trajectory from Ganymede to Europa orbit insertion on the T-P graph.

to $\approx 550\ m/s$, a savings of up to 30% .The Δv could increase as the trajectory is computed in a high-fidelity model, but may also decrease as result of further optimization.

Figure 13 shows the trajectory in the T-P graph. At each flyby, the spacecraft crosses the T-P section on a different point, denoted with green dots (for the first part) and blue dots (for the second part). Note that the dots at 1:1 resonance are missing because the spacecraft loops around the minor body without getting too far from it, thus without crossing the section. The T-P graph reveals that the entire transfer occurs just outside the domain of linked-conics, bounded by the thick vertical and horizontal lines. In fact, the energy at Ganymede ($v_\infty \approx 1.1\ km/s$) is significantly lower than that of a Hohmann transfer; yet Type I flybys can be used to connect the initial orbit reaching Callisto, to the final orbit where the Europa sequence starts. The arrival condition at Europa is again just outside the linked-conics domain, where small Δv maneuvers at apojoves efficiently reduce the energy, until gravitational-capture approaches can be targeted. Such trajectories have proven very effective in reducing the Δv costs;[26–29] one such trajectory has been recently proposed to significantly reduce the cost of the Europa orbiter endgame, from 850 to less than 700 m/s.[29]

CONCLUSIONS

A new approach is presented to provide new insight and practical design tools for the analysis and design of flybys in the planar, circular, restricted three-body problem. The analysis is carried with a new tool, the Flyby map, which improves the Keplerian map accuracy at the expense of extra compute time through the use of using numerical integration. The Flyby map to extends the functionality of the Tisserand graph to low energies beyond the validity of linked conics. The Flyby map is used for a wide range of energies, revealing that (1) there are two families of flybys, Type I (direct flybys) and Type II (retrograde flybys); (2) Type I flybys exist at all energies, while Type II flybys only appear at high energies; and (3) Type I flybys are more efficient than Type II flybys. Finally, an example application trajectory is presented for an Europa orbiter tour and endgame that saves up to 30% in Δv compared to the current baseline, without significant increases to the time of flight or the radiation dose.

ACKNOWLEDGEMENTS

Part of this research was carried out at the Jet Propulsion Laboratory, California Institute of Technology, under a contract with the National Aeronautics and Space Administration. The authors would like to thank

Arnaud Boutonnet and Anastassios Petroupolos for the many discussions on low-energy flybys, and Dan Grebow for his insight and software to compute gravitational-capture trajectories.

NOTATION

a semi-major axis

f true anomaly

H altitude

m mass of the minor body. Subscript, refers to the minor body

r radius

v_∞ spacecraft velocity relative to the moon in the patched-conics models

α pump angle

δ flyby deviation angle

λ longitude of the apsis of reference

φ coordinate chart

μ mass parameter

F Flyby map

G gravitational constant

M mass of the major body. Subscript, refers to the major body

R_{CA} Distance from the minor body at closest approach

R_1 Distance from the major body

R_2 Distance from the minor body

T Tisserand parameter

X state in the rotating frame

$\tilde{}$ Dimensional coordinate

APPENDIX A: LINKED-CONICS FLYBY

At the intersection between the spacecraft orbit and the minor body orbit, the spacecraft velocity can be computed in two ways: from the definition of v_∞

$$v^2 = 1 + 2v_\infty \cos\alpha + v_\infty^2,$$ (20)

and from the Keplerian energy equation

$$\frac{1}{2}v^2 - 1 = -\frac{1}{2a}$$ (21)

Comparing Eq20 and Eq21 results in an expression for the semi-major axis

$$a = \frac{1}{1 - 2v_\infty \cos\alpha - v_\infty^2}. \tag{22}$$

The eccentricity is computed comparing two expressions for the angular momentum at $r = 1$:

$$h = \sqrt{p} = \sqrt{a(1 - e^2)} \tag{23}$$

and

$$h = 1 + v_\infty \cos\alpha. \tag{24}$$

Thus

$$e = \sqrt{1 - \frac{h^2}{a}} = \sqrt{1 + (v_\infty^2 + 2v_\infty \cos\alpha - 1)(1 + v_\infty \cos\alpha)^2}. \tag{25}$$

Similar formulae can be found in the literature.[9,30]

APPENDIX B: THE COORDINATE CHART φ

The direct elliptical domain

The configuration space for the circular restricted three-body problem in a non-inertial frame rotating with the major-minor body axis is $S = \mathbb{R}^2 - \{(-\mu, 0),\ (1 - \mu, 0)\}$, and the corresponding velocity phase space is the tangent bundle TS. There is a natural identification of TS with $S \times \mathbb{R}^2$ given by

$$V \in TS \longleftrightarrow (X, Y, \dot{X}, \dot{Y}) \in S \times \mathbb{R}^2$$

where $\dot{X}, \dot{Y}$ denote the components of V with respect to the $\{\frac{\partial}{\partial X}, \frac{\partial}{\partial Y}\}$ basis. We use both notations interchangeably.

Let $\mathcal{E}$ denote the *direct elliptical domain*, defined as the subset of $T(S - \{(0,0)\})$ corresponding to elliptic orbits moving counterclockwise in the inertial frame. Explicitly

$$\mathcal{E} = \{V \in T(S - \{(0,0)\}) \mid 0 < e(V) < 1,\ -\frac{1}{2a(V)} < 0,\ h(V) > 0\}$$

where e, a, and h are the eccentricity, semi-major axis, and angular momentum respectively. Details of how to compute these functions from $(X, Y, \dot{X}, \dot{Y})$ are given below.

Domain of definition of φ

The paper employs a coordinate chart (φ, U), where U is a dense open subset of $\mathcal{E}$. Let $U_+ \subset \mathcal{E}$ be the set of states V with semi-major axis $a(V) > 1$, not lying on the corresponding Keplerian apocenter, and for which the corresponding pericenter doesn't lie along the negative Y-axis in the rotating frame. Let

$$\varphi_+ : U_+ \longrightarrow (1, \infty) \times \mathbb{R}^+ \times (-\pi, \pi) \times (-\pi, \pi)$$
$$\varphi_+(V) = (a(V),\ T(V),\ \lambda(V),\ f(V))$$

where $\lambda(V)$ is the angle of the Keplerian orbit pericenter with respect to the positive X-axis in the rotating frame, and $f(V)$ is the true anomaly, measured relative to the orbit's pericenter.

Similarly, let $U_- \subset \mathcal{E}$ be the set of states V with semi-major axis $a(V) < 1$, not lying on the corresponding Keplerian pericenter, and for which the corresponding apocenter doesn't lie along the negative Y-axis in the rotating frame. Let

$$\varphi_- : U_- \longrightarrow (0,1) \times \mathbb{R}^+ \times (-\pi, \pi) \times (0, 2\pi)$$
$$\varphi_-(V) = (a(V), T(V), \lambda(V), f(V))$$

where now $\lambda(V)$ is the angle of the Keplerian orbit apocenter with respect to the positive X-axis in the rotating frame, and $f(V)$ is the true anomaly, again measured relative to the orbit's pericenter.

We define $U = U_+ \cup U_-$, and $\varphi : U \to \varphi_+(U_+) \cup \varphi_-(U_-)$ by

$$\varphi(V) = \begin{cases} \varphi_+(V) & \text{if } V \in U_+ \\ \varphi_-(V) & \text{if } V \in U_- \end{cases}$$

Explicit computation of $\varphi : (X, Y, \dot{X}, \dot{Y}) \mapsto (a, T, \lambda, f)$

1. Compute the radius and the angle $\theta \in [-\pi, \pi)$ between the spacecraft and the moon.

$$r = \sqrt{X^2 + Y^2}$$
$$\cos\theta = \frac{X}{r} \quad ; \quad \sin\theta = \frac{Y}{r}$$

2. Compute the radial and transverse velocity in the inertial frame. From the state vector we obtain the radial and transverse unit vectors e_r, e_θ. Then

$$v_r = \left\langle \left(\dot{X}, \dot{Y} \right), e_r \right\rangle$$
$$v_\theta = \left\langle \left(\dot{X}, \dot{Y} \right), e_\theta \right\rangle + r$$

3. Compute the osculating orbital elements $a, h, e, f \in U, E \in U$

$$a = \frac{r}{2 - (v_\theta^2 + v_r^2)\, r}$$
$$h = v_\theta r$$
$$e = \sqrt{1 - h^2/a}$$
$$\cos f = \left(\frac{h^2}{r} - 1 \right) / e \quad ; \quad \sin f = \frac{v_r h}{e}$$
$$E = 2\arctan\left(\sqrt{\frac{1-e}{1+e}} \tan\frac{f}{2} \right)$$

4. Compute λ, T. Using the osculating orbital elements and the definition of the Tisserand parameter

$$T = \frac{1}{a} + 2\sqrt{a(1 - e^2)}$$

The time span from $\overline{f}$ to f is

$$a^{3/2} \left(E - e\sin E - \overline{f} \right)$$

which is also the angle covered by the minor body in the same time span.

$$\Delta = a^{3/2} \left(E - e\sin E - \overline{f} \right)$$

Then λ is

$$\lambda = \theta + \Delta - (f - \overline{f}) \qquad \lambda \in [-\pi, \pi)$$

389

Explicit computation of $\varphi^{-1} : (a, T, \lambda, f) \mapsto (X, Y, \dot{X}, \dot{Y})$

1. Compute the osculating orbital elements: eccentricity, angular momentum, eccentric anomaly $E \in U$

$$e = \sqrt{1 - \frac{(Ta-1)^2}{4a^3}} \tag{26}$$

$$h = \sqrt{a(1-e^2)} \tag{27}$$

$$E = 2\arctan\left(\sqrt{\frac{1-e}{1+e}} \tan \frac{f}{2}\right) \tag{28}$$

2. Compute the radius and the angle $\theta \in [-\pi, \pi)$ between the spacecraft and the moon.

$$r = \frac{h^2}{1 + e\cos f} \tag{29}$$

The time span from $\overline{f}$ to f is

$$a^{3/2}\left(E - e\sin E - \overline{f}\right)$$

which is also the angle covered by the minor body in the same time span.

$$\Delta = a^{3/2}\left(E - e\sin E - \overline{f}\right) \tag{30}$$

Then the angle θ is (see Figure)

$$\theta = \lambda - \Delta + (f - \overline{f}) \tag{31}$$

3. Compute the radial and transverse components of the velocity in the inertial frame

$$v_r = \frac{k}{h}e\sin f = \frac{e\sin f}{h} \tag{32}$$

$$v_\theta = \frac{h}{r} \tag{33}$$

4. Compute the state in the rotating frame:
$$X = r\cos\theta \tag{34}$$
$$Y = r\sin\theta \tag{35}$$
$$\dot{X} = v_r\cos\theta - (v_\theta - r)\sin\theta \tag{36}$$
$$\dot{Y} = v_r\sin\theta + (v_\theta - r)\cos\theta \tag{37}$$

Symmetry property of φ

This section shows that, for any $\alpha \in (0, \pi)$,

$$\varphi^{-1}(a, T, \lambda, \overline{f} + \alpha) = \left(X, Y, \dot{X}, \dot{Y}\right) \iff \varphi^{-1}(a, T, -\lambda, \overline{f} - \alpha) = \left(X, -Y, -\dot{X}, \dot{Y}\right)$$

For this purpose we apply φ^{-1} to $(a', T', \lambda', f') = (a, T, \lambda, \overline{f}+\alpha)$ and to $(a'', T'', \lambda'', f'') = (a, T, -\lambda, \overline{f}-\alpha)$ to find $(X', Y', \dot{X}', \dot{Y}')$ and $(X'', Y'', \dot{X}'', \dot{Y}'')$.

Eq.(26-30) applied to a', T', λ' and a'', T'', λ'' yields to

$$r' = r'', \quad e' = e'', \quad h' = h''$$

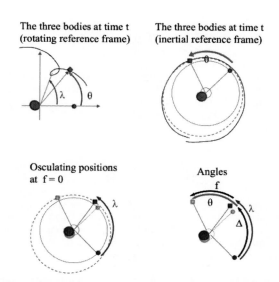

The three bodies at time t
(rotating reference frame)

The three bodies at time t
(inertial reference frame)

Osculating positions
at f = 0

Angles
f

Figure 14. Relation between $\theta, \Delta, \lambda,$ **and** f **in the inertial and rotating frames.**

while

$$\Delta' = -\Delta''$$

because the time from the apsis of reference is opposite for f' and f''. Eq. (31-33) shows that

$$\theta' = -\theta'', \quad v'_r = -v''_r, \quad v'_\theta = v''_\theta,$$

and finally Eq. (34-37) shows that

$$X' = X'', \quad Y' = -Y'', \quad \dot{X}' = -\dot{X}'', \quad \dot{Y}' = \dot{Y}''.$$

REFERENCES

[1] S. D. Ross and M. W. Lo, "Design of a Multi-Moon Orbiter," *Advances in the Astronautical Sciences*, Vol. 114, Univelt, San Diego, 2003, pp. 669–684.

[2] S. Campagnola and R. P. Russell, "Endgame Problem Part 2: Multi-Body Technique and T-P Graph," *Journal of Guidance, Control, and Dynamics*, Vol. 33, No. 2, 2010, pp. 476–486, 10.2514/1.44290.

[3] E. S. Gawlik, J. E. Marsden, S. Campagnola, and A. Moore, "Invariant manifolds, discrete mechanics, and trajectory design for a mission to Titan," *Advances in the Astronautical Sciences*, Vol. 134, PartI, Univelt, San Diego, 2009, pp. 1887–1904.

[4] P. Grover and S. D. Ross, "Designing Trajectories in a Planet-Moon Environment Using the Controlled Keplerian Map," *Journal of Guidance, Control, and Dynamics*, Vol. 32, No. 2, 2009, pp. 437–444, 10.2514/1.38320.

[5] G. Lantoine, R. P. Russell, and S. Campagnola, "Optimization of low-energy resonant hopping transfers between planetary moons," *Acta Astronautica*, Vol. 68, No. 7-8, 2011, pp. 1361–1378, 10.1016/j.actaastro.2010.09.021.

[6] R. L. Anderson, *Low Thrust Trajectory Design for Resonant Flybys and Captures Using Invariant Manifolds*. PhD thesis, University of Colorado at Boulder, 2005.

[7] S. D. Ross and D. J. Scheeres, "Multiple Gravity Assists, Capture, and Escape in the Restricted Three-Body Problem," *SIAM Journal on Applied Dynamical Systems*, Vol. 6, No. 3, 2007, pp. 576–596, 10.1137/060663374.

[8] C. Uphoff, P. H. Roberts, and L. D. Friedman, "Orbit Design Concepts for Jupiter Orbiter Missions," *Journal of Spacecraft and Rockets*, Vol. 13, 1976, pp. 348–355, 10.2514/3.57096.

[9] N. J. Strange, R. P. Russell, and B. B. Buffington, "Mapping the V-Infinity Globe," *AAS/AIAA Astrodynamics Specialist Conference and Exhibit,*.

[10] A. V. Labunsky, O. V. Papkov, and K. G. Sukhanov, *Multiple Gravity Assist Interplanetary Trajectories*, pp. 33–68. Earth Space Institute Book Series, Gordon and Breach Publishers, London, 1998.

[11] N. J. Strange and J. M. Longuski, "Graphical Method for Gravity-Assist Trajectory Design," *Journal of Spacecraft and Rockets*, Vol. 39, No. 1, 2002, pp. 9–16, 10.2514/2.3800.

[12] H. Poincaré, *Les Méthodes Nouvelles de la Mécanique Celeste*. Paris, Gauthier-Villars et fils, 1892.

[13] V. Szebehely, *Theory of orbits. The restricted problem of three bodies*. New York: Academic Press, 1967.

[14] F. F. Tisserand, *Traité de Méchanique Céleste*, Vol. 4, pp. 203–205. Gauthier-Villars et fils, Paris, 1896.

[15] T. H. Sweetser, "Jacobi's Intergal and DV-Earth- Gravity Assist (DV-EGA) Trajectories," *Advances in the Astronautical Sciences*, Vol. 85, Univelt, San Diego, 1993, pp. 417–430.

[16] M. Vaquero and K. C. Howell, "Poincaré maps and resonant orbits in the restricted three-body problems," *AAS 11-428 AAS Astrodynamics Specialists Conference, Girdwood, AK*, 2011.

[17] B. F. Villac and D. J. Scheeres, "Escaping Trajectories in the Hill three Body problem and application," *Journal of Guidance, Control, and Dynamics*, Vol. 26, No. 2, 2003, pp. 224–232, 10.2514/2.5062.

[18] T. Y. Petrosky and R. Broucke, "Area-preserving mappings and deterministic chaos for nearly parabolic motions," *Celestial Mechanics and Dynamical Astronomy*, Vol. 42, 1988, pp. 53–79.

[19] L. Malyshkin and S. Tremaine, "The Keplerian map for the planar restricted three-body problem as a model of comet evolution," *Icarus*, Vol. 141, 1999, pp. 341–353.

[20] W. S. Koon, M. W. Lo, J. E. Marsden, and S. D. Ross, *Dynamical Systems, the Three-Body Problem , And Space Mission Design*. 2006.

[21] G. Lantoine and R. P. Russell, "Near Ballistic Halo-to-Halo Transfers between Planetary Moons," *Journal of the Astronautical Sciences*, 2011.

[22] G. R. Hollenbeck, "New Flight Techniques for Outer Planet Missions," *AAS Microfishe series*, Vol. 26, 1975.

[23] J. A. Sims, J. M. Longuski, and A. J. Staugler, "V-infinity Leveraging for Interplanetary Missions: Multiple-Revolution Orbit Techniques," *Journal of Guidance, Control, and Dynamics*, Vol. 20, No. 3, 1997, pp. 409–415, 10.2514/2.4064.

[24] S. Campagnola and R. P. Russell, "Endgame Problem Part 1: V-Infinity Leveraging Technique and Leveraging Graph," *Journal of Guidance, Control, and Dynamics*, Vol. 33, No. 2, 2010, pp. 463–475, 10.2514/1.44258.

[25] K. W. Kloster, A. E. Petropoulos, and J. M. Longuski, "Europa Orbiter tour design with Io gravity assists," *Acta Astronautica*, Sept. 2010, 10.1016/j.actaastro.2010.08.041.

[26] J. R. Johannesen and L. A. D'Amario, "Europa Orbiter Mission Trajectory Design," *Advances in the Astronautical Sciences*, Vol. 103, part, Univelt, San Diego, 1999, pp. 895–908.

[27] S. Campagnola and R. Jehn, "Use of Gravitational Capture for the BepiColombo Mission to Mercury," *Poster at the Advanced Topics in Astrodynamics workshop, 5-10 July 2004*, Barcelona, Spain.

[28] A. Boutonnet, "Gravitational Capture vs Direct Capture: the Example of Ganymede," Tech. Rep. 49, 2009.

[29] D. J. Grebow, A. E. Petropoulos, and P. A. Finlayson, "Multi-body Capture to Low-Altitude Circular Orbits at Europa," *AAS 11-427 AAS Astrodynamics Specialists Conference, Girdwood, AK*, 2011.

[30] M. Vasile and S. Campagnola, "Design of Low-Thrust Multi-Gravity Assist Trajectories to Europa," *Journal of the British Interplanetary Society*, Vol. 62, Jan. 2009, pp. 15–31.

IDENTIFICATION OF INPUT-OUTPUT MAPS FOR BILINEAR DISCRETE-TIME STATE-SPACE MODELS

Haris Čelik[*] and Minh Q. Phan[†]

This paper presents a formulation to identify the input-output maps of discrete-time bilinear state-space models. The new method uses input-output data from one experiment, and the input data need not be of special types such as extended pulses. The initial conditions can be non-zero and unknown. Recent methods, on the other hand, require data from multiple experiments, specialized input signals, and zero initial conditions. In the present method, a Nonlinear Auto-Regressive model with eXogenous input (NARX) is identified and used to predict the bilinear system response directly without returning to the bilinear state-space format. Numerical examples are provided to illustrate the identification method.

INTRODUCTION

The research areas of linear time-varying systems and bilinear systems have seen a recent spark of interest in the aerospace engineering community, Refs. [1-9]. At one level, bilinear systems can be viewed as a bridge between linear and nonlinear systems. More importantly, bilinear models of sufficiently high orders can be used as a mechanism to approximate a nonlinear dynamical relationship. This application of bilinear models is known as bilinearization. For example, Euler's equations describing the rotation of a rigid body can be approximated by a bilinear model, Ref. [4]. A bilinear state-space model can be viewed as a linear time-varying state-space model, but its system matrix is input-dependent, or its input influence matrix is state-dependent. This feature makes the identification of a bilinear system identification considerably more difficult than the identification of a linear time-varying system.

One approach to identify a bilinear system is to recover the bilinear states first from input-output measurements, then identify the bilinear state-space model matrices. This paper takes another approach, which is to identify an input-output map of a bilinear system and uses such an input-output map directly for output prediction. To accomplish this task, one needs to understand the relationship between a bilinear state-space model and its equivalent input-output model such as a NARX model (Nonlinear Auto-Regressive with eXogenous input). However, despite many years of research on the subject, this relationship is still poorly understood, Refs. [10-14]. Because of this gap there are two definitions of discrete-time bilinear models, one from the state-space perspective, and one from the input-output perspective. There has been no clear relationship between the two representations, except for a few very special cases. It is also understood that the two bilinear system definitions are not equivalent, Refs. [10,11].

[*]Royal Institute of Technology, Stockholm, SWEDEN. This work was performed while H. Čelik was a Visiting Graduate Research Assistant at Thayer School of Engineering, Dartmouth College, Hanover, NH 03755 USA.
[†]Associate Professor, Thayer School of Engineering, Dartmouth College, Hanover, NH 03755 USA.

This paper overcomes the above stated stumbling block by formulating a connection between a discrete-time bilinear model and its input-output representation. By extending the interaction matrix technique that was developed for linear state-space models (time-invariant and time-varying), Refs. [8,9,15], appropriate input-output maps are derived for a discrete-time bilinear state-space model. From the known form of the input-output map, the coefficients of the input-output model can be identified from a set of sufficiently rich input-output measurements. Such an identified input-output map can then be used to predict the bilinear dynamical system response directly without having to convert the identified input-output model back to bilinear state-space form. Compared to recent bilinear system identification results, this new solution offers three key improvements: (a) Only one set of input-output data from one experiment is needed, (b) The input data need not to be of special types as long as it is sufficiently rich (e.g., random input excitation), and (c) The initial conditions need not be zero and can be assumed to be unknown. Recent methods, on the other hand, require multiple sets of data where the inputs are specialized such as multiple extended pulses. They also require zero initial conditions, and the underlying bilinear model is continuous-time, not discrete-time, which is the case considered in this paper.

PROBLEM STATEMENT

Consider an n-state, single-input, q-output bilinear system in state-space form:

$$
\begin{aligned}
x(k+1) &= Ax(k) + Bu(k) + Nx(k)u(k) \\
y(k) &= Cx(k) + Du(k)
\end{aligned}
\tag{1}
$$

Given a single set of input-output data that starts from some unknown initial state $x(0)$,

$$
\begin{aligned}
\{u(k)\} &= \{u(0), u(1), u(2), ..., u(\ell-1)\} \\
\{y(k)\} &= \{y(0), y(1), y(2), ..., y(\ell-1)\}
\end{aligned}
\tag{2}
$$

The objective is to identify the input-output map of system (1) with the input-output data provided in (2). The data set is assumed to satisfy the standard richness condition so that the system (1) can be correctly identified. For simplicity, we focus on the single-input case in this paper. Extension to the multi-input case can be made without conceptual difficulties.

MATHEMATICAL FORMULATION

In the bilinear state-space model (1), the first equation relates the dynamical relationship between the bilinear system state and input measurements, whereas the second equation relates the output in terms of the state and input measurements. Finding an input-output relationship of (1) involves two steps. In the first step, we find an expression that relates the current state in terms of past input and output measurements. In the second step, we combine the result of the first step with the second equation in (1) to arrive at the final input-output map. The first step is where the major difficulty lies as shown in the subsection below.

Input-to-State Relationship of Original Bilinear Model

Propagating Eq. (1) one step forward produces an expression for $x(k+2)$,

$$
\begin{aligned}
x(k+2) &= Ax(k+1) + Bu(k+1) + Nx(k+1)u(k+1) \\
&= A^2x(k) + ANx(k)u(k) + NAx(k)u(k+1) + N^2x(k)u(k)u(k+1) \\
&\quad + ABu(k) + NBu(k)u(k+1) + Bu(k+1)
\end{aligned}
\tag{3}
$$

394

Propagating one more step produces an expression for $x(k+3)$,

$$
\begin{aligned}
x(k+3) = {} & A^3 x(k) + A^2 N x(k) u(k) + A N A x(k) u(k+1) \\
& + A N^2 x(k) u(k) u(k+1) + N A^2 x(k) u(k+2) + N A N x(k) u(k) u(k+2) \\
& + N^2 A x(k) u(k+1) u(k+2) + N^3 x(k) u(k) u(k+1) u(k+2) \\
& + A^2 B u(k) + A N B u(k) u(k+1) + N A B u(k) u(k+2) \\
& + N^2 B u(k) u(k+1) u(k+2) + A B u(k+1) \\
& + N B u(k+1) u(k+2) + B u(k+2)
\end{aligned}
\tag{4}
$$

Notice the rapid build-up of terms involving $x(k)$ in the right hand sides of these expressions. In general, the bilinear system state at any future time step $x(k+p)$ depends on the state at the current time step $x(k)$ which is unknown. Because we are looking for a relationship that expresses the bilinear system state $x(k+p)$ in terms of known quantities, we must find a way to make implicit the dependence on the current state $x(k)$ in these expressions. Yet in (4) it is not possible to eliminate these state-dependent terms because we have no control over the bilinear system matrices A and N. In the following we show a mechanism to alter the dynamics of A and N through the use of interaction matrices.

Interaction Matrices

Adding and subtracting $M_1 y(k)$ and $M_2 y(k) u(k)$ to the original state equation in (1) produces

$$
\begin{aligned}
x(k+1) = {} & A x(k) + B u(k) + N x(k) u(k) + M_1 y(k) - M_1 y(k) \\
& + M_2 y(k) u(k) - M_2 y(k) u(k) \\
= {} & (A + M_1 C) x(k) + (B + M_1 D) u(k) - M_1 y(k) \\
& + M_2 D u^2(k) - M_2 y(k) u(k) + (N + M_2 C) x(k) u(k)
\end{aligned}
\tag{5}
$$

The matrices M_1 and M_2 are called interaction matrices which alter the original system dynamics according to

$$
\bar{A} = A + M_1 C \qquad \bar{N} = N + M_2 C
\tag{6}
$$

$$
\bar{B} = \begin{bmatrix} B + M_1 D & -M_1 & M_2 D & -M_2 \end{bmatrix} \qquad v(k) = \begin{bmatrix} u(k) \\ y(k) \\ u^2(k) \\ y(k)u(k) \end{bmatrix}
\tag{7}
$$

so that the original system now becomes

$$
\begin{aligned}
x(k+1) &= \bar{A} x(k) + \bar{B} v(k) + \bar{N} x(k) u(k) \\
y(k) &= C x(k) + D u(k)
\end{aligned}
\tag{8}
$$

From now on, we will work with Eq. (8) instead of Eq. (1), and the freedom introduced by the interaction matrices will be used to eliminate the state-dependent terms when necessary. These interaction matrices themselves do not need to be found. Rather they are used to create expressions that relate the system state in terms of input-output measurements.

Input-Output-to-State Relationship of Bilinear Model Modified by Interaction Matrices

Before propagating Eq. (8), we group terms that do not depend on $x(k)$. In Eq. (5), this group is defined as $r_1(k)$,

$$r_1(k) = \bar{B}v(k) = (B + M_1D)\,u(k) - M_1y(k) + M_2Du^2(k) - M_2y(k)u(k) \tag{9}$$

so that (8) becomes

$$x(k+1) = \bar{A}x(k) + \bar{N}x(k)u(k) + r_1(k) \tag{10}$$

Now we propagate Eq. (10) one step forward to produce $x(k+2)$,

$$
\begin{aligned}
x(k+2) &= \bar{A}x(k+1) + \bar{N}x(k+1)u(k+1) + r_1(k+1) \\
&= \bar{A}\left[\bar{A}x(k) + \bar{N}x(k)u(k) + r_1(k)\right] \\
&\quad + \bar{N}\left[\bar{A}x(k) + \bar{N}x(k)u(k) + r_1(k)\right]u(k+1) + r_1(k+1) \\
&= \bar{A}^2x(k) + \bar{A}\bar{N}x(k)u(k) + \bar{A}r_1(k) \\
&\quad + \left[\bar{N}\bar{A}x(k) + \bar{N}^2x(k)u(k) + \bar{N}r_1(k)\right]u(k+1) + r_1(k+1) \\
&= \bar{A}^2x(k) + \bar{A}\bar{N}x(k)u(k) + \bar{N}\bar{A}x(k)u(k+1) \\
&\quad + \bar{N}^2x(k)u(k)u(k+1) + r_2(k)
\end{aligned}
\tag{11}
$$

where terms that do not depend on $x(k)$ are grouped together in $r_2(k)$,

$$r_2(k) = \bar{A}r_1(k) + \bar{N}r_1(k)u(k+1) + r_1(k+1) \tag{12}$$

Propagating the state equation once more produces $x(k+3)$,

$$
\begin{aligned}
x(k+3) &= \bar{A}^3x(k) + \bar{A}^2\bar{N}x(k)u(k) + \bar{A}\bar{N}\bar{A}x(k)u(k+1) + \bar{A}\bar{N}^2x(k)u(k)u(k+1) \\
&\quad + \bar{N}\bar{A}^2x(k)u(k+2) + \bar{N}\bar{A}\bar{N}x(k)u(k)u(k+2) \\
&\quad + \bar{N}^2\bar{A}x(k)u(k+1)u(k+2) + \bar{N}^3x(k)u(k)u(k+1)u(k+2) + r_3(k)
\end{aligned}
\tag{13}
$$

where

$$
\begin{aligned}
r_3(k) &= \bar{A}^2r_1(k) + \bar{A}\bar{N}r_1(k)u(k+1) + \bar{N}\bar{A}r_1(k)u(k+2) \\
&\quad + \bar{N}^2r_1(k)u(k+1)u(k+2) + r_2(k+1)
\end{aligned}
\tag{14}
$$

Notice again that terms involving the state $x(k)$ begin to build up, but this time they are multiplied by products of $\bar{A}$ and $\bar{N}$, not A and N. Continuing with $x(k+4)$, we have

$$
\begin{aligned}
x(k+4) &= \bar{A}^4x(k) + \bar{A}^3\bar{N}x(k)u(k) + \bar{A}^2\bar{N}\bar{A}x(k)u(k+1) + \bar{A}^2\bar{N}^2x(k)u(k)u(k+1) \\
&\quad + \bar{A}\bar{N}\bar{A}^2x(k)u(k+2) + \bar{A}\bar{N}\bar{A}\bar{N}x(k)u(k)u(k+2) \\
&\quad + \bar{A}\bar{N}^2\bar{A}x(k)u(k+1)u(k+2) + \bar{A}\bar{N}^3x(k)u(k)u(k+1)u(k+2) \\
&\quad + \bar{N}\bar{A}^3x(k)u(k+3) + \bar{N}\bar{A}^2\bar{N}x(k)u(k)u(k+3) \\
&\quad + \bar{N}\bar{A}\bar{N}\bar{A}x(k)u(k+1)u(k+3) + \bar{N}\bar{A}\bar{N}^2x(k)u(k)u(k+1)u(k+3) \\
&\quad + \bar{N}^2\bar{A}^2x(k)u(k+2)u(k+3) + \bar{N}^2\bar{A}\bar{N}x(k)u(k)u(k+2)u(k+3) \\
&\quad + \bar{N}^3\bar{A}x(k)u(k+1)u(k+2)u(k+3) \\
&\quad + \bar{N}^4x(k)u(k)u(k+1)u(k+2)u(k+3) + r_4(k)
\end{aligned}
\tag{15}
$$

where terms that do not involve $x(k)$ are grouped in $r_4(k)$,

$$
\begin{aligned}
r_4(k) = {} & \bar{A}^3 r_1(k) + \bar{A}^2 \bar{N} r_1(k) u(k+1) + \bar{A}\bar{N}\bar{A} r_1(k) u(k+2) \\
& + \bar{A}\bar{N}^2 r_1(k) u(k+1) u(k+2) + \bar{N}\bar{A}^2 r_1(k) u(k+3) \\
& + \bar{N}\bar{A}\bar{N} r_1(k) u(k+1) u(k+3) + \bar{N}^2 \bar{A} r_1(k) u(k+2) u(k+3) \\
& + \bar{N}^3 r_1(k) u(k+1) u(k+2) u(k+3) + r_3(k+1)
\end{aligned}
\tag{16}
$$

Let us examine (15) closely. Every term in the expression for $x(k+4)$, as written, involves $x(k)$ except for $r_4(k)$ which is expressed in terms of previous input-output measurements only. Examination of $r_4(k)$ reveals that it has the form of unknown coefficients multiplied with certain products of input and output measurements which are known. The state $x(k)$ is not known, but it is multiplied by products of powers of $\bar{A}$ and $\bar{N}$ whose sum adds up to 4 such as $\bar{A}^4, \bar{A}^3\bar{N}, \bar{A}^2\bar{N}\bar{A}, \bar{A}^2\bar{N}^2$, etc. We can generalize this observation to $x(k+p)$ to see that terms involving the state $x(k)$ contain products of $\bar{A}$ and $\bar{N}$ whose sum of the powers adds up to p. It is assumed that for a sufficiently large p, there exist interaction matrices M_1, M_2 to turn $\bar{A}$ and $\bar{N}$ into contraction mappings, then all these explicit state-dependent terms can be neglected [9]. In that case, the state $x(k+p)$ can be expressed in terms of input and output measurements only,

$$
x(k+p) = r_p(k)
\tag{17}
$$

One possible contraction mechanism is that all the singular values of $\bar{A}$ and $\bar{N}$ are less than 1. Although this is not always possible for the original A and N of (1), it might be possible for some $\tilde{A} = TAT^{-1}$ and $\tilde{N} = TNT^{-1}$, with new interaction matrices $\tilde{M}_1 = TM_1$ and $\tilde{M}_2 = TM_2$. The associated new state is $\tilde{x}(k) = Tx(k)$, and bilinear model is $\{TAT^{-1}, TNT^{-1}, TB, CT^{-1}, D\}$ whose input-output relationship is identical to that of the original bilinear model (1). In that case, the rest of the derivation applies to $\tilde{x}(k)$ instead of $x(k)$. In any event, the form of $r_p(k)$, which has coefficients multiplied by certain products of input and output measurements, does not change. We can express that relationship in the following form,

$$
r_p(k) = T_p z_p(k+p)
\tag{18}
$$

where the entries that define $z_p(k+p)$ is summarized in the following subsection.

The General Pattern for $z_p(k+p)$

Let $nCk = \binom{n}{k}$ denote the combinations of k out of n terms, commonly referred to as n-choose-k. The general pattern for $z_p(k+p)$ in (18) can be shown to be:

- $v(k), v(k+1), \ldots$ to $v(k+p-1)$.

- $v(k)$ multiplied with products of $u(k+1)$ to $u(k+p-1)$ in all possible combinations $(p-1)C1, (p-1)C2, \ldots, (p-1)C(p-1)$ of $\{u(k+1), u(k+2), \ldots, u(k+p-1)\}$.

- $v(k+1)$ multiplied with products of $u(k+2)$ to $u(k+p-1)$ in all possible combinations $(p-2)C1, (p-2)C2, \ldots, (p-2)C(p-2)$ of $\{u(k+2), u(k+3), \ldots, u(k+p-1)\}$.

- $v(k+2)$ multiplied with products of $u(k+3)$ to $u(k+p-1)$ in all possible combinations $(p-3)C1, (p-3)C2, \ldots, (p-3)C(p-3)$ of $\{u(k+3), u(k+4), \ldots, u(k+p-1)\}$.

$\vdots$

- $v(k+p-3)$ multiplied with products of $u(k+p-2)$ to $u(k+p-1)$ in all possible combinations $2C1, 2C2$ of $\{u(k+p-2), u(k+p-1)\}$.

- $v(k+p-2)$ multiplied with $1C1$ of $u(k+p-1)$, which of course is $u(k+p-1)$.

Thus, stacking these combinations of input-output data defines the column vector $z_p(k+p)$ where $k \geq 0$. To obtain an expression for $z_p(k)$, $k \geq p$, we simply shift the time indices of $z_p(k+p)$ backwards by p time steps.

Input-Output Relationship of Discrete-Time Bilinear State-Space Model

We are now ready to derive the input-output relationship of a discrete-time bilinear state-space model. By shifting the time indices p steps forward in $y(k) = Cx(k) + Du(k)$, and combining the resultant equation with (17) and (18), one has

$$y(k+p) = CT_p z_p(k+p) + Du(k+p), \qquad k \geq 0 \tag{19}$$

or equivalently,

$$y(k) = CT_p z_p(k) + Du(k), \qquad k \geq p \tag{20}$$

For example, with $p = 1$, the input-output map is $y(k+1) = CT_1 z_1(k+1) + Du(k+1)$, $k \geq 0$, where

$$CT_1 = C\bar{B} \tag{21}$$

$$z_1(k+1) = v(k) \tag{22}$$

With $p = 2$, the input-output map is $y(k+2) = CT_2 z_2(k+2) + Du(k+2)$, $k \geq 0$, where

$$CT_2 = \begin{bmatrix} C\bar{A}\bar{B} & C\bar{B} & C\bar{N}\bar{B} \end{bmatrix} \tag{23}$$

$$z_2(k+2) = \begin{bmatrix} v(k) \\ v(k+1) \\ v(k)u(k+1) \end{bmatrix} \tag{24}$$

With $p = 3$, the input-output map is $y(k+3) = CT_3 z_3(k+3) + Du(k+3)$, $k \geq 0$, where

$$CT_3 = \begin{bmatrix} C\bar{A}^2\bar{B} & C\bar{A}\bar{B} & C\bar{B} & C\bar{A}\bar{N}\bar{B} & C\bar{N}\bar{A}\bar{B} & C\bar{N}^2\bar{B} & C\bar{N}\bar{B} \end{bmatrix} \tag{25}$$

$$z_3(k+3) = \begin{bmatrix} v(k) \\ v(k+1) \\ v(k+2) \\ v(k)u(k+1) \\ v(k)u(k+2) \\ v(k)u(k+1)u(k+2) \\ v(k+1)u(k+2) \end{bmatrix} \tag{26}$$

The general pattern of $z_p(k+p)$ is provided in the previous subsection. Thus (19) or (20) is a NARX model (nonlinear auto-regressive with exogenous input). Figure 1 outlines the path that converts a discrete-time bilinear state-space model to an input-output model described in this paper. Also in this figure is an alternate path that converts the discrete-time bilinear state-space model to an equivalent linear model (ELM) considered in [9].

INPUT-OUTPUT MAP IDENTIFICATION

The relationship in (19) can now be used to identify the input-output map of the original system (1) using the single set of input-output data provided in (2). First we re-package (19) in the following form,

$$y(k + p) = \begin{bmatrix} CT_p & D \end{bmatrix} \begin{bmatrix} z_p(k + p) \\ u(k + p) \end{bmatrix} \tag{27}$$

where $k \geq 0$. By writing (27) repeatedly for all available input-output data, we have

$$Y = PV \tag{28}$$

All the unknown coefficients of the input-output model are grouped in P,

$$P = \begin{bmatrix} CT_p & D \end{bmatrix} \tag{29}$$

and the available input-output data are grouped in Y and V,

$$Y = \begin{bmatrix} y(p) & y(p+1) & \cdots & y(\ell - 1) \end{bmatrix} \tag{30}$$

$$V = \begin{bmatrix} z_p(p) & z_p(p+1) & \cdots & z_p(\ell - 1) \\ u(p) & u(p+1) & \cdots & u(\ell - 1) \end{bmatrix} \tag{31}$$

A solution for P can be found from

$$P = YV^+ \tag{32}$$

where the $+$ sign denotes the pseudo-inverse which can be computed via the singular value decomposition of V. If the conversion from state-space to input-output model is exact, then the matrix V must be full row rank for the minimum-order input-output model. This is the richness condition required for the input-output data. In this case, if p is chosen to be larger than the minimum value, V will not be full rank to reflect the fact that an over-parameterized model is not unique. The identification can still proceed correctly with the pseudo-inverse of V computed via its singular value decomposition, where all zero singular values are eliminated. On the other hand, if the mapping from state-space to input-output models is not exact, then we would require that V be full row rank as a sufficient condition on the richness of the input-output data. These cases will be illustrated in the numerical examples.

RECOVERY OF MARKOV PARAMETERS

So far we have grouped all the parameters of the input-output model in P without examining its entries. In the input-output identification problem, once P is identified, we can use it for simulation without having to go any further. In this section we show that knowing the structural forms of the entries of P allows us to recover additional information about the bilinear state-space model. In particular, we describe how to recover the Markov parameters CA^kB and CN^kB from the first and last group of coefficients of the identified input-output model,

$$P = \begin{bmatrix} CT_p & D \end{bmatrix} = \begin{bmatrix} C\bar{A}^{p-1}\bar{B} & \cdots & C\bar{A}\bar{B} & C\bar{B} & \cdots & C\bar{N}^{p-1}\bar{B} & \cdots & C\bar{N}\bar{B} & D \end{bmatrix} \tag{33}$$

where $\bar{B} = \begin{bmatrix} B + M_1D & -M_1 & M_2D & -M_2 \end{bmatrix}$, $\bar{A} = A + M_1C$, and $\bar{N} = N + M_2C$. We would like to point out that although the interaction matrices M_1 and M_2 are present in all the coefficients that define P, their effect can be removed from these coefficients to recover the Markov parameters CA^kB and CN^kB without having to find M_1 and M_2 explicitly. This feature is particularly remarkable in view of the fact that M_1 and M_2 are embedded in these coefficients in a complicated manner due to $\bar{A}^k$ and $\bar{N}^k$, $k = 1, 2, ..., p - 1$.

The recovery of CA^kB

To recover the Markov parameters CA^kB we focus on the first two (out of four) combinations of parameters present in $C\bar{A}^k\bar{B}$ in P,

$$C\bar{A}^k\bar{B} = \begin{bmatrix} C(A + M_1C)^k (B + M_1D) & -C(A + M_1C)^k M_1 & \cdots & \cdots \end{bmatrix} \tag{34}$$

Now the procedure to recover the Markov parameters CA^kB is described for CB, CAB, and CA^2B. The remaining Markov parameters can be recovered analogously. To find CB we examine

$$C\bar{B} = \begin{bmatrix} C(B + M_1D) & -CM_1 & \cdots & \cdots \end{bmatrix} \tag{35}$$

from which the first Markov parameter CB can be found

$$CB = C(B + M_1D) + (-CM_1)D \tag{36}$$

because the combinations $C(B + M_1D)$, $-CM_1$ are known from (35), and D is explicitly present as the last term in P from (33). To find CAB we examine

$$C\bar{A}\bar{B} = \begin{bmatrix} C(A + M_1C)(B + M_1D) & -C(A + M_1C)M_1 & \cdots & \cdots \end{bmatrix} \tag{37}$$

from which the second Markov parameter CAB can be found

$$CAB = C(A + M_1C)(B + M_1D) + [-C(A + M_1C)M_1]D + (-CM_1)CB \tag{38}$$

because the combinations $C(A + M_1C)(B + M_1D)$, $-C(A + M_1C)M_1$, $-CM_1$, CB, and D are all known. Similarly,

$$\begin{aligned} CA^2B = C(A + M_1C)^2 (B + M_1D) + \left[-C(A + M_1C)^2 M_1\right]D \\ + [-C(A + M_1C)M_1]CB + (-CM_1)CAB \end{aligned} \tag{39}$$

We can recover all remaining Markov parameters up to $CA^{p-1}B$ without having to know M_1 explicitly. The Markov parameters beyond $CA^{p-1}B$ can be recovered in the same manner except that $C(A + M_1C)^k (B + M_1D) = 0$ and $C(A + M_1C)^k M_1 = 0$ for $k \geq p$ due to the condition $\bar{A}^p = (A + M_1C)^p = 0$.

The recovery of CN^kB

The recovery of the Markov parameters CN^kB can proceed similarly. We focus on the combinations that define $C\bar{N}^k\bar{B}$ in P,

$$C\bar{N}^k\bar{B} = \begin{bmatrix} C\bar{N}^k(B + M_1D) & -C\bar{N}^kM_1 & C\bar{N}^kM_2D & -C\bar{N}^kM_2 \end{bmatrix} \tag{40}$$

In order to use the same technique as (35)-(39) to find the Markov parameters CN^kB, we need to find the analogous combinations $C(N + M_2C)^k (B + M_2D)$ and $-C(N + M_2C)^k M_2$. In the recovery of CA^kB, the combinations $C(A + M_1C)^k (B + M_1D)$ and $-C(A + M_1C)^k M_1$ are readily available as the first two groupings of (34). In the recovery of CN^kB, however, although $-C(N + M_2C)^k M_2$ is readily available as the last combination in (40) where $\bar{N} = N + M_2C$, more work is needed to find the analogous combinations $C(N + M_2C)^k (B + M_2D)$ because they

400

do not appear explicitly in (40). Fortunately, the combinations $C(N + M_2C)^k (B + M_2D)$ can be found from the first three combinations of (40) and D as follows,

$$C(N + M_2C)^k (B + M_2D) = C\bar{N}^k (B + M_1D) + \left(-C\bar{N}^k M_1\right) D + C\bar{N}^k M_2 D \qquad (41)$$

Now that the combinations

$$\left[\; C(N + M_2C)^k (B + M_2D) \quad -C(N + M_2C)^k M_2 \;\right] \qquad (42)$$

are known, we can proceed to find the Markov parameters $CN^k B$ in the exact same manner as finding the Markov parameters $CA^k B$ from

$$\left[\; C(A + M_1C)^k (B + M_1D) \quad -C(A + M_1C)^k M_1 \;\right] \qquad (43)$$

Again, the recovery of $CN^k B$ can be achieved without having to know M_2 explicitly. The Markov parameters beyond $CN^{p-1}B$ can be recovered using the condition $\bar{N}^p = (N + M_2C)^p = 0$.

EXAMPLES

We now provide analytical and numerical examples to illustrate how the method works. For the analytical examples, we use Pearson's bilinear state-space model considered in Ref. [10]. This is one of very few examples of a discrete-time bilinear state-space model for which an exact input-output representation is known to exist analytically. Starting with a somewhat general model, we first show how various (sufficient) conditions were imposed on it so that the bilinear state-space model can be converted into an input-output model. This example reveals the difficulties associated with converting a bilinear state-space model to an equivalent input-output model in the general case. We then show how the same input-output map can be achieved by the proposed interaction matrix formulation. The next set of examples will show that it is possible to identify input-output maps for the bilinear state-space model by simply increasing the model order p when Pearson's model conditions are violated. The identification error is found to decrease as p increases.

Example 1: Pearson's Model

The following model illustrates the difficulties involved in converting a discrete-time bilinear state-space model to an equivalent input-output model. Consider the following bilinear model,

$$A = \begin{bmatrix} a_{11} & a_{12} \\ a_{21} & a_{22} \end{bmatrix} \quad N = \begin{bmatrix} n_{11} & n_{12} \\ n_{21} & n_{22} \end{bmatrix} \quad B = \begin{bmatrix} b_1 \\ b_2 \end{bmatrix} \quad C = \begin{bmatrix} 0 & 1 \end{bmatrix} \quad D = 0 \qquad (44)$$

Multiplying out the expressions produces

$$x_1(k+1) = a_{11}x_1(k) + a_{12}x_2(k) + b_1 u(k) + n_{11}x_1(k)u(k) + n_{12}x_2(k)u(k)$$
$$x_2(k+1) = a_{21}x_1(k) + a_{22}x_2(k) + b_2 u(k) + n_{21}x_1(k)u(k) + n_{22}x_2(k)u(k) \qquad (45)$$
$$y(k) = x_2(k)$$

Propagating one step forward produces

$$x_1(k+2) = a_{11}x_1(k+1) + a_{12}x_2(k+1) + b_1 u(k+1) + n_{11}x_1(k+1)u(k+1)$$
$$+ n_{12}x_2(k+1)u(k+1) \qquad (46)$$

$$x_2(k+2) = a_{21}x_1(k+1) + a_{22}x_2(k+1) + b_2u(k+1) + n_{21}x_1(k+1)u(k+1)$$
$$+ n_{22}x_2(k+1)u(k+1)$$
$$= a_{21}\left[a_{11}x_1(k) + a_{12}x_2(k) + b_1u(k) + n_{11}x_1(k)u(k) + n_{12}x_2(k)u(k)\right] \quad (47)$$
$$+ a_{22}x_2(k+1) + b_2u(k+1) + n_{21}\left[a_{11}x_1(k) + a_{12}x_2(k) + b_1u(k)\right.$$
$$+ \left. n_{11}x_1(k)u(k) + n_{12}x_2(k)u(k)\right]u(k+1) + n_{22}x_2(k+1)u(k+1)$$

Examining the right hand sides of (46) and (47), it is not obvious how to remove the explicit dependence of the states $x_1(k)$, $x_1(k+1)$, $x_2(k)$, $x_2(k+1)$ in the right hand sides of these expressions. First recognize that because $C = \begin{bmatrix} 0 & 1 \end{bmatrix}$, $y(k) = x_2(k)$ simplifies the problem considerably. Furthermore, Pearson's model requires $a_{11} = 0$ and $n_{11} = 0$ which will cause $x_1(k+2)$ to be expressible in terms of input-output measurements, $k \geq 0$,

$$x_1(k+2) = a_{12}y(k+1) + b_1u(k+1) + n_{12}y(k+1)u(k+1) \quad (48)$$

Substituting the above expression into (47) produces an expression for $x_2(k+2)$ in terms of input-output measurements only, $k \geq 0$,

$$x_2(k+2) = a_{22}y(k+1) + a_{21}a_{12}y(k) + b_2u(k+1) + a_{21}b_1u(k)$$
$$+ n_{22}u(k+1)y(k+1) + a_{21}n_{12}u(k)y(k) + n_{21}a_{12}u(k+1)y(k) \quad (49)$$
$$+ n_{21}b_1u(k)u(k+1) + n_{21}n_{12}u(k)u(k+1)y(k)$$

Because $y(k+2) = x_2(k+2)$, $k \geq 0$, it follows that

$$y(k+2) = a_{22}y(k+1) + a_{21}a_{12}y(k) + b_2u(k+1) + a_{21}b_1u(k)$$
$$+ n_{22}u(k+1)y(k+1) + a_{21}n_{12}u(k)y(k) + n_{21}a_{12}u(k+1)y(k) \quad (50)$$
$$+ n_{21}b_1u(k+1)u(k) + n_{21}n_{12}u(k+1)u(k)y(k)$$

The input-output map for $y(k)$, $k \geq 2$ can be found by simply shifting Eq. (50) backwards by 2 time steps. We have a NARX model,

$$y(k) = a_{22}y(k-1) + a_{21}a_{12}y(k-2) + b_2u(k-1) + a_{21}b_1u(k-2)$$
$$+ n_{22}u(k-1)y(k-1) + a_{21}n_{12}u(k-2)y(k-2) + n_{21}a_{12}u(k-1)y(k-2) \quad (51)$$
$$+ n_{21}b_1u(k-1)u(k-2) + n_{21}n_{12}u(k-1)u(k-2)y(k-2)$$

In summary, as stated in Ref. [10], if $a_{11} = 0$, $n_{11} = 0$, and $y(k) = x_2(k)$, the bilinear state-space model has an exact input-output representation. From the above analytical example, it was not clear how to proceed when $a_{11} \neq 0$, $n_{11} \neq 0$, and $y(k) \neq x_2(k)$.

Example 2: Derivation of Pearson's Model by Interaction Matrices

We first illustrate how the interaction matrices handle Pearson's model where $a_{11} = 0$, $n_{11} = 0$, and $y(k) = x_2(k)$, then deal with the generalizations. Let the bilinear system to be identified be:

$$A = \begin{bmatrix} 0 & a_{12} \\ a_{21} & a_{22} \end{bmatrix} \quad N = \begin{bmatrix} 0 & n_{12} \\ n_{21} & n_{22} \end{bmatrix} \quad B = \begin{bmatrix} b_1 \\ b_2 \end{bmatrix} \quad C = \begin{bmatrix} 0 & c_2 \end{bmatrix} \quad D = 0 \quad (52)$$

The two interaction matrices involved are

$$M_1 = \begin{bmatrix} -a_{12}/c_2 \\ -a_{22}/c_2 \end{bmatrix} \quad M_2 = \begin{bmatrix} -n_{12}/c_2 \\ -n_{22}/c_2 \end{bmatrix} \quad (53)$$

402

These two interaction matrices transform the original system to the following system,

$$\bar{A} = A + M_1 C = \begin{bmatrix} 0 & 0 \\ a_{21} & 0 \end{bmatrix} \quad \bar{N} = N + M_2 C = \begin{bmatrix} 0 & 0 \\ n_{21} & 0 \end{bmatrix} \tag{54}$$

so that

$$\bar{A}^2 = \begin{bmatrix} 0 & 0 \\ 0 & 0 \end{bmatrix} \quad \bar{N}^2 = \begin{bmatrix} 0 & 0 \\ 0 & 0 \end{bmatrix} \quad \bar{A}\bar{N} = \begin{bmatrix} 0 & 0 \\ 0 & 0 \end{bmatrix} \quad \bar{N}\bar{A} = \begin{bmatrix} 0 & 0 \\ 0 & 0 \end{bmatrix} \tag{55}$$

Referring to Eq. (11) we will see that for $k \geq 0$,

$$\begin{aligned} x(k+2) &= r_2(k) \\ &= \bar{A}r_1(k) + \bar{N}r_1(k)u(k+1) + r_1(k+1) \end{aligned} \tag{56}$$

where

$$r_1(k) = Bu(k) - M_1 y(k) - M_2 y(k)u(k) \tag{57}$$

Combining (57) with (56) produces an expression that relates the current state $x(k)$ in term of past input-output measurements, $k \geq 0$,

$$\begin{aligned} x(k+2) &= \bar{A}Bu(k) - \bar{A}M_1 y(k) - \bar{A}M_2 y(k)u(k) + \bar{N}Bu(k)u(k+1) \\ &\quad - \bar{N}M_1 y(k)u(k+1) - \bar{N}M_2 y(k)u(k)u(k+1) + Bu(k+1) \\ &\quad - M_1 y(k+1) - M_2 y(k+1)u(k+1) \end{aligned} \tag{58}$$

Equivalently, $k \geq 2$,

$$\begin{aligned} x(k) &= \bar{A}Bu(k-2) - \bar{A}M_1 y(k-2) - \bar{A}M_2 y(k-2)u(k-2) + \bar{N}Bu(k-2)u(k-1) \\ &\quad - \bar{N}M_1 y(k-2)u(k-1) - \bar{N}M_2 y(k-2)u(k-2)u(k-1) + Bu(k-1) \\ &\quad - M_1 y(k-1) - M_2 y(k-1)u(k-1) \end{aligned} \tag{59}$$

Finally, because $y(k) = Cx(k)$, input-output map for $k \geq 2$ is

$$\begin{aligned} y(k) &= -CM_1 y(k-1) - C\bar{A}M_1 y(k-2) + CBu(k-1) + C\bar{A}Bu(k-2) \\ &\quad - CM_2 y(k-1)u(k-1) - C\bar{A}M_2 y(k-2)u(k-2) - C\bar{N}M_1 y(k-2)u(k-1) \\ &\quad + C\bar{N}Bu(k-1)u(k-2) - C\bar{N}M_2 y(k-2)u(k-2)u(k-1) \end{aligned} \tag{60}$$

where

$$\begin{aligned} -CM_1 &= a_{22}, \quad -C\bar{A}M_1 = a_{21}a_{12}, \quad CB = b_2 \\ C\bar{A}B &= a_{21}b_1, \quad -CM_2 = n_{22}, \quad -C\bar{A}M_2 = a_{21}n_{12} \\ -C\bar{N}M_1 &= n_{21}a_{12}, \quad C\bar{N}B = n_{21}b_1, \quad -C\bar{N}M_2 = n_{21}n_{12} \end{aligned} \tag{61}$$

Comparing (60), (61) to (51) we arrive at the same NARX expression as Pearson's input-output model. Thus this example demonstrates that the interaction matrix formulation produces the same input-output map derived in Pearson's model.

Example 3: Identification of Pearson's Model

In example 2, we explicitly find the interaction matrices from a known bilinear state-space model to demonstrate how they enable the conversion from discrete-time bilinear state-space model into an input-output model. In the identification problem, the bilinear state-space model matrices are not known, thus we cannot find these interaction matrices before hand. We should note here that as far as the identification problem is concerned, we do not need to find these interaction matrices. Instead, they are used only to reveal the general form of the input-output map whose coefficients can be identified from a set of sufficiently rich input-output data. For example, with $p = 2$, the coefficients of this model are $-CM_1, -C\bar{A}M_1, CB, C\bar{A}B, -CM_2, -C\bar{A}M_2$, etc. To illustrate the identification, consider this model

$$A = \begin{bmatrix} 0 & 0.5 \\ 0.5 & -0.5 \end{bmatrix} \quad N = \begin{bmatrix} 0 & 1 \\ -1 & 1 \end{bmatrix} \quad B = \begin{bmatrix} 1 \\ 2 \end{bmatrix} \quad C = \begin{bmatrix} 0 & 1 \end{bmatrix} \quad D = 0 \tag{62}$$

then analytically, the two interaction matrices for $p = 2$ are

$$M_1 = \begin{bmatrix} -0.5 \\ 0.5 \end{bmatrix} \quad M_2 = \begin{bmatrix} -1 \\ -1 \end{bmatrix} \tag{63}$$

Then,

$$\bar{A} = A + M_1C = \begin{bmatrix} 0 & 0 \\ 0.5 & 0 \end{bmatrix} \quad \bar{N} = N + M_2C = \begin{bmatrix} 0 & 0 \\ -1 & 0 \end{bmatrix} \tag{64}$$

We should expect the input-output model coefficients to be

$$\begin{aligned}
-CM_1 = a_{22} = -0.5, \quad -C\bar{A}M_1 = a_{21}a_{12} = 0.25, \quad CB = b_2 = 2 \\
C\bar{A}B = a_{21}b_1 = 0.5, \quad -CM_2 = n_{22} = 1, \quad -C\bar{A}M_2 = a_{21}n_{12} = 0.5 \\
-C\bar{N}M_1 = n_{21}a_{12} = -0.5, \quad C\bar{N}B = n_{21}b_1 = -1, \quad -C\bar{N}M_2 = n_{21}n_{12} = -1
\end{aligned} \tag{65}$$

Now using one set of input-output data generated from the bilinear state-space model (62) starting from a non-zero initial condition that is unknown to the identification algorithm, we illustrate that the analytical coefficients expected in (65) are indeed identified. With this set of input-output data, the data matrices Y and V are formed as in (30), (31), and P is identified from (32),

$$P = \begin{bmatrix} CT_2 & D \end{bmatrix} = \begin{bmatrix} C\bar{A}\bar{B} & C\bar{B} & C\bar{N}\bar{B} & D \end{bmatrix} \tag{66}$$

where because $D = 0$,

$$\bar{B} = \begin{bmatrix} B + M_1D & -M_1 & M_2D & -M_2 \end{bmatrix} = \begin{bmatrix} B & -M_1 & 0 & -M_2 \end{bmatrix} \tag{67}$$

With the input-output model order $p = 2$, the input-output data must be sufficiently rich so that V is full row rank. The identified P is found to be

$$\begin{aligned}
C\bar{A}\bar{B} &= \begin{bmatrix} C\bar{A}B & -C\bar{A}M_1 & 0 & -C\bar{A}M_2 \end{bmatrix} = \begin{bmatrix} 0.5 & 0.25 & 0 & 0.5 \end{bmatrix} \\
C\bar{B} &= \begin{bmatrix} CB & -CM_1 & 0 & -CM_2 \end{bmatrix} = \begin{bmatrix} 2 & -0.5 & 0 & 1 \end{bmatrix} \\
C\bar{N}\bar{B} &= \begin{bmatrix} C\bar{N}B & -C\bar{N}M_1 & 0 & -C\bar{N}M_2 \end{bmatrix} = \begin{bmatrix} -1 & -0.5 & 0 & -1 \end{bmatrix} \\
D &= 0
\end{aligned} \tag{68}$$

Upon careful inspection, it can be seen that the identified coefficients in (68) match the analytical values in (65) exactly.

We now describe how the identified model can be used for output prediction. This step is used to verify if the identified input-output model is capable of reproducing the output data used in the identification when driven by the same input, or to verify against another independent input-output data set. In the case of a linear system, as long as it is asymptotically stable, any discrepancy in the responses due to initial condition mismatch between the actual system and the model will vanish in the steady-state. In the case of a nonlinear system such as a bilinear system, the system responses can be drastically different for different initial conditions when driven by the same input time history. It is therefore important to ensure that the initial condition of the identified input-output model match the initial condition of the actual system during the model validation process so that proper evaluation of the prediction ability of the identified input-output model can be made.

We explain how to use the identified input-output model as a predictor for the case $p = 2$. The procedure can be easily generalized for any value of p. The very first output value that the input-output model can predict is $\hat{y}(2)$, which according to (27),

$$\hat{y}(2) = \begin{bmatrix} CT_2 & D \end{bmatrix} \begin{bmatrix} v(0) \\ v(1) \\ v(0)u(1) \\ u(2) \end{bmatrix} \tag{69}$$

where $v(k)$ defined in (7) is expressed in terms of $u(k)$ and $y(k)$,

$$v(0) = \begin{bmatrix} u(0) \\ y(0) \\ u^2(0) \\ y(0)u(0) \end{bmatrix} \qquad v(1) = \begin{bmatrix} u(1) \\ y(1) \\ u^2(1) \\ y(1)u(1) \end{bmatrix} \tag{70}$$

The predicted output $\hat{y}(2)$ is expressed in terms of $y(0)$, $y(1)$, and $u(0)$, $u(1)$, $u(2)$. Thus, aside from the direct transmission input $u(2)$, the actual output values $y(0)$, $y(1)$, and input values $u(0)$, $u(1)$ serve as the initial condition for the input-output model. The next predicted output $\hat{y}(3)$ can be computed from $y(1)$, $\hat{y}(2)$, and $u(1)$, $u(2)$, $u(3)$ where the predicted output $\hat{y}(2)$ replaces the actual output $y(2)$,

$$\hat{y}(3) = \begin{bmatrix} CT_2 & D \end{bmatrix} \begin{bmatrix} v(1) \\ \hat{v}(2) \\ v(1)u(2) \\ u(3) \end{bmatrix} \qquad v(1) = \begin{bmatrix} u(1) \\ y(1) \\ u^2(1) \\ y(1)u(1) \end{bmatrix} \qquad \hat{v}(2) = \begin{bmatrix} u(2) \\ \hat{y}(2) \\ u^2(2) \\ \hat{y}(2)u(2) \end{bmatrix} \tag{71}$$

Next, $\hat{y}(4)$ is computed from $\hat{y}(2)$, $\hat{y}(3)$, and $u(2)$, $u(3)$, $u(4)$ where no actual output measurements are used,

$$\hat{y}(4) = \begin{bmatrix} CT_2 & D \end{bmatrix} \begin{bmatrix} \hat{v}(2) \\ \hat{v}(3) \\ \hat{v}(2)u(3) \\ u(4) \end{bmatrix} \qquad \hat{v}(2) = \begin{bmatrix} u(2) \\ \hat{y}(2) \\ u^2(2) \\ \hat{y}(2)u(2) \end{bmatrix} \qquad \hat{v}(3) = \begin{bmatrix} u(3) \\ \hat{y}(3) \\ u^2(3) \\ \hat{y}(3)u(3) \end{bmatrix} \tag{72}$$

Starting from $\hat{y}(4)$, therefore, the prediction relies solely on the output values that the model generates and the input values alone. In general, for an input-output model with order p, the first p values of input and output measurements serve as the initial condition of the model. The very first output measurement that the model can predict is $\hat{y}(p)$. From then on, the predicted output values are fed back into the model, until eventually the model runs on its own when it relies only on its own output values for the prediction.

Next, we investigate the case where the input-output model order p is chosen to be larger than the minimum value of 2. This case is important because in an actual identification problem, we do not know the true order of the system being identified, and we simply pick a value of p corresponding to an assumed model order that is larger than the true (effective) order of the system. Using the same input-output data but selecting $p = 4$, the singular value decomposition of V reveals 6 zero singular values. These zero singular values reflect the fact that the input-output model is no longer unique. By not keeping these zero singular values in the computation of the pseudo-inverse we are picking an input-output model such that the norm of the coefficients is minimized. As expected, the over-parameterized input-output model still reproduces the actual output exactly when driven by the same input time history as shown in Figure 2. The prediction error is found to be $8.6 \times 10^{-13}\%$ which is numerically zero in double-precision calculation (Matlab).

Example 4: Identification with $a_{11} \neq 0, n_{11} \neq 0, c_{11} \neq 0$, and $D \neq 0$

Now we consider the case where all Pearson's model conditions are violated,

$$A = \begin{bmatrix} 0.5 & 0.1 \\ -1.2 & 0.9 \end{bmatrix} \quad N = \begin{bmatrix} 0.99 & 0.22 \\ -1.65 & 0.55 \end{bmatrix} \quad B = \begin{bmatrix} 1 \\ 2 \end{bmatrix} \quad C = \begin{bmatrix} 1 & 1 \end{bmatrix} \quad D = 1 \quad (73)$$

In view of the analysis of Pearson's model, we do not expect that an exact input-output model exists to represent it. However, it is not unreasonable to expect that the approximated input-output models will become increasingly more accurate as p increases. Indeed, our numerical results confirm that with $p = 2, 4, 6, 8$, the prediction errors of the identified input-output models are found to be 31.2%, 1.43%, 0.02%, and 0.00015%, respectively. A comparison of the predicted vs. actual outputs and the prediction error is shown in Figure 3 for $p = 8$. In each of these cases, V is full row rank, hence the richness condition of the input-output data is satisfied, and all singular values are kept in the computation of the pseudo-inverse of V. In these examples we also find that the smaller singular values can be eliminated without significantly affecting the quality of the identified models. The resultant models will then have coefficients with smaller magnitudes, an effect which is often desirable.

Finally, we also compute the first 50 Markov parameters of (A, B, C, D) which are D, CB, CAB, CA^2B, ... up to $CA^{48}B$, and compare them to the Markov parameters recovered from the identified input-output model coefficients according to the procedure described in the previous section. In the same manner, we also compare the actual Markov parameters of (N, B, C, D) which are $D, CB, CNB, CN^2B, ...$ up to $CN^{48}B$ to the similarly recovered Markov parameters. This comparison is shown in the top and bottom portions of Figures 4-7 corresponding to $p = 2, 4, 6, 8$, respectively. The Markov parameters beyond p are computed using the conditions $\bar{A}^p = \bar{N}^p = 0$. The first term in these sequences is $D = 1$. As clearly shown in these figures, as p increases, the recovered Markov parameters match the true Markov parameters of the bilinear system for both CA^kB and CN^kB.

CONCLUSIONS

We have presented a formulation to identify the input-output relationship of a discrete-time bilinear state-space model. Key advances associated with the proposed formulation include the ability to use input-output data from one single experiment for identification. It also avoids the need to require zero initial condition. Instead, the initial conditions can be non-zero and unknown. Also, the input excitation can be general as long as it is sufficiently rich. Current methods, in contrast, require data from multiple experiments, zero initial conditions, and specialized input excitation such as extended pulses. We also addressed a fundamental question on the relationship between a discrete-time bilinear state-space model and its equivalent NARX input-output models. This issue has been outstanding for several decades despite a large amount of work on the subject. By extending the interaction matrix formulation, which was originally developed for linear time-invariant systems, later extended to time-varying systems, and now to discrete-time bilinear systems, we have provided a bridge between the state-space form and the input-output form of the bilinear models. The proposed identification formulation does not require the determination of the interaction matrices themselves, but only their existence.

With numerical simulations we observe that for bilinear state-space models where exact input-output representations are known to exist, our algorithm is able to identify such bilinear systems exactly to the numerical accuracy of the computational software. When the conversion from state-space to input-output models is not exact according to the interaction matrix formulation, we find that the identification algorithm produces approximate input-output models whose prediction accuracies improve as the parameter p, which is the order of the NARX input-output model, increases.

An important question that requires further investigation is the precise mechanism by which the interaction matrices permit the elimination of explicit state-dependent terms in the input-output models in these non-exact cases. There are an infinite number of equivalent bilinear state-space models that produce the same input-output map as the original model. It is possible that the interaction matrices exist for one such model even if they do not exist for the original model. The interaction matrix formulation also establishes the relationship between the Markov parameters of the bilinear state-space model and the coefficients of the identified input-output models. These relationships are used to recover the bilinear state-space model Markov parameters from the identified coefficients of the input-output models. Finally, practical aspects such as computational requirements and robustness to noises, etc., are also very important, and we hope to address these aspects in our future work.

REFERENCES

[1] Majji, M., Juang, J. N., Junkins, J. L., "Continuous-Time Bilinear System Identification Using Repeated Experiments," AAS09-366, *AAS/AIAA Astrodynamics Specialist Conference*, Pittsburgh, PA, 2009.

[2] Juang, J.-N., "Generalized Bilinear System Identification," *The Journal of the Astronautical Sciences*, Vol. 57, No. 1/2, 2009.

[3] Juang, J.-N., Lee C.-H., and Jiang, S.-B., "Continuous-Time Bilinear System Identification Using Single Experiment With Multiple Pulses," AAS10-110, *AAS/AIAA Space Flight Mechanics Meeting*, San Diego, CA, 2010.

[4] Lee C.-H., Juang, J.-N., and Jiang, S.-B., "Nonlinear System Identification - A Continuous-Time Bilinear State-Space Approach," AAS10-328, *Kyle T. Alfriend Astrodynamics Symposium*, The American Astronautical Society, Monterey, CA, 2010.

[5] Majji, M., Juang, J.-N., and Junkins, J.L., "Application of Time Varying Eigensystem Realization Algorithm to Guidance and Control Problems," AAS09-360, *AAS/AIAA Astrodynamics Specialist Conference*, Pittsburg, PA, 2009.

[6] Majji, M. and Junkins, J.L., "Observer Markov Parameter Identification Theory for Time Varying Eigensystem Realization Algorithm," *AIAA Guidance Navigation and Control Conference and Exhibit*, Honolulu, HI, 2008.

[7] Phan, M.Q., Longman, R.W., and Juang, J.-N., "Identification of Linear Time-Varying Systems by Canonical Representation," AAS09-387, *AAS/AIAA Astrodynamics Specialist Conference*, Pittsburgh, PA, 2009.

[8] Phan, M.Q., Longman, R.W., and Juang, J.-N., "A Direct Method For Identifying Linear Time-Varying State-Space Models," AAS09-312, *AAS/AIAA Astrodynamics Specialist Conference*, Pittsburgh, PA, 2009.

[9] Phan, M.Q. and Čelik, H., "A Superstate Method for Discrete-Time Bilinear Model Identification by Interaction Matrices," AAS10-330, *Kyle T. Alfriend Astrodynamics Symposium*, The American Astronautical Society, Monterey, CA, 2010. Accepted for publication in *Journal of the Astronautical Sciences*.

[10] Pearson, R.K., *Discrete-Time Dynamic Models*, Oxford University Press, USA, 1999.

[11] Pearson, R.K. and Kotta, U., "State-Space Discrete-Time Models: State-Space vs. I/O Representations," *Journal of Process Control*, Vol. 14, 2004, pp. 533-538.

[12] Baheti, R.S., Mohler, R.R., and Spang, H.A., "Second-Order Correlation Method for Bilinear System Identification," *IEEE Transactions on Automatic Control*, Vol. AC-45, No. 6, December 1980.

[13] Zhang, Q., and Ljung, L, "Multiple Steps Prediction with Nonlinear ARX Models," *Proceedings in NOLCOS 2004-IFAC Symposium on Nonlinear Control Systems*, Stuttgart, Germany.

[14] Fornasini, E. and Valcher, M.E., "On Some Connections Between Bilinear Input/Output Maps and 2D Systems, Nonlinear Analysis, Theory, Methods and Applications," *Proceedings of the 2nd World Congress of Nonlinear Analysts*, Vol. 30, No. 4, 1997, pp. 1995-2005.

[15] Phan, M.Q., "Interaction Matrices in System Identification and Control," *Proceedings of the Fifteenth Yale Workshop on Adaptive and Learning Systems*, New Haven, CT, 2011.

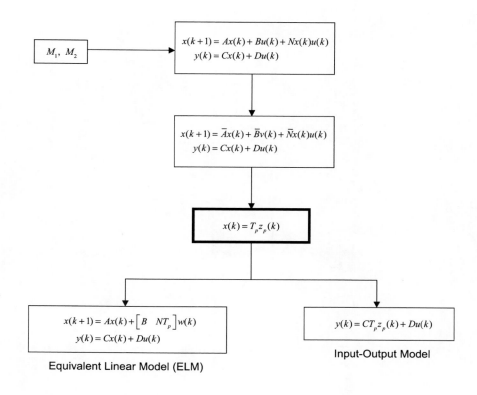

Figure 1. From a bilinear state-space model to an input-output model by interaction matrices.

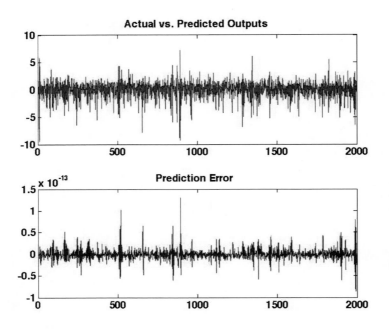

Figure 2. Actual vs. Predicted Outputs and Prediction Error (p=4).

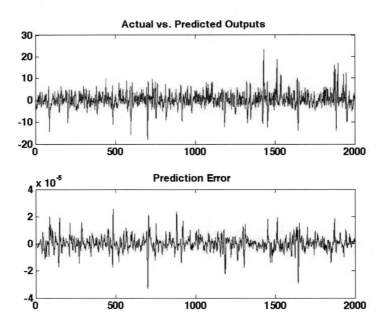

Figure 3. Actual vs. Predicted Outputs and Prediction Error (p=8).

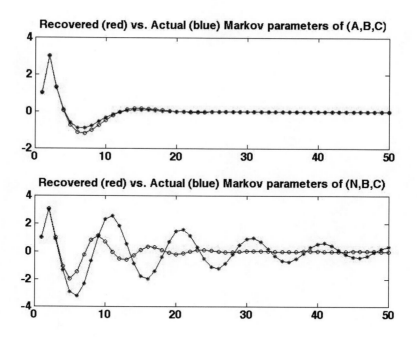

Figure 4. Recovered vs. actual Markov parameters (p=2).

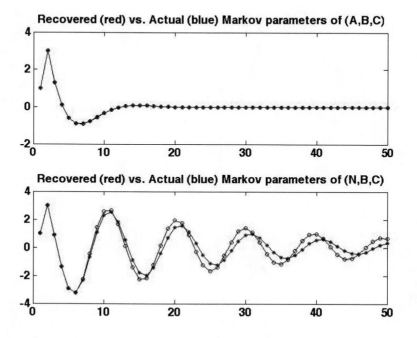

Figure 5. Recovered vs. actual Markov parameters (p=4).

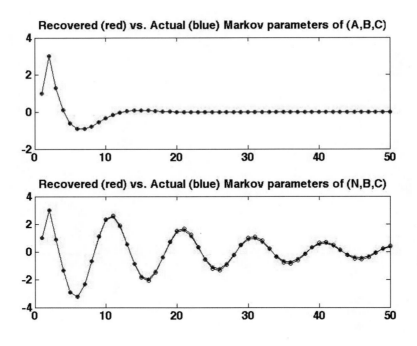

Figure 6. Recovered vs. actual Markov parameters (p=6).

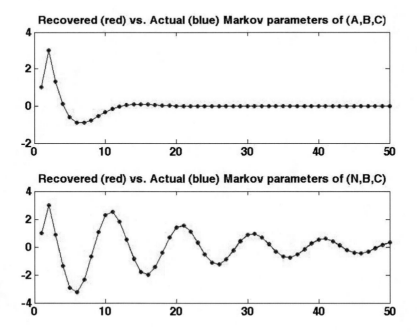

Figure 7. Recovered vs. actual Markov parameters (p=8).

MULTI-BODY CAPTURE TO LOW-ALTITUDE CIRCULAR ORBITS AT EUROPA

Daniel J. Grebow,[*] Anastassios E. Petropoulos[*] and Paul A. Finlayson[*]

For capture to a 200-km circular orbit around Europa, millions of different starting points on the orbit are propagated in the Jupiter-Europa Restricted 3-Body Problem. The transfers exist as members of families of trajectories, where certain families consistently outperform the others. The trajectories are not sensitive to changes in inclination for the final circular orbit. The top-performing trajectories appear to follow the invariant manifolds of L_2 Lyapunov orbits for capture into a retrograde orbit, and in some cases save up to 40% of the Δv from the patched 2-body problem. Transfers are attached to the current nominal mission for NASA's Jupiter-Europa Orbiter, where the total cost is roughly 100 m/s less than the baseline mission.

INTRODUCTION

NASA engineers and scientists have long anticipated a mission to Europa. While a mission to Europa is enticing for many reasons, the primary cause of our allurement is the potential discovery of a "habitable world".[1] Scientists believe that buried beneath the surface of this moon is a water ocean that might support life.

There are many options for a mission to Europa.[1-5] The currently proposed mission architecture consists of two spacecraft: the NASA-led Jupiter-Europa Orbiter (JEO) and the ESA-led Jupiter-Ganymede Orbiter (JGO). The nominal trajectory for JEO would involve many phases, including multiple interplanetary flybys and over 20 flybys of the Jovian moons.[5] Nearing the end of its three-year campaign, eventually the spacecraft would fall into a cadence, or resonance, with Europa's motion on its orbit. This phase would be just the beginning of what researchers have dubbed the *endgame*;[3] however, considering the dance the spacecraft performs with Europa at this time, a more satisfactory description might be *courtship*. For a final play, the spacecraft would capture to a 200-km circular orbit around Europa. As far as the scientists are concerned, the end of this phase marks the beginning of what would hopefully be a long list of discoveries at Europa.

Ignoring Earth launch and Jupiter orbit insertion, Kloster et al.[5] report that the entire tour would require less than 1 km/s in deterministic Δv. Since the bulk of this Δv is at Europa orbit insertion (EOI), the primary motivation for the current work is to develop a practical technique for designing an efficient capture at Europa. Efficient capture means harnessing the gravitational effects of both Europa and Jupiter to lower the insertion cost. This is primarily a three-body problem, and therefore inherits all the features associated with the three-body problem, e.g., numerical integration in highly sensitive regimes. Of course, the radiation dose is also a concern, and therefore a technique cannot lead to unrealistically long trajectories that spend too much time in the radiation belts.

In the literature, there are only a few studies on efficient capture to low altitude orbits at Europa. Koon et al.[6] and Russell and Lam[7] utilize the invariant manifolds of periodic orbits for designing a ballistic capture. While this approach is appealing from a dynamical systems perspective, the final orbit for JEO would be at an altitude from which ballistic capture is impossible. Still the method might be adapted for designing capture trajectories with low insertion costs. Campagnola and Russell[8] mainly focus on methods for minimizing the apoapsis Δv's leading up to EOI, however, in another study[9] they include a multi-body approach that

[*]Mission Design Engineer, Outer Planet Mission Analysis, Jet Propulsion Laboratory, California Institute of Technology, 4800 Oak Grove Drive, Pasadena, CA, 91109-8099.

might be useful for unlocking efficient capture trajectories. Starting from a 100-km circular orbit around Europa, they numerically integrate trajectories backwards in the Jupiter-Europa Restricted 3-Body Problem (R3BP). Sampling various departure geometries, they are able to find a transfer originating from Ganymede that captures with only $\Delta v = 510$ m/s, well below the minimum Δv for parabolic capture in the Patched 2-Body Problem (P2BP). Unfortunately, their method is tied to a very specific mission objective (i.e., transfer from a 100-km Ganymede orbit), and it is difficult to envision how to adapt their approach for a general baseline mission strategy. Furthermore, they only investigate a planar circular orbit at Europa, and the mission requirements stipulate that the orbit must be inclined at 95° to the equator.

Johannesen and D'Amario[3] discuss multiple options for the Jovian tour, each ending with only 520 m/s for EOI. Since their analysis is more focused on mission architectures, they do not provide a detailed description of the method used to generate the trajectories. In fact, the algorithm was developed by one of the authors on this current paper (Finlayson[10]), and, in brief, goes as follows: A database of stored trajectories is calculated by starting from a 200-km circular orbit around Europa and numerically integrating three-body equations backwards in time to the first apojove. The precise initial conditions for integration are obtained by applying a maneuver tangent to the spacecraft's velocity vector for all possible geometries of an orbit at a prescribed inclination. Only the trajectories that yield the highest apojoves are stored. While considering phasing between the spacecraft, Jupiter, and Europa, the final Europa flyby is adjusted until a trajectory matches in position with one of the stored trajectories.

The current work expands on the Finlayson method used by Johannesen and D'Amario to arrive at a more satisfying dynamical understanding of the solutions. Starting with a 200-km circular orbit around Europa, we also apply maneuvers tangent to the spacecraft's velocity vector. Recognizing the sensitivity of the dynamics, a million different locations along the orbit are sampled. Purely prograde and retrograde orbits are investigated, as well as an orbit with inclination of 95° to Europa's orbital plane. The states for the points are propagated backwards in time in the Jupiter-Europa R3BP, where the final apojove values are recorded at an appropriate stopping condition. After repeating the process for various EOI Δv's, we notice that each transfer trajectory exists as a member of a family of trajectories, where certain families consistently outperform others. A continuation method is presented for creating families of trajectories from a seed member. The most desirable family appears to arrive along the invariant manifolds associated with an L_2 Lyapunov orbit. For some of the trajectories, the Δv savings is as high as 40% of the Δv computed in the P2BP to transfer from the same apojove. The study is completed with a method for patching the trajectories into the baseline mission for JEO.

SOLUTION APPROACH

Our goal is discovery of low-Δv capture trajectories that simultaneously leverage the gravitational effects of Jupiter and Europa. Therefore all capture simulations take place in the Jupiter-Europa R3BP. For a particular Δv, we seek to find the optimal insertion location to a 200-km circular orbit that originates from a trajectory with the highest possible apojove. This solution method is equivalent to finding the minimum insertion Δv for a transfer from a particular apojove.

Equations of Motion

For the Jupiter-Europa R3BP, the primary bodies are assumed to move in circular orbits, and the spacecraft possesses negligible mass. The standard rotating, barycentric coordinate frame is used, with the X-axis directed from Jupiter to Europa and the Z-axis parallel to the Jupiter-Europa angular velocity. The nondimensional form of the equations is

$$\ddot{X} = 2\dot{Y} + X + (\mu - 1)\frac{X + \mu}{d^3} - \mu\frac{X + \mu - 1}{r^3},$$
$$\ddot{Y} = -2\dot{X} + Y + (\mu - 1)\frac{Y}{d^3} - \mu\frac{Y}{r^3}, \qquad (1)$$
$$\ddot{Z} = (\mu - 1)\frac{Z}{d^3} - \mu\frac{Z}{r^3}.$$

414

where

$$d^2 = (X + \mu)^2 + Y^2 + Z^2,$$
$$r^2 = (X + \mu - 1)^2 + Y^2 + Z^2. \tag{2}$$

In Eq. (1), X, Y, and Z are the Cartesian components of the spacecraft's position relative to the rotating, barycentric frame. The mass ratio is

$$\mu = \frac{GM_E}{GM_J + GM_E}, \tag{3}$$

where M_J and M_E are the masses of Jupiter and Europa, respectively, and G is the universal gravitational constant. See Szebehely[11] for a more detailed discussion of the R3BP.

Methodology

Starting from a 200-km circular parking orbit around Europa, the approach is to apply a maneuver and integrate Eqs. (1) in backwards time. Since Europa is the dominant gravitating body when the spacecraft is in the 200-km circular orbit, we only consider maneuvers along the spacecraft's velocity vector in the Europa-centered non-rotating frame. The simulations are terminated at the first crossing of the plane $Y = 0$ where $X < 0$, and the osculating apojove is computed. When the trajectory crosses the plane $Y = 0$ where $X < 0$, the osculating apojove is very close to the actual apojove. The method is similar to the one used by Campagnola and Russell,[9] and by Finlayson[10] who used apojove itself as the stopping condition.

To express the capture conditions as initial states for integrating Eq. (1), we first define the spacecraft's position and velocity in a radial, transverse, and normal (RTN) frame. The position and velocity are

$$\mathbf{r} = (r_c, 0, 0)^T, \quad \mathbf{v} = (0, \sqrt{\mu/r_c} + \Delta v, 0)^T, \tag{4}$$

where the quantity r_c is the nondimensional radius of the 200-km circular orbit, and recall μ is the Jupiter-Europa mass ratio, or, equivalently, the nondimensional gravitational parameter of Europa. The transformation $\mathbf{T}$ from the RTN frame to an inertial frame instantaneously aligned with the Jupiter-Europa rotating frame is defined by an Euler 3-1-3 (Ω-i-θ) sequence, i.e.,

$$\mathbf{T} = \begin{bmatrix} \cos\Omega\cos\theta - \sin\Omega\sin\theta\cos i & -\cos\Omega\sin\theta - \sin\Omega\cos\theta\cos i & \sin\Omega\sin i \\ \sin\Omega\cos\theta + \cos\Omega\sin\theta\cos i & -\sin\Omega\sin\theta + \cos\Omega\cos\theta\cos i & -\cos\Omega\sin i \\ \sin\theta\sin i & \cos\theta\sin i & \cos i \end{bmatrix}, \tag{5}$$

where $0° \leq i \leq 180°$. Then, the position and velocity of the spacecraft in the barycentric rotating frame are

$$\mathbf{R} = (X, Y, Z)^T = \mathbf{Tr} + (1 - \mu, 0, 0)^T,$$
$$\mathbf{V} = (\dot{X}, \dot{Y}, \dot{Z})^T = \mathbf{Tv} - (-Y, X + \mu - 1, 0)^T. \tag{6}$$

For circular orbits in the plane of the primaries, $\Omega = 0°$. The orbit can be either pure prograde if $i = 0°$ or pure retrograde when $i = 180°$. For simplicity, hereafter, we refer to pure prograde and pure retrograde as *prograde* and *retrograde*, respectively. The quantities Δv, θ, Ω, and i encompass all possible capture trajectories. Furthermore, by Eq. (6), these parameters uniquely determine an initial state for integrating Eq. (1) backwards in time. In this study we allow Δv, θ, and Ω to vary for particular values of i.

Delta-v for L_2 Jacobi Constant

Jacobi's constant is a well-known integral of the motion in the R3BP, and has been useful in the past for understanding strategic placement of maneuvers.[12] In barycentric rotating coordinates, the integral is

$$C = -\dot{X}^2 - \dot{Y}^2 - \dot{Z}^2 + X^2 + Y^2 + 2(1 - \mu)/d + 2\mu/r. \tag{7}$$

For trajectories coming into the vicinity of Europa from ranges beyond the L_2 radius, the minimum possible Δv for insertion at Europa is the one that makes the Jacobi constant equal to that of L_2. At this Δv a small corridor, or gateway, opens at L_2 enabling low-energy transfer into the vicinity of Europa.[13] To compute this

Δv, i.e., the Δv required to achieve C_{L_2}, we note that Eq. (7) can be expressed in terms of Δv, θ, Ω, and i using Eqs. (6). Setting $C = C_{L_2}$ and solving for Δv yields

$$\Delta v = r_c \cos i - \sqrt{\mu/r_c} + \sqrt{r_c^2 \cos^2 \theta \sin^2 i + X^2 + Y^2 + 2(1-\mu)/d + 2\mu/r - C_{L_2}}. \qquad (8)$$

For a particular value of i, we are interested in the smallest possible Δv for all values of θ and Ω. The global minimum is easily found by looping through θ and Ω and computing Δv with Eq. (8). As shown in Figure 1, the minimum Δv varies with inclination. The minimum Δv to achieve C_{L_2} for polar orbits is *less* than that required if the orbit is prograde. If the orbit is retrograde the Δv necessary is even smaller.

Here we arrive at an important result that is also noticed by Campagnola and Russell.[9] Europa's orbital motion imparts a rotational component of velocity on the spacecraft, reducing the cost for insertion into a retrograde orbit. From Eq. (8), the difference in minimum cost for insertion into a prograde orbit ($\Delta v_{i=0°}$) versus a retrograde orbit ($\Delta v_{i=180°}$) is

$$\Delta v_{i=0°} - \Delta v_{i=180°} = 2r_c. \qquad (9)$$

For a 200-km circular orbit, this difference is

$$\Delta v_{i=0°} - \Delta v_{i=180°} = 72.3 \text{ m/s}. \qquad (10)$$

We note that the difference in minimum cost for insertion to prograde versus retrograde orbits depends only on the radius of the orbit r_c.

Since passing through the L_2 corridor depends also on the phase space stability, implementing a Δv that is slightly higher than those in Figure 1 does not guarantee that the spacecraft will ever pass through the gateway. However, the minimum Δv to achieve C_{L_2} is still useful in that it is the theoretical lower limit for capture in the R3BP (assuming a starting position beyond L_2), and is considerably less than $\Delta v = 558$ m/s, or the Δv for parabolic capture from the P2BP.

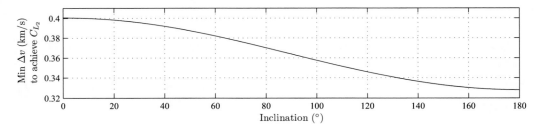

Figure 1. For 200-km circular Europa orbit, Δv necessary to achieve C_{L_2}.

TRANSFERS TO IN-PLANE CIRCULAR ORBITS

The details of our approach are first outlined for transfers to prograde and retrograde circular orbits in Europa's orbital plane. We begin by sampling grid points along the circular orbit. The grid search provides insight into various options for approaching Europa, and ultimately serves as a pool of initial guesses for an algorithm that further refines the trajectories.

Grid Search

Recall that for orbits in the plane of the primaries, $\Omega = 0°$ and $i = 0°$ or $180°$ depending on if the orbit is prograde or retrograde. Then, for a given Δv, the goal of a grid search is to determine the optimal EOI location θ. Due to the sensitivities in the R3BP, it is very difficult to predict a value of θ that maximizes the osculating apojove r_a. To search for these trajectories, we implement an extremely fine grid. For a given

Δv, we examine 1 million capture trajectories where the initial state corresponds to 1 million linearly equally spaced points between $\theta = 0°$ and $360°$. As previously described, the trajectories are integrated to the first crossing of the plane $Y = 0$ where $X < 0$. All simulations are performed in Fortran 90 using Shampine and Watt's[14] Adams-Bashforth-Moulton variable time-step integrator. Up to 500-day transfers are considered to see if long-duration transfers provide significant Δv savings. For each trajectory we store the osculating value of r_a at the end of the simulation. Simulations that reach the 500-day limit before crossing the negative X-axis are discarded, as well as if the Jacobi constant is not preserved within a prescribed tolerance.

The results of the simulations can be visualized in Figure 2, where r_a is plotted in Jupiter-Europa distances. The values of Δv examined are 0.425 km/s, 0.475 km/s, 0.525 km/s, 0.575 km/s, 0.625 km/s, and 0.675

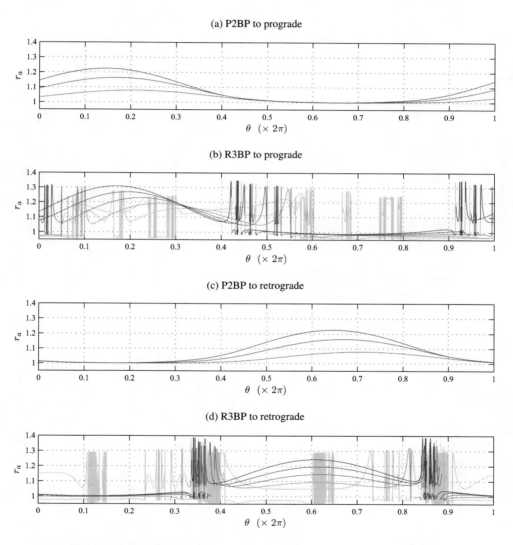

Figure 2. Maximum osculating apojove ending with a maneuver at θ; each line is for a unique Δv ranging from 0.425 (aqua) to 0.675 km/s (magenta); r_a in Jupiter-Europa distances.

417

km/s. We also monitor if the trajectory passes below Europa's surface (gray). Included in Figure 2 are the curves of r_a versus θ for the P2BP for $\Delta v = 0.575$ km/s, 0.625 km/s, and 0.675 km/s. As expected, in the P2BP the curves are smooth and there is one maximum and one minimum for each Δv. The maxima occur when θ is such that the vector $\mathbf{v}_\infty$ is in the direction the Europa's motion. In the P2BP the extremal values of r_a are the same for both prograde and retrograde orbits.

While the shape of the curves in the R3BP are similar to the P2BP, there are some striking and important

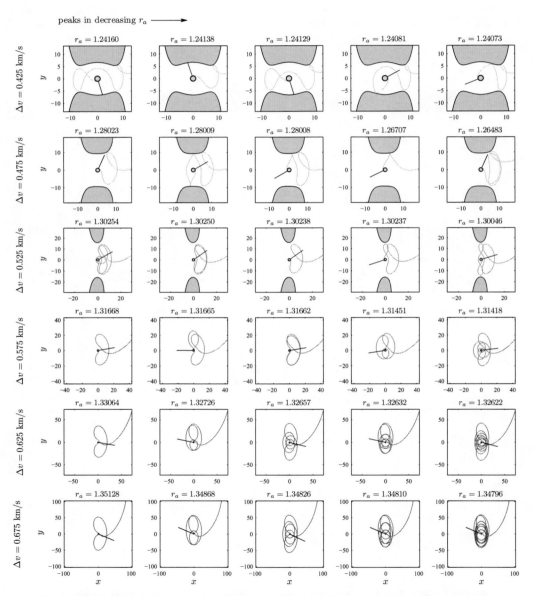

Figure 3. Top transfer to prograde circular orbit; origin is Europa, axes in Europa radii.

418

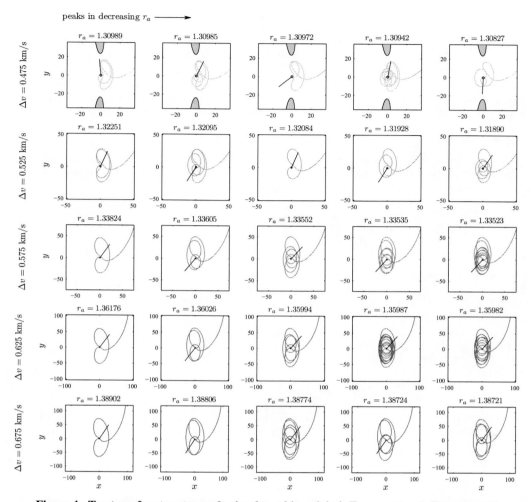

Figure 4. Top transfers to retrograde circular orbit; origin is Europa, axes in Europa radii.

differences. The most noticeable difference is the prominent spiking that occurs in Figures 2b and 2d. The spikes correspond to Europa flybys not modeled in our P2BP analysis. There is spiking as well for resonances in the P2BP (not shown), however, for a particular Δv, the r_a achievable from those resonant encounters cannot exceed the maximum shown in Figures 2a and 2c. Alternatively, for a given Δv in the R3BP, often the spiking peaks yield much larger r_a's than the smooth peaks. For a prograde orbit, we also note that even the smooth peak in Figure 2b has a larger r_a than the corresponding peak in Figure 2a.

All the peaks in Figures 2b and 2d are stored and ordered in descending r_a. For each Δv, the top five trajectories are plotted in Figures 3 and 4, for prograde and retrograde orbits, respectively. The coordinates x, y, and z in the figures are the spacecraft's position with respect to Europa, measured in the rotating frame and units of Europa radii. The gray region is the forbidden zone where the velocity is imaginary, according to Eq. (7). We also include a line corresponding to the angle at arrival θ, and the value of osculating r_a for that case is recorded in the title of each plot. We immediately notice that the same type of transfer consistently performs well for each value of Δv. The best trajectory appears to follow an L_2 Lyapunov orbit for one revolution, where an Europa flyby then ejects the spacecraft with high r_a. In fact, for some cases the spacecraft follows the L_2 Lyapunov orbit for multiple revolutions before leaving the vicinity of Europa. The other transfers also follow well-known periodic orbits in the R3BP. (For an example of some of these orbits, see Broucke.[15]) We notice similar behavior if the orbit is retrograde. (Recall Figure 4.) When the orbit is retrograde, there are no capture trajectories that are not subsurface for $\Delta v = 0.425$ km/s. However, for the other Δv's the r_a values are much higher than for the best prograde trajectories. Considering the similarities of the trajectories found in Figures 3 and 4, these preliminary results suggest that the type of approach trajectory for optimal capture is not sensitive to the orientation of the 200-km circular orbit at Europa.

Families of Transfers

In this section we come to a more satisfying dynamical understanding of the efficient trajectories found in the grid search. From Figures 3 and 4, it is not surprising that each transfer trajectory exists as a subset of a family of trajectories. To this end, we seek to compute a family of trajectories where

$$\frac{dr_a}{d\theta} = 0, \tag{11}$$

$$\frac{d^2 r_a}{d\theta^2} < 0. \tag{12}$$

A targeting scheme is derived that enforces Eq. (11). Provided the initial guess is close to the maximum, the algorithm converges to a solution that satisfies Eq. (12), as well. To formulate the targeter, first we need an expression for the derivative $dr_a/d\theta$. The derivative appears in the variation of r_a, i.e.,

$$\delta r_a = \frac{dr_a}{d\theta} \delta\theta. \tag{13}$$

From Taylor series expansion of $r_a = r_a(\mathbf{X}_f(\mathbf{X}_0(\theta), t))$ and the chain-rule,

$$\delta r_a = \frac{\partial r_a}{\partial \mathbf{X}_f} \frac{\partial \mathbf{X}_f}{\partial \mathbf{X}_0} \frac{\partial \mathbf{X}_0}{\partial \theta} \delta\theta + \frac{\partial r_a}{\partial \mathbf{X}_f} \frac{\partial \mathbf{X}_f}{\partial t} \delta t. \tag{14}$$

Note that $\mathbf{X}_f$ is the resulting six-state from integrating the initial state $\mathbf{X}_0$ backwards to the plane $Y = 0$, $X < 0$. The variation δt in Eq. (14) can be eliminated by recognizing that at the crossing $Y_f(\mathbf{X}_0(\theta), t) = 0$, so the variation is

$$\delta Y_f = \frac{\partial Y_f}{\partial \mathbf{X}_0} \frac{\partial \mathbf{X}_0}{\partial \theta} \delta\theta + \frac{\partial Y_f}{\partial t} \delta t = 0. \tag{15}$$

Solving for δt in Eq. (15) and substituting into Eq. (14) results in the expression

$$\delta r_a = \frac{\partial r_a}{\partial \mathbf{X}_f} \left[\frac{\partial \mathbf{X}_f}{\partial \mathbf{X}_0} - \frac{\dot{\mathbf{X}}_f}{\dot{Y}_f} \frac{\partial Y_f}{\partial \mathbf{X}_0} \right] \frac{\partial \mathbf{X}_0}{\partial \theta} \delta\theta. \tag{16}$$

Hence, to satisfy Eq. (11) we desire that

$$g(\theta, \Delta v) = \frac{\partial r_a}{\partial \mathbf{X}_f} \left[\frac{\partial \mathbf{X}_f}{\partial \mathbf{X}_0} - \frac{\dot{\mathbf{X}}_f}{\dot{Y}_f} \frac{\partial Y_f}{\partial \mathbf{X}_0} \right] \frac{\partial \mathbf{X}_0}{\partial \theta} = 0. \tag{17}$$

Initial guesses for θ and Δv are available from the grid search, and a minimum-norm Newton's method finds the precise conditions $\mathbf{Y}_j = (\theta_j, \Delta v_j)^T$ such that $g(\mathbf{Y}_j) = 0$. From $\mathbf{Y}_j$, a guess for a nearby solution in the family is available from

$$\mathbf{Y}_{j+1} = \mathbf{Y}_j + s\hat{\mathbf{Y}}_j, \tag{18}$$

where $\hat{\mathbf{Y}}_j$ is a unit vector in the nullspace of $Dg(\mathbf{Y}_j)$. To converge to the neighboring trajectory, the new system of equations to solve is

$$\mathbf{F}(\mathbf{Y}_{j+1}) = \left\{ \begin{array}{c} g(\mathbf{Y}_{j+1}) \\ (\mathbf{Y}_{j+1} - \mathbf{Y}_j)^T \hat{\mathbf{Y}}_j - s \end{array} \right\} = \mathbf{0}. \tag{19}$$

Note that included in $\mathbf{F}$ is the pseudo-arclength constraint enforcing that the distance between the jth and $j^{\text{th}} + 1$ solutions, projected into the nullspace of $Dg(\mathbf{Y}_j)$, is a fixed value s. The process repeats in a method of continuation, until either the peak switches from local maximum to minimum, or the trajectory at some point passes below the surface of Europa.

While continuing the family, it is important to monitor the sign of $\hat{\mathbf{Y}}_{j+1}$ to keep moving in the same direction along the family. The sign is determined such that $\hat{\mathbf{Y}}_{j+1}^T \hat{\mathbf{Y}}_j$ is always positive. For each solution, we check that the necessary condition of maximality is satisfied, i.e., $Dg(\theta) < 0$. The scaling of the variables Δv and θ is also important. For all the families in this study, a dimensional value of Δv (km/s) is used, and for θ one revolution is set to unity. In general, the value of s in Eqs. (18) and (19) is allowed to change along the family, however, a fixed value of $s = 0.0075$ is sufficient for computing all the families in this study. This continuation method has found great success in the literature[16] and is a key component to computing various families of trajectories for efficient capture at Europa. As evidenced in Figure 2, these transfers are extremely sensitive to small changes in θ and Δv, and therefore a robust continuation scheme is critical for a successful algorithm.

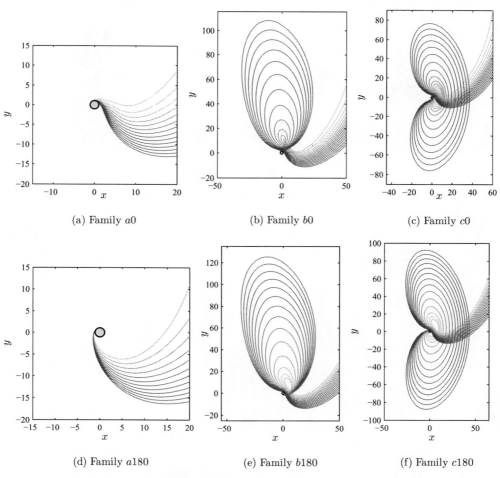

(a) Family $a0$ (b) Family $b0$ (c) Family $c0$

(d) Family $a180$ (e) Family $b180$ (f) Family $c180$

Figure 5. Various families; origin is Europa, axes in Europa radii.

For both prograde (designated by '0') and retrograde (designated by '180') orbits, three families are identified corresponding to the smoother peaks in Figure 2. (See Figure 5.) The peaks outlined by these families are shown in Figure 6. When selecting peaks in Figure 2 to examine more closely, we want to be sure to take a closer look at trajectories that consistently give high performance r_a in Figures 3 and 4. However, we also want to investigate the smooth peak that closely resembles the one in the P2BP. (Since smooth peaks do not always yield the highest r_a, they do not necessarily appear in Figures 3 and 4.) In general, the smoother the peak in Figure 2, the faster the trajectory leaves Europa. Jagged peaks likely correspond to trajectories that orbit Europa many times before leaving the vicinity. While these trajectories are also fascinating, we are more interested in trajectories that quickly depart from Europa. Furthermore, from the results of the grid search, it does not appear that long duration trajectories always yield higher apojoves. For now, we leave the discussion of the performance of these trajectories for a later section.

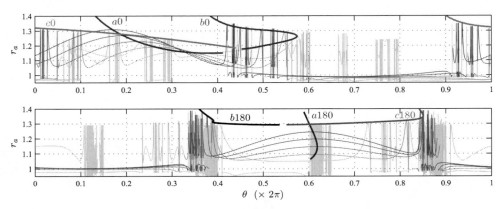

Figure 6. Line of peaks for the families.

TRANSFERS TO 95°-INCLINED CIRCULAR ORBITS

Investigation of planar capture trajectories is fascinating from a dynamical standpoint, yet ultimately we seek transfers to a nearly polar orbit. The currently envisioned mission calls for an orbit inclined at 95° to the equator. Since Europa is tidally locked, we assume the inclination can be measured with respect to the orbit plane of the primaries. When the inclination is fixed at $i = 95°$, in the P2BP there are two peaks in apojove

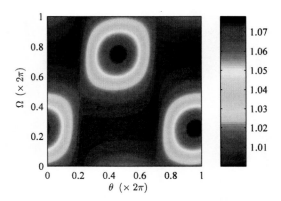

Figure 7. Apojove for all possible θ and Ω in the P2BP, $i = 95°$.

r_a, both for values of θ and Ω that align the vector $\mathbf{v}_\infty$ with Europa's velocity. An example for $\Delta v = 0.575$ km/s is plotted versus θ and Ω in Figure 7. The r_a-axis (z-axis) is attached to the color scale to the right of the plot. Apojove for the two peaks is roughly equal to 1.08 times the distance between Jupiter and Europa.

Similar to the study of planar trajectories, a grid search is performed for three-dimensional transfer trajectories in the R3BP. Once again, trajectories are integrated for each value of Δv, and osculating values of r_a

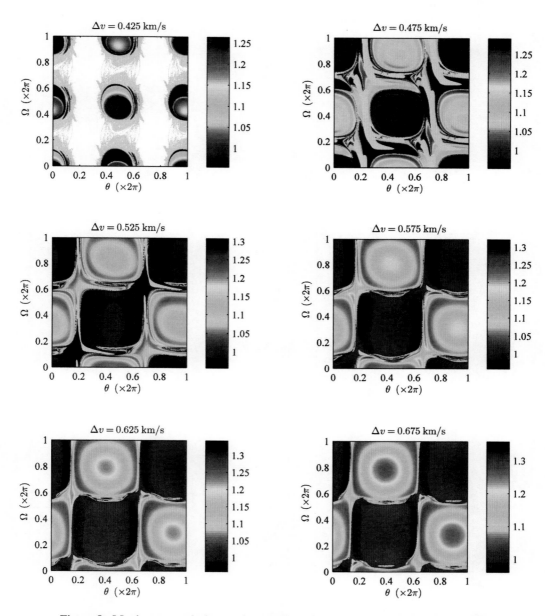

Figure 8. Maximum osculating apojove ending with maneuver at θ and Ω, $i = 95°$; colorbar indicates r_a in Jupiter-Europa distances.

423

are recorded when the trajectory first crosses the plane $Y = 0$, $X < 0$. The initial states correspond to all combinations of 1,000 linearly equally spaced points for θ and Ω ranging from 0° to 360°. The results of the grid search are plotted in Figure 8. Due to symmetries about the X-Y plane in the R3BP, the plots in Figure 8 also possesses symmetry. For initial conditions in the white region, either the Jacobi constant is not preserved to sufficient accuracy, or the trajectories fail to leave Europa after 500 days. Recall that the gray region corresponds to trajectories that pass below Europa's surface. For larger Δv's, there are two gentle peaks and valleys, similar to the P2BP example in Figure 7. The spiking between those peaks and valleys is associated with trajectories that re-encounter Europa before leaving. We note also that the highest peak for

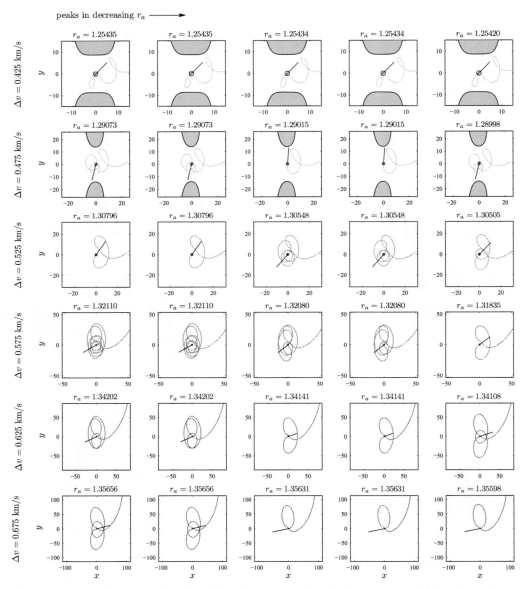

Figure 9. Top transfers to circular orbit where $i = 95°$; origin is Europa, axis in Europa radii.

$\Delta v = 0.575$ km/s is about $r_a = 1.32$, a value much higher than the P2BP maximum of 1.08 (recall Figure 7). The top five trajectories for each Δv are plotted in Figure 9. As expected due to the symmetries in the R3BP, the trajectories shown in Figure 9 occur in pairs. The shapes of the top performing trajectories for $i = 95°$ are similar to the best trajectories from $i = 0°$ and $180°$. The performance of the trajectories that yield the highest r_a is between that of $i = 0°$ and $180°$, with $i = 180°$ giving the best results. (For example, compare the r_a's recorded in each row of Figures 3, 4, and 9.)

As with the planar transfers, transfers to $95°$-circular orbits are characterized as members of families. Each peak in Figure 8 serves as an initial guess for an algorithm that adjusts θ, Ω and Δv until

$$\frac{dr_a}{d\theta} = 0 \quad \text{and} \quad \frac{dr_a}{d\Omega} = 0. \tag{20}$$

These conditions are equivalent to the vector constraint

$$\mathbf{g}(\theta, \Omega, \Delta v) = \left\{ \begin{array}{c} \dfrac{\partial r_a}{\partial \mathbf{X}_f} \left[\dfrac{\partial \mathbf{X}_f}{\partial \mathbf{X}_0} - \dfrac{\dot{\mathbf{X}}_f}{\dot{Y}_f} \dfrac{\partial Y_f}{\partial \mathbf{X}_0} \right] \dfrac{\partial \mathbf{X}_0}{\partial \theta} \\[3mm] \dfrac{\partial r_a}{\partial \mathbf{X}_f} \left[\dfrac{\partial \mathbf{X}_f}{\partial \mathbf{X}_0} - \dfrac{\dot{\mathbf{X}}_f}{\dot{Y}_f} \dfrac{\partial Y_f}{\partial \mathbf{X}_0} \right] \dfrac{\partial \mathbf{X}_0}{\partial \Omega} \end{array} \right\} = \mathbf{0}. \tag{21}$$

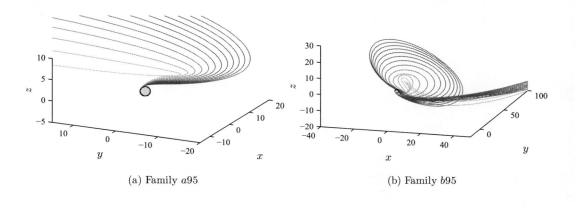

(a) Family $a95$ (b) Family $b95$

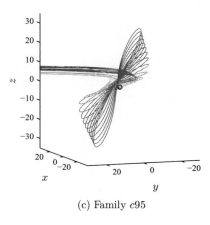

(c) Family $c95$

Figure 10. Various families for $i = 95°$; origin is Europa, axes in Europa radii.

425

Once Eq. (21) is satisfied, Eq. (18) makes a prediction for a nearby transfer in the same family, where now $\mathbf{Y}_j = (\theta_j, \Omega_j, \Delta v_j)^T$, and $\hat{\mathbf{Y}}_j$ is a unit vector in the nullspace of $D\mathbf{g}(\mathbf{Y}_j)$. The equations for continuation are Eq. (19), where g is now replaced by the vector constraint $\mathbf{g}$ of Eq. (21). As the continuation progresses, it is important to monitor the eigenvalues of $D\mathbf{g}(\theta, \Omega)$ to ensure that solution corresponds to a local maximum.

Families analogous to the planar families are now examined for $i = 95°$ and are plotted in Figure 10. From Figure 10c, it appears that the c-type family is following either an L_2 axial orbit before insertion, or the invariant manifolds of an L_2 vertical orbit. (For examples of vertical and axial orbits, see Doedel et al.[16]). While these families are more thoroughly discussed in the following section, for now we briefly mention that the a-, b-, and c-type trajectories appear to exist for all values of i.

ANALYSIS OF RESULTS

The results for the families are discussed and an algorithm is presented for attaching efficient capture trajectories to a baseline mission. Two different capture options are proposed for the current JEO mission architecture.

Comparison of Families

We are now in a position to compare the r_a performance of the a-, b-, and c-type trajectories. In Figure 11, r_a is plotted as a function of Δv for the trajectories in each family. Also included in the plot is the r_a achieved in the P2BP for values above the Δv required for parabolic capture. While the minimum theoretical Δv for capture from $r_a = 1$ is 556 m/s, in the three identified R3BP families there are Δv's as low as 402 m/s that

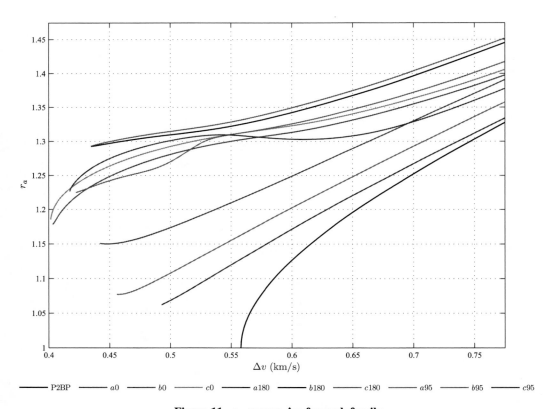

Figure 11. r_a versus Δv for each family.

originate from $r_a = 1.19$. These trajectories are part of the $c0$ family (orange). For only 50 m/s more, the $c180$ family (magenta) includes a transfer from $r_a = 1.3$. We note that while all the R3BP families yield better results than the P2BP (for the range of Δv's examined), the b- and c-type trajectories consistently outperform the a-type trajectories. An interesting trade occurs at $\Delta v = 550$ m/s between the $b95$ (gray) and $c95$ (purple) families. Below $\Delta v = 550$ m/s, the $c95$ family includes trajectories from higher r_a's, whereas above 550 m/s the $b95$ family gives the higher r_a's. In fact, for the $c95$ family, r_a briefly decreases following 550 m/s.

To measure the performance of the trajectories, consider the minimum Δv, single-burn strategy necessary to transfer from an apoapsis range of r_a in the P2BP. Assuming the spacecraft is already on the inbound trajectory from r_a, the minimum Δv corresponds to insertion from a Hohmann transfer arc. The Δv at insertion is

$$\Delta v_{P2BP} = \sqrt{\left(\sqrt{\frac{2r_a(1-\mu)}{1+r_a}} - \sqrt{1-\mu} \right)^2 + \frac{2\mu}{r_c} - \sqrt{\frac{\mu}{r_c}}}. \tag{22}$$

Then, the fractional savings in Δv using a multi-body transfer from the same r_a is

$$\eta = \frac{\Delta v_{P2BP} - \Delta v_{R3BP}}{\Delta v_{P2BP}}. \tag{23}$$

We compute η for the a-, b-, and c-type trajectories, and the results are plotted in Figure 12. To appreciate the importance of these results, compare a multi-body transfer from $r_a = 1.3$ to the equivalent minimum-energy Hohmann transfer. Ignoring the Δv at apojove and assuming the spacecraft is already on the inbound

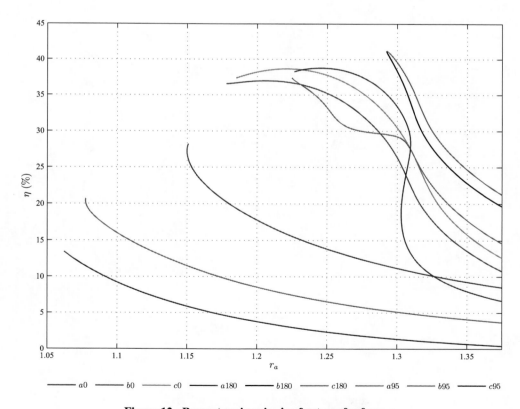

Figure 12. Percent savings in Δv for transfer from r_a.

transfer from $r_a = 1.3$, the Hohmann transfer Δv for insertion is about 750 m/s. For an alternative single burn strategy, from Figure 12 we see there is a transfer trajectory in the $c180$ family that saves 40% of this Δv. The trajectory achieves the same objective for 300 m/s less.

Mission-Oriented Examples

Attaching a multi-body trajectory to the baseline mission is a critical step in verifying the usefulness of these trajectories for mission design. Conversely, when a mission is in the formulation stage, these trajectory families can guide the selection of a baseline mission that most fully exploits the beneficial characteristics. Here we demonstrate that it is not essential to start with an a-, b-, or c-type trajectory that perfectly matches the spacecraft-Jupiter-Europa phasing of a nominal mission.

The envisioned baseline for JEO is the tour T08-008 presented in Kloster et al.[5] The final phase of the tour before insertion is depicted in Figure 13. The last flyby before capture is the E24 flyby on June 12, 2028, where the incoming $v_\infty^- = 1.17$ km/s. Since we desire a ballistic flyby, the magnitude of the post-flyby vector $\mathbf{v}_\infty^+$ must also equal 1.17 km/s, however, in general the direction is allowed to vary. Assuming the position of the spacecraft coincides with Europa, Eqs. (1) are then integrated forward in time from E24 with $\mu = 0$ to successive apojoves $\mathbf{R}_{r_a}^-$. At capture, we note that for each multi-body family of trajectories, θ and Ω are functions of the insertion Δv. Knowing the approximate r_a, we select the family that achieves that r_a with minimum Δv. Guessing a reasonable Δv, we interpolate the values of θ and Ω from the family data and integrate backwards in time to successive apojoves $\mathbf{R}_{r_a}^+$. For the backwards integration, μ is the actual Jupiter-Europa mass ratio. The number of apojoves selected depends on both the resonance of the trajectory and which apoapsis is selected for the match point. For our study, we investigate the effects of placing the

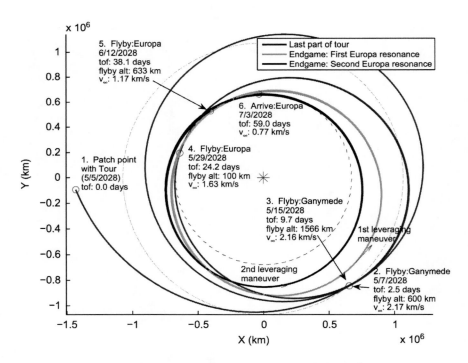

Figure 13. Courtship phase for tour T08-008.[5]

428

match point at all possible apoapses. A velocity discontinuity, or Δv_{r_a}, is allowed at the match point. This velocity discontinuity represents a maneuver at apojove. In brief, the variables of the algorithm are

$$\mathbf{Y} = \left\{ \begin{array}{c} \mathbf{v}_\infty^+ \\ \Delta v \end{array} \right\}, \tag{24}$$

where the constraints to satisfy are

$$\mathbf{F}(\mathbf{Y}) = \left\{ \begin{array}{c} \|\mathbf{v}_\infty^+\| - \|\mathbf{v}_\infty^-\| \\ \mathbf{R}_{r_a}^+ - \mathbf{R}_{r_a}^- \end{array} \right\} = \mathbf{0}. \tag{25}$$

In Eq. (25), both $\mathbf{R}_{r_a}^+$ and $\mathbf{R}_{r_a}^-$ are measured with respect to the Jupiter-Europa barycenter. Guessing a reasonable $\mathbf{Y}$, a Newton's method satisfies the constraint Eqs. (25). Once a solution is found, it is important to check the angle between $\mathbf{v}_\infty^+$ and $\mathbf{v}_\infty^-$ to ensure that the altitude of the flyby is acceptable.

The algorithm successfully attaches a trajectory from the $c95$ family to the end of the T08-008 tour. Following the E24 flyby, the trajectory is plotted in Figure 14. As in Figure 13, the time of flight is measured in days past May 5, 2028. The trajectory requires only 1.6 more days than the T08-008 tour. Kloster et al. report a maneuver between E24 and EOI of 66 m/s. The Δv_{r_a} for the trajectory shown in Figure 14 is 153 m/s. Whereas the insertion Δv for the T08-008 tour is 707 m/s, the $c95$-type trajectory only requires 436 m/s. The total savings is 118 m/s. This is a significant savings representing roughly 15% of the entire Δv allotted for the Jovian tour.

As an alternative, insertion following the E23 flyby is perhaps a better strategy. The E24 flyby puts the spacecraft in a 6:5 resonance with Europa with low apoapses that might be costly in terms of radiation dose. We can discard the 6:5 resonance and capture following the 4:3 resonance by using a $b95$-type trajectory. The post E23 trajectory is shown in Figure 15. Here $\Delta v_{r_a} = 99$ m/s and performed at the first apoapsis following E23. Europa orbit insertion is 17.6 days earlier than the T08-008 tour, and the total Δv required is only 27 m/s more than the nominal T08-008 tour.

We want to stress that the Δv_{r_a} is non-optimal with this method. These options for capture serve as initial guesses for an optimizer that further reduces the total Δv in a full ephemeris model and with fully integrated propagation. We speculate that the total cost can be lowered perhaps by 50 m/s more via optimization.

CONCLUSION

Millions of trajectories leading to a Europa orbit insertion are investigated. Prograde and retrograde orbits are considered, as well as a 200-km circular orbit inclined at 95° to the Jupiter-Europa plane. An algorithm is presented for computing the trajectories as members of a family of transfers in the R3BP, and three new types of transfer are identified. The trajectories are evaluated in terms of apojove and Δv performance. The top-performing trajectories appear to follow L_2 Lyapunov orbit invariant manifolds, leading to capture to a retrograde orbit, and in some cases saving up to 40% of the Δv from the patched 2-body problem. A method is developed for patching the trajectories into a baseline tour, and two capture trajectories are proposed as alternatives for the courtship phase of the current JEO baseline mission. While the first option saves over 100 m/s in Δv, the second option might be more useful in that insertion occurs following the 4:3 resonance and without a significant penalty in Δv.

This solution approach for identifying capture trajectories can easily be adapted for a study of escape trajectories. Due to the symmetries in the R3BP, the apojove performance for the escape trajectories is equivalent to that for capture. Furthermore, the method is not dependent on a specific inclination, nor does it require the circular orbit be at 200-km altitude. An interesting application for this approach might be the investigation of transfers to low-altitude lunar orbits that originate from the smallest possible perigee.

Future work includes exploring unstable periodic orbits as waypoints to Europa. Adapting the method proposed by Koon et al.,[6] the keys to an even better understanding of the results presented in this work may involve the study of invariant manifolds of periodic orbits nearby Europa.

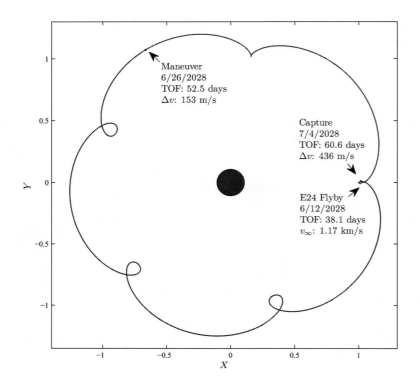

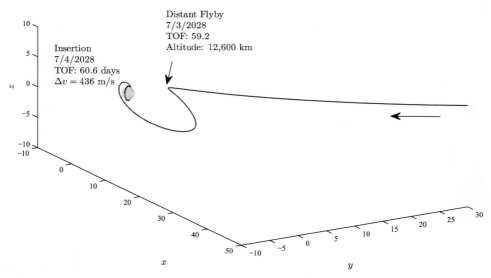

Figure 14.   Attaching a c95-type trajectory at E24 of the T08-008 tour; rotating, barycentric, Jupiter-Europa coordinates (top), and rotating, Europa-centered, coordinates in Europa radii (bottom).

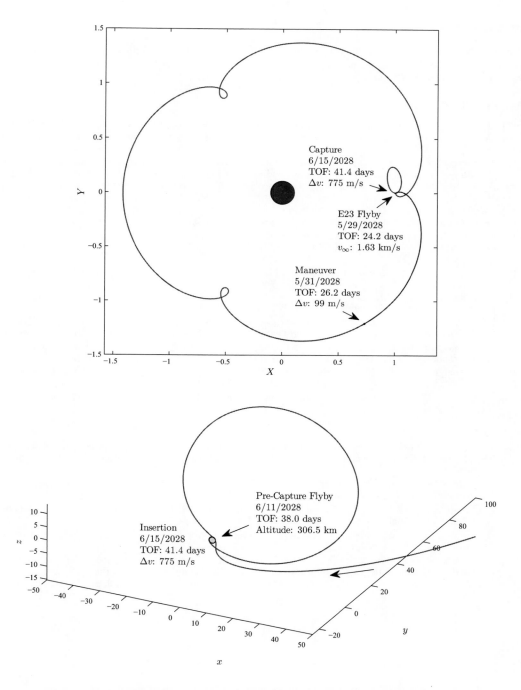

Figure 15. Attaching a $b95$-type trajectory at E23 of the T08-008 tour; rotating, barycentric, Jupiter-Europa coordinates (top), and rotating, Europa-centered, coordinates in Europa radii (bottom).

431

ACKNOWLEDGMENT

This research was carried out at the Jet Propulsion Laboratory, California Institute of Technology, under a contract with the National Aeronautics and Space Administration. The authors thank Stefano Campagnola, Jon Sims, and Chen-Wan Yen for their insights provided for this work.

REFERENCES

[1] "Europa Jupiter System Mission: A Joint Endeavor by ESA and NASA," *Europa Jupiter System Mission Joint Summary Report*, National Aeronautics Space Administration and The European Space Agency, January 16, 2009.

[2] T. Sweetser, R. Maddock, J. Johannesen, J. Bell, P. Penzo, A. Wolf, S. Williams, S. Matousek, and S. Weinstein, "Trajectory design for a Europa Orbiter mission: a plethora of astrodynamics challenges," AAS Paper No. 97-174, *AAS/AIAA Space Flight Mechanics Meeting*, Huntsville, Alabama, February 10-12, 1997.

[3] J. Johannesen and L. D'Amario, "Europa orbit mission trajectory design," AAS Paper No. 99-360, *AAS/AIAA Astrodynamics Specialists Conference*, Girdwood, Alaska, August 15-19, 1999.

[4] M. Khan, S. Campagnola, and M. Croon, "End-to-End mission analysis for a low-cost, two spacecraft mission to Europa," AAS Paper No. 04-132, *AAS/AIAA Space Flight Mechanics Meeting*, Maui, Hawaii, February 8-12, 2004.

[5] K. Kloster, A. Petropoulos, and J. Longuski, "Europa Orbiter tour design with Io gravity assists", *Acta Astronautica*, Vol. 68, No. 7-8, 2011, pp. 931-946.

[6] W. Koon, M. Lo, J. Marsden, and S. Ross, "Constructing a Low Energy Transfer Between Jovian Moons," *Contemporary Mathematics*, Vol. 292, 2002, pp. 129-146.

[7] R. Russell and T. Lam, "Designing Ephemeris Capture Trajectories at Europa Using Unstable Periodic Orbits," *Journal of Guidance, Control, and Dyanmics*, Vol. 30, No. 2, 2007, pp. 482-491.

[8] S. Campagnola and R. Russell, "Endgame Problem Part 1: V-Infinity Leveraging Technique and Leveraging Graph," *Journal of Guidance, Control, and Dyanmics*, Vol. 33, No. 2, 2010, pp. 463-475.

[9] S. Campagnola and R. Russell, "Endgame Problem Part 2: Multi-Body Technique and T-P Graph," *Journal of Guidance, Control, and Dyanmics*, Vol. 33, No. 2, 2010, pp. 476-486.

[10] P. Finlayson, "PTool Version 1.0," Technical Memorandum, Jet Propulsion Laboratory, Pasadena, CA, July 30, 1999.

[11] V. Szebehely, *Theory of Orbits: The Restricted Problem of Three Bodies*. New York: Academic Press, 1967.

[12] T. Sweetser, "Jacobi's Integral and ΔV-Earth-Gravity-Assist (ΔV-EGA) Trajectories," AAS Paper No. 93-635, *AAS/AIAA Astrodynamics Specialist Conference*, Victoria, British Columbia, Canada, August 16-19, 1993.

[13] C. Conley, "Low Energy Transit Orbits in the Restricted Three-Body Problem," *SIAM Journal of Applied Mathematics*, Vol. 16, No. 4, 1968.

[14] L. Shampine and H. Watts, *DEPACK-Design of a User Oriented Package of ODE Solvers*. SAND79-2374, Sandia National Laboratories, Albuquerque, New Mexico, 1980.

[15] R. Broucke, "Periodic Orbits in the Restricted Three-Body Problem with Earth-Moon Masses," NASA Technical Report 32-1168, Jet Propulsion Laboratory, Pasadena, CA, 1968.

[16] E. Doedel, V. Romanov, V. Paffenroth, H. Keller, D. Dichmann, J. Galán-Vioque, and A. Vanderbauwhede, "Elemental Periodic Orbits Associated with the Libration Points in the Circular Restricted 3-Body Problem," *International Journal of Bifurcation and Chaos*, Vol. 17, No. 8, pp. 2625-2677, 2007.

432

POINCARÉ MAPS AND RESONANT ORBITS IN THE CIRCULAR RESTRICTED THREE-BODY PROBLEM

Mar Vaquero[*] and Kathleen C. Howell[†]

The application of dynamical systems techniques to mission design has demonstrated that employing invariant manifolds and resonant flybys enables previously unknown trajectory options and potentially reduces the ΔV requirements. An analysis of planar resonant orbits, as well as the computation and visualization of the associated invariant manifolds is explored in this analysis. Poincaré maps are an effective tool in the search for unstable resonant orbits and potential resonant transitions. Connections between the invariant manifolds associated with two-dimensional unstable resonant orbits for different energy levels are identified in the Saturn-Titan system and resonant periodic homoclinic-type connections are also summarized. As an application of this design process, the accessibility of Hyperion from orbits resonant with Titan is explored.

INTRODUCTION

Much of this work involves the search, identification, and computation of planar resonant orbits in the circular restricted three-body problem (CR3BP). Both the determination of the orbits and their use is facilitated by Poincaré sections. Poincaré sections are successfully employed as a tool to examine the relationships between the invariant manifolds of multiple unstable resonant orbits at a fixed value of Jacobi constant. The intersection of the invariant manifolds associated with these resonant trajectories, as viewed in the Poincaré map, is then employed to search for potential resonance transitions. The resulting transfer trajectories may benefit from a reduced maneuver cost (ΔV) by shadowing the invariant manifold trajectories. Thus, the core of this investigation is the application of Poincaré maps and resonance to the CR3BP. As a result, the techniques can be applied in mission design.

Interplanetary missions, such as the Jupiter Icy Moons Orbiter (JIMO)[1] and the Jupiter Europa Orbiter (JEO),[2] are designed to exploit multiple gravity assists as well as low-thrust propulsion. The complexity of such mission scenarios, as well as the multi-body gravity environments, suggest that dynamical systems techniques might offer important advantages. This investigation is primarily motivated by the work of previous researchers[3–7] involving the analysis of the invariant manifolds emanating from resonant orbits involved in the JEO encounters. One obvious extension is the application to other systems, for example, the Saturn-Titan system. Parker and Lo also explored the use of unstable resonant orbits and their associated invariant manifolds to explore mission designs near Earth involving periodic flybys of the Moon.[8]

In this investigation, a transfer design process that blends manifold arcs associated with unstable resonant orbits is developed. The resulting trajectory is a continuous, cost-free path that transitions between interior and exterior resonances in the Saturn-Titan system at a specific energy level. As an application of this tool, the problem of accessing Hyperion from an orbit resonant with Titan is also explored. Finally, as a further application of dynamical systems theory, a homoclinic-type periodic orbit that cycles indefinitely between two resonances is presented. Lo and Parker demonstrated that unstable periodic orbits can be chained together using their invariant manifolds to produce new periodic orbits, which they termed "chains" and strongly

---

[*]Ph.D. Student, School of Aeronautics and Astronautics, Purdue University, Armstrong Hall, 701 West Stadium Avenue, West Lafayette, Indiana 47907-2045.
[†]Hsu Lo Professor of Aeronautical and Astronautical Engineering, School of Aeronautics and Astronautical, Purdue University, Armstrong Hall, 701 West Stadium Avenue, West Lafayette, Indiana 47907-2045. Fellow AAS; Associate Fellow AIAA.

resemble their generating orbits.[9] These "chains" are similar to the homoclinic cycle summarized here. In contrast, these trajectories are termed periodic 'homoclinic-type' resonant orbits, since they emerge from two resonant orbits and their associated invariant manifolds.

DYNAMICAL MODEL AND NUMERICAL METHODS

Any analysis involving resonances typically defines a resonance initially within the context of the two-body problem and conics. This investigation, however, is focused on resonance conditions involving multiple gravitational fields. Thus, the CR3BP serves as the basis for the majority of this investigation. In the restricted problem, the motion of an infinitesimal third particle, P_3, is modeled in the presence of two gravitationally-attracting bodies of significantly larger mass, P_1 and P_2. A formulation relative to a rotating observer adds great insight and further applications. The rotating frame is an additional reference frame centered at the barycenter, B, of the system such that the x-axis is always parallel to the line connecting P_1 to P_2, and directed from the larger towards the smaller primary. Let $\hat{x}$ represent a unit vector in this direction. Since P_1 and P_2 move on conic paths, their mutual plane of motion remains fixed. This fixed plane is defined as the $\hat{x}\hat{y}$-plane. The third particle P_3 can move in any of the three spatial dimensions. The z-axis of the rotating frame, i.e. $\hat{z}$, is parallel to the orbital angular momentum vector associated with the motion of the system. Then, $\hat{y}$ completes the right-handed vector basis. Let the state vector $\bar{x}$ be defined from B to P_3 and $\bar{x} = [x \ y \ z \ \dot{x} \ \dot{y} \ \dot{z}]^T$. The mass fraction μ is associated with the two system primaries P_1 and P_2,

$$\mu = \frac{m_2}{m_1 + m_2} \tag{1}$$

where m_1 and m_2 are the masses of P_1 and P_2 respectively. This mass ratio is often used to parameterize the ensuing motion. The motion of P_3 is then governed by the well-known scalar, second-order differential equations of motion,

$$\ddot{x} - 2\dot{y} - x = -\frac{(1-\mu)(x+\mu)}{d^3} - \frac{\mu}{r^3}(x - 1 + \mu) \tag{2}$$

$$\ddot{y} + 2\dot{x} - y = -\frac{(1-\mu)}{d^3}y - \frac{\mu}{r^3}y \tag{3}$$

$$\ddot{z} = -\frac{(1-\mu)}{d^3}z - \frac{\mu}{r^3}z \tag{4}$$

where d and r are evaluated as,

$$d = \sqrt{(x+\mu)^2 + y^2 + z^2}, \quad r = \sqrt{(x - 1 + \mu)^2 + y^2 + z^2} \tag{5}$$

and the dot indicates a derivative with respect to the non-dimensional time, τ, and relative to an observer in a rotating reference frame. The form of these equations of motion does admit an integral of the motion known as the Jacobian integral, or Jacobi constant, C, that is,

$$V^2 = 2U^* - C \tag{6}$$

where the speed relative to the rotating frame is denoted V. There are five equilibrium solutions in the CR3BP, denoted Lagrange points or libration points, located in the plane of motion of the primaries: the well-known collinear points L_1, L_2 and L_3 and the equilateral points L_4 and L_5. The equilibrium solutions and the Jacobi constant lead to the concepts of zero relative velocity and the zero velocity surfaces. If the relative velocity V is zero then,

$$x^2 + y^2 + \frac{2}{d}(1-\mu) + \frac{2}{r}\mu = C \tag{7}$$

The solutions to Eq. (7) define a surface in three-dimensional space, that is, the zero-velocity surface which delineates two types of regions: a region available for free movement and a region of exclusion, where motion is physically impossible. Without a maneuver that alters the velocity state and, thus, the value of Jacobi constant, the zero velocity surfaces constrain the motion throughout any time evolution.

The existence of periodic motion in the CR3BP is well-known and its computation in the nonlinear system involves the use of a multi-dimensional version of a Newton-Raphson differential corrections process implemented as a shooting method. With the availability of the appropriate mathematical model, that is, the equations of motion and the state transition matrix (STM), the nonlinear differential equations are numerically integrated to any future time. The STM is essentially a linear map associated with a trajectory arc and predicts adjustments in the initial state to shift the final state to a desired set of values at the end point. Thus, this approximation is used to adjust the initial state such that the current trajectory evolves and reaches some desired state downstream; with the appropriate constraints, a periodic orbit is generated.

An infinite number of periodic orbits exist in the CR3BP but only two types are considered in this investigation: 2D libration point orbits and resonant orbits. Lyapunov orbits are examples of planar periodic motion around the libration points. Resonant orbits, by definition, are periodic as well, but in contrast to Lyapunov orbits, these are not typically defined in terms of the Lagrange points.

RESONANT ORBITS AND MAPS

The solar system possesses a high degree of organization. Under Newton's laws of motion, subtle gravitational effects determine this dynamical structure. One result is the phenomenon of resonance. Within the context of conics, a resonance exists when there is a simple numerical relationship between periods.[10] Resonances occur under different conditions, such as mean motion, Laplace, secular, and Kozai resonance. However, the focus of this investigation is orbit-orbit resonance, when the periods involved represent the orbits of two or more bodies.

Two-Dimensional Resonant Orbits

Consider two bodies of arbitrary mass, denoted as A and B, and consider the relationship that may exist between the periods of their motion. In the two-body model, an orbit-orbit resonance is defined by the ratio $p{:}q$, where p indicates the period of motion for body B and q represents the period of motion for body A in resonance with body B. In this analysis, the primary body represents Saturn; thus, body A represents Titan and body B models a spacecraft. The spacecraft is in orbital resonance with Titan when it completes exactly p orbits about Saturn in the same time that is required for Titan to complete q orbits. In this definition of orbital resonance, p and q are positive integers, and by convention, p is associated with the spacecraft and q reflects the period of Titan. For example, a spacecraft in a 1:2 resonance with Titan completes one revolution around Saturn in the same time that Titan completes two periods. Assume that the spacecraft and Titan possess orbital periods T_p and T_q respectively, such that the ratio between periods is,

$$\frac{p}{q} = \frac{n_p}{n_q} = \frac{\frac{1}{T_p}}{\frac{1}{T_q}} = \frac{T_q}{T_p} \tag{8}$$

The mean motion n_i corresponding to body i, is a function of the mass of the planet and the semi-major axis of the orbit, i.e., $n_i = \sqrt{\frac{Gm_1}{a_i^3}}$, where Gm_1 is the gravitational parameter of the planet in this two-body model. The orbital period T_i is proportional to the inverse of the mean motion, n_i.

In the CR3BP, the $p{:}q$ resonant ratio is not precisely equal to the ratio of the orbital periods corresponding to the bodies in resonance. In a multi-body problem, with the gravity of two or more bodies incorporated in the model, the time to complete a revolution is not even constant. Instead, for a $p{:}q$ resonance in the circular restricted three-body problem, the spacecraft completes p orbits around Saturn in *approximately* the same time required for Titan to complete q revolutions; thus, the ratio of the orbital periods is not rational, but rather an approximate rational fraction. However, actual resonant orbits in the CR3BP are still closed and periodic trajectories as observed in the rotating reference frame.

The addition of a third gravity field to the two-body model adds perturbations to the trajectory, generally resulting in a orbit that is not closed or periodic. Hence, a strategy is required to compute closed, periodic, resonant orbits in the CR3BP. A simple targeting scheme is applied to the computation of periodic resonant orbits. A reasonably accurate starting estimate for the initial state is generated from the two-body model. This starting vector seeds the corrections scheme to target a perpendicular crossing of the x-axis in a nonlinear propagation. An example of a planar, periodic, resonant orbit with multiple nonperpendicular crossings in the Saturn-Titan system is plotted in Fig. 1(a). Along this 3:5 resonant trajectory, the spacecraft completes three revolutions around Saturn in the time required for Titan to complete five revolutions. To illustrate the perturbating effects of the additional gravity field, the initial guess computed from the two-body model and the corrected initial state in the three-body model for the 3:5 resonant orbit are listed in Table 1. For comparison, the periods for both trajectories are listed in the table as well. For this particular resonant orbit, adding a third attracting center results in an orbital period that is 7.1 hours shorter.

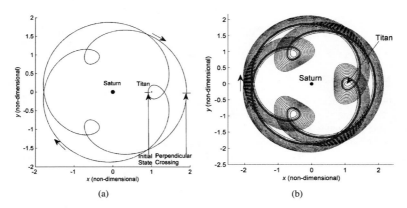

(a)   (b)

Figure 1: A Periodic 3:5 Resonant Orbit in (a) and Representative Orbits in a Family of 3:5 Resonant Trajectories in (b) - Plotted in the Rotating Frame

Table 1: Two-Body and Three-Body Initial States of the 3:5 Resonant Orbit in Fig. 1(a)

3:5 resonance	x (km)	y (km)	$\dot{x}$ (km/sec)	$\dot{y}$ (km/sec)	Period (days)
2-Body model	1.115474×10^6	0	0	1.693619	79.726015
3-Body model	1.115474×10^6	0	0	1.747992	79.420632

Resonant orbits as viewed from the perspective of the rotating frame offer valuable insight since this view illustrates the relationship between resonance and the frequency of conjunctions,[10] in this case, with Titan. A conjunction occurs when Saturn, Titan and the spacecraft are aligned. A special feature of resonant orbits, and one that occurs only in the rotating frame, is the formation of "loops". These loops are apparent in Fig. 1 and occur at pericenter and apocenter. Resonant orbits are categorized based on the p:q ratio. Exterior resonant orbits have a p:q ratio such that $p<q$, while in an interior resonance the ratio p:q is such that $p>q$.

Once a single, periodic, resonant orbit is determined, it is possible to generate multiple resonant orbits with the same characteristics, that is, a family of p:q resonant orbits, by employing a continuation scheme with the corrections process. Members of a representative family of 3:5 resonant orbits appear in Fig. 1(b). The original member in the family is highlighted in blue. Note that the same strategy is employed to generate almost any family of interior and exterior resonant orbits.

Three-Dimensional Resonant Orbits

Similar to families of Lyapunov orbits, these families of resonant orbits also include bifurcating orbits to three-dimensional, periodic resonant orbits. These bifurcating orbits are identified by examining the eigenvalues of the monodromy matrix corresponding to each orbit in the family. The presence of a bifurcating orbit is indicated by an abrupt change in stability. In addition to other scenarios, the stability properties change whenever the eigenvalues depart from or arrive at the unit circle in the complex plane.

436

Once the bifurcating orbit is identified, it is possible to target an out-of-plane orbit and, thus, 3D families by employing an algorithm based on a scheme similar to one used to compute halo orbits from a bifurcating Lyapunov orbit. Once the bifurcating orbit is isolated, it is slightly perturbed in the z-direction and the resulting state seeds the corrections scheme to target a three-dimensional resonant orbit. Representative members from the 3D family of 3:5 resonant orbits that intersect the 2D family in Fig. 1(b) are plotted in Figs. 2-3, which includes two-dimensional views of this three-dimensional family of resonant orbits. For completeness, Table 2 includes the non-zero initial conditions, value of Jacobi constant, and orbital period corresponding to the smallest three-dimensional orbit represented in this family. The zero elements in the set of initial conditions are y and $\dot{x}$, that is, $y = \dot{x} = 0$. Similar families of three-dimensional resonant orbits are straightforwardly computed for different values of the mass fraction μ.[11]

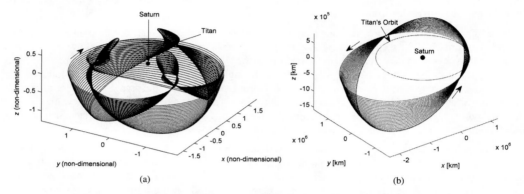

Figure 2: Representative Orbits in a 3D Family of 3:5 Resonant Orbits Plotted in the Rotating Frame in (a) and in the Inertial Frame in (b)

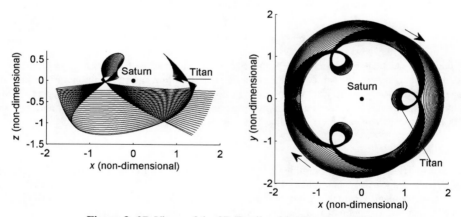

Figure 3: 2D Views of the 3D Family of 3:5 Resonant Orbits

Poincaré Maps

In general, maps are used to describe the time evolution of a vector at discrete intervals. The use of very simple maps allows the representation of the properties of generic dynamical systems that are described by the differential equations. Maps have been used extensively in the last few decades, especially to add insight and expose dynamical structure in complex systems. This technique offers three main advantages: reduction

437

p:q	x (km)	z (km)	$\dot{y}$ (km/sec)	C	P (days)
3:5	1.094489×10^{6}	1.078303×10^{5}	1.890196	2.91169	79.55

of dimension, global dynamics, and conceptual clarity. The construction of a Poincaré map eliminates at least one variable in the problem, resulting in the analysis of a lower-dimensional system. In lower-dimensional problems, numerically computed Poincaré maps deliver an insightful and, sometimes, dramatic display of the global dynamics of a system. In fact, for this application, Poincaré sections highlight the existence of periodic and quasi-periodic orbits.[3]

The computation of a Poincaré map for an autonomous higher-dimensional system in $\Re^n$ requires the use of a hyperplane or surface of section, labeled as Σ in $\Re^{n-1}$ which is located transverse to the flow. A trajectory intersecting the hyperplane is integrated until it returns to the hyperplane surface. Hence, the mapping is from one intersection to the next, and so on. A periodic orbit originates in the plane and returns to intersect the plane after exactly one period. A truly periodic orbit returns to exactly the same point on the plane after each revolution. Such a point is denoted a 'fixed point', labeled $\bar{x}^*$. Then, for any point $\bar{x} \in \Sigma$ sufficiently close to the fixed point, $\bar{x}^*$, a propagation of the differential equation through $\bar{x}$, intersects the plane again at the first return point $P(\bar{x})$, generally near the original fixed point.

For the planar CR3BP in $\Re^4$, the surface of section, or hyperplane Σ, is typically specified by fixing one of the coordinates, usually $y = 0$, producing a surface in $\Re^3$. The 3D surface is projected onto a plane by specification of another parameter. For example, to generate a two-dimensional Poincaré section in the CR3BP, a value for the Jacobi constant is specified and a grid of initial conditions for x and $\dot{x}$ are selected and integrated forward in time. The grid represents a range of initial conditions originally in the hyperplane, generating many trajectories. The intersections of each trajectory with the surface of section create the Poincaré map. With C, x and $\dot{x}$ initially defined, as well as the hyperplane $y = 0$, the corresponding initial values for $\dot{y}$ can be calculated from the expression for the Jacobi constant in Eq. (6), that is,

$$\dot{y} = \pm \sqrt{x^2 + y^2 + \frac{2(1 - \mu)}{d} + \frac{2\mu}{r} - \dot{x}^2 - C} \tag{9}$$

where d and r are calculated from Eq. (5). Alternatively, an initial range of values for $\dot{y}$ is defined and the corresponding values for $\dot{x}$ are then computed from Eq. (6). In a Poincaré map, the points defined by the mapping are then plotted. A variety of quantities can be computed and displayed at each iteration of the map. The quantities used to plot the intersections in this investigation are x and $\dot{x}$, although other authors consider quantities such as Delaunay variables, as well as other dynamical quantities.[3]

Invariant Manifolds

The role of invariant manifolds is significant in building a framework to model the dynamical structure in the CR3BP. Knowledge of any manifold structure improves the efficiency of trajectory design in this regime. The use of invariant manifolds in the design of transfers between resonant orbits in the Saturn-Titan system is the focus of this effort. The geometrical theory of dynamical systems is based on the phase portrait associated with solutions to a nonlinear set of differential equations.

Once the periodic orbits and their associated invariant manifolds are identified, the search for potential transfers to and from these orbits in the CR3BP requires the computation of the actual unstable and stable manifolds. The invariant manifolds corresponding to a periodic orbit essentially represent the flow to and from the orbit and are frequently computed by using the eigenvector corresponding to the unstable and stable eigenvalues, denoted λ_u and λ_s, respectively. The algorithm to compute manifold trajectories is defined as follows: $\bar{x}_{u+}$ ($\bar{x}_{u-}$) is defined as a point on the local unstable manifold and along the positive direction, $W_{loc}^{u^+}$ ($W_{loc}^{u^-}$). Then, integrating forward and backward from point $\bar{x}_{u+}$ ($\bar{x}_{u-}$) yields W^{u^+} W^{u^-}. Calculating a half manifold involves locating a point on $W_{loc}^{u^+}$ ($W_{loc}^{u^-}$), and integrating from this point. To locate a point locally near $\bar{x}^*$, $W_{loc}^{u^+}$ ($W_{loc}^{u^-}$) is approximated to first order by the unstable eigenvector $\bar{v}_u$, where $\bar{v}_u$ is normalized with respect to the position components of the eigenvector. Then, an initial state on the unstable manifold is approximated by selecting a point close to $\bar{x}^*$ that lies on $\bar{v}_u$, that is,

$$\bar{x}_{u\pm} = \bar{x}^* \pm d\,\bar{v}_u \tag{10}$$

In Eq. (10), d is the offset in the direction of the unstable eigenvector, and its value is of critical importance. If d is too large, the computed value for $\bar{x}_{u\pm}$ is not a good approximation; if d is too small, the trajectory spends too long near the fixed point and the integration error accumulates with little progress along the path. In this investigation, an offset value of 30 km is used in the computation of the stable and unstable manifolds associated with periodic orbits in the Saturn-Titan system. Similarly, the positive and negative branches of the local stable manifold are computed via propagation from $\bar{x}_{s\pm}$. To better identify the manifold structure, it is desirable to compute the trajectories from multiple fixed points along the orbit. Note that the eigenvalues and eigenvectors are independent of the number of fixed points selected, and whether these points are evenly spaced in time or position.

RESONANCE TRANSITION

Given the necessary background in periodic orbits and dynamical systems theory, the relationship between unstable resonant orbits and their invariant manifolds is explored. Unstable resonant orbits in the Saturn-Titan systems serve as the focus in the following examples and Poincaré maps are constructed to display the associated stable and unstable manifolds. A transfer design tool is developed once potential resonance transitions are identified from the maps that employs a corrections scheme to blend the periodic orbits and the manifolds arcs into a continuous path.

Computation and Visualization of Invariant Manifolds Associated with Resonant Orbits

The trajectories along the invariant manifolds corresponding to the unstable resonant orbits possess their own distinctive behavior. However, the arcs are tangled, so plotting these paths in the xy-plane does not offer any insight. In contrast to libration point orbits, the trajectories along the resonant orbit manifolds frequently pass close to different resonances, but also remain in the vicinity of the original resonant orbit in configuration space.[3] A Poincaré section that reflects the behavior in the vicinity of these resonant periodic orbits as well as the manifolds also emerges. Maps that identify, and potentially isolate, these manifold trajectories aid in visualization and supply valuable insight concerning the relationships between these manifolds and other structures in the phase space.

Recall that the original motivation for this investigation is an extension of the work of previous researchers who considered the application of invariant manifolds to the Europa Orbiter mission.[3,5–7] The original Europa Orbiter trajectory was designed without the use of manifolds[2,12] but Anderson and Lo examine various techniques in considering low-thrust trajectory design for missions to the Jovian moon, as well as the Europa Orbiter (EO) spacecraft. In their investigations, Lo and Anderson first use Poincaré sections to search for unstable resonant orbits in support of the Europa Orbiter mission concept.[5–7] The invariant manifolds from these unstable resonant orbits reflect the transitions of the actual EO trajectory between resonances. The actual trajectory clearly exploits invariant manifolds associated with quasi-periodic orbits.[6] Extending the work of Lo and Anderson, this investigation focuses on the use of these tools to search for potential resonance transitions in the Saturn-Titan system.

Consider the exterior 3:4 orbit that is resonant with Titan as illustrated in Fig. 4. The non-zero initial state, Jacobi constant value, and unstable eigenvalue associated with this resonant orbit are listed in Table 3. The invariant manifolds associated with this 3:4 resonant trajectory are computed using an offset value of 30 km and a total of 100 fixed points evenly spaced in time along the orbit. The trajectories along the stable manifold are propagated backwards in time for 50 non-dimensional time units, equivalent to 126.8 days. Similarly, the trajectories along the unstable manifold are integrated forward in time for the same period of time. For a wider view of the invariant manifolds and their relationship to other dynamical structures, it is necessary to plot them against a background that includes these structures. The set of initial conditions used to generate this surface of section is selected to be in the vicinity of the resonant orbit. A planar problem, the bounds are defined with $y = 0$ and $z_0 = \dot{z}_0 = 0$; the corresponding value of $\dot{y}_0$ is calculated from the value of Jacobi constant. In propagating the initial conditions, long integration times are necessary to produce sufficient crossings to yield a dense and well-defined map. For this particular example, an integration time of approximately 7 years is employed to generate the background map in Fig. 5. The regions along the x-axis that are used as initial conditions for the maps are noted in Fig. 4. The invariant manifolds associated with the 3:4 resonant trajectory appear in the figure plotted against the background map in Fig. 5; the stable and unstable manifolds are plotted in blue and magenta, respectively.

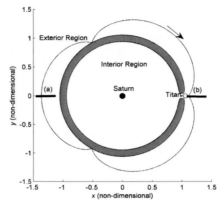

Figure 4: A Periodic 3:4 Resonant Orbit in the Saturn-Titan Three-Body System. Lines Indicate Initial Condition Regions for the Maps in Fig. 5

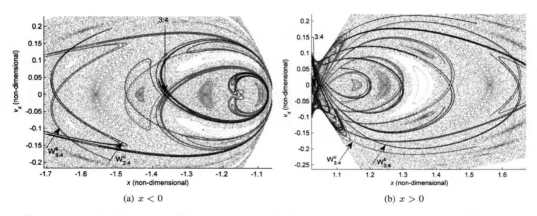

(a) $x < 0$ (b) $x > 0$

Figure 5: Poincaré Section Illustrating the Invariant Manifolds Associated with the 3:4 Resonant Orbit. Stable Manifolds Plotted in Blue and Unstable Manifolds Plotted in Magenta

Potential resonant transitions can be identified and exploited from the Poincaré map that includes the invariant manifolds. From the map, it is apparent that these manifolds 'travel' extensively to different regions of the map. Different areas of the map are potentially associated with other unstable resonant orbits, therefore, promoting possible resonance transitions. Thus, it is necessary, at the given energy level, to further examine the relationship between the 3:4 resonance and other structures. Hence, some of the crossings of the invariant manifolds associated with the 3:4 resonant orbit are investigated using a method to estimate the period of the potential resonant orbit from its intersection in the Poincaré map using two-body approximations. The estimated period and state from the map are then used as the initial guess in the corrections algorithm to compute the corresponding unstable resonant orbit in the CR3BP. As a result, a variety of exterior and interior resonant orbits are determined. Once the unstable resonant orbits are identified on the surface of section, it is necessary to compute their invariant manifolds to confirm that a transition is possible between these trajectories and the 3:4 resonant orbit. These resonant orbits expose manifold structures similar to those of the 3:4 resonant orbit. The integration times that are required to compute the invariant manifolds varies from orbit to orbit. Of course, the manifolds for orbits that are more unstable depart or approach the orbit faster than the manifolds associated with orbits possessing a smaller stability index.

For illustration purposes, consider an interior orbit resonant with Titan as well as the L_1 and L_2 Lyapunov orbits at $C = 3.01$. These three orbits are plotted in Figs. 6(a)-6(b). The orbital periods, unstable eigenvalues and initial states for these orbits are listed in Table 3. The resonant orbit in Fig. 6(a) is computed from an initial guess obtained from the Poincaré map associated with the 3:4 unstable resonant orbit. This periodic orbit together with the L_1 and L_2 Lyapunov orbits possess manifold structures that are very similar to those of the 3:4 resonant orbit, and thus, it is expected that there exists a special relationship between them. Potential resonant transitions are identified from the maps and some of the stable and unstable manifold arcs associated with each of these orbits are used to construct the transitions between them.

Table 3: Initial State, Periods and Unstable Eigenvalues for Selected Periodic Orbits

Periodic Orbits	x (km)	$\dot{y}$ (km/sec)	Period (days)	λ_u
3:4 resonant orbit	1.258688×10^6	0.477301	66.331165	2,129.812
6:5 resonant orbit	1.142136×10^6	0.545759	71.263798	191.641
L_1 Lyapunov orbit	1.158974×10^6	0.447315	8.282961	1,004.722
L_2 Lyapunov orbit	1.252306×10^6	0.549329	79.726015	892.850

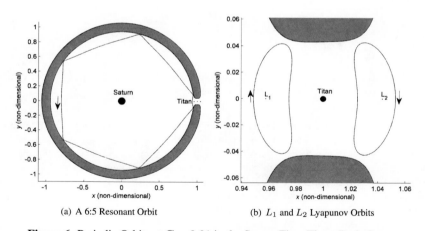

(a) A 6:5 Resonant Orbit   (b) L_1 and L_2 Lyapunov Orbits

Figure 6: Periodic Orbits at $C = 3.01$ in the Saturn-Titan Three-Body System

Transfer Design Process

A transfer process is designed to yield a continuous trajectory that transitions between periodic orbits of interest. It employs the stable and unstable manifold arcs associated with these periodic orbits. Once the connecting arcs are identified from the Poincaré map, they are patched together with the periodic orbits and the complete path is then decomposed into smaller subarcs. A multiple shooting algorithm reconverges these subarcs into a full trajectory, enforcing continuity in position and velocity at each subarc interface. The resulting trajectory is maneuver-free and serves as a connection between resonant orbits. Note, however, that as long as there exists a relationship between the invariant manifolds associated with different periodic orbits, virtually any connection can be accommodated using this technique. A selection of trajectory design scenarios illustrate the usefulness of this process:

Scenario 1: 3:4 Resonance $\rightarrow L_2$ Lyapunov Orbit $\rightarrow L_1$ Lyapunov Orbit $\rightarrow$ Titan impact.

The spacecraft in this first design scenario is originally moving about Saturn in a 3:4 periodic orbit resonant with Titan. After completing one full cycle in this orbit, a transition occurs and the path merges into an unstable manifold arc that departs the 3:4 resonant orbit and approaches the L_2 Lyapunov orbit at $C = 3.01$. This manifold arc is defined with a duration of 39.7 days. Arriving at the L_2 libration point orbit, one revolution is complete and the path merges into a stable manifold arc associated with the L_1 Lyapunov orbit, thus, approaching the L_1 libration point orbit in 12.4 days. After a full revolution in the L_1 libration point orbit, the path transitions onto an unstable manifold arc associated with this L_1 Lyapunov orbit for 2.47 days that eventually results in a Titan impact. After corrections, the resulting trajectory, as plotted in Figs. 7(a) and 7(b), is continuous in position and velocity, with the desired Jacobi constant value of $C = 3.01$.

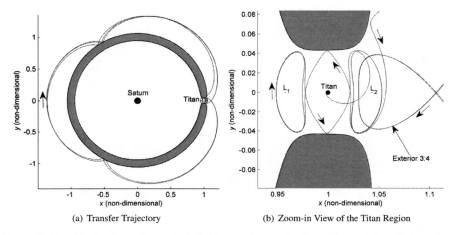

(a) Transfer Trajectory

(b) Zoom-in View of the Titan Region

Figure 7: Transfer Design - Scenario 1: 3:4 Resonance $\rightarrow L_2$ Lyapunov Orbit $\rightarrow L_1$ Lyapunov Orbit $\rightarrow$ Titan impact

Scenario 2: 3:4 Exterior Resonance $\rightarrow$ 6:5 Interior Resonance $\rightarrow L_1$ Lyapunov Orbit $\rightarrow$ Titan impact.

The spacecraft in this second design scenario departs from the original 3:4 resonant orbit on a manifold arc that approaches an interior 6:5 resonant orbit. The time of flight along this unstable manifold arc is approximately 72.5 days. The spacecraft then wanders in the interior region under the influence of Saturn for one revolution and merges into a stable manifold arc associated with the L_1 Lyapunov orbit, approaching the libration point orbit after 43.8 days. After one revolution in the L_1 libration point orbit, departure from the periodic orbit occurs along an unstable manifold arc that again results in an impact with Titan. The final, continuous trajectory appears in Figs. 8(a) and 8(b).

Scenario 3: 3:4 Exterior Resonance $\rightarrow$ 6:5 Interior Resonance $\rightarrow L_1$ Lyapunov Orbit $\rightarrow$ Titan Capture.

This third design scenario is similar to the second scenario but, in contrast to a final unstable manifold arc associated with the L_1 Lyapunov orbit that results in an impact on Titan, the spacecraft follows a different manifold arc that subsequently surrounds Titan and remains in the moon vicinity. At a specified point along this manifold arc, a maneuver is implemented to decrease the energy level and close the zero velocity curve. Thus, a capture orbit around Titan results. The maneuver occurs in a specific location so that the resulting capture trajectory maintains a minimum distance from Titan's surface. The magnitude of this $\Delta \bar{V}$ is 123.6718 m/s and the maneuver is entirely in the $\dot{y}$-direction. The resulting transfer trajectory appears in Fig. 9(a) and

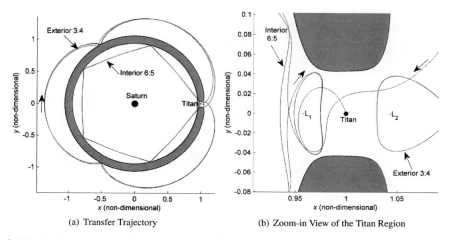

(a) Transfer Trajectory

(b) Zoom-in View of the Titan Region

Figure 8: Transfer Design - Scenario 2: 3:4 Exterior Resonance $\rightarrow$ 6:5 Interior Resonance $\rightarrow$ L_1 Lyapunov Orbit $\rightarrow$ Titan impact

the maneuver location is indicated with a black dot. The trajectory in Fig. 9(b) is a plot of the capture trajectory integrated for 500 nondimensional units, which is equivalent to 3.476 years. The energy level post-maneuver is $C = 3.015861511039047$ and, thus, in this dynamical model, the spacecraft remains in orbit around Titan unless another force is introduced (e.g., a second maneuver) to again shift the energy level. Note that this maneuver is not optimal; it is simply applied for illustration.

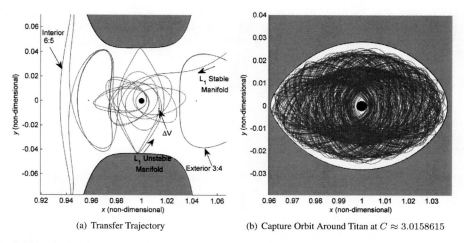

(a) Transfer Trajectory

(b) Capture Orbit Around Titan at $C \approx 3.0158615$

Figure 9: Transfer Design - Scenario 3: 3:4 Exterior Resonance $\rightarrow$ 6:5 Interior Resonance $\rightarrow$ L_1 Lyapunov Orbit $\rightarrow$ Titan Capture

Scenario 4: 3:4 Exterior Resonance $\rightarrow$ Interior Region.
In this last design scenario, the spacecraft departs from the 3:4 resonant orbit along an unstable manifold arc that enters the interior region, that is, the region in the vicinity of Saturn. If propagated for a long period of time, this manifold trajectory eventually exits the interior region, passing a second time through the L_1 and L_2 gateways into the exterior region. However, in this scenario it is desired to depart the 3:4 resonant

443

orbit and enter a capture orbit around Saturn, maintaining a sufficient altitude to avoid collision with Saturn's rings. Thus, after traveling on the unstable manifold arc associated with the 3:4 resonant orbit for 91 days, a maneuver of 20.26 m/s occurs in the interior region such that the spacecraft is inserted into a Saturn capture orbit. The resulting trajectory is plotted in Fig. 10(a); the capture trajectory is numerically integrated for 3.476 years in the CR3B model and appears in Fig. 10(b).

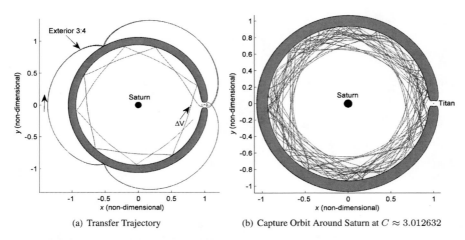

(a) Transfer Trajectory (b) Capture Orbit Around Saturn at $C \approx 3.012632$

Figure 10: Transfer Design - Scenario 4: 3:4 Exterior Resonance $\rightarrow$ Interior Region

The relationship between unstable resonant orbits and their invariant manifolds is explored with the aid of Poincaré maps, which are effective in locating and computing unstable resonant orbits and displaying their manifold structures. The associated surface of section demonstrates that, for the specified energy level, a relationship exists between the invariant manifolds of multiple periodic orbits. Thus, it is possible to construct continuous trajectories that transition between resonances or specific regions of interest. Four selected scenarios are illustrated in this section, but others are also available for different energy levels.

PERIODIC HOMOCLINIC-TYPE RESONANT ORBITS

Poincaré maps are also a powerful tool in the search and identification of other type of trajectories. An intersection in the Poincaré map is an intersection in phase space. That is, an intersection of the stable and unstable manifolds on the Poincaré section – generated for a particular value of Jacobi constant – is a point that approaches the resonant orbit when integrated into the future as well as into the past.[3] Such a trajectory is frequently termed a 'homoclinic' connection. Consider the invariant manifolds associated with the 3:4 unstable resonant orbit in Figs. 5(a)-5(b). A homoclinic connection associated with the 6:5 resonant orbit is determined from the intersection of the stable and unstable manifolds corresponding to the 3:4 resonance near the fixed point on the Poincaré map corresponding to the 6:5 resonant orbit, as illustrated in Fig. 11, particularly at the Jacobi constant value in Fig. 11(a). A particular subset of the manifolds from the 3:4 resonance travel to the interior region, shadowing the 6:5 resonant orbit. Hence, the path that results from propagating this intersection point on the map forward and backward in time is associated with both resonant orbits, that is, the interior 6:5 and the exterior 3:4. To illustrate this relationship, the initial state corresponding to this homoclinic connection is obtained from the Poincaré map in Fig. 11(a) and is integrated forward and backward in time until the path reaches both resonant orbits and appears plotted in Fig. 12(a). The integrated trajectory with the initial state near the return of the 6:5 resonant orbit on the map shadows the invariant manifolds of the 3:4 resonant orbit, and thus, asymptotically arrives and departs the 3:4 resonant orbit after a half period. That is, for $0 \leq \tau \leq \frac{1}{4}P$, the homoclinic trajectory follows the 6:5 resonant trajectory, and for $\frac{1}{4}P \leq \tau \leq \frac{1}{2}P$, it switches to shadow the 3:4 resonant orbit. For $\frac{1}{2}P \leq \tau \leq \frac{3}{4}P$, it continues on the exterior 3:4 resonant path, and finally, for $\frac{3}{4}P \leq \tau \leq P$, the path returns to follow the interior 6:5 resonant trajectory, closing the cycle at the same point where it started.

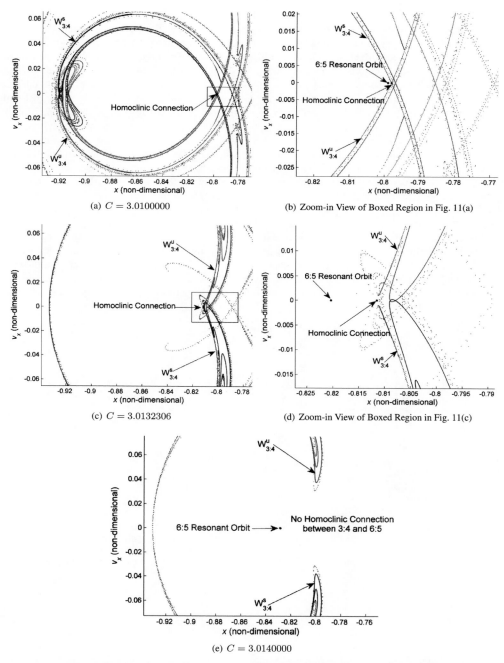

(a) $C = 3.0100000$

(b) Zoom-in View of Boxed Region in Fig. 11(a)

(c) $C = 3.0132306$

(d) Zoom-in View of Boxed Region in Fig. 11(c)

(e) $C = 3.0140000$

Figure 11: Poincaré Maps Displaying the Invariant Manifolds Associated with a 3:4 Resonance at Different Energy Levels

445

It is possible to numerically correct these type of homoclinic trajectories to obtain a periodic orbit that shadows the invariant manifolds associated with the two resonant orbits, thus, creating a cycle between two resonances. The periodicity of the orbit in Fig. 12(a) is represented by the perpendicular crossings. Consistent with previous resonant orbits, it is possible to generate a family of periodic homoclinic-type resonant orbits, although the size of these families is dependent on the relationship between their associated invariant manifolds. Note that each member represented in this family possesses a different value of Jacobi constant. The family of periodic homoclinic-type resonant orbits plotted in Figs. 13(a)-13(b) is generated using the invariant manifolds from the Poincaré maps associated with each particular energy level. The appropriate manifold arcs are selected from the intersection on the map near the 6:5 resonant orbit and are subsequently corrected in a numerical scheme to obtain a periodic trajectory that cycles between the two resonances. The intersection on the map occurs at a different location in position for each value of Jacobi constant, that is, as the energy changes, the manifolds "shift" in space and so does the location of the intersection representing the homoclinic trajectory. Thus, the existence of the family of periodic homoclinic orbits is limited to the existence of a connection between manifolds. For a given energy level, if the stable and unstable manifolds of the 3:4 resonant orbit do not intersect in the vicinity of the 6:5 resonance, it is not possible to generate a homoclinic-type periodic orbit at this energy level. This phenomenon is illustrated in Figs 11(c)-11(e). It is possible to observe that for a value of Jacobi constant equal to $C = 3.0132306$, the intersection between the stable and unstable manifolds associated with the 3:4 resonant orbit is still available, whereas for a value of $C = 3.014$ the manifolds do not cross in the vicinity of the 6:5 resonant orbit. The gap between the stable and the unstable manifolds in Fig. 11(e) indicates that there is no intersection between that particular set of manifolds at $C < 3.0140$. Thus, it is suspected that this family of periodic homoclinic-type resonant orbits ends for a value of Jacobi constant $C < 3.0140$.

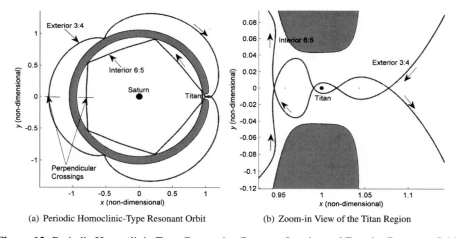

(a) Periodic Homoclinic-Type Resonant Orbit   (b) Zoom-in View of the Titan Region

Figure 12: Periodic Homoclinic-Type Connection Between Interior and Exterior Resonant Orbits

APPLICATION TO HYPERION

Hyperion is characterized by its irregular shape, its chaotic rotation, its fairly eccentric orbit, and, perhaps most notable here, for its proximity to Titan.[13] Hyperion is known to be in a 3:4 resonance with Titan, that is, Hyperion completes three revolutions around Saturn in the time Titan completes four. The transfer design process from this preliminary investigation is employed to access Hyperion's orbit from an orbit around Saturn.

To investigate the accessibility of Hyperion, it is first necessary to approximate its orbit as a 3:4 resonant orbit in the restricted three-body model. The development of a model for Hyperion within the context of the CR3BP requires information on the moon, period, location, orientation, and Jacobi constant. The ephemeris

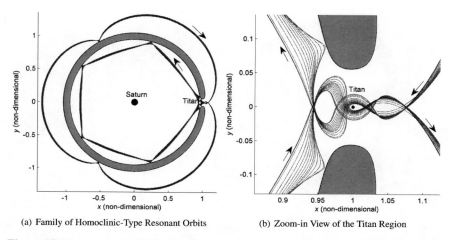

(a) Family of Homoclinic-Type Resonant Orbits

(b) Zoom-in View of the Titan Region

Figure 13: Representative Orbits in a Family of Periodic Homoclinic-Type Resonant Orbits

data for Hyperion's trajectory is obtained over the course of 20 years, from 01/01/2000 to 01/01/2020, using the Horizons database.[14] Hyperion's orbit is plotted in Fig. 14(c). Note that the approximate value of Jacobi constant for the ephemeris data ranges from $C = 3.025$ to $C = 2.995$, as illustrated in Fig. 14(b). For illustration purposes, a value of $C = 3.009368211888420$, denoted C_{Hyp}, is selected for this investigation, which corresponds to Hyperion's orbit approximately in August 2019. This value of Jacobi constant is highlighted by a red line in Fig. 14(b). The ephemeris data is viewed in a rotating frame and plotted in Fig. 14(a). The shape of the 3:4 resonance is apparent from the observational data. Then, a subset of this ephemeris data is used in a numerical corrections scheme that reconverges the ephemeris trajectory in the CR3B model. The converged 3:4 resonant orbit appears in Fig. 14(c). The results from this section vary as different 3:4 resonances are considered.

Hyperion's 3:4 resonant orbit as modeled in the CR3BP is a stable orbit, i.e., the eigenvalues associated with the monodromy matrix are complex. Even though this result is not surprising, there is no natural flow to and from the orbit that can be exploited to construct continuous transfer paths that asymptotically approach the orbit. Hence, a maneuver is required to access or depart the 3:4 stable resonance. However, the use of invariant manifolds to access the vicinity of this orbit may offer viable trajectory concepts. Transfers to this orbit from different departure orbits are explored and the associated costs of insertion to this orbit are demonstrated.

Consider the L_1 and L_2 libration point orbits at $C = C_{Hyp}$. The invariant manifolds associated with the L_1 Lyapunov orbit are displayed on a surface of section plotted against a background that highlights other dynamical structures at this particular energy level in Figs. 15-16. The maps in Fig. 15 correspond to the regions highlighted in Fig. 14(c) on the negative x-axis, that is, the regions on the x-axis labeled (1) and (2). The maps in Fig. 16 correspond to the regions (3) and (4) on the positive x-axis. Recall that the surfaces of sections are located at $y = 0$ and the maps represent the intersections of the manifolds and other dynamical structures plotted in x and $\dot{x}$. These maps are used to identify other stable and unstable resonant orbits that could serve as potential departure orbits to reach the 3:4 orbit of Hyperion. For illustration purposes, other stable resonant orbits are identified at this energy level and labeled on the maps. Each of these stable orbits is located at the center of a region of quasi-periodic behavior.

The stable interior and exterior resonant orbits that are labeled in Figs. 15-16 are plotted in Fig. 17. Each of these periodic orbits is associated with two fixed points on the maps. To identify the location of these orbits, the fixed points on the maps are associated with the colored dots on the orbits. For example, the location of the 4:5 exterior resonance on the map is represented by two red dots in Fig. 15(a) and Fig. 16(b) to indicate

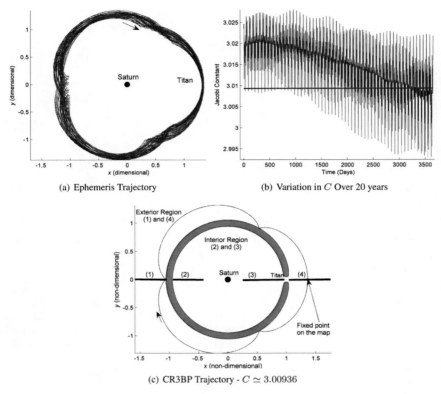

(a) Ephemeris Trajectory

(b) Variation in C Over 20 years

(c) CR3BP Trajectory - $C \simeq 3.00936$

Figure 14: Hyperion's Orbit in the Ephemeris and CR3B Models

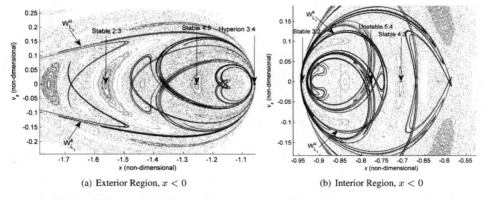

(a) Exterior Region, $x < 0$

(b) Interior Region, $x < 0$

Figure 15: Poincaré Section Illustrating the Invariant Manifolds Associated with the L_1 Lyapunov Orbit at $C = C_{Hyp}$; Maps that Correspond to Crossings (1) and (2) in Fig. 14(c)

the location where the Poincaré section pierces the orbit.

The chaotic regions on the maps are also explored to search for the presence of unstable resonant orbits at this energy level that may be used in the design of transfer trajectories to Hyperion. As illustrative examples,

448

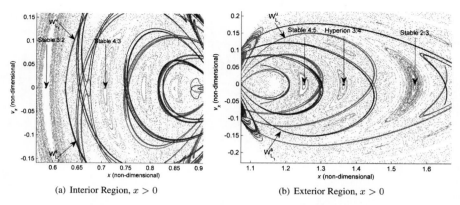

(a) Interior Region, $x > 0$ (b) Exterior Region, $x > 0$

Figure 16: Poincaré Section Illustrating the Invariant Manifolds Associated with the L_1 Lyapunov Orbit at $C = C_{Hyp}$; Maps that Correspond to Crossings (3) and (4) in Fig. 14(c)

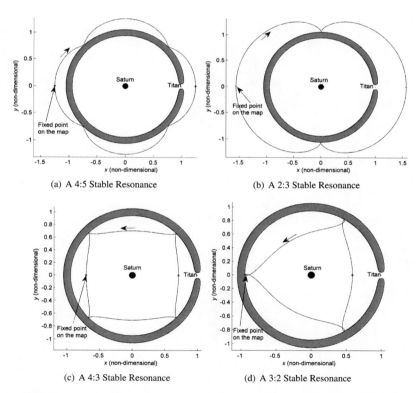

(a) A 4:5 Stable Resonance (b) A 2:3 Stable Resonance

(c) A 4:3 Stable Resonance (d) A 3:2 Stable Resonance

Figure 17: Stable Interior and Exterior Resonant Orbits at $C = C_{Hyp}$; Fixed Points Plotted in Figs. 15-16

consider two unstable periodic orbits in resonance with Titan: a 3:5 exterior resonance and a 5:4 interior resonance. The fixed point on the map corresponding to the unstable 5:4 resonance is labeled in Fig. 15(b). Two transfers from these orbits to Hyperion's 3:4 resonant orbit are produced for illustration. The design approach to construct these transfer trajectories is similar to that used in the previous section. The manifold arcs from

449

the unstable resonant orbits are employed to depart the orbits and approach the vicinity of Hyperion's orbit, where a maneuver is introduced to insert onto the stable orbit. Note that the transfer arc along the trajectory that is used to depart the initial orbit is continuous along an unstable manifolds and requires no maneuvers.

Transfer Trajectory A: The continuous transfer illustrated in Fig. 18 departs from an initial interior 5:4 resonant orbit along an unstable manifold arc that merges with a stable manifold arc associated with the L_2 Lyapunov orbit, approaching the orbit after 41.5 days. After one revolution in the L_2 Lyapunov, the path departs the Titan region on an unstable manifold arc that eventually approaches the vicinity of Hyperion's orbit, actually near L_3. The time of flight along this manifold arc is 105.5 days. At the point indicated in Fig. 18(c), a maneuver of 61.9 m/s yields insertion into Hyperion's orbit.

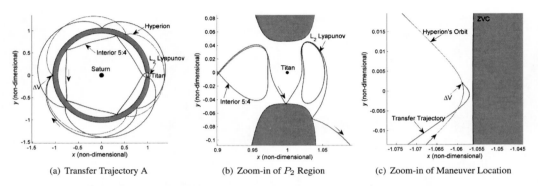

(a) Transfer Trajectory A (b) Zoom-in of P_2 Region (c) Zoom-in of Maneuver Location

Figure 18: Transfer Trajectory to Hyperion from Interior 5:4 Resonant Trajectory

Transfer Trajectory B: The transfer trajectory that appears in Fig. 19 is designed to depart along an unstable manifold from an initial exterior 3:5 resonant orbit. The unstable manifold approaches the vicinity of Hyperion's orbit after 121.9 days, again in the vicinity of L_3, even though the L_3 point is unavailable due to the ZVC's. Note that this transfer trajectory does not enter the P_1 or P_2 region and does not exploit any of the libration point orbits considered in previous transfer design. At the point indicated in Fig. 19(b), a maneuver of 121.9 m/s is added to insert into Hyperion's orbit. The full, continuous transfer trajectory is illustrated in Fig. 19(a).

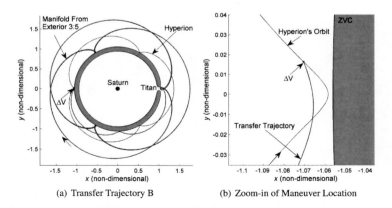

(a) Transfer Trajectory B (b) Zoom-in of Maneuver Location

Figure 19: Transfer Trajectory to Hyperion from Exterior 3:5 Resonant Trajectory

450

CONCLUSION

Planar families of unstable resonant orbits in the Saturn-Titan system are computed and families of three-dimensional resonant orbits are also observed to bifurcate from most of these planar families of resonant orbits. As an illustrative example, a family of 3:5 resonant orbits is demonstrated to exist both in plane and out-of-plane.

Poincaré sections are particularly effective in locating and computing unstable resonant orbits and displaying their manifold structures. Results from the analysis for the design of planar trajectories that transition between interior and exterior resonant orbits as well as between libration point orbits are successfully produced in the Saturn-Titan system. The associated surfaces of section demonstrate that, for the specified energy level, a relationship exists between the invariant manifolds of multiple periodic unstable orbits. In addition, a homoclinic cycle is constructed for the 3:4 and 6:5 resonant orbits.

This transfer design process is also applied to the problem of accessing Hyperion from both an interior and exterior orbits that are resonant with Titan. Two sample transfer trajectories are computed and the associated cost of insertion into Hyperion's orbit is detailed. These trajectories both exploit invariant manifolds as transfer arcs.

ACKNOWLEDGMENT

The authors wish to thank the School of Aeronautics and Astronautics at Purdue University for supporting this work. The authors appreciate access to the computational facilities in the Barbara and Rune Eliasen Visualization Laboratory as well as the assistance of Cody Short in the visualization of some of the results presented in this paper.

REFERENCES

[1] Jet Propulsion Laboratory, "Jupiter Icy Moons Orbiter (JIMO)," http://www.jpl.nasa.gov/jimo.

[2] Jet Propulsion Laboratory, "Jupiter Europa Orbiter (JEO)," http://opfm.jpl.nasa.gov.

[3] R. L. Anderson, "Low Thrust Trajectory Design for Resonant Flybys and Captures Using Invariant Manifolds," Ph.D. Dissertation, School of Aeronautics and Astronautics, University of Colorado, Boulder, Colorado, 2005.

[4] J. R. Johannesen and L. A. D'Amario, "Europa Orbiter Mission Trajectory Design," *AAS/AIAA Astrodynamics Specialist Conference*, Girdwood, Alaska, August 16-19 1999. Paper AAS 99-360.

[5] M. W. Lo, R. L. Anderson, G. Whiffen, and L. Romans, "The Role of Invariant Manifolds in Low Thrust Trajectory Design (Part I)," *AAS/AIAA Spaceflight Dynamics Conference*, Maui, Hawaii, February 2004. Paper AAS 04-288.

[6] R. L. Anderson and M. W. Lo, "The Role of Invariant Manifolds in Low Thrust Trajectory Design (Part II)," *AAS/AIAA Spaceflight Dynamics Conference*, Providence, Rhode Island, August 2004. Paper AIAA 2004-5305.

[7] M. W. Lo, R. L. Anderson, T. Lam, and G. Whiffen, "The Role of Invariant Manifolds in Low Thrust Trajectory Design (Part III)," *AAS/AIAA Spaceflight Dynamics Conference*, Tampa, Florida, January 2006. Paper AAS 06-190.

[8] J. S. Parker and M. W. Lo, "Unstable Resonant Orbits near Earth and Their Applications in Planetary Missions," *AIAA/AAS Astrodynamics Specialist Conference*, Providence, Rhode Island, August 2004. AIAA 2004-22819,.

[9] M. W. Lo and J. S. Parker, "Chaining Simple Periodic Three-BodyOrbits," *AIAA/AAS Astrodynamics Specialist Conference*, Lake Tahoe, California, August 7-11 2005. Paper AAS-05-380.

[10] C. D. Murray and S. F. Dermott, *Solar System Dynamics*. Cambridge, United Kingdom: Cambridge University Press, Cambridge, 1999.

[11] M. Vaquero, "Poincaré Sections and Resonant Orbits in the Restricted Three-Body Problem," M.S. Thesis, School of Aeronautics and Astronautics, Purdue University, West Lafayette, Indiana, 2010.

[12] A. F. Heaton, N. J. Strange, J. M. Longuski, and E. P. Bonfiglio, "Automated Design of the Europa Orbiter Tour," *Journal of Spacecraft and Rockets*, Vol. 39, No. 1, January-February 2002.

[13] Jet Propulsion Laboratory, "Cassini Solstice Mission," http://saturn.jpl.nasa.gov/science/moons/hyperion/.

[14] Jet Propulsion Laboratory, "JPL Solar System Dynamics," http://ssd.jpl.nasa.gov/, 1994.

SPECIAL TOPIC:
AUTONOMOUS AEROBRAKING

SESSION 4

Chair: Angela Bowes
                                   NASA Langley Research Center

The following paper was not available for publication:

AAS 11-472
  (Paper Withdrawn)

AUTONOMOUS AEROBRAKING ALGORITHM TESTING IN A FLIGHT SOFTWARE SIMULATION ENVIRONMENT

Daniel J. O'Shaughnessy,[*] David J. Carrelli,[†] James T. Kaidy,[†] Thomas E. Strikwerda[*] and Hollis Ambrose[†]

Aerobraking has been successfully used to lower the propulsive ΔV required to achieve a desired science orbit for a number of missions, but it requires significant resources for tracking, navigation, modeling and maneuver planning. NASA is now exploring the transition of the technology to a spacecraft environment to enable autonomous aerobraking. This paper describes the modifications to flight and testbed software from a prior interplanetary mission that were made to incorporate aerobraking and navigation algorithms. The flight architecture and algorithms are presented along with preliminary simulation results for several typical orbits around Mars.

INTRODUCTION

Aerobraking has been used effectively by NASA to deliver a spacecraft to its final orbit around a target body with an atmosphere. This is a mission enabling technology to bodies such as Mars, Venus and the Saturn's moon, Titan, as it serves to reduce the propellant required to achieve a desired science orbit. While aerobraking reduces the propulsive ΔV requirements (or conversely increases the dry mass allocated to payload), it does so at the expense of time (typically 3-6 months), continuous Deep Space Network (DSN) coverage, and a large staff to design maneuvers to control the aerobraking process and achieve the desired final orbit. To facilitate a lower-risk transition from the current technique to a lower cost, autonomous capability, the NASA Engineering and Safety Center (NESC) has assembled a team of experts in aerobraking, navigation, and guidance and control to develop a high-fidelity simulation to demonstrate the feasibility of autonomous aerobraking.[1] This will assist NASA in evaluating the potential for the reductions in DSN coverage and staff resources required to fly future aerobraking missions.

As a member of the NESC-led team, the Johns Hopkins University Applied Physics Laboratory (JHU/APL) is developing an Autonomous Aerobraking High-Fidelity Simulation (AAHFS) to assess the performance of the new algorithms required for such a mission.[2] The simulation is based on the flight software and truth models previously developed for the JHU/APL-designed MErcury Surface, Space ENvironment, GEochemistry, and Ranging (MESSENGER) spacecraft,

---

[*] Principle Professional Staff, Space Department, The Johns Hopkins University Applied Physics Laboratory, Laurel, MD, 20723.

[†] Senior Professional Staff, Space Department, The Johns Hopkins University Applied Physics Laboratory, Laurel, MD, 20723

currently orbiting Mercury.[3,4] The aerobraking simulation is comprised of the existing MESSENGER algorithms and software in the Mathworks Matlab/Simulink Real Time Workshop (RTW) environment to which have been added aerobraking algorithms adapted for a flight system and the associated testbed. This effort is intended to study tradeoffs in the approach and design and, in the end, generate a high degree of confidence in this technology as a precursor to implementation in a flight program.

Figure 1 shows the AAHFS software in block diagram form. The color-coding demonstrates the organization responsible for each software element. The JHU/APL software is MESSENGER heritage, although some adaptation to the aerobraking application is necessary, particularly in the flight software. The truth models provided by one of the team-members, NASA Langley Research Center (LaRC), have a rich aerobraking flight heritage. These elements include an atmosphere model and aerodynamics models, and are integrated into the MESSENGER Simulink environment to allow testing of the flight software. The Autonomous Aerobraking Development Software (AADS) is new algorithm and code development specific to this project. This code is a collaborative effort between the aerobraking and deep-space navigation experts at LaRC and KinetX, Inc, respectively. These algorithms ensure the spacecraft remains safe and performs aerobraking in the desired manner with limited ground intervention. The AAHFS simulation is developed as a reliable validated test environment to demonstrate the performance of these AADS algorithms.

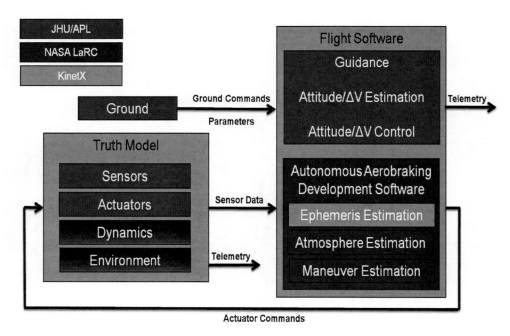

Figure 1. AAHFS Block Diagram

The truth model integration is currently complete and undergoing testing using baseline cases for a Mars mission. The AADS software is currently being tested by other team members prior to integration into the AAHFS. Initial simulations have been run demonstrating the spacecraft performance through a typical aerobraking drag pass. These results show the 6-DOF performance of the vehicle under the influence of the drag forces and torques and demonstrate the aerodynamic stability of the vehicle and the gradual reduction in the orbit due to the drag force.

Conventional Aerobraking Overview

Aerobraking uses atmospheric drag to reduce the propellant required to achieve a desired orbit about a target body. An aerobraking spacecraft makes numerous passes through the upper atmosphere, allowing aerodynamic drag to incrementally reduce the apoapsis of the orbit. These drag passes require periodic propulsive modifications to ensure that the atmospheric drag remains within design limits. These limits define an allowable altitude (or dynamic pressure, or thermal limit) corridor. Although deeper passes through the atmosphere would allow more drag and consequently a more rapid reduction of the spacecraft orbital energy, in general, the spacecraft design limits preclude these high temperatures experienced with the increased drag. These design limits define a minimum allowable altitude required to maintain spacecraft safety and as a result, aerobraking operations have historically been time consuming. The first planetary aerobraking mission, Magellan Venus, took 70 days and over 700 orbits.[5] This opportunistic flight demonstration of aerobraking was conducted during the extended mission, and also served to enhance the scientific return by providing a characterization of the Venus gravity field. After the successful demonstration at Venus, three Mars aerobraking missions have been flown.[6,7,8] These Mars missions had aerobraking operational phases that ranged from 77 days (Mars Odyssey) up to 17 months (MGS).

These main aerobraking operational periods can be broken into four phases. The first phase follows the propulsive orbit capture maneuver (generally into a high-eccentricity orbit), and serves to gradually lower the periapsis altitude until the sensible atmosphere is encountered and can be initially characterized. This "walk-in" period also allows for calibration of the spacecraft hardware and validation of the system performance during the drag passes. The second phase is the main aerobraking phase, where the spacecraft transitions from a long period, high eccentricity orbit to short period, low eccentricity orbit. During this second phase, many orbits are made with the orbital periapsis passing through the upper atmosphere of the central body, successively lowering the orbital energy to achieve the desired orbit. Orbital spacecraft are not normally designed to be aerodynamic, or with a thermal protection system to shield them from atmospheric heating. Therefore, the vehicle's dynamic pressure and thermal loads are monitored and maintained by a large ground team to ensure that these loads remain within design parameters. By using small, corrective propulsive maneuvers at apoapsis, these limits are controlled. This keeps the periapsis altitude within the desired corridor. Although periapsis control maneuvers are not required on every orbit, the ground team must repeatedly analyze data from prior drag passes and predict the conditions of the ensuing orbit to ensure the corridor requirements are met. Ground operators reevaluate the corridor roughly every week based on spacecraft performance, and adjust the corridor limits up or down as necessary. These ground planners also schedule the necessary corridor control maneuvers, although to reduce the burden on ground staff, these maneuvers are generally limited to once daily. Because this phase requires the ground to decide when and what corridor control maneuvers are required, this aerobraking phase is expensive. The cost is not only derived from the ground staff required, but also the DSN support to ensure that all of the necessary telemetry from each spacecraft burn and drag pass is available for analysis. As the orbit period shortens, the spacecraft enters the third phase where a minimum orbital lifetime must be maintained to ensure that spacecraft safety constraints are met. This allows adequate time to respond to a spacecraft problem without danger of deorbiting. The final phase is the termination of aerobraking by raising the periapsis out of the atmosphere via a propulsive maneuver and ultimately reaching the desired (circular or near-circular) final orbit.

Autonomous Aerobraking Overview

The standard approach to aerobraking has been very successful at delivering a payload into a desired orbit. However, the nature of the aerobraking operations is repetitive, and the timeliness of a response to problems could be improved if much of the orbit-to-orbit operations were conducted onboard. Also, in some cases ground operator constraints affect the course of aerobraking, and the process would be more efficient if conducted without these constraints. An example is that ground teams would avoid maneuver execution on a holiday or weekends, even if that manuever may allow aerobraking to proceed in a more optimal fashion. If the main aerobraking phase could be conducted with limited ground interaction, the cost of aerobraking could be significantly reduced, making it a much more attractive approach to orbiting solar system bodies with a sufficient atmosphere.

Various approaches to automating aerobraking have been in work for over a decade.[9,10,11,12,13,14] The proposed autonomous aerobraking approach for this project is to move the orbit estimation and corridor control maneuver design to the spacecraft flight software. This prevents the need for ground contact to telemeter the drag accelerations following every aerobraking pass. Although this onboard ephemeris estimation is less accurate than could be achieved via orbit reconstruction on the ground, it proposed that it is sufficient to ensure safe operation of the spacecraft. Even with autonomous aerobraking, periodic ground updates will be required to adjust the corridor limits as well as to re-initialize the orbital state for the ephemeris estimation scheme. The goal of this development effort is to demonstrate that these ground contacts can, in general, be weekly without jeopardizing spacecraft safety.

The evolution of a typical autonomous aerobraking orbit is shown in Figure 2. The orbit is arbitrarily assumed to begin just after the atmospheric passage (also referred to as a drag pass)

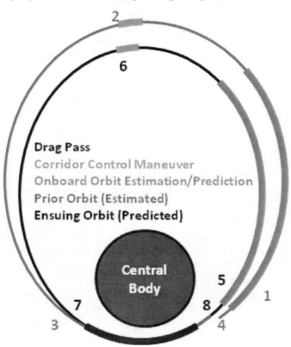

Figure 2: Autonomous Aerobraking Orbit Evolution

at point 5. All of the onboard calculations to estimate the orbit begin at this point and must complete with sufficient time to prepare to execute any potential corridor control maneuver shown at point 6. The figure shows the prior orbit just completed in green, as much of the data collected from this orbit is used to estimate the ensuing trajectory. The initial spacecraft trajectory estimate is provided by the onboard estimation software from the prior orbit, shown as point 1, or could be initialized with a ground state as necessary.

These onboard algorithms will estimate two complete orbits, where the first orbit is a reconstruction of the orbit just flown (points 1-4) and the second orbit is a prediction of the following orbit (points 5-8). The prediction at point 5 uses accelerometer data collected during a corridor control maneuver (if used) from the prior orbit (point 2) and from the prior drag pass (points 3-4) to estimate the prior orbit. Once the estimation of this prior orbit is complete, the onboard software predicts the following orbit through the next drag pass (point 8) to ensure the proper corridor is met. This orbit propagation is refined based on a prediction of the next atmospheric pass based on the accelerometer data collected during the last orbit. If an adjustment to the orbit is required, the onboard software would compute a corridor control maneuver at point 6 to ensure the predicted drag pass (points 7-8) meets the necessary vehicle design requirements. This sequence of events would need to occur on every aerobraking orbit. Eventually, as the orbit knowledge degrades due to errors in the propagation, a ground contact would reinitialize the onboard orbital state.

AAHFS TRUTH MODEL

The AAHFS truth model software replicates the true behavior of the spacecraft in its environment. The environment and spacecraft characteristics of a typical aerobraking mission are similar to many other deep-space missions. This makes the MESSENGER truth model a good initial starting point for developing a test environment for autonomous aerobraking. The MESSENGER 6-DOF truth model includes the spacecraft dynamics, sensors, actuators and environmental disturbances necessary to faithfully model the performance of the spacecraft in all orbital scenarios. Although the actuator models were developed to emulate the characteristics of the MESSENGER flight hardware, they provide a convincing, validated environment for testing the autonomous aerobraking approach since these sensors are typical of an aerobraking spacecraft as well. The environment models approximate all known disturbances sources external to the vehicle. These disturbances affect both the trajectory and the attitude dynamics, so it is natural to encapsulate these effects in a full 6-DOF simulation. A key addition is that autonomous aerobraking modeling also requires detailed atmospheric and aerodynamic models to determine the forces and torques due to the atmosphere during the drag passes. These models were not a part of the original MESSENGER truth models, but are easily incorporated into the code by adopting the architecture shown in Figure 3. This figure highlights the high-level interface between the MESSENGER heritage software, depicted in red, and the new development to support autonomous aerobraking, depicted in purple. Minimizing the interaction between the heritage code and the aerobraking models reduces the complexity of the model and ensures the MESSENGER-based software is unperturbed. The new aerobraking models have their own rich flight heritage as well, as they are based on software used for testing and operations of prior NASA aerobraking missions. The forces and torques that result from these models are integrated by the full equations of motion to predict the vehicle state. Sensor models are used to emulate the data inputs to the Guidance Navigation and Control (GN&C) system. These models also make use of the MESSENGER flight heritage to include flight performance characteristics, further enhancing the fidelity of the simulation environment.

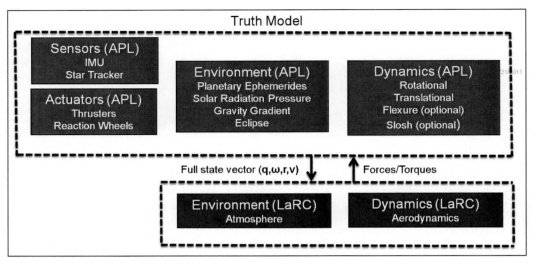

Figure 3. AAHFS Truth Model Block Diagram

MESSENGER Heritage Truth Models

The MESSENGER heritage software contains complete actuator models that are sufficient for the AAHFS demonstration. These models include both thruster and reaction wheel models, which operate at 200 Hz to ensure that thruster transient characteristics are correctly modeled. Although the MESSENGER reaction wheels are undersized for a typical aerobraking mission (as the aerobraking mission inertias are 3-5 times the MESSENGER values), the model can be scaled appropriately to ensure the torque and momentum characteristics are consistent with the simulated vehicle inertias. There is significant flexibility built into these models, as modifications can easily be made to static and running friction, wheel alignments and inertia variability, allowing for trade study and (if desired) Monte Carlo analysis. The MESSENGER propulsion system is perhaps overly complex for the autonomous aerobraking studies, but this model has simplified modes that are consistent with propulsive maneuver operations during prime aerobraking missions. Thruster capabilities allow corridor control maneuvers to be simulated with appropriate fidelity. The propellant supply mechanism can run in a fixed pressure mode or simulate tank blowdown for producing realistic thrust and specific impulse, as well as ensuring mass changes are modeled realistically. Thrust transients due to valve/thruster/thermal effects are modeled to accurately mimic system performance. Additional performance variation may be included with a thruster plume impingement model. These actuator models have undergone an extensive correlation with flight data, ensuring that they mimic the actual hardware performance, thereby ensuring a high-fidelity test environment for AAHFS.

The MESSENGER heritage software also includes high-fidelity sensor models running at rates that are consistent with the device operation. This includes multiple star trackers for attitude determination, running at 10 Hz. These star tracker models have easily adjusted alignments and noise characteristics for sensitivity studies. The 100-Hz IMU model is critical for AAHFS simulation and study, since AADS algorithms heavily rely on acceleration data from the IMU. A variety of trade studies may be useful involving this model, as it is of interest to determine the accuracy required of the IMU data (in particular, the accelerometer readings through the drag pass) to assure the proposed autonomous aerobraking approach meets the performance goals. The IMU model includes a convenient environment for studying AADS sensitivity to accelerometer (and gyro) misalignments, scale factor errors, biases, noise (white and readout), IMU clock walk, data collection frequency and sensor latencies.

The environment models in the AAHFS simulation model all of the salient perturbations that the spacecraft would experience when in orbit about the central body. This simulation can extract ephemeris information for any solar system body of interest from a SPICE Spacecraft Planet Kernel (SPK) file. The SPK file is the de facto storage framework for interplanetary spacecraft and celestial body trajectories. The bodies of interest are easily changed, allowing the simulation to be quickly adapted to different central bodies of interest (as well as modifying the desired gravitational perturbative bodies). The central body can include an optional harmonic gravity model, which can be of arbitrary degree and order; this allows the highest possible fidelity in integrating the translational equations of motion. Disturbance forces include the effects of solar radiation pressure (SRP) with a full umbra/penumbra eclipse model. This SRP model is specific to the MESSENGER spacecraft, but is scaled to get the effect to be consistent with an aerobraking mission (based on the ratio of the Sun-facing areas between a notional aerobraking mission and MESSENGER). For missions where this force is negligible (at Titan, for instance), this effect can be disabled. Additionally, disturbance torque models include those due to SRP as well as the gravity gradient. In general, most of these environment models are run at 1 Hz as the resulting disturbance forces and torques are slowly varying and don't require higher execution rates. The exception is the ephemeris models, since the planetary states are used to calculate the right-hand side of the translational equations of motion. In this case, the SPICE file extractions are done at 1 Hz, but the planet states are interpolated up to the model integration rate of 200-Hz.

The AAHFS dynamics models integrate the translational and rotational dynamics at 200 Hz. This rate is selected to capture thrust transients for thrusters pulsed at 50 Hz. A smaller step size would be possible, but testing revealed that it did not provide additional fidelity but it did reduce the execution speed of the simulation. Simulation speed is of critical importance, as the goal of the project is to demonstrate autonomous aerobraking is plausible for durations on the order of a week, so the AAHFS code must be capable of running simulations in excess of seven days. Additionally, the AAHFS truth models include propellant slosh dynamics and a structural model, which are optional models for the purposes of this study. While these models do enhance the fidelity of the truth model software, they are spacecraft specific, and would need to be updated to be consistent with the vehicle of interest for a real aerobraking flight program. Further, this model does not respond or get excited by the atmosphere, limiting its utility. It does provide some mechanism to conduct simulations on a non-rigid body, particularly to model the IMU response to a flexible environment, so it is retained for future study purposes. Both the slosh and the structural model are easily disabled for the initial AAHFS testing.

AAHFS Truth Model New Development

Figure 4 shows a detailed block diagram for the new AAHFS truth model development. Of particular interest for this discussion are the heritage elements provided by the LaRC team members, the atmosphere model and the aerodynamic models. These new models have been added to support aerobraking specific capabilities these models have been calibrated using aerobraking flight data from prior NASA aerobraking missions. This produces a very convincing environment for testing the 6-DOF behavior of an aerobraking spacecraft.

The fidelity of the atmosphere model is of particular importance to the demonstration of an end-to-end autonomous aerobraking simulation. Additionally, flexibility of this model is of paramount importance, as this study aims to use atmospheric variability as one means of investigating the robustness of the proposed AADS algorithms. The Mars Global Reference Atmospheric Model (Mars-GRAM) is an engineering-level atmospheric model widely used for prior Mars

461

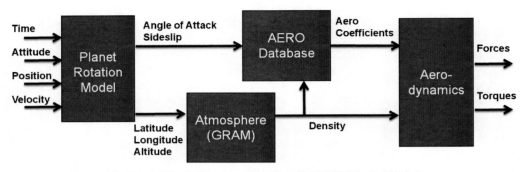

Figure 4. Block Diagram for New AAHFS Truth Models

aerobraking study and mission analyses.[15],[16] In addition to providing high-fidelity predictions of the mean density, temperature, pressure, and wind components at any planet position and altitude, Mars-GRAM also allows for the simulation of perturbed profiles about the mean conditions, thereby offering great flexibility for testing the autonomous aerobraking approach. The most recent version of Mars-GRAM (2010) has updates to reconcile the models with the aerobraking data of MRO, Mars Odyssey and MGS, making it a highly useful model for this aerobraking study. For the two other proposed central bodies a Titan-GRAM model and Venus-GRAM model were utilized. C versions of these GRAM models have been provided, and through the use of the Simulink Legacy Code Tool, these models have been directly integrated into the AAHFS truth model software. It is of minor consequence that this code was originally conceived in FORTRAN, and relies on namelist files for parametric modification. Prior to running the Simulink simulation, these namelist files are easily modified by Matlab scripts. The significant capability that the GRAM code provides does come at the price of execution speed. For this reason, the AAHFS only executes the GRAM model at 1 Hz. The output atmospheric densities are generally quite smooth and slowly varying, so interpolation up to the 200-Hz integration time step is easily accomplished. This allows use of the high-fidelity GRAM models without sacrificing simulation speed. The AAHFS atmosphere modeling strategy allows a wide variety of studies of missions to Mars, Venus and Titan with a single simulation.

An aerodynamic model has also been added to allow conversion of the atmospheric data generated by the GRAM software into the forces and torques operating on the vehicle. This model uses an underlying database of aerodynamic coefficients that are interpolated based on the spacecraft attitude and atmospheric density. This database is spacecraft specific (the current one in use is based on MRO data), and although this step in the process is mission dependent, the data currently in use is consistent with a typical aerobraking spacecraft. If an aerodynamic data set was available for a proposed spacecraft, it is trivial to modify the software to adopt an alternate database. Any future flight program that uses the autonomous aerobraking approach would substitute their vehicle model in for the MRO model when that data became available. As such, the use of MRO data for the vehicle aerodynamic properties is notional for this study. However, this database has been validated against an aerobraking flight mission, thereby serving to produce more convincing test results. Once this model produces the necessary aerodynamic coefficients, the forces and torques are produced via standard aerodynamic equations.[17] It is important that these dynamic quantities are calculated at a high rate, as the attitude can be very active during a drag pass. The AAHFS software computes these forces and torques at the integration rate of 200-Hz to ensure faithful modeling of the aerodynamics during the atmospheric pass.

AAHFS FLIGHT SOFTWARE

The flight software portion of the AAHFS model represents all of the guidance and control functions and algorithms necessary to ensure control of the spacecraft. As with the AAHFS truth model algorithms, the framework for this software was the MESSENGER guidance and control flight software. Where appropriate, AAHFS uses the same control code for the demonstration of the autonomous aerobraking capability. This heritage software includes a typical set of attitude, momentum, and maneuver guidance, estimation and control algorithms. The primary responsibility of this code is to ensure the attitude follows the desired pointing profiles, that angular momentum remains within desired limits, and that the propulsive maneuvers are executed successfully. One major advantage of this architecture is that the portion of the flight software that is inherited from MESSENGER is the actual onboard software used for the flight mission. The only significant differences are that the simulation runs in a workstation much faster than realtime and responds to simulated environmental data, whereas the onboard guidance and control software runs in real time as an embedded application on the flight processor and experiences the true flight environment. The MESSENGER heritage code alone is insufficient to demonstrate autonomous aerobraking. The AADS is a new block of software developed to handle the additional functions necessary to implement the aerobraking corridor control onboard. While this set of algorithms represents a small part of the AAHFS software, the development of these algorithms is the primary focus of the demonstration of the autonomous aerobraking capability. The remainder of the AAHFS acts as a testbed for these algorithms.

Heritage Flight Software Algorithms

Much of the AAHFS flight software block depicted in Figure 5 is heritage code from the MESSENGER mission. A standard set of algorithms is used to ensure the necessary control goals are achieved. The addition of the AADS software as well as the additional drag pass operations of an aerobraking spacecraft levy additional requirements on the standard MESSENGER software. This required modification to all elements of the software functionality to enhance the autonomy of the system and to ensure control is maintained through the drag pass.

The MESSENGER heritage software contains a very complete set of guidance algorithms. These algorithms maintain knowledge of all relevant solar system bodies to allow construction of

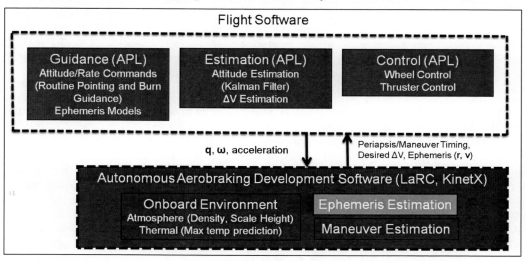

Figure 5. AAHFS Guidance and Control Flight Software Block Diagram

a variety of pointing commands as well as to ensure satisfactory execution of planned ΔV maneuvers.[18] Transitions and parameterization of these pointing scenarios are typically handled with ground commands, but in the case of autonomous aerobraking, these mode transitions must happen autonomously. This means the spacecraft must determine when and how to configure itself for an aerobraking drag pass as well as handle the appropriate configuration for executing a corridor control maneuver. These events cannot be triggered via ground command, as their timing is not known in advance, but rather, they must be orbit-event driven. As an example, the spacecraft guidance system must know the expected time of the ensuing periapse passage. Based on this timing, the spacecraft must determine the duration of the aerobraking drag pass, and ensure that the proper reconfiguration is handled to orient a preferred axis into the wind prior to entering the atmosphere, thereby ensuring the necessary aerodynamic stability. As the orbit period changes during aerobraking from a long period to a short period, the drag pass durations also change and the spacecraft must respond accordingly. As a result, the MESSENGER guidance algorithms have been modified to ensure these pointing transitions occur autonomously based on timing information about the orbit coming from the AADS. Likewise, to ensure maneuvers are executed correctly, the spacecraft must be able to determine its own attitude command and maneuver timing to ensure the desired corridor control maneuver executes properly. The AADS function computes the desired corridor control ΔV and maneuver epoch, and the guidance system must use this information to autonomously slew to burn attitude and execute the maneuver. So while much of the functionality of the onboard guidance system is unchanged, the level of autonomy is increased significantly.

Much of the estimation tasks provided by the MESSENGER flight software are reused directly for AAHFS. This software runs a model replacement Kalman Filter to estimate the spacecraft attitude from the gyro and star tracker data. Although fault scenarios are beyond the scope of the AAHFS test program, the attitude estimation is robust to missing or incomplete sensor data, as is typical for flight software. The filter executes at 1 Hz, and attitude estimates are propagated with high-rate gyro data up to the control task rate of 50-Hz. The MESSENGER software also supports a high-rate (50-Hz) estimation of accumulated ΔV based on the accelerometer data. This includes the onboard estimation of accelerometer biases prior to the maneuver. This process has been modified to execute autonomously, as for the MESSENGER flight program, the bias estimation and maneuver estimation are all accomplished with command sequences carefully planned by ground operators. An identical process to maneuver estimation is proposed for estimating the accelerations (or alternately, ΔV) from the aerobraking drag pass. This estimation must happen autonomously, so the software has been configured to execute the necessary commands autonomously to perform the accelerometer bias estimation as well as to estimate and buffer the accelerations from the drag pass. This buffer of accelerations will be used in the AADS software, discussed in the next subsection.

The control functionality required for an aerobraking mission is similar to that provided by the MESSENGER heritage flight software. This software contains algorithms for attitude control on reaction wheels and thrusters. The wheel control law is a hybrid approach that performs an eigenaxis slew for large angle maneuvers using a bang-bang control law, and for small angle errors, the controller transitions to a PID law. The thruster control law uses a phase plane to control each thruster individually, and is typically only employed during maneuvers and momentum dumps. Momentum control is generally accomplished via ground command, but autonomous momentum control is a part of the MESSENGER heritage code, and is used for AAHFS as necessary. The only significant modification to the MESSENGER code to support AAHFS simulations is to develop a control mode for the aerobraking drag pass. Much of the attitude control during aerobraking is accomplished by the aerodynamic stability of the vehicle. It is assumed that the vehicle is stable in pitch and yaw (which is typical for an aerobraking spacecraft). The roll axis is the only element that requires control, and this torque is assumed to be reasonably small. The control concept adopted for AAHFS simulations is to enter the drag pass on wheel control, ensuring that a pre-defined vehicle axis (the "nose") is pointed into the wind. Once in the drag pass and the aerodynamics take over, the wheels spin down (off-loading momentum), and pitch and yaw are controlled by the aerodynamic stability. The rolling motion is controlled with thrusters, although very few thruster pulses are required, due to the small roll torque and the large thruster deadbands. This strategy maintains vehicle and momentum control with minimal propellant usage. This also ensures that all thruster pulses are captured by the buffered acceleration data to allow accurate orbit determination by the AADS software.

AAHFS Flight Software New Development, AADS

The primary software development effort to demonstrate autonomous aerobraking is the AADS algorithms.[19,20,21] The AADS is responsible for performing orbit determination, and then based on predictions of the atmospheric conditions of the subsequent drag pass, deciding what maneuver (if any) is required at the orbit apoapsis. The AAHFS flight software is designed such that AADS is embedded as a single unit that is executed once during each central body orbit, immediately after each drag pass completes. As discussed in the prior subsection, the main input to the AADS consists of a buffer of time tagged acceleration and quaternion data obtained during the prior drag pass and any control maneuver that may have been performed. The key outputs from the AADS are the parameters defining any corrective control maneuver required to maintain the vehicle in the proper aerobraking corridor as well as information about the spacecraft ephemeris. AADS is executed as a low priority batch process, which completes its computations by a designated deadline so the resultant maneuver commands can be performed at the allotted time, typically at or near apoapsis. This approach minimizes the impact on normal real-time processing associated with the usual guidance and control software functions. However, care must be taken to ensure that as aerobraking reduces the orbital period, there are sufficient computational resources for the AADS to complete its execution by the allotted deadline.

The onboard AADS is composed of the following elements:

- Ephemeris Estimator (EE) – The EE, developed by KinetX Inc., estimates and predicts the spacecraft ephemeris and provides predictions of the next apoapsis and periapsis states using the on-board IMU accelerometer data.

- Atmospheric Estimator (AE) – The AE uses the on-board IMU accelerometer data to predict the density and scale height at the next periapsis.

- Maneuver Estimator (ME) – The ME determines the direction, magnitude and timing of any required periapsis control maneuver.

These elements are detailed in the following paragraphs.

Successful autonomous aerobraking requires accurate onboard spaceacrft ephemeris estimation. For a typical deep-space mission, the orbit determination is conducted on the ground using radiometric (and possibly optical) data to produce a filtered estimate of the reconstructed trajectory. This end state is then propagated using a full-fidelity model to estimate the future spacecraft trajectory. For autonomous aerobraking, the onboard software lacks the standard navigational data to estimate the trajectory history and it lacks the computational resources to propagate the trajectory with the highest level of fidelity. Instead, the onboard EE uses the available acceleration data and prior knowledge of the state (initialized from the ground) to run an orbital estimation of the prior orbit and a prediction of the ensuing orbit. Although this approach is not as accurate as using the standard navigational data, the largest disturbance to producing an accurate propagation is the variability in the atmospheric drag passes. This variability is measured by the accelerometers and buffered by the flight software, and using this information to reconstruct the trajectory allows for sufficient accuracy in estimation of the historical trajectory. Simply stated, the trajectory estimate must be accurate enough to predict periapsis timing and altitude. If the periapsis timing drifts too far from the true periapsis, the vehicle is at risk for not being configured properly for aerobraking, and the attitude control during the drag pass could be unstable and expose vehicle surfaces to excessive heating. If the periapsis altitude is incorrect, the aerodynamic heating could exceed allowable limits. The onboard ephemeris estimation is therefore the most challenging and critical task to achieving autonomous aerobraking, and its accuracy is likely to dictate the frequency of ground contact to reinitialize the integrator.

Fidelity of the numerical integration is important in accurately determining the spacecraft ephemeris. In the current design the EE uses an eighth-order Runge-Kutta-Fehlberg integrator with embedded seventh order automatic step-size selection to perform the orbital propagation. It includes a harmonic gravity model of the central body for maximum fidelity. Additionally, the EE includes the effects due to solar radiation pressure. At Mars, solar pressure affects may play a role but are not large. The solar pressure at Venus is expected to be significant and the effects at Titan are expected to be negligible. The integration also includes the effects of perturbing gravitational bodies, such as the Sun, or in the case on a Titan mission, Saturn. Finally the EE includes the ability to integrate the sensed accelerometer readings from the executed maneuvers and drag passes. These acceleration terms are much larger than any of the other terms considered in the integrator, and this requires careful consideration of these sensed accelerations to ensure accuracy. The rate of this data is also important to ensure sufficient fidelity in reconstructing the orbit. The software will provide the spacecraft state data at 10 Hz. This rate is expected to be fast enough to accurately reproduce the inertial accelerations, but will still produce a reasonably-sized data buffer during the longest drag passes. Furthermore, these accelerations must be compensated for all known error sources, such as bias, latency and IMU rotational effects. These compensations are done outside the AADS, prior to the accelerations being put into the data buffer. The accuracy of these accelerations strongly influences the quality of the ephemeris estimate.

The acceleration measurements collected for the EE task are also supplied to the AE. These data are used to estimate atmospheric density profiles as the drag acceleration is directly related to the aerodynamic forces. The atmospheric density provides information about phenomena such as gravity waves, longitude dependent wave characteristics, latitudinal gradients, atmospheric temperature and orbit-to-orbit variability. Future atmospheric conditions can be predicted by atmospheric scientists from this information. In the AADS the AE must provide all these functions in a subsystem that consumes minimal computational resources while simultaneously being robust and reliable. This is a challenging problem especially given the amount and nature of the information available for the various central bodies under consideration. Titan, in particular, has very limited existing atmospheric information at the resolution necessary to perform aerobraking. More data are available from the Magellan aerobraking experience at Venus but are still limited. Mars has significant amounts of information available but is a taxing environment to perform aerobraking due to the highly variable nature of its atmospheric density. LaRC researchers are actively investigating various potential methods for representing and recovering density profiles derived from IMU/accelerometer data during aerobraking and are evaluating algorithms based on simplicity, robustness and applicability to onboard limitations.[6,20]

The remaining component of the AADS is the maneuver logic. Using the orbit predicted by the EE and the predicted atmospheric conditions at the next drag pass from the AE, this software determines what maneuver, if any, is required to ensure the desired corridor is maintained during

466

this drag pass. The corridor in the ME can be specified a number of ways (heat rate, dynamic pressure, etc..), but ultimately the code translates this into a required maneuver to achieve a desired periapsis altitude . The flight software autonomously responds to this maneuver command as necessary to implement the desired maneuver. This would include a slew to the desired attitude, burn ignition, closed-loop monitoring of the accumulated ΔV, burn cutoff, and buffering of the burn accelerations for the next execution of the EE task. The ME would (in general) request a maneuver only if one of the corridor limits (either high or low) were going to be violated. The ME software would then retarget back to the center of the corridor. This software could also easily have autonomy built into it such that if problem conditions were encountered during the prior drag pass, a pop-up maneuver could be commanded so that the spacecraft would raise periapsis out of the atmosphere and wait for ground intervention for fault diagnosis and correction.

AAHFS MODELLING AND SIMULATION ENVIRONMENT IMPROVMENTS

The MESSENGER portion of the AAHFS models were developed using the Simulink graphical programming tool. This tool provides an intuitive and natural way for GN&C analysts to design algorithms but may not be familiar to flight software developers. Furthermore, this environment may not always be well suited to satisfying all the all the constraints that the software developers must meet.

To convert the flight algorithms developed in the Simulink environment to flight software the RTW toolbox was used to generate C code from the Simulink models, a process called auto code generation. The resulting C code has a hand generated interface code wrapper applied following which it is incorporated into the main flight software executable. Additionally a similar process is followed for generating a truth model executable. The resulting flight and truth model executables are then loaded onto a flight processor board and test bed respectively. Detailed hardware in the loop (HWIL) testing is then performed.

The code generation process is also used to create executables that are used for non-realtime workstation simulation tasks such as Monte Carlo runs and individual test cases. This provides significantly improvements in speed, for example a model run natively in the Simulink environment typically runs 4 to 5 times faster than real time, whereas an executable version of the same model runs approximately 50 times faster than real time (64-Bit Linux, x86, 2.66GHz.) This increase in simulation speed is crucial when demonstrating scenarios having real time durations measured in weeks, as would be expected in a typical autonomous aerobraking simulation.

As previously mentioned, the AAHFS is based on the MESSENGER mission software. Although every attempt has been made to retain or minimize the changes made to the functionality associated with the MESSENGER software the AAHFS has benefitted from numerous upgrades and modification made to the modeling and simulation environment. These enhancements resulted from infrastructure upgrades previously developed for a number of different projects actively being pursued by the GN&C group at JHU/APL. The objectives of these upgrades are numerous, but key elements are outlined below, together with the original MESSENGER limitations, most of which resulted from previous customizations of the auto-code generation process:

1)   Provide multiple platform (Windows, Linux, and Mac) support for model development, debugging and simulation. The prior MESSENGER model development was limited to the Linux operating system. The new AAHFS simulation has been successfully demonstrated on all three of the named platforms.

2)   Support simulations containing multiple sample rates, including asynchronously executed objects, ensuring that simulations accurately reproduce the effects of task switching in an embedded flight system. While the MESSENGER model previously contained multiple rates the execu-

tables generated for workstation simulations assumed that all GN&C calculations would be executed as a single task although not all calculations would be executed during every task activation. This approach could not accurately reflect task switching if separate tasks were assigned to each execution rate, which is desirable to maximize processor availability. This results in potentially algorithm errors that are not identified until HWIL testing is performed. This single tasking rate constraint resulted from customizations that permitted the "tuning" of simulation parameters during the simulation, emulating the upload of parameters to the spacecraft during flight and the modification of parameters during complex Monte-Carlo runs. AAHFS would not be able to accurately demonstrate the AADS operation without these changes as AADS is expected to run as a separate asynchronous task in the final flight software.

3) Improve the interface to external code. The original MESSENGER model contained interfaces to complex (multi-element) external code modules used in ephemeris determination. Additionally the AADS, GRAM, and aero models are supplied as monolithic code deliveries that must be incorporated into the AAHFS Simulink models while still maintaining the ability to generate executable via auto-code. To satisfy these requirements a more generalized approach (which is also platform independent) was established for importing these external code components.

4) Improve the management of model parameters. The complete MESSENGER model contains over 1000 named parameters and although a significant attempt was made to provide structure to the management of these variables the underlying code infrastructure provided no comprehensive way to ensure that all these variables remained independent and well ordered. In the AAHFS this has been rectified by using tunable parameter structures. This change has enabled the modeling infrastructure to provide database-like functionality in the ordering and grouping of parameters. It ensures no side effects due to inadvertent parameter name reuse while enhancing and potentially simplifying the syntax associated with updating and tuning parameters both at the start of model execution and during a model run, and also when manipulating values during Monte-Carlo runs. Additionally it helps reduce the number of simulation executable code rebuilds by only forcing code regeneration when in lined (as opposed to tunable) parameters are changed and can significantly aid in the reuse of parameter setup files enhancing the ability to reuse models.

All the above-mentioned modeling and simulation environment improvements have been added to the MESSENGER model to create the AAHFS without functionally changing the results produced by the models. The exception to this is discussed in point 2 above which helps highlight algorithmic errors much earlier in the development process.

AAHFS TESTING

Initial tests have been run with the current version of the AAHFS. Because the AADS algorithms have not yet been integrated with the MESSENGER heritage software, these tests do not demonstrate the full concept of autonomous aerobraking. That is, the results in this section demonstrate the complete functionality of the AAHFS truth model environment but not the onboard ephemeris estimation and maneuver execution. It is important to remember that the role of AAHFS testing is to provide a high-fidelity 6-DOF dynamic simulation of each aerobraking orbit, so the performance of the truth models are critical to achieving this objective. The execution speed of the AAHFS model is not sufficient for studying entire mission runouts, as were demonstrated with the Program to Optimize Simulated Trajectories (POST).[22,23] Instead, AAHFS is useful for looking at the detailed 6-DOF performance of the aerobraking algorithms and, in particular, the attitude dynamics of the vehicle during the drag pass. To date, simulations have been run testing a variety of typical orbit scenarios about Mars, including long-period orbits consistent with initial aerobraking orbit conditions (~30-35 hour orbital period) and short-period orbits consistent with final aerobraking orbit conditions (~2 hour orbital period). Although the density profiles and drag durations differ somewhat for the varying orbits, from an attitude dynamics and orbital mechanics point of view, the performance through the drag passes are quite similar.

Figures 6-8 demonstrate the spacecraft performance through two different drag passes. The two cases presented are for two different MRO-like orbits, a long period (33 hour) orbit and a shorter period (6 hour) orbit. All the plots show time histories of various parameters within 10 minutes of periapsis. Figure 6 shows the altitude and atmospheric density for each of these orbits. The longer period orbit spends less time in the sensible atmosphere (<250 km), and the periapsis altitude is slightly higher than the short-period orbit (120 km versus 104 km, respectively). This leads to approximately three times higher atmospheric density for the short period orbit, although the cases do not have the same planet relative geometry, and would not see the same atmospheric conditions if the altitudes were identical.

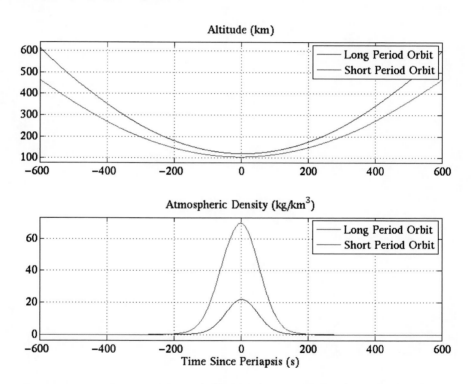

Figure 6. AAHFS Simulation Results for Two Sample Aerobraking Orbits

It is useful to understand the aerobraking attitude configuration for interpreting the results shown in Figures 7 and 8. To begin aerobraking, the onboard guidance system aligns the spacecraft +x-axis with the planet-relative orbital velocity direction. This approximates the wind-relative velocity direction, although it ignores the wind contribution due to planet rotation and surface-relative winds. The spacecraft roll is constrained to keep the −z-axis toward nadir. This roll condition is somewhat arbitrary, and is chosen for convenience and consistency with POST simulations and the underlying spacecraft aerodynamic database. The spacecraft control system attempts to maintain this attitude throughout the drag pass, but as the vehicle descends deeper into the atmosphere, the aerodynamic torques begin to overwhelm the control system. At this point, the spacecraft demonstrates the desired aerodynamic stability provided by the underlying MRO aerodynamic database. As a result, the spacecraft begins to oscillate around its trim point in both pitch and yaw.

The resulting aerodynamic forces and torques in the spacecraft body frame for each of the two orbits are provided in Figure 7. As expected, the most pronounced force for each orbit is in the $-x$ direction, and opposes the spacecraft wind-relative velocity. The ordinate scale of the long and short period orbits are the same for the forces and torques, demonstrating the effect of the increased density during the short period orbit in the right-hand graphics. This force serves to reduce the apoapsis of the orbit, and the integral over the drag pass provides an equivalent ΔV of 1.6 m/s and 5.0 m/s for the short and long period orbits, respectively. This scaling is similar to the threefold increase in atmospheric density shown in Figure 6. The torque demonstrates the expected aerodynamic stability. This is reflected in the oscillatory behavior in the y- and z-axes, and a small secular roll torque which is easily managed by the reaction wheels, although the torques are higher and more oscillatory for the longer, deeper drag pass.

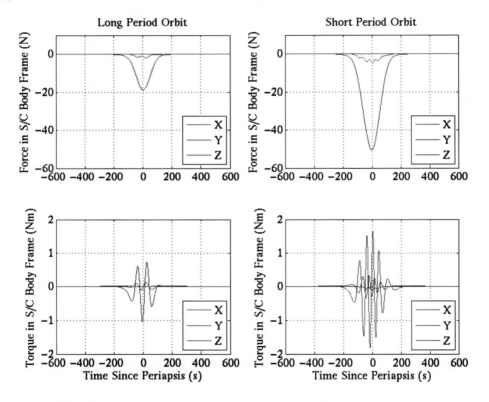

Figure 7. AAHFS Aerodynamic Forces and Torques for Two Aerobraking Orbits

Figure 8 plots the wind-relative attitude in terms of the angle of attack, α (where positive angles represent nose-up), and sideslip angle, β (where positive angles represent nose-left) for the short and long period orbit. These plots show that once in the atmosphere, the vehicle angle of attack moves close to -6° and begins to oscillate about that point, clearly showing the aerodynamic stability. As the spacecraft emerges from the atmosphere, the angle of attack returns

470

(under reaction wheel control) to zero. The sideslip angle follows a similar pattern, although this angle is complicated by the winds due to the rotation of the planet, making the sideslip trim point time-varying, and latitude/longitude dependent.

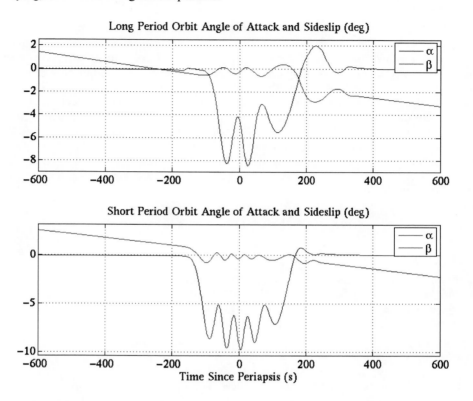

Figure 8. AAHFS Wind-Relative Attitude for Long and Short Period Orbits

While the results shown in the above figures are preliminary and subject to validation with POST, they are an encouraging step to producing the full AAHFS simulation. Once the AAHFS simulation is complete, testing will focus on demonstrating the functionality of AADS for a minimum of seven days in the Mars environment. Initial tests will work to demonstrate this capability for the long and short period orbits. Once those cases are complete, tests will be conducted to show how AADS responds to perturbed atmosphere cases and to study how the required accuracy of the accelerometer data impacts the autonomy. There will not be any demonstration of spacecraft safing capability as a part of this initial development effort. This would be done for a real flight program, but since much of this testing is sensor/actuator/configuration dependant, testing is of somewhat limited utility, and beyond the scope of this demonstration effort. The safing strategy employed for an autonomous aerobraking mission is not expected to be drastically different from a conventional aerobraking mission, since the risks to the spacecraft are similar. Normally, the approach to safing an aerobraking spacecraft is to execute a pop-up maneuver to ensure the spacecraft is out of the atmosphere, allowing the ground to recover from the fault without posing a danger to the spacecraft from atmospheric heating or stability concerns. It is expected that autonomous aerobraking may provide a more robust/responsive safing methodology, since the ground is not required to execute the necessary pop-up maneuver, although this demonstration is not addressed as a part of this project. Testing in future phases of the AA development may address these fault scenarios and provide a comprehensive vehicle safing methodology.

CONCLUSION

The AAHFS software is being used to demonstrate the performance of the autonomous aerobraking algorithms. The foundation for this software was the MESSENGER Simulink/RTW models, which allows for rapid integration of the additional software functionality needed to demonstrate autonomous aerobraking. The resulting 6-DOF test environment will be used to study the performance of the AADS with a flight proven set of truth models and flight software. An additional advantage of the AAHFS test environment is that the architecture of the flight software algorithms, which includes AADS, is flight-like, making future steps to a flight demonstration of autonomous aerobraking easier. With the successful demonstration of AAHFS, the NESC may elect to fund additional phases of this project where the software algorithms are embedded in a realtime test environment for further study and testing.

ACKNOWLEDGMENTS

This work is sponsored by the NASA Engineering and Safety Center. Their assessment can be found in the final report NESC-RP-09-00605 due in November 2011.

REFERENCES

[1] J. L. Prince, D. Murri, "Autonomous Aerobraking: A Design, Development, and Feasibility Study," AAS 11-473, AAS/AIAA Astrodynamics Specialist Conference, Girdwood, AK, 2011.

[2] D. J. Carrelli et al., "Autonomous Aerobraking for Low-Cost Interplanetary Missions," 9th IAA Low-Cost Planetary Missions Conference, Laurel, MD, June 21-23, 2011.

[3] S. C. Solomon et al., "The MESSENGER Mission to Mercury: Scientific Objectives and Implementation," Planetary and Space Science, Vol. 46, Issues 14-15, pp. 1445-1465, Dec 2001.

[4] R. M. Vaughan, D. J. O'Shaughnessy, H. S. Shapiro, and D. R. Haley, "The MESSENGER Spacecraft Guidance and Control System," NASA 2005 Flight Mechanics Symposium, Goddard Space Flight Center, Greenbelt, MD, October 18-20, 2005.

[5] D. T. Lyons, "Aerobraking Magellan: Plan Versus Reality," AAS/AIAA Space Fight Mechanics Meeting, Vol. 87, Pt. 2, edited by J. E. Cochran Jr., C. D. Edwards Jr., S. J. Hoffman, and R. Holdaway, Univelt, San Diego, CA, 1994, pp. 663–680.

[6] D. T. Lyons, J. Beerer, P. Esposito, M. Johnston, and W. Willcockson, "Mars Global Surveyor: Aerobraking Mission Overview," Journal of Spacecraft and Rockets, Vol. 36, No. 3, 1999, pp. 307–313.

[7] R. H. Tolson et. al., "Application of Accelerometer Data to Mars Odyssey Aerobraking and Atmospheric Modeling," Journal of Spacecraft and Rockets, Vol. 42, No. 3, pp 435-443.

[8] J. L. Prince, S. A. Striepe, "Mars Reconnaissance Orbiter Operational Aerobraking Phase Assessment," 17th Annual AAS/AIAA Space Flight Mechanics Conference, Sedona, AZ, 07-244.

[9] D. T. Lyons, "Aerobraking Automation Options," Advances in the Astronautical Sciences, Vol. 109, Pt. 2, 2001, pp. 1231–1246.

[10] W. R. Johnson, J. M. Longuski, and D. T. Lyons, "Pitch Control During Autonomous Aerobraking for Near-Term Mars Exploration," Journal of Spacecraft and Rockets, Vol. 40, No. 3, 2003, pp. 371–379.

[11] W. R. Johnson, J. M. Longuski, and D. T. Lyons, "Six-Degree-of-Freedom Modeling of Semi-Autonomous Attitude Control During Aerobraking," Journal of Spacecraft and Rockets, Vol. 41, No. 5, 2004, pp. 797-804.

[12] J. L. Hanna, and R. H. Tolson, "Approaches to Autonomous Aerobraking at Mars," The Journal of the Astronautical Sciences, Vol. 50, No. 2, Apr-Jun 2002.

[13] J. L. Hanna, R. H. Tolson, A. D. Cianciolo, and J. A. Dec, "Autonomous Aerobraking at Mars," 5th International ESA Conference on Guidance Navigation and Control Systems and Actuator and Sensor Product Exhibition, Frascati, Italy, October 22-25, 2002.

[14] J. L. Prince, D. Murri, R. W. Powell, R, H. Tolson, M. K. Lockwood, B. Williams, "Development Plan for Autonomous Aerobraking," Proceedings of 7th International Planetary Probe Workshop, Barcelona, Spain, June 2010.

[15] C. G. Justus, "A Mars Global Reference Atmospheric Model (MARS-GRAM) for Mission Planning and Analysis," AIAA-1990-4 28th Aerospace Sciences Meeting, Reno, NV, Jan 8-11, 1990.

[16] H. L. Justh et al., "The Next Generation of Mars-GRAM and Its Role in the Autonomous Aerobraking Development Plan." AAS 11-478, AAS/AIAA Astrodynamics Specialist Conference, Girdwood, AK, 2011.

[17] B. L. Stevens and F. L. Lewis, *Aircraft Control and Simulation*, John Wiley and Sons, Inc., Hoboken, New Jersey, p100-106, 2003.

[18] D. J. O'Shaughnessy and R. M. Vaughan, "MESSENGER Spacecraft Pointing Options," AAS 03-149, AAS/AIAA Spaceflight Mechanics Meeting, Ponce, Puerto Rico, Feb, 2003.

[19] D. L. Skinner, R. W. Maddock, "Autonomous Aerobraking Ephemeris Estimator." AAS 11-472, AAS/AIAA Astrodynamics Specialist Conference, Girdwood, AK, 2011.

[20] R. W. Maddock, A. D. Cianciolo, A. Bowes, J. L. Prince, and R. W. Powell, "Implemenation and Simulation Results Using Autonomous Aerobraking Development Software." AAS 11-476, AAS/AIAA Astrodynamics Specialist Conference, Girdwood, AK, 2011.

[21] R. H. Tolson, J. L. Prince, "Onboard Atmospheric Modeling and Prediction for Autonomous Aerobraking Missions." AAS 11-477, AAS/AIAA Astrodynamics Specialist Conference, Girdwood, AK, 2011.

[22] S. A. Striepe et al., "Program To Optimize Simulated Trajectories (POST II): Volume 2, Utilization Manual," Martin Marietta Corporation, 2004.

[23] G. L. Brauer et al., "Program To Optimize Simulated Trajectories (POST): Volume 1, Formulation Manual," Martin Marietta Corporation, 1990.

AAS 11-473

AUTONOMOUS AEROBRAKING:
A DESIGN, DEVELOPMENT, AND FEASIBILITY STUDY

Jill L. H. Prince,[*] Richard W. Powell[†] and Dan Murri[‡]

Aerobraking has been used four times to decrease the apoapsis of a spacecraft in a captured orbit around a planetary body with a significant atmosphere utilizing atmospheric drag to decelerate the spacecraft. While aerobraking requires minimum fuel, the long time required for aerobraking requires both a large operations staff, and large Deep Space Network resources. A study to automate aerobraking has been sponsored by the NASA Engineering and Safety Center to determine initial feasibility of equipping a spacecraft with the onboard capability for autonomous aerobraking, thus saving millions of dollars incurred by a large aerobraking operations workforce and continuous DSN coverage. This paper describes the need for autonomous aerobraking, the development of the Autonomous Aerobraking Development Software that includes an ephemeris estimator, an atmospheric density estimator, and maneuver calculation, and the plan forward for continuation of this study.

INTRODUCTION

NASA uses aerobraking to reduce the fuel required to deliver an orbiter into its desired final orbit around a target planet or moon that has an appreciable atmosphere. Rather than using the propulsion system to decelerate the spacecraft after initial orbit insertion, aerobraking decelerates the spacecraft using aerodynamic drag. An orbital spacecraft is not normally designed with aerodynamics in mind or with a thermal protection system to protect it from atmospheric heating. Therefore, while the spacecraft is aerobraking, it must traverse through the upper atmosphere of the planet or moon multiple times while keeping the aerodynamic loads and heating to very low levels during each pass. Small propulsive maneuvers at apoapsis are used to control the altitude at periapsis to maintain the spacecraft within its designed periapsis control corridor as illustrated in figure 1. The periapsis control corridor may in terms of dynamic pressure, a heat rate indicator, or even atmospheric density, but typically the corridor is constrained by spacecraft temperature, which is the limiting parameter on the vehicle. Using this multiple-pass through the upper atmosphere approach enables the spacecraft's design loads to remain within its designed parameters and while achieving an appropriate final science orbit.

---

[*] Senior Engineer, Atmospheric Flight and Entry Systems Branch, NASA Langley Research Center MS 489 Hampton, VA 23681.
[†] Senior Engineer, Analytical Mechanics Association, NASA Langley Research Center MS 489 Hampton, VA 23681.
[‡] NASA Technical Fellow, NASA Engineering Safety Center, Hampton, VA 23681.

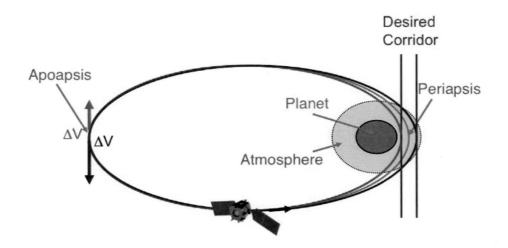

Figure 1. A spacecraft using apoapsis maneuvers to control periapsis altitude during aerobraking.

NASA has used aerobraking four times to modify a spacecraft's orbit to one with lower energy, reduced apoapsis altitude, and smaller orbital period. Aerobraking was first demonstrated by the Magellan spacecraft at Venus[1]. For this spacecraft operations cycle, aerobraking was completed at the end of its primary mission, demonstrating the concept of aerobraking and reducing the orbital period from just over three hours to just under two. This successful demonstration led to the use of aerobraking as a mission enabling capability for three Mars orbiters: Mars Global Surveyor (MGS)[2], Mars Odyssey[3], and Mars Reconnaissance Orbiter (MRO)[4]. A brief comparison of these four missions can be found in Table 1.

Table 1. A comparison of aerobraking spacecraft.

	Magellan	MGS	Odyssey	MRO
Launch Year	1989	1996	2001	2005
Dry Mass (kg)	1035	677	380	968
AB Orbits	730	886	330	428
AB Days	70	17 months	77	149
AB Period Change (hr)	3.2-1.6	45-1.9	18-2.0	34-1.9
ΔV Savings (m/s)	1220	1220	1090	1190
Propellant Savings (kg)	490	330	320	580

Although aerobraking reduces the propellant required to reach the final orbit, this reduction comes at the expense of time, continuous Deep Space Network (DSN) coverage, and a large ground staff currently required for aerobraking operations. This combination of DSN and workforce results in aerobraking being an expensive operational phase of a mission[5]. The first aerobraking demonstration, Magellan, held the shortest aerobraking operations phase completing in 70 days. With such a small orbital period change in this duration, however, it is understood that a mission-enabling aerobraking phase to reduce a large-period orbit to a small science orbit at Venus would be considerably longer. If holding to the same relatively benign (low dynamic pressure, low heat rate indicator) periapsis corridor, aerobraking a Venus spacecraft could take years.[6]

With the development of Autonomous Aerobraking (AA), much of the daily operations could be moved to the spacecraft, thus reducing the cost of the aerobraking phase by several millions of dollars. The concept of autonomous aerobraking has been studied in depth over the past decade[7,8,9]. A first step in autonomous aerobraking occurred with the implementation of a periapsis timing estimator on MRO[10] that was tested during Mars Odyssey aerobraking operations. Further development that includes maneuver execution is required and is the subject of further discussion here. In the AA development described in this paper, the spacecraft would calculate and predict its own ephemeris (all aerobraking activities are referenced to a periapsis time and all periapsis altitude correction burns are performed at apoapsis). Using the subsequent orbit's predicted periapsis, the spacecraft would estimate its next predicted periapsis density using an onboard atmospheric model. If the predicted parameter control value (dynamic pressure, heat rate, temperature) is predicted to fall outside of the corridor, the spacecraft would determine the maneuver strategy to remain within the specified corridor. The spacecraft would design and execute any required maneuvers. Ground based weekly activities such as corridor updates (the operational corridor may change weekly if the spacecraft is off of its intended schedule), updates to model parameters (e.g. AADS gains), and overall mission strategy would remain as ground-based activities. Not only would providing this functionality of moving daily maneuver assessment to the spacecraft save significant cost in staff and DSN usage, but because the spacecraft would no longer be tied to the work schedule of the ground personnel (e.g., previously, maneuvers were ideally performed during staff's prime shift and outside of weekends and holidays), autonomous aerobraking also has the potential to reduce risk, as the maneuver could be conducted at the optimal time and executed even if DSN or other required ground elements were unavailable.

AA has been developed with support of the NASA Engineering Safety Center (NESC) over the past year and has demonstrated preliminary concept feasibility. This initial feasibility study is the first phase of an anticipated 4-year, three-phased study to develop and test the Autonomous Aerobraking Development Software (AADS). The concept study and overview of the AA development will be discussed in this paper.

AUTONOMOUS AEROBRAKING SUPPORT

The Autonomous Aerobraking development team consists of core members from three NASA centers, industry, and academia. The NESC provided programmatic support; NASA Langley Research Center provided study team leadership, thermal modeling, aerodynamic modeling, trajectory analysis, and simulation support. NASA Johnson Space Center provided aerodynamic and aerothermodynamic support. NASA Marshal Space Flight Center provided atmosphere modeling. Kinetx provided the Ephemeris Estimator. The Johns Hopkins University Applied Physics Laboratory (APL) developed a MESSENGER-based high fidelity simulation. The National Institute of Aerospace provided atmosphere models and analysis. Outside of this core development team, NESC support consisted of several technical fellows as consultants to the AA development work. In addition, a peer review consisting of a review board of technical fellows is scheduled for November 2011 to assess the results of Phase 1.

AUTONOMOUS AEROBRAKING: PHASE 1

During Phase 1 of the AA development study, atmospheric[11,12], aerodynamic[13], and thermal models[14] for a representative spacecraft were developed for both the onboard AADS as well as a ground-based "truth" simulation that is developed for testing purposes. An autonomous ephemeris estimator was developed and incorporated into the AADS. In previous aerobraking mission experience, an increase in error in predicting the time of periapsis passage requires frequent (daily) ephemeris updates from the ground using tracking data from DSN. If high quality ephemeris estimation can be performed onboard, the number of required updates will be reduced. The goal for AA is the capability to allow over one week before requiring a ground update. This eliminates the requirement for continuous DSN coverage.

The "truth" simulations were developed using two separate tools: Program to Optimize Simulated Trajectories II (POST2)[15] at NASA Langley Research Center and a MESSENGER-based simulation at APL, the Autonomous Aerobraking High Fidelity Simulation (AA-HFS)[16]. The AADS is the onboard set of models and algorithms that is called from and tested against both "truth" simulations. This suite of models and algorithms within the AADS consists of the ephemeris model, an atmospheric density predictor, a thermal model (for Venus only), and maneuver logic. The maneuver logic was an adaptation of that which was developed for the ground-based Mars Odyssey mission analyses and refined for the Mars Reconnaissance Orbiter for mission design and operations[17]. This logic is used for onboard determination of daily maneuver decisions and execution based on AADS algorithms.

Three versions of the AADS were tested during Phase 1: one that carried a baseline heat-rate indicator (1/2 * atmospheric density*velocity^3) corridor at Mars, the second was a solar-panel temperature corridor at Venus, and a third held a dynamic pressure corridor at Titan. At each destination, nominal and some stressing aerobraking situations were designed to stress-test the software. For example, the benign polar orbit that was originally used for testing the AADS was not sufficient in identifying potential errors in the software. Modifying the orbit to cross the Tharsis Ridge over mars uncovered small, simulated gravitational differences that might not have been noticed over the "nominal" simulated state.

During Phase 1, performance was analyzed of the AADS against the "truth" simulations[18]: POST2 and the AA-HFS. Detail of the initial performance of the AADS-Mars against the POST2 simulation can be found in reference 19.

AUTONOMOUS AEROBRAKING: PHASE 2

Pending project approval, a second phase (14 months in duration) of development will follow Phase 1 that includes the transportation of the AA modules to a flight-like processor and for additional testing of the AADS. This hardware-in-the-loop processor will provide an interface by which it can be determined if a spacecraft is capable of processing and transmitting the necessary data for AADS computation and if that spacecraft can successfully execute the maneuvers dictated by the AADS. In addition phase 2 will determine the necessary processor characteristics, including storage requirements. The ephemeris and atmospheric density estimator require the accelerometer time history during the atmospheric pass, and the ephemeris estimator also requires the accelerometer history during any propulsive maneuver.

In addition to the flight-like processor analysis of autonomous aerobraking, the AADS will undergo further stress-testing in the POST2 and the high fidelity simulation environment. During Phase 1, the AADS was built for three destinations: Mars, Venus, and Titan. During Phase 2, more anomalistic environments will be introduced to ensure that the AADS is robust and will select the appropriate maneuver while considering spacecraft risk. For example, the AADS will select a maneuver that places the next periapsis within the designed corridor. Further development of the AADS will include additional error checks to ensure that this maneuver does not put the spacecraft in a situation in which a statistically feasible high-density could put the spacecraft at risk. These error checks and further investigation of 3-sigma atmospheric events will be a focus of Phase 2. Phase 2 will also incorporate emergency maneuver implementation into the AADS. As AADS is running after atmospheric exit, there will be a determination of the maximum heating of the drag pass just completed. If the heating is far higher than statistically anticipated and it crosses an "immediate action" pre-determined criteria, an overriding "up" maneuver must be made prior to the next drag pass to raise the periapsis altitude so that a ground based team can determine the next course of action. This emergency maneuver is something that has been calculated for every spacecraft aerobraking operations on the ground. For autonomous aerobraking, this contingency situation must be automated as well. These additions and improvements to the AADS will be ongoing within Phase 2 and Phase 3.

AUTONOMOUS AEROBRAKING: PHASE 3

Following the Phase 2 activity, Phase 3 is dedicated to determining the physical cost of aerobraking (e.g. dedicated processor, if required, implementation of autonomous aerobraking code within the MESSENGER-based code, etc.) as well as the limitations of autonomous aerobraking. Success is defined by the ability of AADS to maintain aerobraking effectiveness for up to one week at a time, without uploads from ground staff, for nominal as well as off-nominal aerobraking scenarios at Mars, Venus, and Titan. AADS improvements, tuning, and stress-testing will continue throughout Phase 3.

AUTONOMOUS AEROBRAKING: PHASE 4

It is anticipated that one of the next orbiters to use aerobraking to achieve science orbit will use AADS in a listen-only mode as a technology demonstration. This will be Phase 4 of AA. AADS, after three phases of ground-testing, will be implemented onboard an aerobraking orbiter, will employ AADS and will calculate desired maneuvers. It will not, however, execute these maneuvers. Aerobraking for this spacecraft will remain ground-based in which engineers in a mission control will continue to simulate trajectories and compute maneuver magnitude and timing. During aerobraking operations, the AADS-derived maneuvers, ephemeris and atmospheric density estimation capability will be compared to those determined by the ground-based staff. This will determine the efficacy and actual improvement over ground-based aerobraking operations that AADS could benefit a science mission. This Phase 4 shadow mode demonstration will also help identify any operational situations that would produce anomalous results that must be corrected before committing to flight.

The next aerobraking orbiter after this Phase 4 AA demonstration will then reap the benefits of autonomous aerobraking in reducing cost and risk to the orbiter mission.

CONCLUSION

Aerobraking is a long and arduous process that bears considerable cost and risk associated with ground-based analysis and maneuver determination. Autonomous Aerobraking is currently being developed in four phases that will lead to the elimination of millions of dollars in cost of a large aerobraking operations staff and continuous DSN coverage. Phase 1 will be completed in

November 2011 and will have produced three versions of the AADS for three periapsis control corridors at three potential destinations. Phase 2 is intended to test these modules in a flight-like environment, determining the physical cost of employing AADS on a spacecraft. Phases 2 and 3 will be spent stress-testing the software, ensuring that proper risk is assessed onboard. Phase 4 is a demonstration of the AA software in a shadow mode. This demonstration is intended to prove the efficacy of autonomous aerobraking and quantify the benefits to an aerobraking orbiter. The next orbiter to use AA in a flight operations environment should then see a comparable maneuver strategy with the spacecraft staying within the design corridor without the staffing burden of ground-based analysis and cost burden of continuous DSN coverage.

ACKNOWLEDGMENTS

This work was sponsored by the NASA Engineering and Safety Center. This assessment can be found in the final report NESC-RP-09-00605 in November 2011. Team members who have significantly contributed to Phase 1 of the Autonomous Aerobraking assessment include Bobby Williams and Dave Skinner from Kinetx for the ephemeris model; Bob Tolson for the onboard Atmosphere Estimator; Jere Justus, Hilary Justh, and Holly Ramey for the "truth" atmosphere models used: MarsGRAM, VenusGRAM, and TitanGRAM; Chris Pastore for software conversion; John Dec and Mark Thornblom for the temperature models; Derek Liechty and Forrest Lumpkin for aerodynamic and aerothermodynamic assessments; Rob Maddock, Angela Bowes, and Alicia Cianciolo for trajectory and simulation modeling; and Dan O'Shaughnessy, Jim Kaidy, David Carrelli, Hollis Ambrose, and Tom Strikwerda from the Applied Physics Laboratory in modeling aerobraking within the MESSENGER-based high-fidelity simulation.

NOTATION

AA	Autonomous Aerobraking
AADS	Autonomous Aerobraking Development Software
AA-HFS	Autonomous Aerobraking – High Fidelity Simulator
APL	Applied Physics Laboratory
DSN	Deep Space Network
MESSENGER	MErcury Surface, Space ENvironment, GEochemistry and Ranging
MGS	Mars Global Surveyor
MRO	Mars Reconnaissance Orbiter
NESC	NASA Engineering and Safety Center
ODY	Mars Odyssey
POST2	Program to Optimize Simulated Trajectories

REFERENCES

[1] Willcockson, W. H., "Magellan Aerobraking Control Corridor: Design and Implementation", Adv. Astronautical Sciences. Vol. 87, Part II, 1994. Pp 647-662.

[2] Lyons, D. T., Beerer, J. G., Esposito, P., Johnston, M. D., "MGS: Aerobraking Mission Overview" Journal of Spacecraft and Rockets, Vol. 36, No. 3, 1999, pp 307-313.

[3] Tartabini, Paul, Michelle M. Munk, Richard W. Powell. "Development and Evaluation of an Operational Aerobraking Strategy for Mars Odyssey". *Journal of Spacecraft and Rockets 2005* 0022-4650 vol 42 no. 3 pp. 423-434.

[4] Johnston, M. D., Graf, J. E., Zurek, R. W., Eisen, H. J., and Jai, B. "The Mars Reconnaissance Orbiter Mission". IEEAC paper #1174 2004 IEEE Aerospace Conference Proceedings

[5] Spencer, D. A., Tolson, R. H., "Aerobraking Cost and Risk" Journal of Spacecraft and Rockets. Vol. 44, No. 6, Nov-Dec 2007, pp 1285-1293.

[6] Hibbard, K., Glaze, L., Prince, J., "Aerobraking at Venus: A Science and Technology Enabler". International Astronautical Congress Proceedings, Prague, Czech Republic. AA-D-11-00125.

[7] Hanna, J. L., Tolson, R. H. Approaches to Autonomous Aerobraking at Mars" AAS/AIAA Astrodynamics Specialist Conference, Quebec City, Canada. July 30-August 2, 2001. AAS 01-387.

[8] Daniel T. Lyons, "Aerobraking Automation Options." AAS-01-385, AAS/AIAA Astrodynamics Specialist Conference, Quebec City, CA, 2001.

[9] Hanna, J.L., Tolson, R.H., Cianciolo, A.M.D, and Dec, J.A., "Autonomous Aerobraking at Mars", presented at 5th International ESA Conference on Guidance Navigation and Control Systems and Actuator and Sensor Product Exhibition, Frascati, Italy, October 22-25, 2002. (ESA SP-516, February 2003)

[10] Willcockson, W. H. and Johnson, m. A., "Mars Odyssey Aerobraking: The First Step Towards Augonomous Aerobraking Operations" 2003 IEEE Aerospace Conference, Big Sky, MT. March 9-14, 2003.

[11] Robert H. Tolson, Jill L. Prince, "Onboard Atmospheric Modeling and Prediction for Autonomous Aerobraking Missions." AAS 11-477, AAS/AIAA Astrodynamics Specialist Conference, Girdwood, AK, 2011.

[12] Hilary L. Justh et al., "The Next Generation of Mars-GRAM and Its Role in the Autonomous Aerobraking Development Plan." AAS 11-478, AAS/AIAA Astrodynamics Specialist Conference, Girdwood, AK, 2011.

[13] Takashima, N., Wilmoth, R., "Aerodynamics of Mars Odyssey". AIAA Atmospheric Flight Mechanics Conference and Exhibit, Monterey, California, Aug 5-8, 2002. AIAA-2002-4809.

[14] John A. Dec et al., "Autonomous Aerobraking: Thermal Analysis and Response Surface Development." AAS 11-474, AAS/AIAA Astrodynamics Specialist Conference, Girdwood, AK, 2011.

[15] S.A. Striepe et al., "Program To Optimize Simulated Trajectories (POST II): Volume 2, Utilization Manual." Martin Marietta Corporation, 2004.

[16] David Carrelli et al., "Autonomous Aerobraking Algorithm Testing In Flight Software Simulation Environment." AAS 11-471, AAS/AIAA Astrodynamics Specialist Conference, Girdwood, AK, 2011

[17] Prince, J.L. H., Striepe, S. A., "NASA Langley Simulation Capabilities for the Mars Reconnaissance Orbiter", presented at the 15th Annual AAS/AIAA Space Flight Mechanics Conference, Copper Mountain, Colorado, January 23-27, 2005.

[18] Robert W. Maddock, "Implementation and Simulation Results Using Autonomous Aerobraking Development Software ." AAS 11-476, AAS/AIAA Astrodynamics Specialist Conference, Girdwood, AK, 2011.

AUTONOMOUS AEROBRAKING: THERMAL ANALYSIS AND RESPONSE SURFACE DEVELOPMENT

John A. Dec[*] and Mark N. Thornblom[†]

A high-fidelity thermal model of the Mars Reconnaissance Orbiter was developed for use in an autonomous aerobraking simulation study. Response surface equations were derived from the high-fidelity thermal model and integrated into the autonomous aerobraking simulation software. The high-fidelity thermal model was developed using the Thermal Desktop software and used in all phases of the analysis. The use of Thermal Desktop exclusively, represented a change from previously developed aerobraking thermal analysis methodologies. Comparisons were made between the Thermal Desktop solutions and those developed for the previous aerobraking thermal analyses performed on the Mars Reconnaissance Orbiter during aerobraking operations. A variable sensitivity screening study was performed to reduce the number of variables carried in the response surface equations. Thermal analysis and response surface equation development were performed for autonomous aerobraking missions at Mars and Venus.

INTRODUCTION

There are several challenges associated with placing a spacecraft in orbit around any planetary body. Often, mission design trade studies are made to maximize payload and minimize propellant mass. A mass efficient technique in terms of propellant use that has been used successfully by past missions is aerobraking.[1,2,3,4] After propulsively establishing a high-eccentricity, long-period orbit, aerobraking reduces an orbital period and eccentricity to a desired science orbit by passing through the upper atmosphere multiple times and using the drag on the spacecraft to reduce velocity. Atmospheric drag reduces the periapsis velocity of the spacecraft, thereby lowering the apoapsis altitude and velocity on each pass through the atmosphere. A larger drag, results in a larger change in velocity (ΔV) for a given orbit pass. The spacecraft passes through the upper atmosphere at hypersonic speeds and as a result is subjected to aerodynamic heating. The aerodynamic heating causes the temperature of both the internal and external spacecraft components to increase during the drag pass. The atmospheric drag and the aerodynamic heating are both functions of the atmospheric density and spacecraft velocity. One of the fundamental trades in performing an aerobraking maneuver is to achieve the largest ΔV possible while keeping all spacecraft components within defined temperature limits. As the spacecraft passes deeper into the atmosphere, the atmospheric density increases which results in a larger drag and a larger ΔV. However, an increase in atmospheric density causes a corresponding increase in the aerodynamic

---

[*] Senior Aerospace Engineer, Structural and Thermal Systems Branch, NASA Langley Research Center, MS 431.
[†] Aerospace Engineer, Structural and Thermal Systems Branch, NASA Langley Research Center, MS 431.

heating and hence, an increase in the spacecraft temperatures. Typically, most science orbiters are designed to minimize structural mass in order to maximize the science payload. The materials used in the construction of these spacecraft have finite temperature limits which cannot be exceeded without loss of structural integrity or functional performance. The temperature limits on these materials introduce a constraint to the aerobraking process and dictate how large the aerodynamic heating can become and thus, how much ΔV can be obtained on a given drag pass.

Aerobraking was first demonstrated by the Magellan spacecraft in orbit around Venus1. Mars Global Surveyor (MGS), Mars Odyssey, and Mars Reconnaissance Orbiter (MRO) all successfully performed aerobraking maneuvers around Mars.[2,3,4] The one character all of these missions had in common was that during the drag pass, the maximum temperature limit of the spacecraft was the most limiting factor in determining how many drag passes would be needed to arrive at the final science orbit. In particular, it was the temperature of the solar array of the spacecraft that was the most limiting. Because of orbit-to-orbit variations in atmospheric density and uncertainty in its prediction, the temperature of the solar array for an upcoming drag pass cannot be accurately predicted. In addition to the uncertainties associated with the atmospheric density, uncertainties also exist in the high-fidelity thermal model used to make the temperature predictions. The uncertainties in the thermal model can be classified into three groups; environmental, material property, and modeling. The environmental group encompasses the external inputs to the thermal model which include, heat transfer coefficient distribution, solar heating, etc. The material property group includes the uncertainties in the thermophysical properties of the materials used in the construction of the spacecraft. The modeling group is somewhat abstract and includes uncertainties introduced by modeling a physical object with a nodalized, lumped capacitance representation. This group includes modeling constructs such as contact resistance and mass distribution.

Traditionally, the aerobraking operations phase has required many teams (navigation, atmospheric scientist, mission designers, thermal analyst, etc.) to constantly monitor the mission and spacecraft. The aerobraking operations phase can last between 3 to 6 months and automating this process would reduce workload, cost, and risk of human error. Automation may also increase aerobraking mission flexibility by providing the means with which to choose maneuvers that are not limited to times occurring during a workday.[5] In addition, all aerobraking operations have relied on surrogate variables such as maximum dynamic pressure or maximum incident heat flux for mission control in lieu of the driving constraint which is solar array temperature. The thermal analysis performed on the MRO was unique in that a new thermal analysis technique was developed to account for the uncertainties in the analysis and improve the accuracy of the temperature predictions. The new technique called thermal response surface analysis was demonstrated during aerobraking operations.[6] The thermal response surface analysis technique provides the means with which to use onboard temperature measurements to make maneuver decisions. The purpose of this paper is to describe the thermal model and response surface development as well as the response surface equation integration into an autonomous aerobraking simulation.

THERMAL MODEL DEVELOPMENT

A high-fidelity thermal model, originally developed in MSC PATRAN[®7] and Thermal Desktop[®8] for MRO aerobraking operations[9], was modified to develop the response surface equations for this autonomous aerobraking simulation. Originally, Thermal Desktop was used to compute the view factors to space and the solar heating. The PATRAN model was used to compute the temperatures during the drag pass, utilizing the view factor and solar heating data from Thermal Desktop, and the aerodynamic heating from the direct simulation Monte Carlo (DSMC) code as boundary conditions. The original high-fidelity PATRAN thermal model was used as a starting point because model was already correlated to flight data.[10] One of the objectives of the autonomous aerobraking study was to consolidate the thermal analysis models into one universal model which would compute the view factors, solar heating inputs and solar array temperatures. To accomplish this objective, the original MRO thermal model, shown in Figure 1, was converted to Thermal Desktop and correlated to MRO flight data.[11] The results of the correlation effort compare well to flight data. An example of the correlation results is provided in Figure 2 and Figure 3 for orbit pass 262.

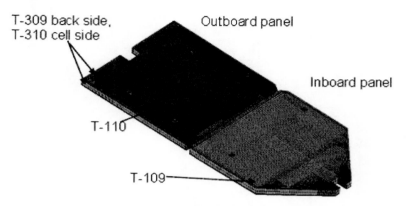

Figure 1. Original MRO solar array model and sensor locations.

After the MRO model was converted to Thermal Desktop and was correlated to flight data, several modifications were made to utilize the model as a tool for autonomous aerobraking and response surface development. First, the model was parameterized to allow variation in the key environmental, material property, and modeling variables needed for response surface development. This parameterization involved creating symbols within the model that either explicitly define the value of specific variables, or, as in most cases, establishes a multiplier or bias to known values to represent the defined uncertainty of the variable.

The next modification of the model is made to enable autonomous running of multiple analyses in parametric mode with multiple variables, where the user can select a desired number of variables and change the values between a defined upper and lower limit. Currently, Thermal Desktop has no design of experiment (DOE) capabilities; the code only has the built-in ability to run in parametric mode while varying a single variable. For response surface equation development of the MRO model, it is necessary to vary between twelve and fifteen parameters. Therefore, custom logic and operation blocks are added to the Thermal Desktop model that allows for multiple cases being run with variation of a user-defined number of variables. Additionally, these logic blocks allow specification of the total number of cases to run as well as the nominal, the high, and the low values of each variable.

The logic block also provides the ability to input a matrix of numbers that define the values of each parameter for each run. For a DOE, this matrix would be N by M elements, where N represents the number of cases in the study, and M represents the number of variables being investigated. The values in the matrix consist of either a 0 or ±1, where, in the case of the MRO model, 0 indicates that the nominal value of the variable used in the study, and ±1 indicates that the ±3 σ value is used. The variables are coded to range between -1 and +1 so that they are all on the same scale. This matrix is then input to an array data block, within the Thermal Desktop logic manager. While this approach limits the user to only the nominal, high and low values, minimal effort would be required to populate this matrix with any values between -1 and +1, based on either a uniform or Gaussian distribution, and the variable set according to the corresponding value, thus allowing the user to run Monte Carlo analyses, but that aspect is beyond the scope of this study.

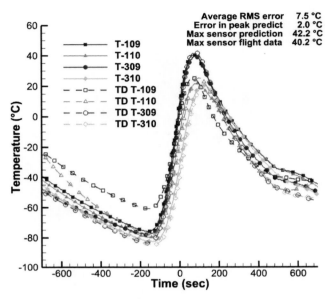

Figure 2. Correlation of the Thermal Desktop model to flight temperature data for drag pass 262 [11]

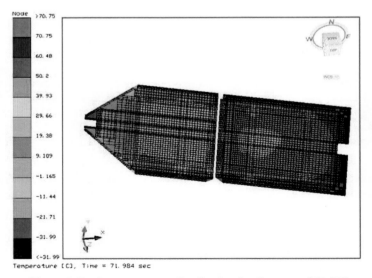

Figure 3. Peak temperature distribution for drag pass 262 (°C)

DESIGN OF EXPERIMENTS, SENSITIVITY STUDY AND RESPONSE SURFACE DEVELOPMENT

For an autonomous aerobraking mission, it is impractical, from a time perspective, with current onboard spacecraft computer technology to run a high-fidelity thermal model onboard the spacecraft. For autonomous aerobraking, the spacecraft must be able to compute the temperatures within seconds, minutes at most. One solution to satisfy this calculation speed requirement is to develop a response surface model for the temperatures which is derived from the high-fidelity thermal model. A response surface model is typically a polynomial equation that can be used to determine how a given response is affected by a set of quantitative independent variables or factors over a specified range. In the case of a high-fidelity thermal model the response is the temperature at a discrete point. The general form of the response surface equation representing the thermal response of the spacecraft solar arrays is given in Eq. (1).[12]

$$T_m = b_0 + \sum_{i=1}^{n} b_i x_i + \sum_{i=1}^{n} b_{ii} x_i^2 + \sum_{i=1}^{n-1} \sum_{j=i+1}^{n} b_{ij} x_i x_j + \sum_{i=1}^{n-2} \sum_{j=i+1}^{n-1} \sum_{k=j+1}^{n} b_{ijk} x_i x_j x_k \qquad (1)$$

Eq. (1) captures the main effects, 1st and 2nd order interactions and captures non-linearities with the quadratic terms and 3rd order interaction terms. Main effects are how the response of the system changes as a single factor changes. Interactions occur when the effect of one factor on the response depends on the level of another factor.[13]

Without a priori knowledge of how the temperatures calculated via a thermal analysis of a complex system will respond to variations and uncertainty in the input parameters, analysts are forced to include every variable they can think of in the development of a response surface representation of the thermal analysis. One way to generate the data necessary to create a response surface is to perform a DOE. A DOE is a systematic way of varying the design variables so that the data obtained can be analyzed to yield valid and objective conclusions.[13] In the case of the thermal analysis for autonomous aerobraking, the objective is to create a response surface model of the high-fidelity thermal model. As the number of variables or factors, as they are called in statistics, increases, the number of runs required for the DOE and hence, required to define the response surface increases dramatically. For example, in a full factorial design, which is a DOE that includes all possible combinations of the factors, if there are three levels for each factor and ten factors, then the number of required runs of the thermal analysis model would be 59,049, or l^k, where l is the number of levels and k is the number of factors. A level is defined as a discrete value for a particular factor, hence three levels represents three discrete values for a factor. Typically, when three levels are used the minimum, maximum, and midpoint values are used.

There are other types of DOEs that reduce the number of runs, but the trade off is that not every combination of the factors is represented. A face-centered central composite design (CCD) for example is one type of DOE that reduces the number of runs. A face-centered CCD is made up of three parts; center points, axial points, and fractional factorial points. For the same example of ten factors at three levels, if a face-centered CCD is chosen with two center points and a ¼ fractional factorial contribution, the number of runs required of the thermal model would be reduced to 278. The variation in the number of required runs as a function of the number of analysis variables for a full factorial design and a face-centered CCD are compared in Figure 4.

The trends in Figure 4 indicate that the number of factors being used to create the response surface should be minimized in order to minimize the number of required runs of the thermal model. In practical terms, if the thermal model takes 2 hours for one run, the 10 factor face-centered

CCD requiring 278 runs would take over 23 days running on a single computer to generate the data required to create the response surface. For autonomous aerobraking, updates to the thermal response surface may be required so minimizing the number of required runs, and hence, the time necessary for an update are essential. Additionally, reducing the number of factors reduces the amount of data that needs to be passed back-and-forth and maintained within the autonomous aerobraking simulation software.

To accomplish the goal of minimizing the number of factors, a sensitivity study can be performed to determine which factors initially selected are significant contributors to the solar array temperature response. Creating a screening DOE is a way to examine which of the factors main effects and which interactions are important. A screening DOE is similar to a CCD, except that a screening DOE does not include axial points, may or may not include center points, and the fraction factorial portion is much, much smaller. If a factor is deemed insignificant, it does not mean that particular factor contributes nothing to the response; it just means that particular factors variation is insignificant.

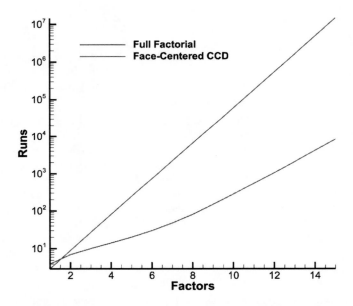

Figure 4. Comparison of required runs for different DOEs

For this study, the MRO spacecraft is used to simulate autonomous aerobraking around both Mars and Venus. The thermal model described in the thermal model section is used for both the Mars and Venus mission scenarios. The only differences in the model come from the external heating environments. At Mars, the solar heating input is relatively low and the affect of solar occultation on the initial temperatures is large. The atmospheric density and corresponding aerodynamic heating encountered during the drag pass are also relatively low, but due to the low initial temperatures prior to the drag pass, only the aerodynamic heating dominates the thermal response during the drag pass. At Venus, the solar heating inputs are relatively high and the affect of solar occultation in lowering the initial temperatures is lessened. The density and corresponding aerodynamic heating are also relatively high and combined with the solar heating both dominate the thermal response during the drag pass. The differences in the corresponding thermal response for both mission scenarios necessitate that a screening sensitivity study be performed for each mission scenario.

Starting with the initial list of factors used in the actual MRO aerobraking thermal response surface analysis[6], a screening DOE was generated using the JMP® statistical software.[14] The factors and their definitions are given in Table 1. The factors can be classified into three general categories: environmental, material property, and modeling. For these 15 factors, the screening DOE only required 129 runs, 128 from the fraction factorial part and 1 center point.

The JMP software performed an analysis of variance on the resulting temperatures calculated for each case in the DOE matrix. The statistical p-value was an indication as to whether the variation in the factor contributes significantly to the analysis. P-values less than 0.05 typically indicate a significant contribution. For the Mars autonomous aerobraking mission, the main effects for factors that had p-values greater than 0.05 are summarized in Table 2. If the only concern was the main effects, all six of these factors could be eliminated from the subsequent DOE and would not be carried in the response surface equation. However, the interactions between factors must also be examined. In the Mars mission scenario, interactions between all but two of the factors had p-values less than 0.05 when interacting with other factors. The only factors that could be dropped were the drag pass duration, and the solar cell emissivity, hence the face-centered CCD DOE for generating the response surface equation for the Mars mission scenario will contain 13 factors.

Table 1. MRO analysis variables

Category	Factor	Abbreviation
Environmental	Drag pass duration	DP
	Density	RHO
	Heat transfer coefficient	C_H
	Periapsis velocity	V
	Initial solar array temperature	IT
	Orbital heat flux	Q_s
Material Property	M55J graphite emissivity	FSE
	ITJ solar cell emissivity	ITJE
	M55J graphite thermal conductivity	FSk
	M55J graphite specific heat	FSC_p
	Aluminum honeycomb core thermal conductivity	ALk
	Aluminum honeycomb core specific heat	ALC_p
Modeling	Outboard solar panel mass distribution	OFM
	Solar cell layer mass distribution	MD
	Contact resistance	CR

Table 2. Factor screening for Mars mission scenario

Factor	Abbreviation	p-value
Drag pass duration	DP	0.8100
Orbital heat flux	Q_s	0.5987
ITJ solar cell emissivity	ITJE	0.6443
M55J graphite thermal conductivity	FSk	0.7929
Outboard solar panel mass distribution	OFM	0.4642
Contact resistance	CR	0.7929

Since different environmental conditions are encountered for the Venus mission scenario, the screening sensitivity must be performed again. Also, the drag pass duration was replaced by the orbital period. This new factor was used since it was deemed a better representation of the variation in the orbit geometry, which was the original intent of the drag pass duration factor. Following the same procedure as in the Mars mission scenario, an identical screening DOE was generated and the resulting data analyzed. For the Venus autonomous aerobraking mission, the main effects for factors that had p-values greater than 0.05 are summarized in Table 3.

Table 3. Factor screening for Venus mission scenario

Factor	Abbreviation	p-value
Orbital period	P	0.1097
Periapsis velocity	V	0.7999
M55J graphite specific heat	FSC_p	0.5526
M55J graphite thermal conductivity	FSk	0.5232
Aluminum honeycomb core thermal conductivity	ALk	0.9832
Aluminum honeycomb core specific heat	ALC_p	0.5684
Solar cell layer mass distribution	MD	0.5291
Outboard solar panel mass distribution	OFM	0.5496
Contact resistance	CR	0.5081

For Venus, some of the factors that are found to be insignificant are the same as the Mars mission scenario, however, there are others that are insignificant for Venus. but were significant for Mars, and vice-versa. The difference arises due to how different the missions are in terms of their environment and underscores the need to repeat the screening study for every mission scenario. Both scenarios illustrate the need to examine the interaction between factors. It was found that all but two factors had significant interactions with other factors. For Venus, the periapsis velocity and the contact resistance are dropped; hence the face-centered CCD DOE for generating the response surface equation for the Venus mission scenario will also contain 13 factors.

A face-centered CCD with 13 factors was generated using the JMP statistical software. The CCD had 26 axial points, 10 center points and 128 point from the fractional factorial contribution. JMP automatically reduces the fraction used to compute the fractional factorial contribution as the number of factors increases; in this case the fraction was 1/64th. The temperatures calculated for each of the 164 total runs for both Mars and Venus was analyzed using JMP where a least squares fit was constructed using the stepwise regression option in JMP. The result of the regression is a quadratic equation, one unique to the Mars mission scenario and one unique to the Venus mission scenario. The coefficient of determination or R^2 adjusted value was measured and used to determine how well the assumed functional form of the response measures the variability of the supplied data. In this case, the R^2 adjusted value measured how well the quadratic response surface represented the variability in the temperatures generated by the DOE cases. In the Mars mission scenario, the resulting response surface equation had an R^2 adjusted value of 0.9948. For the Venus mission scenario, the R^2 adjusted value is 0.9991. An R^2 adjusted value greater than 0.9 was desirable, but was not sufficient to determine the goodness of fit of the response surface.

To get a clear picture of how well the response surface equation is fitting the response data from the DOE runs, a plot of the actual versus predicted values, a plot of the residual versus predicted values, and the model fit distributions must be examined. The actual versus predicted plot shows the temperatures calculated by the thermal model for the cases described in the DOE plotted against the temperatures calculated by the quadratic response surface equation and is given in Figure 5 for the Mars mission scenario.

The centerline of the plot represents a perfect fit of the data; the plot shows that the data points lie close to the center line which indicates a good fit. The residual is the error in the fitted model and is the difference between the actual temperature calculated by the thermal model and the temperature calculated by the response surface equation. The residual for the maximum solar panel temperature versus the predicted maximum temperature is plotted in Figure 6.

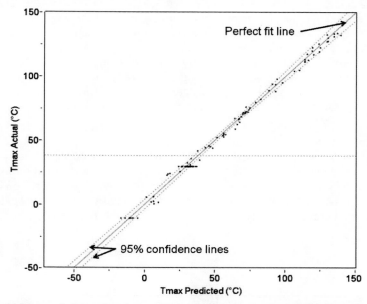

Figure 5. Mars mission scenario actual temperatures versus predicted temperatures

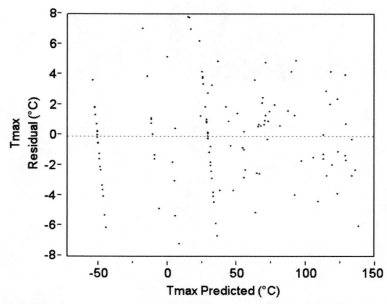

Figure 6. Mars mission scenario maximum solar panel temperature residual versus predicted maximum temperature

In general, the data points are randomly scattered in Figure 6 indicating a good fit of the temperature data. However, there are two areas on both Figure 5 and Figure 6 where the data points are clustered together; this clustering indicates that one of the factors may be dominating the response. For aerobraking, the peak temperatures are highly influenced by the peak density which is the primary reason for this clustering. One way to alleviate the occurrence of clustering is to break the density up into smaller intervals and develop a different response surface equation for each interval as in Reference 6. For simplicity in implementing the response surface equations into the autonomous aerobraking simulation, a goal is to try to have a single response surface equation. As a result of the goodness of fit analysis, a recommendation is that the density be broken up into three ranges and three separate response surface equations used.

One final check of the goodness of fit is to examine the model fit and model representation error distributions. Both model error distributions should approximate a normal distribution with mean around zero and standard deviation less ≤ 1.0. The model fit error is how well the response surface fits the temperature data in the DOE. The model fit error distribution for the maximum temperature for the Mars mission scenario is plotted in Figure 7. The distribution is approximately normal and has a mean of 0.0158 and a standard deviation of 1.0359. The standard deviation is slightly above 1.0, but is sufficiently close to 1.0 to conclude that the model is accurate.

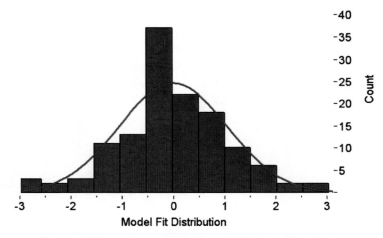

Figure 7. Mars mission scenario model fit error distribution

The model representation error is how well the response surface fits actual temperatures calculated by the thermal model for points other than those on the DOE. For the Mars mission scenario, the model representation error for the maximum temperature is plotted in Figure 8. The distribution is approximately normal with a mean of -0.1103 and standard deviation of 0.6177. Hence, it can be concluded that the response surface equation is an accurate representation of the high-fidelity thermal model.

The model fit and model representation errors are accounted for in the response surface equation when the temperature calculation is made from within the autonomous aerobraking simulation. Another error is also added as a bias to the temperature calculated by the response surface. This error is present because the high-fidelity thermal model will typically not be correlated to the aerobraking flight temperature data. This error is typically unknown until the first couple of drag passes are made and the flight temperatures and predicted temperatures compared. Therefore, a short calibration period is required but this can be accomplished during walk in which makes up the first initial orbits where the spacecraft periapsis is gradually lowered into the aerobraking altitude corridor.

One important aspect of response surface modeling that must be emphasized is that the response surface equation is only valid over the range for which it was defined. It must be stressed that even a small amount of extrapolation in any factor included in the equation can produce results that are invalid.

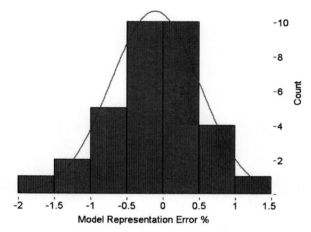

Figure 8. Mars mission scenario model representation error distribution

AUTONOMOUS AEROBRAKING SIMULATION

A generic response-surface equation thermal analysis (GRETA) computer program was written for use in the autonomous aerobraking development software (AADS). There are two versions, one written as a standalone program which includes the ability to run Monte Carlo simulations, the other for use with AADS which does not have a Monte Carlo simulation. AADS accesses the GRETA routines via an external function call. This architecture is beneficial in that the response surface equation coefficients or GRETA routines can be updated independently of AADS. The main feature of GRETA is that GRETA will accept any number of variables and hence any number of response surface coefficients so long as the program follows the form of Eq. (1). GRETA will also allow the user to modify any set of factors and thus calculate a new response. Additionally, GRETA allows the user to input a value for the response and calculate the value of one specific factor, holding all others constant. For autonomous aerobraking, the ability to calculate the value of a factor is crucial. For autonomous aerobraking the response is the temperature and the factor which needs to be determined is the atmospheric density. During the autonomous aerobraking simulation a temperature within the temperature corridor is sent by AADS to GRETA and the density is calculated. Hence, the temperature can be used to control the spacecraft during aerobraking. Using the temperature represents a major step forward since the temperature is measured directly onboard the spacecraft and can be used to determine what temperature is input to GRETA for the next orbit pass. The temperature and corresponding density for the Mars Mission run out is shown in Figure 9 and Figure 10.

Similar simulations were run using the Venus response surface equation and similar results were obtained, however, since the MRO spacecraft was used, the temperature results were unrealistically high and will not be shown in this paper to avoid confusion. The reason the temperatures were unrealistically high comes from the fact that the solar heating was almost 4.5 times higher at Venus as compared to Mars in addition to a higher aerodynamic heating. The MRO spacecraft was not designed to aerobrake at Venus and hence, the generated thermal response was not consistent with a spacecraft specifically designed for Venus aerobraking. For the autonomous aerobraking simulation at Venus, for demonstration purposes, the maximum temperature obtained from the thermal analysis was scaled to match the maximum temperature calculated for a proposed Venus aerobraking spacecraft; a spacecraft which had a more robust thermal design and had solar panels tailored to minimize the aerodynamic heating.

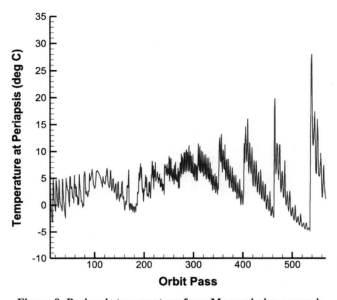

Figure 9. Periapsis temperature for a Mars mission scenario

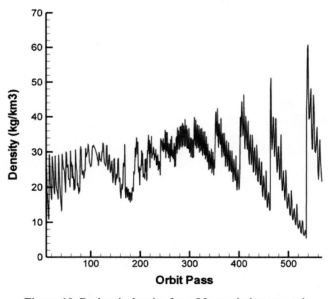

Figure 10. Periapsis density for a Mars mission scenario

494

SUMMARY

The original high-fidelity thermal model using both PATRAN and Thermal Desktop was described and converted for analysis in Thermal Desktop. The new Thermal Desktop model was successfully correlated to flight data obtained from the MRO mission. The response surface development and the response surface equation integration into an autonomous aerobraking simulation were described and implemented. Analysis variable screening was performed and it was determined that for each mission scenario, two different variables could be dropped from the subsequent response surface equation derivation. A goodness of fit analysis was performed confirming the response surface equations were adequate representations of the high-fidelity thermal model. The generic response surface equation thermal analysis program was developed and demonstrated within the autonomous aerobraking development software.

ACKNOWLEDGMENTS

The authors would like to thank Ruth Amundsen for converting the MRO thermal model to Thermal Desktop and making the comparison between the original PATRAN thermal model. This work was sponsored by the NASA Engineering and Safety Center (NESC). This assessment can be found in the final report NESC-RP-09-00605 in November 2011. In particular we would like to thank Steven Rickman the NESC Passive Thermal Control Technical Fellow for his review of this work.

NOTATION

AADS	autonomous aerobraking development software
ALC_p	aluminum honeycomb core specific heat, J/kg-K
ALk	aluminum honeycomb core thermal conductivity, W/m-K
b_0	response surface intercept coefficient
b_i	response surface equation main effect term coefficients
b_{ii}	response surface equation quadratic term coefficients
b_{ij}	response surface equation 2nd order interaction term coefficients
b_{ijk}	response surface equation 3rd order interaction term coefficients
C_H	heat transfer coefficient
CCD	central composite design
CR	contact resistance, W/m^2-K
DP	drag pass duration, sec
DOE	design of experiments

DSMC	direct simulation Monte Carlo
FSC$_p$	M55J composite facesheet specific heat, J/kg-K
FSE	M55J composite facesheet emissivity
FSk	M55J composite facesheet thermal conductivity, W/m-K
GRETA	generic response-surface equation thermal analysis program
i	summation index
ITJE	improved triple junction solar cell emissivity
IT	initial solar panel temperature, °C
k	number of factors
l	number of levels
m	point on the spacecraft for which a response surface equation has been derived
M	DOE matrix dimension
MD	solar cell mass distribution, kg
MGS	Mars Global Surveyor
MOI	mars orbit insertion
MRO	Mars Reconnaissance Orbiter
n	number of factors
N	DOE matrix dimension
OFM	outboard panel M55J facesheet mass distribution, kg
P	orbit period, hr
Q$_s$	solar and planetary heat flux, W/cm^2
R^2 adj	coefficient of determination, R squared adjusted
RHO	atmospheric density, kg/km^3
RSE	response surface equation
T$_m$	temperature (°C) of the mth point on the solar array
V	periapsis velocity, km/s

X_i	independent variable
ΔV	change in velocity, km/s
ρ_∞	freestream density, kg/km^3
σ	standard deviation

REFERENCES

[1] Carpenter, A. S., "The Magellan Aerobraking Experiment: Attitude Control Simulation and Preliminary Flight Results", AIAA Paper 93-3830, August 1993.

[2] Lyons, D., Beerer, J., Esposito, P., Johnston, M. D., and Willcockson, W., "Mars Global Surveyor: Aerobraking Mission Overview", *Journal of Spacecraft and Rockets*, Vol. 36, No 3, 1999, pp. 307-313.

[3] Smith, J. C., and Bell, J. L., "2001 Mars Odyssey Aerobraking", *Journal of Spacecraft and Rockets,* Vol. 42, No. 3, 2005, pp. 406-415.

[4] Lyons, D., "Mars Reconnaissance Orbiter: Aerobraking Reference Trajectory", AIAA Paper 2002-4821, August 2002.

[5] Prince, J. L., Dec, J. A., and Tolson, R. H., "Autonomous Aerobraking Using Thermal Response Surface Analysis", *Journal of Spacecraft and Rockets,* Vol. 46, No 2, 2009, pp 292-298.

[6] Dec, J. A., "Probabilistic Thermal Analysis During Mars Reconnaissance Orbiter Aerobraking", AIAA Paper 2007-1214, January 2007.

[7] MSC/PATRAN User Manual, MacNeal-Schwendler Corporation, Version 2010, February 2010.

[8] Thermal Desktop User Manual, Cullimore and Ring Technologies, Inc., Version 5.3, January 2010.

[9] Dec, John A., Gasbarre, Joseph F., and Amundsen, Ruth M., "Thermal Modeling of the Mars Reconnaissance Orbiter's Solar Panel and Instruments During Aerobraking," 07ICES-64, 37th International Conference On Environmental Systems, Chicago, Illinois, July 2007.

[10] Amundsen, Ruth M., Dec, John A., Gasbarre, Joseph F., "Thermal Model Correlation for Mars Reconnaissance Orbiter", 07ICES-17, 37th International Conference on Environmental Systems, Chicago, Illinois, 2007.

[11] Amundsen, Ruth M., "Aeroheating Mapping to Thermal Model for Autonomous Aerobraking Capability", 22nd Annual Thermal Fluids and Analysis Workshop, Newport News, Virginia, 2011.

[12] Breyfogle, F. W., *Implementing Six Sigma: Smarter Solutions Using Statistical Methods*, 2nd Ed., John Wiley & Sons, Inc., Hoboken, NJ, 2003.

[13] *NIST/SEMATECH e-Handbook of Statistical Methods*, http://www.itl.nist.gov/div898/handbook/, 2011.

[14] JMP, Version 8. SAS Institute Inc., Cary, NC, 1989-2011.

IMPLEMENTATION AND SIMULATION RESULTS USING AUTONOMOUS AEROBRAKING DEVELOPMENT SOFTWARE

Robert W. Maddock,[*] Alicia Dwyer Cianciolo,[*] Angela Bowes,[*]
Jill L. H. Prince[*] and Richard W. Powell[†]

An autonomous aerobraking software system is currently under development with support from the NASA Engineering and Safety Center (NESC) that would move typically ground-based aerobraking operations functions to on-board a spacecraft, reducing mission risk and cost. The software suite that will enable autonomous aerobraking is the Autonomous Aerobraking Development Software (AADS) and consists of an ephemeris model, onboard atmosphere estimator, temperature and loads prediction, and a maneuver calculation. The software calculates the maneuver time, magnitude and direction commands to maintain the spacecraft periapsis parameters within the desired design structural load and/or thermal constraints. The AADS is currently tested in simulations at Mars, with plans to also evaluate feasibility and performance at Venus and Titan.

INTRODUCTION

Several past NASA missions have used the aerobraking technique to reduce the fuel required to deliver a spacecraft into a desired orbit around a target planet or moon with an appreciable atmosphere. Aerobraking was first demonstrated at Venus with Magellan in 1993 and then was used to achieve the science orbit of three Mars orbiters: Mars Global Surveyor in 1997, Mars Odyssey in 2001, and Mars Reconnaissance Orbiter in 2006. Instead of using only the propulsion system to decelerate the spacecraft, aerobraking is used after the initial orbit insertion to further decelerate the spacecraft using aerodynamic drag. The spacecraft traverses the upper atmosphere of the planet or moon multiple times while controlling periapsis altitude using small propulsive maneuvers at apoapsis in order to hold the spacecraft within a specified corridor. This corridor is designed to keep the spacecraft safely within required structural and/or thermal design limits until the desired orbit is achieved.

Although aerobraking itself reduces the propellant required to reach the final orbit, this reduction comes at the expense of additional mission time (typically 3–6 months), a large mission operations staff, and significant Deep Space Network (DSN) coverage. This combination of critical resources results in an expensive operational phase of a mission. The concept of automating this complex process has been studied for over a decade[1,2]. The NASA Engineering and Safety Center (NESC) is currently developing the Autonomous Aerobraking Development Software (AADS) to demonstrate that many of the aerobraking operations functions, which have typically been per-

---
[*] NASA Langley Research Center, Engineering Directorate, M.S. 489, Hampton, VA 23681.
[†] Analytical Mechanics Associates, 303 Butler Farm Rd., Hampton, VA 23666.

formed on the ground, can be performed autonomously onboard the spacecraft, thus reducing the required ground staff and DSN coverage saving millions of dollars in project costs[3].

Aerobraking operations occur in four phases. The first phase, referred to as "walk-in", begins after the propulsive capture and is used to gradually lower the periapsis until the sensible atmosphere is encountered and can be initially characterized. The second phase is the main aerobraking phase and guides the spacecraft from the initial long period orbits to short period orbits, using maneuvers to remain within the operational corridor. The third phase, often referred to as the "endgame", adds a minimal orbital lifetime to the spacecraft safety constraints to allow adequate time to respond to a spacecraft problem without danger of deorbiting. The final phase is the termination of aerobraking by raising periapsis out of the atmosphere. Operations during the main aerobraking phase can be broken down into daily and weekly operations. The weekly operations determine the flight corridor design for the next week, and the daily operations are used to determine any required periapsis adjust maneuvers to maintain the spacecraft within the design corridor. The AADS system currently being developed through NESC would allow for these ground operations functions to be moved to the spacecraft and performed autonomously.

AEROBRAKING MISSION RUNOUT

The mission runout is a ground based simulation of a reference mission designed to achieve the final desired orbit conditions via aerobraking while maintaining the mission operational constraints and the required margins on spacecraft design limits[4]. Desired final orbit conditions can include altitude, inclination, argument of periapsis, and longitude of the ascending node required to attain a specific local mean solar time (LMST) orientation, or any combinations of the above. Spacecraft design and mission operational constraints may consist of spacecraft thermal and structural limits, such as freestream heat rate, solar array temperature, dynamic pressure, power, attitude, and capability to handle atmospheric density fluctuations, as well as orbit lifetime requirements, maneuver frequency restrictions, maneuver magnitude limitations, and required propellant remaining post aerobraking to achieve mission objectives.

The mission runout begins after walk-in and lasts until the final desired orbit conditions are achieved. A corridor is determined based on a heat rate indicator, dynamic pressure, or temperature to keep the spacecraft within the appropriate design margins. Maneuvers are performed at apoapsis that raise or lower periapsis to maintain the spacecraft within the pre-determined corridor. The upper limit of the corridor is determined by the required operational constraint margin to ensure spacecraft safety, and therefore defines the maximum aerobraking rate (i.e. shortest duration) that can be achieved within that constraint margin. For any of these corridor constraints, the lower the spacecraft is in the corridor, the higher altitude the atmospheric passes, the lower the delta-v from aerodynamic drag, resulting in an overall increased aerobraking mission duration. The lower corridor limit may be set to reduce the frequency of maneuvers required to stay in the corridor and/or to maintain the maneuver magnitudes above some minimum threshold. A particular lower corridor limit may also be required to ensure the aerobraking rate is such that the desired final orbit conditions can be reached by a certain time. For instance, in the case where there is a required final orbit LMST, the initial orbit node must have enough time to precess with respect to the Sun in order to achieve the desired LMST. The amount of time required for the precession varies as a function of the initial orbit conditions, current orbit conditions, central body, gravity, atmospheric environment, and other forces such as third body perturbations and solar radiation pressure. Aerobraking either too quickly or too slowly could cause the final desired orbit apoapsis altitude to be reached at a different LMST than required.

The corridor limits can change as a function of time since the specific conditions that the spacecraft is experiencing are a function of orbit geometry. A corridor target, specified as a percentage of the corridor width, is set and can vary with time or orbit geometry as well. The minimum amount of time allowed between maneuvers is also set. Whether or not a maneuver is performed when it is "allowed" is based on predicting ahead by the minimum time between maneuvers plus one additional day. If a corridor violation occurs at any time during the predicted time period, a maneuver will be performed at the next allowable apoapsis.

Operationally, the mission runout is used to establish the actual spacecraft flight design corridor each week and can be adjusted if necessary during the flight to accommodate observed atmosphere fluctuations. The daily operations are used to determine any required periapsis adjust maneuvers to maintain the spacecraft within the design corridor.

AADS OVERVIEW AND INTERFACES

The Autonomous Aerobraking Development Software (AADS) is a suite of models and algorithms intended to test the feasibility of an autonomous aerobraking system[5]. Three separate AADS packages are being developed for this NESC study, one each for Mars, Venus, and Titan. AADS for application at Mars and Titan consists of three distinct modules: (1) the Ephemeris Estimator which processes spacecraft Inertial Measurement Unit (IMU) acceleration data to estimate current and future spacecraft states, (2) the Atmosphere Estimator[6] which processes spacecraft acceleration data along with Ephemeris Estimator state data to estimate the atmosphere's density and scale height, and (3) the Maneuver Estimator which processes data from both the Ephemeris and Atmosphere Estimators to determine whether or not a maneuver is required in order to keep the spacecraft within the desired operational corridor. The AADS for Venus will also include a fourth module containing temperature models to predict the maximum temperature the spacecraft will encounter during the next atmospheric pass[7].

The AADS is designed to output a maneuver vector and its associated apoapsis time to the spacecraft. With these pieces of information, the spacecraft can autonomously execute maneuvers at apoapsis to correct its periapsis altitude such that its design parameters are maintained within the specified heat rate, temperature, or dynamic pressure corridor. In addition, the AADS outputs the periapsis and atmospheric entry/exit time estimates so that the spacecraft can properly slew to aerobraking configuration and begin its atmospheric data collection at the appropriate times.

The AADS flight software interfaces with the spacecraft through the use of data structures[8], as shown in Figure 1. The AADS software is not always running, but instead is called once per orbit, typically at some time after an atmospheric pass ends and prior to the next apoapsis. The required AADS input data is passed into AADS through two structures; the first includes data which will or may change at each AADS call (e.g. spacecraft acceleration data), and the second which contains data not likely to change during the aerobraking mission, but is desirable to upload to the spacecraft in case a change is necessary (e.g. planetary constants). At each AADS call, all calculations are performed and the results (maneuver time, size, and direction) are then passed back to the spacecraft through a separate data structure. At this time, the AADS software can be placed in stand-by mode or terminated until after the next atmospheric pass in order to free up spacecraft resources for other activities. Some AADS data does need to be preserved between AADS calls (e.g. Ephemeris Estimator current state prediction and Atmosphere Estimator atmosphere archive data), so some memory will be allocated and preserved while AADS is not running.

The AADS has been developed for testing using aerodynamic and thermal models of the Mars Reconnaissance Orbiter (MRO). These models are used with a generalized spacecraft model for AADS feasibility testing purposes only. When a flight vehicle is selected for AADS implementation, the simulation aerodynamic and AADS thermal models must be adapted to that specific vehicle. The maneuver calculation, atmosphere estimation and ephemeris estimation models are not vehicle specific and do not require modification once validated. The testing of AADS presented here is performed with the Program to Optimize Simulated Trajectories II (POST2).

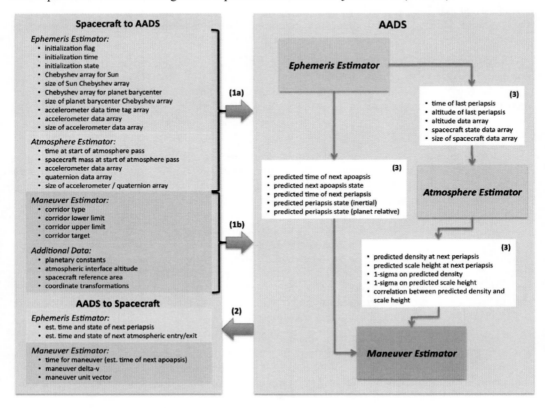

**Figure 1. AADS interfaces with the spacecraft using data structures:
(1a) spacecraft inputs to AADS which will or may change each AADS call, (1b) spacecraft inputs to AADS which are not likely to change during the aerobraking mission, (2) AADS outputs to the spacecraft, and (3) intra-AADS.**

Program to Optimize Simulated Trajectories II (POST2)

The Program to Optimize Simulated Trajectories II (POST2) is a generalized point mass, rigid body, discrete parameter targeting and optimization trajectory simulation program based on the POST software initially developed in the 1970's by NASA Langley Research Center in partnership with the Martin Marietta Co.[9, 10] Throughout the years, POST has been continually upgraded and modified to support a large variety of aerospace vehicle development and mission flight operations through trajectory simulation, flight dynamics analyses, vehicle system development and evaluation, as well as integrated system performance assessments. The program was significantly improved with additional capabilities added in the area of vehicle modeling, trajectory simulation, and targeting and optimization. Three and six degree-of-freedom (DOF) versions of POST have been available since the 1980's.

POST2 development began in the mid-1990's in an effort to update the software architecture and expand the modeling capability of the original POST computer code. POST2 has been used successfully to solve a wide variety of atmospheric ascent and re-entry problems, as well as exo-atmospheric orbital transfer problems. The versatility of the program is evidenced by its multiple vehicle, multiple phase simulation capability that features generalized planet and vehicle models. POST2 also contains many basic models (such as atmosphere, gravity, propulsion and navigation system models) while maintaining modularity in the code structure. As a result, the user has substantial flexibility to modify existing models, or include mission specific models of varying fidelity, such as vehicle specific aerodynamic data, planetary (e.g. gravity) and atmosphere models, vehicle and sensor models, and even onboard flight/mission specific software. POST2 has become an industry standard trajectory simulation and optimization tool that has been transferred to hundreds of organizations throughout government, industry, and academia, where it is used to evaluate, design, develop, test, and operate numerous current and future aerospace systems.

SIMULATION ENVIRONMENT AND MODELS

AADS and POST2 Integration

Because of the high level of flexibility and modularity of POST2, it was possible to integrate the AADS code with POST2 in a way that is very "flight-like". In this simulation environment, POST2 takes on the role of the physical environment as well as the spacecraft, where AADS is then executed through the POST2 flight software interface, in much the same way it would be implemented onboard the spacecraft. The interface data structures described earlier are created on the spacecraft/POST2 side and passed into AADS. As would be the case onboard the spacecraft, the AADS code has no other connection to POST2 or the "outside world", and vice versa, except through this data structure interface. Once integrated, the POST2 and AADS code are compiled into a single executable which is then run using the POST2 user interface.

As just described, it is necessary for POST2 to take on many of the roles and responsibilities of the spacecraft, including the generation and passing of critical data needed by AADS, such as:

1. 10 Hz time-tagged sensed acceleration vector during both maneuvers and atmospheric passes for the Ephemeris Estimator.

2. 1 Hz sensed acceleration vector and quaternion (central body inertial to spacecraft body frame) during the atmospheric passes for the Atmosphere Estimator.

3. Planetary ephemeris data (e.g. central body, Sun) over the time period of interest for the Ephemeris Estimator

The data are collected during the trajectory simulation, saved in the appropriate AADS interface data structure arrays, and then passed to AADS when it is called. In actual flight, the acceleration data would be collected from the spacecraft IMU, processed, and stored in the data structures for AADS usage. The planetary ephemeris data would likely be uploaded to the spacecraft from the ground, possibly updated at some interval, and then sent to the AADS when called.

Other Models and Simulation Inputs

As previously described, POST2 has many built-in planetary and environment models, but also has the capability to integrate mission specific models. For the AADS POST2 simulation environment, this was done in several areas, including planetary constants, gravity, atmosphere, and spacecraft aerodynamics[11]. Additional models required for both mission runout and AADS simulations were also developed and integrated into the POST2 simulation environment, including solar radiation pressure and 3rd body gravitational effect.

AADS PERFORMANCE FOR MARS

Mission Runout

In order to assess the operational advantages and estimate performance of the AADS software, a comparison must ultimately be made with an aerobraking mission runout. POST2 (without AADS integrated) was used to simulate this mission runout in an application at Mars. For this analysis, an initial orbital state was selected from the Mars Reconnaissance Orbiter (MRO) flight profile after the "walk-in" phase of the aerobraking mission was completed. Generalized space-craft geometry and mass properties were also used as simulation inputs. In addition, the Mars-GRAM-2010 atmosphere model[12] was integrated with POST2, along with an 85x85 Mars gravity field and an MRO / Mars Odyssey aerodynamics model[13]. A full aerobraking mission was then simulated until the apoapsis altitude is brought to 450 km. In addition, the Mars mission runout maneuvers were constrained to occur no more frequently than once a week.

For aerobraking at Mars, the estimated freestream heat rate at periapsis is used as the operational corridor to which the spacecraft must be kept during the main aerobraking phase, and is given by:

$$\dot{q} = \frac{1}{2}\rho V^3 \tag{1}$$

were $\dot{q}$ is the freestream heat rate, ρ is the atmospheric density, and V is the spacecraft speed. For this analysis, the corridor was set to 0.11 to 0.17 W/cm^2. Since maneuvers were constrained to once a week, it was necessary to bias the target within this corridor as a function of orbit period: 80% for orbit periods greater than 10.5 hrs, 70% for orbit periods between 10.5 and 2.5 hours, and 50% for orbit periods less than 2.5 hrs.

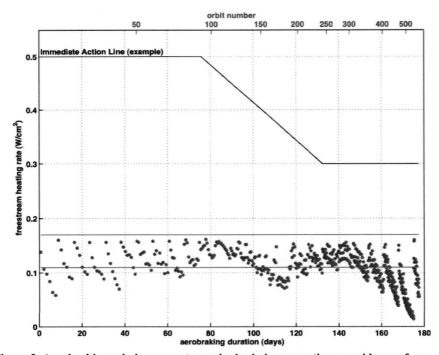

Figure 2. Aerobraking mission runout: nominal mission operations corridor performance

Figure 2 shows the operational corridor performance for the mission runout simulation. As noted earlier, the corridor target was varied as a function of orbit period in order to ensure the corridor was maintained (upper limit not exceeded) throughout the aerobraking mission while constraining maneuvers to no more frequently than once a week. The corridor performance for the AADS is expected to be similar to that of the mission runout. However, with the added advantage of a fixed corridor target and maneuvers allowed on each orbit, the AADS system should complete the aerobraking mission much more efficiently (i.e. in a shorter amount of time), by doing a much better job of remaining within the corridor (lower limit). A representative operational immediate action line is also shown to provide context as to how the corridor would be established to provide sufficient margins during the main aerobraking phase.

AADS Performance

With the AADS software successfully integrated into the POST2 simulation environment, AADS performance has been assessed for application at Mars. The AADS POST2 simulation utilizes the same planetary, atmosphere, gravity, spacecraft and aerodynamics models as the mission runout. The initial state for the AADS simulation, however, is extracted from the mission runout results. The apoapsis state of the 7th orbit of the mission runout is used in order to allow data from the first 7 atmospheric passes to be used to build the atmosphere archive needed by the Atmosphere Estimator. (During actual operations, this archive would likely be constructed during the "walk-in" phase, while there is still ground interaction and prior to initiation of the AADS system.) The same operational corridor as the mission runout is also used for the AADS simulation; however, the target is fixed at 50% of the corridor width for the duration of the aerobraking mission. In addition, since this system is fully autonomous, maneuvers are allowed to occur at any apoapsis.

The Ephemeris Estimator performance can be assessed by examining how well the AADS module estimates the current periapsis state as compared to POST2. Figure 3 (a and b) illustrates this performance, showing the estimated differences in terms of periapsis time and altitude. At the start of the simulation, when the Ephemeris Estimator is initialized with a POST2 state, the performance is quite good, showing excellent agreement (sub-second and meter level) between the Ephemeris Estimator and POST2 estimates. As time progresses, drifting in the Ephemeris Estimator propagation, as well as a build up of error from the lack of precision (i.e. frequency) in the acceleration data provided by the spacecraft (during both the atmospheric pass and maneuver), causes the Ephemeris Estimator estimates to diverge (10-20 seconds and 100's of meters). In order to mitigate this during implementation in flight, an initialization state update would be provided to the Ephemeris Estimator at some regular interval. For this AADS simulation, this was done once per week. As the mission progresses and the orbit period reduces, the Ephemeris Estimator propagation relies more heavily on acceleration data as the atmospheric passes become longer and more frequent, resulting in increased divergence due to the increased atmospheric pass duration and the number of orbits between Ephemeris Estimator initialization state updates. This is evident in the more rapid fall-off of the Ephemeris Estimator estimates towards the end of the aerobraking mission. Increased acceleration data rates (e.g. 100 Hz) have been shown to improve the performance at these later mission times (Figure 3c). However, the impact on the spacecraft resources to save this amount of additional data is significant. Another option would be to increase the frequency of the initialization state updates to minimize the Ephemeris Estimator divergence (Figure 3d). The time where this performance drop-off is most likely to occur, however, is after the main aerobraking phase ends, when the mission would have transitioned into the lifetime constraint or orbit safety phase, and AADS would likely no longer be utilized. Regardless, preliminary results show overall the Ephemeris Estimator performance shown here is sufficient for successful AADS operation over the main aerobraking phase of the mission.

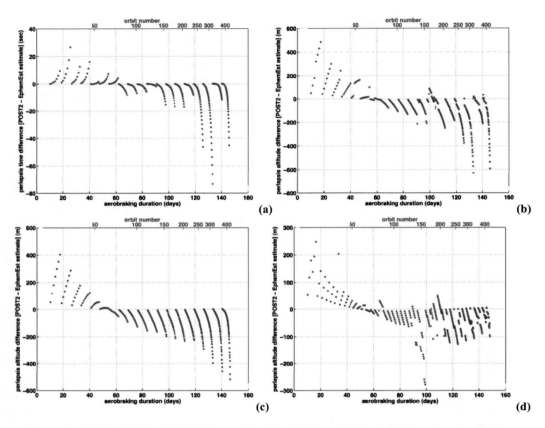

Figure 3. AADS Ephemeris Estimator performance (difference) for current periapsis estimate:
(a) periapsis time, (b) periapsis altitude, (c) periapsis altitude using 100 Hz acceleration data, and
(d) periapsis altitude for initialization state updates every 3 days.

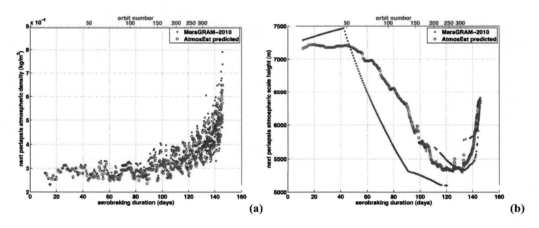

Figure 4. AADS Atmosphere Estimator performance:
(a) periapsis atmospheric density, (b) periapsis atmospheric scale height

506

The Atmosphere Estimator performance can be assessed by comparing the density and scale height estimates for the next periapsis against the actual MarsGRAM-2010 atmosphere model values, as shown in Figure 4. The density prediction is generally within 10% and the scale height within 1 km (~15%) of the MarsGRAM-2010 model. The difference in the scale height estimates can be tied to the drift in the Ephemeris Estimator periapsis time and altitude (profile) estimates. Efforts to tune the Atmosphere Estimator and update the algorithm to be independent of altitude estimates are underway and should provide additional improvements (see Reference 7).

The Maneuver Estimator and AADS performance are highly coupled and can be assessed by determining how well the spacecraft remains within the desired operational corridor. Data from the Ephemeris and Atmosphere Estimators are used to estimate the freestream heat rate at periapsis during the next atmospheric pass. If the estimate is outside of the operational corridor, a maneuver is calculated such that the predicted heat rate for the next periapsis is at the target location within the corridor (50%, or 0.14 W/cm^2). First, a desired change in altitude is calculated using:

$$\Delta h = -H_s \cdot \ln(\frac{\rho_{desired}}{\rho_{predicted}}) = -H_s \cdot \ln(\frac{\dot{q}_{desired}}{\dot{q}_{predicted}}) \qquad (2)$$

where Δh is the required altitude change and H_s is the predicted atmospheric scale height. This change in altitude is then added to the current orbit semi-major axis and a new velocity at apoapsis is determined. The difference between this new apoapsis velocity and the current estimate of the apoapsis velocity is the required maneuver magnitude. This value is positive for a periapsis raise (decrease freestream heating rate) and negative for a periapsis lowering (increase freestream heating rate). The maneuver direction is estimated to be that of the pre-maneuver velocity vector at apoapsis. Since these maneuvers are typically small (< 0.5 m/s), this assumption works well, even when considering a finite burn. (The mission runout simulation calculates required maneuvers in much the same way.)

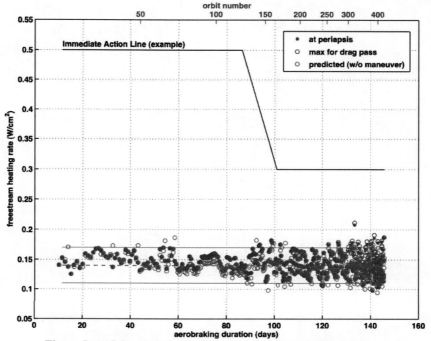

Figure 5. AADS: nominal mission operations corridor performance

507

A summary of the AADS performance for the Mars aerobraking mission simulation, in terms of how well the spacecraft stays within the mission operations corridor, is provided in Figure 5. It shows that the AADS system is successful in keeping the spacecraft within the specified corridor. Figure 5 also illustrates the difference between the AADS predicted freestream heat rate and the actual heat rate, which is mainly driven by the differences between the Atmosphere Estimator density and scale height estimates from those of the MarsGRAM-2010 atmosphere model.

As previously discussed, near the end of the aerobraking mission, the very long atmospheric passes and increased number of atmospheric passes due to the shorter orbit period tend to emphasize the effects of acceleration data precision on the Ephemeris Estimator (and Atmosphere Estimator) performance. These effects are also represented in the corridor performance (Figure 5). It is important to remember that in flight operations, AADS functions would very likely terminate well before this threshold is reached when the aerobraking mission transitions from the main aerobraking phase, when orbit period reduction is the focus, to the endgame phase, when orbit safety and lifetime is of greatest concern.

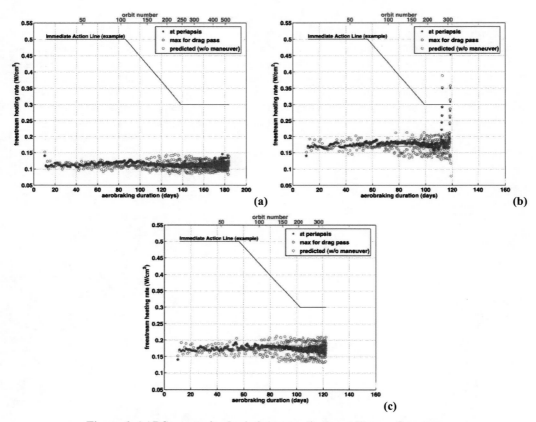

Figure 6. AADS constrained mission operations corridor performance:
(a) fixed at nominal corridor lower limit, (b) fixed at nominal corridor upper limit (c) at nominal corridor upper limit with 3 day updates

Changing the corridor limits can have an effect on the aerobraking mission duration. To illustrate this, the AADS aerobraking mission was simulated again using a very tight operational corridor (0.02 W/cm^2 in width) centered at the corridor lower limit (0.11 W/cm^2) and again at the corridor upper limit (0.17 W/cm^2). Figure 6 illustrates the corridor performance for these cases and a summary of the mission performance is also provided in Table 1.

Table 1. Summary of AADS performance for runs using the nominal operational corridor, a corridor constrained to the nominal corridor upper limit, and one to the nominal corridor lower limit.

	Nominal	*Lower Limit* (Figure 6a)	*Upper Limit* (Figure 6b)
aerobraking duration (days)	145.9	183.8	119.3
total Δv (m/s)	9.0	40.8	30.6
no. of maneuvers	37	479	294

Figure 6b does show violations of the desired corridor as the aerobraking mission progresses. This divergence is driven by the aggressive (e.g. low altitude = higher density) corridor constraint and its impact on the accuracy of the Ephemeris Estimator's integration of the atmospheric pass acceleration data, and thus the Atmosphere Estimator's density estimates. Since density information is estimated from acceleration data, and AADS will be more sensitive to these estimates due to the higher density environment, and lack of sufficient resolution of the acceleration data will result in earlier and/or more rapid divergence within the AADS. The Ephemeris Estimator's integration of the maneuver acceleration data also plays a role in this behavior. Small maneuvers (< 0.5 m/s, < 1 sec burn duration) coupled with the fixed resolution of the acceleration data (10 Hz) means that in many cases, the acceleration data may not capture the entire maneuver, thus resulting in poor Ephemeris Estimators estimates of the maneuver delta-v. For the nominal run, maneuvers, although allowed on every orbit, were relatively sparse, particularly early in the aerobraking mission, so this error is not very pronounced. For these extreme cases, however, maneuvers occur on practically every orbit, and the effects of this error in the delta-v estimate can quickly build up. In addition, the Ephemeris Estimator predictions of atmospheric entry and exit times (as a function of altitude) are used as the start and end time of acceleration data collection. If the Ephemeris Estimator tends to estimate altitudes higher than the actual (as Figure 3b appears to indicate), then these entry and exit times, will result in a reduced acceleration data set for the Ephemeris Estimator (and Atmosphere Estimator), further increasing the likelihood of divergence. As suggested previously, increased precision of the Ephemeris Estimator data, either in higher rate acceleration data and/or more frequent initialization state updates, should improve this behavior. This is illustrated in Figure 6c for a run where the Ephemeris Estimator initialization state update is provided every 3 days compared to every 7 days for the nominal case. Again, it is important to note this performance degradation appears to occur late in the aerobraking mission, after the main aerobraking phase (where AADS would be used) ends, and into the "endgame".

The accuracy at which AADS can maintain such a tight operational corridor will also be driven by the accuracy in the predicted freestream heat rate. Any improvements in the Atmosphere Estimator density and scale height estimates will narrow the spread between the predicted and actual, improve the required maneuver estimate to reach the target in the corridor, and thus further improve the overall corridor performance.

AADS Comparisons to Mission Runout

With simulations complete for both the Mars aerobraking mission runout and AADS implementation, it is now possible to compare the system performance between these two analyses.

Figure 7 provides a comparison of the aerobraking mission profile of both the AADS and mission runout simulations, including the difference between the aerobraking "glide slope" (orbit period versus time), as well as a comparison of the commanded maneuvers, orbit periapsis altitudes, and periapsis locations (areocentric latitude) as a function of time. Table 2 also provides a summary comparison of the mission performance for both simulations.

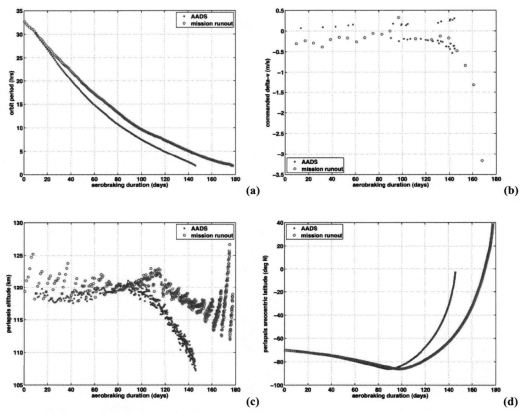

Figure 7. AADS versus mission runout comparisons: (a) orbit period "glide slope", (b) commanded maneuver Δv, (c) periapsis altitude, and (d) periapsis areocentric latitude

Table 2. Summary of AADS performance compared to Mars mission runout.

	Nominal	*Runout*
aerobraking duration (days)	145.9	177.7
total Δv (m/s)	9.0	9.6
no. of maneuvers	37	22

These results show the efficiency of the AADS system. It should be noted that although maneuvers were allowed at any apoapsis for the AADS simulation, in actual flight operations, this may not be desired or allowed. Practical limits may exist on the spacecraft propulsions system in both how frequently maneuvers can be performed, as well as the magnitude of those maneuvers. For very small maneuvers, these constraints may require the AADS system to postpone execution until a point at which the spacecraft drifts sufficiently outside of the operational corridor to meet any minimum burn duration or Δv requirements. However, the flexibility AADS provides allows the ground operations team to tailor the aerobraking mission to meet any desired glide slope, LMST, or any other constraint.

CONCLUSION

Summary of Results

The results shown here indicate that the AADS system does provide sufficient performance to successfully complete an aerobraking mission at Mars under nominal conditions. By creating code and integrating it in a "flight-like" manner, there is high confidence that the performance level will be maintained once AADS is converted to flight software and executed on flight hardware or onboard a spacecraft. At the Applied Physics Laboratory of Johns Hopkins University, AADS work includes the development of a High Fidelity Simulation using flight hardware and a modified MESSENGER spacecraft testbed to run and evaluate the AADS system[14]. Even at this early development stage, these results show that much of the ground operations functions can be performed autonomously onboard while still ensuring spacecraft safety. With this realized, the resource savings (in the form of reduced ground staff, reduced DSN coverage, and even possibly reduced operations time) for future aerobraking missions utilizing an autonomous system such as AADS can be dramatic.

Moving Forward / Future Work

The development of the AADS system is still ongoing. There is additional work to be done to ensure smooth transition to flight software, as well as verify application at other bodies of interest. Phase 1 of the planned AADS development is nearing completion, and Phase 2 is expected to begin once nominal Phase 1 testing is completed.

The results presented were based on nominal / non-perturbed environments. Now that the AADS system has been shown to work well under nominal conditions, the next step is to verify it can still perform adequately in off-nominal situations. This will require continued stress testing of the simulation and AADS code to ensure successful operation under all conceivable environments and conditions. One example of where this will be of great importance is the atmosphere model. Obviously, atmospheric conditions very rarely conform to some nominal profile, particularly when considering a pass through a wide swath of the atmosphere over a period of several minutes. Understanding the effects of a perturbed atmosphere will be crucial to ensuring the AADS system will still perform well under "real-life" flight conditions. Additional spacecraft models, such as an IMU, can also be added to the POST2 simulation to provide more realistic acceleration data containing expected in-flight noise levels.

In addition to verifying the AADS system performance under more flight-like conditions, the system must also perform when aerobraking at bodies other than Mars. Continued work will include simulation of aerobraking missions at both Venus and Titan. At Venus, where solar radiation pressure and 3rd body effects from the Sun will become significant, and heating from the thick atmosphere a greater concern, thermal models will be used to estimate the spacecraft (e.g. solar array) temperature that will act as the operational corridor during the aerobraking mission. At Titan, when Saturn 3rd body gravitational effects dominate, dynamic pressure will be used as the operational corridor throughout aerobraking. Only small changes in the Atmosphere Estimator are required to account for the differences in the atmospheres at Mars, Venus, and Titan. The Ephemeris Estimator would only need to account for the differences in the gravity field and other body characteristics (most of these provided by the spacecraft through the interface structure). Finally, updates and modifications to the models used to determine where the spacecraft is with respect to the desired operational corridor are all that remains to create versions of the AADS system that will successfully, safely, and autonomously execute a full aerobraking mission at any of these destinations.

ACKNOWLEDGMENTS

This work is sponsored by the NASA Engineering and Safety Center. Their assessment can be found in the final report NESC-RP-09-00605 due in November 2011. The authors would also like to recognize David Skinner (Kinetx, Inc.) and Robert Tolson (National Institute of Aerospace) for the development of the Ephemeris Estimator and the Atmosphere Estimator respectively, and for their tremendous support in the integration and testing of these models into the AADS-POST2 simulation. Special thanks also goes the Chris Pastore (Analytical Mechanics Associates) for his outstanding support in the development and integration of the AADS-POST2 simulation.

REFERENCES

[1] Jill L. Hannah, Robert H. Tolson, "Approaches to Autonomous Aerobraking at Mars." The Journal of the Astronautical Sciences, Volume 50, No. 2, April-June 2002.

[2] Daniel T. Lyons, "Aerobraking Automation Options." AAS-01-385, AAS/AIAA Astrodynamics Specialist Conference, Quebec City, CA, 2001.

[3] David A. Spencer, et al., "Aerobraking Cost and Risk Decisions." Journal of Spacecraft and Rockets, Volume 44, No. 6, November-December 2007.

[4] J.L. Prince H., S. A. Striepe, "NASA Langley Simulation Capabilities for the Mars Reconnaissance Orbiter", AAS/AIAA Space Flight Mechanics Conference, Copper Mountain, Colorado, January 23-27, 2005.

[5] Jill L. Prince, et al., "Autonomous Aerobraking: A Design, Development, and Feasibility Study." AAS 11-473, AAS/AIAA Astrodynamics Specialist Conference, Girdwood, AK, 2011.

[6] Robert H. Tolson, Jill L. Prince, "Onboard Atmospheric Modeling and Prediction for Autonomous Aerobraking Missions." AAS 11-477, AAS/AIAA Astrodynamics Specialist Conference, Girdwood, AK, 2011.

[7] John A. Dec et al., "Autonomous Aerobraking: Thermal Analysis and Response Surface Development." AAS 11-474, AAS/AIAA Astrodynamics Specialist Conference, Girdwood, AK, 2011.

[8] *Autonomous Aerobraking Development Software Interface Document, DRAFT v1.0*, 21 February 2011, project document.

[9] S.A. Striepe et al., "Program To Optimize Simulated Trajectories (POST II): Volume 2, Utilization Manual." Martin Marietta Corporation, 2004.

[10] G. L. Brauer et al., "Program To Optimize Simulated Trajectories (POST): Volume 1, Formulation Manual." Martin Marietta Corporation, 1990.

[11] *Autonomous Aerobraking Planetary Constants and Models, v0.06*, 9 June 2011, project document.

[12] Hilary L. Justh et al., "The Next Generation of Mars-GRAM and Its Role in the Autonomous Aerobraking Development Plan." AAS 11-478, AAS/AIAA Astrodynamics Specialist Conference, Girdwood, AK, 2011.

[13] Takashima, N. and Wilmoth, R.G., "Aerodynamics of Mars Odyssey." AIAA 2002- 4809, AIAA/AAS Astrodynamics Specialist Conference and Exhibit, Monterey, California, 5-8 August 2002.

[14] Daniel O'Shaughnessy, et al., "Autonomous Aerobraking Algorithm Testing In a Flight Software Simulation Environment." AAS 11-471, AAS/AIAA Astrodynamics Specialist Conference, Girdwood, AK, 2011.

ONBOARD ATMOSPHERIC MODELING AND PREDICTION FOR AUTONOMOUS AEROBRAKING MISSIONS

Robert H. Tolson[*] and Jill L. H. Prince[†]

For capture to a 200-km circular orbit around Europa, millions of different starting points on the orbit are propagated in the Jupiter-Europa Restricted 3-Body Problem. The transfers exist as members of families of trajectories, where certain families consistently outperform the others. The trajectories are not sensitive to changes in inclination for the final circular orbit. The top-performing trajectories appear to follow the invariant manifolds of L_2 Lyapunov orbits for capture into a retrograde orbit, and in some cases save up to 40% of the Δv from the patched 2-body problem. Transfers are attached to the current nominal mission for NASA's Jupiter-Europa Orbiter, where the total cost is roughly 100 m/s less than the baseline mission.

INTRODUCTION

NASA engineers and scientists have long anticipated a mission to Europa. While a mission to Europa is enticing for many reasons, the primary cause of our allurement is the potential discovery of a "habitable world".[1] Scientists believe that buried beneath the surface of this moon is a water ocean that might support life.

There are many options for a mission to Europa.[1-5] The currently proposed mission architecture consists of two spacecraft: the NASA-led Jupiter-Europa Orbiter (JEO) and the ESA-led Jupiter-Ganymede Orbiter (JGO). The nominal trajectory for JEO would involve many phases, including multiple interplanetary flybys and over 20 flybys of the Jovian moons.[5] Nearing the end of its three-year campaign, eventually the spacecraft would fall into a cadence, or resonance, with Europa's motion on its orbit. This phase would be just the beginning of what researchers have dubbed the *endgame*;[3] however, considering the dance the spacecraft performs with Europa at this time, a more satisfactory description might be *courtship*. For a final play, the spacecraft would capture to a 200-km circular orbit around Europa. As far as the scientists are concerned, the end of this phase marks the beginning of what would hopefully be a long list of discoveries at Europa.

Ignoring Earth launch and Jupiter orbit insertion, Kloster et al.[5] report that the entire tour would require less than 1 km/s in deterministic Δv. Since the bulk of this Δv is at Europa orbit insertion (EOI), the primary motivation for the current work is to develop a practical technique for designing an efficient capture at Europa. Efficient capture means harnessing the gravitational effects of both Europa and Jupiter to lower the insertion cost. This is primarily a three-body problem, and therefore inherits all the features associated with the three-body problem, e.g., numerical integration in highly sensitive regimes. Of course, the radiation dose is also a concern, and therefore a technique cannot lead to unrealistically long trajectories that spend too much time in the radiation belts.

In the literature, there are only a few studies on efficient capture to low altitude orbits at Europa. Koon et al.[6] and Russell and Lam[7] utilize the invariant manifolds of periodic orbits for designing a ballistic capture. While this approach is appealing from a dynamical systems perspective, the final orbit for JEO would be at an altitude from which ballistic capture is impossible. Still the method might be adapted for designing capture trajectories with low insertion costs. Campagnola and Russell[8] mainly focus on methods for minimizing the apoapsis Δv's leading up to EOI, however, in another study[9] they include a multi-body approach that

---
[*]Mission Design Engineer, Outer Planet Mission Analysis, Jet Propulsion Laboratory, California Institute of Technology, 4800 Oak Grove Drive, Pasadena, CA, 91109-8099.

into atmospheric density at one second intervals along the orbit. The recovered density profiles were analyzed to determine atmospheric temperature, gravity wave phenomena, orbit to orbit variability, longitude dependent wave characteristics, latitudinal gradients and other information.[3] To predict upcoming atmospheric conditions, this information was evaluated on a day-by-day basis by a team of atmospheric scientist, the Atmospheric Advisory Group (AAG). Implementation of autonomous AB will require the development of robust, reliable, and simple methods for the estimation of atmospheric density profiles from the IMU data and the prediction of future atmospheric conditions without the human interpretation provided by the AAG.

Mars, Venus and Titan are targets for autonomous AB missions. It is well know that the Mars atmosphere provides a challenging environment for autonomous AB because of the high orbit to orbit variability in atmospheric density.[3] An abundance of AB data provides adequate information for testing autonomous AB at Mars. High orbit to orbit variability has also been detected near the terminator and on the night side of Venus,[4] but there are no accelerometer data for validation or detection of small scale variations. Little is known about the variability of the Titan atmosphere on the temporal and spatial scales of interest for AB. However, during the Huygens descent through the atmosphere, significant wave structure was found in the density and temperature profiles in the altitude range of interest,[5] and Cassini mass spectrometer measurements during Titan flybys in the altitude range from 1000 to 1600 km identified relevant vertical and horizontal wave structure in various constituents and in total density.[6]

The current paper presents various potential methods for representing density profiles derived from IMU data during AB, for recovering profile parameters from IMU data, and for optimal combinations of profiles for prediction. Algorithms are evaluated based on simplicity, robustness, and applicability to onboard limitations. The atmospheres of Mars is the primary focus due to the wealth of data, but Venus and Titan are discussed briefly.

ATMOSPHERIC ESTIMATION DURING PAST AEROBRAKING MISSIONS

Magellan entered orbit in August 1990 with an orbit eccentricity of about 0.4. After the 4-th Venusian day, spanning over 7000 orbits, the AB phase was initiated to reduce the eccentricity to about 0.03 after 70 days and over 700 AB passes. During AB, the active side of the solar array was turned away from the free stream direction to minimize the temperature encountered by the cells, adhesives and structure. Maximum solar array (SA) temperature was the limiting factor constraining the rate of AB.[1] Pre-aerobraking studies provided a relationship between free stream dynamic pressure and maximum SA temperature, but atmospheric density was required to determine dynamic pressure. The method for determining atmospheric density during each Magellan pass relied on Doppler radio tracking data. Pre-pass and post-pass tracking data were process in a single orbit determination (OD) that included density at a specified altitude as a solution parameter. This approach provides continuity of the equations of motion across the unobserved AB pass. To provide a unique solution for density, a model for density vs. altitude was used. The contemporary VIRA model[7] provided density every 5 km and a constant scale height was used for interpolation. Density at 140 km altitude was the solution parameter in the OD process and the scale heights from the VIRA model were used to map density to other altitudes. For a hydrostatic atmosphere, this is equivalent to assuming that the temperature profile is given and the density profile is defined within a multiplicative factor.

Magellan AB was so successful that AB was considered a validated technology and was enabling for the MGS mission in 1997. The MGS AB corridor was again defined in terms of the surrogate variable, free stream dynamic pressure. However, after the discovery of the broken solar array on orbits 11 through 15, the corridor criteria changed from limiting SA temperature to limiting torque on the broken SA yoke[8] and for the only time, the maximum dynamic pressure became the most relevant control variable.

During MGS operations, density at periapsis was estimated by two different methods. Members of the AAG used the IMU data at a one per second sample rate to model the atmospheric density profile. IMU accelerometer measurements were mapped to the vehicle center of mass using the IMU angular rate data and the resulting center of mass acceleration was converted to atmospheric density using a data base of aerodynamic force coefficients. Density at periapsis and density scale height were extracted using a least squares solution from three data sets that included all data within 1, 1.5 and 2 scale heights of periapsis.[9] The "best" model was selected by visual comparison of the model and the data density profiles. Estimated scale heights were averaged over a few orbits and provided to the NAV team to be used for corridor control maneuver calculations and orbit determination. The NAV team used this scale height to estimate the density at periapsis using radio tracking data in the same way as was done for Magellan. The need for more autonomy[10] was recognized well before the end of the 15 months required to complete MGS AB. When adjusted for the different between predicted and observed scale height (equation (A-5)), the AAG and NAV estimates of periapsis density were within 3%, 1σ.

The periapsis altitude, density at periapsis, density scale height, latitude, solar longitude, and local solar time as determined during operations, are shown in Figure 1. In an idealized atmosphere, density scale height is proportional to temperature, so this variable can be thought of as the local average atmospheric temperature. The first 202 orbits of MGS were termed "phase 1," after which there was a six month "hiatus" while periapsis regressed over the north pole. Aerobraking "phase 2" began on orbit 573 and ended on orbit 1285 about 2 weeks after periapsis regressed over the south pole during the winter.

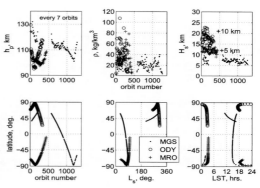

Figure 1. Summary of aerobraking conditions for MGS, ODY and MRO

ODY, the most aggressive AB mission, went to the lowest altitude and experienced the highest densities, unintentionally reaching 107 kg/km^3 on orbit 106. Like MGS and MRO, the science orbit required a particular LST, which meant that the AB phase had to end within a few days of the planned final day. Both ODY and MRO used MarsGRAM[11] to define the density profile and the OD process determined the density by solving for a multiplier to be applied to the MarsGRAM density profile. In addition, as the latitude of AB precessed toward the north pole, it was expected that thermospheric temperature would decrease. Instead, the temperature increased dramatically as indicated by the density scale height in Figure 1. The inferred temperature increase has been interpreted as a polar warming[12] and lead to accelerometer derive density scale heights between 7 and 14 km with an average above 10 km. The nominal atmosphere scale height was expected to be closer to 6 km and did returned to that value after the periapsis latitude regressed south of 60°N. The difference in scale height partially lead to the large density differences between MarsGRAM and the IMU derived densities.

ODY also tested a couple of new techniques. Though ODY used maximum dynamic pressure to define the AB corridor, it was the first mission to have a near real time prediction of the solar array temperatures for a comparison with the measured temperatures.[13] Based on this comparison over a number of orbits, the AB safety margin was reduced, permitting ODY AB to proceed at a faster rate. During this mission the first onboard algorithm,[14] called the Periapsis Timing Estimator (PTE), designed to reduce the work load of the ground flight team, was tested.

MRO had a less risky AB phase than ODY because there was 6 months between MOI and the time when the orbit would have the proper local solar time (LST). Aerobraking was initially performed with nearly a 200% safety margin as opposed to the 100% margins used for MGS and ODY. However, as suggested by the significant increase in density after orbit 200, MRO fell behind the time line during the early conservative approach and AB was more aggressive for the last 200 orbits. PTE was used operationally during this mission with an estimated saving of about $1m dollars. The operational process for density estimation was essentially the same as Odyssey.

ATMOSPHERIC PREDICTION PERFORMANCE DURING OPERATIONS

During Mars AB operations, the AAG monitored the characteristics of recent AB passes to anticipate major changes in the atmosphere. The simplest variation used for modeling the density (ρ) profile was the exponential or constant scale height (CSH) model

$$\rho(h) = \rho_p \exp\left[\frac{-(h - h_p)}{H_s}\right] \tag{1}$$

where density, as determined from IMU data,[9] is a function only of the altitude (h) above some reference or base altitude, here taken as periapsis, with the density at h_p of ρ_p and density scale height, H_s. Such a model results for a homogeneous, isothermal atmosphere in hydrostatic equilibrium, and the density scale height is related to the atmospheric temperature (T), the local gravity acceleration (g) and the mean molecular weight by $H_s = kT/mg$, where k is the Boltzmann constant. Using this as the basic model, the AAG studied density and temperature latitudinal gradients, amplitude of gravity waves, and among others, the accuracy of predicting the periapsis density for the next orbits using the density and scale height from the current orbit. This latter metric was called "persistence' and is a measure of the atmospheric variability that the AB system must accommodate. The ratio of observed to predicted periapsis density for orbit n+1 is

$$\frac{\rho_{obs_{n+1}}}{\rho_{pred_{n+1}}} = \frac{\rho_{obs_{n+1}}}{\rho_{obs_n}} \exp\left[\frac{h_{n+1} - h_n}{H_{s_n}}\right] \tag{2}$$

where the altitudes are provided by the OD process and "observed" density and scale height are determined from IMU data. Orbit n is called the "base' orbit and orbit n+1 is the "predict" orbit.

Figure 2 provides the persistence for all three Mars missions. The means over the entire missions are between 1.06 and 1.08, with the deviation from unity mostly being an artifact of averaging a positive ratio. ODY has the largest 19 orbiting running mean at 1.38 and maximum standard deviation of 1.10, i.e. over a factor of two variation orbit to orbit. Mission wide standard deviations range form 37% for MRO to 47% for ODY. The large ODY value are perhaps due to the very large variations early in the mission between 70° and 80° latitude. Except for ODY during this time, the deviations from the means are much smaller at high latitudes than in the mid latitudes and equatorial regions. Poleward of 60° latitude, the 1σ deviations are generally between 20% and 30%. Just from a geometric argu-

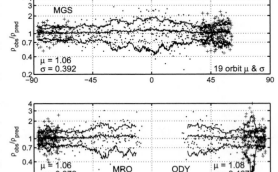

Figure 2. Persistence for MGD, ODY and MRO missions. Dots are data and lines are the 19 orbit running mean and mean +/- one standard deviation. Total mission μ and σ are also shown. Dots become + as periapsis regresses past the pole.

ment, it might be expected that the deviations would become smaller near the pole since great circle distances between successive periapsis locations become shorter. The large ODY deviations near the pole are likely due to the polar warming producing strong winds and large, asymmetric temperature variations around the pole.[12,15]

In the tropics persistence, is the largest for all three missions likely due to the global scale tides that appear as stationary waves to a nearly sun synchronous orbiter.[16] These waves were sufficiently persistent and observable during MGS that models were developed during operations to include their influence on predicting subsequent periapsis densities and to plan orbit trim maneuvers. Latitude dependent empirical models were developed post flight for inclusion of such waves in Monte Carlo simulations of AB missions.[17] These waves appeared for brief periods during ODY and MRO, but not with sufficient consistency to be included in operational decisions.

Ignoring the latitudinal, seasonal, diurnal and other dependencies and considering the orbit to orbit variability as a random process provides very similar results for all three missions. It was found[17] that persistence can be reasonably represented by a gamma probability distribution. Maximum likelihood estimates (95%) of the two gamma distribution parameters for each mission results in probability density distributions shown

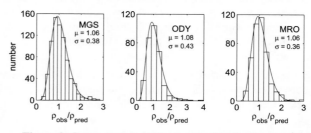

Figure 3. Gamma probability density distribution based on maximum likelihood fits to persistence data for three Mars aerobraking missions.

in Figure 3. The histograms are from the same ratios shown in Figure 2. Within the 95% confidence interval, the values of σ and μ are indistinguishable from each other and compare well with the simple standard deviations in Figure 2. Since underestimating density is usually of higher mission risk than underestimation, these distributions can be used to approximate the probability associated with any ratio of ρ_{obs} to ρ_{pred}. For example, for MGS, ODY and MRO, the probabilities that the ratio will be less than 2 are 98.5%, 97% and 98.6% respectively. These probabilities are consistent with the AB rule of thumb requiring a design safety factor of 2 uncertainty in density. The distributions might also be used for Monte Carlo simulations of AB missions. Since the variance clearly depends on latitude, latitudinal band statistical models might be considered for a little higher fidelity Monte Carlo simulations.

RELEVANT ATMOSPHERIC PARAMETERS FOR AEROBRAKING

The relevant atmospheric parameters depend on the criterion selected to define the AB corridor. If the limiting condition is related to maximum aerodynamic force or torque, then maximum dynamic pressure is likely the relevant parameter. If maximum temperature is the limiting factor for a component with rapid thermal response, maximum free stream heat flux might be the relevant parameter. If temperature is the limiting factor for a component with slow thermal response (e.g. high thermal inertia or low radiative cooling), total or integrated heat flux may be most relevant. Here thermal response time is relative to the duration of the AB pass. To calculate any of these parameters requires knowledge of some characteristic of atmospheric density along the trajectory. To predict the variation for subsequent orbits requires an atmospheric model.

For this discussion, consider Figure 4 which shows the recovered density vs. time and vs. areodetic altitude for a typical Mars AB orbit. A least squares fit to data with $\rho > 2$ kg/km^3 using the CSH model produced the "model" results. For this orbit, maximum density occurs 57 sec. before periapsis, a feature not captured by CSH. There is considerable asymmetry in the time profiles, with density rising faster than it falls. If maximum dynamic pressure or maximum heat flux are the selected corridor criteria, then recovering the density at periapsis using the data or the model is inadequate. Further, when maximum temperature is the criterion, the shape of the heat flux as well as the total heat flux could become a consideration and only a detailed thermal analysis[18] can address these issues. The CSH scale

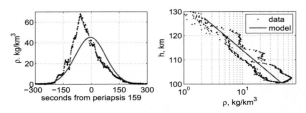

Figure 4. ODY orbit 159 atmospheric density inferred from accelerometer data

height of 8.9 km, which might be used to predict density for the next orbit, represents the inbound, outbound and mean density profiles reasonably well. Maximum density occurs 2 km above periapsis and density varies by nearly a factor of 3 within this altitude range. This gradient is likely due to a strong along track density gradient. Within this range, ODY spend about 110 seconds and traveled about 360 km along track. The high frequency deviation from a "smoothed" density profile are generally attributed to gravity waves[19] and are a common feature at high latitudes. Note that accelerometer noise becomes relevant above altitudes of 125 km. Early and late in the AB pass, accelerometer data noise dominates the signal and the recovered "density" is often negative. These phases of the pass are used to determine a time linear approximation to the accelerometer bias, which is used to correct the data during the pass.[9]

Although the density variation is usually modeled as a function of only altitude, as seen above, along track variations may dominate over the altitudinal. Large scale variations in atmospheric properties, from those assumed for the simple CSH model, might be expected to include an along track variation in base density and/or base temperature, and an altitudinal variation in temperature. Examples of how such variations affect the density profiles are shown in Figure 5.

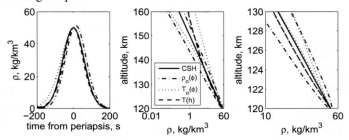

Figure 5. Effects of along track and altitudinal density and temperature gradients on density profiles

Although there are obvious deviation in the altitudinal profiles, the differences in the temporal variation are more subtle. The CSH model is of course a straight line in the two right panels and for this case has a scale height of 7 km. Assuming base density varies linearly with along track angle (ϕ) provides different inbound and outbound profiles and a substantial difference in the two densities within a kilometer or two of periapsis that is comparable with the altitudinal variation in density. An along track linear temperature variation produces a linear variation in scale height resulting again in different inbound and outbound profiles. This variation causes little density differences in the vicinity of periapsis but an increasing difference with altitude. The model with temperature increasing linearly with altitude (T(h)) has the same inbound and outbound altitude profiles and no significant deviation in the first 10 km, but deviates significantly 20 km above periapsis and higher. One can assume that some combination of these and other effects influence every AB pass. For autonomous AB, the first issue is to quantify such effects and the second issue is to decide whether or not to include them in the atmospheric estimation process.

As examples of some of the multiplicity of effects on real AB passes, consider Figure 6 which provides examples of Odyssey profiles that are representative of the types of phenomena seen during all the Mars AB missions. The noticeable increase in data noise is due to halving the IMU sample rate on orbit 134 and again on orbit 270. Clearly the "bell shaped" density variation with time, derived in APPENDIX I, is not representative of any of these orbits. For orbit 44, the factor of two change in density over 10 seconds is not atypical for Mars. The time or altitude of maximum density are meaningless concepts for pass 157. The

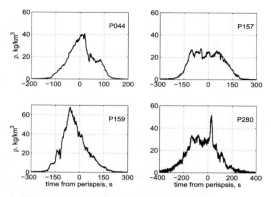

Figure 6. Four Odyssey orbits.

large asymmetry for orbit 159 results in maximum density occurring a full minute before periapsis. Generally solar power and Earth communications are lost during the AB pass. Thus, there are clear reasons to want to minimize the duration that the vehicle is in the AB orientation. The AB phase is usually designed to be centered on periapsis. With such large asymmetries, extra time may have to be allocated, or if the asymmetries are consistent from orbit to orbit, biasing the center of the pass away from periapsis may be desirable. The AB passes for orbits 157 and 159 are 7 hours apart in time, 2 km apart in altitude and essentially at the same latitude, yet the profiles and the maximum density are dramatically different. These phenomena are the sort of natural orbit to orbit variability that are difficult to predict and therefore must be included as uncertainties in the design of any AB mission and requires a particularly robust design for an autonomous AB mission. It will be seen that there is some orbit to orbit persistence in the density, density scale height and temporal asymmetry.

Near factor of two density spikes like P280 are uncommon but would be important if maximum density or heat flux is the consideration and not so important if total heat flux is the consideration. Even in the former case, the characteristic response time of the system will play a role. At Mars, the lack of persistence in the shape and maximum value of the density profile from orbit to orbit and the small-scale deviation are attributed to global scale longitudinal waves and vertically propagating gravity waves. The longitudinal waves during MGS have been modeled[17] and are attributed to non-migrating thermal tides[16] in the lower atmosphere that propagate to the upper atmosphere in the equatorial and mid-latitude regions. On the other hand, the source of the gravity waves is not known, but they are believed to originate in the lower atmosphere and, at high latitudes, propagate vertically while increasing in amplitude with subsequent "breaking" in the lower thermosphere.[19] Their latitudinal, seasonal, diurnal variations of rms amplitude have been partially defined from previous AB data.[3] Whether or not they are significant for a particular mission depends on the criteria that limit AB. In the modeling approaches that follow, neither of these wave types will be a consideration as they are very difficult to model at this time.

The observed density asymmetries in time could be due to either an along track density gradient at a fixed altitude or to the areodetic altitude gradient at a constant distance from the center of the planet. First consider a possible density gradient. ODY, like the other Mars AB missions, is in a near polar orbit so along track is essentially latitudinal. The polar regions are generally colder than the tropics and consequently density scale height is smaller in polar regions. This would suggest that, for a fixed altitude, a lower density would be expected near the pole than in the tropics and strong latitudinal density gradients have been seen in all three Mars missions. On the second possible reason for a density asymmetry, periapse is the point in the orbit that is closest to the center of mass; but, due to planetary flattening, does not usually correspond to the point of lowest areodetic altitude. Planetary flattening is defined by the reference ellipsoid which approximates the equipotential surface at the surface of the planet. The reference ellipsoid is selected to approximate such a surface by defining an equatorial radius (a) and a flattening (f) that give a polar radius of a(1-f). For the Earth, the ellipsoid can be thought of as defining "mean sea level." On solid planets, the ellipsoid is selected to provide an equatorial radius that approximates the physical mean radius and the flattening is usually selected to represent the equipotential defined by the central gravitational potential, J_2 and the centrifugal potential due to planetary rotation. In an idealized, isothermal atmosphere, surfaces of constant planetodetic altitude correspond to surfaces of constant pressure and density. Hence, in a real atmosphere, density should be approximately constant on surfaces of constant planetodetic altitude. Many empirical atmospheric models, as will this paper, use this surface as the reference from which altitude is measured.

Density: In this paper it is assumed that the AB corridor is defined in terms of variables that require a knowledge of atmosphere density. But it should be kept in mind that density is often a surrogate for some other physical quantity that actually defines the limits on the execution of AB.

Density Scale Height: Density scale height plays two roles in AB. First, for maneuver calculations to stay within a density corridor, the scale height, or equivalent, must be known to calculate the required dV, equation (10). Second, if total heat flux or integrated density is important, the integral depends on the reference altitude density and scale height as shown by equation (A-5).

Asymmetry of Density Profile: As mentioned above, during AB at Venus or Mars, the vehicle would be generally turned from sun-point and would be operating on batteries. In this case it may be desirable to minimize the time in the AB orientation. If the density profile is skewed or asymmetric in time, an allowance may be made for the potential skewness. If the skewness is predictable, then it can be included in the design and the AB pass can be accordingly biased in time.

Figure 7 shows the influence of planet flattening on shifting the density profile for a Mars AB mission. The upper left chart provides the variation of altitude above periapsis along the orbit, where the orbit parameters are given in the figure. The second line shows the variation in altitude above the reference ellipsoid along the orbit. The upper right panel provides the difference over three density scale heights or 21 km. The lowest areodetic altitude and highest density occurs 64 seconds before periapsis. The 0.59 km difference in altitude would cause a 9% higher density than the density at periapsis. This shift would also cause a least squares density estimation process, centered on periapsis, to overweight the outbound leg of the pass. The time and altitude shifts for other latitudes and orbit periods are shown in the lower two panels. The differences approach zero at the equator and pole, are maximum at mid latitudes, and decrease rapidly with orbit period. This latter effect is due to shortening of the AB pass as eccentricity increases with orbital period. Non-polar orbits will show smaller effects at every latitude. The size of the altitude difference and time shift are increased with planetary flattening, AB pass duration and angular velocity at periapsis. This phenomena is not an issue at Venus due to very slow rotation and the nearly spherical gravity field. The Titan rotational period is 15.9 days and Saturn produces tidal bulges of

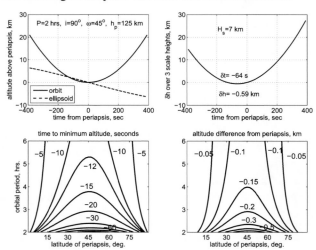

Figure 7. Mars reference ellipsoid flattening effect on density profiles.

less than one kilometer resulting in a flattening that is less than 1/10 of Mars, so the effects on Titan AB are likely ignorable as well

POTENTIAL ATMOSPHERIC MODELS AND USES

Here it is assumed that no preflight empirical model of the atmosphere exist that is accurate enough to perform AB without using onboard data to adjust model parameters during the flight. Selection criteria for onboard atmospheric models include (1) capture the relevant characteristics of the atmosphere, (2) be robust against unexpected phenomena, (3) allow for linear estimation of the parameters, (4) permit prediction of atmospheric properties for the next AB pass and (5) support the calculation of corridor control maneuvers. A number of models are discussed and evaluated using Mars AB data. All the models assume that atmospheric density data have been derived from an onboard source, e.g IMU accelerometer and gyro data.

Constant Scale Height

The constant scale height model (CSH) given by equation (1) was used successfully as the fundamental model during the MGS mission. Successful use of this model, or any model using altitude, depends on an accurate representation of altitude vs. time. This could be an issue for onboard ephemeris integration. There are two disadvantages to using this form for estimation. First, the density is not linear in the estimation parameters $\rho(h_p)$ and H_s and second, a simple least squares process will overweight residuals at the lowest altitude and nearly ignore residuals a few scale heights above the reference altitude. One approach is to use $\log(\rho)$ as the observable and use

$$\log \rho(h) = a \log \rho_p + b(h - h_p) \tag{3}$$

where a and b are the regression parameters. The equation is linear in a and b and the least squares method, within the linear regime, now minimizes the sum of squares of the density difference divided by the density, i.e. the fractional deviation in the density. This approach provides equal weight to high or low density data and is more suitable when scale height is among the estimated parameters. This model can, to a limited extent, provides asymmetric temporal variation like the left panel in Figure 4, but the inbound and outbound altitude profiles will be identical so that the model is a straight line in the left panel. Clearly equation (3) is not applicable early and late in the AB pass when accelerometer data noise produces negative density. This model is simple and captures the dominate local variations in density. It also permits prediction of the atmospheric density at the next periapsis by assuming that the scale height is the same for the next orbit and that the density at periapsis can be obtained from equation (1) at the next periapsis. Since the AB pass is not vertical, the two parameters in this model also absorb an unknown amount of along track variation. The persistence results in Figure 2 show the real world limitations to this approach.

Quadratic Time

In APPENDIX I it is shown that, for the constant density scale height model, the temporal variation in density in the vicinity of periapsis can be approximated by

$$\rho(t) = \rho_p \exp\left[\frac{-(t - t_p)^2}{2\sigma^2}\right] \tag{4}$$

$$\text{where} \qquad \sigma^2 = H_s r_p^2 / \mu e \tag{5}$$

depends on orbit parameters and scale height. Again, to assure linear estimation, $\log \rho$ is used as the observable and $a = \log \rho_p$ and $b = -1/2\sigma^2$ are the parameters. This model has the advantage that a precision trajectory is not required to generate altitude vs. time. To predict to other altitudes, the scale height can be approximated from the solution for σ^2. It is seen that a disadvantage is that the model is symmetric in time about the time of periapsis and that maximum density occurs at periapsis, whereas few of the Martian density profiles satisfy either of these conditions. A shift in the time of maximum density is easily accomplished by adding a linear term to get

$$\log \rho(t) = a \log \rho(t_p) + b(t - t_p) + c(t - t_p)^2 \tag{6}$$

which is still symmetric in time but centered at the model maximum density which occurs at $t_{max} = t_p - b/2c$ and has a value of $\exp(a + b(t_{max} - t_p)/2)$. This model (QdT) does however permit different inbound and outbound altitude profiles, but with the same scale height.

Cubic and Quartic Time

One can introduce both asymmetry and a shift in the time of maximum density by extending the quadratic model to either a cubic (CubT) or a quartic model (QtT) in time, e.g.

$$\log \rho(t) = a \log \rho(t_p) + b(t - t_p) + c(t - t_p)^2 + d(t - t_p)^3 + e(t - t_p)^4 \tag{7}$$

The quartic term might be included to assure that density decreases with altitude outside the data set or to provide a better estimate of the maximum density during the pass. There are profiles for which $e > 0$, so this model would not be recommended for extrapolation. For both models, H_s can be extracted from the quadratic coefficient. However, it was found that the $(t - t_p)^4$ term often absorbed enough of the quadratic dependence that the H_s estimates were substantially biased. Consequently, no further consideration will be given to the quartic representation.

Constant Scale Height with Time

A hybrid model (CSHT), with constant scale height but different density profiles for the inbound and outbound legs, can be obtained by adding a linear time term to equation (3) to get

$$\log \rho(h, t) = a \log \rho_p + b(h - h_p) + c(t - t_p) \tag{8}$$

where the reference altitude and time are taken at periapsis. The model permits some variation in local scale height with altitude. It is unlikely that this model should be used to extrapolate beyond the data interval, since, unless $c = 0$, the predicted density will eventually increase with altitude.

Constant Inbound and Outbound Scale Heights

Another three parameter hybrid model is one that permits different inbound and outbound scale heights but only one density at periapsis (CSHIO).

Periapsis Timing Estimator

Satellite ephemeris propagation errors are usually dominated by along track deviations which for AB are manifested as time of periapsis errors. The PTE[14] was consequently designed to adjust the flight sequence so that it would be centered on the centroid of the density history. Based on the PTE Δt from one orbit, the initiation of the AB sequence for the next orbit is adjusted by Δt. PTE was run in shadow mode and validated during ODY and was operational for MRO. Although the details are not exactly known, results of the above models will be compared to an implementation based on Reference 14. The implementation is a simple density weighted time from periapsis to provide the location of the density centroid relative to periapsis

$$\Delta t = \sum t_i \rho_i / \sum \rho_i \tag{9}$$

where time is measured from periapsis and the sum is taken over all the density data above a threshold determined by the density noise level.

Single Orbit Examples

Each of these models was applied to the four Odyssey orbits in Figure 6. Data within 14 km altitude of periapsis are used for the LS solutions. Results are shown in Figure 8 for both density vs. time and density-altitude profiles, where the density data are shown as dots. Relevant solution parameters for these orbits are tabulated in Table 1. For the QdT and CubT models, the scale height was calculated using Equation (5) where the position and velocity at periapsis was used to calculate the eccentricity. For orbits 44, 157 and 280, little difference between the models is seen in the plots. In fact, for these orbits, the CSHT and time quadratic (QdT) models are nearly identical and the differences in the parameters in the Table 1 are ignorable. Examination of the orbit 44 profile shows that the cubic (CubT) model is beginning to diverge above 110 km and $\rho=10$ kg/km^3 with one branch going to zero density and the other going to an infinite den-

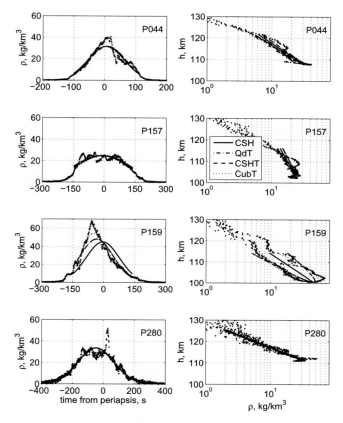

Figure 8. Density model least square fits to four Odyssey orbits. Data range δh=14 km.

sity with further increase in altitude. To fit the "flat" top of orbit 157, all models produced a very large scale height near 23 km, whereas the remaining orbits have scale heights of less than 11 km. Similar statements can be made for the time of the maximum density. Estimation of the scale height is very consistent among the models, but of course all the orbit 157 estimates are much greater than estimates from nearby orbits and it would likely be unwise to use the anomalistically large scale height for orbit 157 to predict the density for orbit 158. In fact, to do so would give 21.8 kg/km^3 verses the measured value of 38.8. Predicting orbit 159 from the 157 values gives 21.9 kg/km^3. Orbits like this demonstrate the need to combine estimates from a number of orbits and even then, large differences might be expected.

Model	Odyssey Orbit			
	44	157	159	280
ρ_{max}, kg/km^3				
Data	40.8	27.8	68.1	51.8
CSH	31.5	24.9	45.0	33.6
QdT	31.6	25.0	48.0	33.5
CSHT	31.6	25.0	48.1	33.6
CubT	31.7	25.1	54.5	33.6
t_{max}, sec				
Data	20.0	-44.5	-58.5	29.5
CSH	5.0	-3.5	-4.5	-49.4
QdT	9.0	-15.5	-34.5	-45.4
CSHT	9.0	-15.5	-34.5	-46.4
CubT	-1.0	-19.5	-48.6	-44.4
PTE	6.8	-5.4	-28.6	-41.3
Hs, km				
CSH	8.6	23.1	8.9	5.1
QdT	8.7	23.6	9.2	5.0
CSHT	8.6	23.1	8.9	5.1
CubT	8.3	23.8	9.7	5.0

Multiple Orbit Comparisons

The four algorithms in Table 1 and the CSHIO algorithm were applied to all three Mars missions. Only data during the "main" AB phase were included. In addition, MGS data for orbits 910 through 980 were also excluded because of an onboard computer issue that significantly reduced the quality of the accelerometer data. There is a subtle difference in how the data are selected for the three constant scale height models and the two time polynomial models. For the former, data are selected within a specified altitude range of periapsis, which for all these results is 14 km or about 2 density scale heights. Unless periapsis is at the equator or a pole, planetary flattening results in these data being asymmetric in time. Conversely, for the latter two models, the data are selected symmetric in time around periapsis with a time interval that corresponds to a planetocentric radius change of 14 km. The resulting in planetodetic altitude distribution is generally asymmetry. This small difference has a noticeable effect on the results.

Density: As a basis for comparison, the "mean" density for each orbit was calculated by averaging all five solutions for density at periapsis. Results are presented as ratios of recovered density to this mean density. For MGS it was found that this ratio varied from 0.92 to 1.06. The orbit average difference between CSH and CSHIO had a μ=0.0045 with σ=0.02 and between QdT and CubT μ<10^{-5} and σ<10^{-3}. Because these pairs of recoveries are so similar, only one of the pair will be shown for some of the results. Figure 9 shows these ratios for the CSH, CSHT and QdT methods. There are couple of general trends evident. First, when the CSH ratios are generally greater than one, the QdT ratios are generally less than one. Second, the CSHT method provides results closest to unity over the entire mission. Third, there are two places where all three methods

524

give nearly the same density, near orbits 860 and 1190. It will be seen in the next paragraph that a couple of these trends can be explained in terms of the method for selecting data as discussed above and the time between periapsis and the minimum planetodetic altitude. The ODY and MRO analyses showed similar trends in ratio ranging from 0.92 to 1.06, model agreement near the pole, and CSH and QdT providing opposite deviations from unity. The CSHT model providing result closer to the mean than the other two models, but with slightly larger deviations than MGS.

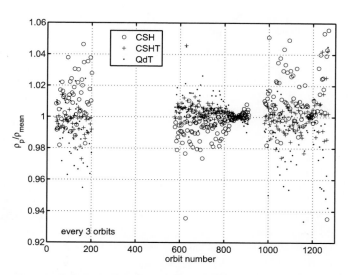

Figure 9. MGS estimated periapsis density for three methods normalized by mean periapsis density of all five methods.

Time of Maximum Density: Consider Figure 10 which shows the time from periapsis to the time when the various models predict the maximum density. For the CSH model, this is time from periapsis to minimum planetodetic latitude, i.e. the same "time to minimum altitude" presented in Figure 7. Time difference changes slowly because latitude and orbit eccentricity are changing slowly until near the final orbits when the orbit is nearly circular. During the first 200 orbits, MGS is passing from north to south as periapsis regresses northward. Consequently, minimum altitude occurs after periapsis. The CSHT and QdT results suggest there is an additional effect that further delays the time. This would be consistent with a equatorward increase in density, which is a general trend. The periapsis regresses past the equator on orbit 860 and here the altitude data distribution will be symmetric in time and conversely. So, the models should predict essentially the same atmospheric parameters. It is seen from

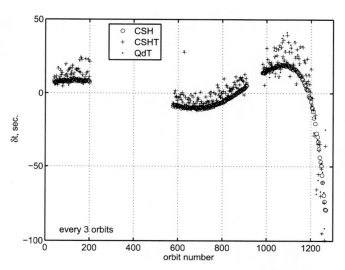

Figure 10. MGS time from periapsis to time of maximum density as predicted by three models.

Figure 9 that this is true for density, but not so for the δt values. Again there is an along track density gradient that delays the epoch of maximum density. At the risk of over analysis, one possibility is that the maximum density is occurring in the northern hemisphere since during all of phase 2,

L_s (Figure 1) is between 0° and 90°, so it is hemisphere spring and the Sun is in the northern hemisphere. The balance of the orbits after 860 are readily explained by a minimum density occurring near the pole. Maximum positive δt occurs near orbit 1060 as periapsis regresses past 45° latitude, the region of maximum gradient in the planetocentric altitude. As periapsis passes over the pole, there will be symmetry in the data distributions and the densities are nearly identical. One final note, the difference between the δt for CSHT and QdT has a μ=0.2 sec. and σ=1.9 sec. These two methods are providing excellent agreement in δt.

ODY and MRO analyses provided similar results. MRO had generally smaller deviations from the δt caused by flattening than MGS. ODY on the other hand, while periapsis regressed toward the pole, showed up to 40 sec. positive δt deviations which rapidly switched to negative values up to -40 sec. while moving away from the pole. Perhaps these large, rapid variations were due to the polar warming.

Density Scale Height: H_s is the final variable of interest for predicting the periapsis density at subsequent orbits. As might be expected, the estimation of scale height is more sensitive than density to the altitude span of the data set. Orbit 157 in Figure 8 illustrates the difficulty. The solution used data within δh=14 km of periapsis, i.e. about two expected scale heights. The resulting H_s=23 km given in Table 1 is not a realistic value to use for predicting density at the next periapsis. From the figure it can be expected that as the altitude range δh is increased, the value of H_s would decrease perhaps to more realistic values, but the estimated periapsis density will likely increase. The data above 100 km appears to follow a straight line with a scale height of about 7.5 km, but using just these data would yield a periapsis density of about 100 kg/km^3. Hence, using a much larger data set would lead to a significantly higher density prediction. Orbit 158 occurred 1 km lower in altitude than 157 and had a density of 41 kg/km^3. So the predictions using a 14 km altitude range underestimated the density for 158 and using a very large altitude range would have overestimated the density. Studies for all missions using δh=7, 11, 14 and 21 km altitude ranges showed that for orbits with "bell shaped" density histories, even with time shifts, the estimates of H_s generally differed by less than 0.5 km between the 11 and 14 km cases and 0.3 km between the 14 and 21 km cases. Differences between the 7 and 14 cases were around 1 km. For orbits that vary significantly for the "bell shape," the results are mixed. Using an altitude interval of δh=2H_s seems to be a reasonable compromise.

Like the other parameters, the estimation of H_s within a family of methods e.g. (CSH, CSHT, CSHIO) or (QdT, CubT) were very consistent with standard deviations for the differences of less than σ=50m. Between the two families σ<500m. Consequently, only the CSHT results are shown in Figure 11. The means of the three MGS

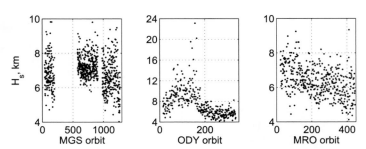

Figure 11. Density scale height recovered using the CSHT method and δh=14 km.

data segments (H_s=6.9, 7,3, 6.6 km) have trends that are consistent with temperature decreasing toward the poles. The standard deviations are 1.1, 0.7 and 1.1 km, from left to right. ODY scale heights (i.e. temperature) were the means of discovering the polar warming but outside the polar region the mean scale height drops to about 5.6 km, well below the expected value. Global circulations model simulations of a polar warming[15] show strong adiabatic heating near the pole due to subsiding flow and an adjacent region of cooling. This region is likely the reason for these small scale heights. In this region $\sigma = 0.76$ km. MRO also shows a decreasing H_s trend as periapsis regresses toward the pole. If there was a sudden south polar warming, it occurred after periapsis passed the pole. Averaging over 100 orbit blocks, H_s varies from $\mu = 6.9$ and $\sigma = 0.86$ to $\mu = 5.7$ and $\sigma = 1$ km over the mission.

AEROBRAKING CORRIDOR MAINTENANCE

As mentioned earlier, a model of atmospheric density has a couple of purposes: (1) to quantify characteristics of the atmosphere for the current pass which might be used for heating calculations[18], (2) to provide a prediction of the characteristics of the next pass, and (3) provide information needed to calculate the orbit trim maneuvers to stay in the AB corridor.

Corridor Maintenance Maneuvers

To maintain the AB corridor, orbit trim maneuvers are generally performed near apoapsis to adjust the altitude of subsequent periapses and thereby control the atmospheric density.[20] For tangential, impulsive maneuvers, the first order δV_a required at apoapsis to raise periapsis altitude by an amount δr_p is first given for two body motion and the secondly is given by relating the altitude change through the CSH model to obtain the desired fractional change in periapsis density $\delta \rho_p / \rho_p$

$$\delta V_a = \frac{n}{4}\sqrt{\frac{r_a}{r_p}}\ \delta r_p = -\frac{n}{4}\sqrt{\frac{r_a}{r_p}}H_s\left(\frac{\delta \rho_p}{\rho_p}\right) \tag{10}$$

where δr_p has been approximated by δh_p, n is the orbital mean motion, r_a (r_p) is the apoapsis (periapsis) radius and H_s and ρ_p are the expected density scale height for the next orbit. Even without a precision trajectory, the previous results strongly suggest that the latter two variables are likely to contribute the majority of the uncertainty in calculating the desired δV_a.

Predicting Atmospheric Parameters for the Next Pass

For autonomous AB it will be necessary to have a prediction of atmospheric density for the next pass through the atmosphere. From past experience with Mars AB it is clear that there are likely to be large variations between predicted and observed density that are not within the current ability to predict from either empirical or numerical models of the atmosphere. Any of the density models discussed above might be used to generate parameters for predicting the conditions at the next periapsis as was demonstrated in the study of "persistence." All the models have persistence values that deviate up to a factor of 2 from unity. This naturally raised the question if some averaging of the estimates would produce a better "prediction" ratio. As mentioned, for both Magellan and MGS, some form of atmospheric density was averaged over a number of orbits to be used to predict the density at the next periapsis. Using the extensive set of data from Mars, a study was performed of two averaging methods over a range of altitudes (δh) used to obtain model coefficients and over the number of orbits used in the averaging process. One would anticipate both of these variables would influence the results. Only the CSH and CSHT models were included as CSH is the simplest model and CSHT provided prediction results that were the closest to the average of all the methods. The data collection altitude ranges studied were $\delta h = 7, 10, 14$ and 21 km. This range starts near the mean H_s averaged all latitudes and times. The values of 10 and 14 can be thought of as 1.5 or 2 times the $H_s = 7$ km value or 1 and 1.5 times the $H_s \sim 10$ that was seen during the polar warming. The number of orbits for the averaging was varied from 1 to 20. It might be anticipated that a low number of averaging orbits will have a large standard deviation for the prediction ratio while estimates using very long data arcs may be biased by the time dependent (latitudinal, seasonal, diurnal) variations in atmospheric characteristics.

Figure 12 show the results for MGS. The prediction σ is the standard deviation over all the values of the ratio of observed to predicted density across the entire mission. Two simple averaging methods were explored for both the CSH and CSHT models. For notational convince, let n+1 be the orbit number at which density is to be estimated using model values from orbits n, n-1,...n-k+1, where k is the "number of orbits in the estimate." When the number of orbits in the estimate k=1, the prediction value is the standard deviation of all the points in Figure 9 for each model. For the "CSH AVG" results the previous k values of 'a' and 'b' in equation (3) are used to get a value of 'a' at the periapsis altitude of orbit n+1. These k values are

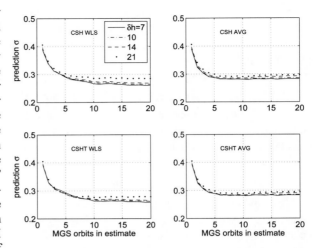

Figure 12. Density prediction capability of various methods for the MGS mission

simply averaged to obtain the "estimated" density at orbit n+1. This value is used in the denominator of the prediction ratio. A similar process is used for the CSHT model where the time dependence in this model is ignored. The second averaging method attempted to account for the "accuracy" of the estimated parameters. The LS process was turned into a WLS method by using the reciprocal of the rms deviation between observed and model predicted density to "weight" the data. Orbits with large deviations, like orbit 159 (Figure 8), would be weighted lower than orbits which had a smaller rms, like orbit 280. So the second method is the weighted sum of the estimates, much like a minimum variance linear combination of random variables. No probabilistic interpretation is attempted for these results for obvious reasons.

Referring to the figure, the standard deviation across all orbits starts near 40% 1σ. The initial downward trend as the number of orbits increases is to be expected. From a practical standpoint little is to be gained in reducing σ after 10 to 15 orbits and the AVG results start to increase slightly after 10 orbits are averaged. The three lower values of δh provide similar results and noticeable lower than the δh=21 case, although this different is likely not significant from an autonomous AB standpoint. This residual deviation of about 28% is interpreted as the natural variability of the atmosphere and can not be reduced without significantly more knowledge of the atmosphere than is available from onboard measurements alone.

The standard deviation does not tell the whole story on prediction for autonomous AB. The probability of the ratio being greater than a specified value may be more relevant. The gamma distributions shown in Figure 3 provide a more rigorous means of making probabilistic statements. Here a simpler approach is taken by just tracking the fraction of total orbits for which the ratio of observed to predicted density ratio exceeds 1.5. For MGS this result is shown in Figure 13 for the same methods and data as Figure 12. There appears to be little advantage to using more than 10 to 15 orbits for the prediction and WLS provides about 1 to 2% improvement over the AVG approach. Note that WLS is computationally more cumbersome than the AVG approach, which is a consideration for onboard computation. For prediction the shorter data spans, δh<10 provided a small advantage, for Figure 13 the lines cross repeatedly with δh=14 being lower than the others in more cases. Setting δh at about 2 scale heights may be a good rule of thumb and unless time of maximum density is a desirable parameter to estimate, the simple CSH method seems like a good candidate. Selecting between AVG and WLS is less obvious.

Just to complete this story, similar results are shown for ODY and MRO in Figure 14 for just the CSH model and the WLS prediction method. The ODY prediction has a minimum at 0.3 which is 10% higher than either MGS or MRO, but still over a 30% reduction below the initial persistence values. This higher variability also appears in the prediction greater than 1.5 have nearly 10% of the orbits above this limit. Also the longer the span of orbits used in the prediction, the smaller the σ. The δh=21 appears to be optimal for ODY, consistent

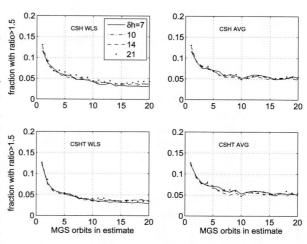

Figure 13. Fraction of total MGS orbits for which the ratio of observed to predicted density exceeded 1.5

with ODY having Hs>10 km for a significant fraction of the mission. Of course, MRO behaves in a different manner from the other two missions with an initial rise in σ followed by a steep fall eventually becoming 0.28 like MGS. The decline in the 1.5 fraction is slower than MGS, but does get near 5% eventually.

SUMMARY

1. Mars is a challenging environment for autonomous aerobraking due to the large, natural orbit to orbit variability in the density profiles. With the plethora of data from MGS, ODY and MRO, some latitudinal seasonal trends have been identified, but, the best that can be done to date is to reduce the variability by about one third.

2. Because of thermospheric waves due to thermal tides in the

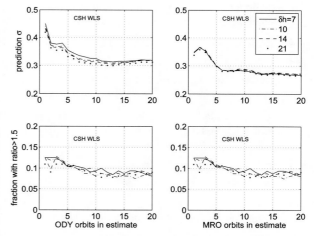

Figure 14. prediction and orbit fractions for ODY and MRO

lower atmosphere, aerobraking in temperate latitudes has nearly twice the average variability as aerobraking near the poles.

3. Five different formulations for the density variation with altitude and time were investigated. If maximum density or the time of maximum density are not relevant, then the simple constant density scale height model (CSH) performs nearly as well as more complicated models. If time is important, the hybrid CSHT is the likely choice.

4. Two methods were used to combine data from numerous orbits to improve the prediction for subsequent orbits. A weighted least squares method performed a little better than simple averaging, but at the cost of additional software on the vehicle. Both methods reduced the variability by

about 30%. The remaining 1σ deviations of about 30% are likely due to natural variability that will have to be included in vehicle design.

5. Models that depend on altitude are likely to be sensitive to ephemeris errors and combined studies of atmospheric model parameterization and ephemeris propagation errors should be performed before final model selection is made. If ephemeris errors in altitude vs. time become too large, models that depend only on time can be considered without loss of performance.

6. Similar analyses can not be performed for aerobraking at Venus and Titan due to lack of data. However, significant orbit to orbit variation has been noted at Venus and gravity waves have been seen at both bodies. Because of the basic physics, neither body will likely be as challenging as Mars, but prudence suggest not attempting autonomous aerobraking until more is known about the atmospheres.

ACKNOWLEDGEMENT

This work was sponsored by the NASA Engineering and Safety Center (www.nesc.nasa.gov). This assessment can be found in the final report NESC-RP-09-00605 in November 2011.

REFERENCES

1. Willcockson, W. H., Magellan Aerobraking Control Corridor: Design and Implementation, *Adv. Astronautical Sciences*, Vol. 87, Part II, 1994, pp. 647-662.

2. Spencer, D. A. & Tolson, R. H., "Aerobraking Cost and Risk," *J. Spacecraft and Rockets*, Vol. 44, No. 6, Nov.-Dec., 2007, pp.1285-1293

3. Tolson, R. H., Keating, G. M., Zurek, R. W., Bougher, S. W., Justus, C. J., Fritts, D. C., "Application of Accelerometer Data to Atmospheric Modeling During Mars Aerobraking Operations." *J. Spacecraft and Rockets*, Vol. 44, No. 6, 2007, pp. 1171-1179.

4. Konopliv, A. S. & Sjogren, W. L., "Venus Gravity Handbook," JPL Pub.96-2, Jan. 1996.

5. Striepe, S. A., Blanchard, R. C., Kirsch, M. F., Fowler, W. T.,"Huygens Titan Probe Trajectory Reconstruction Using Traditional Methods and the Program to Optimize Trajectories II", AAS/AIAA Space Flight Mechanics Meeting, Sedona, AZ, 2007, AAS 07-226.

6. Muller-Wodarg, I. C. F., Yelle, R. V., Borggren, N., Waite, J. H., "Waves and horizontal structures in Titan's thermosphere," *J. Geophysical Research*, Vol. 111, A12315, doi:10.1029/2006JA011061, 2006.

7. Keating, G. M., et al.,"Models of Venus Neutral Upper Atmosphere: Structure and Composition," *Adv. Space Res.*, Vol, 5, No. 11, 1985, pp. 117-171.

8. Lyons, D. T., Beerer, J. G., Esposito, P., Johnston, M. D., "MGS: Aerobraking Mission Overview," *J. of Spacecraft and Rockets*, Vol. 36, No. 3, 1999, pp. 307-313.

9. Tolson, R. H., Keating, G. M., Cancro, G. J., Parker, J. S., Noll, S. N., and Wilkerson, B. L., "Application of Accelerometer Data to Mars Global Surveyor Aerobraking Operations," *J. Spacecraft and Rockets*, Vol. 36, No. 3, May-June, 1999, pp. 323-329.

10. Hanna, J. L. & Tolson, R. H., "Approaches to Autonomous Aerobraking at Mars," AAS/AIAA Astrodynamics Specialist Conference, Quebec City, Canada, July 30-August 2, 2001. AAS 01-387

11. Justus, C. G., Duvall, A., Keller, V. W., "Atmospheric Models for Aeroentry and Aeroassist," Proceedings of the 2nd International Planetary Probe Workshop, NASA Ames Research Center, Moffett Field, CA, pp 41-48, August 23-27, 2004. Also published in NASA/CP-2004-213456, April 2005.

12. Keating, G.M., et al., "Detection of winter polar warming in Mars upper atmosphere," Paper PS1.02-1TH2A-006, EGS XXVII General Assembly, Nice, France, April 2002.

13. Dec, J. A., Gasbarre, J. F., George, B. E., "Thermal Analysis and Correlation of the Mars Odyssey Spacecraft's Solar Array During Aerobraking Operations," AIAA/AAS Astrodynamics Conference, Monterey CA, Aug. 5-8, 2002.

14. Willcockson, W. H. & Johnson, M. A., "Mars Odyssey Aerobraking: The First Step Towards Autonomous Aerobraking Operations" 2003 IEEE Aerospace Conference, Big Sky, MT, March 9-14, 2003.

15. Bougher, S. J., Bell, J. M., Murphy, J. R., Lopez-Valverde, M. A., Withers, P. G., "Polar warming in the Mars thermosphere: Seasonal variations owing to change in insolation and dust distributions," *Geophysical Research Letters*, Vol. 33, 2006.

16. Wilson, R. J., "Evidence for nonmigrating thermal tides in the Mars upper atmosphere from the MGS Accelerometer Exp.", *Geophys. Res. Lett.*, 27(21), 3563-3566, 2002.

17. Dwyer, A. M., Tolson, R. H., Munk, M. M., Tartabini, P. V., "Development of a Monte Carlo Mars-GRAM Model for Mars 2001 Aerobraking Simulations," J. of the Astronautical Sciences, 2001, Vol. 109, pp 1293-1308.

18. Dec, J. A. & Thormblom, M. N., "Autonomous Aerobraking: Thermal Analysis and Response Surface Development", AAS/AIAA Astrodynamics Specialist Conference, July 31-August 3, 2011, Gildwood, Alaska, AAS 11-474.

19. Fritts, D. C., Wang, L., Tolson, R. H., "Mean and gravity wave structured and variability in the Mars upper atmosphere inferred from Mars Global Surveyor and Mars Odyssey aerobraking densities," *J. Geophy. Res.*, Vol. 111, 2006.

20. Maddock, R. W., et al., "Implementation and Simulation Results Using Autonomous Aerobraking Development Software," AAS/AIAA Astrodynamics Specialist Conference, July 31-August 3, 2011, Gildwood, Alaska, AAS 11-476.

21. King-Hele, D. G., "Satellite Orbits in an Atmosphere: Theory and Applications," Blackie and Sons, Ltd., Glasgow and London, 1987, ISBN 0-216-92252-6.

APPENDIX I

Aerobraking in a Constant Density Scale Height Atmosphere

Consider an AB pass for which atmospheric density can be modelled using equation (1). To produce the familiar "bell" shaped density vs. time profile,[21] assume two body motion about a spherical planet and expand the altitude in a Taylor series about the time of periapsis to get

$$h(t) = h(t_p) + \frac{1}{2}\ddot{h}(t_p)(t - t_p)^2 + O((t - t_p)^4) \qquad \text{(A-1)}$$

where $\ddot{h}(t_p)$ is the second derivative of altitude with respect to time evaluated at periapsis. Under the above assumptions, altitude is symmetric in time so odd derivatives vanish and the truncated terms are of order $(t-t_p)^4$ and negligible for most AB orbits. Eliminating altitude in equation (1) in favor of time in equation (A-1) yields the "bell" shape variation of density with time,

$$\rho(t) = \rho(t_p)\exp\left[\frac{-\ddot{h}(t_p)(t - t_p)^2}{2H_s}\right] \qquad \text{(A-2)}$$

The $\ddot{h}$ term can be written in terms of the orbit parameters as $\ddot{h}(t_p) = \mu e / r_p^2$, giving a function of scale height, orbit eccentricity, periapsis distance and gravitational constant (μ). To demonstrate the "square root of scale height" law, start with the Gaussian density function

$$f(x,\xi,\sigma) = \frac{1}{\sigma\sqrt{2\pi}}\exp(-(x-\varepsilon)^2/2\sigma^2) \tag{A-3}$$

where ξ is the mean and σ is the standard deviation and $\int_{-\infty}^{\infty} f(x)dx = 1$.

The last two equations suggest the substitution $\sigma^2 = H_s/\ddot{h}_p = H_s r_p^2/\mu e$, leading to

$$\rho(t) = \rho(t_p)\sqrt{\frac{2\pi r_p^2 H_s}{\mu e}}\left[\frac{1}{\sigma\sqrt{2\pi}}\exp\left[\frac{-(t-t_p)^2}{2\sigma^2}\right]\right] = \rho_p\exp\left[\frac{-(t-t_p)^2}{2\sigma^2}\right] \tag{A-4}$$

and the integral over the entire pass is

$$\int_{-\infty}^{\infty}\rho(t)dt = \rho(t_p)\sqrt{2\pi r_p^2 H_s/\mu e} \tag{A-5}$$

This result shows that the integral of ρ is proportional to the density at periapsis times the square root of H_s. Since the velocity decrease due to drag is approximately proportional to the integral of ρ, over estimation of the scale height will result in underestimating the density as determined by an OD approach that process tracking data before and after the unobserved AB pass.

The only approximation to arrive at (A-4) and (A-5) is the truncation of the Taylor series and as long as the $H_s \ll e r_p$, the higher order terms are not significant. For example, for Mars with e=0.1, H_s=7 km, h_p=125 km, and $\rho_p = 50\,\text{kg/km}^3$, the error in altitude is less than 1 km and the error is density is less than 0.1 kg/km^3 over an altitude range from periapsis to 5 scale heights above periapsis.

The integrals of dynamic pressure ($\frac{1}{2}\rho V^2$) for total drag effect or heat flux ($\frac{1}{2}\rho V^3$) for total heat input may be more important variables than density. Under the same assumptions for which (equation (A-1) is valid, the velocity variation throughout the AB pass varies by only a few percent from the value at periapsis. So the total heat input during a pass is closely approximated by the value of the heat flux at periapsis times the radical in equation (A-5).

Finally, the "drag duration" (T_d) is often defined as the time from the inbound occurrence of 1% of maximum density to the outbound time when the density is 1% of maximum density, then the drag duration is twice the time for the spacecraft to increase in altitude above periapsis by 4.6H_s. From equation (A-2) and equation (A-5)

$$T_d = 2\sqrt{\frac{9.2 H_s r_p^2}{\mu e}} \tag{A-6}$$

THE NEXT GENERATION OF MARS-GRAM AND ITS ROLE IN THE AUTONOMOUS AEROBRAKING DEVELOPMENT PLAN

Hilary L. Justh,[*] Carl G. Justus[†] and Holly S. Ramey[‡]

The Mars Global Reference Atmospheric Model (Mars-GRAM) is an engineering-level atmospheric model widely used for diverse mission applications. Mars-GRAM 2010 is currently being used to develop the onboard atmospheric density estimator that is part of the Autonomous Aerobraking Development Plan. In previous versions, Mars-GRAM was less than realistic when used for sensitivity studies for Thermal Emission Spectrometer (TES) MapYear=0 and large optical depth values, such as tau=3. A comparison analysis has been completed between Mars-GRAM, TES and data from the Planetary Data System (PDS) resulting in updated coefficients for the functions relating density, latitude, and longitude of the sun. The adjustment factors are expressed as a function of height (z), Latitude (Lat) and areocentric solar longitude (Ls). The latest release of Mars-GRAM 2010 includes these adjustment factors that alter the input data from MGCM and MTGCM for the Mapping Year 0 (user-controlled dust) case. The greatest adjustment occurs at large optical depths such as tau >1. The addition of the adjustment factors has led to better correspondence to TES Limb data from 0-60 km as well as better agreement with MGS, ODY and MRO data at approximately 90-135 km. Improved simulations utilizing Mars-GRAM 2010 are vital to developing the onboard atmospheric density estimator for the Autonomous Aerobraking Development Plan. Mars-GRAM 2010 was not the only planetary GRAM utilized during phase 1 of this plan; Titan-GRAM and Venus-GRAM were used to generate density data sets for Aerobraking Design Reference Missions. These data sets included altitude profiles (both vertical and along a trajectory), GRAM perturbations (tides, gravity waves, etc.) and provided density and scale height values for analysis by other Autonomous Aerobraking team members.

INTRODUCTION

The Mars Global Reference Atmospheric Model (Mars-GRAM) has been utilized during the aerobraking operations of the Mars Global Surveyor (MGS), Mars Odyssey (ODY) and Mars Reconnaissance Orbiter (MRO) spacecraft and was part of the Mars Aerocapture System Study (MASS) as well as the Aerocapture Technology Assessment Group (TAG). Mars-GRAM's per-

---

[*] Aerospace Technologist, Natural Environments Branch, NASA, Marshall Space Flight Center, Mail Code: EV44, Marshall Space Flight Center, AL 35812, USA.

[†] Senior Scientist, Natural Environments Branch, Dynetics Technical Services, Marshall Space Flight Center, Mail Code EV44, Marshall Space Flight Center, AL 35812, USA.

[‡‡] Terrestrial Environments Engineer, Natural Environments Branch, Jacobs ESTS Group, Marshall Space Flight Center, Mail Code EV44, Marshall Space Flight Center, AL 35812, USA.

turbation modeling capability is commonly used, in a Monte-Carlo mode, to perform high fidelity engineering end-to-end simulations for entry, descent, and landing (EDL)[1]. Mars-GRAM 2005 has been validated[2] against Radio Science data, and both nadir and limb data from TES[3].

Traditional Mars-GRAM options for representing the mean atmosphere along entry corridors include: (1) TES mapping year 0, with user-controlled dust optical depth and Mars-GRAM data interpolated from NASA Ames Mars General Circulation Model (MGCM)[4] results driven by selected values of globally-uniform dust optical depth, or (2) TES mapping years 1 and 2, with Mars-GRAM data coming from MGCM results driven by observed TES dust optical depth. From the surface to 80 km altitude, Mars-GRAM is based on NASA Ames MGCM. Above 80 km, Mars-GRAM is based on the University of Michigan Mars Thermospheric General Circulation Model (MTGCM)[5].

MGCM results that were used for Mars-GRAM with MapYear=0 were from a MGCM run with a fixed value of tau=3 for the entire year at all locations. This choice of data has led to discrepancies that have become apparent during recent sensitivity studies for MapYear=0 and large optical depths. Unrealistic energy absorption by time-invariant atmospheric dust leads to an unrealistic thermal energy balance on the polar caps. The outcome is an inaccurate cycle of condensation/sublimation of the polar caps and, as a consequence, an inaccurate cycle of total atmospheric mass and global-average surface pressure. Under an assumption of unchanged temperature profile and hydrostatic equilibrium, a given percentage change in surface pressure would produce a corresponding percentage change in density at all altitudes. Consequently, the final result of a change in surface pressure is an imprecise atmospheric density at all altitudes.

MARS-GRAM 2010 ADJUSTMENT FACTORS

In determining a possible solution to this discrepancy Mars-GRAM was evaluated at locations and times of TES limb observations, and adjustment factors (ratio of observed TES density to Mars-GRAM density) were determined. The adjustment factors [F(z,Lat,Ls)] were expressed as a function height (z), Latitude (Lat) and areocentric solar longitude (Ls). For altitudes above 80 km, Mars-GRAM (MTGCM) densities were compared to aerobraking densities measured by MGS, ODY, and MRO. For Mars-GRAM 2010, MGCM and MTGCM data values are modified by these adjustment factors.

Adjustment Factor Requirements

The adjustment factors generated by this process had to satisfy the gas law: $p = \rho RT$ as well as the hydrostatic relation: $dp/dz = -\rho g$. If T is assumed to be unchanged and both p and ρ are adjusted by a common factor, F, both relations are preserved. This adjustment factor, F, is applied to the daily mean MGCM density and pressure (0-80 km) and MTGCM density and pressure (above 80 km). The pressure scale height (RT/g) is unchanged by this process. However, since the pressure has been changed by the adjustment factor, the height of the 1.26 nbar pressure level, referred to as ZF in Mars-GRAM, has also been changed.

The daily mean MGCM or MTGCM density, DTA0, and the daily mean MGCM or MTGCM pressure, PTA0, depend on height (z), latitude (Lat), solar longitude (L_s), dust amount (tau), and solar activity parameter (F10). The adjusted values of DTA0' and PTA0' are computed from the adjustment factors F using the following equations:

$$DTA0' = DTA0 * F(z, Lat, L_s) \qquad (1)$$

$$PTA0' = PTA0 * F(z, Lat, L_s) \qquad (2)$$

where the adjustment factor F has been determined as described above.

Adjustment factors F are also used to adjust ZF by the relation:

$$ZF' = ZF + H \ln(F) \tag{3}$$

where H is local pressure scale height.

Development of MTGCM Factors

The Mars-GRAM density and pressure need to be consistent at 80 km, where the transition from MGCM to MTGCM data occurs. Thus, the assumption was made that $F(80, Lat, L_s)$ for the MTGCM data had to be the same as the adjustment factor at 80 km for the MGCM data. After adjustment factors $F(80, Lat, L_s)$ were determined from the MGCM analysis, they were used to determine MTGCM adjustment factors by use of the following equation:

$$F(z, Lat, Ls) = F(80, Lat, L_s)*(1 + A\zeta + B\zeta^2) \tag{4}$$

where the height parameter $\zeta = (z - 80)$ and the coefficients A and B depend on Lat and L_s.

Final adjustment factors $F(z, Lat, L_s)$ for MTGCM data were implemented into Mars-GRAM and a validation run comparing Mars-GRAM 2010 vs. MGS, ODY, and MRO aerobraking data from the Planetary Data System (PDS) was completed. Any residual variation of aerobraking density about mean values that became apparent during this process was used to update the height dependence of Mars-GRAM perturbation standard deviations.

IMPROVEMENT IN MARS-GRAM 2010 RESULTS

Improvement of Mars-GRAM 2010 at Lower Altitudes

Application of adjustment factors for the MGCM data yields improved comparisons between Mars-GRAM and TES limb data, as shown by density ratios (Mars-GRAM/TES Limb) given in Figure 1. Prior to adjustment these density ratios were as low as 0.65 near 60 km.

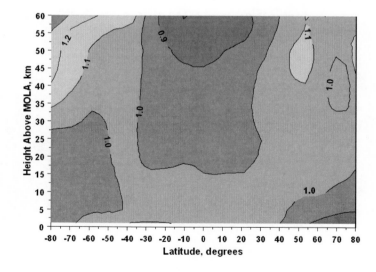

Figure 1. Latitude-Height Contours of Density Ratio (Mars-GRAM/TES Limb) After Application of MGCM Adjustment Factors

Mars-GRAM 2005 and Mars-GRAM 2010 MapYear = 0 results have also been compared for three locations at Local True Solar Time (LTST) 2 and 14.

- Location 1 (L1) = 22.5° S, 180° E, L_s = 90 ± 5, tau=.11
- Location 2 (L2) = 22.5° S, 180° E, L_s = 75 ± 5, tau=.12
- Location 3 (L3) = 2.5° N, 180° E, L_s = 210 ± 5, tau=2.65 *Dust Storm case*

Figure 2 provides the density ratios of Mars-GRAM to TES for Mars-GRAM 2005. As Figure 3 shows, the application of the adjustment factor in Mars-GRAM 2010 results in ratios of approximately 1 at lower altitudes.

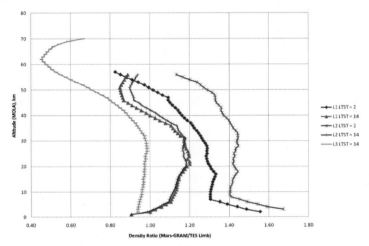

Figure 2. Density Ratio (Mars-GRAM/TES) for Mars-GRAM 2005

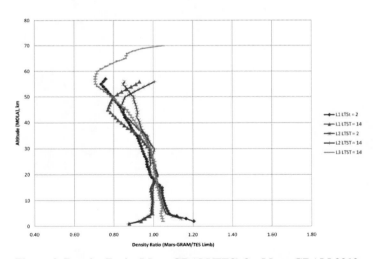

Figure 3. Density Ratio (Mars-GRAM/TES) for Mars-GRAM 2010

At the higher altitudes, Mars-GRAM 2010 results have corrected the effect of the underestimated dust aloft in the MGCM. At location 3, the Mars-GRAM 2010 density ratio has shifted closer to 1. This demonstrates that the addition of adjustment factors to Mars-GRAM 2010 has improved the results for the MapYear = 0 cases for large tau values.

Improvement of Mars-GRAM 2010 at Aerobraking Altitudes

Mars-GRAM modeled data output has improved at aerobraking altitudes by adding MTGCM adjustment factors which included height parameters and thermosphere coefficients. Improvement has been quantified by examining all of the profile data density ratios for each PDS orbiter. The 99th percentile profile shows the most extreme cases of ratio values while eliminating outliers that do not contribute to the standard profile. Density ratios for the old and updated Mars-GRAM versions will be shown versus height and latitude globally for Mars; these results will show the variability in certain regions on the red planet. All of these results will show that the updated Mars-GRAM is producing more realistic results, which will assist in future autonomous aerobraking procedures.

All of the density ratios from the PDS profile datasets are shown in Figures 4, 5, and 6. Each of these figures shows the density ratio of the PDS density to the Mars-GRAM output density versus height, with the blue lines representing the old Mars-GRAM output and the red lines showing the updated Mars-GRAM 2010 output using the thermosphere coefficients. Each one of the datasets showed an improvement with the ratio values for the latest version of Mars-GRAM. The MGS/Mars-GRAM density ratio originally was an average 2.6 with a maximum value of 16.1, but the updated Mars-GRAM 2010 ratio data averaged 1.8 with a maximum value of 10.7. The initial MRO/Mars-GRAM density ratio reached a maximum of 10.0 and averaged 2.0, whereas the new ratio only reached a maximum of 3.6 and averaged 0.9—close to the optimal 1.0 ratio. The Odyssey/Mars-GRAM ratio exceeded all of the other ratios with a maximum ratio of 39 but had an average of 3.9, which means that there were several outlying profiles that skewed the average profile. However, the newly-modeled ODY/Mars-GRAM 2010 ratio only reached a maximum of 8.2 with an average of 0.99. As these results show, the updated Mars-GRAM 2010 with MTGCM adjustment factors including thermosphere coefficients greatly improves the results of the modeled data when compared to observed data.

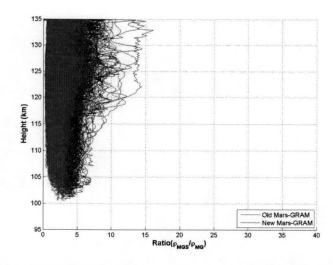

Figure 4. Density Ratios of MGS data to the New and Old Mars-GRAM Output Data

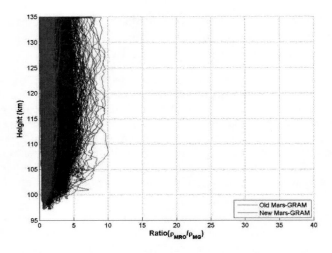

Figure 5. Density Ratios of MRO data to the New and Old Mars-GRAM Output Data

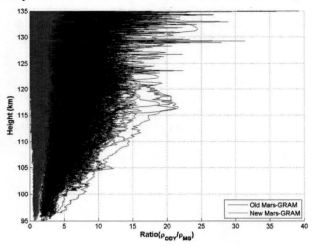

Figure 6. Density Ratios of ODY data to the New and Old Mars-GRAM Output Data

Taking the 99th percentile of all the density profiles illustrates the significant change the updated Mars-GRAM 2010 has on the profile density ratios. As shown in Figure 7, the least amount of change was observed in the MGS data over the 99th percentile profile data, with an overall change of 2.0 units across the altitude range. The MRO data showed a significant improvement from the old version of Mars-GRAM, reducing the higher altitude ratios from 6.0 to close to the optimal value of 1.0 on the updated data. However, the greatest change in ratio values occurred with the Odyssey data where the older data reached values close to 20.0 but the newer data brought the ratios down to a range between less than 1.0 to over 4.0 at the higher altitudes. All of the ratio values of the datasets improved from the old Mars-GRAM data output to the updated Mars-GRAM 2010 version; therefore, the inclusion of MTGCM adjustment factors has shown to be valid in providing more realistic output to be used in future endeavors.

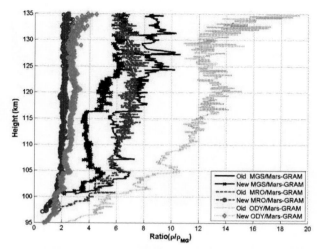

Figure 7. The 99th percentile density ratios of the profile data from MGS, MRO, and ODY to Mars-GRAM 2010 output versus height

Although autonomous aerobraking procedures are sensitive to density values at certain altitude levels, showing the density ratio values according to latitude is also beneficial for mission planning operations. Figures 8 and 9 show the ratio of the observed density values to the Mars-GRAM output values for the old version and the updated Mars-GRAM 2010 version versus height and Mars latitude. Before the MTGCM adjustment factors including thermosphere coefficients were added to the Mars-GRAM code (Figure 8), the ratio values were higher than the optimal value of 1.0, especially at locations towards the poles. The contour lines are very tight near the poles, meaning lots of variability exists with the comparisons. In the updated plot shown in Figure 9, a large area of the map is covered with the 1.0 ratio value, especially between -30°S and 15°N. Although a large discrepancy of ratio values still exist towards the poles, the variability has decreased with the inclusion of the adjustment factors. Improvement in density ratio values across latitudes can be beneficial for planning autonomous aerobraking procedures on Mars.

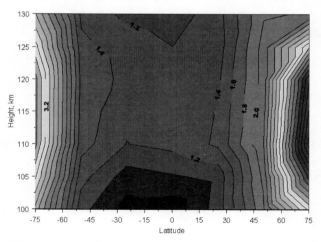

Figure 8. Contour plots of the ratio of observed PDS density values to Mars-GRAM output values (before adjustment) versus height and latitude.

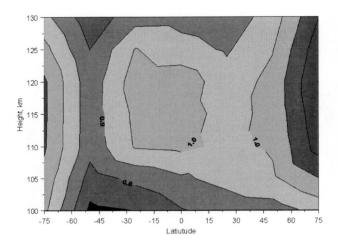

Figure 9. Contour plots of the ratio of observed PDS density values to Mars-GRAM 2010 output values (after adjustment) versus height and latitude.

CONCLUSION

Mars-GRAM 2010 has been developed, validated and is ready for distribution. Mars-GRAM in the past has been export controlled (EAR-99), but is now classified as publically available. This change in distribution classification has increased the availability of Mars-GRAM 2010 to users. Mars-GRAM 2010 has been updated to Fortran 90/95. Mars-GRAM 2010 now includes adjustment factors that are used to alter the input data from MGCM and MTGCM for the Mapping year 0 (user-controlled dust) case. The greatest adjustment occurs at large optical depths such as tau>1. The addition of the adjustment factors has led to better correspondence to TES Limb data from 0-60 km as well as better agreement with MGS, Odyssey and MRO data at approximately 90-130 km. Improved simulations utilizing Mars-GRAM 2010 are vital to developing the onboard atmospheric density estimator for the Autonomous Aerobraking Development Plan.

ACKNOWLEDGMENTS

This work was sponsored by the NASA Engineering and Safety Center. This assessment can be found in the final report NESC-RP-09-00605 in November 2011.

REFERENCES

[1]Striepe S. A. at al., AIAA Atmospheric Flight Mechanics Conference and Exhibit, Abstract # 2002-4412, 2002.

[2]Justus C. G. et al., "Mars Aerocapture and Validation of Mars-GRAM with TES Data." 53rd JANNAF Propulsion Meeting, 2005.

[3]Smith M. D. "Interannual variability in TES atmospheric observations of Mars during 1999-2003." *Icarus*, 167, 2004, pp. 148-165.

[4]Haberle, R. M., Pollack, J. B., Barnes, J. R., et al., "Mars Atmospheric Dynamics as Simulated by the NASA Ames General Circulation Model 1. The Zonal-Mean Circulation." *Journal of Geophysical Research*, Vol. 98, No. E2 1993, pp. 3093-3123.

[5]Bougher, S.W., et al., "The Mars Thermosphere: 2. General Circulation with Coupled Dynamics and Composition." *Journal of Geophysical Research*, Vol. 95, No. B9, 1990, pp. 14,811-14,827.

ASTEROID AND NEO II

SESSION 5

Chair: Dr. Shyam Bhaskaran
                                            Jet Propulsion Laboratory

The following paper was not available for publication:

AAS 11-442
   (Paper Withdrawn)

A NEW APPROACH ON THE LONG TERM DYNAMICS OF NEO'S UNDER YARKOVSKY EFFECT

Jesús Peláez,[*] Hodei Urrutxua,[†]
Claudio Bombardelli[‡] and Isabel Perez-Grande[**]

A classical approach to the many-body problem is that of using special perturbation methods. Nowadays and due to the availability of high-speed computers is an essential tool in Space Dynamics which exhibits a great advantage: it is applicable to any orbit involving any number of bodies and all sorts of astrodynamical problems, especially when these problems fall into regions in which general perturbation theories are absent. One such case is, for example, that Near Earth Objects (NEO's) dynamics. In this field, the Group of Tether Dynamics of UPM (GDT) has developed a new regularization scheme —called DROMO— which is characterized by only 8 ODE. This new regularization scheme allows a new approach to the dynamics of NEO's in the long term, specially appropriated to consider the influence of the anisotropic thermal emission (Yarkovsky and YORP effects) on the dynamics. A new project, called NEODROMO, has been started in GDT that aims to provide a reliable tool for the long term dynamics of NEO's.

INTRODUCTION

Some Near-Earth Objects (NEO's) of the Solar System mean a real threat for the life on Earth. The geological and biological history of our planet is punctuated by evidence of repeated, devastating cosmic impacts. References [1, 2] deal with the asteroid threats in a detailed way; also, the volume 2 of the *Journal of Cosmology* is entirely devoted to these kind of threats. In Ref. [1] we can read:

International NEO decision-making should take the following factors into consideration:

- *Damage caused by asteroids and other Near Earth Objects might affect the entire international community and/or major parts of the world. A truly global response is required.*

- *Capabilities (unevenly spread among the international community) are available to humankind to undertake responsive action against NEO threats, especially if the appropriate decisions are made sufficiently in advance.*

- *The discovery rate of NEOs posing a potential threat will increase significantly within the next 10-15 years.*

- *Because a substantial lead time is usually required to execute an asteroid deflection operation, the international community may have to act before it would be certain an impact would occur.*

[*] Technical University of Madrid (UPM), ETSI Aeronáuticos, Pz Cardenal Cisneros 3, 28040 Madrid, Spain. E-mail: j.pelaez@upm.es.

[†] Technical University of Madrid (UPM), ETSI Aeronáuticos, Pz Cardenal Cisneros 3, 28040 Madrid, Spain. E-mail: hodei.urrutxua@upm.es.

[‡] Technical University of Madrid (UPM), ETSI Aeronáuticos, Pz Cardenal Cisneros 3, 28040 Madrid, Spain. E-mail: claudio.bombardelli@upm.es.

[**] Technical University of Madrid (UPM), ETSI Aeronáuticos, Pz Cardenal Cisneros 3, 28040 Madrid, Spain. E-mail: isabel.perez.grande@upm.es.

- *Efforts to deflect a NEO could cause a temporary shift in the impact site from one populated region of the planet to another.*

- *Delays in decisions to undertake responsive actions will limit the relevant options. Such delays will increase the risk that the remaining options may cause undesirable political consequences or even physical impact damage.*

As a consequence, asteroid deflection is becoming a key topic in astrodynamics. Although no asteroid has been deflected so far, altering the trajectory of a small-sized asteroid to avoid a catastrophic impact with the Earth has been shown to be, in principle, technically feasible [3], and different techniques, ranging from nuclear detonation to kinetic impact and low-thrust methods, have been proposed [3, 4, 5]. Each one of these methods shows advantages and drawbacks that, in general, depend on the mass and orbital characteristics of the particular asteroid to be deflected as well as its physical property (porosity, composition, surface reflectivity, etc.) and rotation state.

Recently a new concept, the **Ion Beam Shepherd (IBS)**, has been introduced by our group[1]. This concept allows the introduction of a controlled force on a spacecraft, or a celestial body, by means of a highly collimated high-velocity ion beam which is produced by an ion thruster onboard a shepherd spacecraft. The ion beam is pointed against a target to modify its orbit and/or attitude with no need for docking. It can be used to deflect a threatening asteroid (see [6]) or to remove space debris (see [7]). In the context of the *Ariadna Call for Ideas: Active Removal of Space Debris*, the IBS concept has been partially developed in Ref. [8], a project carried out in collaboration with the EP2 team[2] of the UPM.

Regardless of the chosen deflection method, accurate orbit propagation and determination is of paramount importance in any deflection mission. However, when using low-trust deflexion techniques the accurate knowledge of the asteroid dynamics turns out to be a key point of the mission, since a substantial lead time should be provided in order to execute the deflection operation with the required reliability.

The dynamics of a NEO, specially in the long term, is always a n-body problem with additional perturbations. A classical approach to the many-body problem is that of using **special perturbation methods**. Nowadays, and due to the availability of high-speed computers, special perturbation methods are an essential tool in space dynamics which exhibit a great advantage: they are applicable to any orbit involving any number of bodies and all sorts of astrodynamical problems, especially when these problems fall into regions in which general perturbation theories are absent. This is the case of NEO's dynamics.

Two-body regularization is an efficient tool to integrate perturbed two-body problems numerically. This is true not only in Keplerian astrodynamics but also in n-body simulations. Originally regularization was developed to avoid the numerical difficulty in integrating nearly parabolic orbits such as those of comets. However, its effectiveness was confirmed even for nearly circular orbits due to its better numerical stability than unregularized Keplerian motion [9]. A numerical comparison of different *regularized* schemes together with the unregularized formulation in the light of their computational cost and performance can be found in [10].

Our group has developed a new regularization scheme —called DROMO— which is characterized by only 8 ODE. This special perturbation method was presented for the first time in the 2005 winter meeting of the AAS [11], but the basic theory of DROMO can be found in [12] that was published in 2007 almost simultaneously with the Fukushima report (DROMO is not evaluated in [10]).

This novel method is especially appropriated to carry out the propagation of **complex orbits**, like, for example, NEO's orbits. The formulation of DROMO is flexible and it permits, in some cases, to obtain analytical or semi-analytical solutions; an example of this flexibility can be found in [13] where a new asymptotic solution has been obtained for the constant tangential thrust acceleration case. However, the best performances of DROMO are obtained when it is used in the numerical propagation of orbits. Thus, DROMO turns out to be one of the most accurate propagators when compared with similar formulations. Due to the plus of accuracy provided by the DROMO formulation (see section 4 in page 565), this scheme is quite appropriated for the propagation of orbits when a high-fidelity description of the trajectory is mandatory. This tool will be used to study the dynamical behavior of small celestial bodies.

Aside from the gravitational perturbations, NEO's dynamics is affected by non-conservative perturbations of thermal origin. The effects of thermal radiation forces and torques on small bodies of our Solar System have

---

[1]Group of Tether Dynamics of UPM (GDT)

[2]Team of Space Propulsion and Plasmas, web.fmetsia.upm.es/ep2

been extensively studied during the last decades. An excellent description of these phenomena can be found in two Ph.D. thesis defended in Charles University (see [14, 15]) focusing on its influence on the dynamics of asteroids and small bodies. The main effects of these perturbations of thermal origin are called the **Yarkovsky effect** and the **YORP effect** (Yarkovsky - O'Keefe - Radzievskii - Paddack).

YARKOVSKY AND YORP EFFECTS

The Yarkovsky effect is a tiny nongravitational force due to radiative recoil of the anisotropic thermal emission. When the temperature of the surface of the body is not uniform the radiation emitted by the body varies from one point to another. This causes a force —responsible for the Yarkovsky effect— and a torque —responsible for the YORP effect— acting on the body.

In general, the Yarkovsky effect induces a secular deviation on the semimajor axis of a heliocentric orbit of asteroids of appropriate size. In addition, the forces associated to this thermal phenomenon also modifies the rotational dynamics of the asteroid, due to the non-vanishing torque on its center of mass; this additional effect —commonly called the YORP effect— is responsible for the variation of the attitude dynamics of the body due to thermal effects.

These effects are important in the long-term because, unlike gravitational perturbations, they can permanently increase or decrease orbital and/or rotational energy. As a consequence of the secular evolution of the semimajor axis the body may migrate from one heliocentric zone to another. Similarly, rotation rate and obliquity of the spin axis could be permanently changed such that a normal rotator may be moved to the category of fast or slow, or even tumbling, rotators.

The intensity of the coupling between orbital and attitude motion depends on many factors; the size is one of the most important together with the spin of the asteroid. Thus, the above mentioned coupling cannot be neglected in some asteroids and a joint description is mandatory in order to predict its orbit with accuracy.

To properly calculate the force associated with this particular effect the temperature distribution on the surface of the asteroid should be determined; but this temperature depends on the asteroid orbit, its size and shape, spin axis orientation and period, mass, density of surface layers, albedo, thermal conductivity, capacity and IR emissivity of the material (see [16]). The uncertainty of many of these parameters invites to develop simplified methods to calculate the influence of the thermal effects on long term dynamics of asteroids as, for example, the excellent paper [17].

The elemental force $\mathrm{d}\vec{f}$ due to thermal radiation on a surface element of area $\mathrm{d}S$ is normal to the surface and takes the value

$$\mathrm{d}\vec{f} = -\frac{2\varepsilon\sigma T^4}{3c}\,\vec{n}\mathrm{d}s$$

where ε is the emissivity of the surface, $\sigma = 5.67 \times 10^{-8}$ W/(m^{2}K^4) the Stefan-Boltzman constant, $c = 2.998 \times 10^8$ m/s the speed of light in vacuum, $\vec{n}$ is the unit vector normal to the surface and T the temperature of the surface, which has to be determined in order to integrate the force over the entire surface.

The resultant of these forces and the torque at the center of mass of the body are:

$$\vec{f} = -\frac{2\sigma}{3c}\int_\Sigma \varepsilon T^4\,\vec{n}\mathrm{d}s, \qquad \vec{T} = -\frac{2\sigma}{3c}\int_\Sigma \varepsilon T^4\,\vec{x}\times\vec{n}\mathrm{d}s$$

where both integrals should be extended to the external surface Σ of the body. Obviously, a geometric model for the surface should be available. Some preliminary but very interesting results have been obtained assuming simple geometries as in [18].

To obtain the surface's temperature distribution, $T(\vec{x},t)$, the heat diffusion equation is applied. Assuming that heat conduction is one-dimensional (see [19, 20]), that is, assuming that the main temperature gradients are perpendicular to the body surface, the equation is

$$\rho\,c_t\frac{\partial T}{\partial t} = \frac{\partial}{\partial z}(k\frac{\partial T}{\partial z})$$

where ρ is the density of the body, c_t its specific thermal capacity and k its thermal conductivity. In this equation z is the depth accounted from the body surface. To solve this partial differential equation, boundary and initial conditions must be given.

The first boundary condition comes from the energy balance equation on the body surface. Thus,

$$\varepsilon \sigma T^4(z=0,t) = k \frac{\partial T}{\partial z}(z=0,t) + \alpha E(t)$$

In this equation α is the solar absorptance of the body surface and $E(t)$ the solar irradiation on the surface element. It can be calculated from the solar intensity at the distance d (in AU) between the body and the Sun and θ is the angle between the solar rays and the vector normal to the surface. Thus,

$$E(t) = G_s \left(\frac{d_{SE}}{d}\right)^2 \cos\theta$$

where $G_s = 1366.1$ W/m^2 is the solar constant at the distance between the Earth and the Sun: $d_{SE} = 1$ AU.

The second boundary condition is related to the fact that after certain depth, the effect of the Sun on the body temperature is not perceived. Then

$$\lim_{z \to \infty} \frac{\partial T}{\partial z}(z,t) = 0$$

Regarding, the initial conditions, a periodicity restriction is applied, so that

$$T(z,t) = T(z,t+P)$$

where P is the rotational period of the celestial body.

The solution of the differential equation with the boundary and initial conditions described above is quite complex, even for spherical bodies, mainly due to the non-linearity of the boundary conditions. In some works (see [21, 22]) solutions have found by assuming that the temperature distribution of the body fluctuates about an average value $T = T_{av} + T$ and linearizing the radiation term. But, even in this case, the mathematical apparatus necessary to solve the problem is quite complex. More details about these models can be found in [16, 15]. A model similar to the models described in ,[19, 20] will be used in a first step in NEODROMO.

Impact of Yarkovsky effect on NEO dynamics

Non-gravitational perturbations, regardless being many orders of magnitude weaker than gravity [23], hold keys to fully understand the dynamical evolution of asteroids. These forces produce small but meaningful effects on asteroid orbits and rotation rates over long timescales, which suggests that they should be considered as important as collisions and gravitational perturbations for the understanding of asteroid evolution [24].

For meteoroids and small asteroids in the 10 cm - 10 km range, the principal non-gravitational force and torque arise from an anisotropic thermal emission of the absorbed solar radiation [23].

Historically the Yarkovsky perturbation was believed to be negligible assuming that its acceleration, opposed to the gravitational attraction of the Sun, could be modeled by adjusting the gravitational constant of the Sun, and the asteroids were anyway too large objects. However, it can be proved [25] that none of these conditions is typically satisfied for real NEOs, so the effects of direct solar radiation pressure and reflected radiation should also be taken into account, since may lead to observable displacements of the orbit whenever the asteroid is not spherical or its surface albedo is not homogeneous. The Yarkovsky effect may in fact become important in the dynamics of asteroids, since it leads to long-term perturbations accumulating over long time spans.

The most important implication of the Yarkovsky perturbations is the steady and size-dependent semimajor axis drift as a function of the body's spin, orbit and material properties [25, 26, 24]. This effect results in an orbit displacement that accumulates quadratically with time, compared with the linear perturbations due to the eccentricity and inclination [25].

Besides, further Yarkovsky/YORP-driven processes [23] include: secular changes of the rotational period and obliquity, efficient transport towards low-order resonances, interaction with weaker higher-order resonances, or captures in secular and spin-orbit resonances. According with [27] *two major mechanisms are suspected to alter the rotation rates and states of NEOs once they get into planet crossing orbits: close encounters with the planets and YORP.*

As a significative example to the relevance of non-gravitational perturbations, the Yarkovsky/YORP force could push a 10 meter meteoroid's semimajor axis by 0.1-0.2 AU, before being disrupted by a random collision with another body (see Ref. [23]).

NEODROMO PROJECT

Predicting the trajectory of a given asteroid —we are thinking basically in NEO's— involves the knowledge of several standard models of the solar system that includes the gravity of the Sun, Moon, other planets and the three largest asteroids: Ceres, Vesta and Pallas. The ephemeris of all these celestial bodies are needed and *high fidelity prediction requires high fidelity ephemeris.*

Additional factors influence the long-term predicted trajectory in a substantial way: the spin of the asteroid, its mass, the way it reflects and absorbs sun-light, radiates heat, and the gravitational pull of other celestial bodies passing nearby. Most of these factors are associated with small perturbations which act on the asteroid and produce the slow evolution of its classical elements. However, close encounters with celestial bodies introduce a much faster time scale and the dynamical state of the asteroid could change drastically.

When studying the dynamics of NEO's on long time intervals numerical methods of integration of the equations of motion are practically mandatory since the dynamics of these objects is not easily studied by analytical methods because of large eccentricities and close encounters with planets. In addition, the elements of the NEO orbits are known with some uncertainty due to errors associated with the observations used to determine the orbit or the initial conditions used to start the propagation. The presence of these errors, in some cases, invites the use of probabilistic methods to solve the problem (see, for example, the paper [28]).

However, we adopt another point of view. During the last years, the observation techniques and the procedures used to determine orbits have experienced important improvements (see [29, 30, 31]). This is one of the reason why the number of well known NEO's has increased spectacularly. Similarly, the knowledge about the spin rates of asteroids is increasing steadily (see [32, 33]) and it is natural to assume that this bulk of knowledge will increase even more during the next decades. Some recent examples in this sense can be found in [34, 35].

This paper tries to describe the main characteristics of NEODROMO, which is being developed in our group. The idea of NEODROMO project is to offer a propagation tool, specially tailored for the NEO's dynamics, including models of increasing complexity that can be used for the determination of orbits and the prediction of trajectories. The main objective of this project is to obtain numerically an accurate description of the dynamics of a NEO in the general case in which the thermal radiation induce both, the Yarkovsky and the YORP effects. To do that we use the DROMO propagator together with an attitude propagator (see section 5 in page 570) also developed in our group.

ORBIT PROPAGATION. DROMO

DROMO is based in a new special perturbation method whose theory is developed in papers [11, 12] where a set of non-classical elements $(q_1, q_2, q_3, \varepsilon_1^0, \varepsilon_2^0, \varepsilon_3^0, \varepsilon_4^0)$ has been introduced. DROMO provides the time evolution of these elements when the perturbations forces are known.

Starting from the original variable, an slight improvement of the performances of DROMO can be obtained by carrying out the following change of variables:

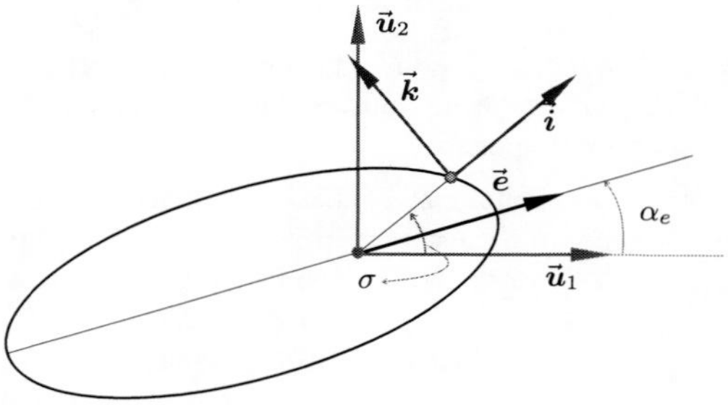

$$\zeta_1 = \frac{q_1}{q_3}, \quad \zeta_2 = \frac{q_2}{q_3}, \quad \zeta_3 = q_3$$

Figure 1: Reference frames

This way the eccentricity vector can be expressed like

$$\vec{e} = \zeta_1 \, \vec{u}_1 + \zeta_2 \, \vec{u}_2$$

where the unit vectors $(\vec{u}_1, \vec{u}_2)$, which lie in the orbital plane, are defined by:

$$[\vec{u}_1, \vec{u}_2] = [\vec{i}, \vec{k}] \, Q_0, \qquad Q_0 = \begin{pmatrix} \cos \sigma & \sin \sigma \\ -\sin \sigma & \cos \sigma \end{pmatrix}$$

They rotate with angular velocity $+\dot{\sigma}\,\vec{j}$ relative to the orbital frame $(\vec{i},\,\vec{k})$.

Expressed in terms of these new variables the governing equations take the form:

$$\frac{d\zeta_1}{d\sigma} = \frac{1}{\zeta_3^4 \hat{s}^3}\left[+\hat{s}\sin\sigma f_{px} + \{\zeta_1 + (1+\hat{s})\cos\sigma\}f_{pz}\right]$$

$$\frac{d\zeta_2}{d\sigma} = \frac{1}{\zeta_3^4 \hat{s}^3}\left[-\hat{s}\cos\sigma f_{px} + \{\zeta_2 + (1+\hat{s})\sin\sigma\}f_{pz}\right]$$

$$\frac{d\zeta_3}{d\sigma} = -\frac{1}{\zeta_3^3 \hat{s}^3}f_{pz}$$

$$\frac{d\tau}{d\sigma} = \frac{1}{\zeta_3^3 \hat{s}^2}$$

$$\frac{d\varepsilon_1^0}{d\sigma} = -\frac{\lambda(\sigma)}{2}\{\sin(\sigma-\sigma_0)\varepsilon_2^0 + \cos(\sigma-\sigma_0)\varepsilon_4^0\}$$

$$\frac{d\varepsilon_2^0}{d\sigma} = +\frac{\lambda(\sigma)}{2}\{\sin(\sigma-\sigma_0)\varepsilon_1^0 - \cos(\sigma-\sigma_0)\varepsilon_3^0\}$$

$$\frac{d\varepsilon_3^0}{d\sigma} = +\frac{\lambda(\sigma)}{2}\{\cos(\sigma-\sigma_0)\varepsilon_2^0 - \sin(\sigma-\sigma_0)\varepsilon_4^0\}$$

$$\frac{d\varepsilon_4^0}{d\sigma} = +\frac{\lambda(\sigma)}{2}\{\cos(\sigma-\sigma_0)\varepsilon_1^0 + \sin(\sigma-\sigma_0)\varepsilon_3^0\}$$

These equations should be integrated, taking into account the relations:

$$\lambda(\sigma) = \frac{1}{\zeta_3^4 \hat{s}^3}f_{py}$$

$$\hat{s} = 1 + \zeta_1\cos\sigma + \zeta_2\sin\sigma$$

$$z = \frac{1}{r} = \zeta_3^2\{1 + \zeta_1\cos\sigma + \zeta_2\sin\sigma\}$$

$$\frac{dr}{d\tau} = \zeta_3(\zeta_1\sin\sigma - \zeta_2\cos\sigma)$$

$$\chi = \frac{\sigma - \sigma_0}{2}$$

$$\begin{pmatrix}\varepsilon_1 \\ \varepsilon_3 \\ \varepsilon_2 \\ \varepsilon_4\end{pmatrix} = \begin{pmatrix}\cos\chi & \sin\chi & 0 & 0 \\ -\sin\chi & \cos\chi & 0 & 0 \\ 0 & 0 & \cos\chi & -\sin\chi \\ 0 & 0 & \sin\chi & \cos\chi\end{pmatrix}\begin{pmatrix}\varepsilon_1^0 \\ \varepsilon_3^0 \\ \varepsilon_2^0 \\ \varepsilon_4^0\end{pmatrix}$$

Here (f_{px}, f_{py}, f_{pz}) are the non-dimensional components of the perturbing force acting upon the body. The integration must start from the appropriate initial conditions at $\sigma = \sigma_0$ $(\tau = 0)$.

The initial conditions should be obtained from the initial values $(\vec{r}_0, \vec{v}_0)$ of the position and velocity of the body. In particular σ_0 is the true anomaly of the initial position at the initial osculating orbit; the initial values of $(\varepsilon_1^0, \varepsilon_3^0, \varepsilon_2^0, \varepsilon_4^0)$ are obtained directly from the orbital frame at perigee of the initial osculating orbit. The other initial values are:

$$\text{at}\quad \sigma = \sigma_0: \quad \tau = 0, \quad \zeta_1 = e_0, \quad \zeta_2 = 0, \quad \zeta_3 = \frac{\sqrt{\mu}|\vec{r}_0|}{|\vec{r}_0 \times \vec{v}_0|}$$

where e_0 is the eccentricity of the initial osculating orbit and μ the gravitational constant of the attractive center (the Sun in heliocentric orbits).

The mains characteristics of DROMO are:

- Unique formulation for the three types of orbits: elliptic, parabolic and hyperbolic. So, the singularity that appears in the proximity of parabolic motion when using different formulations for elliptic and hyperbolic orbits disappears.

- It uses orbital elements as generalized coordinates (as the Lagrange's Planetary equations); as consequence, the truncation error vanishes in the unperturbed problem and is scaled by the perturbation itself in the perturbed one. The method doesn't have singularities for small inclination and/or small eccentricities, unlike the Lagrange's planetary equations. The orbital plane attitude is determined by Euler parameters which are free of singularities.

- The use of Euler parameters gives easy auto-correction as well as robustness. The error propagation shows better performances than in the cases of Cowell's or Encke's methods. Easy programming, since they use the components of perturbation forces in the orbital frame. This makes easy the use of models proper of Orbital Dynamics.

- A precise and fast simulator is obtained by using this method with variable step routines with effective step control, as Runge-Kutta-Fehlberg or Dormand-Prince types. However, routines with fixed step can be used also without reduction in performances. Multistep routines —like the classical one of Shampine & Gordon [36] (DE)— can be used also. In fact, this kind of routines show excellent characteristics because, from a practical point of view, keep the accuracy and reduce the number of function calls significantly.

- It is not necessary to solve Kepler's equation in the elliptic case, nor the equivalent for hyperbolic and parabolic cases, since time is one of the dependent variables determined by the method itself.

548

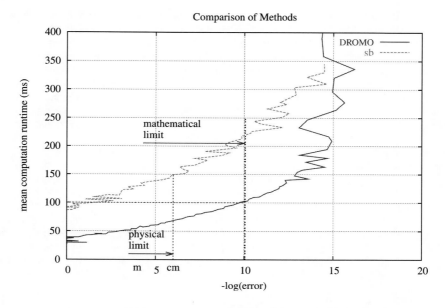

Figure 2: Comparison between DROMO and Sperling-Bürdet

In terms of *accuracy* DROMO with a classical Runge-Kutta-Fehlberg routine of order 7 —RKF7(8)— turn out to be one of the best combinations than can be used for high fidelity propagation of orbits. In [12] we shown that DROMO beats the Sperling–Bürdet's method solving the *example 2b* of the famous book of Stiefel and Scheifele: [9]; such an example has been used also in other works (for example, in the book [37]).

In that comparison the *exact solution* is not the one given in the book [9]. Instead, we recalculated the solution two times using both propagators with the maximum accuracy; we took as *exact solution* the common part obtained in both calculations.

The computations have been done: 1) in the same computer (Intel Xeon 3056 MHz microprocessor, 2 Gb RAM), 2) with the same compiler (Intel C++ 8.1.022), 3) with the same integrating algorithm (Runge-Kutta-Fehlberg (RKF) 7(8) of variable step-size better than the RKF 4(5) taken from the [38]), and 4) in the same computer conditions (processor load, etc). Moreover, to minimize the effect of uncontrolled factors on the computation time we have repeated the former task 30 times and we have obtained the mean value of runtime.

Figure 2 which has been taken from Ref. [12] shows the results of the comparison. The mean computation runtime is plotted in ordinates and the common logarithm of the norm of the error vector ($-\log(|\Delta \bar{x}|)$ in abscissas. This last quantity is a measure of the quality of the solution: it is approximately equivalent to the number of exact decimal digits of the solution plus one.

The plot shows better performances for DROMO; it seems to be quicker for the same precision, or equivalently, it seems to be more accurate for identical computational time.

These differences are mainly due to the lower order of DROMO (8 ODE's) compared with the Sperling-Bürdet's method (13 ODE's). But there are other reasons also: in the Sperling-Bürdet's method the calculation of the "second members" of equations requires to process perturbation forces through numerical treatments of some length; this also happens in similar methods based on regularization techniques as the KS's method. In our method however, forces hardly require manipulation. Note that the right hand sides of equations only include their components in the orbital frame, which are obtained by simple scalar products. Moreover, the simplicity of programming, joined to the clearness and the simplicity of equations governing the evolution of Euler parameters, strengthens our conviction in the method's advantages.

In [39] a comparison between DROMO and Cowell's method have been carried out in the field of inter-planetary trajectories; the idea was to evaluate the accuracy of both methods calculating the post-trajectory of a spacecraft when a planet fly-by is included in the mission. Figure 5 shows the results of two simulations performed in that paper. In that comparison, and regarding the numerical integration methods, a variable step routine with effective step control has been programmed. In particular, the chosen scheme is an 8th order embedded Runge-Kutta method implemented by Dormand-Prince (DOPRI853). This method also allows an accurate dense output and the possibility of implementing events detection with a slight cost in additional function evaluations [40]. These brand-new capabilities, that are becoming strongly demanded, together with the reasonably good performance, numerical precision and easy implementation, make this type of single-step methods worth considering for applications in the field of orbital mechanics [41]. The propagation tool have been programmed in C although some combined C/FORTRAN90 programming has been necessary in order to use the SOFA routines for Earth Attitude, that are provided in FORTRAN90 by the International Astronomical Union.

The comparison of the results obtained by means of DROMO and Cowell's method for the integration of several direct transfers to outer planets in the Solar System exhibits the great differences in the final position that has been computed. This is particularly critical in the cases where gravity-assisted maneuvers are performed, since they are extremely sensible missions in which slight shifts in the conditions at the arrival to the sphere of influence of the target body may lead to completely different subsequent trajectories.

The comparison performed in [39] is not completely fair for the Cowell method. The reasoning is as follows: for any method, DROMO or Cowell's method, exist a numerical integrator that provides the best performances of the method by achieving the required numerical accuracy after propagation over some specified simulation time. The point is that these integrators need not be the same for the different methods considered. Thus, for each method, we should select the numerical integrator that minimizes the CPU time needed to achieve the specified error.

In general, the Cowell method reach its better performances when is used in conjunction with the Störmer-Cowell algorithms to integrate the equations. Thus, in [42] we performed a comparison between DROMO and the Störmer-Cowell method by using an analytical solution which appears in the well known *problem of Tsien*: a satellite perturbed by a constant radial thrust.

In the Tsien's problem and for a critical value of the perturbing thrust, there is an asymptotic motion from a circular orbit of radius R_0 to a final circular orbit of radius $2R_0$ (see figure 3). This last circle is an unstable limit cycle which can be calculated analytically but the *numerical* obtention of such an analytical solution is not easy.

A suitable measure to evaluate performance of both propagators is to calculate the number of orbits until the numerical solution starts to deviate from the asymptotic orbit. A deviation is considered, when the relative error of the numerically computed position is larger than a threshold. Here R is the current orbital radius which must be compared with the radius of the asymptotic orbit $2R_0$.

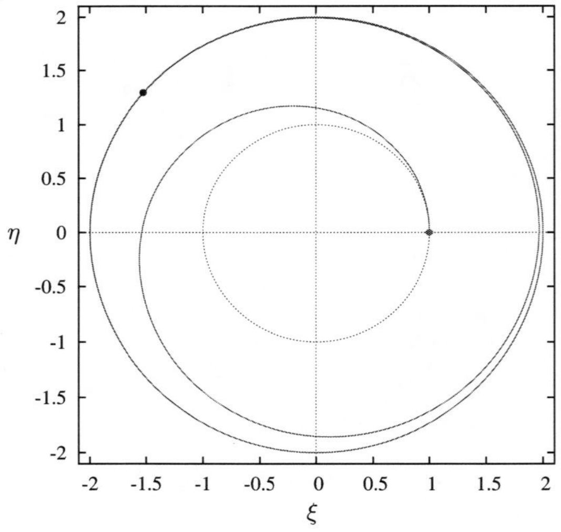

$$\frac{|2R_0 - R|}{2R_0} < 10^{-3}$$

Figure 3: Satellite trajectory in the asymptotic case of the Tsien problem

To allow for a fair comparison, integrators of same order are used for the DROMO and Störmer-Cowell formulations. For DROMO, the integrators of the Runge-Kutta-Fehlberg family have proven to be very efficient and accurate. These schemes [43, 44] of order 5 to 8 are compared to Störmer-Cowell implementations [45] of equal maximum order. In addition, integrators of the multistep method of Shampine & Gordon [36] (DE 5-8) are tested and compared to Störmer-Cowell, too. The implementations for Störmer-Cowell and the DE integrators are modified to obtain a fixed order version to be compared with RKF integrators.

550

Figure 4 shows the number of stable orbits based on the initially given relative tolerance of the integrators. It is evident that DROMO in combination with RKF integrators has a better stability than Störmer-Cowell. However the runtime of the DROMO method is higher than of the Störmer-Cowell method of equal order. This drawback can in part be accounted for by using the DE integrator, which is faster but less accurate, for DROMO.

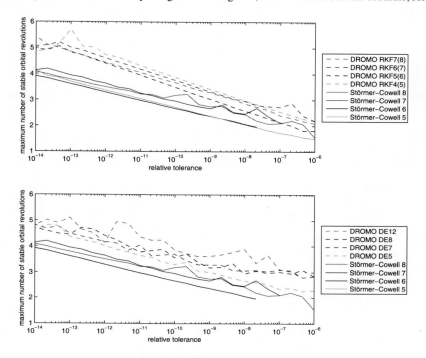

Figure 4: Comparison of method stability versus relative tolerance

In order to evaluate the computational cost of the different methods under equal conditions, the integrators have to be tuned to a similar performance. Therefore a common integration range and accuracy is chosen for them. According to figure 4, all integrators can be stable for up to 4 orbital revolutions. For fair comparison, the relative errors are chosen in such a way, that the integrators are stable only within that specified range. DROMO RKF7(8) and RKF6(7) can achieve this with $\epsilon_{rel} = 10^{-11}$ while the equal order Störmer-Cowell propagators need a tighter tolerance of $\epsilon_{rel} = 10^{-14}$. The results show comparison only of integrators of order 7 and 8 because, for both methods, they perform significantly better in terms of runtime. The evaluation is performed 100 times and table 1 shows the mean runtime, the number of steps and the function calls. It indicates similar processing time for DROMO RKF and Störmer-Cowell of the same order even though the number of function calls of DROMO is higher. This is due to the specific characteristics of the Tsien problem. The higher number of function calls in DROMO does not influence the runtime significantly, because the calculation of the perturbations is not very costly. In the Störmer-Cowell method the runtime is influenced by the fact, that coefficients have to be recalculated for each integration step. Using DROMO formulation in combination with the multistep DE integrator requires less function calls. For these integrators the runtime are not shown because they are implemented in a different programming environment.

From the analysis carried out in [42] some conclusions can be drawn.

- In terms of *accuracy* DROMO with the Runge-Kutta-Fehlberg routine RKF7(8) turn out to be the best combination since they provide a longer and more stable description of the asymptotic orbit.

Method	DROMO RKF7(8)	DROMO RKF6(7)	DROMO DE8	DROMO DE7	SC 8th order	SC 7th order
Rel tolerance	1e-11	1e-11	1e-11	1e-12	1e-14	1e-14
Runtime in s	0.21	0.47	-	-	0.24	0.24
Function calls	2379	4850	1113	1623	439	536
Number of steps	181	483	-	-	431	529

Table 1: Runtime comparison for 4 complete orbits

- In terms of *function calls* the Störmer-Cowell formulations turns out to be the best formulation since it provides the lower number of call to the derivative functions.

Due to the plus of accuracy provided by the DROMO formulation, this scheme is the most appropriated for the propagation of orbits when a high-fidelity description of the trajectory is mandatory. This plus of accuracy, however, has a cost: the higher number of function calls due to the Runge-Kutta-Fehlberg routine used to perform the integration.

However, and from a *global point of view*, the combination of DROMO with the multistep method of Shampine & Gordon [36] (DE) shows excellent characteristics because: 1) the accuracy worsens in a small amount, relative to the accuracy provided by the combination DROMO + RKF7(8), and 2) the number of function calls reduce in a significant way. Regarding this last point, it should be noticed that the Störmer-Cowell formulas requires one function call per step, and the multistep method of Shampine & Gordon [36] (DE) requires two function call per step due to the second evaluation that takes place in the *correction* part of the algorithm.

ATTITUDE PROPAGATION

In recent years a considerable amount of effort has been devoted to the development of a comprehensive theory that it provides a deeper insight into the complex dynamic behavior involved in the motion of rotating rigid bodies. Some of these efforts have been focused on alternatives ways of describing the kinematics of this motion (see for instance the complete survey [46] by M.D. Shuster); some other have been focused on the dynamics. From the kinematic point of view, one has a certain degree of freedom, since the rotation matrix which determines the relative orientation between two reference frames can be parameterized in more than one way. By having available several different approach for viewing the kinematics, more insight can be gained into a specific problem. In general, the best approach is clearly problem dependent. The most commonly used parameterizations for the attitude kinematics are the Eulerian angles, the Euler-Rodrigues parameters (quaternion formulation), the Andoyer variables, the Cayley-Klein parameters and the Cayley-Rodrigues parameters (see [46, 47, 48, 49, 50, 51]).

The dynamics of the rotational motion may be deduced from the angular momentum equation which describes the influence of the external torques on the attitude of the rigid body, through the angular velocity concept. Basically, the rotational dynamics of a rigid body is an initial value problem: for a given orientation and its change rate with respect to an inertial frame at an initial time and the force acting on it, find its attitude at any instant. From this point of view, Euler equations of motion provide a complete and well-defined framework. However, the complete analytical solution of this system of three nonlinear, coupled differential equations is still unknown in the general case. Special cases for which solutions have been found include the torque-free motion (Euler-Poinsot case) and the motion of the symmetric top forced by gravitation (Lagrange case). The existence of analytical solutions for such special cases cherished hopes about the existence of a general analytical solution which should be discovered some day. However, deeper analysis shown later that this hope it was just wishful thinking. In fact, a complete description of the rotational motion of a rigid body turned out to be a formidable task; many of the most prominent mathematicians of our time failed in their attempt to solve this problem (see [52]).

DROMO is based on a method which combines regularization, linearization and perturbations techniques and it turns out to be clearly advantageous when it is compared to other traditional methods. A question arises here in a natural way: is it possible to use a similar technique with the attitude dynamics of a celestial body?

The attitude motion of a rigid spacecraft reduces to the Euler-Poinsot case when all the perturbations torques are neglected. This torque-free motion can be considered as the unperturbed case and its analytical solution is very well known. The idea underneath the NEODROMO project tries to take advantage of the knowledge of the analytical solution of this *unperturbed problem* in order to solve with more accuracy the **perturbed problem**. Some effort have been made in our group GDT trying to obtain a formulation similar to the one carried out in [12] for the *Attitude Problem* of a rigid spacecraft. The goal was to obtain a global propagation tool with the ability to include, when necessary, both aspects of the Space Dynamics: the orbital motion of the center of mass and the attitude dynamics. Simultaneously, we opted for the quaternion formulation taking as generalized coordinates the Euler-Rodrigues parameters trying to follow, if possible, the trail of papers [53, 54]. **This theory has been developed in [55] for the case of an axisymmetric satellite**. Similar approaches have been considered in references [56, 57, 58] for the triaxial case. Also in [59] can be found a similar formulation; there is an important difference, however, since in [55] a perturbation technique is used that is absent in [59].

From a logical point of view, the procedure usually followed to solve the *unperturbed problem* —torque-free motion— requires the following two steps:

1. in a first step the time evolution of the coordinates (p, q, r) —in the body frame— of the angular velocity $\vec{\omega}$ of the celestial body is obtained. The triaxial case involves a greater complexity due to the nature of the solution of the unperturbed problem. The time evolution of (p, q, r) is given by the Jacobi elliptical functions. However, in the axisymmetric case the time evolution of (p, q, r) is given by simple harmonic functions.

2. in a second stage the coordinates fixing the attitude of the celestial body are obtained from the known expressions of (p, q, r). There are several options since the rotation matrix which determines the relative orientation between the body frame and an inertial frame can be parameterized by using: 1) Euler angles, 2) Andoyer variables or 3) Euler parameters.

In our opinion the Euler parameters is the best option, from a numerical point of view, due to the lack of singularities in the parametrization of the configuration space. However, when using **Euler parameters**, and from a practical point of view, the triaxial case cannot be handled since the time evolution of the Euler parameters is given by unmanageable expressions. On the contrary, the axisymmetric case can be solved easily and the time evolution of the Euler parameters is given by simple and elegant expressions which permit to develop a perturbation theory as it is shown in [55].

The key point in the NEODROMO formulation is the following: the triaxial case can be considered as a perturbed problem of an equivalent axisymmetric case. This is the main difference with the concepts developed in references [56, 57, 58] where the triaxial case is tackle directly.

In effect, let (I_1, I_2, I_3) be the principal central moments of inertia of the triaxial celestial body. The Euler equations governing the attitude dynamics of the body take the form:

$$\dot{p} + \frac{I_3 - I_2}{I_1} q r = \frac{L}{I_1} \tag{1}$$

$$\dot{q} + \frac{I_1 - I_3}{I_2} p r = \frac{M}{I_2} \tag{2}$$

$$\dot{r} + \frac{I_2 - I_1}{I_3} p q = \frac{N}{I_3} \tag{3}$$

where (L, M, N) are the coordinates, in the body frame, of the perturbation torque which is acting on the center of mass of the body. Let us assume that $|I_1 - I_2| < |I_1 - I_3|$ and $|I_1 - I_2| < |I_2 - I_3|$. By introducing the value

$$I_0 = \frac{1}{2}(I_1 + I_2) \tag{4}$$

the governing equations take the following form

$$\dot{p} + \frac{I_3 - I_0}{I_0} q r = \frac{1}{I_1}\{L + \tilde{L} q r\} \tag{5}$$

$$\dot{q} + \frac{I_0 - I_3}{I_0} p r = \frac{1}{I_2}\{M + \tilde{M} p r\} \tag{6}$$

$$\dot{r} = \frac{1}{I_3}\{N + \tilde{N} p q\} \tag{7}$$

where the values $(\tilde{L}, \tilde{M}, \tilde{N})$ are given by:

$$\tilde{L} = \tilde{M} = \frac{(I_2 - I_1)(I_1 + I_2 - I_3)}{I_1 + I_2}, \quad \tilde{N} = I_1 - I_2 \tag{8}$$

Thus, the governing equations (4-8) turn out to be a **perturbed problem** of an *equivalent axisymmetric body* which includes an additional perturbation torque, due to the triaxiality of the body, which has the following coordinates

$$(\tilde{L} q r, \tilde{M} p r, \tilde{N} p q)$$

in the body frame. Obviously, when $I_1 = I_2$ this perturbing torque vanishes, since $\tilde{L} = \tilde{M} = \tilde{N} = 0$ in such a case.

From a numerical point of view, this approach is quite convenient for the propagation of the attitude motion of NEO's since in many cases two principal inertia moments take similar values and the perturbation torque due to the triaxiality of the body is small. But this numerical scheme, can be used also with bodies strongly triaxials, with a slight deterioration in performances.

ORBIT DETERMINATION

One of the main goals involved in the accurate determination of NEO's orbits is the reliable assessment of the real risk of a collision between a potentially hazardous asteroid and the Earth. Orbit determination and long time span forward propagation of NEOs is particularly difficult, mainly due to the large amount of uncertainties involved when compared to artificial satellites. These difficulties advocate for a 100-year time horizon for routine impact monitoring in space surveillance issues, since the analysis of impact possibilities further in the future is strongly dependent on the action of the Yarkovsky effect, which raises new challenges in the careful assessment of longer term impact hazards [60]. We must notice that the Yarkovsky effect is the largest single source of uncertainty in trajectory predictions of < 2 km diameter asteroids [61].

Additionally, even for NEOs with very accurately determined orbits, a future close approach to another body would scatter the possible trajectories to the extent that the problem becomes like that of a newly discovered asteroid with a weakly determined orbit. Actually, both orbital integrations and direct measurements predict Yarkovsky-induced position offsets of millions of kilometers on timescales of decades to centuries when coupled with such close planetary encounters [61].

According to [60], *if the scattering takes place late enough so that the target plane uncertainty prevails over Yarkovsky accelerations, then the asteroid's thermal properties, typically unknown, play a major role in the impact assessment. In contrast, if the strong planetary interaction takes place sooner, while the Yarkovsky dispersion is still relatively small, then precise modeling of the non-gravitational acceleration may be unnecessary.*

This sensitivity to close encounters suggests the use of regularized formulations —such as DROMO or similar schemes as the reviewed in Ref. [10]— in order to stretch the uncertainties related to orbit propagation from the point of view of numerical error accumulation. The importance of the close encounters in the real NEO's orbits is crucial. Thus, in some comparisons performed between different propagation schemes (see [10]), the number of encounters involved in the NEO's trajectory to be propagated plays a significant role.

We should underline one of the strong points of DROMO: its ability to manage close encounters in a better way than other perturbation methods. Figure 5 —which has been taken from Ref. [39]— shows the heliocentric post-encounter trajectories of a spacecraft, in Uranus and Neptune respectively, calculated with the Cowell

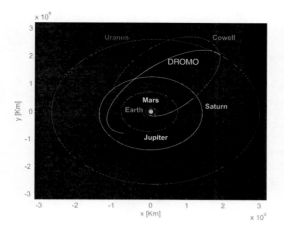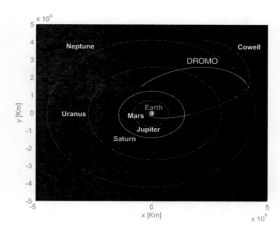

Figure 5: Close encounters with Uranus and Neptune

method and DROMO; the same numerical algorithm —the Dormand-Prince routine DOPRI853 with dense output— have been used to propagate the non-Keplerian orbits in both cases. The post-encounter trajectories are quite different due basically to the error accumulated in the Cowell propagation. Due to this differences, the entry point to the planet's sphere of influence and the entry spacecraft velocities are different in both propagations. These small differences are strongly amplified in the later encounter and give place to quite different post-encounter trajectories.

According with [62]: *the main limit to the time span of a numerical integration of the planetary orbits is no longer set by the availability of computer resources, but rather by the accumulation of the integration error. By the latter we mean the difference between the computed orbit and the dynamical behaviour of the real physical system, whatever the causes.* It is a well known fact that propagation error is exponential in the Cowell method (see [37]); this exponential growth of the errors, should be reduced as much as possible in order to increase the accuracy of the long term propagation of NEO's. For reasons that are not clear for us, the error propagation of DROMO is lower than in other formulations.

In order to put some kind of approximate bound to these behaviours, we could consider that Yarkovsky semimajor-axis drifts of the order ~ 10 km per 10 years becomes crucial for an accurate orbit determination and even for estimates of an impact hazard [63]. Especially, when the calculation of an impact probability depends on the fact, if the asteroid misses of hits a phase-space "keyhole", which is much smaller than the diameter of the Earth.

To assess the possibility of impacts taking into account the Yarkovsky effect with its full uncertainty, Monte Carlo methods are usually employed. These methods are based on construction of a set of possible orbits (by applying small variations to the initial conditions) which represent the region of possible motions [64].

The accuracy of a NEO trajectory prediction depends on the fraction of the orbit sampled by astrometry, the accuracy and precision of those measurements, the interval between the time of measurement and time of prediction, and the dynamics of the model used to propagate the non-linear equations of motion [34, 64]. The Standard Dynamical Model, used for routine asteroid solutions and propagations, includes n-body relativistic gravitational forces caused by the Sun, planets, Moon, Ceres, Pallas, and Vesta, but no single non-gravitational perturbation is considered, a matter that has recently brought the debate to use an Extended Dynamical Model instead.

A meaningful example of the convenience of considering the Yarkovsky effect is that of asteroid Apophis, whose uncertainty in accelerations related to solar radiation can cause, according to [34], between 82 and 4720 Earth-radii of trajectory change relative to the Standard Dynamical Model by its 2036 Earth encounter.

In the NEODROMO project the propagation of the attitude of the NEO's is performed by the numerical scheme described in page 570. This scheme is based in a perturbation method for which the unperturbed

555

motion corresponds to an equivalent axisymmetric body. For a real axisymmetric body the state variables are "constants" of the unperturbed solution. For a slightly triaxial body the state variables are "quasi-constants" of the unperturbed motion.

The NEODROMO project will be able, as a consequence, to simulate the *full-two-body problem* under the action of different perturbations. In general, the numerical simulation of the *full-two-body problem* introduces stiffness in the integration, due to the differences between the characteristic times associated with the attitude dynamics and the orbital dynamics. However, due to the perturbation scheme used in the propagation of the attitude, in the case of NEO's affected by the YORP effect, the stiffness is practically removed for axisymmetric bodies and it is substantially decreased for quasi-axisymmetric asteroids. For the triaxial case, the stiffness of the problem should be taken into account by selecting an appropriated integration algorithm.

Finally we should underline that the numerical simulation of the *full-two-body problem* allows to introduce a plus of accuracy in the basic problem of determine the orbit of a NEO. Thus, some parameters used to model the dynamics of the body —for example, direction of the spin axis in the body frame— could be determined inside the level of accuracy permitted by the observations.

CONCLUSIONS

In this paper we reviewed the different elements involved in the NEODROMO project:

- a special perturbation method capable to propagate with accuracy the complex orbits of the center of mass of any celestial body. It opens a new approach in the field of NEO's dynamics due to its many good qualities and, in particular, its robustness.

- an additional propagator of the attitude of any celestial body. It is based on a perturbation scheme in which the unperturbed dynamics is selected as the motion of an equivalent axisymmetric body. The perturbation scheme is described, from a kinematic point of view, in terms of Euler parameters (a quaternion), and turns out to be more accurate than other classical and sophisticated schemes based on Hamiltonian dynamics.

- both propagators can be used together in order to simulate the *full-two-body problem* from a numerical point of view. The full simulation of a triaxial body introduces stiffness in the integration. Due to the perturbation scheme used in the propagation of the attitude, in the case of NEO's affected by the YORP effect, the stiffness is practically removed for axisymmetric bodies and it is substantially decreased for quasi-axisymmetric asteroids.

- in future editions of this meeting we will present some interesting simulations performed inside the NEODROMO project.

ACKNOWLEDGEMENTS

The work of J. Peláez, H. Urrutxua and C. Bombardelli is part of the research project entitled **Dynamic simulation of complex space systems** (AYA2010-18796) supported by the DGI of the Spanish Ministry of Science and Innovation.

REFERENCES

[1] R.L. Schweickart, T.D. Jones, and F. von der Dunk. Asteroid threats: A call for global response. *Association of Space Explorers International Panel on Asteroid Threat Mitigation, report to the UN*, 25, 2008.

[2] R.L. Schweickart. Decision program on asteroid threat mitigation. *Acta Astronautica*, 65(9-10):1402–1408, 2009.

[3] T. Ahrens and A. Harris. Deflection and fragmentation of near-earth asteroids. *Nature*, 360(6403):429–433, 1992. doi:10.1038/360429a0.

[4] H. Melosh, I. Nemchinov, and Y. Zetzer. Non-nuclear strategies for deflecting comets and asteroids. *Hazards due to Comets and Asteroids*, 1:1111–1132, 1994. Univ. of Arizona Press, Tucson, AZ.

[5] E.T. Lu and S.G. Love. Gravitational tractor for towing asteroids. *Nature*, 438(7065):177–178, 2005. doi:10.1038/438177a.

[6] C. Bombardelli and J. Peláez. Ion beam shepherd for asteroid deflection. *Journal of Guidance, Control and Dynamics*, 34(4):1270–1272, July-August 2011. DOI: 10.2514/1.51640.

[7] C. Bombardelli and J. Peláez. Ion beam shepherd for contactless space debris removal. *Journal of Guidance, Control and Dynamics*, 34(3):916–920, May-June 2011. DOI: 10.2514/1.51832.

[8] C. Bombardelli, M. Merino-Martinez, E. Ahedo, J. Peláez, H. Urrutxua, J. Herrero-Montojo, A. Iturry-Torrea, J. Olympio, D. Petkow, and L. Summerer. Ion beam shepherd for contactless debris removal. Technical Report ESTEC contract No. 4000101447/10/NL/CBi, ARIADNA Programme, Advanced Concept Team, ESA - ESTEC, 2011.

[9] E. L. Stiefel and G. Scheifele. *Linear and Regular Celestial Mechanics*. Springer, 1971.

[10] T. Fukushima. Numerical comparison of two-body regularizations. *The Astronomical Journal*, 133:2815, 2007.

[11] J. M. Hedo J. Peláez and P. Rodríguez de Andrés. A special perturbation method in orbital dynamics. Paper AAS 05-167 of the 15th AAS/AIAA Space Flight Mechanics Meeting, Copper Mountain, Colorado, USA, 23-27 January 2005, 2005.

[12] Jesús Peláez, José Manuel Hedo, and Pedro Rodriguez de Andrés. A special perturbation method in orbital dynamics. *Celestial Mechanics and Dynamical Astronomy*, 97:131–150, 2007. 10.1007/s10569-006-9056-3.

[13] C. Bombardelli, G. Baù, and J. Peláez. Asymptotic solution for the two-body problem with constant tangential thrust acceleration. *Celestial Mechanics and Dynamical Astronomy*, pages 1–18, 2011. DOI: 10.1007/s10569-011-9353-3.

[14] Miroslav Brož. *Yarkovsky Effect and the Dynamics of the Solar System*. Charles University, Prague, 2006. Ph.D. Thesis.

[15] David Čapek. *Thermal effects in the physics and dynamics of the small solar system bodies*. Charles University, Prague, 2007. Ph.D. Thesis.

[16] D. Capek and D. Vokrouhlicky. Accurate model for the yarkovsky effect. In *Dynamics of populations of planetary systems: proceedings of the 197th colloquium of the International Astronomical Union held in Belgrade, Serbia and Montenegro August 31-September 4, 2004*, volume 197, page 171. Cambridge Univ Pr, 2005.

[17] DJ Scheeres. The dynamical evolution of uniformly rotating asteroids subject to yorp. *Icarus*, 188(2):430–450, 2007.

[18] S. Breiter, H. Michalska, D. Vokrouhlickỳ, and W. Borczyk. Radiation-induced torques on spheroids. *Astronomy and Astrophysics*, 471(1):345–353, 2007.

[19] S. Breiter and H. Michalska. Yorp torque as the function of shape harmonics. *Monthly Notices of the Royal Astronomical Society*, 388(2):927–944, 2008.

[20] S. Breiter, P. Bartczak, and M. Czekaj. Yorp torques with 1d thermal model. *Monthly Notices of the Royal Astronomical Society*, 2010.

[21] D. Vokrouhlicky. Diurnal yarkovsky effect as a source of mobility of meter-sized asteroidal fragments. i. linear theory. *Astronomy and Astrophysics*, 335:1093–1100, 1998.

[22] D. Vokrouhlický, A. Milani, and SR Chesley. Yarkovsky effect on small near-earth asteroids: Mathematical formulation and examples. *Icarus*, 148(1):118–138, 2000.

[23] Miroslav Brož, D. Vokrouhlický, W.F. Bottke, D. Nesvorný, A. Morbidelli, and D. Čapek. Non-gravitational forces acting on small bodies. In D. Lazzaro, S. Ferraz-Mello, and J.A. Fernández, editors, *Proceedings of the International Astronomical Union*, volume 1, page Symposium S229. International Astronomical Union, 2005.

[24] W.F. Bottke, D. Vokrouhlický, D. P. Rubincam, and M. Brož. *Asteroid III*, chapter The Effect of Yarkovsky Thermal Forces on the Dynamical Evolution of Asteroids and Meteoroids, pages 395–408. The University of Arizona Press, 2002.

[25] D. Vokrouhlický and A. Milani. Direct solar radiation pressure on the orbits of small near-earth asteroids: observable effects? *Astronomy & Astrophysics*, 362:746–755, 2000.

[26] W.F. Bottke et al. Dynamical evolution of main belt meteoroids: Numerical simulations incorporating planetary perturbations and yarkovsky thermal forces. *Icarus*, 145(2):301–331, 2000.

[27] A. Rossi, F. Marzari, and D.J. Scheeres. Computing the effects of yorp on the spin rate distribution of the neo population. *Icarus*, 202(1):95 – 103, 2009.

[28] L.E. Bykova and T.Yu. Galushina. Investigation of the motion of (99942) apophis asteroid using the skif cyberia multiprocessor computing system. *Cosmic Research*, 48(5):409–416, 2010.

[29] B.Ts. Bakhshiyan, A.A. Sukhanov, and K.S. Fedyaev. Estimation of the determination accuracy of orbit parameters of the apophis asteroid from measurement results. *Cosmic Research*, 48(5):417–423, 2010.

[30] G.F. Gronchi, L. Dimare, and A. Milani. Orbit determination with the two-body integrals. *Celestial Mechanics and Dynamical Astronomy*, 107(3):299–318, 2010.

[31] G.F. Gronchi, D. Farnocchia, and Dimare. Orbit determination with the two-body integrals.ii. *Celestial Mechanics and Dynamical Astronomy*, 2011. DOI 10.1007/s10569-011-9357-z.

[32] A. Kryszczynska, A. La Spina, P. Paolicchi, AW Harris, S. Breiter, and P. Pravec. New findings on asteroid spin-vector distributions. *Icarus*, 192(1):223–237, 2007.

[33] P. Pravec, AW Harris, D. Vokrouhlicky, BD Warner, P. Kusnirak, K. Hornoch, DP Pray, D. Higgins, J. Oey, A. Galád, et al. Spin rate distribution of small asteroids. *Icarus*, 197(2):497–504, 2008.

[34] Jon D. Giorgini, Lance A.M. Benner, Steven J. Ostro, Michael C. Nolan, and Michael W. Busch. Predicting the earth encounters of (99942) apophis. *Icarus*, 193(1):1 – 19, 2008.

[35] A. S. Zabotin and Yu. D. Medvedev. On the accuracy of the orbit of asteroid (99942) apophis at the time of its encounter with the earth in 2029. *Astronomy letters*, 35(4):278–285, 2009.

[36] L. F. Shampine and M. K. Gordon. Local error and variable order adams codes. *Applied Mathematics and Computation*, 1:47–66, 1975.

[37] V. R. Bond and M. C. Allman. *Modern astrodynamics: fundamentals and perturbation methods*. Princeton University Press, 1996.

[38] W.H. Press, S.A. Teukolsky, W.T. Vetterling, and B.P. Flannery. *Numerical recipes in C*. Cambridge Univ. Press Cambridge, 1992.

[39] J. Esteban-Dones and J. Peláez. Advanced propagation of interplanetary orbits in the exploration of jovian moons. In *4th Int. Conference on Astrodynamics Tools and Techniques*, 2010. 3-6 May 2010, ESAC Villafranca, Madrid, Spain.

[40] E. Hairer and G. Wanner. *Solving ordinary differential equations II: Stiff and differential-algebraic problems*, volume 14. Springer Verlag, 2010.

[41] O. Montenbruck and G. Eberhard. *Satellite orbits: models, methods, and applications*. Springer Verlag, 2000.

[42] J. Peláez H. Urrutxua, C. Bombardelli and A. Huhn. High fidelity models for orbit propagation: Dromo vs. störmer-cowell. European Space Surveillance Conference 7-9 June 2011, INTA HQ, Madrid, Spain, 2011.

[43] William H. Press, Saul A. Teukolsky, William T. Vetterling, and Brian P. Flannery. *Numerical Recipes - The Art of Scientific Computing*. Cambridge University Press, third edition, 2007.

[44] Erwin Fehlberg. Classical fifth-, sixth-, seventh-, eight-order runge-kutta formulas with stepsize control. Technical Report NASA TR R-287, George C. Marshall Space Flight Center, 1968.

[45] Matthew M. Berry. *A Variable-Step Double-Integration Multi-Step Integrator*. PhD thesis, Virginia Tech, Blacksburg, 2004.

[46] M.D. Shuster. A survey on attitude representation. *The Journal of the Astronautical Science*, 41(4):439–517, October-December 1993.

[47] J. Stuelpnagel. On the parametrization of the three-dimesnional rotation group. *SIAM Review*, 6:422–430, October 1964.

[48] J. R. Wertz. *Spacecraft attitude determination and control*. D. Reidel Publising Company, Dordrecht, Holland, 1980.

[49] P. Tsiotras and J.M. Longuski. A new parametrization of the attitude kinematics. *The Journal of the Astronautical Science*, 43(3):243–262, 1993.

[50] P. Gurfil, A. Elipe, W. Tangren, and M. Efroimsky. The serret-andoyer formalism in rigid-body dynamics: I. symmetries and perturbations. *Regular and Chaotic Dynamics*, 12(4):389–425, 2007.

[51] A. Bloch, P. Gurfil, and K.Y. Lum. The serret-andoyer formalism in rigid-body dynamics: Ii. geometry, stabilization, and control. *Regular and Chaotic Dynamics*, 12(4):426–447, 2007.

[52] E. Leimanis. *The general problem of the motion of coupled rigid bodies about a fixed point*. Springer-Verlag, New York, 1965.

[53] A. Elipe M. Arribas and M. Palacios. Quaternions and the rotation of a rigid body. *Celestial Mechanics and Dynamical Astronomy*, 96(3):239–251, 2006. DOI: 10.1007/s10569-006-9037-6.

[54] W.I. Newman and M. Efroimsky. The method of variation of constants and multiple time scales in orbital mechanics. *Chaos*, 13(2):476–485, June 2003.

[55] A. Pizarro-Rubio and J. Peláez. On the attitude propagation of an axisymmetric satellite. In *Advances in the astronautical sciences*, volume 130, pages 535–554. AAS/AIAA, 2008. AAS/AIAA 18th Space Flight Mechanics Meeting, Galveston, TX, Jan 28-Feb 01, 2008.

[56] L.G. Kraig and J.L. Junkins. Perturbations formulations for satellite attityude dynamics. In *AIAA Mechanics and control of flight conference, Anaheim, CA, August 5-9*, 1974. AIAA Paper No. 74-785.

[57] L.G. Kraig and S.B. Skaar. A variation of parameters approach to the arbitrarily torqued, asymmetric rigid body problem. *The Journal of the Astronautical Sciences*, XXV(3):207–226, July-September 1977.

[58] L.G. Kraig and D.A. Ulman. Rectification of the encke perturbation method as applied to rigid body rotational motion. *The Journal of the Astronautical Sciences*, XXVII(3):311–319, July-September 1979.

[59] T. Fukushima. Simple, regular, and efficient numerical integration of rotational motion. *The Astronomical Journal*, 135:2298, 2008.

[60] Andrea Milani, Steven R. Chesley, Maria Eugenia Sansaturio, Fabrizio Bernardi, Giovanni B. Valsecchi, and Oscar Arratia. Long term impact risk for (101955) 1999 rq36. *Icarus*, 203(2):460 – 471, 2009.

[61] Michael W. Busch, Shrinivas R. Kulkarni, Walter Brisken, Steven J. Ostro, Lance A.M. Benner, Jon D. Giorgini, and Michael C. Nolan. Determining asteroid spin states using radar speckles. *Icarus*, 209(2):535 – 541, 2010.

[62] A. Milani and A.M. Nobili. Integration error over very long time spans. *Celestial Mechanics and Dynamical Astronomy*, 43(1):1–34, 1987.

[63] J.D. Giorgini, S.J. Ostro, L.A.M. Benner, P.W. Chodas, S.R. Chesley, R.S. Hudson, M.C. Nolan, A.R. Klemola, E.M. Standish, R.F. Jurgens, R. Rose, A.B. Chamberlin, D.K. Yeomans, and J.-L. Margot. Asteroid 1950 da's encounter with earth in 2880: Physical limits of collision probability prediction. *Science*, 296:132–136, 2002.

[64] J. Desmars, J.-E. Arlot, and A. Vienne. Estimation of accuracy of close encounter performed by the bootstrap method. *Cosmic Research*, 48(5):472–478, 2010.

A SURVEY OF POTENTIAL HUMAN-PRECURSOR ROBOTIC ASTEROID MISSIONS

Michael L. Cupples,[*] Roberto Furfaro,[†] Carl W. Hergenrother,[‡] Daniel R. Wibben[§] and John N. Kidd Jr.[**]

A preliminary mission analyses survey of conceptual robotic asteroid missions that are precursor to potential human asteroid missions is provided, yielding a set of parametric data that can be used for preliminary mission planning. For a set of carefully chosen asteroids, this study generated a table of delta-v data that extends over a range of launch opportunity dates and a range of total transfer times. A subjective comparison of missions was performed and the comparison results are reported, further evaluating the low delta-v analyses data based on a set of Key Performance Parameters that included Earth departure energy (C3) and total transfer time, as well as total delta-v. The key parameter comparison yielded a table of data that synthesizes the rather large set of mission analyses data into a set of "best" cases.

INTRODUCTION

Within the Robotic and Human Space Exploration communities there exists a surge of interest in Near Earth Asteroid (NEA) missions. NEA objects are interesting for a variety of reasons. Chief among those reasons is the science value related to understanding solar system evolution, understanding the risk for Earth-NEA collision, and better determination of NEA potential for an abundant source of extraterrestrial natural resources such as metals[††]. Current interest in the space exploration community includes robotic science missions to investigate asteroid carbonaceous compositions, leading to an understanding of solar system origin and evolution. A specific NASA New Frontiers mission in point is the recently awarded asteroid sample return mission OSIRIS REx[‡‡]. In addition to purely science objectives, robotic asteroid missions that are precursor to human exploration of NEA's are currently under study for the opportunity years including 2014-2020. Such missions will pave the way for potential human visits to asteroids that can lead to transportation technology validation required for eventual human exploration of Mars[1].

Robotic and human conceptual NEA mission studies are not new to the space exploration communities. For example, a conceptual human mission to 433 EROS was touted in 1966[§§]. The objective of the EROS mission study was to demonstrate mission hardware and other capabilities required to achieve exploration of solar system destinations such as the Moon and Mars. Other significant study efforts, including those that unfolded under the Space Exploration Initiative (SEI) in the late 80's and early 90's, examined potential missions to NEA's to show many asteroid destinations are more accessible than comparable Moon missions. To date, there have been only two

---

[*] Principal Systems Engineer, Modeling & Simulation, Raytheon Missile Systems, 1151 E. Hermans Rd, Tucson, AZ 85756.
[†] Associate Professor, Industrial & Systems Engineering, University of Arizona, Tucson, AZ 85721.
[‡] Research Scientist, Lunar & Planetary Laboratory, University of Arizona, Tucson, AZ 85721.
[§] Graduate Student, Industrial & Systems Engineering, University of Arizona, Tucson, AZ 85721.
[**] Student, Lunar & Planetary Laboratory, University of Arizona, Tucson, AZ 85721.
[††] http://beyondapollo.blogspot.com/2010/03/manned-eros-flyby-1966.html
[‡‡] http://www.nasa.gov/centers/goddard/news/releases/2011/11-037.html
[§§] http://echo.jpl.nasa.gov/~lance/delta_v/delta_v.rendezvous.html

asteroid rendezvous spacecraft missions, i.e. the NASA NEAR Shoemaker mission that visited asteroid 433 Eros in 1999[***], and the JAXA Hayabusa probe that visited the asteroid 25143 Itokawa in 2005[†††]. As of mid-2011, 8019 NEA's have been discovered. During calendar year 2010, over 5000 asteroids were newly discovered, 920 of which were NEAs[‡‡‡]. The rate of asteroid discovery will increase as next-generation surveys such as PanSTARRS and the LSST come online in the near future. The limited scope of early mission studies, as well as the proliferation of new NEA discoveries, may point to the need for a more modern and comprehensive study to identify a range of asteroid mission opportunities to highly desirable objects. This paper outlines a mission survey study based on a particular set of asteroids of current interest to the space exploration communities. Even though this study does not reach the lofty goal of "comprehensive", it is a first step in that direction through performing a relative comparison on a finite set of asteroids judiciously culled from the relatively large number of asteroids known to the space community.

DESCRIPTION OF THE CONCEPTUAL MISSION SURVEY

This study reports the survey results of conceptual asteroid mission opportunities covering a range of asteroid destinations. This study focuses on asteroids of current high interest (19 asteroids in number) with the asteroids broadly categorized as carbonaceous (C-type) and non-carbonaceous asteroids (e.g. S-group), and thus are of interest to both the robotic exploration and human exploration communities. For this aforementioned set of asteroids, the study delineated in this paper emphasizes preliminary mission analyses results. By preliminary, we mean data of low fidelity and of first-look quality. Although our study covers a fairly wide range of asteroids and two significantly different mission profiles, we did not perform a truly comprehensive study, and is the follow-on to a recent report of 12 asteroids of interest to the space community[2]. This more extensive study covers a 7 more asteroids of current discovery vintage. Presently, we considered only one-way, non-sample return missions. Consequently, our primary focus was on trajectories that can be applied to robotic missions that would also be a precursor to a human visit to the asteroids. The asteroid study set will be further evaluated in a follow-on study that will consider the set of asteroids for a potential human mission.

Study Strategy

For this study, the assumed mission class is NASA Discovery. NASA Discovery class missions are very sensitive to mission cost, and thus mission planners must emphasize cost minimization. Thus, this survey strategy focuses on finding low cost missions with the stated goals of 1) a low energy mission which in turn implies a minimal launch vehicle, 2) a low spacecraft mass which in part implies a low delta-v mission, and 3) a short mission duration to reduce operations cost. Our survey study includes mission analyses objectives that can be summarized as follows:

A. To minimize launch vehicle requirements, our study aims at reducing the Earth escape energy (C3) as part of the trajectory optimization. A low C3 mission implies minimal launch vehicle requirements, with everything else remaining constant. By "low" C3, we mean that C3 has been made a part of the overall trajectory optimization process where emphasis is on reducing the mission C3 as a part of the delta-v cost function. A more detailed exposition of the optimization process is forthcoming in this report.

B. Minimizing the spacecraft cost can be related to reducing the spacecraft size and mass. This study attempts to address spacecraft cost by minimizing the total delta-v (including C3); note that mission delta-v can, in turn, be related to spacecraft size and mass. When delta-v is reported in this report, the C3 component is removed, and the sum deterministic delta-v is actually tabulated. A more detailed exposition of the precise composition of the "total" delta-v is delineated in a subsequent section of this report.

C. Costs can also be reduced by limiting operations. Lower transfer times are an emphasis in this study, and can lead to reduced operations cost through reduction in time required to reach the targeted asteroid.

[***] http://neo.jpl.nasa.gov/stats/

[†††] http://wise.ssl.berkeley.edu/documents/WISE-CryoStatusReport-8-10-10%20(2).pdf?release=2010-238

[‡‡‡] http://ssd.jpl.nasa.gov/?horizons

A preliminary mission design tool called Mission Design and Trajectory Optimization Program[3] (MDTOP) is our primary mission analysis and design tool to find suitable launch dates, mission trajectories, and delta-v sequences that minimize the overall mission delta-v (cost function). As explained later in this paper, MDTOP is based on the Differential Evolution[4] global optimizer which is a stochastic approach to finding the global minimum of a defined cost function. Since the algorithm is initiated by selecting a random set of candidate solutions based in the mission constraints, MDTOP is very well suited to perform the survey in an automated fashion.

Asteroid Study Set

Small bodies such as asteroids and comets may be found throughout the Solar System. In fact, there is no region of the Solar System, whether a few solar radii from the Sun to the distance of the Oort cloud, that does not contain a significant population of small Solar System bodies. According to the IAU Minor Planet Center (MPC), as of July 2011 there are over 556,366 known asteroids and comets[§§§]. This number only includes those objects observed over a long enough span of time to determine an orbit. The number of objects observed over the course of only one or two nights adds at least another 100,000 objects to the total.

With so many known asteroids and comets, it seems fair to assume that future spacecraft missions have an unlimited number of objects to choose from. This is true when the focus of the mission is the flyby and reconnaissance of an asteroid of any type. In the case of mission types that require rendezvous or a return-to-Earth profile, however, the number of viable mission targets is severely limited due to high delta-v requirements for many of the asteroids.

The aforementioned 8019 NEA's are classified as near-Earth asteroids if the perihelia (minimum distance from the Sun) is less than or equal to 1.30 AU. Though these objects can be located relatively close to Earth, the majority are on orbits that are not conducive to supporting a human or unmanned mission due to the high delta-v and/or expected high rotation rates (related to size). Also, it should be noted that this report is not a comprehensive study of all possible asteroid targets for a human mission, but rather will focus on objects previously identified as likely targets for a human mission to an asteroid during the 2020-2035 timeframe or for an unmanned sample return mission to a carbonaceous asteroid.

Asteroid destinations should ideally be selected based on the following criteria:

1) Possess Earth-like orbits with low eccentricity and low inclination;

2) Make very close approaches to Earth, within ~0.05 AU;

3) Single-axis slow rotators with rotation periods on the order of several hours;

4) Single, solitary objects and do not possess any satellites;

5) Bodies consisting of asteroidal origin and not active, extinct, or dormant comets;

6) An average diameter on the order of 50 m or greater;

7) Suitable for resource utilization such as H_2O;

8) Support a human visit with a total mission duration on the order of 150-210 days[5,6].

The asteroids chosen as the study set for this survey are shown in Table 1 and are of three categories:

1) Objects that have been previously identified by the NASA community as being of interest to human space exploration, labeled the "Big Six[7]" in Table 1;

2) Carbonaceous asteroids that were previously identified as being of interest to the space science community as potential targets for a sample return mission, labeled "carbonaceous" in Table 1.

3) Asteroids that have not yet been classified into a group (e.g. carbonaceous, silicaceous), but are neither too small nor rotate too quickly to allow for a future manned mission.

The so-called "Big Six" list of potential asteroid targets for a human visit actually consists of seven objects (see Table 1). These objects have been identified by NASA studies as providing "good" opportunities to conduct a

---

[§§§] http://www.minorplanetcenter.net/

human visit in the 2020-2035 windows. It is important to note, however, that our understanding of the physical properties of the "Big Six" is limited. The Big Six are actually not well known and therefore may not be good candidates for a human mission. Also, the Big Six may not be good targets for an asteroid sample return mission because of their small size. Every object on the list is relatively small with diameters less than 150 m. Surveys of the rotation state of small asteroids have found that most asteroids with diameters smaller than 150 m rotate rapidly, with rotation periods on the order of minutes. It is possible that every object on the "Big Six" list rotates too rapidly to support a safe human visit. Further, given that some of the Big Six asteroids are "lost", due to their small size and hence faintness, they will be difficult to find. We show in Table 1 the asteroid orbital elements used for this asteroid mission survey. Note that in the case of the Big Six asteroids, 1999 AO10, 2001 BB16, and 2001 QJ142 are most likely hopelessly lost, with 2009 OS5 as possibly "findable".

Table 1 Asteroid Mission Analyses Survey Set

Asteroid	Category	Semi Major Axis (AU)	e	i (deg)	Argument of Perihelion (deg)	Longitude of Ascending Node (deg)	Epoch of Perihelion (Calendar Date)
1999 JU3	Carbonaceous	1.1895	0.1903	5.8833	211.4117	251.6367	8/19/2010 19:03
1999 RQ36	Carbonaceous	1.1260	0.2038	6.0350	66.2268	2.0613	6/20/2009 1:06
2001 FC7	Carbonaceous	1.4358	0.1145	2.6206	234.3942	99.1460	7/6/2010 23:32
2002 CD	Carbonaceous	0.9796	0.1765	6.8777	331.7116	8.7212	6/19/2010 11:05
2008 EV5	Carbonaceous	0.9583	0.0835	7.4361	234.7438	93.4252	8/12/2009 10:16
1999 AO10	Big Six, **lost**	0.9114	0.1110	2.6244	7.6493	313.3234	11/15/2010 18:01
1998 HG49	Big Six	1.2006	0.1131	4.1953	324.1662	44.8937	9/24/2010 1:16
2001 BB16	Big Six, **lost**	0.8549	0.1725	2.0267	195.5609	122.5681	3/13/2010 5:15
2003 SM84	Big Six	1.1253	0.0820	3.1065	63.8555	184.4723	3/6/2010 11:38
2000 AE205	Big Six	1.1646	0.1375	4.4589	150.3094	271.6775	12/9/2009 21:25
2001 QJ142	Big Six, **lost**	1.0622	0.0863	3.1065	63.8555	184.4723	3/6/2010 11:38
2009 OS5	Big Six, **findable**	1.1442	0.0966	1.6947	120.7979	145.3868	9/4/2010 12:17
1993 BX3	Unknown	1.0033	0.2806	2.7902	289.9493	175.5851	2/18/2011 21:17
2000 EA14	Unknown	0.8907	0.2025	3.5547	206.0584	203.9717	7/1/2010 18:41
2001 US16	Unknown	1.0132	0.2527	1.9044	66.9922	176.0166	9/14/2010 11:36
2002 NV16	Unknown	0.9653	0.2200	3.5078	179.4149	183.5659	12/25/2010 18:57
2006 KL21	Unknown	1.0463	0.1279	9.3593	214.0793	117.2927	8/20/2010 7:01
2006 SU49	Unknown	0.9717	0.3122	2.5186	198.9462	303.2053	8/24/2010 10:55
2008 DG5	Unknown	0.9510	0.2427	5.7066	59.5960	244.0902	1/26/2010 11:48

Carbonaceous asteroids represent the original building blocks of the terrestrial planets. The presence of complex organic compounds in carbonaceous meteorites has led to speculation that they may have seeded the early Earth with prebiotic material that led to the emergence of life. The existence of volatile-rich carbonaceous asteroids in the Main Belt suggests that carbonaceous NEAs may contain a significant fraction of water and other ices. Such ices could be utilized by visiting astronauts for propellant production and human consumption. The selection of carbonaceous asteroids suitable for asteroid sample return are based on: 1) the asteroids have an Earth-like orbit with low eccentricity and low inclination; 2) in order to minimize the cost and complexity of spacecraft power and thermal systems, the asteroids have an orbit that approach no closer than 0.80 AU of the Sun and travels no further than 1.60 AU from the Sun; 3) the asteroids are slow rotators with rotation periods on the order of a few hours or greater; 4) the asteroids possess a spectral signature consistent with primitive carbonaceous material; and 5) the asteroids contain a significant amount of retrievable regolith on its surface. Selected by the NASA New Frontiers Program, the OSIRIS-REx mission's target is the asteroid 1999 RQ36, and 1999 JU3[8] is the primary target of the proposed JAXA Hayabusa-2 sample return mission[11].

A survey of larger and slower rotating asteroids identified seven targets experiencing close, low velocity flybys of Earth in the 2020-2040 timeframe. The seven asteroids include (65717) 1993 BX3, 2000 EA14, (89136) 2001 US16, 2002 NV16, 2006 KL21, 2006 SU49 and 2008 DG5. There is no taxonomic information for these asteroids, so whether or not they are carbonaceous is unknown. The criteria for selection are: 1) Earth-asteroid miss distance of less than 0.05 AU; 2) asteroid velocity relative to Earth of less than 6.5 km/s; and 3) absolute magnitude (H) greater than 21.5. An H of 21.5 corresponds to a diameter of 130-m for an object with a typical S-type albedo and 300-m for a typical C-type albedo. Nearly 75% of asteroids fainter than H = 21.5 are rapid rotators with rotation periods less than 2 hours[9]. Such rapid rotation increases mission risk for close proximity operations of both manned and unmanned missions.

ANALYSIS APPROACH

To facilitate our study objectives of finding trajectories that minimize the cost of performing the mission, this study includes a range of trajectory profiles. Even though we are optimizing the trajectories for minimum delta-v, our optimization approach allows us to capture a set of data that covers a range of delta-v, a range of Earth departure C3, and a range of transfer times. By parameterizing these key variables and searching across the mission space that include a wide range of these parameters, we are attempting to find the lowest cost mission. Therefore, we base our study results on a set of "Key Performance Parameters" that provide the avenue for comparison of mission cases.

Key Performance Parameters

Based on the low cost mission objective, a set of Key Performance Parameters (KPP) were chosen to compare various mission cases. The KPPs are closely related to the mission trajectory and parameterize the trajectory performance. Used to rank over-all mission performance, the KPPs allow for a more useful ranking than simply choosing the absolute lowest delta-v case.

KPP1 ≡ Total Mission delta-v
The total mission delta-v is the sum of the magnitudes of V-infinity and deterministic delta-v components of the mission. Low delta-v implies lower propulsion requirements, which in turn can imply smaller spacecraft. Thus, spacecraft cost can be directly related to the relative value of KPP1
KPP2 ≡ Earth Departure Energy (C3)
This study focus was on lower Earth departure energies, which can imply a smaller launch vehicle for the same mass. Thus, the LV requirements can be directly related to KPP2.
KPP3 ≡ Total Transfer Time to Asteroid
Shorter transfer times imply shorter mission support costs, assuming the actual asteroid operations remain constant for any mission transfer time. Thus, mission cost can be directly related to KPP3

Essentially, the KPPs were used as a decision tool to determine the best overall cases for each of the survey asteroids. Asteroid missions that result in low delta-v, low departure energy, and low transfer times are most desirable from a mission analysis standpoint.

Transfer Assumptions

To ferret out the low KPP missions, analyses were undertaken to design transfer trajectories with lower valued KPP's. Our approach entails optimization of the mission by using a global trajectory design process. Trajectory design entails a parameterization of the mission trajectory yielding a range of mission trajectory options that can be ranked according to the KPPs. As a conceptual example of the process, the trajectory will first be broken into a set of nodes and legs. A node defines a point that an event occur, including a departure from a point in space such as a planet, a delta-v maneuver location, or an arrival at a point such as a planet or asteroid. A leg defines the transfer that occurs between nodes. Importantly, the mission trajectory parameterization includes the time of transfer between nodes and the delta-v of a maneuver at a node. The two trajectory profile categories included in this study are "Direct" missions and "Gravity Assist" missions.

For a Direct mission, the nodes of the trajectory are Earth Departure, Deep Space Maneuver (DSM), and the Asteroid Arrival, as shown in Figure 1. There can be at most two legs for a Direct mission, with a DSM embedded between the Earth departure node and asteroid arrival node. For a zero DSM (or very near zero DSM), the mission consist of only one leg.

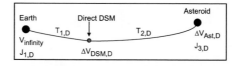

Figure 1 Notional Direct Mission Profile

For a Gravity Assist (GA) type mission, the 5 nodes include Earth Departure, DSM1, an Earth GA, DSM2, and the Asteroid Arrival. The legs of the mission can be as many as 4 (if both DSM's are non-zero) as shown in Figure 2.

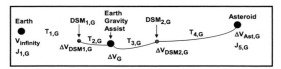

Figure 2 Notional Gravity Assist Mission Profile

A summary of assumptions that characterize the missions investigated in this survey include those listed in Table 2. Where the language "allowed" is used in the table, the meaning is related to the optimization process. The trajectory design process was set up to allow the optimizer to "zero-out" DSM's if the total delta-v (the optimization pay-off function) was reduced. More details will be provided concerning the optimization process in upcoming paragraphs of this study. In the next section, a more thorough delineation of the maneuvers, including the DSM, is provided.

Table 2 General Mission Analyses Assumptions

Mission Assumption	Comment
Asteroids	See the 19 asteroids in Table 1
Departure years (Opportunities)	Investigation includes 2014-2020
Total trip time range	1 to 4 years in total length
Direct Mission cases	By definition, no GAs were allowed; A single plane-change DSM is allowed in the transfer; The DMS can be zero;
GA cases	An Earth GA is required during transfer; A single plane-change DSM is allowed on either side of the Earth GA; The DMS can be zero;

Patched Conic Trajectories

Given the preliminary nature of this mission analysis survey, non-integrated patched conic trajectories were employed in trajectory delta-v determination. The patched conic approach is well known, and has been used for decades to provide first-order mission analysis data[10,11]. The patch conic results are considered, as a rule of thumb, to fall within 10-20% of the multi-body integrated trajectory results. The trajectory maneuvers employed in the trajectory optimization process include only those found in Table 3.

Table 3 Delta-V Maneuvers Investigated in Trajectory Optimization

Maneuver	Comment
Earth Departure	Earth departure delta-v is not actually evaluated; it is assumed that the launch vehicle provides the Earth departure delta-v in this study. Thus, the Earth departure is associated with Earth departure energy C3. The actual trajectory optimization parameter is V-infinity.
Deep Space Maneuvers	Any leg of a trajectory may have an embedded DSM, depending on whether the minimization of the sum delta-v shows an optimization benefit from a non-zero DSM.
Powered/Unpowered GA	For this study, all GAs are assumed to be Earth flybys. A GA can be either non-powered or powered, depending on whether the trajectory optimization process determines the benefit for a powered flyby at Earth.
Asteroid Arrival	Asteroid arrival is assumed to be executed as a intercept with the asteroid based on an overall optimal delta-v.

All delta-v maneuvers were modeled as deterministic burns and no margins or contingencies were included in the estimates. Likewise, all burns were instantaneous in nature, and no finite burn loss estimates (gravity losses) were included. In addition, no trajectory correction maneuvers were included in this preliminary work. Ephemeris positions of the Earth were derived from the JPL 405 ephemeris, with positions of the asteroids derived from classical elements taken from JPL's Horizon Systems[****].

TRAJECTORY OPTIMIZATION APPROACH

The primary objective of this survey entails finding a set of best case trajectories, one for each of the survey asteroids. To find this best case for each asteroid, a large number of trajectory optimization runs were performed, and a subjective determination of "best" was made based on the aforementioned KPPs. The optimized mission trajectories were realized, in part, by finding the trajectory that yielded the lowest sum-distributed delta-v magnitude for the Earth-Asteroid transfer. A delta-v in this study defines the burn maneuver vector. For Earth departure, the magnitude of the V-infinity vector is used rather than an Earth departure delta-v. Using the departure V-infinity vector as part of the optimization leads to a direct optimization link to departure C3 which in turn can be related to launch vehicle choice by traditional Launch Mass vs. C3 data. The asteroid arrival delta-v is assumed as an intercept maneuver. The total delta-v is defined as the sum of magnitudes of the deterministic delta-v vectors previously mentioned in Table 3, with the exception of the Earth departure V-infinity.

The optimized trajectory design process entails the components of trajectory design assumptions, trajectory design constraints, and trajectory design parameters. We now provided a summary of the assumptions, constraints and key design parameters.

Trajectory Design Assumptions. All design processes include assumptions, and the trajectory design process of this study is no exception. The primary trajectory design assumptions include the following:
- One-way missions to asteroid…no sample return trajectories considered
- Missions have a specific given epoch date
- Earth departure dates must come on or after the epoch
- All trajectory leg transfer times are greater than the set minimum number of days
- Launch vehicle performance is sufficient to reach the DLA at Earth departure
- Range Safety launch azimuth angle are not considered in this study

Trajectory Design Constraints. In general, the trajectory optimization process integrally employs a set of trajectory design constraints. For this study, there were three constraints as defined below:
- Launch Window Constraint: The mission launch window is 1 calendar year from the epoch date.
- Maximum Transfer Time: Missions have a maximum transfer time explicit in the trajectory optimization.
- Sum of the Transfer Time for each leg of mission must be less than or equal to Maximum Transfer Time.
- Solar Central Distance: Min perihelion is 0.8 AU; max aphelion is 3 AU

Key Trajectory Design Parameters. The survey employs a trajectory optimization process that was formulated by varying a set of parameters within the above mentioned constraint limits and consistent with the trajectory design assumptions. These parameters include the launch date, the position of the DSMs, the time of the GA, and each trajectory leg transfer time. All the other trajectory parameters, including V-infinity, delta-v maneuvers, and arrival time, are implicitly dependent on the key design parameters shown here:
- Direct Case: $J_{1,D}$, $T_{1,D}$, Position of DSM, $T_{2,D}$
- GA Case: $J_{1,G}$, $T_{1,G}$, Position of DSM1, $T_{2,G}$, Time of GA, $T_{3,G}$, Position of DSM2, $T_{4,G}$

Optimization Technique

Methods and tools for preliminary mission analysis and design have become a critical topic for solar system exploration. In particular, global optimization applied to space mission design is currently witnessing an intense research effort. Over the past few years, various global optimization techniques have been employed to find optimal solutions for interplanetary mission design. Examples of global optimization algorithms proposed and tested by various authors include 1) Genetic Algorithms[12,13], 2) Differential Evolution[14,15], 3) Particle Swarm Optimization[16] as well as a variety of hybrid methods[17]. While the objective of applying such techniques to the problem of finding

[****] http://ssd.jpl.nasa.gov/?horizons

optimal interplanetary trajectories is to improve over a pure grid search, each method exhibits advantages and disadvantages. In recent years, two studies were commissioned by the European Space Agency (ESA) to assess the performance of the most popular global optimizers[18,19]. Importantly, it was found that the DE technique, which is a subset of the most general evolutionary algorithms, outperformed every other method. Indeed, this optimization technique, which has been under study for a number of years[20], has been pitted against a wide array of other global techniques in finding optimal trajectories of various complexities in terms of number of GAs and DSMs. Recently, the DE optimizer has been embedded in the previously mentioned preliminary space trajectory design tool called MDTOP. The program has proven to be effective in finding minimum delta-v solutions for a variety of real missions (e.g. Cassini, Galileo) and represents the principal tool that our team has chosen to perform the asteroid mission survey study presented in this paper. The DE algorithm, as implemented within the MDTOP framework, is described next.

DE is a stochastic direct search method that utilizes a set of parameter vectors that are mathematically manipulated in a way that is inspired by the theory of the evolution of living species. Figure 3 shows a notional graphical representation of a DE population used for a simple trajectory optimization problem. In Fig. 3, each of the NP members of the population is named X_i, where i is the member index. Each vector has D elements, where the j-th element is a design variable (for this study, a trajectory design variable). The j-th element corresponds to the same continuous design variable for each vector, though its value can vary among the population.

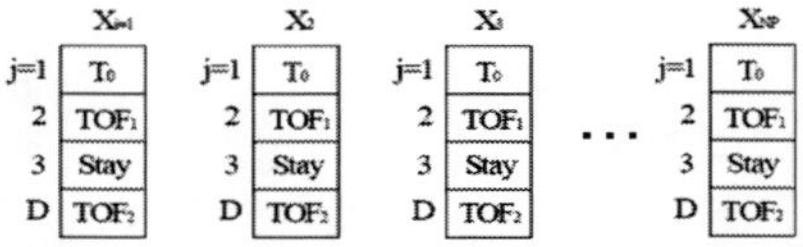

$X_{i=1}$		X_2		X_3			X_{NP}	
j=1	T$_0$	j=1	T$_0$	j=1	T$_0$		j=1	T$_0$
2	TOF$_1$	2	TOF$_1$	2	TOF$_1$	...	2	TOF$_1$
3	Stay	3	Stay	3	Stay		3	Stay
D	TOF$_2$	D	TOF$_2$	D	TOF$_2$		D	TOF$_2$

Figure 3 Notional Trajectory Parameter Vectors (Population)

DE initializes the population by assigning variable values from a uniform random distribution between the upper and lower limits of each design variable. We now define a "generation" as the process of varying each member of the population individually and measuring solutions against the cost function of sum-distributed delta-v. For each these generations, the parameter vectors are modified in order to locate better solutions (lower delta-v). DE uses three operations during a generation, viz. Mutation, Crossover, and Selection, to spawn successive generations. Each of the three operations of the DE process is successively repeated for each member of the current generation, $X_{i,G}$. First, two unique individuals are randomly chosen from the population: $X_{r2,G}$, and $X_{r3,G}$, where r2, and r3 are different indexes. Next, a "differential variation" vector is generated by subtracting vector $X_{r3,G}$ from vector $X_{r2,G}$. This differential variation term is multiplied by a mutation scale factor, F, and added to $X_{i,G}$ to form a mutant vector $V_{i,G}$. This process is called "Mutation" and is mathematically described by equation (1) :

$$V_{i,G} = X_{1,G} + F \cdot \left(X_{r2,G} - X_{r3,G} \right) \tag{1}$$

Following Mutation, a process known as "Crossover" is performed. The Crossover process mixes the parameters of the target vector $X_{i,G}$ and the mutant vector $V_{i,G}$ to form a trial vector $U_{i,G}$. A Crossover constant, CR $\in$ [0, 1], is now used in the Crossover process, where CR is equivalent to the probability that a trial vector element will come from the mutant vector. For each of the D design elements, a uniform random number rand(j) $\in$ [0,1] is generated and compared with CR to determine if the j-th value of $U_{i,G}$ will come from $X_{i,G}$ or $V_{i,G}$. The Crossover process is graphically illustrated notionally in Figure 4.

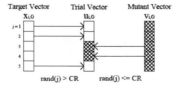

Figure 4 DE Crossover Operations to Form a Trial Vector

After Crossover, an operation known as "Selection" is undertaken. In Selection, the better of the $U_{i,G}$ and $X_{i,G}$ vectors is chosen to survive to the next generation, $G+1$. Herein, "better" is based on the optimization criterion which is the sum magnitude of the delta-v. If $U_{i,G}$ is a better solution than $X_{i,G}$, then $U_{i,G}$ will be assigned to $X_{i,G+1}$ and $X_{i,G}$ is discarded. Otherwise, $X_{i,G}$ moves into the next generation as $X_{i,G+1}$ and $U_{i,G}$ is discarded. For each generation, Mutation, Crossover, and Selection are repeated for all NP $X_{i,G}$ vectors in order to form a new population of NP $X_{i,G+1}$ vectors. The optimization continues until the prescribed number of generations (10,000 in this study) is undertaken or until the convergence condition is satisfied.

In order to tailor DE to a particular problem, there are three parameters that may be varied, i.e. population size NP, Mutation constant F, and Crossover probability CR. The optimization is terminated when the maximum number of generations is reached, which, for our investigation, is set as the iteration number where progress is observed to cease for most runs (the population size, NP, was 36; the maximum number of generations was set at 10,000; F was a constant of 0.6; CR was a constant of 0.8). It should be noted that the DE scheme detailed here is of type rand/1/bin[††††]. This means that the vector to be mutated is selected at random, only one difference vector is used for mutation, and crossover is determined by independent binomial experiments. Whereas there are many other variants of the DE procedure in existence, the above mentioned scheme is the most well-known, and it is the method used for all optimization in this study.

Within the MDTOP framework, the DE technique is invoked to locate the optimal patched conic trajectories based on deterministic delta-v, including the degrees-of-freedom of launch window, maximum total transfer time, single GA, and Deep Space Maneuvers. Note that the probability of finding the global optimal, based on the mission space encompassed by the constraints and trajectory design parameters, is directly related to the number of runs performed in the primary search. In this study, 500 runs of 10,000 generations each were performed for each particular case of asteroid and opportunity year. Through inspection, the 500 runs appeared to be sufficient to find most of the possible sub-optimal cases (local delta-v buckets in the mission space). Yet, the mission space is complex enough that more runs could be needed to actually find the global optimal (perhaps several thousand runs), thus there is no guarantee that the selected case is the actual global minimum based on the cost function. It should be made clear to the reader that we are implying that there were 500 optimal solutions found for each case that we investigated, and a lowest sum-distributed delta-v case was chosen as our "low-delta-v" solution.

ANALYSIS RESULTS

The large number of solutions generated by the global optimal solution method employed in this study was consolidated into a group of low delta-v cases for further investigation. These low delta-v cases were then compared by taking into account the remaining KPPs of launch energy and the total transfer time. A final set of mission cases were compiled that yielded a set of "best" cases identified.

Delta-V Results Summary

Depicted in Figure 5, a synthesis of results highlighting a set of low delta-v cases is provided in a format that attempts to allow easy comparison between each of the survey asteroids. Note that this synthesis of results represents a large number of trajectories over a full sweep of the survey asteroid set, departure years, and total trip times (not shown directly, but implicit to the results). The color contour-like properties of this figure permit a quick overview of the delta-v trends across all the asteroids and departure years, allowing the selection of a possible trajectory that would best suit the particular mission requirements. Note that Figure 5 data emphasizes the delta-v KPP, and does not attempt to address transfer time or departure C3.

[††††] http://www.icsi.berkeley.edu/~storn/code.html

min dV (m/s)	0	501	1001	1501	2001	2501	3001	3501
max dV (m/s)	500	1000	1500	2000	2500	3000	3500	7200

Direct Cases

	1999 JU3	1999 RQ36	2001 FC7	2002 CD	2008 EV5	1999 AO10	1998 HG49	2001 BB16	2003 SM84	2000 AE205	2001 QJ142	2009 OS5	1993 BX3	2000 EA14	2001 US16	2002 NV16	2006 KL21	2006 SU49	2008 DG5
2014	1379	2175	1818	1194	617	251	950	213	1188	661	1216	632	1165	2239	1997	356	1695	385	3184
2015	1342	323	2081	1288	2509	2147	1008	563	1412	685	1458	594	1169	1825	779	391	2308	1709	1950
2016	147	1981	2969	1687	1171	2699	1982	146	1393	583	1123	1125	1160	1076	854	2145	3419	286	2221
2017	1382	614	1816	1692	2107	3325	1005	3650	1339	525	906	1648	1167	2179	854	400	3376	375	2808
2018	1353	993	2977	1694	215	1100	857	2209	1638	522	381	1523	1199	715	1133	1385	861	1304	2767
2019	1365	1686	1816	1700	1445	233	1035	742	1199	649	945	873	1170	716	2154	2065	684	383	1969
2020	153	2127	2717	1664	156	230	879	209	1283	656	953	611	1173	1123	854	1102	2268	358	2093

Gravity Assist Cases

	1999 JU3	1999 RQ36	2001 FC7	2002 CD	2008 EV5	1999 AO10	1998 HG49	2001 BB16	2003 SM84	2000 AE205	2001 QJ142	2009 OS5	1993 BX3	2000 EA14	2001 US16	2002 NV16	2006 KL21	2006 SU49	2008 DG5
2014	651	1875	2863	1136	2493	752	930	702	1867	1050	2008	636	1440	1402	1479	1783	1717	1676	2390
2015	774	504	1979	1101	1891	1574	2173	261	1933	1188	2347	1252	1197	2181	2022	863	2130	884	2273
2016	929	1010	2520	4227	2051	1609	934	618	3612	1373	2950	1848	1512	1659	1398	584	699	373	541
2017	1474	1168	1817	3494	1878	796	1103	1156	2749	599	2765	972	1882	950	1641	531	1549	272	348
2018	345	1565	2621	2525	556	245	915	786	1517	942	362	700	1257	902	1090	1438	2906	494	2359
2019	727	1721	2957	1372	1479	251	1252	310	1025	854	1401	758	1860	762	1618	1123	2119	1750	1246
2020	130	1410	1732	1593	926	364	1271	261	1544	2400	1037	688	1196	1121	1586	1087	1006	354	1506

Figure 5 Delta-V Results Displaying Sweep of Survey over Target Bodies and Departure Years

Several points can be easily derived from the table, including the observation that there are a number of cases with total mission delta-v (KPP1) of less than 1 km/s (denoted by the light and dark blue colors). The particular mission requirements must be called into play to further analyze the mission in terms of Earth departure energy (KPP2) and trip time (KPP3) in order to find the subjective "best" case. Of interest are asteroids 1999 JU3, 2000 AE205, 2008 EV5, 2006 SU49, and 1999 AO10, given that those asteroids have relatively low delta-v cases in nearly every departure year that was examined in this survey. In addition, while only one value for each combination of asteroid and departure year is shown, there are quite a number of related cases for alternate trajectories that might be superior depending on the individual objectives and constraints of a specific mission.

Trajectory Results Summary

This section provides five example trajectory plots taken from a larger set of scenario data that were presented in the previously given Delta-V Results Summary section. As a sample of the data generated through this study, typical Direct and GA trajectories plots are shown in Figures 6a, 7a, 8a, 9a, and 10a. It should be noted that these sample trajectory plots are taken from some of the lowest delta-v mission cases generated. In the case for the Direct trajectory transfers, the trajectory of the spacecraft very nearly overlaps the target asteroid orbit for much of the transfer. This overlapping effect can also be seen clearly in Figure 7a.

The first example, illustrated in Figure 6a, shows a trajectory plot of a conceptual Direct mission to asteroid 1999 JU3 with a total mission delta-v of 154 m/s, launch C3 of 19.26 km^2/s^2, and a total trip time of 1.72 years. The precise sequence of trajectory events for the JU3 mission, along with the associated delta-v maneuvers and classical orbital elements (COE), is delineated in Figure 6b. Essentially, the Earth departure event provides the heliocentric transfer energy that places the spacecraft on an orbit with inclination of approximately 5.8 degrees. This transfer inclination is near the asteroid orbital inclination. Next, the DSM event of approximately 142 m/s places the spacecraft on an intercept trajectory with the asteroid. Finally, the 11 m/s asteroid rendezvous maneuver completes the plane change and matches the remaining asteroid orbital elements. Figure 6c delineates the mission event position and velocity change required to place the spacecraft on the associated trajectory leg. It should be noted that this table includes the Event Node's escape energy, applicable only to the Earth Departure. At this node, the tabulated delta-v elements actually correspond to the components of the V-infinity vector necessary for Earth departure and are not actual delta-v components provided by the spacecraft bus. Following the data of Figures 6a-6c, additional Direct mission data sets have been provided in Figures 7a-7c and 8a-8c.

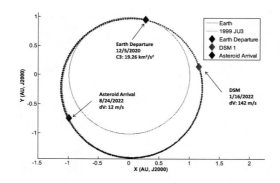

Figure 6a 1999 JU3 Direct Mission Trajectory

The total transfer time for this JU3 mission is 1.72 years, with a delta-v of approximately 154 m/s.

Trajectory Leg	Semi Major Axis (AU)	e	i (deg)	Longitude of Ascending Node (deg)	Argument of Periapsis (deg)	Initial True Anomaly (deg)	Final True Anomaly (deg)
Earth to DSM	1.197	0.19	5.76	253.76	207.21	332.80	265.70
DSM to Asteroid	1.189	0.19	5.86	251.76	211.20	263.69	113.90

Figure 6b 1999 JU3 Direct Mission Trajectory Legs

Event Node	Time (Julian)	C3 (km²/s²)	X (AU)	Y (AU)	Z (AU)	dV_x (m/s)	dV_y (m/s)	dV_z (m/s)	dV_MAG (m/s)
Earth Departure	2459189.2354	19.26	0.276	0.948	0.000	$V_{inf,x}=$ -2213	$V_{inf,y}=$ -1245	$V_{inf,z}=$ 3579	$V_{inf}=$ 4389
DSM	2459595.7255	N/A	1.158	0.137	0.109	1.2	-98	-103	142
Asteroid Arrival	2459815.8689	N/A	-0.990	-0.746	0.073	2	5	10	11

Figure 6c 1999 JU3 Direct Mission Trajectory Nodes

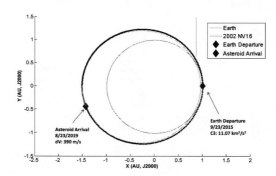

Figure 7a 2002 NV16 Direct Mission Trajectory

The total transfer time for this NV16 mission is 2.92 years, and the total delta-v is approximately 390 m/s. Note that the total transfer true anomaly is greater than 360 degrees.

Trajectory Leg	Semi Major Axis (AU)	e	i (deg)	Longitude of Ascending Node (deg)	Argument of Periapsis (deg)	Initial True Anomaly (deg)	Final True Anomaly (deg)
Earth to Asteroid	1.259	0.20	2.84	179.97	181.84	358.16	196.44

Figure 7b 2002 NV16 Direct Mission Trajectory Legs

Event Node	Time (Julian)	C3 (km^2/s^2)	X (AU)	Y (AU)	Z (AU)	dV$_x$ (m/s)	dV$_y$ (m/s)	dV$_z$ (m/s)	dV (m/s)
Earth Departure	2457288.6870	11.06	1.007	-0.001	0.000	V$_{inf,x}$= -1419	V$_{inf,y}$= 2274	V$_{inf,z}$= 1912	V$_{inf}$= 3327
Asteroid Arrival	2458354.4902	N/A	-1.420	-0.468	0.023	33	-297	-245	389

Figure 7c 2002 NV16 Direct Mission Trajectory Nodes

Figures 8 displays the result of an Earth GA mission involving asteroid 2008 DG5 with a total mission delta-v of 350 m/s, launch C3 of 44.18 km^2/s^2, and a total trip time of 2.70 years. After the energy-pumping Earth departure maneuver which places the spacecraft on relatively high energy transfer that sets up the spacecraft for an Earth GA, the remaining trajectory legs follow very nearly the orbit of 2008 DG5. Similarly, there are other examples of missions to asteroids 2006 KL21 and 1999 RQ36 illustrated in Figures 9a-9c and 10a-10c.

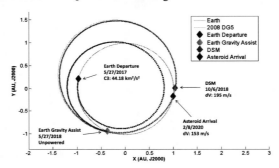

Figure 8a 2008 DG5 Gravity Assist Mission Trajectory

This DG5 mission requires a total of 2.70 years for transfer to the asteroid, with a total delta-v of 348 m/s distributed between the DSM and the asteroid rendezvous.

Leg	Semi Major Axis (AU)	e	i (deg)	Longitude of Ascending Node (deg)	Argument of Periapsis (deg)	Initial True Anomaly (deg)	Final True Anomaly (deg)
Earth to Earth Flyby	1.000	0.067	12.14	246.41	102.87	257.14	55.09
Earth to DSM	1.225	0.236	5.47	246.41	52.20	307.81	89.56
DSM to Asteroid	1.242	0.239	5.61	245.26	56.34	86.57	73.11

Figure 8b 2008 DG5 GA Mission Trajectory Legs

Event Node	Time (Julian)	C3 (km^2/s^2)	X (AU)	Y (AU)	Z (AU)	dV$_x$ (m/s)	dV$_y$ (m/s)	dV$_z$ (m/s)	dV (m/s)
Earth Departure	2457900.7384	44.18	-0.404	-0.926	0.000	V$_{inf,x}$= 5199	V$_{inf,y}$= -1186	V$_{inf,z}$= -3968	V$_{inf}$= 6647
Earth GA	2458265.9680	N/A	-0.404	-0.926	0.000	0	0	0	0
DSM	2458397.8225	N/A	1.015	0.547	0.068	-58	156	-100	194
Asteroid Arrival	2458887.5102	N/A	1.056	0.280	0.083	241	-125	85	153

Figure 8c 2008 DG5 GA Mission Trajectory Nodes

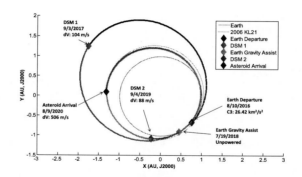

Figure 9a 2006 KL2 Gravity Assist Mission Trajectory

The total transfer 4.00 years puts us at the maximum constrained transfer time for our analyses, with a total delta-v of 699 m/s distributed between two DSM's and the asteroid rendezvous.

Leg	Semi Major Axis (AU)	e	i (deg)	Longitude of Ascending Node (deg)	Argument of Periapsis (deg)	Initial True Anomaly (deg)	Final True Anomaly (deg)
Earth to DSM 1	1.586	0.340	0.00	155.39	163.22	0.017	185.97
DSM 1 to Earth	1.576	0.368	0.00	168.58	150.26	185.75	337.91
Earth to DSM 2	1.156	0.155	9.30	116.76	224.52	315.47	276.50
DSM 2 to Asteroid	1.164	0.157	9.31	116.74	222.44	278.60	197.16

Figure 9b 2006 KL21 GA Mission Trajectory Legs

Event Node	Time (Julian)	C3 (km^2/s^2)	X (AU)	Y (AU)	Z (AU)	dV$_x$ (m/s)	dV$_y$ (m/s)	dV$_z$ (m/s)	dV (m/s)
Earth Departure	2457610.9972	26.42	0.762	-0.671	0.000	V$_{inf,x}$= 4366	V$_{inf,y}$= -2702	V$_{inf,z}$= 251	V$_{inf}$= 5140
DSM 2	2457999.6019	N/A	-1.752	1.246	0.000	52	89	-1	104
Earth GA	2458318.5347	N/A	0.458	-0.908	0.000	0	0	0	0
DSM 2	2458730.7812	N/A	-0.227	-1.080	0.113	86	8	-15	87
Asteroid Arrival	2459070.9881	N/A	-1.319	0.092	0.186	-165	475	-55	506

Figure 9c 2006 KL21 GA Mission Trajectory Nodes

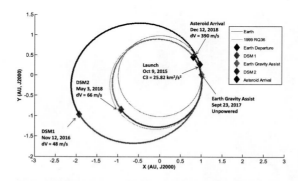

Figure 10a 1999 RQ36 Gravity Assist Mission Trajectory

573

This RQ36 mission required approximately 3.18 years of total transfer, with 504 m/s distributed between the two DSM's and the asteroid rendezvous.

Leg	Semi Major Axis (AU)	e	i (deg)	Longitude of Ascending Node (deg)	Argument of Periapsis (deg)	Initial True Anomaly (deg)	Final True Anomaly (deg)
Earth to DSM 1	1.586	0.368	0.001	187.32	191.23	357.12	188.02
DSM 1 to Earth	1.581	0.372	0.001	187.14	191.53	187.90	342.29
Earth to DSM 2	1.095	0.180	5.858	0.96	72.79	287.21	148.79
DSM 2 to Asteroid	1.091	0.182	5.902	1.34	71.54	149.67	318.18

Figure 10b 1999 RQ36 GA Mission Trajectory Legs

Event Node	Time (Julian)	C3 (km2/s2)	X (AU)	Y (AU)	Z (AU)	dVx (m/s)	dVy (m/s)	dVz (m/s)	dV (m/s)
Earth Departure	2457304.7661	25.825	0.965	0.271	0.000	$V_{inf,x}$= -5060	$V_{inf,y}$= 457	$V_{inf,z}$= -127	V_{inf}= 5082
DSM 1	2457704.5238	N/A	-1.929	-0.965	0.000	-24	41	0	47
Earth GA	2458020.1675	N/A	1.007	0.017	0.000	0	0	0	0
DSM 2	2458242.0684	N/A	-0.923	-0.842	-0.085	-26	57	-19	66
Asteroid Arrival	2458465.3849	N/A	0.796	0.477	0.047	202	-310	-122	390

Figure 10c 1999 RQ36 GA Mission Trajectory Nodes

Note that for all cases identified in this survey, further trajectory optimization could be performed to meet specific mission criteria, and thus our study purports to identify only cases as survey examples. Further work should be done on any cases provided in this study to validate the results and perform a more detailed optimization based on specific mission requirements.

Summary of "Best" Robotic Cases from the Survey Set

Data from Figure 5 has been further consolidated into Table 4 displaying the "best" cases determined by considering the full set of KPP's. These best cases are among the lowest delta-v for their respective asteroid, but also combine an attempt to factor-in low Earth departure energies and relatively short trip times for their class of mission (Direct or GA). In addition, the launch dates and delta-v break-downs are provided in table 4, providing a delineation of total delta-v distributed across the mission. Cases with an N/A inserted for the GA delta-v and DSM2 delta-v values are Direct transfer cases. Note cases such as the one listed for 1998 HG49 that have values of 0 m/s for some maneuvers. These 0 m/s cases are indicative of the optimizer finding a trajectory with maneuvers very near zero in magnitude (essentially, the maneuver in point has been "optimized-out"). If the delta-v of the Earth GA maneuver is listed as 0 m/s, the GA Earth flyby does occur as an "unpowered" flyby of Earth.

Table 4 Best Cases for Each Asteroid of Study Set

Asteroid	Launch	DSM1	Earth Flyby	DSM2	Arrival	DLA (deg)	RLA (deg)	Trip Time (years)	DepartC3 (km²/s²)	Total dV (m/s)	dV DSM1 (m/s)	dV GA (m/s)	dV DSM2 (m/s)	dV Arrival (m/s)
1999 JU3	12/5/2020	1/16/2022	N/A	N/A	8/24/2022	-48.1	118.9	1.72	19.26	154	142	N/A	N/A	12
1999 RQ36	10/9/2015	11/12/2016	9/23/2017	5/3/2018	12/12/2018	-0.02	15.62	3.18	25.82	504	48	0	66	390
2001 FC7	7/15/2017	2/3/2018	N/A	N/A	8/5/2019	-13.2	64.6	2.06	9.92	1817	486	N/A	N/A	1331
2002 CD	10/7/2017	3/20/2019	N/A	N/A	9/10/2019	58.9	47.3	1.93	12.06	1695	0	N/A	N/A	1695
2008 EV5	12/24/2020	2/17/2022	N/A	N/A	10/1/2022	58.6	25.3	1.77	19.73	156	0	N/A	N/A	156
1999 AO10	2/2/2020	7/23/2020	N/A	N/A	5/4/2021	-30.5	65.7	1.26	6.90	232	129	N/A	N/A	103
1998 HG49	4/16/2014	9/22/2014	10/20/2014	8/10/2015	1/29/2016	-87.7	24.99	1.79	5.75	1061	0	3	1058	<1 m/s
2001 BB16	1/25/2020	8/15/2020	N/A	N/A	5/20/2021	17.9	39.2	1.32	10.01	214	76	N/A	N/A	138
2003 SM84	4/3/2019	6/7/2020	4/2/2021	12/15/2021	2/19/2023	0.02	167.8	3.88	25.62	1025	0	0	903	122
2000 AE205	12/21/2018	12/1/2019	N/A	N/A	1/29/2021	-55.2	55.2	2.11	9.05	525	84	N/A	N/A	441
2001 QJ142	5/1/2014	5/21/2015	N/A	N/A	6/29/2016	30.8	121.3	2.17	3.18	1217	0	N/A	N/A	1217
2009 OS5	7/6/2020	4/29/2021	N/A	N/A	12/17/2021	-10.5	81.10	1.45	3.60	771	402	N/A	N/A	369
1993 BX3	12/13/2018	2/25/2020	12/10/2020	9/20/2021	2/27/2022	-0.1	80.6	3.21	25.17	1256	0	0	0	1256
2000 EA14	4/21/2019	5/10/2019	10/24/2019	6/8/2020	10/29/2020	-87.6	29.2	1.52	6.67	1193	0	0	694	499
2001 US16	5/21/2015	9/3/2016	N/A	N/A	4/24/2018	7.7	106.7	2.93	14.40	779	351	N/A	N/A	428
2002 NV16	9/23/2015	11/3/2017	N/A	N/A	8/23/2019	-28.9	5.3	2.92	11.07	391	1	N/A	N/A	390
2006 KL21	8/10/2016	9/3/2017	7/19/2018	9/4/2019	8/9/2020	0.0	43.43	4.00	26.42	698	104	0	88	506
2006 SU49	2/17/2017	8/6/2018	N/A	N/A	7/8/2020	-18.3	148.2	3.45	18.90	375	248	N/A	N/A	127
2008 DG5	5/27/2017	10/20/2017	5/27/2018	10/6/2018	2/8/2020	68.5	6.1	2.70	44.18	348	0	0	195	153

Human Mission Analyses

For the set 19 chosen asteroids, we conducted a set of Human mission runs over the matrix of asteroids and over the opportunity years from 2024-2035. The results of those optimizations are shown in Figure 11. For each of the 19 asteroids, the overall mission optimization was performed to determine the best year to perform the mission. This overall best year is labeled as "Opportunity Year" in Figure 11. Then, further optimization work was performed to determine the dependency of mission delta-v with asteroid stay time. Except for the lone case of the 210 day missions to 2002 NV16, the total delta-v increased with increasing stay time at the asteroid. Notably for some cases such as 1999 AO10 and 2001 QJ142, there exist cases with delta-v as low as 6 km/s for 120 day missions with asteroid stay time of 30 days and with delta-v of less than 7 km/s for 90 missions with stay times of up to 10 days. For a nominal mission time of 180 days, there exist missions with delta-v of just over 7 km/s and asteroid stay times of 10 days for eleven asteroids : 1999 JU3, 2002 CD, 2008 EV5, 1999 AO10, 2001 BB16, 2003 SM84, 2001 QJ142, 2009 OS5, 2001 US16, 2006 KL21, and 2008 DG5.

Max dV (m/s)	3000	4000	5000	6000	7000	8000	35000												
Min dV (m/s)	0	3001	4001	5001	6001	7001	8001												
Opportunity Year																		
	2033	2030	2034	2034	2024	2025	2031	2030	2034	2033	2024	2031	2025	2025	2034	2024	2031	2028	2025
90 Day Mission																		
Stay Time	1999 JU3	1999 RQ36	2001 FC7	2002 CD	2008 EV5	1999 AO10	1998 HG49	2001 BB16	2003 SM84	2000 AE205	2001 QJ142	2009 OS5	1993 BX3	2000 EA14	2001 US16	2002 NV16	2006 KL21	2006 SU49	2008 DG5
3 Days	12978	23232	25724	13728	14231	6178	18865	10873	17764	21697	5976	13442	20154	9448	8592	11270	13638	7337	12047
5 Days	13182	23522	25963	14100	14542	6302	20667	11044	18187	21934	6105	13720	20457	9710	8659	11538	13931	7500	12388
10 Days	13692	24343	26665	15105	15392	6671	19465	11520	18214	22617	6458	14461	21303	10431	8912	12263	14732	7985	13304
20 Days	15342	26513	28593	17526	17457	7640	20685	12872	19227	24431	7266	16253	23562	12215	9736	14006	16699	9379	15107
30 Days	17406	29746	31463	20706	20213	9012	22561	14907	20765	27151	31464	18659	26942	14646	11057	16271	19346	12325	17588
120 Day Mission																		
Stay Time	1999 JU3	1999 RQ36	2001 FC7	2002 CD	2008 EV5	1999 AO10	1998 HG49	2001 BB16	2003 SM84	2000 AE205	2001 QJ142	2009 OS5	1993 BX3	2000 EA14	2001 US16	2002 NV16	2006 KL21	2006 SU49	2008 DG5
3 Days	11371	19198	23422	10027	11392	5188	15351	8839	13960	18371	4540	9355	17190	8653	7141	9906	12192	6921	11860
5 Days	11197	19331	23567	10147	11565	5241	15599	8875	14160	18475	4615	9492	17336	8877	8878	10043	12358	7069	12146
10 Days	10995	19683	23956	10494	12027	5375	16265	9017	14682	18763	4819	9850	17739	9479	7450	10396	12781	7461	12902
20 Days	11709	20576	24820	15090	13097	5668	17508	9496	15860	19505	5303	10708	18725	10370	8045	11173	13839	8544	12605
30 Days	13210	21759	25959	12600	14408	6036	18154	10675	17314	20500	5913	11801	20003	12560	8856	12116	15182	10045	13764
150 Day Mission																		
Stay Time	1999 JU3	1999 RQ36	2001 FC7	2002 CD	2008 EV5	1999 AO10	1998 HG49	2001 BB16	2003 SM84	2000 AE205	2001 QJ142	2009 OS5	1993 BX3	2000 EA14	2001 US16	2002 NV16	2006 KL21	2006 SU49	2008 DG5
3 Days	6902	17081	21829	7178	9029	4030	11747	6144	10725	16568	3901	6862	15953	8426	6582	8563	11568	6767	11803
5 Days	7031	17148	22232	7281	9130	4042	11916	6376	10818	16627	3959	6961	16044	8636	6670	8609	11737	6915	9942
10 Days	7375	17347	22811	7566	9399	4072	12375	6376	11079	16790	4109	7222	16286	9188	6918	8727	12107	7330	8713
20 Days	8207	17849	23335	8248	10000	4177	13408	6753	11709	17201	4461	7815	16880	10423	7486	8975	12694	8373	9602
30 Days	9306	18486	24103	9105	10702	4360	14622	7245	12504	17731	4881	8521	17609	11850	8189	9291	13130	9759	10765
180 Day Mission																		
Stay Time	1999 JU3	1999 RQ36	2001 FC7	2002 CD	2008 EV5	1999 AO10	1998 HG49	2001 BB16	2003 SM84	2000 AE205	2001 QJ142	2009 OS5	1993 BX3	2000 EA14	2001 US16	2002 NV16	2006 KL21	2006 SU49	2008 DG5
3 Days	5125	15753	19103	6190	7034	3218	9273	5035	8010	17222	3068	5558	12585	8406	6567	7050	11169	6725	6679
5 Days	5198	15805	19426	6300	7094	3234	9418	5098	8067	15231	3716	5619	12759	8610	6659	7038	11279	6780	6780
10 Days	5391	15948	20276	6592	7250	3282	9790	5269	8288	15397	3836	5782	13224	9139	6891	7016	11532	7285	7058
20 Days	5830	16300	22117	7257	7586	3417	10621	5646	8770	15842	4112	6178	15530	10278	7425	7016	11745	8320	7715
30 Days	6339	16769	23329	8043	7961	3612	11568	6083	9342	16229	4426	6705	15980	11444	8070	7120	11566	9666	8531
210 Day Mission																		
Stay Time	1999 JU3	1999 RQ36	2001 FC7	2002 CD	2008 EV5	1999 AO10	1998 HG49	2001 BB16	2003 SM84	2000 AE205	2001 QJ142	2009 OS5	1993 BX3	2000 EA14	2001 US16	2002 NV16	2006 KL21	2006 SU49	2008 DG5
3 Days	4810	14579	16702	6517	5805	2904	7852	4772	6151	13856	3650	4709	10310	8406	6728	5686	7739	6728	7087
5 Days	4877	14623	17012	6648	5827	2916	7970	4847	6218	13929	3592	4787	10352	8610	6869	5672	7844	6869	7122
10 Days	5059	14749	17809	6947	5896	2962	8276	5038	6399	14119	3799	4991	10731	9139	7099	5651	8177	7280	7222
20 Days	5471	15077	19353	7547	6018	3107	8952	5444	6806	14589	4014	5441	11591	8125	7541	5705	9012	8317	7511
30 Days	5955	15499	21055	8242	6168	3324	9722	5886	7280	14961	4225	5953	12600	8964	8117	5887	9941	9657	7882

Figure 11 Delta-V Human Mission, Sweep Over Departure Years, Stay Time, & Mission Time

Further, based on the aforementioned KPP's and in vein with the way that we derived Table 4, we summarize in Figure 12 the set of "best" cases from Figure 11 for the mission times of 180 and 210 days. Note that some of the missions are not exactly 180 and 210 days because the optimization was actually performed on 180 and 210 days as upper bounds on the total mission time. We assume an upper bound on delta-v for the human missions of approximately 8000 m/s. From Figure 12, there are eight cases that have high delta-v (> 7000 m/s) and are thus not candidates for human missions during the opportunity years 2024-2035 with total mission time of up to 210 days: 1999 RQ36, 2001 FC7, 2008 EV5, 1998 HG49, 2000 AE2005, 1993 BX3, 2000 EA14, and 2006 KL2. The remaining eleven asteroids have delta-v in the acceptable range for consideration as human missions. Yet, of those eleven asteroids with reasonable delta-v, 4 of those are "lost" asteroids, leaving 7 possible asteroids for human missions.

As a finale for our exposition of potential cases for human-precursor robotic asteroid missions, we summarize in Figure 13 a set of human mission candidates corresponding to the robotic missions in Table 4. Note that essentially it was found that 13 out of the 19 asteroids yielded potential human missions (highlighted in tan in Table 9), yet given the effective "lost" state of four out of the eleven, 1999 AO10, 2001 BB16, 2001 QJ142, and 2009 OS5, the plausible human missions synthesized from our original 19 are 1999 JU3, 2002 CD, 2008 EV5, 2003 SM84, 2001 US16, 2002 NV16, 2006 KL21, 2006 SU49, and 2008 DG5. The JU3 case corresponds to the 2020 robotics mission in Table 4, but there are a number of good robotic cases including GA cases in 2014-2019 and a fairly low delta-v direct case in 2016.

Asteroid	Launch Date	Arrival Date	Departure Date	Return Date	Mission Time (days)	Leg 1 Flight Time (days)	Leg 2 Flight Time (days)	Stay Time (days)	C3 (km²/s²)	TOTAL dV (m/s)	Arrival dV (m/s)	Departure dV (m/s)	Earth Arrival dV (m/s)
1999 JU3	11/5/2033	1/1/2034	1/31/2034	5/4/2034	180	57	93	30	20.152	6339	2464	3875	0
	10/24/2033	12/29/2033	1/28/2034	5/22/2034	210	66	114	30	13.547	5955	2850	3105	0
1999 RQ36	4/14/2030	9/18/2030	9/21/2030	10/11/2030	180	157	20	3	28.019	24892	3066	12867	8959
	3/31/2030	10/4/2030	10/7/2030	10/27/2030	210	187	20	3	22.614	24133	2448	12131	9554
2001 FC7	6/12/2034	9/15/2034	9/18/2034	12/9/2034	180	95	82	3	62.175	19453	9754	9349	350
	5/11/2034	9/8/2034	9/11/2034	12/7/2034	210	120	87	3	57.556	16702	8455	8247	0
2002 CD	9/11/2034	11/29/2034	12/9/2034	3/10/2035	180	79	91	10	30.582	7362	3659	2933	770
	8/27/2034	11/24/2034	12/4/2034	3/25/2035	210	89	111	10	22.817	7078	4267	2680	131
2008 EV5	1/1/2024	3/6/2024	3/9/2024	6/28/2024	179	65	111	3	46.693	8395	2614	4421	1360
	1/1/2024	4/25/2024	4/28/2024	7/28/2024	209	115	91	3	32.266	7868	1667	4137	2064
1999 AO10 (L)	9/4/2025	1/11/2026	1/14/2026	3/3/2026	180	129	48	3	2.393	3218	2166	1052	0
	8/12/2025	1/15/2026	1/18/2026	3/8/2026	208	156	49	3	2.140	2904	1844	1060	0
1998 HG49	5/11/2031	7/31/2031	8/3/2031	11/7/2031	180	81	96	3	19.132	11044	4724	4548	1772
	5/2/2031	8/6/2031	8/9/2031	11/28/2031	210	96	111	3	13.464	9284	4028	3825	1431
2001 BB16 (L)	12/18/2030	3/8/2031	3/11/2031	6/16/2031	180	80	97	3	14.902	5035	1201	3834	0
	12/8/2030	3/4/2031	3/7/2031	7/6/2031	210	86	121	3	11.403	4772	1491	3281	0
2003 SM84	1/25/2034	4/14/2034	4/17/2034	7/24/2034	180	79	98	3	14.176	8710	3954	4056	700
	1/27/2034	4/20/2034	5/10/2034	8/25/2034	210	83	107	20	14.294	7258	3578	3229	452
2000 AE205	12/9/2033	3/17/2034	3/20/2034	6/7/2034	180	98	79	3	72.269	18253	8802	8419	1032
	11/8/2033	3/4/2034	3/7/2034	6/6/2034	210	116	91	3	76.024	14389	7378	6479	532
2001 QJ142 (L)	4/17/2024	7/20/2024	7/23/2024	10/14/2024	180	94	83	3	2.875	3669	1796	1873	0
	4/9/2024	7/18/2024	7/21/2024	10/21/2024	195	100	92	3	2.762	3650	1838	1812	0
2009 OS5 (L)	2/8/2031	5/12/2031	5/15/2031	8/7/2031	180	93	84	3	7.658	5557	2744	2813	0
	1/24/2031	5/15/2031	5/18/2031	8/22/2031	210	111	96	3	4.906	4710	2479	2231	0
1993 BX3	11/3/2025	2/2/2026	2/5/2026	5/2/2026	180	91	86	3	90.794	16282	5367	7218	3697
	10/16/2025	1/30/2026	2/2/2026	5/14/2026	210	106	101	3	65.149	12412	3987	6223	2202
2000 EA14	5/7/2025	8/29/2025	9/1/2025	10/20/2025	166	114	49	3	3.059	8407	4943	3464	0
	5/7/2025	8/29/2025	9/1/2025	10/20/2025	166	114	49	3	3.059	8407	4944	3463	0
2001 US16	3/28/2034	5/25/2034	6/4/2034	9/24/2034	180	58	112	10	4.422	6891	2830	4061	0
	3/15/2034	5/26/2034	5/31/2034	10/11/2034	210	72	133	5	3.359	6918	3008	3910	0
2002 NV16	5/18/2024	9/11/2024	10/1/2024	11/14/2024	180	116	44	20	9.932	7016	4604	2413	0
	4/18/2024	8/29/2024	9/28/2024	11/14/2024	210	133	47	30	9.167	5887	3612	2274	0
2006 KL21	3/24/2031	7/17/2031	7/20/2031	9/19/2031	179	115	61	3	1.246	11169	5689	5480	0
	6/13/2031	8/22/2031	8/25/2031	1/9/2032	210	70	137	3	12.767	7739	4742	2997	0
2006 SU49	8/21/2028	1/21/2029	1/26/2029	2/17/2029	180	153	22	5	0.298	6871	5041	1830	0
	8/9/2028	1/22/2029	1/27/2029	2/17/2029	192	166	21	5	0.264	6869	4943	1926	0
2008 DG5	6/1/2025	8/1/2025	8/6/2025	11/28/2025	180	61	114	5	22.493	6780	2067	4713	0
	5/17/2025	7/31/2025	8/3/2025	12/13/2025	210	75	132	3	14.749	7087	2715	4372	0

Figure 12 Delta-V Human Mission Best Cases Summary

The human missions assumed Direct trajectories to the asteroids with no DSM's or GAs. Note that an important mission constraint invoked on the trajectory optimization was an Earth return entry interface speed constrained to ≤ 11.9 km/s. A particular case where an explanation is due includes the case for 2000 EA14, in which both the 210 day and 180 day cases are very similar in mission time. This similarity is because the optimal mission for this target is 166 days, and so both the 180 and 210 day cases report this optimal result.

Figure 13 Human Precursor Robotic Asteroid Missions; 210 day and 180 day Missions

Asteroid	Robotic				Human (210 Day Mission)						Human (180 Day Mission)					
	Launch Date	Transfer time (years)	C3 (km²/s²)	Total dV (m/s)	Launch Date	Return Date	Stay Time (days)	Mission Time (days)	C3 (km²/s²)	Total dV (m/s)	Launch Date	Return Date	Stay Time (days)	Mission Time (days)	C3 (km²/s²)	Total dV (m/s)
1999 JU3	12/5/2020	1.72	19.26	154	10/24/2033	5/22/2034	30	210	13.55	5955	11/5/2033	5/4/2034	30	180	20.15	6339
1999 RQ36	10/9/2015	3.18	25.82	504	3/31/2030	10/27/2030	3	210	22.61	24133	4/14/2030	10/11/2030	3	180	28.02	24892
2001 FC7	7/15/2017	2.06	9.92	1817	5/11/2034	12/7/2034	3	210	57.56	16702	6/12/2034	12/9/2034	3	180	62.18	19453
2002 CD	10/7/2017	1.93	12.06	1695	8/27/2034	3/25/2035	10	210	22.82	7078	9/11/2034	3/10/2035	10	180	30.58	7362
2008 EV5	12/24/2020	1.77	19.73	156	1/1/2024	7/28/2024	3	209	32.27	7868	1/1/2024	6/28/2024	3	179	46.69	8395
1999 AO10	2/2/2020	1.26	6.90	232	8/12/2025	3/8/2026	3	208	2.14	2904	9/4/2025	3/3/2026	3	180	2.39	3218
1998 HG49	4/16/2014	1.79	5.75	1063	5/2/2031	11/28/2031	3	210	13.46	9284	5/11/2031	11/7/2031	3	180	19.13	11044
2001 BB16	1/25/2020	1.32	10.01	214	12/8/2030	7/6/2031	3	210	11.40	4772	12/18/2030	6/16/2031	3	180	14.90	5035
2003 SM84	4/3/2019	3.88	25.62	1025	1/27/2034	8/25/2034	20	210	14.29	7258	1/25/2034	7/24/2034	20	180	14.18	8710
2000 AE205	12/21/2018	2.11	9.05	525	11/8/2033	6/6/2034	3	210	76.02	14389	12/9/2033	6/7/2034	3	180	72.27	18253
2001 QJ142	5/1/2014	2.17	3.18	1217	4/9/2024	10/21/2024	3	195	2.76	3650	4/17/2024	10/14/2024	3	180	2.88	3669
2009 OS5	7/6/2020	1.45	3.60	771	1/24/2031	8/22/2031	3	210	4.91	4710	2/8/2031	8/7/2031	3	180	7.66	5557
1993 BX3	12/13/2018	3.21	25.17	1257	10/16/2025	5/14/2026	3	210	65.15	12412	11/3/2025	5/2/2026	3	180	90.79	16282
2000 EA14	4/21/2019	1.52	6.67	1195	5/7/2025	10/20/2025	3	166	3.06	8407	5/25/2025	10/20/2025	3	180	3.06	8407
2001 US16	5/21/2015	2.93	14.40	779	3/15/2034	10/11/2034	5	210	3.36	6918	3/28/2034	9/24/2034	10	180	4.42	6391
2002 NV16	9/23/2015	2.92	11.07	391	4/18/2024	11/14/2024	30	210	9.17	5887	5/18/2024	11/14/2024	20	180	9.93	7016
2006 KL21	8/10/2016	4.00	26.42	699	6/13/2031	1/9/2032	3	210	12.77	7739	3/24/2031	9/19/2031	3	179	1.25	11169
2006 SU49	2/17/2017	3.45	18.90	375	8/9/2028	2/17/2029	5	192	0.26	6869	2/18/2028	2/17/2029	5	180	0.30	6871
2008 DG5	5/27/2017	2.70	44.18	348	5/17/2025	12/13/2025	3	210	14.75	7087	6/1/2025	11/28/2025	5	180	22.49	6780

SUMMARY

An analysis survey of conceptual asteroid missions was completed, providing a set of parametric data that can be used for preliminary mission planning related to human-precursor asteroid missions. For a carefully chosen set of 19 asteroids, this study generated a table of "low" delta-v mission data that extended over a range of launch opportunity dates (2014 – 2020) and a range of total transfer times (1-4 years). The delta-v data demonstrates a wide range of "low" delta-v including high ranking missions like the 2016 opportunity for 1999 JU3 at approximately 150 m/s to the relatively low ranking 2008 DG5 cases coming in at near 4 km/s. From the table of delta-v data, several asteroids sharply stood-out. First, asteroids 2001 FC7, 2002 CD, and 2008 DG5 demonstrated generally high delta-v over the mission space investigated, as well as 2003 SM84 and 2001 QJ142 showing quite marginal comparisons to the other asteroids in the study set. Generally, 1999 JU3, 2008 EV5, 1999 AO10, 2001 BB16, 2000 AE205, 2009 OS5, and 2006 SU49 showed cases with comparatively low delta-v, with the big winners being 2008 EV5 and 1999 AO10 with relatively low delta-v cases for all opportunities from 2014-2020. Marginal comparisons were given light by 1999 JU3 and 1999 RQ36, where an Earth Gravity Assist was an enabling mission approach for the 2015 and 2016 launch opportunities for asteroid 1999 RQ36. Asteroids 2006 KL21 and 2008 DG5 demonstrated several rather widely scattered good cases in both Direct and GA missions. Another example of a GA enabled mission was the 2017 opportunity for asteroid 1998 HG49.

A subjective comparison was performed that further evaluated the low delta-v analyses data by a set of Key Performance Parameters that included Earth departure C3 and total transfer time. The key parameter comparison yielded a table that synthesized the rather large set of mission analyses data for each of the study asteroids into a set of "best" cases. A summary of the findings include:

- Over the set of asteroids, mission opportunities exist for each year 2014-2020, where a good Direct case for 1999 JU3 exists for 2016 (not shown in Table 4)

- Transfer times cover the range of 1.3 years for 2001 BB16 to approximately 4.0 years for 2006 KL21.

- Earth departure energies range from approximately 3 km²/s² for 2009 OS5 to 45 km²/s² for 2008 DG5.

- Total delta-v ranged from approximately 130 m/s for 1999 JU3 to over 4000 m/s for 2002 CD.

- GA trajectories made significant difference in mission delta-v for 2001 BB16, 1999 JU3, and 1999 RQ36. The remainder of the asteroids showed the best cases for Direct trajectory missions.

- Candidates for Human missions included eleven asteroids: 1999 JU3 in 2020, 2002 CD in 2017, 2008 EV5 in 2024, 1999 AO10 in 2020, 2001 BB16 in 2020, 2003 SM84 in 2019, 2001 QJ142 in 2014, 2009 OS5 in 2020, 2001 US16 in 2015, 2002 NV16 in 2015, 2006 KL21 in 2031, 2002 SU49 in 2017, and 2008 DG5 in 2017. Note that QJ142, AO10, BB16, and OS5 are considered lost asteroids, resulting in nine potentially good candidates for a human precursor robotic asteroid, viz., JU3, CD, EV5 (for the 210 day mission), SM84 (for the 210 day mission), US16, NV16, 2006 KL21 (for the 210 day mission), SU49, and DG5.

- The nine "good" missions are summarized in terms of stay-time at the asteroid as follows: JU3 has a maximum stay time of 30 days, CD has 10 days, EV5 has 5 days, US16 has 5 days for the 210 day mission and 10 days for the 180 day mission, NV16 has 30 days for the 210 day mission and 20 days for the 180 day mission, KL21 has 3 days, SU49 has 5 days for the 210 day mission and 5 days for the 180 day mission, 2008 DG5 has 3 days for the 210 day mission and 5 days for the 180 day mission.

REFERENCES

[1] NASA Request for Information, Exploration Enterprise Workshop, "Enabling Technology Development and Demonstration Program", Solicitation Number NNH10ZTT004L, May 21, 2010.

[2] Cupples, M.L., Furfaro, R., Hergenrother, C.W., Adebonojo, B.O., Wibben, D.R., Kidd, J.N., "A Mission Analysis Survey of Potential Human-Precursor Robotic Missions", *Proceedings of AAS/AIAA Space Flight Mechanics Meeting, (AAS 11-100), 2011.*

[3] Olds, A., Kluever, C., and Cupples, M., "Interplanetary Mission Design Using Differential Evolution", *Journal of Spacecraft and Rockets*, Vol. 44, No. 5, 2007, pp. 1060–1070.

[4] *Differential Evolution. A Practical Approach to Global Optimization*, Price, K.V., Storn, R. M., and Lampinen, J. A., , Natural Computing Series, Springer–Verlag, New York, 2005.

[5] Abell, P.A., Korsmeyer, D.J., Landis, R.R., Jones, T.D., Adamo, D.R., Morrison, D.D., Lemke, L.G., Gonzales, A. A. , Gersham, R., Sweetser, T.H., Johnson, L. L., Lu, E., "Scientific exploration of near-Earth objects via the Orion Crew Exploration Vehicle", *Meteoritics & Planetary Sciences*, Vol. 44, Nr 12, 1825-1836, 2009.

[6] Landis, R.R., Abell, P.A., Kosmeyer, D.J., Jones, T.D., Adamo, D.R., "Piloted Operations at a Near-Earth Object (NEO) ," *Acta Astronautica*, Vol 56, Issues 11-12, 1689-1697, 2009.

[7] "Asteroids Emerge as Next Frontier of Space Exploration", Vergano, D., USA Today, May 23, 2010.

[8] http://www.jspec.jaxa.jp/e/activity/hayabusa2.html.

[9] Hergenrother, C.W. and Whiteley, R.J. 2011. A survey of small fast rotating asteroids among the near-Earth asteroid population. Icarus 214, 194-209.

[10] *Spacecraft Mission Design*, Brown, C.D., American Institute of Aeronautics and Astronautics, Washington DC, 1992, pp 111-133.

[11] *Orbital Mechanics*, Prussing, J.E., Conway, B.A., Oxford University Press, New York and Oxford, 1993, pp 124-128.

[12] Abdelkhalik, O., and Mortari, D., "N-Impulse Orbit Transfer Using Genetic Algorithms," *Journal of Spacecraft and Rockets*,Vol. 44, No. 2, March–April 2007, pp. 456–459.

[13] Gage, P. J., Braun, R. D., and Kroo, I. M., "Interplanetary Trajectory Optimization Using a Genetic Algorithm," *Journal of the Astronautical Sciences*, Vol. 43, No. 1, 1995, pp. 59–75.

[14] *Interplanetary Trajectory Optimization with Differential Evolution*, Olds, Aaron D., Thesis, University of Missouri-Columbia, Dec 2005.

[15] Olds, Aaron D., Cupples, Michael L., "End-to-end optimization of Conceptual Roundtrip Mars Missions with Exact Precession Elliptical Parking Orbits", *Proceedings of the AAS/AIAA Space Flight Mechanics Meeting (AAS 08 – 194)*, 2008.

[16] Kennedy, J. and Eberhart, R. C., "Particle Swarm Optimization," *Proceedings of IEEE International Conference on Neural Networks*, 1995, pp. 1942–1948.

[17] Vasile, M., Summerer, L., and De Pascale, P., "Design of Earth-Mars Transfer Trajectories using Evolutionary Branching Techniques," *Acta Astronautica*, Vol. 56, No. 8, 2005, pp. 705–720.

[18] Myatt, D. R., Becerra, V. M., Nasuto, S. J., and Bishop, J. M., "Advanced Global Optimization Tools for Mission Analysis and Design," Final Rept. of ESA Ariadna ITTAO4532/18138/04/NL/MV, Call03/4101, 2004.

[19] Di Lizia, P., and Radice, G., "Advanced Global Optimization Tools for Mission Analysis and Design," Final Rept. of ESA Ariadna ITTAO4532, Call 03/4101, 2004.

[20] Price, K.V., Storn, R. M., and Lampinen, J. A., Differential Evolution. A Practical Approach to Global Optimization, Natural Computing Series, Springer–Verlag, New York, 2005.

AAS 11-443

LAUNCH ANALYSES SUPPORTING CONCEPTUAL HUMAN-PRECURSOR ROBOTIC ASTEROID MISSIONS

Badejo O. Adebonojo Jr.,[*] Michael L. Cupples,[†] Roberto Furfaro[‡] and John N. Kidd Jr.[§]

From a set of carefully selected asteroids, a study of conceptual asteroid missions was conducted using a stochastic direct search global optimization process, assuming a set of Key Performance Parameters (KPP's). The key parameters from the best case set included the minimum Escape Energy (C3) as well as the minimum mission total delta V for each asteroid, for both direct and gravity assisted missions. The objective of the current study to determine the launch window times required to achieve ascent and injection onto the outbound trajectory required for either the direct or gravity assisted mission to the selected asteroid, taking into consideration the impact of the range safety limits on the launch azimuths. A set of flyout trajectory orbital elements corresponding to the launch windows will be provided, and a preliminary assessment of the resulting launch vehicle payload delivery capability and margins will be conducted provided based on launch vehicle vendor data.

INTRODUCTION

A study of robotic asteroid missions[1,2], was conducted which identified a set of 19 "best case" asteroid missions based on a selection process which employed a stochastic direct search global optimization utilizing a set of Key Performance Parameters (KPP's) to find the best trajectories that minimize the cost of the missions required to achieve the optimal Earth departure conditions, including the Right Ascension of the Launch Asymptote (RLA) and Declination of the Launch Asymptote (DLA), for the mission. The primary mission analysis optimization parameters were the Earth Escape Energy (C3) and the total mission delta-v for each asteroid, for both direct and gravity assisted missions. That study, however, did not include an assessment of the mission launch limitations and constraints due to launch site range safety requirements nor launch vehicle payload capability, a problem which will be addressed by this paper.

Table 1 below, shows the subjective "best" case KPP's for each Asteroid as well as the Launch Epoch, DLA and RLA. The primary focus of the current study is to extend the Asteroid Robotic Mission Analysis to include launch and fly out trajectory analysis for the selected launch epochs based on launch site and departure asymptote geometries, and to determine the capability of achieving the desired C3 based on the set of available launch vehicles, and further to provide a set of preliminary data to be utilized for first-look

---

[*] Senior Systems Engineer, Modeling & Simulation, Raytheon Missile Systems, 1151 E. Hermans Rd, Tucson, AZ 85756.
[†] Principal Systems Engineer, Modeling & Simulation, Raytheon Missile Systems, 1151 E. Hermans Rd, Tucson, AZ 85756.
[‡] Associate Professor, Industrial & Systems Engineering, University of Arizona, Tucson, AZ 85721.
[§] Student, Lunar and Planetary Laboratory, University of Arizona, Tucson, AZ 85721

mission planning efforts for these asteroid missions. The analyses will also yield mission launch windows, fly out trajectory elements, as well as a set of launch geometry parameters for further spacecraft sizing and launch vehicle analyses considerations.

Table 1. Summary of the Overall Best Cases for the Asteroid Study Set.

Target	Launch	Mission Time (years)	DSM1	Earth Flyby	DSM2	Arrival	DLA (deg)	RLA (deg)	Depart C3	Total dV (m/s)
1999 JU3	12/5/2020	1.72	1/16/2022	N/A	N/A	8/24/2022	-48.1	118.9	19.26	154
1999 RQ36	10/9/2015	3.18	11/12/2016	9/23/2017	5/3/2018	12/12/2018	-0.02	15.6	25.82	504
2001 FC7	7/15/2017	2.06	2/3/2018	N/A	N/A	8/5/2019	-13.2	64.6	9.92	1817
2002 CD	10/7/2017	1.93	3/20/2019	N/A	N/A	9/10/2019	58.9	47.3	12.06	1695
2008 EV5	12/24/2020	1.77	2/17/2022	N/A	N/A	10/1/2022	58.6	25.3	19.73	156
1999 AO10	2/2/2020	1.26	7/23/2020	N/A	N/A	5/4/2021	-30.5	65.7	6.9	232
1998 HG49	4/16/2014	1.79	9/22/2014	10/20/2014	8/10/2015	1/29/2016	-87.7	25	5.75	1063
2001 BB16	1/25/2020	1.32	8/15/2020	N/A	N/A	5/20/2021	17.9	39.2	10.01	214
2003 SM84	4/3/2019	3.88	6/7/2020	4/2/2021	12/15/2021	2/19/2023	0.02	167.7	25.62	1025
2000 AE205	12/21/2018	2.11	12/1/2019	N/A	N/A	1/29/2021	-55.2	55.2	9.05	525
2001 QJ142	5/1/2014	2.17	5/21/2015	N/A	N/A	6/29/2016	30.8	121.3	3.18	1217
2009 OS5	7/6/2020	1.45	4/29/2021	N/A	N/A	12/17/2021	-10.5	81.1	3.6	771
1993 BX3	12/13/2018	3.21	2/25/2020	12/10/2020	9/20/2021	2/27/2022	-0.1	80.6	25.17	1257
2000 EA14	4/21/2019	1.52	5/10/2019	10/24/2019	6/8/2020	10/29/2020	-87.6	29.2	6.67	1195
2001 US16	5/21/2015	2.93	9/3/2016	N/A	N/A	4/24/2018	7.7	106.7	14.4	779
2002 NV16	9/23/2015	2.92	11/3/2017	N/A	N/A	8/23/2019	-28.9	5.3	11.07	391
2006 KL21	8/10/2016	4	9/3/2017	7/19/2018	9/4/2019	8/9/2020	0.05	43.4	26.42	699
2006 SU49	2/17/2017	3.45	8/6/2018	N/A	N/A	7/8/2020	-18.3	148.2	18.9	375
2008 DG5	5/27/2017	2.7	10/20/2017	5/27/2018	10/6/2018	2/8/2020	68.5	6.1	44.18	348

ANALYSES ASSUMPTIONS AND APPROACH

Launch Site location Assumption

Launch site location is an independent variable of launch geometry. The launch geometry properties which most strongly influence the ascent trajectory are, a) the launch site location and the launch asymptote. Because the missions for this study come from a set of previous conceptual Discovery Class robotic asteroid missions, any spacecraft launch for these missions will most likely occur out of Cape Canaveral Air Station (CCAS) into a launch corridor in an easterly (pro-grade) direction.

This study involves the determination of the launch window times within the azimuth limits which allow the launch vehicle to execute a fly out to the launch asymptote without violating range safety requirements for land masses and populated areas which could result from spent stage impacts, vehicle over-flight and other debris generated as a result of destruct actions which might need to be taken. CCAS impact areas lie in the Atlantic Ocean between the azimuths of 44 degrees and 110 degrees, however, with acceptable risk analysis, launch azimuths between 37 and 114 degrees9 have been permitted, yielding orbital inclinations of approximately 28.5 degrees to 52.5 degrees without performing a dogleg ascent maneuver. For the purposes of this analysis, the limits of 50 to 115 degrees were used as a conservative range.

Launch Constraints

There are a number of important constraints typically considered for interplanetary mission analyses which include interplanetary trajectory geometry, injection energy requirements, payload mass/size, guidance, tracking & telemetry and safety. For this study, a primary launch assumption was that for analyses purposes, missions would launch from the Cape (CCAS). A CCAS launch imposes a number of launch constraints primarily driven by range safety considerations. Other launch analysis assumptions include the following:

- The CCAS launch location is Φ_L = Latitude 28.3 deg, λ_L = Longitude 279.4 deg East
- Launch azimuth range safety requirements (50 - 115 degrees)
- Motion of launch vehicle after launch remains in the flyout plane established at launch

- No intermediate phasing parking orbit is considered in this analysis, though in nearly all cases the optimal ascent to the injection point will require a phasing orbit
- We do not consider retrograde orbits in these analyses

It is important for a general understanding of this launch analyses to keep in mind that by adhering to the above launch constraints, several key facts are implicit to the forthcoming results:

- For DLA > Φ_L, the minimum flyout plane inclination is the DLA.
- For DLA < Φ_L, the minimum flyout plane inclination is the launch site latitude of 28.3 deg.

Approach

The inputs for this study are taken from the previously mentioned mission analysis. The analysis provided four primary input parameters to the current study. Those four parameters together with launch site position make up the entire set of required inputs for this study:

- Launch Epoch (Epoch$_L$)
- Declination of the Launch Asymptote (DLA)
- Right Ascension of the Launch Asymptote (RLA)
- Earth Escape Energy (C3)
- Launch site latitude and longitude (Φ_L, λ_L respectively)

Table 2 below shows the conceptual mission analysis inputs derived from the aforementioned preliminary mission analysis study that also includes the V∞ vector and its components and is placed in a format most useful for our analyses.

Table 2. Analysis Input Data.

Analysis Inputs
Launch Site Geocentric Latitude, Φ_L = 28.3 deg; Launch Site Geocentric East Longitude , λ_L = 279.4 deg

	Epoch$_L$ Julian	Epoch$_L$ Gregorian	DLA (deg)	RLA (deg)	VinfMag (km/s)	Vinf,x (km/s)	Vinf,y (km/s)	Vinf,z (km/s)	C3 (km2/sec2)
1999 JU3	2459189.235	2020 12 5	-48.078	118.868	4.388	-1.416	2.568	-3.265	19.259
1999 RQ36	2457304.766	2015 10 9	-0.025	15.618	5.082	4.894	1.368	-0.002	25.825
2001 FC7	2457950.154	2017 7 15	-13.151	64.612	3.149	1.315	2.771	-0.717	9.918
2002 CD	2458034.465	2017 10 7	58.904	47.346	3.473	1.215	1.319	2.974	12.060
2008 EV5	2459208.331	2020 12 24	58.569	25.290	4.442	2.094	0.990	3.790	19.730
1999 AO10	2458881.684	2020 2 2	-30.531	65.741	2.626	0.929	2.062	-1.334	6.896
1998 HG49	2456764.287	2014 4 16	-87.729	24.995	2.398	0.086	0.040	-2.396	5.750
2001 BB16	2458874.028	2020 1 25	17.854	39.195	3.164	2.334	1.903	0.970	10.010
2003 SM84	2458576.675	2019 4 3	0.024	167.762	5.061	-4.946	1.073	0.002	25.616
2000 AE205	2458473.508	2018 12 21	-55.223	55.228	3.008	0.978	1.409	-2.470	9.045
2001 QJ142	2456779.269	2014 5 1	30.798	121.306	1.783	-0.796	1.309	0.913	3.180
2009 OS5	2459037.248	2020 7 6	-10.500	81.097	1.897	0.289	1.842	-0.346	3.597
1993 BX3	2458465.746	2018 12 13	-0.104	80.600	5.017	0.819	4.950	-0.009	25.172
2000 EA14	2458594.915	2019 4 21	-87.557	29.222	2.584	0.096	0.054	-2.581	6.675
2001 US16	2457163.883	2015 5 21	7.676	106.702	3.795	-1.081	3.602	0.507	14.400
2002 NV16	2457288.687	2015 9 23	-28.909	5.270	3.327	2.900	0.268	-1.608	11.070
2006 KL21	2457610.997	2016 8 10	0.049	43.428	5.140	3.733	3.534	0.004	26.424
2006 SU49	2457788.138	2017 2 17	-18.253	148.219	4.347	-3.510	2.174	-1.362	18.900
2008 DG5	2457900.738	2017 5 27	68.475	6.059	6.647	2.425	0.257	6.183	44.180

From the set of constraints and initial parameters, we apply the analytical method outlined in Appendix A, yielding a set of orbital elements and launch windows parameters for the launch and fly out trajectory for each asteroid.

The Significance of the Launch Asymptote Vector

The Spacecraft is launched onto an ascent and fly out trajectory, which places it on a path traveling radially outward from the earth, where it is first influenced primarily by the Earth's gravity, and then after reaching the Earth-Sun gravitational sphere of influence, primarily by the sun's gravity. The defining quantities of the launch trajectory of the near earth conic are the launch date, the right ascension and declination of the launch asymptote as well as the Escape energy, C3. The launch asymptote is a primary independent variable of the launch geometry, and it has a considerable influence on the ascent trajectory geometry. The launch asymptote points in the same direction as the Vinfinity vector ($\mathbf{V}_\infty$) and defines the direction of the outgoing asymptote of the escape hyperbola.

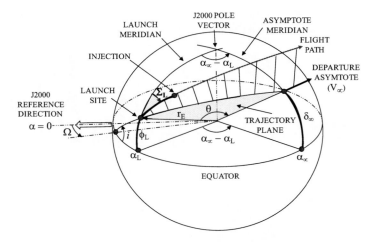

Figure 1. Launch and Injection Plane Geometry.

Figure 1 shows the launch injection plane geometry. The figure shows the earth centered J2000 inertial reference system with the X axis in the direction of the J2000 reference vector and the Z axis in the direction of the Earth rotational axis. The center of this reference system, together with the earth departure asymptote vector ($\mathbf{V}_\infty$) and the launch site vector (r_E), define the launch and flyout trajectory plane. The launch azimuth angle (Σ_L), in this figure, is measured clockwise from the local north. The algorithms used in the execution of this study are based on these parameters and on the solutions of the launch and injection geometry problem[6-8](Eq. (1-17), shown in Appendix A).

Analysis starts at launch epoch and covers twenty-four hours for each of the following parameters:
- $\Sigma_L \equiv$ Launch Azimuth
- $i \equiv$ Launch Plane Inclination
- $\theta \equiv$ Range Angle
- $\Omega \equiv$ Right Ascension of Ascending Node (RAAN)
- $\alpha_L \equiv$ Right Ascension of the Launch Site
- perigee of flyout trajectory (not shown)

where $\delta_\infty \equiv$ DLA
and $\alpha_\infty \equiv$ RLA

The algorithms were coded in FORTRAN and Matlab and executed to determine the launch windows for each mission. Analyses output reports are generated for each asteroid mission covering a twenty-four hour period following the launch epoch, and the data is summarized in Tables.

ANALYSES RESULTS

The primary finding is that asteroids 1999 JU3, 2002 CD, 2008 EV5, 1998 HG49, 2000 AE205, 2000 EA14 and 2008 DG5 have no launch window which could be identified during the 24 hour period following the proposed launch epochs which came from the original optimization study. Additionally, two of the cases, 2001 QJ142 and 2006 SU49 have launch windows which are open over three smaller time spans during the 24 hour launch period. This case is applicable when the first launch window has been open for some time prior to the start of the launch epoch. Additionally, the analyses outputs include, as a function of time from the assigned launch date, a set of figures for the Right Ascension of the Launch Site,

Launch Azimuth Angle, Launch Plane Inclination Angle, Range Angle and Right Ascension of the Ascending Node.

Non-Temporal Flyout Trajectory Elements

Table 3 which follows, shows the non-temporal launch and fly out trajectory orbital elements computed for those asteroid sets which produced clearly identifiable launch windows. This data indicates the flyout trajectory and constitutes the first three of the fly out trajectory elements which include the trajectory true anomaly, semi major axis and the eccentricity. Note that these trajectory elements assume that the launch vehicle has performed the final injection maneuver.

Table 3. Launch and Fly Out Trajectory Elements.

Analysis Outputs		
vθ (deg)	a (km)	e
1999 JU3	No launch window	
1999 RQ36	146.9	-30872.2	1.19
2001 FC7	158.0	-80381.3	1.06
2002 CD	No launch window	
2008 EV5	No launch window	
1999 AO10	161.4	-115604.2	1.06
1998 HG49	No launch window	
2001 BB16	157.9	-79646.4	1.08
2003 SM84	147.0	-31123.3	1.19
2000 AE205	No launch window	
2001 QJ142	167.1	-250710.7	1.03
2009 OS5	166.3	-221629.8	1.03
1993 BX3	147.2	-31672.8	1.19
2000 EA14	No launch window	
2001 US16	154.0	-55365.3	1.11
2002 NV16	156.9	-72019.9	1.09
2006 KL21	146.6	-30172.0	1.20
2006 SU49	150.8	-42183.1	1.15
2008 DG5	No launch window	

Launch Windows

The launch window is the time range during which a launch from CCAS can occur either directly into the plane of the flyout trajectory or indirectly via an intermediate parking orbit or another maneuver. The launch is generally centered on an optimal launch time with the window duration being driven by range safety limits, lighting/weather conditions, and other mission related requirements.

There are typically two launch windows per day for missions with a $\mathbf{V}_\infty$ vector whose DLA is greater or less than the launch site latitude, while there is only one launch window per day for missions with a $\mathbf{V}_\infty$ vector whose DLA is equal to the launch site latitude (i.e. the window is not bifurcated into two segments during the 24 hour period).

Tables 4 - 10 below, show the analyses output summaries for the asteroids. They include
- Right Ascension of the Launch Site (Table 4),
- The Launch Azimuth Angle (Table 5),
- The Trajectory Plane Inclination (Table 6),
- The Range Angle (Table 7),
- Right Ascension of the Ascending Node (Table 8),
- Right Ascension of the Ascending Node of the Launch Trajectory (Table 9),
- Argument of Perigee (Table 10).

Together with the elements in Table 3 above, Table 8, Table 9 and Table 10 provide the set of fly out trajectory elements at the window open and close times for each of the asteroid missions.

The tables provide values of the fly out trajectory parameters at the time of launch window open as well as at the time of launch window close. From the set of tables, we see that asteroids QJ142 and SU49 have windows which are open over at least three periods during the 24 hour launch epoch window. It should be noted that in the usual way of considering launch windows over a 24 hour period, there are only

583

two actual launch windows. There can be a rather "short" first or third window that is actually the end or the beginning of the next day's launch window respectively.

The launch window analyses shows from these tables, that seven out of the nineteen best-case missions, 1999 JU3, 2002 CD, 2008 EV5, 1998 HG49, 2000 AE205, 2000 EA14 and 2008 DG5, have no launch windows during the 24 hour period following the optimal launch epochs. Hence, no launch azimuths are available on that day which would satisfy the range safety requirements of a Cape launch.

Of the remaining 12 missions, eight missions have launch windows which support the direct (ref Table 1) asteroid mission based on range safety launch azimuths constraints: 2001 FC7, 1999 AO10, 2001 BB16, 2001 QJ142, 2009 OS5, 2002 NV16, 2006 SU49 and 2001 US16.

Four of the missions, 1999 RQ36, 2003 SM84, 1993 BX3 and 2006 KL21, have launch windows which support the Gravity Assist (ref Table 1) asteroid mission based on range safety launch azimuths constraints.

Table 4. Right Ascension of the Launch Site at window Open and Close.

Right Ascensions of the Launch Site	Window 1 Open:		Window 1 Close:		Window 2 Open:		Window 2 Close:		Window 3 Open:		Window 3 Close:	
	Epoch$_L$ (+Hrs)	Σ_L (deg)	Epoch$_L$ (+Hrs)	RALS (deg)	Epoch$_L$ (+Hrs)	RALS (deg)	Epoch$_L$ (+Hrs)	RALS (deg)	Epoch$_L$ (+Hrs)	RALS (deg)	Epoch$_L$ (+Hrs)	RALS (deg)
1999 JU3	No launch window											
1999 RQ36	0.84	45.4	7.82	150.4	12.79	225.1	19.78	330.2				
2001 FC7	1.20	106.5	8.57	217.4	11.52	261.8	18.14	1.4				
2002 CD	No launch window											
2008 EV5	No launch window											
1999 AO10	0.72	128.1	8.35	242.9	8.95	252.0	14.09	329.2				
1998 HG49	No launch window											
2001 BB16	2.14	266.1	9.65	19.1	11.83	51.9	18.26	148.7				
2003 SM84	1.58	197.5	8.57	302.6	13.54	17.3	20.52	122.3				
2000 AE205	No launch window											
2001 QJ142	0.00	55.7	4.13	117.8	4.82	128.3	9.84	203.7	20.50	4.0	24.00	56.7
2009 OS5	0.46	120.6	7.73	230.0	11.11	280.9	17.81	21.6				
1993 BX3	1.37	110.5	8.35	215.5	13.32	290.3	20.30	35.3				
2000 EA14	No launch window											
2001 US16	1.82	325.3	9.02	71.6	12.86	129.4	19.63	231.2				
2002 NV16	5.11	65.3	13.03	184.5	13.20	187.0	18.91	272.9				
2006 KL21	1.01	72.9	7.99	178.0	12.98	253.1	19.97	358.1				
2006 SU49	0.00	282.9	1.73	308.9	3.82	340.3	10.25	77.1	18.12	195.5	24.00	283.9
2008 DG5	No launch window											

Table 5. Launch Azimuths at window Open and Close.

Launch Azimuths	Window 1 Open:		Window 1 Close:		Window 2 Open:		Window 2 Close:		Window 3 Open:		Window 3 Close:	
	Epoch$_L$ (+Hrs)	Σ_L (deg)	Epoch$_L$ (+Hrs)	Σ_L (deg)	Epoch$_L$ (+Hrs)	Σ_L (deg)	Epoch$_L$ (+Hrs)	Σ_L (deg)	Epoch$_L$ (+Hrs)	Σ_L (deg)	Epoch$_L$ (+Hrs)	Σ_L (deg)
1999 JU3	No launch window											
1999 RQ36	0.84	50.3	7.82	115.2	12.79	50.1	19.78	115.1				
2001 FC7	1.20	50.1	8.57	115.2	11.52	50.0	18.14	115.2				
2002 CD	No launch window											
2008 EV5	No launch window											
1999 AO10	0.72	50.2	8.35	47.0	8.95	113.9	14.09	115.1				
1998 HG49	No launch window											
2001 BB16	2.14	50.2	9.65	115.1	11.83	50.9	18.26	115.1				
2003 SM84	1.58	50.3	8.57	115.2	13.54	50.0	20.52	115.0				
2000 AE205	No launch window											
2001 QJ142	0.00	70.1	4.13	49.7	4.82	114.1	9.84	115.0	20.50	50.1	24.00	70.4
2009 OS5	0.46	50.3	7.73	115.2	11.11	50.1	17.81	115.1				
1993 BX3	1.37	50.4	8.35	115.2	13.32	50.3	20.30	115.2				
2000 EA14	No launch window											
2001 US16	1.82	50.1	9.02	115.1	12.86	50.4	19.63	115.1				
2002 NV16	5.11	50.2	13.03	49.2	13.20	112.4	18.91	115.0				
2006 KL21	1.01	50.1	7.99	115.1	12.98	50.1	19.97	115.1				
2006 SU49	0.00	93.5	1.73	115.4	3.82	50.4	10.25	115.1	18.12	50.2	24.00	94.0
2008 DG5	No launch window											

Table 6. Trajectory Plane Inclination Angles at window Open and Close.

Trajectory Plane Inclinations	Window 1 Open:			Window 1 Close:		Window 2 Open:			Window 2 Close:		Window 3 Open:			Window 3 Close:	
	Epoch (+Hrs)	i (deg)	i min (deg)	Epoch (+Hrs)	i (deg)	Epoch (+Hrs)	i (deg)	i min (deg)	Epoch (+Hrs)	i (deg)	Epoch (+Hrs)	i (deg)	i min (deg)	Epoch (+Hrs)	i (deg)
1999 JU3	No launch window														
1999 RQ36	0.84	47.4	28.3	7.82	37.2	12.79	47.5	28.3	19.78	37.1					
2001 FC7	1.20	47.5	28.3	8.57	37.2	11.52	47.6	28.3	18.14	37.2					
2002 CD	No launch window														
2008 EV5	No launch window														
1999 AO10	0.72	47.5	30.5	8.35	49.9	8.95	36.4	30.5	14.09	37.1					
1998 HG49	No launch window														
2001 BB16	2.14	47.4	28.3	9.65	37.1	11.83	46.9	28.3	18.26	37.1					
2003 SM84	1.58	47.3	28.3	8.57	37.2	13.54	47.6	28.3	20.52	37.1					
2000 AE205	No launch window														
2001 QJ142	0.00	34.1	30.8	4.13	47.8	4.82	36.5	30.8	9.84	37.1	20.50	47.5	34.0	24.00	34.0
2009 OS5	0.46	47.4	28.3	7.73	37.2	11.11	47.5	28.3	17.81	37.1					
1993 BX3	1.37	47.3	28.3	8.35	37.2	13.32	47.3	28.3	20.30	37.2					
2000 EA14	No launch window														
2001 US16	1.82	47.5	28.3	9.02	37.1	12.86	47.3	28.3	19.63	37.1					
2002 NV16	5.11	47.5	28.9	13.03	48.2	13.20	35.5	28.9	18.91	37.1					
2006 KL21	1.01	47.5	28.3	7.99	37.1	12.98	47.5	28.3	19.97	37.1					
2006 SU49	0.00	28.5	28.5	1.73	37.3	3.82	47.3	28.3	10.25	37.1	18.12	47.4	28.3	24.00	28.6
2008 DG5	No launch window														

Table 7. Range Angles at window Open and Close.

Range Angles	Window 1 Open:		Window 1 Close:		Window 2 Open:		Window 2 Close:		Window 3 Open:		Window 3 Close:	
	Epoch (+Hrs)	θ (deg)	Epoch (+Hrs)	θ (deg)	Epoch (+Hrs)	θ (deg)	Epoch (+Hrs)	θ (deg)	Epoch (+Hrs)	θ (deg)	Epoch (+Hrs)	θ (deg)
1999 JU3	No launch window											
1999 RQ36	0.84	319.8	7.82	231.6	12.79	140.0	19.78	51.8				
2001 FC7	1.20	302.0	8.57	209.5	11.52	158.0	18.14	73.8				
2002 CD	No launch window											
2008 EV5	No launch window											
1999 AO10	0.72	276.4	8.35	183.3	8.95	174.1	14.09	109.1				
1998 HG49	No launch window											
2001 BB16	2.14	115.3	9.65	21.2	11.83	344.3	18.26	262.3				
2003 SM84	1.58	319.9	8.57	231.7	13.54	140.0	20.52	51.8				
2000 AE205	No launch window											
2001 QJ142	0.00	56.3	4.13	3.9	4.82	353.4	9.84	290.0	20.50	96.0	24.00	55.4
2009 OS5	0.46	305.6	7.73	214.1	11.11	154.3	17.81	69.3				
1993 BX3	1.37	319.7	8.35	231.5	13.32	140.0	20.30	51.8				
2000 EA14	No launch window											
2001 US16	1.82	129.6	9.02	39.0	12.86	330.3	19.63	244.5				
2002 NV16	5.11	278.9	13.03	180.9	13.20	178.4	18.91	105.1				
2006 KL21	1.01	320.1	7.99	231.9	12.98	139.9	19.97	51.7				
2006 SU49	0.00	222.6	1.73	200.3	3.82	165.0	10.25	83.0	18.12	294.8	24.00	221.7
2008 DG5	No launch window											

Table 8. Right Ascension of Ascending Nodes at window Open and Close.

Right Ascension of the Ascending Nodes	Window 1 Open:		Window 1 Close:		Window 2 Open:		Window 2 Close:		Window 3 Open:		Window 3 Close:	
	Epoch (+Hrs)	Ω (deg)	Epoch (+Hrs)	Ω (deg)	Epoch (+Hrs)	Ω (deg)	Epoch (+Hrs)	Ω (deg)	Epoch (+Hrs)	Ω (deg)	Epoch (+Hrs)	Ω (deg)
1999 JU3	No launch window											
1999 RQ36	0.84	15.6	7.82	15.7	12.79	195.6	19.78	195.6				
2001 FC7	1.20	77.0	8.57	82.5	11.52	232.3	18.14	226.7				
2002 CD	No launch window											
2008 EV5	No launch window											
1999 AO10	0.72	98.5	8.35	216.0	8.95	118.9	14.09	194.6				
1998 HG49	No launch window											
2001 BB16	2.14	236.4	9.65	244.4	11.83	21.7	18.26	14.0				
2003 SM84	1.58	167.7	8.57	167.7	13.54	347.8	20.52	347.8				
2000 AE205	No launch window											
2001 QJ142	0.00	3.0	4.13	88.6	4.82	355.0	9.84	69.2	20.50	334.4	24.00	3.6
2009 OS5	0.46	90.9	7.73	95.2	11.11	251.3	17.81	246.9				
1993 BX3	1.37	80.7	8.35	80.7	13.32	260.5	20.30	260.5				
2000 EA14	No launch window											
2001 US16	1.82	293.8	9.02	297.0	12.86	99.6	19.63	96.5				
2002 NV16	5.11	35.7	13.03	155.7	13.20	56.0	18.91	138.3				
2006 KL21	1.01	43.4	7.99	43.4	12.98	223.5	19.97	223.5				
2006 SU49	0.00	185.6	1.73	173.9	3.82	310.5	10.25	302.4	18.12	165.8	24.00	185.5
2008 DG5	No launch window											

Table 9. RAAN of the Launch Trajectory at window Open and Close.

Right Ascension of the Ascending Nodes of the Launch Trajectory											
	Window 1 Open:		Window 1 Close:		Window 2 Open:		Window 2 Close:		Window 3 Open:		Window 3 Close:
	Epoch$_L$ (+Hrs)	Ω_L (deg)	Epoch$_L$ (+Hrs)	Ω_L (deg)	Epoch$_L$ (+Hrs)	Ω_L (deg)	Epoch$_L$ (+Hrs)	Ω_L (deg)	Epoch$_L$ (+Hrs)	Ω_L (deg)	Epoch$_L$ (+Hrs)	Ω_L (deg)
1999 JU3	No launch window										
1999 RQ36	0.84	15.6	7.82	15.7	12.79	195.6	19.78	195.6				
2001 FC7	1.20	77.0	8.57	82.5	11.52	232.3	18.14	226.7				
2002 CD	No launch window										
2008 EV5	No launch window										
1999 AO10	0.72	98.5	8.35	216.0	8.95	118.9	14.09	194.6				
1998 HG49	No launch window										
2001 BB16	2.14	236.4	9.65	244.4	11.83	21.7	18.26	14.0				
2003 SM84	1.58	167.7	8.57	167.7	13.54	347.8	20.52	347.8				
2000 AE205	No launch window										
2001 QJ142	0.00	88.6	4.13	88.6	4.82	355.0	9.84	69.2	20.50	334.4	24.00	3.0
2009 OS5	0.46	90.9	7.73	95.2	11.11	251.3	17.81	246.9				
1993 BX3	1.37	80.7	8.35	80.7	13.32	260.5	20.30	260.5				
2000 EA14	No launch window										
2001 US16	1.82	293.8	9.02	297.0	12.86	99.6	19.63	96.5				
2002 NV16	5.11	35.7	13.03	155.7	13.20	56.0	18.91	138.3				
2006 KL21	1.01	43.4	7.99	43.4	12.98	223.5	19.97	223.5				
2006 SU49	0.00	185.6	1.73	173.9	3.82	310.5	10.25	302.4	18.12	165.8	24.00	185.6
2008 DG5	No launch window										

Table 10. Argument of Perigee at window Open and Close.

Arguments of Perigee											
	Window 1 Open:		Window 1 Close:		Window 2 Open:		Window 2 Close:		Window 3 Open:		Window 3 Close:
	Epoch$_L$ (+Hrs)	ω (deg)	Epoch$_L$ (+Hrs)	ω (deg)	Epoch$_L$ (+Hrs)	ω (deg)	Epoch$_L$ (+Hrs)	ω (deg)	Epoch$_L$ (+Hrs)	ω (deg)	Epoch$_L$ (+Hrs)	ω (deg)
1999 JU3	No launch window										
1999 RQ36	0.84	213.1	7.82	213.1	12.79	5.7	19.78	326.8				
2001 FC7	1.20	184.1	8.57	180.1	11.52	5.6	18.14	315.8				
2002 CD	No launch window										
2008 EV5	No launch window										
1999 AO10	0.72	205.0	8.35	299.8	8.95	3.8	14.09	284.0				
1998 HG49	No launch window										
2001 BB16	2.14	357.5	9.65	351.6	11.83	4.0	18.26	232.7				
2003 SM84	1.58	146.9	8.57	146.9	13.54	0.6	20.52	33.0				
2000 AE205	No launch window										
2001 QJ142	0.00	306.9	4.13	123.4	4.82	0.8	9.84	108.9	20.50	31.1	24.00	53.6
2009 OS5	0.46	180.6	7.73	183.9	11.11	0.5	17.81	31.3				
1993 BX3	1.37	147.3	8.35	147.4	13.32	0.6	20.30	33.0				
2000 EA14	No launch window										
2001 US16	1.82	15.6	9.02	13.2	12.86	2.5	19.63	141.2				
2002 NV16	5.11	197.9	13.03	296.4	13.20	3.7	18.91	283.6				
2006 KL21	1.01	213.5	7.99	213.5	12.98	5.7	19.97	326.6				
2006 SU49	0.00	168.1	1.73	178.1	3.82	0.9	10.25	60.4	18.12	176.0	24.00	168.2
2008 DG5	No launch window										

Specific Examples of Launch Window Analyses

We now provide two illustrative examples of launch window analyses results. The first set of figures show examples of analyses results for RQ36, where viable launch windows were identified. The second set of figures show examples of analyses results for JU3 where viable launch windows cannot be found for the given launch epoch. Figures 2-6 detail analyses plots for asteroid 1999 RQ36, and Figures 7-11 detail analyses plots for asteroid 1999 JU3. The figures included represent the following parameters:

- Right Ascension of the Launch Site,
- Launch Azimuth Angle,
- Inclination (Flyout plane),
- Range Angle,
- Right Ascension of the Ascending Node (RAAN) (Flyout plane),.

For the asteroid RQ36, Table 2 provides the critical analyses data: DLA = -0.03 deg, RLA = 15.6 deg, C3 = 28.8 km^2/sec^2, Epoch = 2457304.766 days.

Figure 2: Shows the evolution of the Right Ascension of the Launch Site angle between the node of the launch site meridian and the J2000 reference direction. The transition of the angle back to zero, which is clearly visible at the asymptote, occurs at the crossing of the J2000 reference direction.

586

Figure 3: Shows the variation of the launch Azimuth angle with time, starting from the launch Epoch. The launch azimuth range safety limits are shown on the figure. The figure illustrates that asteroid RQ36 has two launch windows. The first window opens at launch Epoch + 0.84 hours and lasts for approximately 7 hours. The second window opens at launch Epoch +11.5 hours and lasts for approximately 6.6 hours. The green bars along the launch Epoch axis highlight these windows. The further observation can be made that, with the absolute value of the DLA less than the launch site latitude of 28.3 deg, the minimum flyout plane inclination expected for this mission is 28.3.

Figure 4: Shows the Inclination angle of the flyout plane, where it is clearly illustrated that the DLA is less than the launch site latitude of 28.3 deg, the minimum fly out plane inclination being 28.3 deg.

Figure 5: Shows the time variation of the launch site Range Angle where it is noted that transitions in the value of the range angle occur when the launch meridian crosses the asymptote meridian at both 0 and 180 degrees.

Figure 6: Shows that the value of the RAAN of the trajectory plane remains relatively constant between meridian crossings due to the low DLA of -0,02 deg.

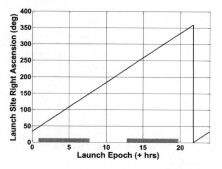

Figure 2. Right Ascension of Launch Site

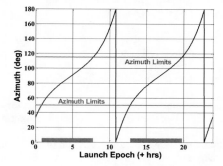

Figure 3. Launch Azimuth

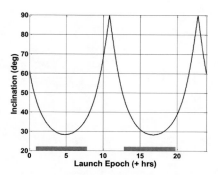

Figure 4 Flyout Plane Inclination

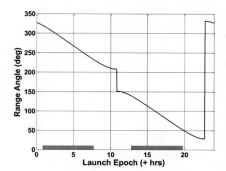

Figure 5. Flyout Range Angle

587

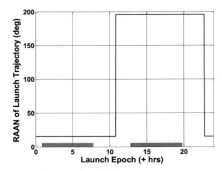

Figure 6. RAAN of Flyout Trajectory.

For the asteroid JU3, Table 2 provides the critical analyses data of: DLA = -48.1 deg, RLA = 118.9 deg, C3 = 19 km^2/sec^2, Epoch = 2459189.235 days.

Figure7: Shows the evolution of the Right Ascension of the Launch Site angle with the same characteristic transition back to zero at the crossing with the J2000 reference direction.

Figure8: Shows that no launch window was found for this asteroid given that the achievable launch azimuths did not fall within the 50-115 degree range safety limits. An observation can be made immediately that with the DLA greater than the launch site latitude of 28.3 deg, the minimum flyout plane inclination expected for this mission is 48.1

Figure 9: Shows the inclination of the trajectory plane. For JU3, the DLA is greater than the launch site latitude of 28.3 deg therefore, the expected minimum fly out plane inclination is 48.1 deg

Figure 10: Shows the time variation of the launch site Range Angle with the expected transitions at the launch meridian and the asymptote meridian crossings.

Figure 11: Shows that the variation of the RAAN of the trajectory plane, where in this case the DLA is -48.1 deg.

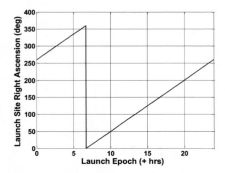

Figure 7. Right Ascension of the Launch Site

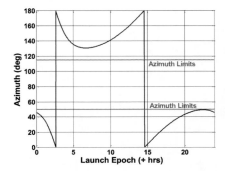

Figure 8. Launch Azimuth Angle

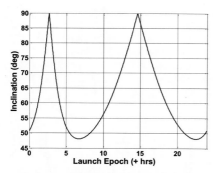

Figure 9. Launch Plane Inclination Angle.

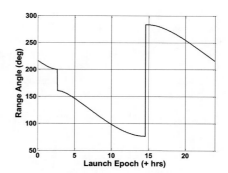

Figure 10. Range Angle.

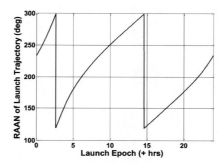

Figure 11. RAAN of Flyout Trajectory.

LAUNCH VEHICLE PAYLOAD ANALYSES

Figures 12 and 13 show the of payload mass delivery capability for the set of optimized missions, with and without an available launch window for the Direct and Gravity Assisted missions, respectively. The information provided from the plots allows a comparison between suitable launch vehicles available for Discovery class missions for further mission analysis and systems engineering.

Utilizing the data from the various launch vehicle manuals available for Discovery class missions, the plots illustrate each mission C3 against the published payload capabilities for SpaceX Falcon 9, Lockheed Martin Atlas V 401 and Athena II[3] and the Boeing Delta II 7925[4]. The SpaceX Falcon 9, is a newer launcher which provides payload capability between that of the Delta II and Atlas V. Falcon 9 launch capability from Kourou is currently under consideration and will be included in a further analysis once launch data becomes available. Such capability is expected to considerably enhance the launch vehicle payload capabilities and margins for these missions.

The Delta II LV has been phased-out of operations and no further Delta II will be manufactured but its profile provides a well-documented benchmark for NASA missions. The Athena II is a lighter launcher with noticeably lower payload capabilities, but may be a cost effective solution for unique low-mass missions.

The 1107.25 kg launch mass of the MESSENGER[5] spacecraft is shown for reference as the dashed horizontal line in the figures. The MESSENGER spacecraft was chosen as a benchmark in this study as it reflects the approximate mass properties of a Discovery class spacecraft capable of an interplanetary mission and is used for assessing potential mission margins for enhancing capability and performance.

From the set of asteroids shown in figure 12, for example, for a due-east launch from Kennedy, the payload mass capability with the Atlas V 401 ranges from 1930 kg for 2006 SU49 to 2830 kg for 2001 QJ142 for the direct mission. The Falcon 9 payload mass capability for the same missions range from 1325 to 2260 kg, while for the Athena II launch vehicle, payload, the payload mass capability range is 290 kg to 320 kg. Asteroids 2001 FC7, 1999 AO10, 2001 BB16, 2001 QJ142, 2009 OS5, 2002 NV16, 2006 SU49 and 2001 US16 have launch windows for Direct asteroid mission trajectory, with QJ142 and SU49 having windows which are open over at least three periods during the 24 hours launch epoch window.

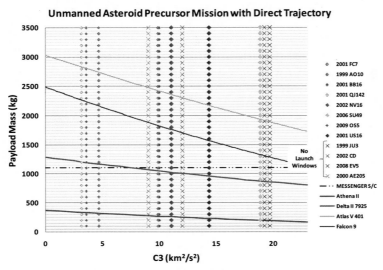

Figure 12. LV Payload Mass vs. C3 for Direct Trajectory Missions.

From asteroid 1999 RQ36 in Figure 13 for a due-east launch from Kennedy, the payload mass capability with the Atlas V 401 is about 1560-1620 kg for the Gravity Assist mission while in the case of the Falcon 9, the payload mass capability is approximately 960-1010 kg. For the Athena II launch vehicle, the payload mass capability is just 150 kg. The same general payload capability appears to apply to the other Gravity Assist type missions.

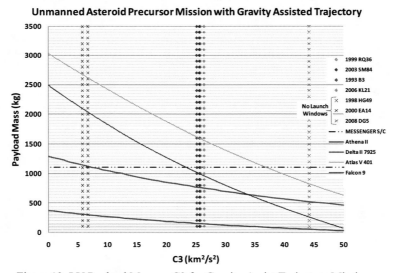

Figure 13. LV Payload Mass vs C3 for Gravity Assist Trajectory Missions.

590

Table 11 shows the potential spacecraft payload margin for each of the asteroids on the two launch vehicles currently approved for Discovery missions. The Athena launch vehicle is not shown in the table because it does not provide margin for any of the missions.

Table 11. Potential Launch Vehicle Payload Margins.

		Atlas V		Falcon 9	
	Asteroid	Payload Capability	Spacecraft Payload Margin*	Payload Capability	Spacecraft Payload Margin*
Direct	QJ142	2830	1723	2260	1153
	OS5	2810	1703	2240	1133
	AO10	2740	1633	2170	1063
	FC7	2430	1323	1830	723
	BB16	2420	1313	1820	713
	NV16	2360	1253	1760	653
	US16	2180	1073	1570	463
	SU49	1930	823	1325	218
Gravity Assist	B3	1620	513	1010	No Margin
	SM84	1600	493	1000	No Margin
	RQ36	1590	483	990	No Margin
	KL21	1560	453	960	No Margin

* The Spacecraft payload margin considers the Messenger
Spacecraft payload of 1107 kg as the baseline

SUMMARY

For the set of 19 best-case optimized asteroids missions, a launch trajectory study was conducted for launch out of CCAS subject to the required range safety limits imposed on the launch azimuth (50-115 degrees) for launch missions required to achieving the Earth departure V∞ vector. From the resulting analyses, the following observations have been drawn:

1. In satisfaction of the range safety requirements for launching out of the Cape, Asteroids 1999 JU3, 2002 CD, 2008 EV5, 1998 HG49, 2000 AE205, 2000 EA14 and 2008 DG5 were found to have no launch windows which could be identified during the 24 hour period following the optimal Launch Epoch.

2. Asteroids QJ142 and SU49 have windows which are open over at least three periods during the 24 hours launch epoch window. The remaining asteroids have two launch windows which are generally open twice on the day of the launch epoch for approximately 5-7 hours each.

3. While the published launch vehicle payload capability refers to capability for launch azimuths due-east from Kennedy, the payload capability for the missions for which launch windows have been identified show that the Atlas V provides payload margin for all of the direct and gravity assisted missions, while the Falcon 9 provides payload margin only for the direct missions and no margin for the gravity assisted missions.

4. The cases with no Launch Windows, namely 1999 JU3, 2002 CD, 2008 EV5, 1998 HG49, 2000 AE205, 2000 EA14 and 2008 DG5, require re-runs of the mission analyses in order to find a lower DLR including consideration of lunar gravity assist to obtain optimal DLA.

591

APPENDIX A: LAUNCH ANALYSES AND INJECTION GEOMETRY ALGORITHM

The asymptote direction is represented by a unit vector $\bar{S}$ in the J2000 X-Y-Z Cartesian frame where X points in the J2000 reference direction, Z points along the J2000 earth spin vector and Y completes the triad and where i-j-k corresponds to the unit vectors in the direction of the $\bar{S}$ components.

Launch Asymptote Unit Vector:

For the purposed of these analyses, the outgoing launch asymptote unit vector was taken as

$$\bar{S} = i\, S_x + j\, S_y + k\, S_z$$

or

$$\bar{S} = i\, \cos\alpha_\infty\, \cos\delta_\infty + j\, \sin\alpha_\infty\, \cos\delta_\infty + k\, \sin\delta_\infty \tag{1}$$

with α_∞ being the right ascension (RLA) and δ_∞ the declination (DLA) of the launch asymptote.

Vinfinity Vector:

The V_∞ vector and its vector components were derived from the Earth Departure Energy, C3, as

$$V_\infty = \sqrt{C3} \tag{2}$$
$$\mathbf{V}_{\infty,xyz} = V_\infty * \bar{S}$$

Launch Azimuth Angle:

The Launch Azimuth angles determined for this study depend mainly on the Geocentric Latitude of the Launch Site (ϕ_L) and the Right Ascension (related to the Sidereal Time) of the Launch Site (α_L). The Right Ascension of the Launch Site was determined from the Greenwich Mean Sidereal Time (GMST), measured starting at Launch Epoch (JDUT1). From this it is possible to determine the Right Ascension of the Launch Site and the Launch Azimuth. The following relationships are used

$$GMST = 280.461+360.986*days+ 0.000388*TimeUT1^2 - TimeUT1^3/38710000$$

with

$$TimeUT1 = (JDUT1 - 2451545.0)/36525.0$$

where the ΔT in JDUT1 was selected as .001 sec.

$$\alpha_L = GMST + \lambda_L \tag{3}$$

λ_L is the Geographic East Longitude of the Launch Site

and the Launch Azimuth angle (Σ_L) is derived from

$$\cot\Sigma_L = \cos\phi_L * \tan\delta_\infty - \sin\phi_L * \cos(\alpha_\infty - \alpha_L) / \sin(\alpha_\infty - \alpha_L) \tag{4}$$

Launch and Fly Out Trajectory Elements:

Inclination Angle:

The Launch Azimuth angle allows the determination of the Inclination angle (i) as well as the Range Angle (θ) of the launch trajectory from the following relationships

$$\cos i = \cos \phi_L * \sin \Sigma_L \tag{5}$$

Range Angle:

$$\cos \theta = \sin \delta_\infty * \sin \phi_L + \cos \delta_\infty * \cos \phi_L * \cos (\alpha_\infty - \alpha_L)$$

$$\sin \theta = \sin (\alpha_\infty - \alpha_L) * \cos \delta_\infty / \sin \Sigma_L \tag{6}$$

Launch Site Radius Unit Vector:

With the launch geometry properties established, the launch fly out trajectory is determined by recognizing that the trajectory plane contains both the Outgoing Launch Asymptote unit vector ($\bar{\mathbf{S}}$), and the Launch Site Radius unit vector ($\bar{\mathbf{R}}_L$) which depends on the Right Ascension of the Launch Site.

$$\bar{\mathbf{R}}_L = (\cos \phi_L * \cos \alpha_L, \cos \phi_L * \sin \alpha_L, \sin \phi_L) \tag{7}$$

The orientation of the launch and fly out trajectory plane in the X-Y-Z system can then be determined from the unit vector perpendicular to the plane or the unit Angular Momentum vector.

Angular Momentum Vector:

$$\bar{\mathbf{h}}_0 = \bar{\mathbf{S}} \times \bar{\mathbf{R}}_L \tag{8}$$

where

$$h_z = \cos i$$

$$h_y = \frac{hz * Sy * Sz \pm Sx * \sqrt{1 - Sz^2 - hz^2}}{Sx^2 - Sy^2}$$

$$h_x = - \frac{hy * Sy + hz * Sz}{Sx}$$

As shown above, the components of the $\bar{\mathbf{h}}_0$ vector, h_x, h_y and h_z, are resolved in terms of the components of the vector $\bar{\mathbf{S}}$ and the launch and fly out trajectory inclination angle i. The result is two angular momentum vectors and two possible planes, one retro-grade and the other pro-grade. From the unit angular momentum vector, the Right Ascension of Ascending Node of the Launch Trajectory is determined by

$$\mathbf{n} = [0,0,1] \times \bar{\mathbf{h}}_0 = (- h_y, h_x, 0)$$

$$\Omega_L = \arctan \left(- \frac{hx}{hy} \right) \tag{9}$$

with [0,0,1] being the vector in the direction of the Earth's rotation axis.

Right Ascension of Ascending Node:

$$\Omega = \arccos \frac{nx}{|\mathbf{n}|} \quad (n_y \geq 0) \qquad (10)$$

$$\Omega = 2\pi - \arccos \frac{nx}{|\mathbf{n}|} \quad (n_y \leq 0) \qquad (11)$$

Eccentricity of the Hyperbolic Orbit:

with Periapsis Radius (r_P) 6578.3 km,

$$e_H = \text{sqrt}(1 + r_P * V_\infty^2 / \mu_E) \qquad (12)$$

True Anomaly of the Launch Asymptote:

$$\nu_\theta = \arccos(-1 / e_H) \qquad (13)$$

Semi-Major Axis:

$$a = -\mu_E / 0.5 * V_\infty^2 \qquad (14)$$

For both the direct or indirect launch and fly out trajectory, the Periapsis vector determines the injection point on the fly out hyperbola. In general, a phasing parking orbit would be required to optimally reach this injection point; this parking orbit is not included our analyses.

Periapsis Vector and Radius:

$$\mathbf{V_P} = \bar{\mathbf{s}} \times \bar{\mathbf{h}}_0 \qquad (15)$$

$$\mathbf{r_P} = r_P * (\cos \nu_\infty * \bar{\mathbf{s}} + \sin \nu_\infty * \mathbf{V_P}) \qquad (16)$$

Argument of Periapsis:

$$\omega = \arccos(\bar{\mathbf{r}}_P \cdot \mathbf{n}) \qquad (17)$$

REFERENCES

[1] A Survey of Potential Human-Precursor Robotic Asteroid Missions - Michael L. Cupples, Roberto Furfaro, Carl W. Hergenrother, Daniel R. Wibben, John N. Kidd Jr., *2011 Astrodynamics Specialist Conference (AAS 11-441)*.

[2] Cupples, M.L., Furfaro, R., Hergenrother, C.W., Adebonojo, B.O., Wibben, D.R., Kidd, J.N., "A Mission Analysis Survey of Potential Human-Precursor Robotic Missions", *Proceedings of AAS/AIAA Space Flight Mechanics Meeting, (AAS 11-100), 2011*.

[3] NASA Launch Services Program, Flight Dynamics Branch of the NASA Launch Services Program at Kennedy Space Center, Launch Vehicle Performance Website <http://elvperf.ksc.nasa.gov/elvMap/>.

[4] "Delta II Payload Planners Guide", ULA: United Launch Alliance, 2006, pp 2.15-2.16.

[5] http://discovery.nasa.gov/messenger.html

[6] "Interplanetary Mission Design Handbook", Volume 1, Part 2 - Andrey B. Sergeyevsky, Gerald C. Snyder, Ross A. Cunniff, JPL Publication 82-43.

[7] "Design of Lunar and Interplanetary Ascent Trajectories", Vincent C. Clark, Technical Report No. 32-30, Revision # 1

[8] "A Computer Simulation of Orbital Launch Window Problem", Archie C. Young and Pat R. Odom, NASA Marshall Space Flight Center, AIAA Paper No. 67-615

[9] Launch Safety Assessment, 45th Space Wing/Patrick Air Force Base, March 1999, RTI/6462/219-01F

METHODOLOGY AND RESULTS OF
THE NEAR-EARTH OBJECT (NEO) HUMAN SPACE FLIGHT
(HSF) ACCESSIBLE TARGETS STUDY (NHATS)

Brent W. Barbee,[*] **Ronald G. Mink,**[†]
Daniel R. Adamo[‡] **and Cassandra M. Alberding**[§]

Near-Earth Asteroids (NEAs) have been identified by the Administration as potential destinations for human explorers during the mid-2020s. Planning such ambitious missions requires selecting potentially accessible targets from the growing known population of 8,008 NEAs. NASA is therefore conducting the Near-Earth Object (NEO) Human Space Flight (HSF) Accessible Targets Study (NHATS), in which the trajectory opportunities to all known NEAs are being systematically evaluated with respect to a set of defined constraints. While the NHATS algorithms have identified hundreds of NEAs which satisfy purposely inclusive trajectory constraints, only a handful of them offer truly attractive mission opportunities in the time frame of greatest interest. In this paper we will describe the structure of the NHATS algorithms and the constraints utilized in the study, present current study results, and discuss various mission design considerations for future human space flight missions to NEAs.

INTRODUCTION

Near-Earth objects (NEOs) are asteroids and comets with perihelion distance < 1.3 AU, permitting many of them to closely approach or cross Earth's orbit. The vast majority of NEOs are asteroids, classified as near-Earth asteroids (NEAs). These objects are largely unchanged since the early days of our solar system and may have even deposited the seeds of life on the young Earth; studying them therefore provides vital scientific knowledge about the formation and evolution of both the solar system and our own planet. However, there is evidence of many past impacts on Earth by these objects, some of which were sufficiently energetic to destroy life on a planetary scale. These objects therefore bear careful monitoring for the possibility of future impacts that we would hopefully be able to prevent. The close proximity of some of these objects' orbits to Earth's orbit and the fact that some of them contain usable resources, such as water, raises the possibility of sending human explorers to visit them. While that is the primary focus of this paper, it is important to recognize that the study and exploration of NEAs is simultaneously motivated by fundamental science, planetary defense against impacts, and human space exploration.

NEAs have been identified by the current presidential administration as potential destinations for human explorers during the mid-2020s. While the close proximity of these objects' orbits to Earth's orbit creates the aforementioned risk of highly damaging or catastrophic impacts, it also makes some of these objects potentially accessible to spacecraft departing from and returning to Earth; this presents unique opportunities for solar system science and humanity's first ventures beyond cislunar space.

The planning and execution of such ambitious missions presents formidable technical, programmatic, and political challenges. The first challenge, which is of a technical nature, is to develop and implement a process capable of identifying potentially accessible targets from within the large and growing known population of

---

[*] Aerospace Engineer, NASA GSFC, Code 595, 8800 Greenbelt Road, Greenbelt, MD 20771, USA. Member AIAA.
[†] Mission Systems Engineer, NASA GSFC, Code 592, 8800 Greenbelt Road, Greenbelt, MD 20771, USA.
[‡] Astrodynamics Consultant, 4203 Moonlight Shadow Ct., Houston, TX 77059, USA. Senior Member AIAA.
[§] Aerospace Engineer, NASA GSFC, Code 595, 8800 Greenbelt Road, Greenbelt, MD 20771, USA.

8,038 NEAs*. To accomplish this, NASA is conducting the Near-Earth Object (NEO) Human Space Flight (HSF) Accessible Targets Study (NHATS). Phase I of the NHATS was executed during September of 2010, and Phase II was completed by early March of 2011. Both phases of the study considered only NEAs; near-Earth comets (NECs) were not included because their orbits are typically more difficult to reach due to their very high eccentricities and long periods, and because their active nature could create a hazardous environment for a human crew. The NHATS is ongoing because previously undetected NEAs are being discovered constantly and the ephemerides of known NEOs are updated when new observations are incorporated into the orbit determination process. These factors have motivated an effort to automate the analysis process in order to provide continuous monitoring of NEA accessibility.

The NHATS analysis process consists of a trajectory filter and a minimum estimated size criterion. The trajectory filter employs the method of embedded trajectory grids[1] to compute all possible ballistic round-trip mission trajectories to every NEA in the Jet Propulsion Laboratory (JPL) Small-Body Database (SBDB); all round-trip trajectory solutions that satisfy the trajectory filter criteria are stored. An NEA must offer at least one qualifying trajectory solution to pass the trajectory filter, and it's estimated size must be greater than or equal to the minimum estimated size criterion. The trajectory filter criteria are purposely inclusive, and the estimated size criteria is based on a notional lower limit for NEA albedo, making it an optimistic estimated size and therefore also inclusive. The inclusive nature of the NHATS constraints on trajectory performance and object size is motivated by the desire to obtain a sufficiently comprehensive view of the NEA accessibility landscape before down-selecting candidate targets. This comprehensive view provides useful context and helps to inform current research efforts towards a dynamical theory of round-trip accessibility for NEAs.

While the NHATS has identified hundreds of NEAs which pass the purposely inclusive trajectory filter and meet minimum estimated size constraints which are arguably rather small (30 - 50 m), only a few of these offer potentially attractive mission opportunities during the time frame of greatest interest (mid-2020s to mid-2030s). However, it must be stressed that NASA considers the NHATS results to be pre-decisional as potentially accessible trajectory solutions are only one factor of many in the design and consideration of a future human space flight program. Moreover, the actual NEA population ≥ 30 m is likely to consist of at least several tens of thousands of members, and quite possibly more (hundreds of thousands or even millions), of which we have discovered $< 9,000$. This has led the technical community concerned with NEOs to recommend the deployment of a space-based NEO survey telescope which would avoid the geometrical constraints associated with observing solely from Earth and thus provide a very comprehensive NEO population survey within only a few years of deployment.[2] Such a survey would simultaneously benefit the scientific, HSF, and planetary defense communities.

In this paper we will describe and discuss the workings of the NHATS algorithms, the assumptions built into their operation, and the constraints selected for the study. We will then present the results of the NHATS to date and discuss the trends and features of the data. The ongoing and future work for the project will also be discussed.

MISSION PHASES

Certain fundamental assumptions about mission design had to be made in order to perform round-trip trajectory calculations over billions of combinations of Earth departure dates and trajectory segment flight times for thousands of NEAs. Assumptions were limited to only those which are necessary for Δv calculations; no assumptions were made regarding specific mission architecture elements such as the types of propulsion systems used, the masses of vehicle elements, or the performance capabilities of launch vehicles. In the future it may be possible to define a realistic reference architecture that would permit the computation of Initial Mass in Low Earth Orbit (IMLEO) and the attendant number of required launches, but the forward path for Human Space Flight (HSF) architecture is currently too uncertain to make such a calculation meaningful.

Nevertheless, the basic segments of a HSF mission to a NEO are reasonably well defined. As shown in Figure 1, the spacecraft will depart Earth by performing some Earth departure maneuver which places the

---

*This population number is current as of 07/19/2011. Population statistics are continually updated at http://neo.jpl.nasa.gov/stats/

spacecraft onto a heliocentric trajectory that intercepts the NEO some time later. Upon intercepting the NEO, the spacecraft will then perform a velocity change maneuver to match the NEO's heliocentric velocity. After remaining in the vicinity of the NEO for some period of time, the spacecraft will change its velocity so as to place it onto a heliocentric orbit that will intercept the Earth some time later. Upon arrival at Earth, the spacecraft may have to perform a final maneuver to reduce its velocity with respect to the Earth.

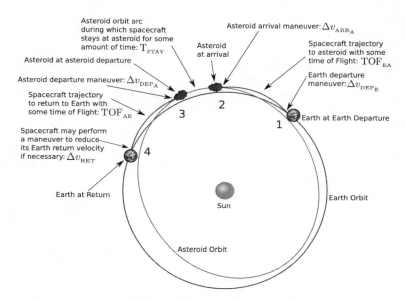

Figure 1. Profile of an HSF Mission to a NEO

The NEO arrival and departure maneuvers are quite straightforward, but certain assumptions were required to compute Earth departure and Earth return maneuvers. These assumptions and their rationale are discussed in the sections that follow.

Earth Departure

The nature of the spacecraft's Earth departure maneuver, which may be referred to as Trans-NEO Injection (TNI), depends on the architecture and concept of operations for the mission. While the design of the spacecraft and the way in which it departs Earth may vary, it is almost certain that the total required spacecraft mass cannot be assembled on Earth's surface and delivered to orbit using only a single launch. Thus the spacecraft will have to be assembled in space and then depart from a particular parking orbit. Assembly could be as simple as launching the crew vehicle and a propulsion stage to a circular Low Earth Orbit (LEO) on one launch vehicle, launching the habitat module with another propulsion stage on a second launch vehicle to the same LEO, and then carrying out a single rendezvous and docking sequence to assemble the complete spacecraft stack. If more than two launches are required then the assembly sequence quickly becomes much more costly and complicated, and the probability of mission success drops accordingly.[2]

Various concepts have been proposed, ranging from the aforementioned assembly in LEO to crew rendezvous with pre-deployed resources at an Earth-Moon Lagrangian point prior to TNI. The NHATS elected to adopt the most straightforward option, which is departure from LEO. We currently have no experience with rendezvous, proximity operations, and docking in any orbit besides LEO*, and we currently have no in-

---

*The only exception to this is rendezvous in a circular Low Lunar Orbit (LLO) during the Apollo missions, but that orbital regime does not differ significantly from LEO for the purposes of spacecraft rendezvous, apart from slower dynamics (orbit rate comparable to that of Geosynchronous orbit).

frastructure in place to support the staging of equipment or propellant in a Lagrangian point orbit. In general, considerable non-existent infrastructure is required to make Earth departure from novel/exotic orbits practical for a NEO mission. By contrast, the only non-existent infrastructure item required to make departure from LEO practical is a heavy lift launch vehicle capable of delivering at least 100 t to LEO per launch. A heavy lift launch capability is important due to the high cost of launch vehicles and the safety/reliability penalty associated with using multiple launches to assemble the spacecraft prior to TNI. In fact, computing the IMLEO for a particular NEO mission opportunity, and from that deriving the required number of launches, provides a good metric for the quality, affordability, and attractiveness of a mission opportunity, where a smaller number of launches is better.

Modeling the TNI maneuver as being performed in LEO provides a conservative Δv calculation since other orbits can require less TNI Δv to achieve the same Earth departure C_3. For instance, the TNI Δv required at perigee on a highly elliptical orbit, such as a Geosynchronous Transfer Orbit (GTO), would be less than that required in LEO, all else being equal. Of course, a launch vehicle's capacity to deliver mass to a GTO is greatly reduced compared to the mass that can be delivered to LEO, so the overall advantage of performing TNI in a high energy orbit is unclear and depends on more than mass and Δv considerations. As an example, the Δv required to achieve a C_3 of 24 km^2/s^2 from a 400 km circular LEO is 4.232 km/s, whereas the Δv is only 1.902 km/s if performed at perigee on a typical GTO. However, to complete the example, the mass to LEO for an Atlas V 551 launch vehicle is approximately 18.8 t, whereas its approximate mass to GTO is only 8.9 t.

Thus, for the purposes of the NHATS, the Earth departure (TNI) maneuver is computed according to

$$\Delta v_{\text{TNI}} = \sqrt{C_3 + \frac{2\mu_{\text{E}}}{r_{\text{EPO}}}} - \sqrt{\frac{\mu_{\text{E}}}{r_{\text{EPO}}}} \tag{1}$$

where C_3 is the characteristic energy required for the particular mission opportunity, μ_{E} is Earth's gravitational parameter (3.986004415×10^5 km^3/s^2), and r_{EPO} is the radius of the circular Earth Parking Orbit (EPO)*. The NHATS assumes a 400 km altitude for the EPO, yielding a value for r_{EPO} of 6778.136 km (with an assumed Earth radius of 6378.136 km).

Another factor that can significantly impact the Earth departure phase of the mission is the asymptotic declination angle associated with the departure hyperbola. The inclination of the EPO should ideally be the same as the asymptotic declination angle, but the latitude of the launch site, along with restrictions on launch azimuth imposed for safety reasons (these vary between launch sites and among launch vehicles), will limit the EPO inclinations achievable from a particular launch site. The general result is that, as the absolute value of the asymptotic declination angle grows to exceed the magnitude of the launch site latitude, the mass that the launch vehicle can deliver to the EPO is reduced. If the asymptotic declination angle requires an EPO inclination that the launch site simply cannot provide due to the combination of launch site latitude and azimuth restrictions, then an achievable inclination for the EPO must be selected and additional Earth departure maneuvers must be performed to make up for the difference between EPO inclination and asymptotic declination angle. Reduced mass delivered to an EPO inclination that is achievable from the launch site chiefly impacts the required number of launches and is therefore not part of the NHATS calculations. The Δv penalty arising from an unachievable EPO inclination is best evaluated on a specific case-by-case basis and is therefore relegated to a post-processing step when necessary as it is beyond the scope of the NHATS analysis.

Earth Return

The NHATS assumes a direct atmospheric re-entry for the crew upon Earth return; that is, the crew vehicle arrives at Earth's Sphere of Influence (SOI) with some hyperbolic excess velocity, v_∞, and proceeds to

---

*Note that for departure from an elliptical orbit, the $\sqrt{\mu_{\text{E}}/r_{\text{EPO}}}$ term in Eq. (1) can simply be replaced with the velocity from the Vis-Viva or 2-body energy integral.

directly re-enter Earth's atmosphere when the incoming hyperbolic trajectory crosses Earth's effective atmospheric entry interface altitude. Thus the key consideration for this mission phase is the magnitude of the spacecraft's inertial velocity with respect to Earth at the effective atmospheric entry interface altitude. This velocity magnitude must be no greater than that which can be tolerated by the spacecraft's heat shield. For NHATS Phase I a maximum entry velocity magnitude of 12.5 km/s is assumed, and this threshold is reduced to 12.0 km/s for the Phase II analysis. For reference, the fastest re-entry velocity experienced by humans was 11.069 km/s during Apollo 10,[3] and in 2006 the fastest un-crewed Earth re-entry was performed by the Stardust Sample Return Capsule* at 12.9 km/s.

The velocity at Earth's entry interface, v_{EI}, depends on the incoming v_∞ and the radius of the entry interface, r_{EI}, according to

$$v_{EI} = \sqrt{v_\infty^2 + \frac{2\mu_E}{r_{EI}}} \qquad (2)$$

where r_{EI} is equal to 6503.136 km (corresponding to an effective atmospheric entry interface altitude of 125 km). If the natural incoming v_∞ of the spacecraft produces a v_{EI} greater than the specified maximum, then the spacecraft must perform a maneuver that reduces v_{EI} to make it equal to the specified maximum. During NHATS Phase I, this maneuver is assumed to occur at the atmospheric entry interface and so is simply equal to the difference between the natural and maximum allowable v_{EI}. After further consideration we determined that it would be operationally infeasible to perform such a critical maneuver shortly before atmospheric entry. A better option is to perform the maneuver much farther from Earth, at Earth's SOI boundary. Thus in Phase II the maximum allowable v_{EI} is converted to the equivalent incoming v_∞ (by solving Eq. (2) for v_∞) and a maneuver at Earth's SOI to control v_∞ is modeled as

$$\Delta v_{RET} = v_\infty - v_{\infty_{max}} \qquad (3)$$

Apart from being more operationally sound, physics dictates that this entry speed control strategy will require more Δv than performing the control maneuver at or near r_{EI} and thus it provides a more conservative value for the required Δv. Application of additional small maneuvers at certain points along the trajectory prior to Earth return can ensure that the spacecraft re-enters at favorable angles and within desirable latitude/longitude windows. That analysis is considered to be a post-processing step for NHATS, and will be applied to specific mission opportunities of interest rather than globally across all possible trajectory solutions.

While the direct entry strategy for Earth return is straightforward and has been successfully demonstrated during the Apollo missions, there are potential drawbacks. For instance, there is no way to salvage the crew's habitat module (e.g., transfer it into a parking orbit for later reuse), unless an additional propulsion module for that purpose is included in the vehicle design. Capturing into any kind of Earth orbit from an incoming hyperbolic trajectory requires substantial Δv and so carrying along the necessary propellant to perform such a maneuver for the habitat module would substantially increase the mission's required IMLEO. Thus an aerocapture for the habitat module (possibly using a ballute to augment the habitat module's ballistic coefficient) would be preferable when possible. However, aerocapture is unlikely to be practical for the crew vehicle, and it would be very difficult to provide the crew vehicle with sufficient propellant to insert itself into some sort of Earth-captured orbit upon return. Nevertheless, the ability to do so would be highly desirable if, for example, the crew vehicle's heat shield was damaged somehow during NEO proximity operations. In that case it would be necessary for the crew to insert into some sort of Earth orbit upon return so that they could be rescued since their heat shield would no longer be capable of withstanding atmospheric re-entry.

Optimal Circular Orbit Capture The goals of reusing the habitat module and providing a rescue option for the crew are certainly worthwhile, but the cost in terms of Δv (and therefore IMLEO) may be prohibitive for most NEO mission scenarios; pre-emplaced propellant at the NEO, or *in situ* resource utilization (ISRU) derived from the NEO, are examples of scenarios which would mitigate the effects on IMLEO. The significance of the Earth return capture cost can be readily understood by examining the Δv required to capture into

---

*http://en.wikipedia.org/wiki/Stardust_(spacecraft)

Earth orbit from an incoming hyperbola. Consider Eq. (1), which specifies the Δv necessary to perform TNI from the EPO. The same equation specifies the Δv necessary to capture into a circular orbit at a particular radius from an incoming hyperbola if we substitute the square of the incoming hyperbolic excess velocity, v_∞^2, for the Earth departure C_3 and substitute the desired capture orbit radius, r_{CAP}, for the departure parking orbit radius (r_{EPO}). The capture Δv is therefore determined by v_∞ and r_{CAP}. For a given v_∞ we can compute the value of r_{CAP} that minimizes the capture Δv by evaluating the derivative of the Δv equation with respect to r_{CAP}, equating the derivative to zero, and solving for the value of r_{CAP} that satisfies the equation.[4] This yields the capture orbit radius which minimizes capture Δv as

$$r_{CAP} = \frac{2\mu_E}{v_\infty^2} \tag{4}$$

If the capture orbit radius given by Eq. (4) is used, then the corresponding minimized capture Δv is

$$\Delta v_{CAP} = \frac{v_\infty}{\sqrt{2}} \tag{5}$$

For the set of minimum total Δv and minimum duration trajectory solutions generated during NHATS Phase II, the minimum *natural* (no control maneuver applied) Earth return v_∞ is 0.528 km/s, the mean is 4.443 km/s ($\sigma = 1.034$ km/s), and the maximum is 8.034 km/s. Most values of v_∞ for NEO missions will therefore lie between 3 and 5 km/s, but for completeness we will allow v_∞ to vary between 0.528 and 8.034 km/s in the brief analysis that follows. Table 1 presents particular optimal circular orbit capture solutions for various values of v_∞, including 4.627 km/s, which corresponds to the NHATS Phase II maximum allowable v_{EI} of 12.0 km/s.

Table 1. Selected Minimum Δv Solutions for Capture Into Circular Earth Orbit

Incoming v_∞, km/s	Optimal Capture Altitude, km	Capture Δv, km/s
0.528	2,853,187	0.373
3.000	82,200	2.121
4.627	30,858	3.272
5.000	25,510	3.536
8.034	5,973	5.681

Figures 2(a) and 2(b) show circular capture orbit altitude and associated minimum capture Δv, respectively, as a function of incoming v_∞. In Figure 2(a) it is clear that the minimum Δv circular capture orbit altitude increases to approximately 1 lunar distance from Earth as v_∞ decreases to approximately 1.4 km/s and quickly becomes much larger for $v_\infty < 1.4$ km/s; for $v_\infty < 0.925$ km/s, the minimum Δv capture orbit altitude actually exceeds Earth's SOI. Capturing into an orbit at greater than lunar distance does not seem practical operationally, and so from that standpoint the *practical* minimum capture Δv for a circular orbit will always be at least 1 km/s.

Furthermore, the incoming v_∞ will generally be greater than 1.4 km/s, most likely in the range of 3 to 5 km/s. Table 1 shows that the optimal capture orbit altitudes for v_∞ of 3 and 5 km/s are 82,200 and 25,510 km, respectively. These are rather large but not necessarily unreasonable. However, the associated capture Δv of 2.121 to 3.536 km/s is significant, considering that total mission Δv for most reasonable NEO mission designs ranges from approximately 4 to 7 km/s. An increase in Δv of 2 to 3.5 km/s to facilitate circular orbit capture at Earth return would dramatically increase the required IMLEO.

Elliptical Orbit Capture One possibility for reducing the necessary capture Δv is to capture into an elliptical orbit. This is an intuitive result considering that the spacecraft begins on a hyperbola with respect to Earth (escaped) and minimizing capture Δv therefore means reducing the spacecraft's energy only as much as necessary for an effective capture. Repeating the foregoing analysis with an elliptical capture orbit will show that there is no true minimum capture Δv associated with a given incoming v_∞, but that capture Δv

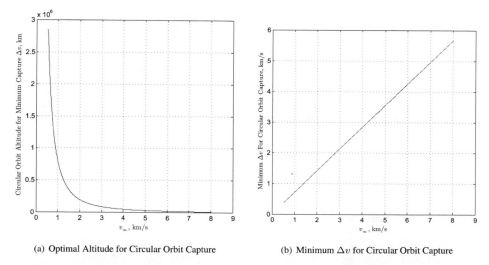

(a) Optimal Altitude for Circular Orbit Capture

(b) Minimum Δv for Circular Orbit Capture

Figure 2.   Altitude and Corresponding Δv for Optimal Circular Orbit Capture as a Function of Incoming v_∞

decreases as the perigee of the elliptical capture orbit decreases and as the eccentricity of the capture orbit increases.

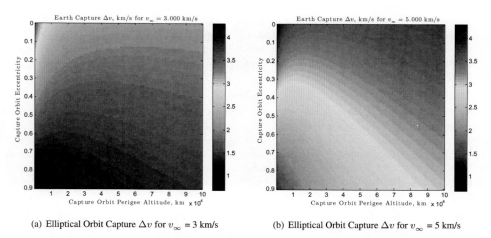

(a) Elliptical Orbit Capture Δv for $v_\infty = 3$ km/s

(b) Elliptical Orbit Capture Δv for $v_\infty = 5$ km/s

Figure 3.   Elliptical Orbit Capture Δv for v_∞ of 3 and 5 km/s

Figures 3(a) and 3(b) present the required Δv to capture into elliptical orbits for v_∞ of 3 and 5 km/s, respectively. In each case the perigee altitude varies between 200 and 100,000 km and the eccentricity varies between 0 and 0.9. These figures show that the capture orbit must be rather eccentric (generally an eccentricity of 0.4 or greater) to yield any substantial capture Δv savings compared to optimal circular orbit captures at similar altitudes. The figures also illustrate the aforementioned behavior of the capture Δv (decreasing with decreasing elliptical capture orbit perigee and increasing eccentricity). Even with a perigee altitude of 200 km and an eccentricity of 0.9, the capture Δv is 0.680 km/s for a v_∞ of 3 km/s, and 1.361 km/s for a v_∞ of 5 km/s.

Thus even for an impractically eccentric capture orbit and minimal capture perigee, the capture Δv remains formidable. It is worth noting that crew rescue on a significantly elliptical orbit could be complicated by our lack of contemporary experience with rendezvous, proximity operations, and docking on elliptical orbits of any kind (much less extremely eccentric orbits). The only historical example of this sort of scenario occurred during Apollo lunar missions, during which CSM/LM transposition and docking was routinely performed post-TLI in a geocentric ellipse whose eccentricity exceeded 0.9.

Incoming Asymptotic Declination Angle Finally, note that the spacecraft will have some natural incoming asymptotic declination angle which will dictate the plane of the capture orbit (whether circular or elliptical) unless additional maneuvers are performed to adjust the plane, and that Δv would be in addition to the already formidable capture Δv discussed previously. The natural incoming asymptotic declination angle also constrains the latitudes and headings at which the spacecraft can re-enter Earth's atmosphere during a direct re-entry, and so some control of this angle may be necessary for logistical reasons even if no orbit capture is performed.

ANALYSIS METHODOLOGY

The objective of the NHATS is to identify all known NEAs which offer trajectory solutions within a given trajectory performance envelope and which also meet some minimum estimated size constraint. The fundamental process by which this analysis is performed was developed between November of 2009 and March of 2010, documented during the Summer of 2010 in Reference 1, and modified for the purposes of the NHATS during September of 2010. The primary difference between the pre-NHATS algorithm documented in Reference 1 and the NHATS version presented herein is that the pre-NHATS version of the algorithm includes notional launch vehicle and crew vehicle performance parameters used to filter out trajectory solutions which could not be flown under those vehicle performance constraints. That algorithm is modified for NHATS by removing the vehicle performance parameters and instead filtering trajectory solutions according to a trajectory performance envelope chiefly characterized by total mission Δv, mission duration, and Earth departure date. This permits a much broader assessment of the potential HSF accessibility of the known NEA population and allows all vehicle performance constraints to be applied in post-processing. A large database of trajectory solutions is thereby produced which can then be used repeatedly to perform a series of trade studies on mission architecture, vehicle performance, and launch requirements. In that way, the modified algorithm for the NHATS is more general and versatile.

One of the key findings from the studies presented in Reference 1 is that there is no simple way to determine whether a particular NEA will offer trajectory solutions within a given trajectory performance envelope, much less what the exact values of the trajectory solutions, if any, will be. For instance, there are no formulae operating on a NEA's heliocentric osculating orbital elements which will provide such an assessment. The only option is therefore to compute all of the possible round-trip trajectory solutions for the NEA in an efficient, organized manner. Reference 1 develops the necessary theory and framework for accomplishing this, facilitated by algorithms which require no propagation of Earth/NEA ephemeris or spacecraft trajectories and which readily admit to trivially parallelized distributed computing.

The core of the NHATS algorithm is based upon the method of embedded trajectory grids, illustrated in Figure 4. This method is described in detail in Reference 1 and constitutes an extension of the usual method by which so-called Pork Chop Contour (PCC) plots are generated for one-way trajectory opportunities between two orbit ephemerides (e.g., to simply travel from Earth to an asteroid, or from Earth to Mars. In those analyses, Lambert's problem is solved for every combination of departure date and Time of Flight (TOF) to yield the total Δv required to fly each possible one-way trajectory. The result is a grid of Δv values forming contours in the departure date vs. TOF space that allow all feasible trajectory opportunities to be identified (including the optimal solution(s)), and the "launch windows" or available departure seasons for the mission, which tend to repeat according to the synodic period between the departure and destination orbits.

Performing this sort of assessment for round-trip missions dramatically increases the complexity of the problem, as shown in Figure 4, because now the amount of time spent at the destination must be allowed to vary, along with the TOF to return to the starting location (e.g., Earth) on the initial departure orbit.

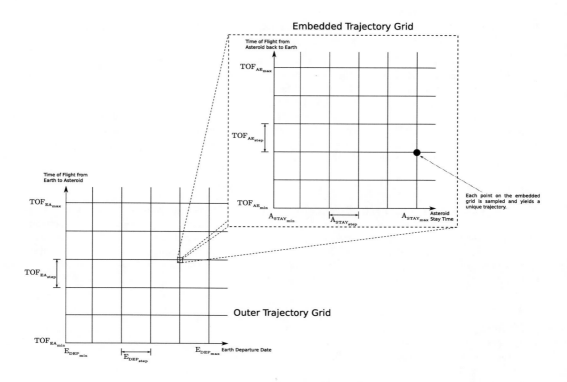

Figure 4. Embedded Trajectory Grids

Thoroughly assessing all the combinations of departure date, outbound TOF, stay time, and inbound TOF requires that secondary trajectory scan grids be "embedded" at every point on the traditional "outer grid" (which parametrizes only the outbound trajectory segment). Doing so causes a geometric increase in the total number of grid points that must be evaluated; furthermore, Lambert's problem must be solved *twice* (once for the outbound trajectory, and again for the inbound trajectory) for each of those grid points. In this context a "grid point" is defined as a particular set of values for (Earth departure date, outbound TOF, stay time, inbound TOF). Eq. (6) yields the total number of grid points, N, present within an embedded grid structure.

$$N = \left(\frac{E_{DEP_{max}} - E_{DEP_{min}}}{E_{DEP_{step}}} + 1 \right) \times \left(\frac{TOF_{EA_{max}} - TOF_{EA_{min}}}{TOF_{EA_{step}}} + 1 \right) \times \left(\frac{A_{STAY_{max}} - A_{STAY_{min}}}{A_{STAY_{step}}} + 1 \right) \times \left(\frac{TOF_{AE_{max}} - TOF_{AE_{min}}}{TOF_{AE_{step}}} + 1 \right) \quad (6)$$

The parameters in Eq. (6) are defined visually in Figure 4 and specify the boundaries and step sizes for the embedded grid structure.

Further constraints must still be applied to determine the actual value of N for a given case. First, only grid points which meet the total mission duration constraint are admissible, as specified in Eq. (7)

$$TOF_{EA} + A_{STAY} + TOF_{AE} \leq TOF_{TOT_{max}} \quad (7)$$

Secondly, the algorithm will stop in the outer grid whenever the maximum Earth departure C_3 constraint is violated; the number of grid points that will be excluded due to that is therefore unpredictable. Nevertheless, Eq. (6) subject to the Eq. (7) constraint provides a reasonable working estimate for N. Perhaps more importantly, it provides a good *relative* measure of N between different embedded grid parameter sets. A closed form solution for N, i.e., a single equation that incorporates the Eq. (7) constraint into Eq. (6), has not yet been obtained and may not be obtainable. In the meantime, it is straightforward to write a simple computer program that counts to N using nested loops, with Eq. (7) enforced.

If the maximum Earth departure C_3 constraint is satisfied in the outer grid, the algorithm proceeds to evaluate the associated embedded grid. The total mission Δv for each combination of grid points is computed as the sum of the Earth departure Δv, the NEA arrival Δv, the NEA departure Δv, and the re-entry speed control Δv necessary upon Earth return, if any. Trajectory solutions for which the total mission Δv is less than or equal to the specified maximum value are then stored in an output data file; individual output data files are generated for each NEA that offers at least one trajectory solution that satisfies all constraints. Note that once N has been determined, it must be multiplied by the number of NEAs to be processed to yield the approximate number of grid points that will be processed in total.

STUDY CONSTRAINTS

The Phase I and Phase II iterations of the NHATS both utilized purposely inclusive trajectory filter constraints. This is motivated by the desire to obtain a broad view of the accessibility landscape and understand the correlations between trajectory performance envelopes (chiefly characterized by total mission duration, total mission Δv, and Earth departure date) and the numbers of NEAs offering trajectory solutions within those performance envelopes. *Due to the highly inclusive nature of the trajectory filter constraints, it is important to stress that passing the trajectory filter does not necessarily make a NEO accessible for HSF.*

Constraints Common to Phases I and II

Most of the constraints utilized in Phase I are modified in Phase II, but several constraints are left the same in both phases and are presented in Table 2. The constraints that change between the Phase I and Phase II studies are presented and compared in Table 3. The comparison and commentary in Table 3 make it clear that Phase II is intended to be even more inclusive than Phase I, while treating the atmospheric re-entry speed aspect of the problem more conservatively.

Table 2. Common NHATS Constraints for Phases I and II

Parameter	Value
Earth Departure Date	01/01/2015–12/31/2040
Minimum Stay Time at NEA (days)	8
Total Mission Δv (km/s)	≤ 12.0
EPO Altitude (km)	400.0

Table 3. Differing NHATS Constraints for Phases I and II

Parameter	Phase I	Phase II	Phase II More/Less Inclusive?
SBDB Polling Date/Time	09/01/2010, 00:00 UTC	02/03/2011, 13:19 EST	More Inclusive
Earth Departure C_3 (km^2/s^2)	≤ 24	≤ 60	More Inclusive
Atmospheric Re-entry Speed (km/s)	≤ 12.5	≤ 12.0	Less Inclusive
Atmospheric Entry Interface Altitude (km)	121.92	125.0	Minor Change
Re-entry Speed Control Maneuver	$v_{\text{EI}} - v_{\text{EImax}}$	$v_\infty - v_{\infty\text{max}}$	Less Inclusive
Trajectory Grid Step Size (days)	6 (2 for stay time)	8 for all	Likely about the same
Minimum Outbound/Inbound TOF (days)	4	1	More Inclusive
Maximum Stay Time at NEA (days)	40	Unconstrained	More Inclusive
Maximum Mission Duration (days)	365	450	More Inclusive
Minimum Max. Estimated Size (m)	50	30	More Inclusive

The increase of the trajectory grid step sizes from 6 days to 8 days in Phase II is motivated by a desire to keep the total number of grid points per NEA, N, (as determined by Eq. (6) subject to Eq. (7), evaluated via a simple counting program) approximately the same as (but no greater than) it is in Phase I*. This necessitates

---

*This will be a non-issue in future study iterations when larger computing clusters are utilized.

a grid step size change because the maximum Phase II mission duration is increased to 450 days and the maximum NEA stay time constraint is removed. Note that while the NEA stay time is not explicitly constrained in Phase II, the total mission duration constraint is always in effect. The value of N for Phase I is 4.30×10^7, and the value of N for Phase II turns out to be 3.67×10^7 with the 8 day step size for the embedded grids.

The relationship between absolute magnitude, H, estimated NEO diameter, D (in km), and geometric albedo, p, is given by[5]

$$D = \frac{1329}{\sqrt{p}} 10^{-0.2H} \tag{8}$$

Eq. (8) is solved for H to convert the minimum estimated size constraints in Table 3 to H values. The reason that the estimated size constraint is couched as a "maximum" estimated size constraint in Table 3 is that a notional lower limit for NEA albedo of 0.05 is used when converting between diameter and H. Thus the size value computed for a given H is about as large as we would expect it to be; we are therefore being optimistic about the NEA's size (the NEA might actually have a higher albedo and thus would have a smaller diameter for a given H). This yields an absolute magnitude criterion in Phase I of $H \leq 25.37$; for Phase II the criterion is $H \leq 26.5$.

RESULTS

Phase I

In Phase I the 7,116 NEAs within the SBDB as of 09/01/2010, 00:00 UTC were processed in 6 hours using 158 CPU cores. 666 of those NEAs offer at least one NHATS-qualifying trajectory solution, and the total number of NHATS-qualifying trajectory solutions was 82,691,955. 433 of those 666 NEAs also meet the constraint of estimated size ≥ 50 m ($H \leq 25.37$). The total number of unique trajectory solutions for those 433 NEAs is 34,021,464.

The minimum, mean, and maximum of the absolute magnitudes of the 433 Phase I NHATS-qualifying NEAs are 15.750, 22.867, and 25.366, respectively. These correspond to maximum, mean, and minimum estimated sizes (at $p = 0.05$) of 4207.654, 254.446, and 50.216 m, respectively. The minimum total mission duration found is 34 days, and the mean across all trajectory solutions is 232 days. The overall minimum total Δv found is 3.549 km/s, and the average minimum total Δv is 9.495 km/s. The minimum number of viable trajectory solutions found for a NEA is 1, the mean for all 433 NEAs is 78,571, and the maximum is 4,153,445.

The minimum, mean, and maximum values for semimajor axis, a, across the 433 NEAs are 0.770, 1.150, and 1.665 AU, respectively. For orbital eccentricity, e, the minimum, mean, and maximum values are 0.012, 0.224, and 0.444, respectively, and for orbital inclination, i, the minimum, mean, and maximum values are 0.111°, 6.194°, and 16.226°, respectively. In terms of NEA orbit classification, the 433 NHATS-qualifying NEAs consist of 115 Atens (26.56%), 234 Apollos (54.04%), and 84 Amors (19.40%). The definitions of these NEA orbit classifications are presented in Figure 5.

Phase II

In Phase II the 7,665 NEAs within the SBDB as of 02/03/2011, 13:19 EST were processed in 52 hours using 20 CPU cores. 765 of those NEAs offer at least one NHATS-qualifying trajectory solution, and the total number of NHATS-qualifying trajectory solutions is 79,157,604. 590 of those 765 NEAs also meet the constraint of estimated size ≥ 30 m ($H \leq 26.5$). The total number of unique trajectory solutions for those 590 NEAs is 39,428,709.

The minimum, mean, and maximum of the absolute magnitudes of the 590 Phase II NHATS-qualifying NEAs are 15.750, 23.459, and 26.468, respectively, and the distribution of H for the Phase II NHATS-qualifying NEAs is shown in Figure 6(a); the distribution of H is quite similar in Phase I. The statistics for H correspond to maximum, mean, and minimum estimated sizes (at $p = 0.05$) of 4207.654, 214.946, and 30.230 m, respectively, and the estimated size distribution is shown in Figure 6(b); again, the distribution for

Amors

Earth-approaching NEAs with orbits
exterior to Earth's but interior to Mars'
(named after asteroid (1221) Amor)

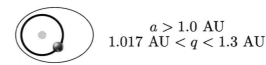

$a > 1.0$ AU
1.017 AU $< q < 1.3$ AU

Apollos

Earth-crossing NEAs with semi-major
axes larger than Earth's
(named after asteroid (1862) Apollo)

$a > 1.0$ AU
$q < 1.017$ AU

Atens

Earth-crossing NEAs with semi-major
axes smaller than Earth's
(named after asteroid (2062) Aten)

$a < 1.0$ AU
$Q > 0.983$ AU

Atiras

NEAs whose orbits are contained
entirely within the orbit of the Earth
(named after asteroid (163693) Atira)

$a < 1.0$ AU
$Q < 0.983$ AU

(q = perihelion distance, Q = aphelion distance, a = semi-major axis)

Figure 5. NEA Orbit Classifications

the Phase II results is quite similar to that for the Phase I results. The minimum total mission duration found is 34 days, and the mean across all trajectory solutions is 245 days. The overall minimum total Δv found is 3.551 km/s, and the average minimum total Δv is 9.458 km/s. The minimum number of viable trajectory solutions found for a NEA is 1, the mean for all 590 NEAs is 66,828, and the maximum is 3,302,638.

The minimum, mean, and maximum values for semimajor axis, a, across the 590 NEAs are 0.770, 1.154, and 1.699 AU, respectively. For orbital eccentricity, e, the minimum, mean, and maximum values are 0.012, 0.228, and 0.417, respectively, and for orbital inclination, i, the minimum, mean, and maximum values are 0.021°, 5.726°, and 15.485°, respectively. In terms of NEA orbit type, the 590 NHATS-qualifying NEAs consist of 150 Atens (25.42%), 332 Apollos (56.27%), and 108 Amors (18.31%).

Considering the semilatus rectum values for the NEA orbits allows the semimajor axis, eccentricity, and inclination envelope of the NHATS-qualifying NEAs to be visualized on a single two-dimensional plot since the semilatus rectum is equal to $a\left(1 - e^2\right)$. This plot is shown in Figure 7(a) and indicates that as inclination increases, the semilatus rectum must become closer to 1 AU (generally, more Earth-like) in order for the NEA to pass the NHATS trajectory filter. Figure 7(b) shows that as eccentricity increases, semimajor axis must become greater than or less than 1 AU to permit close approaches to Earth at NEA perihelion or aphelion, respectively. Likewise, as eccentricity decreases, semimajor axis must be closer to 1 AU to permit close approaches between the NEA and Earth. The trends shown in Figures 7(a) and 7(b) for the Phase II results are essentially the same as the trends associated with the Phase I data.

The top 25 NEAs, in terms of the number of viable trajectory solutions offered by each, are shown in Table 4. 48% of the top 25 NEAs are Atens, 36% are Apollos, and 16% are Amors. Table 4 presents two trajectory solutions for each NEA: the overall minimum duration solution and the overall minimum total round-trip Δv solution. The minimum and maximum estimated size values shown for each NEA in Table 4 are computed from Eq. 8 using the aforementioned values for p of 0.25 and 0.05, respectively.

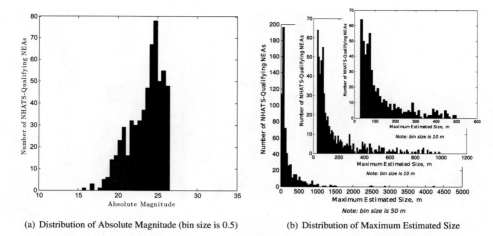

(a) Distribution of Absolute Magnitude (bin size is 0.5)   (b) Distribution of Maximum Estimated Size

Figure 6.   Distributions of Absolute Magnitude and Maximum Estimated Size for the Phase II NHATS-Qualifying NEAs

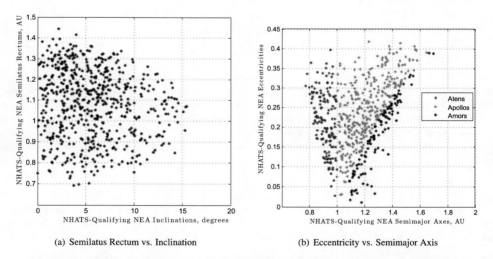

(a) Semilatus Rectum vs. Inclination   (b) Eccentricity vs. Semimajor Axis

Figure 7.   Relationships Between Phase II NHATS-Qualifying NEA Orbital Elements

Table 4. Top 25 NEAs in NHATS Phase II, Ranked by Number of Viable Trajectory Solutions

Rank	Designation	# Viable Sol.	H	Est. Size (m)	Orbit Type	Min. TOF (days)	Δv (km/s)	Dep. Date	Min. Δv (km/s)	TOF (days)	Dep. Date
1	2000 SG$_{344}$	3,302,638	24.79	29 - 66	Aten	34	11.558	6 Apr. 2028	3.551	370	10 Oct. 2029
2	2006 BZ$_{147}$	1,674,416	25.43	22 - 49	Apollo	58	11.928	20 Jul. 2037	4.110	370	13 Feb. 2035
3	2001 FR$_{85}$	1,618,888	24.51	33 - 75	Aten	58	11.631	3 Aug. 2039	4.292	362	28 Sep. 2039
4	2010 UJ	1,082,350	26.18	15 - 34	Aten	50	11.821	26 Aug. 2033	4.376	450	27 Sep. 2033
5	2009 HE$_{60}$	970,582	25.67	20 - 44	Aten	210	11.998	9 Dec. 2016	6.962	442	15 Jul. 2035
6	2007 YF	791,134	24.77	30 - 66	Aten	58	11.929	8 Oct. 2034	5.431	346	25 Nov. 2034
7	2010 JK$_1$	773,964	24.42	35 - 78	Apollo	106	11.789	17 Sep. 2035	4.854	402	12 Apr. 2033
8	2004 VJ$_1$	679,319	24.27	37 - 83	Aten	122	11.749	20 Oct. 2015	6.034	450	14 May 2036
9	2009 YF	663,423	24.69	31 - 69	Aten	74	11.928	21 Sep. 2028	5.660	450	2 Dec. 2028
10	1993 HD	656,700	25.63	20 - 44	Amor	98	11.917	24 Feb. 2036	6.045	442	31 Jan. 2036
11	2001 QJ$_{142}$	638,089	23.42	55 - 123	Apollo	74	11.947	15 Feb. 2024	5.425	362	3 Oct. 2035
12	2006 FH$_{36}$	630,084	22.92	69 - 155	Aten	114	11.946	21 Jun. 2035	5.996	362	14 Mar. 2034
13	2009 HC	555,180	24.77	30 - 66	Apollo	66	11.752	7 Feb. 2027	4.430	362	17 Apr. 2026
14	2011 AA$_{37}$	546,096	22.78	74 - 165	Amor	122	11.895	12 Jun. 2026	5.835	386	20 Jun. 2026
15	1999 CG$_9$	541,015	25.23	24 - 53	Apollo	66	11.770	8 Dec. 2033	5.216	370	10 Aug. 2033
16	2007 UY$_1$	537,599	22.88	71 - 158	Aten	122	11.970	16 Dec. 2033	5.505	362	2 Mar. 2021
17	2005 QP$_{11}$	491,888	26.43	14 - 31	Aten	122	11.731	12 Jul. 2031	5.805	394	28 Feb. 2029
18	2009 OS$_5$	478,949	23.57	51 - 115	Amor	42	11.914	30 May 2036	6.072	410	15 Jun. 2036
19	2009 DB$_{43}$	477,581	26.46	14 - 30	Apollo	82	11.614	26 Aug. 2030	6.249	378	25 Aug. 2015
20	2001 CQ$_{36}$	473,574	22.70	77 - 171	Apollo	162	11.943	25 Jan. 2031	5.826	354	30 Jun. 2021
21	2004 JN$_1$	465,681	23.45	54 - 121	Apollo	106	11.562	25 Oct. 2020	6.220	354	4 Jun. 2029
22	1999 AO$_{10}$	462,650	23.86	45 - 101	Aten	50	11.766	26 Dec. 2025	5.780	418	27 Jan. 2026
23	2003 SM$_{84}$	445,022	22.73	76 - 169	Amor	74	11.889	23 Apr. 2040	6.360	370	20 Sep. 2039
24	2009 CV	434,988	24.25	37 - 84	Apollo	50	11.891	27 Jan. 2029	5.709	322	9 Aug. 2015
25	2009 TP	433,374	23.54	52 - 117	Apollo	154	11.981	2 Aug. 2033	5.916	370	4 May 2035

Phase IIa

A follow-on to Phase II was performed on 05/28/2011 in order to update the NEA trajectory database while NHATS automation work continued. The SBDB contained 7,974 NEAs as of 05/28/2011, 00:34 EDT, an increase of 309 NEAs since the Phase II SBDB polling date. Since 114 days elapsed between the Phase II SBDB polling date of 02/03/2011 and the Phase IIa polling date of 05/28/2011, the *average* rate at which NEAs were added to the SBDB during that interval was approximately 2.7 NEAs per day, or approximately 80 NEAs per lunation.

These 309 NEAs were processed in 10.6 hours using 4 CPU cores. 63 of the NEAs passed the trajectory filter, yielding 3,605,931 trajectory solutions, and 49 of those also meet the minimum estimated size constraint, yielding 1,747,060 trajectory solutions. This raises the total number of NEAs which pass the Phase II trajectory filter to 828, and raises the total number of NEAs which pass the Phase II trajectory filter and also meet the Phase II minimum estimated size constraint to 639.

The minimum, mean, and maximum of the absolute magnitudes of the 49 Phase IIa NHATS-qualifying NEAs are 20.530, 24.452, and 26.450, respectively. These correspond to maximum, mean, and minimum estimated sizes (at $p = 0.05$) of 465.629, 107.470, and 30.482 m, respectively. The minimum total mission duration found is 66 days, and the mean across all trajectory solutions is 249 days. The overall minimum total Δv found is 5.916 km/s, and the average minimum total Δv is 9.780 km/s. The minimum number of viable trajectory solutions found for a NEA is 3, the mean for all 49 NEAs is 35,654, and the maximum is 230,661.

The minimum, mean, and maximum values for semimajor axis, a, across the 49 NEAs are 0.810, 1.144, and 1.670 AU, respectively. For orbital eccentricity, e, the minimum, mean, and maximum values are 0.050, 0.236, and 0.390, respectively, and for orbital inclination, i, the minimum, mean, and maximum values are 0.410°, 5.394°, and 13.920°, respectively. In terms of NEA orbit type, the 49 NHATS-qualifying NEAs consist of 14 Atens (28.57%), 25 Apollos (51.02%), and 10 Amors (20.41%).

Discussion

The number of NEAs added to the SBDB between Phase I and Phase II is 549, representing a 7.715% increase in the known NEA population. Since 155 days elapsed between the Phase I and Phase II SBDB polling times, the *average* NEA discovery rate over that interval was about 3.5 NEAs per day, or 104.6 NEAs per lunation; this is slightly higher than the average rate of 2.7 NEAs per day / 80 NEAs per lunation between Phase II and Phase IIa. Of the 549 NEAs discovered between Phases I and II, 97 (17.668% of the new discoveries) passed the Phase II trajectory filter, and of these, 62 (11.293% of the new discoveries) also met the minimum estimated size constraint ($H \leq 26.5$).

The higher discovery rate between Phase I and Phase II is attributable to the fact nearly all NEO surveys are performed in the Northern Hemisphere, which is in winter during the September 2010 - February 2011 interval. During winter the nights are longer, allowing more time for telescopes to identify faint NEOs. Another effect which tends to increase the discovery rate during winter in the Northern Hemisphere is the fact that the ecliptic is high in the sky during the fall and winter months, and searches are optimized by searching both sides of the ecliptic. During summer months the ecliptic is much lower relative to the horizon and so it is more difficult for telescopes to provide coverage south of the ecliptic. Finally, NEO discoveries are also hampered during summer months because the ecliptic passes through galactic latitude of zero, presenting a more dense star background.[*]

The number of NEAs that pass the trajectory filter increases from 666 in Phase I to 765 in Phase II; the 99 additional NEAs represent a 14.865% increase. The number of NEAs that pass the trajectory filter *and* meet the minimum size constraint increases from 433 in Phase I to 590 in Phase II; the 157 additional NEAs represent a 36.259% increase. However, recall that only 97 of the NEAs discovered between Phases I and II pass the Phase II trajectory filter, and of those only 62 also meet the minimum estimated size constraint.

The differences in trajectory filter and minimum estimated size constraint must also be accounted for when comparing Phase I and II results. Of the 765 NEAs that pass the Phase II trajectory filter, 48 did not originally pass in Phase I. Also, 46 of the 666 NEAs from Phase I did not pass the trajectory filter in Phase II. Likewise, 128 of the 590 NHATS-qualifying NEAs found in Phase II are not among the 433 NHATS-qualifying NEAs identified in Phase I. Further, 33 of the 433 Phase I NEAs did not pass the trajectory and size filters in Phase II.

Thus, the increase in the number of qualifying NEAs in Phase II, as compared to Phase I, is not solely due to the increase in the known NEA population. The careful comparison outlined above demonstrates that changes in the trajectory filter parameters and, to a somewhat greater extent, the reduction in the minimum estimated size constraint (from 50 to 30 m) have an appreciable effect on the outcome. In terms of the total number of NHATS-qualifying NEAs, the net increase in Phase II from Phase I is due to the relaxation of the minimum estimated size constraint to 30 m, the net difference between the more and less inclusive trajectory filter parameters described in Table 3, and the increase in the known NEA population due to discoveries between 09/01/2010 and 02/03/2011.

Also of interest is the subtle change in the distribution of heliocentric osculating orbital elements for the 590 Phase II NHATS-qualifying NEAs as compared to the distribution found in the 433 Phase I NEAs. In particular, the Phase II trajectory filter selects slightly lower inclination NEAs than those found during Phase I. This is likely due to the combination of reduced maximum allowable atmospheric re-entry speed and the more conservative re-entry speed control maneuver calculation since those are the only constraints which become less inclusive in Phase II.

Table 4 presents the top 25 NEAs identified in NHATS Phase II, ranked in descending order of the number of viable trajectory solutions offered. While not a perfect metric for absolute accessibility (particularly in the absence of a well-defined mission architecture and vehicle elements), the number of viable trajectory solutions does provide a good measure of *relative* accessibility, correlates reasonably well with the availability of low Δv mission opportunities with reasonable durations, and is representative of Earth departure season duration. This can be seen by examining the PCC plots for the top 4 NEAs, shown in Figure 8.

Note that while 2000 SG$_{344}$, 2006 BZ$_{147}$, and 2010 UJ all offer at least some low Δv, low duration mission opportunities within the 2025 - 2035 time frame (with 2000 SG344 clearly offering the best accessibility season), the accessibility season offered by 2001 FR85 does not begin until shortly after 2035 and its best opportunities (which include some relatively low Δv mission opportunities with duration $\leq$ 180 days) do not occur until the late 2030s.

---

[*]Abell, Paul (2011), personal correspondence of July 21st. Lead Scientist for Planetary Small Bodies, Astromaterials Research & Exploration Science Directorate, NASA Johnson Space Center, Houston, TX.

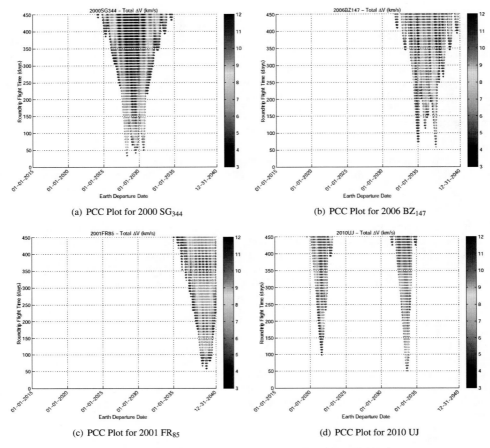

(a) PCC Plot for 2000 SG$_{344}$

(b) PCC Plot for 2006 BZ$_{147}$

(c) PCC Plot for 2001 FR$_{85}$

(d) PCC Plot for 2010 UJ

Figure 8. PCC Plots for the Top 4 NEAs from Table 4

ADVANCED TRAJECTORY MODELING

The University of Maryland (UMD) and Arizona State University (ASU) collaborated during the Fall 2010 and Spring 2011 semesters to complete a senior design project dubbed the Manned Vehicle for Exploration and Research Into the Cosmos (MAVERIC). The goal of the project is to create a comprehensive design for a space program that includes multiple six-month HSF missions to NEAs which launch between 2020 and 2030, use current and near term technology, and carry robotic assistants called Exo-SPHERES. The Exo-SPHERES are fully autonomous robots built and designed by UMD to carry multiple science packages designed by ASU and assist the astronauts in exploring and characterizing the destination NEA. The spacecraft design also includes an inflatable structure called the X-Hab, which is an inflatable habitat attached to the service module of the MAVERIC vehicle. It provides the primary living quarters for the astronauts, protecting them from the deep space environment and providing sufficient habitable volume.

Previous NEA trajectory surveys are examined when deciding which NEA to visit, including the NHATS. The following NEAs are selected using NHATS data, based on estimated NEA diameter, available launch years, mission durations, and low Δv mission opportunities: 2007 XB$_{23}$, 2001 QJ$_{142}$, 1999 AO$_{10}$, and 2000 SG$_{344}$. The NHATS trajectory data show these four NEAs all offer low total Δv solutions (all < 7 km/s) with opportunities for missions with durations of approximately six months that launch between 2020 and

2030. PCC plots are then examined to find specific launch opportunities and the best trajectory solution for each asteroid is then located in the NHATS trajectory data files. The MAVERIC team has designed complete missions to all four NEAs, but for the sake of brevity we will only present results for 2000 SG344$_{344}$ as an example of the trajectory analysis performed for each NEA.

The trajectory analysis is performed using AGI's Satellite Tool Kit Version 9 (STK 9). Parameters are varied slightly in an effort to notionally optimize the trajectory solutions whilst respecting mission constraints and satisfying requirements. The Astrogator module in STK 9 is seeded with the parameters for the best trajectory solution found within the NHATS trajectory data file, including Earth departure date, EPO altitude, EPO inclination (to match departure asymptotic declination angle when possible), and flight times (outbound, NEA stay time, and inbound). Astrogator's differential corrector is then used with STK's built-in high-fidelity force models to converge on the notionally optimized trajectory solution for each NEA. The HSF NEA mission profile shown previously in Figure 1 serves as the primary model for the STK 9 scenario, and the resulting STK 9 heliocentric trajectory solution for a mission to 2000 SG344$_{344}$ is shown in Figure 9. Earth's orbit is rendered in green and 2000 SG344$_{344}$'s orbit is rendered in a teal color. The mission sequence begins with an Earth departure maneuver that places the spacecraft onto the outbound trajectory, rendered in red, which intercepts the NEA. An arrival maneuver to match NEA velocity is then performed as the spacecraft nears the NEA. The spacecraft remains in the vicinity of the NEA for a specified amount of time (rendered in blue), after which an NEA departure maneuver places the spacecraft onto an Earth return trajectory, rendered in yellow.

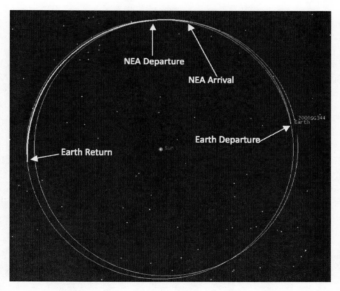

Figure 9. Round-Trip Trajectory Solution Generated with STK/Astrogator for 2000 SG$_{344}$ Mission

Using STK 9 for the trajectory analysis is advantageous because the parameters for a notionally optimal solution identified on a PCC plot can be provided as input and then other mission/trajectory parameters can be easily varied as mission requirements change. The complete set of geocentric parameters for the EPO can also be determined, particularly Right Ascension of the Ascending Node (RAAN) and true anomaly necessary for Earth departure near the specified date/time. Note that the NHATS trajectory solution utilizes a reference value for circular EPO altitude and computes the necessary asymptotic declination angle for Earth departure. The asymptotic declination angle would ideally drive the EPO inclination, but this is impractical in some cases due to launch safety concerns. Here again Astrogator proves useful because the EPO inclination can be constrained whilst allowing Astrogator to vary the exact time of the Earth departure maneuver so as to correct for the inability of the EPO's inclination to match the specified asymptotic declination angle.

The outbound trajectory sequence is divided into the following segments: departure from the EPO, propagation to 100,000 km from Earth using the high-fidelity HPOP propagator, propagation to Earth's SOI (925,000 km from Earth) using the cislunar propagator, and propagation to arrival near the NEA using the heliocentric propagator. The spacecraft's stay time at the NEA is also propagated with the heliocentric propagator, and the inbound trajectory sequence is constructed using the same segments as the outbound sequence, ending with Earth return at the 125 km atmospheric entry interface altitude. All heliocentric propagations included gravitational perturbations from the major solar system bodies. Note that only the spacecraft's motion is propagated; the NEA's ephemeris is supplied by a spice file downloaded from JPL HORIZONS, while STK internally uses DE405 ephemeris for all major solar system bodies.

Using STK 9 with NHATS data, the MAVERIC team has been able to determine how the total mission Δv is impacted by the combination of launch site constraints, EPO altitude, and asymptotic declination angle. These studies are very valuable because the NHATS assumes a 400 km altitude EPO and does not constrain EPO inclination. For the case of 2000 SG344$_{344}$, a launch from Kennedy Space Center (KSC) is assumed, from which launch azimuths are constrained so as to confine available EPO inclinations to be between 28.5° and 62°; these limits did not include any launch vehicle-specific constraints. The results for the 2000 SG344$_{344}$ case are presented in Table 5 and compared to the NHATS trajectory solution. Since the 2000 SG344$_{344}$ trajectory solution calls for an asymptotic declination angle of -22.066°, the minimum available inclination from KSC was used for the EPO and Astrogator was set to allow the exact time of the departure maneuver to vary so as to achieve the desired outbound trajectory.

A second validation of this trajectory solution was recently performed using the MacHILT (HILT = Heliospheric Interactive Lambert Targeting) precision trajectory design software. The MacHILT results are presented alongside the results from NHATS and STK 9 / Astrogator in Table 5, and a geocentric mission trajectory plot from MacHILT is presented in Figure 10. The close agreement of results between the NHATS software, STK 9, and MacHILT shown in Table 5 demonstrates the accuracy of the NHATS data and highlights the capability of both STK 9 / Astrogator and MacHILT to utilize NHATS data, in combination with realistic mission constraints, to produce fully integrated precision trajectory solutions for round-trip NEA missions.

While all three trajectory design solutions in Table 5 agree quite closely, it is important to note that both the STK 9 and MacHILT solutions are able to reduce the total Δv required for the mission by about 1% while essentially preserving the other design features to within < 1%. Although this very small Δv reduction is unremarkable on its own, the fact that it is a reduction and not an increase demonstrates that the NHATS software is not underestimating the Δv requirements for NEA missions; rather, the NHATS software is inherently overestimating the Δv by a very, very small margin. This slight inherent conservatism is highly desirable in a broad trajectory survey tool.

Table 5. 2000 SG$_{344}$ Trajectory Design Results Obtained from the NHATS, STK 9, and MacHILT

Parameter	NHATS	STK	MacHILT
Earth Departure Date & Time (UTCG)	6 Jul. 2029, 00:00	5 Jul. 2029, 23:26	5 Jul. 2029, 21:07
Earth Departure C_3 (km^2/s^2)	1.475	1.180	1.128
Δv to Depart Circular LEO (km/s)	3.244	3.229	3.224
Departure LEO Altitude (km)	400	400	400
Earth Departure Asymptotic Declination	-22.066°	-21.879°	-21.939°
Flight Time from Earth to NEA (days)	73	72.22	70.62
NEA Arrival Δv (km/s)	0.684	0.675	0.702
NEA Stay Time (days)	16	16	18.5
NEA Departure Δv (km/s)	0.814	0.767	0.777
Flight Time from NEA to Earth Return	89	88.652	89.416
Earth Return v_∞ (at SOI crossing) (km/s)	1.073	0.965	0.938
Earth Return Asymptotic Declination	19.773°	19.169°	19.128°
Atmospheric Re-entry Speed at 125 km Altitude (km/s)	11.124	11.114	11.112
Total Mission Δv (km/s)	**4.742**	**4.671**	**4.703**
Total Mission Duration (days)	**178.00**	**176.87**	**178.659**

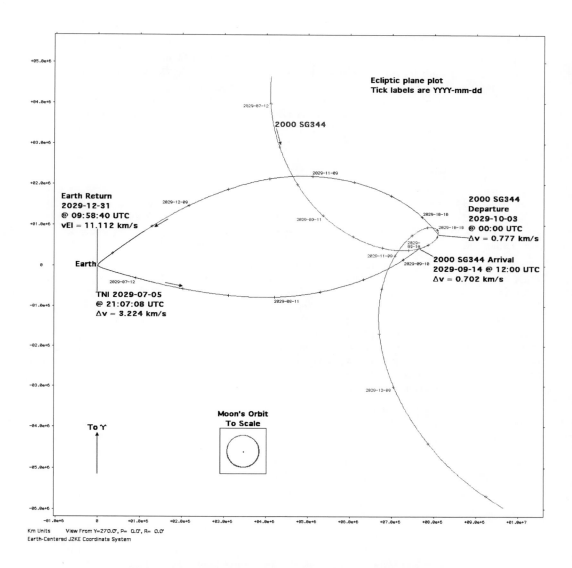

Figure 10. MacHILT Geocentric Precision Trajectory Design

CONCLUSION

The NHATS has identified hundreds of NEAs which pass a purposely inclusive trajectory filter, but only a handful of them may offer truly viable opportunities for HSF exploration between the mid-2020s and mid-2030s. The more important result is that the NHATS has established an efficient, comprehensive, and repeatable process by which the growing known NEA population may be systematically monitored for HSF accessibility as more and more NEAs are discovered, akin to the way in which JPL and the University of Pisa in Italy currently monitor the entire NEO population for Earth impact risk. As NASA's forward path gains clarity and momentum, and as the future of HSF architecture becomes defined, the NHATS will be keeping pace with NEA discoveries so that we find the best targets for our future explorers, human and robotic.

Ongoing and Future Work

NASA is currently automating the NHATS process in order to provide the most efficient systematic monitoring of NEA accessibility for HSF. A dedicated computer will perform a daily check for NEAs newly added to the SBDB, process them using the algorithms described herein, and add any new results to the growing database of trajectory solutions and vital statistics. An email notification system will be put in place to provide timely notification of interesting NEAs as soon as the NHATS system identifies them. A website will also be created to provide easy access to trajectory statistics and complete trajectory data and PCC plots for specific NEAs. Once that system is in place, additional features will be added, such as NHATS-style computation of all possible one-way trajectories for scientific and HSF robotic precursor purposes, and re-processing of NEAs when their ephemerides are updated by new observations.

Additional software tools are currently being considered to compliment the NHATS algorithm set. One example is an NHATS-style tool to compute all possible abort trajectory options during the outbound leg of any NEA mission opportunity of interest. The quality of abort options, in conjunction with the quality of robotic precursor opportunities, could serve as an important discriminator between NEAs which otherwise appear to fare equally well in terms of the HSF mission opportunities they offer.

A new software tool currently under construction will automate the process described herein whereby STK/Astrogator is utilized manually to convert a particular NHATS trajectory solution into a fully integrated trajectory within the STK analysis environment. The new tool will use the STK COM interface between MATLAB and STK to allow an analyst to simply compose an input file containing a pointer to the NHATS trajectory solution database, constraints, vehicle parameters, and a host of analysis option flags, and then have the trajectory solution process execute automatically. This tool will be able to quickly compute notionally optimal trajectory solutions with highly detailed analysis, enabling rapid and detailed assessments. STK's built-in modules will permit a host of rapid analyses, including conversion of all impulsive maneuvers to finite burns, sizing of vehicle elements, communications link budget analysis, attitude analysis for vehicle pointing constraints, and even modeling of proximity operations trajectories during the stay time at the NEA.

Finally, the NHATS algorithms are currently being used to study round-trip trajectory dynamics for NEAs in an effort to develop dynamical theories of round-trip accessibility. These efforts are yielding new insights into why certain NEAs are highly accessible compared to others, and which classes of NEA orbit may prove most accessible for HSF. A complimentary line of research currently under consideration is the development of an IMLEO definition that is meaningful even in the context of a currently ill-defined future HSF mission architecture. Such an IMLEO definition has the potential to provide a more relevant metric for assessing relative accessibility for NEAs, which would in turn aid dynamical accessibility theory investigations.

REFERENCES

[1] Barbee, B. W., Esposito, T., Piñon, E. III, Hur-Diaz, S., Mink, R. G., and Adamo, D. R., "A Comprehensive Ongoing Survey of the Near-Earth Asteroid Population for Human Mission Accessibility," *Proceedings of the AIAA/AAS Guidance, Navigation, and Control Conference*, Toronto, Ontario, Canada, 2-5 August 2010. Paper 2010-8368.

[2] Barbee, B. W., ed., *Target NEO: Open Global Community NEO Workshop Report*. 2011. downloadable from URL http://www.targetneo.org.

[3] Orloff, R. W. and Harland, D. M., *Apollo: The Definitive Sourcebook*, p. 581. Springer-Praxis, 2006.

[4] Wie, B., *Space Vehicle Dynamics and Control*, pp. 281–2. American Institute of Aeronautics and Astronautics, Inc., 1998.

[5] Chesley, S. R., Chodas, P. W., Milani, A., Valsecchi, G. B., and Yeomans, D. K., "Quantifying the Risk Posed by Potential Earth Impacts," *Icarus*, Vol. 159, October 2002, pp. 423–432. doi:10.1006/icar.2002.6910.

MISSION ANALYSIS AND TRANSFER DESIGN FOR THE EUROPEAN STUDENT MOON ORBITER

Willem van der Weg[*] and Massimiliano Vasile[†]

This paper presents an overview of the mission analysis performed for the European Student Moon Orbiter (ESMO). Scheduled for launch in 2014 – 2015 as a piggyback payload, it is currently the only ESA planned mission to the Moon. The launch period was systemically scanned by an automatic transfer generation algorithm, which process is described herein, to compile a large database of nominal transfer options. The database contains 2 types of transfer; transfers with free starting conditions and transfers fixed to a certain launch hour and date using an Ariane 5 launch vehicle. ESMO is inserted into a highly eccentric frozen orbit at the Moon, to minimize the propellant used to insert into, and maintain, its lunar orbit. Between launch and actual departure from the Earth, ESMO will perform a series of apogee raising maneuvers that inject the spacecraft into a trans-lunar transfer within the limits of the current propulsion system.

INTRODUCTION

The European Student Moon Orbiter (ESMO) is the fourth small satellite mission within ESA's Education Satellite Program, and is currently the only scheduled ESA mission to the Moon. The spacecraft is designed, built, and operated entirely by students, under the guidance of Surrey Satellite Technology Limited, which was awarded the position of primary contractor in 2009 (before then, the design was led by the ESA Education Office and a team of students). 23 student teams from 19 European Universities are taking part, where the University of Strathclyde provides the teams responsible for mission analysis and flight dynamics.

ESMO is currently scheduled for launch in 2014 – 2015 as a secondary payload. Although the choice of launcher is as of yet uncertain, the analysis in this paper assumes the use of an Ariane 5 to bring the spacecraft into Geostationary Transfer Orbit (GTO). The shared launch allows for little to no control over exact launch date and time, and so a substantial amount of analysis must be performed in order to cover the two years of possible launch opportunities. The scientific payload consists of a narrow angle camera to take high resolution images of the lunar surface (especially of the South Pole). In addition, a number of other scientific payloads are under development.

The spacecraft will use its chemical propulsion system (a chemical propulsion system was chosen over a solar electric propulsion system after a trade-off during a prior study [1]) to transfer

---

[*] PhD Candidate, SpaceART, Advanced Space Concepts Laboratory, Department of Mechanical Engineering, James Weir Building, University of Strathclyde, e-mail: willem.van-der-weg@strath.ac.uk.
[†] Reader, SpaceART, Advanced Space Concepts Laboratory, Department of Mechanical Engineering, James Weir Building, University of Strathclyde, e-mail: massimilaino.vasile@strath.ac.uk.

itself from GTO at the Earth to its lunar operational orbit at the Moon using a Weak Stability Boundary (WSB) transfer[2]. This type of transfer has been selected due to its associated propellant savings, and to cope consistently with a variety of injection conditions resulting from the shared launch. Departure from the Earth is performed by employing a number of apogee raising maneuvers before using a final maneuver to begin the transfer to the Moon. This is necessary due to limitations of the propulsion system.

The critical design driver for ESMO is mission cost. In addition to the aforementioned shared launch and propellant saving WSB transfer, further cost saving measures are also implemented. Commercial off the shelf parts and flight spares are extensively used in order to reduce cost. The use of a highly eccentric frozen polar orbit serves to reduce the propellant necessary to inject into orbit, and to reduce the propellant necessary to maintain the operational orbit. Finally, a single ground station reduces the operating cost of the ground segment.

MISSION OVERVIEW

ESMO has 4 main goals[*]. The project provides an opportunity for students to gain experience and training for the space industry. It serves as an outreach to younger students across schools in Europe, encouraging them to pursue careers in engineering. ESMO will also contribute to scientific knowledge of the Moon. Finally, it will also test several new technologies in space. Below is an overview of the mission objectives.

Mission Objectives

The official project mission objectives are listed as: (1.) to launch the first lunar spacecraft to be designed, built, and operated by students across ESA Member States and ESA Cooperating States, (2.) to place and operate the spacecraft in lunar orbit, (3.) to acquire images of the Moon from a stable lunar orbit and transmit them back to Earth for education outreach purposes, and finally, (4.) to perform new measurements relevant to advanced technology demonstration, lunar science and exploration[*].

Payload

There are a number of payloads under development for ESMO. The primary payload is a high resolution narrow angle camera to take images of the lunar surface (high school students will be able to propose a lunar site to be imaged). Further scientific payloads are a radar to provide radar observations of the Moon (radar observations from Earth are limited to the Earth-facing side of the Moon), a passive microwave radiometric sounder to measure thermal and dielectric properties of the lunar regolith, and a compact and low power radiation monitor that can provide inputs for space environment models. Finally, a technology demonstration payload for an internet-like network at the Moon for communication between future spacecraft in lunar orbit, landers, rovers, and ground stations on the Earth will be onboard. The experiment, named LunaNet, will test the associated communication protocols for the lunar internet[*].

Spacecraft Characteristics

ESMO will have an initial mass of about 300 kg, and a volume of roughly 1 cubic meter. It is equipped with two bi-propellant engines that provide a combined thrust of 44 N at a specific impulse of 285 s. The two solar panels provide 170 W of power (beginning of life) and are body-mounted in the shape of two sides of a triangular prism (c.f. Figure 1).

---

[*] http://www.esa.int/esa/Education/SEML0MPR4CF_0.html

Figure 1. Preliminary structural design of ESMO.

Requirements

The major requirements placed upon the mission analysis subsystem are to provide an overview of transfers for the launch window of 2014 – 2015 for multiple launchers, to design the transfers such that they accommodate the limited propulsion system (no single maneuver larger than 250 m/s and a total mission ΔV budget of 1,330 m/s), to provide a minimum 30 day waiting period in GTO, and finally to insert the spacecraft into a lunar orbit that is stable for 6 months, requires little to no maintenance, and provides low altitude passes across the Southern surface of the Moon.

TRANSFER

To help keep the total mission ΔV of ESMO at a minimum a Weak Stability Boundary (WSB) transfer was selected [2]. This type of transfer employs the 3-body dynamics of the Sun, Earth, and Moon advantageously in order to change the orbit plane, and to raise the perigee of the orbit from the Earth up to the Moon. The drawback is an increased transfer time (when compared to a more traditional Hohmann transfer) of approximately 3 months.

A WSB transfer for ESMO typically takes 3 months to complete and consists of nominally 6 maneuvers. In principle, 3 maneuvers would suffice – one maneuver at the Earth, followed by a single course correction, and finally a maneuver to inject at the Moon. In ESMO's case the departure maneuver at the Earth is split into 4 parts to avoid excessive gravity losses. The total cost in ΔV of these 4 maneuvers is in the region of 750 m/s. The first 3 apogee raising maneuvers occur at perigee, while the fourth maneuver brings the spacecraft more than 10^6 km away from the Earth toward the WSB region. A small maneuver is performed at the WSB region, allowing the spacecraft to return back toward the Earth-Moon system, but now such that spacecraft can be inserted into lunar orbit using a final maneuver of roughly 70 m/s.

Transfer Generation Algorithm

The current developed software supports two different approaches to the design of transfers:

1.) The program is supplied with the orbital parameters of the initial and final orbits, however the initial orbit parameters may be chosen as optimization variables (e.g. allowing the ascending node to be chosen freely to allow for any orientation of the orbit). The time of departure is also free and an optimization variable.

2.) Just as in the previous case, the program is supplied with initial and final orbital parameters. However, a particular launcher is selected that places limitations on the hour and date of the launch. In this case the initial conditions and time of departure are no longer optimization parameters. For example, ESMO is launched as a secondary payload onboard an Ariane 5, the

617

time of launch is fixed to be launched just before midnight local time from Kourou in French Guiana. In this case the initial orbit parameters are completely fixed.

After all inputs have been supplied the process of creating initial guesses begins. The band of minimum and maximum allowable distance the spacecraft may travel from the Earth is chosen as being between $1.2 \cdot 10^6$ km and $1.8 \cdot 10^6$ km [2]. This represents the spacecraft travelling out towards the WSB region. The minimum and maximum ΔV values to achieve the corresponding minimum and maximum apogee altitudes from the Earth GTO are then calculated, as well as those to reach minimum and maximum apolune from the Moon orbit. The impulsive shot is stepped through (between minimum and maximum ΔV values) at the Earth for a particular departure date and the trajectory is propagated forward by integrating the dynamics equation that considers the Sun, Earth, and Moon gravitational point masses [3].

$$\frac{d\boldsymbol{r}}{dt} = -\mu_E \cdot \frac{\boldsymbol{r}_{ESc}}{|\boldsymbol{r}_{ESc}|^3} - \mu_S \cdot \left(\frac{\boldsymbol{r}_{SSc}}{|\boldsymbol{r}_{SSc}|^3} - \frac{\boldsymbol{r}_{SE}}{|\boldsymbol{r}_{SE}|^3} \right) - \mu_M \cdot \left(\frac{\boldsymbol{r}_{MSc}}{|\boldsymbol{r}_{MSc}|^3} - \frac{\boldsymbol{r}_{ME}}{|\boldsymbol{r}_{ME}|^3} \right) \tag{1}$$

The propagation is continued until the trajectory passes the plane (henceforth referred to as crossing plane) spanned by the GTO line of apsides and a vector normal to the GTO plane (to create the initial guesses the maneuvers always occur within the plane of orbit), or until the maximum allowable time of flight is reached. The resulting trajectories are checked whether they cross the plane and whether they do not escape away from the Earth towards the Sun. Individual trajectories are discarded if they don't meet both these criteria. A similar process is performed for the Moon. Two values are stepped through in this case; the impulsive maneuver magnitude is sampled between the minimum and maximum values, and for each magnitude of maneuver the time of flight is sampled between a minimum transfer time of 70 days and a maximum of 120 days (the time of flight determines the position of the Moon during injection of the spacecraft). The trajectories are propagated backwards until they also meet the crossing plane. The orientation of the lunar orbit, and hence the direction of the maneuver at the Moon, is determined such that the injection at the Moon will occur via the Lagrange L2 point of the Earth-Moon dynamic system. The same criteria as for the Earth trajectories are applied to cull the number of trajectories.

The pool of Earth forward trajectories and Moon backward trajectories are now matched together on the basis of how well they meet at the crossing. Criteria are that a pair of candidate trajectories must meet at the crossing plane within a certain maximum difference in time, within a certain maximum difference of alignment (the velocity vectors are compared), and finally within a certain maximum difference of space (the end positions are compared). At first, the criteria are set quite strictly and a number of initial guesses are created. If there are no guesses or the number is too low, the criteria are relaxed until a minimum number of guesses is found. If there are too many guesses, the criteria are tightened in order to select only the best candidates. The resulting initial guesses are used for optimization. In addition to this, the criteria are loosened progressively until a great number of initial guesses are generated. This group of guesses is then evaluated for total ΔV (departure at Earth, the Moon, and the corrective maneuver to match the Earth forward and Moon backward trajectories are summed) and for positional difference at the crossing plane (i.e. the positional difference at the WSB region), and a small selection of guesses that scored best in either category is also added to the list of initial guesses that are kept for optimization. In this way a robust set of initial guesses is selected from three sources, but the selection is small enough to allow for rapid computation. The initial guesses are locally optimized in the following manner

$$\min_{x \in \mathbb{R}^{13}} f(\boldsymbol{x}) \tag{2}$$

where 3 objective functions

$$f(\boldsymbol{x}) = \Delta v_{tot}, \quad f(\boldsymbol{x}) = \Delta v_{wsb}, \quad \text{and} \quad f(\boldsymbol{x}) = \Delta r_{wsb} \tag{3}$$

are used in a successive manner to locate an optimum. The objective function is subject to 3 inequality constraints

$$g(\boldsymbol{x}) \leq 0 \leftrightarrow \begin{cases} \Delta r_{wsb} \leq 100 \ km \\ r_{max} \leq 1.8 \cdot 10^6 \ km \\ r_{min} \geq 1.2 \cdot 10^6 \ km \end{cases} \tag{4}$$

The process starts the local optimization with as objective the connecting ΔV near the crossing plane. A local optimization with as objective the total ΔV then follows. Finally, the difference in position between the end of the Earth trajectory and the start of the Moon trajectory is used as objective. Between each optimization the progress is observed to determine whether an improvement of the objective function occurs. If this is so, the following optimization (with different objective) is started with the resultant set of design parameters. This entire process is repeated 5 times (leading to a total of 15 optimization runs, 5 for each objective). To maintain computational speed each optimization may only run for a limited number of function evaluations. In addition, if the algorithm spends too many cycles trying to locate the local minimum (making the Hessian positive definite) the optimization run is broken off for that particular initial guess.

Table 1. Optimization parameters of the transfer generation algorithm.

t_{dep}	Time of departure (transfer starting date)	ϑ_E	True anomaly of spacecraft at departure Earth
T_{E-WSB}	Duration Earth-WSB leg	ϑ_M	True anomaly of spacecraft at arrival Moon
T_{WSB-M}	Duration WSB-Moon leg	$\alpha_{\Delta V_E}$	In-plane right ascension of maneuver at Earth
ΔV_E	Maneuver magnitude at Earth	$\delta_{\Delta V_E}$	In-plane declination of maneuver at Earth
ΔV_M	Maneuver magnitude at Moon	$\alpha_{\Delta V_M}$	In-plane right ascension of maneuver at Moon
Ω_E	Ascending node of the orbit at Earth	$\delta_{\Delta V_M}$	In-plane declination of maneuver at Moon
Ω_M	Ascending node of the orbit at Moon		

The design parameters

$$\boldsymbol{x} = \begin{bmatrix} t_{dep} & T_{E-WSB} & T_{WSB-M} & \Delta V_E & \Delta V_M & \Omega_E & \Omega_M & \vartheta_E & \vartheta_M & \alpha_{\Delta V_E} & \delta_{\Delta V_E} & \alpha_{\Delta V_M} & \delta_{\Delta V_M} \end{bmatrix} \tag{5}$$

used for the optimization are shown in Table 1. For the first approach, the parameter set of the 7 values on the left of Table 1 are initially used (the 6 remaining on the right are kept constant). The second approach uses a more restricted parameter set where the variables on the right of Table 1, the time of departure, and the ascending node of the orbit at Earth are kept constant (leaving 5 parameters free to optimize). The time of departure and ascending node are fixed because the launcher prescribes their value. For both approaches, further refinement can occur by allowing some of the parameters on the right of Table 1 to be free during the optimization.

Most code for the algorithm was implemented in Matlab, with a number of supporting C++ Mex functions for computational speed. The inbuilt Dormand-Prince Runge-Kutta method (using 6 function evaluations to compute the 4th and 5th order solutions) was used to integrate the equations of motion. The ephemeris for the Sun, Earth, and Moon was obtained using an analytical ephemeris [3] [4]. The algorithm generally performs all computations in the Earth centered Earth equatorial inertial reference frame, where the Earth orbit inputs are fed into the algorithm in this same frame while the Lunar orbit inputs are fed into the algorithm in the Moon centered Moon equatorial inertial reference frame.

Location of Good Initial Guesses

Prior research by Belbruno & Carrico [2] indicates that the angle between the Earth to Sun and Earth to Moon vectors at launch is roughly 130° for an ideal 2nd quadrant transfer (a 2nd quadrant transfer is defined as having its apogee toward the Sun, while a 4th quadrant transfer has its apogee away from the Sun – this is an effective rotation of 180° for the transfer).

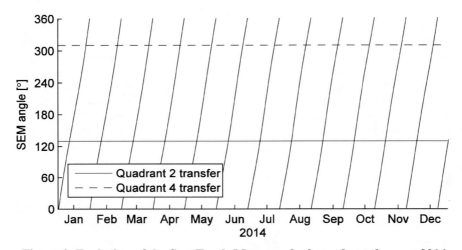

Figure 2. Evolution of the Sun-Earth-Moon angle throughout the year 2014.

Figure 2 shows the occurrences of this angle being 130° and 310° throughout the year 2014. Although the dates that these occur are good starting points for generating transfers, many transfers can also be found on departure dates between these occurrences.

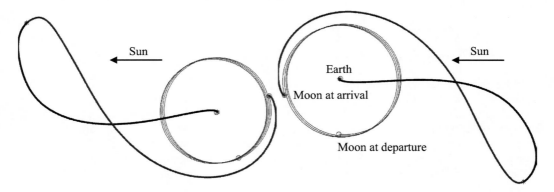

Figure 3. 2nd (shown left) and 4th (shown right) quadrant transfers in Sun-Earth rotating reference frame.

Figure 3 shows the difference in geometry between a 2nd and 4th quadrant transfer. The type of transfer has some practical implications on the design, for example it may be difficult to communicate with the spacecraft during certain periods of the 2nd quadrat transfer when the spacecraft is near the Sun (i.e. the angle between the Earth – Spacecraft and Earth – Sun lines is small).

Example Transfer

A transfer from the database is presented in more detail here. The nominal transfer consists of 6 maneuvers, and the total ΔV cost is 824.4 m/s.

Table 2. Overview of maneuvers for example transfer.

Maneuver	Epoch (MJD2000)	Δt (day)	ΔV magnitude (m/s)
1st perigee passage	5169.4579	30.2590	–
1st apogee raise	5199.7169	2.6242	187.5
2nd apogee raise	5202.3411	2.3063	187.5
3rd apogee raise	5204.6474	2.9318	187.5
4th apogee raise	5207.5792	22.7573	187.2
WSB correction	5230.3364	74.6328	15.0
Lunar injection	5304.9692	–	59.8

Table 2 provides an overview of the maneuvers of a possible transfer for ESMO. Launch occurs on the 25th of February 2014, where the first perigee passage after GTO insertion occurs just before 23:00 Kourou local time. A series of apogee raises bring the spacecraft more than 10^6 km away from the Earth towards the WSB region. A corrective maneuver there ensures that the spacecraft returns for orbital injection at the Moon.

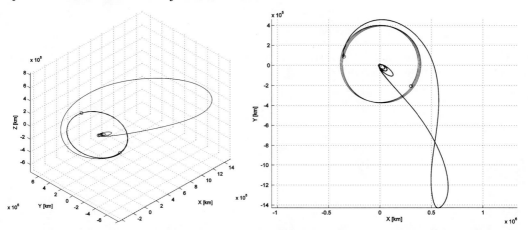

Figure 4. Transfer in inertial reference frame (left) and in Earth-Sun rotating reference frame (right).

Figure 4 provides a graphical overview of the transfer, showing it both in inertial and rotating reference frame. The total ΔV budget is constructed by adding a number of margins to the nominal budget.

Table 3. Construction of the total ΔV budget of ESMO.

Nominal ΔV (m/s)	824.4
Navigation +8% (m/s)	66.0
Contingency +5% (m/s)	41.2
Gravity losses + 5% (m/s)	41.2
Total ΔV (m/s)	972.8

As shown in Table 3, 13% of the nominal budget is added to create the total ΔV budget, which for this case is 972.8 m/s.

LAUNCH

There is a direct impact on the design if ESMO is launched onboard an Ariane 5 as a secondary payload. As launch date and hour are ultimately chosen by the owners of the primary payload there will be little flexibility to select these parameters freely. Launch date and hour influence the ascending node parameter of the GTO.

Table 4. Orbital parameters of a standard Ariane 5 GTO [5].

Semi-major axis	24603 km
Eccentricity	0.72
Inclination	6°
Perigee altitude	250 km
Apogee altitude	35943 km
Argument of perigee	178°
Ascending node	179.9°

The values in Table 4 are defined east of the Greenwich Meridian in the Earth centered Earth equatorial rotating reference frame [5].

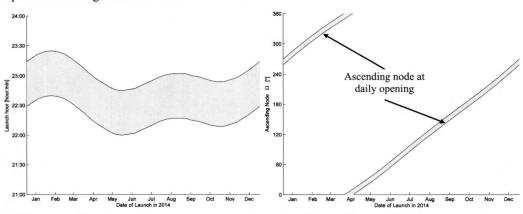

Figure 5. Opening and closing launch times of Ariane 5 in 2014 (left) and corresponding opening and closing ascending nodes in the Earth centered Earth equatorial inertial reference frame (right) [5].

The left plot in Figure 5 indicates in grey the band of time (i.e. opening and closing of the daily launch window) in which can be launched each day during 2014. The right plot defines the resulting band in ascending node (converted from Earth-fixed to inertial reference frame), where the rightmost values of the ascending node correspond to the opening of the daily launch window. The values of the ascending node are converted from fixed to inertial frame by first converting to a Cartesian state vector, and then using a rotation matrix

$$U = \begin{bmatrix} \cos\varphi & -\sin\varphi & 0 \\ \sin\varphi & \cos\varphi & 0 \\ 0 & 0 & 1 \end{bmatrix} \tag{6}$$

where the angle φ is determined by

$$\varphi = 280.4606° + 360.9857 \cdot d \tag{7}$$

The date d is provided in MJD2000, where a round value is defined as midday on that date (a new day starts at half values such as 5200.5 MJD2000).

APOGEE RAISING

The departure burn from GTO to WSB region is too large to be performed in a single maneuver by the propulsion system. For this reason the departure burn is split into a number of smaller burns. Two methods of implementing the series of apogee raising maneuvers at the Earth were inspected for ESMO. They are largely the result of the two different methods (mentioned above in the section of the transfer algorithm) of constructing the database, in which one method creates transfers where the orbital parameters are free, and another where the orbital parameters and launch date are fixed.

Matching Launch and Departure

If one assumes a certain launch date and initial GTO parameters, a cloud of solutions (such as those shown in Figure 13 can be generated, and then a search is conducted to find a suitable 'path' towards one or more of the solutions in the cloud. Multiple 'paths' can be found by altering the number of maneuvers, the epochs of the maneuvers, and the magnitude and direction of the maneuvers. The cloud of solutions must naturally be generated such that the difference between launch conditions and departure conditions is not insurmountable, otherwise the ΔV cost will too high.

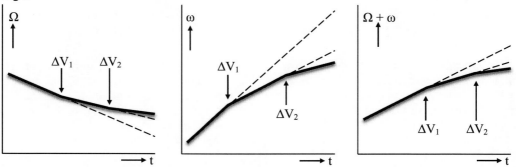

Figure 6. Influence of raising the apogee on the orbital drift.

Figure 6 shows an illustration of how the secular rate of change of the ascending node Ω and argument of perigee ω can be controlled by varying the number, timing, and magnitude of the apogee raising maneuvers. For instance, by altering the initial maneuver to occur at a later perigee passage with a smaller burn the final conditions at a later date are changed.

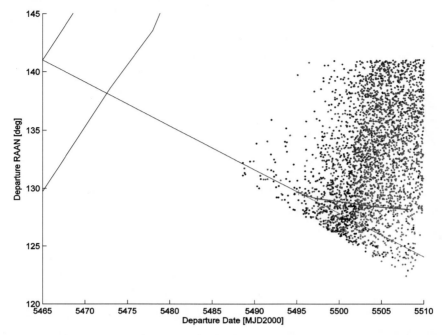

Figure 7. An example path between launch ascending node and departure ascending node.

Figure 7 shows an example, where the spacecraft is launched on the 18th of December 2014. The blue line represents the change in ascending node of the GTO that occurs during the mandatory 30 day waiting period. Afterwards the maneuvers raise the apogee in such a way that a particular solution in the nearby cloud is met (the argument of perigee at departure of the initial guesses was chosen to be around that of the launcher plus a 40 day drifting time). The departure solutions here represent the state at perigee necessary to start the transfer. For the example in Figure 7 the result is a solution with 4 maneuvers that adds almost 50 m/s to the budget (in comparison to a single departure burn). Typical sets of maneuvers can raise the ΔV budget from very little, ca. 10 m/s, to about 100 m/s (of course, even more expensive paths can be found but are prohibitively expensive), depending on the launch parameters and selected solution to target. The analysis can be run for a number of launches at different times and with different departure solutions as target.

The procedure is begun by selecting a trial launch date, from there a first culling of departure solutions in the cloud is performed by removing all those that require a change that is greater than the natural orbital drift in GTO for either the ascending node or argument of perigee. This translates to discarding all solutions below the blue and red line in Figure 7 (for the case of the ascending node) as well as those solutions that lie above the value of orbital parameter at the opportunity of first maneuver (i.e. drawing a horizontal line from the red cross in Figure 7 that occurs after 30 days in GTO). A grid search varying the number and magnitude of the maneuvers (but keeping the total sum the same), and varying the time between each maneuver (with a minimum of 2 days due to operational concerns), is performed to obtain suitable initial guesses. These are used for a local optimization that attempts to minimize the objective – total ΔV – while satisfying the constraints – the final conditions must match those of the departure for a successful transfer.

Ariane 5 Evening Launch

An Ariane 5 evening launch generally provides favorable conditions for an immediate departure to perform a 2nd quadrant WSB transfer to the Moon. However, time spent waiting in GTO will slowly deteriorate the departure conditions, driving the ΔV budget up. The problem is further exacerbated by the sequence of apogee raising maneuvers at the Earth before departure. This waiting period and time spent raising the apogee has an impact on the ability to find feasible transfers for that particular launch time.

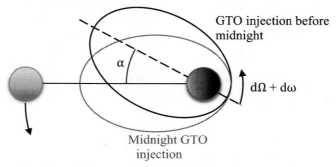

Figure 8. Geometry of an Ariane 5 launch.

Figure 8 shows the geometry of the Ariane 5 GTO compared to the Earth and the Sun. The angle α (describing the angle between the orbit line of apsides and Earth-Sun vector) is found in the literature to be suitable for WSB transfers for values of 25° to 40°[2].

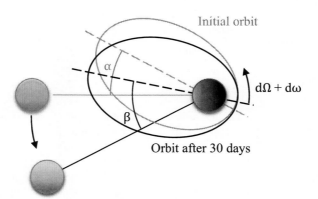

Figure 9. Geometry change over time.

Once the spacecraft is injected into GTO no maneuvers may be performed for a 30 days waiting period. During this time the orbit of the spacecraft orbit will drift due to perturbations. Expressed in orbital parameters, the right ascension of the ascending node and the argument of perigee will change, and are of most interest to us. The secular variation of the ascending node is roughly -0.4° per day in Ariane 5 GTO, while the secular rate of change of the argument of perigee is roughly +0.8° per day. If it is assumed the plane of the orbit is in the plane of reference (in this case the equator) the sum of the ascending node and argument of perigee (+0.4°) can be used to describe the rotation (this is not a bad assumption in this case, as the inclination of an Ariane 5

GTO is only 6°). The plot in Figure 9 shows a rotated orbit due to the shift of orbital parameters after some time, from the original situation (shown in grey) to the new situation (shown in black). During this time, the Sun's position also shifts (also shown in Figure 9) by roughly 1° per day.

An example of a 30 days waiting period is now used to study the effect of waiting on the departure conditions. For the purposes of this example it is assumed the orbit plane is equatorial, and thus for a waiting period of 30 days in GTO the orbit will rotate by 12° (30 × 0.4°). During this time the Sun's position will shift by roughly 30°. If the initial angle α were to be 25°, then β would be 43° after a period of 30 days.

During the process of incremental apogee increasing the rates of change for the ascending node and argument of perigee will diminish (for instance, when the semi-major axis is increased threefold, the secular rate of change for the argument of perigee ω is about 0.15° per day while for the ascending node Ω it is roughly -0.08°), while the Sun will still move ca. 1° per day, meaning the angle (α) will increase at an even higher rate, away from ideal departure conditions. It is therefore in most situations advantageous to spend as little time as possible performing the sequence of apogee raising maneuvers before departure.

LUNAR OPERATIONAL ORBIT

To keep the ΔV budget to a minimum, the selected lunar orbit is a highly eccentric frozen orbit[6][7][8]. The high eccentricity serves to reduce the injection ΔV while the frozen orbit reduces the necessity of station keeping maneuvers.

Table 5. Orbit parameters of reference lunar operational orbit.

Semi-major axis	13084 km
Eccentricity	0.8
Inclination	56.2°
Perigee altitude	879 km
Apogee altitude	21813.2 km
Argument of perigee	270°
Ascending node	Free

The reference target orbit listed in Table 5 is used to provide the arrival conditions for the backward propagation to create transfers. This target orbit is generally stable for 6 months for all cases, and thus this orbit serves ideally to create a uniform set of transfers that allows comparison with each other. However, the frozen orbit can be adapted to improve the performance of the mission. By increasing the eccentricity and varying the inclination one can arrive at an orbit that serves the payload of ESMO more appropriately. This is done on a case by case basis (through the design, not online during the mission) per transfer as the arrival geometry (the angle between spacecraft and lunar velocity vectors, and the position of the Sun and Earth) influence whether particular orbits remain stable for the required 6 months. For the case of the transfer shown in Figure 4 the arrival is such that the eccentricity is increased from 0.8 to 0.83 and the inclination from 56.2° to 66°. This is done to improve the performance of the payload over the entire mission while still keeping the orbit stable for the minimum of 6 months. Changing these parameters does not have negative consequences for the required ΔV to inject into the orbit. On the contrary, the increase of eccentricity reduces the necessary ΔV and the altered inclination introduces little to no change for the maneuver magnitude.

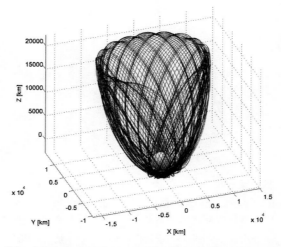

Figure 10. Lunar orbit of 6 months after arriving by transfer shown in Figure 4 (red lines indicate spacecraft in umbra and cyan lines indicate spacecraft in penumbra).

The orbit shape is shown in Figure 10 (in the Moon centered Moon equatorial reference frame), where the operational orbit is propagated for 6 months around the Moon. The propagation is performed using the Dormand-Prince Runge-Kutta method implemented in Matlab considering the point masses of the Sun, Earth, and Moon (using the same analytical ephemeris as for the transfer generation algorithm [4]). Because the numerical fidelity should be sufficiently high to properly indicate whether the orbit remains stable for long periods of time, the solution was verified using an STK propagation that considers also the full lunar gravity field to a high degree of accuracy and a higher order integrator.

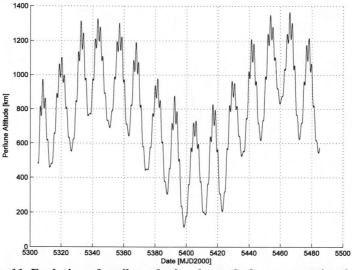

Figure 11. Evolution of perilune during 6 months lunar operational orbit.

The development of the perilune during the lunar orbit, shown in Figure 11, is of critical importance as low altitudes improve the performance of the payload.

627

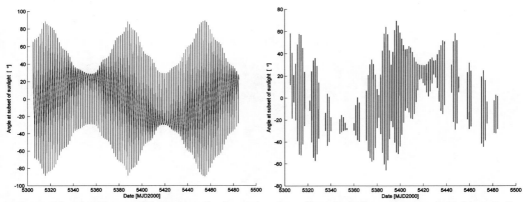

Figure 12. Lighting conditions on the lunar surface directly below spacecraft (left) and directly below spacecraft when it is below 1000 km altitude (right).

The lighting during low altitude is also of great importance for the performance of the camera. The values for the angle shown in Figure 12 are defined by the elevation of the Sun in the sky (i.e. the angle between the local horizon on the lunar surface directly below the spacecraft and the vector from that point towards the Sun). As can be seen in the rightmost plot of Figure 12 there are many occasions where the spacecraft is below 1000 km altitude and the lunar surface is sunlit during the operational lifetime.

LAUNCH WINDOW RESULTS

Free Departure Database

Earlier research was focused on generating optimal transfers using the first method (described above in the section covering the transfer generation algorithm), as it was unknown what launcher was to be employed. Some parameters for a launch to standard GTO were assumed, where the launch time (and hence the ascending node) was a free optimization variable. A systematic search was performed for the years 2014 and 2015 for trajectories with a nominal ΔV beneath the limit of 1,330 m/s. The resulting database contains roughly 300,000 solutions (of which about 40,000 score below the 1 km/s mark).

628

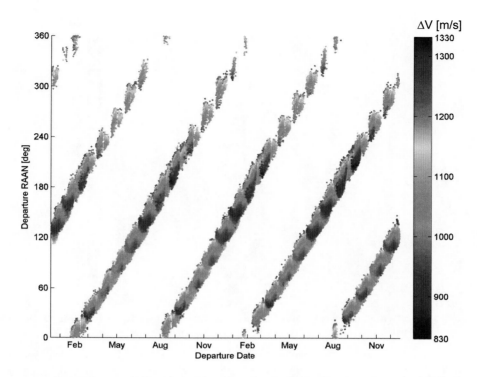

Figure 13. Departure right ascension of the ascending node as a function of departure date for found solutions (colored according to nominal ΔV cost).

The results of this search are shown in Figure 13. Each dot shown represents a solution with an associated time of departure and GTO orientation determined by the ascending node (the argument of perigee is identical for all the solutions shown). The color of the dot represents the cost. As discussed previously, launch and departure conditions will have to be matched up in order to perform a successful transfer. Using the strategy of changing the number and magnitude of the apogee raising maneuvers, and their epoch, the launch GTO may be varied over time to match those of a departure (the success of this is based on how much time there is between launch and departure and whether the values of the orbital parameters are not too far apart). It can also be observed that 2 solutions separated by roughly 180° are possible each launch date. These correspond to the 2nd and 4th quadrant transfers mentioned earlier.

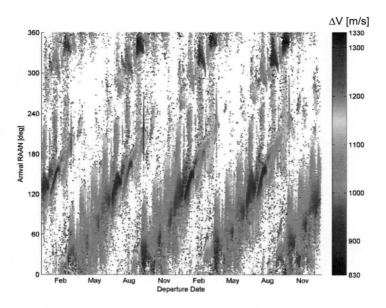

Figure 14. Arrival right ascension of the ascending node as a function of departure date for found solutions (colored according to nominal ΔV cost).

Figure 14 shows the arrival ascending node at the Moon (given in Moon centered Moon equatorial inertial reference frame) as a function of departure date. Good solutions generally arrive at Moon such that the angle between the spacecraft velocity vector and the Moon velocity vector is small.

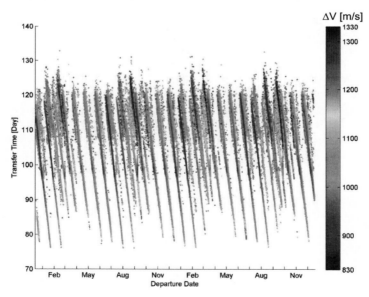

Figure 15. Transfer time of flight as a function of departure date for found solutions (colored according to nominal ΔV cost).

630

The transfer time from departure at the Earth to arrival at the Moon (so not including any time spent performing apogee raising maneuvers or waiting time in GTO around the Earth) is plotting in Figure 15. The empty spaces between the angled lines of solutions represent the periodicity of the Moon's orbit around the Earth.

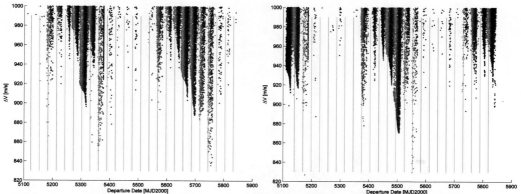

Figure 16. Nominal ΔV for 2nd (shown left) and 4th (shown right) quadrant WSB transfers as a function of departure date for 2014 and 2015 (transfers above 1 km/s not shown).

If the solutions are plotted purely as a function of ΔV and departure date (c.f. Figure 16) some information can be gleaned on whether the solutions are truly best when the Sun – Earth – Moon angle is 130° (2nd quadrant) or 310° (4th quadrant). The vertical lines in Figure 16 indicate the times that the geometry is at this specific angle. The solutions are shaded according to whether the initial guess was close to the ideal geometry or not (lighter shaded solutions are closer, while darker shaded solutions are farther). Figure 16 shows that a great number of good solutions are also found between the ideal geometry cases of 130° and 310°.

Ariane 5 Fixed Departure Database

A second database was also constructed, but now using the second method (described previously) where the initial conditions of departure and time are considered as constant inputs. The departure conditions here coincide strictly to the conditions that are achieved due to an Ariane 5 launch at a specified time. Figures 17 and 18 show the results obtained by the transfer generation algorithm for launches between 20:00 and 24:00 Kourou local time for the period of 2014 of 2015. The color of the area determines the optimality of the solution found, while the dark shaded areas denote launch conditions where no solution could be found lower than 2 km/s, or the constraints are not satisfied (the distance between the forward and backward propagation end points is too large). The 2 white lines represent the band of time Ariane 5 is normally launched within during that time of the year. The departure conditions for all the solutions were generated by taking the state of the spacecraft at first perigee passage after launch, and propagating this for at least 30 days until the next perigee is reached (69 perigee passages). Three apogee raising maneuvers of 187.5 m/s are performed at the perigees, keeping at least 2 days between each maneuver. After the third maneuver the state is propagated again for at least 2 days to the next perigee passage. This state then constitutes the fixed departure conditions that are used to search for valid transfers to the Moon. In this sense, solutions shown in Figures 17 and 18 incorporate a set of 3 fixed (in terms of their direction, magnitude, and epoch) maneuvers for every solution, and a 4th maneuver that varies between the solutions, at the Earth to achieve departure. An analysis of the gravity losses incurred during apogee raising showed that a total sequence of 4 maneuvers for departure was satisfactory to reduce the losses to an acceptable level with the current propulsion system.

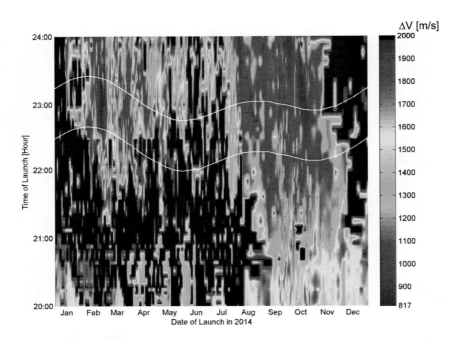

Figure 17. Total ΔV for daily launches occurring between 20:00 and 24:00 Kourou local time in 2014.

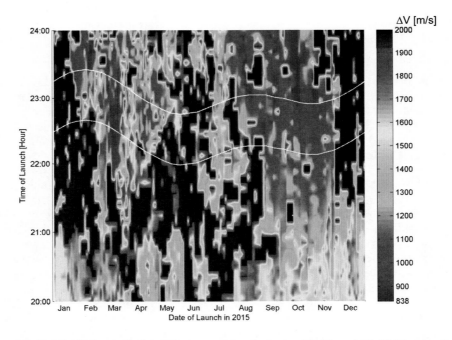

Figure 18. Total ΔV for daily launches occurring between 20:00 and 24:00 Kourou local time in 2015.

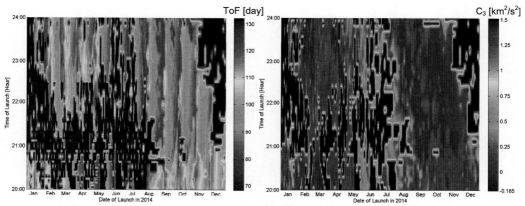

Figure 19. Corresponding transfer time of flight (left) and C_3 value (right) at lunar injection for values plotted in Figure 17.

The corresponding transfer times (from departure to arrival at the Moon) and C_3 values for 2014 are shown in Figure 19. The distribution of C_3 values is quite uniform for the more optimal (in terms of ΔV) solutions. This is perhaps partially a result of the generation algorithm, which provides an initial guess of the arrival geometry typical for a ballistic capture.

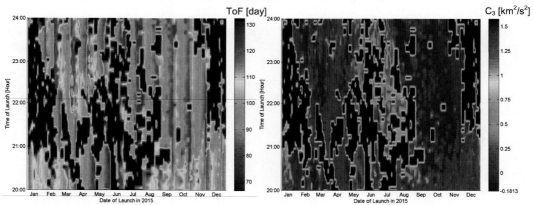

Figure 20. Corresponding transfer time of flight (left) and C3 value (right) at lunar injection for values plotted in Figure 18.

Similar to Figure 19, Figure 20 shows the corresponding transfer times (from departure to arrival at the Moon) and C_3 values for 2015.

CONCLUSIONS

This paper provided a broad overview of the ongoing mission analysis for ESMO. An automatic WSB transfer generation algorithm has been created and used to create two transfer databases: one containing transfers with free departure conditions of launch time and GTO orientation, and one made with the entirely fixed departure conditions of Ariane 5 coupled with a standard apogee raising strategy of 4 maneuvers in total (providing 3 identical maneuvers and apogee altitudes for every launch time). As shown, the focus of the mission analysis for ESMO is to achieve a design fulfilling the requirements for as low a cost as possible, with the resources at hand. This is evidenced by the use of a WSB transfer, and the selection of a highly eccentric frozen orbit. A strategy to cope with varying the ascending node and argument of perigee to align the GTO with a valid departure solution has also been presented, this allows some flexibility in choosing the time of launch without the need for costly maneuvers that change these parameters in orbit directly. Some of the future work for the ESMO mission analysis team will include performing launch window analysis for shared launches on other launch vehicles, refining the dynamic models used (as the project progresses, the generation of more refined trajectories is necessary), to adjust arrival lunar orbits automatically to achieve optimal results in terms of ΔV and payload performance, to study contingencies and recovery strategies (especially for the case when the engine does not properly fire during lunar injection).

ACKNOWLEDGMENTS

The authors would like to thank Mark Taylor at Surrey Satellite Technology Limited and Johannes Schoenmaekers at the European Space Operations Centre for their invaluable advice, and also Richard Martin at the University of Strathclyde for his help in making use of the University's computation facilities. This research is partially supported by Surrey Satellite Technology Limited in the framework of the European Student Moon Orbiter project.

REFERENCES

[1] Croisard, Nicolas, et al., et al. *European Student Moon Orbiter Mission Analysis Phase A1 Report*. Glasgow : University of Glasgow, 2009.

[2] *Calculation of Weak Stability Boundary Ballistic Lunar Transfer Trajectories*. Belbruno, Edward A and Carrico, John P. Denver : AIAA, 2000. AIAA/AAS Astrodynamics Specialist Conference. pp. 1-10.

[3] Vallado, David A. *Fundamentals of Astrodynamics and Applications*. El Segundo : Space Technology Library, Microcosm Press, 2001. 1-881883-12-4.

[4] Dysli, P. *Analytical Ephemeris for Planets*. 1977.

[5] Arianespace. *Ariane 5 User's Manual Issue 5*. Evry-Courcouronnes : Arianespace, 2008.

[6] *Stable Constellations of Frozen Elliptical Inclined Lunar Orbits*. Ely, Todd A. 3, Purdue : American Astronautical Society, 2005, Vol. 53.

[7] *Constellations of Elliptical Inclined Lunar Orbits Providing Polar and Global Coverage*. Ely, Todd A and Lieb, Erica. Lake Tahoe : AIAA/AAS, 2005. AAS/AIAA Astrodynamics Specialists Conference. pp. Paper AAS 05-343.

[8] *Lunar Frozen Orbits*. Folta, David and Quinn, David. Keystone : AIAA/AAS, 2006.

NEAR-EARTH ASTEROIDS ACCESSIBLE TO HUMAN EXPLORATION WITH HIGH-POWER ELECTRIC PROPULSION

Damon Landau[*] and Nathan Strange[†]

The diverse physical and orbital characteristics of near-Earth asteroids provide progressive stepping stones on a flexible path to Mars. Beginning with cislunar exploration capability, the variety of accessible asteroid targets steadily increases as technology is developed for eventual missions to Mars. Noting the potential for solar electric propulsion to dramatically reduce launch mass for Mars exploration, we apply this technology to expand the range of candidate asteroid missions. The variety of mission options offers flexibility to adapt to shifting exploration objectives and development schedules. A robust and efficient exploration program emerges where a potential mission is available once per year (on average) with technology levels that span cislunar to Mars-orbital capabilities. Examples range from a six-month mission that encounters a 10-m object with 65 kW to a two-year mission that reaches a 2-km asteroid with a 350-kW system.

INTRODUCTION

In the wake of the schedule and budgetary woes that led to the cancellation of the Constellation Moon program, the exploration of near-Earth asteroids (NEAs) has been promoted as a more realizable and affordable target to initiate deep space exploration with astronauts.[1,2] Central to the utility of NEAs in a progressive exploration program is their efficacy to span a path as literal stepping stones between cislunar excursions and the eventual human exploration of Mars.[3-8] In the search for initial mission targets, several studies have demonstrated that the Constellation paradigm (specifically short duration habitats propelled by massive propulsion systems that require Saturn V-class launchers) limits the set of "attractive" missions to sporadically spaced launches encountering a few dozen of the easiest to reach objects.[9-16] These targets tend to be relatively small (< 100 m) with uncertain orbits, which introduces significant issues for both public engagement and mission design. Noting the paucity of exploration targets possible with Constellation capability, many in the NEA community have called for a dedicated NEA survey in order to discover a new set of easily accessible targets.[17] Such tactics arise from a desire to find NEAs accessible within the capability of architectures like Constellation or Apollo that were originally formulated for cislunar exploration. By only pursuing cislunar architectures, the exploration program would be limited to the small fraction of asteroids with Earth-like orbits.

---

[*] Mission Design Engineer, Outer Planet Mission Analysis Group, Jet Propulsion Laboratory, California Institute of Technology, M/S 301-121, Pasadena, CA.

[†] Lunar and Planetary Mission Architect, Mission Systems Concepts, Jet Propulsion Laboratory, California Institute of Technology, M/S T1809, Pasadena, CA.

After the publication of the Augustine Commission,[1] we became interested in how technologies useful for Mars exploration could pertain to NEAs, and how these technologies map back to cislunar missions. Such strategic technologies could open the exploration program to a larger fraction of asteroids that span out to Mars. Noting the dramatic reduction in injected mass to low-Earth orbit (IMLEO) enabled by solar electric propulsion (SEP) for Mars surface missions,[18–21] we sought applications that would bring exploration capability to NEAs as well. The underlying premise is that the investment in a high-power SEP stage[22] potentially reduces overall program cost by decreasing the number of required launches or by allowing the use of more economical launch vehicles. We found that power levels comparable to the International Space Station (the ISS arrays can produce up to 260 kW[23]) enabled several 1–1.5 year NEA missions to relatively large (>300 m) targets with well characterized orbits.[24] These missions seemed ideal to bridge the gap between cislunar missions with durations of several months and Mars missions, which can take up to three years round trip. Further analysis expanded the flight time range from 270 to 720 days and demonstrated that SEP reduces IMLEO by a factor of two to three when compared to all chemical architectures, and can be as efficient as nuclear thermal rockets to increase the variety of accessible targets in a NEA exploration campaign.[25] These previous analyses examined NEA mission design from an architectural and technological perspective, while the present analysis seeks programmatic flexibility through a diverse set of mission opportunities. These individual missions provide the building blocks upon which a robust and worthy exploration program can emerge.

EXPLORATION ARCHITECTURE AND TECHNOLOGIES

Mission Profile

The four major flight elements are (1) an in-space transit habitat that provides sufficient room and equipment to keep the crew happy and productive while protecting them from deep-space radiation during, (2) a launch/entry capsule that is optimized to ferry the crew between Earth and the transit habitat in cisluanr space, (3) a SEP stage that transports the crew, habitat, and capsule from Earth to the NEO and back, and (4) a cryogenic propulsion system that injects the entire stack on an interplanetary transfer from Earth orbit. These elements may be launched separately and combined in Earth orbit over an extended time period to become a Deep Space Vehicle (DSV). The launch/entry capsule is based on the relatively mature Orion Multi-Purpose Crew Vehicle design comprising a 9 t capsule and 5 t service module (dry).[15, 26, 27] The Orion capsule is ideal to transport the crew to and from the DSV because it is designed for cislunar missions and provides 21 days of life support for four.[26] However, Orion is not ideal for missions longer than three months because its relatively cramped quarters (10 m^3, or about the room inside two minivans[15]) is right at the "performance limit" for a crew of only one.[28] Instead, a permanent in-space transit habitat can provide adequate room and necessary shelter from deep space (e.g. plenty of radiation protection) without compromising crew safety during launch and reentry (provided by Orion). We allocate 22 t for the NEO missions as a midpoint between ISS[29] and Mars surface[27] designs, while providing development margin for other flexible path missions.[30] In addition to the 22 t dry mass, the habitat also carries 20 kg/d of consumables for a crew of four.[27,31] The chemical propulsion system is assumed to be a cryogenic, zero boil-off LOX/LH2 system (450 s Isp) with 20% of the fuel mass as inert mass.[27, 32] The SEP stage is based on the NEA Design Reference Mission concept of Brophy et al.[22] Their design makes use of recent advances in large, light weight solar array technology[33–36] to provide 300 kW to the SEP thrusters. We limit the amount of time the crew spends in space by setting the SEP I_{sp} to a relatively low value of 1600 s, which increases the thrust (acceleration) at a fixed power level. A higher I_{sp} of 3000 s is used when the crew is not on board the DSV to reduce propellant mass at the expense of longer flight times. This range of Isp is ideal for Hall-effect thrusters,[37-39] which have an additional benefit of long lifetimes compared to other thruster types.[40] The margined mass of the SEP stage is calculated from a specific power of 30 kg/kW plus an additional inert mass of 15% of the propellant.

The DSV is assembled in LEO and spirals with SEP to an elliptical High Earth Orbit (HEO) with a C_3 of -2 km^2/s^2 (about a 10-day period). The individual element launches are not time critical because the spiral begins about two years before Earth departure.[25] The crew then is launched in the crew capsule for a rendezvous with the DSV in this orbit. The DSV with crew then performs an indirect escape maneuver at a 400 km perigee to reach the desired outbound hyperbolic asymptote for the interplanetary trajectory, which is then flown entirely with SEP. This staging and escape sequence is illustrated in Figure 1.

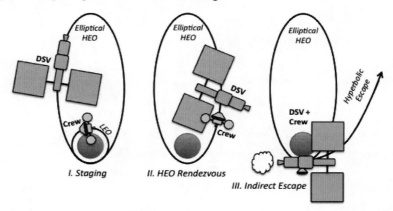

Figure 1. High Earth Orbit (HEO) Staging and Escape Sequence.

Because this architecture uses low-thrust propulsion, the pre-departure staging strategy provides a substantial performance benefit. Staging in the 10-day elliptical HEO with a departure burn at a 400 km perigee can reduce the chemical departure burn by 3.1 km/s for the DSV mass. A 2-year SEP LEO to HEO spiral provides this ΔV much more efficiently than a chemical burn. After the spiral, the DSV can be staged in orbits with perigee above the Van Allen belt and Lunar Gravity-Assists (LGAs) can be used to lower perigee to 400 km and orient the elliptical HEO prior to the departure burn. The crew capsule still uses chemical propulsion for the 3.1 km/s LEO to HEO ΔV, so the crew flight time is not affected by the duration of the SEP spiral and LGA trajectory. After departure, the crew pilots the DSV to the target asteroid with the SEP system. The minimum stay time at the asteroid is 30 days to provide ample exploration time with margin. Upon Earth return, the crew enters Earth's atmosphere directly from the inbound asymptote with an maximum entry speed of 12 km/s. (In comparison, lunar returns are around 11 km/s.) The transit habitat and SEP stage fly by Earth and capture into HEO a year later for refurbishment. By parking a reusable DSV in HEO, the IMLEO on subsequent missions is reduced by about 50 t. A summary of the parameters used to calculate mass and power is provided in Table 1.

Table 1. Mission Design Parameters

Parameter	Description	Value
Capsule dry mass	Crew module for launch and Earth entry, includes 21 d life support for crew of 4	14 t
Habitat dry mass	Reusable module to keep crew safe, happy, and productive in deep space	22 t
Crew consumables	Food, water, and air for a crew of 4	20 kg/day
Stay time at NEA	Provide ample time for exploration	30 d minimum
Departure orbit	Lunar crossing HEO with low perigee for efficient maneuvering	400 km alt. peri., 10 d per.
Maximum entry speed	Limits capsule entry requirements	12 km/s or 4.621 km/s V_∞
CPS I_{sp}	Cryogenic liquid H_2 and O_2	450 s
CPS inert/propellant	Expendable module with zero-boil-off	20 %
SEP spiral time	DSV from LEO to HEO without crew, based on Earth-Mars synodic period	2.14 yr
SEP spiral I_{sp}	High I_{sp} for mass-efficient LEO to HEO	3000 s, 63% jet/array
SEP interplanetary I_{sp}	Lower Isp increases thrust to limit in-space flight time for crew	1600 s, 50% jet/array
SEP inert/power	Reusable SEP stage including margin	30 kg/kW
SEP inert/propellant	Includes tanks and propellant margin	15%

Trajectory search and optimization

We set up a two-stage process to design low-thrust round-trip NEA missions. The first step is a broad search of computationally efficient impulsive trajectories, followed by computationally intensive optimization of low-thrust transfers filtered from the broad search. The entire catalog of known near-Earth asteroids (NEAs) in the JPL Small Body Database (http://ssd.jpl.nasa.gov/sbdb_query.cgi) comprising 7650 objects (as of January 29, 2011) was used in the near-Earth asteroid trajectory search. The trajectory search parameters included launch between 2019 and 2036, minimum 30-d asteroid stay time, maximum 720-d mission duration, and maximum 12-km/s total mission ΔV. A grid with seven-day intervals was applied to the launch, NEA arrival, NEA departure and Earth return dates and all combinations (within the flight time and ΔV limits) were examined. To save computational time the Earth-NEA legs where calculated independently of the NEA-Earth legs, then only combinations that satisfied the stay time and mission duration constraints were kept. The trajectory legs were computed using a robust and efficient (and highly recommended) Lambert solver algorithm from Gooding.[41] Once the mission ΔV was calculated the trajectories were sorted and filtered to provide the minimum ΔV for maximum flight times of 180, 270, 360, 540, and 720 days and for launch opportunities in 90-day increments. In this way the minimum ΔV trajectory in each quarter year for each of the maximum flight times was saved. The end result was ~50,000 filtered trajectories to ~1,400 unique targets.

The trajectories in the filtered set were used as the seed trajectories (initial guesses) in the low-thrust optimizer, MALTO.[42] The trajectories were optimized for maximum net mass assuming

240 t IMLEO and 300 kW maximum SEP power with the design parameters provided in Table 1. The net mass is the arrival mass at Earth minus the propulsion system inert mass. A second MALTO run with a maximum SEP power of 150 kW augmented this initial set to introduce lower power alternatives. The mass and power of the resulting trajectories are then scaled to provide the desired payload mass (transit habitat, capsule, and consumables) while maintaining the same C_3, ΔV, and flight time of the original trajectories.[43]

TRAJECTORIES TO NEAR-EARTH ASTEROIDS

NEA campaign considerations

The overall design objective is to determine the best target sets for different combinations of mass, power, and flight times, where the different capabilities represent flexible points in an evolving technology program and "best" targets are highly speculative based on the small amount of NEA data available. The NEA trajectories are grouped by maximum round trip flight time in Table 2–Table 5, where the 270-day trajectories provide options for the first asteroid missions following cislunar test flights and 720-day trajectories maximize exploration capability before the first Mars orbital missions. The IMLEO values are given for only the deep space vehicle (habitat, consumables, chemical departure stage, and interplanetary SEP) because the DSV is launched separate from the crew and drives the maximum launch vehicle capability. The crew rendezvous with the DSV in HEO a few days prior to departure via a separate launch that places 35 t (14 t capsule and 21 t LEO-HEO upper stage) into LEO. The power values (specified at 1 AU) also only pertain to the DSV because the interplanetary trajectory is independent of the LEO-HEO spiral trajectory. The nominal LEO-HEO SEP stage is sized to complete the spiral within 2.14 years, which requires a power/IMLEO ratio of 2 kW/t (at 3,000 s I_{sp}), and higher power ratios would reduce spiral time if desired. For example if the DSV IMLEO is 153 t (including spiral stage), then either a single 306 kW SEP system or two separate 153 kW stages could transport the DSV components from LEO to HEO in 2.14 years. Similarly, two 306 kW stages would transport the DSV to HEO in a little over 1 year. At a fixed power level, higher I_{sp} values decrease IMLEO but increase LEO-HEO spiral time. Once the crew and DSV rendezvous in HEO, they fly the same interplanetary trajectory regardless of how they reached the staging node. The C_3 and SEP ΔV columns indicate a relative breakdown of work performed by the cryogenic departure stage and the interplanetary SEP system. We note that the SEP ΔV will generally increase for I_{sp} values greater than 1600 s, even with the same initial acceleration (requiring higher power), because the mass ratio across the entire trajectory will change at a different rate. With this caveat, the C_3 and ΔV values are useful for broad system-level trade studies. The maximum Earth arrival V_∞ is 4.621 km/s, corresponding to an atmospheric entry speed of 12.0 km/s, though many trajectories return with a slower speed.

The spectral type and diameter of the targets give a rough portrait of their physical characteristics. Relatively little is known about the NEA population as a whole, so many targets are missing spectral and size information. In general B- and C-types are considered to be primitive carbonaceous objects and tend to have lower albedos (< 15%), while S-types are more stony and shiny (albedo > 15%), and X types are of uncertain physical nature, but have a known spectral curve. The diameter values for objects that have an unmeasured size and unknown albedo is estimated from the absolute magnitude (brightness) assuming a 15% albedo. Darker objects will tend to have higher actual diameters, while shinier ones will tend to have smaller diameters, and can easily range by a factor of two from the estimates in the tables. However, since other physical data tends to be unknown, we tend to favor larger objects to small ones when selecting example missions. While there is no reason to believe that the orbital distribution of small objects is any different than big ones, it is generally easier to find a viable trajectory to a small object due to the simple fact that there are so many more of them. Statistically speaking, an exploration program that can reach the top N% largest asteroids should also be able to include the top N% of any other figure of merit for asteroid target selection. In this case, size is used as a proxy for the degree of target variety and flexibility a given mission architecture provides.

Just as the physical characteristics of many asteroids are not well defined, the orbits of some asteroids are also uncertain. The last column in the tables provides the orbit condition code (as defined by the Minor Planet Center http://www.minorplanetcenter.org/iau/info/UValue.html) where low values (0–1) are considered to be well determined orbits (trajectory to the NEA likely exists as is), moderate values (2–3) are more uncertain (trajectory likely requires slight modifications), and large values (4 and above) represent objects that may not be easily recovered (general trajectory characteristics likely still exist, but at a different launch epoch). Therefore, not all of the trajectories in Table 2–Table 5 are guaranteed to exist after further orbital refinements.

Programmatic overview

For each of the maximum mission durations in Table 2–Table 5, around forty unique mission opportunities were picked "by hand" based on accessibility and speculative target value. The most accessible targets are marked in bold and generally have a combination of IMLEO < ~150 t and SEP power < ~150 kW, though the 720-day missions are purposefully biased toward more advanced technology assuming the exploration program provides more overall capability once astronauts can survive for up to two years in space. We also include targets that are more difficult to reach to examine how the accessible population varies as mission capability begins to approach the Mars exploration stage. For both "easy" and "difficult" targets sets, we seek mission sequences that provide a steady cadence of launch opportunities that not only sustains exploration but also accounts for uncertainty in the technology development schedule. Because technology development does not always keep up with shifts in space policy, a variety of mission options should remain on the table as the exploration program evolves.

For short duration missions (less than 270 days, with 30 days at the target) the accessible targets are largely limited to the large population of small and uncharacterized asteroids with poorly determined orbits. In Table 2 there are 15 opportunities (in bold) over the ~2020–2035 timeframe that are achievable with IMLEO and power levels commensurate with extended stays in lunar orbit. If larger SEP systems are available (up to 400 kW), then larger targets (at least 50 m) with lower orbit uncertainty (of 3 or less) are accessible at least six times during this timeframe. Only one well characterized asteroid, 2004 MN4 (Apophis) famous for its close approach to Earth in April 2029, provided reasonable IMLEO and power for short duration missions.

If one-year round trip missions are acceptable, then a more attractive set of accessible NEAs begins to emerge. In Table 3 there are 14 mission opportunities to targets that are estimated to be 100 m diameter or larger with a SEP system of at most 300 kW. If 300 kW systems are not developed, then a 200 kW SEP system can enable 19 missions (in bold) to moderately sized NEAs (larger than about 30 m) with at most 120 t launched to LEO for the DSV. A more modest technology development program would produce at least five missions achievable with 100 kW SEP systems and 100 t IMLEO.

These short-duration, low-power missions may be desirable to test the waters of deep space beyond the vicinity of the Earth and Moon, but eventually more difficult missions will be desired to begin testing systems for the exploration of Mars. A round trip mission to Phobos and Deimos is achievable for around 300 t IMLEO with 600–800 kW SEP systems and a round trip flight time of three years.[44] (Mars surface exploration is generally considered more difficult than a mission to its moons, though the natural gravity and radiation shielding of the planet provides some benefit.) The mission capabilities required for Mars exploration set a threshold on technology development during the NEA campaign (assuming "Mars is the ultimate destination for human exploration"[1]), which in turn informs the investment in technologies that provide the most leverage during the transition from cislunar excursions to sustainable deep space exploration. It is noteworthy that from this sustainable program perspective, the technologies and architectures that enable the quickest and cheapest NEA mission are not necessarily the most expedient for the overall program.

The development of a 200 kW SEP stage to propel a deep space habitat that can keep the astronauts safe, happy, and productive for up to 540 days enables the exploration of a diverse set of NEAs. In Table 4, there are 13 opportunities to visit an asteroid with a known spectral type and well-determined orbit for DSV IMLEO less than 130 t and SEP power up to 200 kW. With a 300 kW SEP stage there are 20 missions with 540 d flight time to targets that are estimated to be at least 500 m diameter. As exploration capability approaches levels required for Mars the variety of accessible NEAs continues to proliferate. A program that develops 250 t IMLEO capability (with separate launches), 400 kW SEP systems, and in-space mission durations of up to two years introduces regular access to kilometer-sized NEOs with nine examples in Table 5 and three others in Table 4. The exploration of a variety of targets that are relatively difficult to reach builds a proficiency in performing deep space missions that sets the stage for the human exploration of Mars.

The frequency of launch opportunities for a given mission increases not only with the ability to reach a range of targets but also when a NEA becomes accessible over multiple launch years. The ability to design a mission to a single target with multiple backup opportunities adds flexibility to the program schedule. While sets of mission opportunities emerge with impulsive-maneuver trajectories, they appear to be more common with low-thrust trajectories. The relatively high specific impulse of SEP reduces the sensitivity of IMLEO to the variations in ΔV across different opportunities, which makes it more likely for a given target to have similar mass and power requirements for separate launch years. For example, in Table 2 there is a pair of mission opportunities to both 2000 SG344 and 2004 MN4 in 2028 and 2029, and two separate opportunities to 2006 FH36. For 360 day missions in Table 3 there are three opportunities to 2007 UY1, and two pairs of launches to 2001 CQ36. With 540 day mission durations, 1989 UQ and 2002 OA22 have three opportunities over the timeframe of interest; there is a cluster of three potential missions to 1991 JW in 2026 and 2027; and there are two pairs of opportunities to 2001 CC21 in the early 2020s. Certain targets become accessible at regular intervals with longer flight times, where 1998 WT24, 2000 EX106, and 2003 UC20 appear three times, while 2002 RW25 and 2003 SD220 appear four times in Table 5. These last two targets have a semi-major axis less than Earth's (classified as an Aten orbit) and perihelia below Venus' orbit. While the frequency of opportunities to these targets is desirable from a programmatic perspective, the low perihelia increase thermal and, more notably, radiation doses that are less desirable from a mission design perspective. Thus the mission parameters provided in Table 2–Table 5 give an overview of which targets are accessible with a given technology, but they do not provide all of the information necessary to determine the suitability of a given mission.

Table 2. 180 and 270 Day Missions

Designation	Launch Date	DSV[a] IMLEO (t)	Power (kW)	C_3 (km^2/s^2)	SEP ΔV (km/s)	Spectral Type	Diameter (m)[b]	Orbit Code
2009 YF	6/18/2019	153	320	34.165	5.731		40	7
2008 EA9	11/19/2019 [c]	83	314	5.888	4.005		10	5
2001 GP2	**1/5/2020**	**61**	**90**	**6.898**	**2.033**		**14**	**6**
2007 UN12	**5/29/2020**	**71**	**170**	**2.856**	**3.525**		**6**	**4**
2007 UY1	10/16/2020	156	380	31.752	5.894		91	2
2006 FH36	11/9/2020	165	293	41.518	5.627		90	3
2011 AU4	3/31/2021	90	257	5.388	4.918		23	6
2010 UE51	5/9/2023	87	246	4.095	4.78		7	2
2010 UE51	8/11/2023 [c]	83	355	1.821	4.336		7	2
2001 QJ142	1/25/2024	100	323	3.988	5.668		71	6
2008 CM74	**9/30/2024**	**82**	**179**	**9.551**	**3.853**		**8**	**6**
2007 XB23	**12/10/2024** [c]	**61**	**65**	**19.153**	**0.776**		**13**	**6**
2008 ST	**5/19/2025**	**79**	**184**	**7.157**	**3.789**		**13**	**5**
2008 JL24	9/22/2025	106	282	12.185	5.405		4	3
2009 HC	7/11/2026	99	253	16.305	4.242		38	4
2000 SG344	**5/26/2028**	**58**	**86**	**5.415**	**1.736**		**38**	**3**
2006 RH120	6/23/2028 [c]	73	279	1.605	3.644		4	1
2004 MN4	7/22/2028	141	257	32.724	5.527	Sq[45]	270[46]	0
2008 UA202	**1/20/2029**	**65**	**94**	**9.708**	**2.088**		**4**	**6**
2000 SG344	1/31/2029 [c]	72	224	6.238	3.223		38	3
2004 MN4	4/13/2029	129	208	34.407	4.594	Sq[45]	270[46]	0
2002 XY38	6/2/2029	177	397	32.427	7.067		89	1
2000 SG344	**11/23/2029**	**67**	**104**	**8.324**	**2.616**		**38**	**3**
2006 DQ14	8/25/2030 [c]	95	301	15.68	3.986		13	6
2009 YR	**9/6/2030**	**73**	**145**	**9.26**	**2.959**		**9**	**5**
2001 CQ36	2/3/2031	132	244	32.309	4.931		68[47]	2
2008 EA9	**10/1/2033**	**81**	**198**	**6.088**	**4.089**		**10**	**5**
2010 TE55	**6/11/2034**	**88**	**190**	**13.18**	**3.927**		**9**	**3**
2010 JK1	7/2/2034	131	323	25.459	5.292		46	6
2007 VU6	**10/14/2034**	**75**	**122**	**12.782**	**2.928**		**17**	**5**
2006 FH36	10/31/2034	151	363	27.066	6.312		90	3
2007 YF	**11/30/2034**	**83**	**158**	**14.214**	**3.446**		**38**	**5**
2010 JK1	2/2/2035	157	270	42.322	5.113		46	6
2007 VU6	**5/10/2035**	**84**	**130**	**17.935**	**3.169**		**17**	**5**
2006 BZ147	**10/25/2036**	**90**	**141**	**22.1**	**3.218**		**28**	**3**

[a]IMLEO given for deep space vehicle only. The separate crew launch adds 35 t.
[b]Diameter approximated from absolute visual magnitude assuming 15% albedo unless otherwise referenced
[c]180 day flight time

Table 3. 360 Day Missions

Designation	Launch Date	DSV[a] IMLEO (t)	Power (kW)	C_3 (km^2/s^2)	SEP ΔV (km/s)	Spectral Type	Diameter (m)[b]	Orbit Code
2008 RH1	9/20/2019	100	236	13.564	4.372		102	3
2002 BF25	7/20/2020	155	189	45.984	4.558		103	0
2001 CQ36	12/30/2020	118	272	16.938	5.427		68[47]	2
2007 UY1	**4/4/2021**	**106**	**144**	**24.428**	**4.090**		**91**	**2**
2001 CQ36	6/23/2021	94	254	2.729	5.315		68[47]	2
2006 SY5	9/7/2022	133	192	28.711	5.518		90[47]	3
2006 GB	9/26/2022	156	191	39.877	5.555		304	2
2008 EV5	12/30/2022	158	192	46.206	4.728	C[48]	450[49]	0
2007 SQ6	**10/3/2023**	**95**	**126**	**22.53**	**3.281**		**143**	**3**
2008 EV5	**6/23/2024**	**99**	**132**	**23.624**	**3.592**	C[48]	**450[49]**	**0**
1999 RA32	**9/14/2024**	**108**	**140**	**27.986**	**3.714**		**226**	**2**
2001 CC21	10/15/2024	206	410	33.020	8.163	L[50]	711	0
1999 RA32	3/13/2025	191	343	38.327	6.996		226	2
2010 WR7	12/10/2025	147	182	41.273	4.788		67	6
2009 HC	**4/18/2026**	**60**	**86**	**4.614**	**1.782**		**38**	**4**
1991 JW	6/3/2026	173	343	30.785	7.029	S[51]	500	0
2007 UP6	10/27/2026	162	197	45.836	5.029		91	2
1991 JW	5/9/2027	129	255	21.741	5.727	S[51]	500	0
2010 WR7	**7/23/2027**	**115**	**147**	**28.921**	**4.238**		**67**	**6**
2000 SG344	**4/9/2028**	**48**	**37**	**1.136**	**0.536**		**38**	**3**
2007 UP6	**4/21/2028**	**106**	**138**	**28.842**	**3.370**		**91**	**2**
2004 MN4	**4/24/2028**	**101**	**192**	**8.871**	**5.631**	Sq[45]	**270[46]**	**0**
2004 MN4	**4/13/2029**	**99**	**130**	**33.048**	**2.006**	Sq[45]	**270[46]**	**0**
2000 SG344	**10/22/2029**	**48**	**38**	**1.876**	**0.489**		**38**	**3**
2006 BJ55	**2/6/2030**	**102**	**134**	**26.760**	**3.345**		**49**	**6**
2001 CQ36	2/9/2030	187	223	53.676	5.296		68[47]	2
2001 CQ36	1/29/2031	105	201	23.066	3.727		68[47]	2
2006 BJ55	**8/14/2031**	**87**	**131**	**11.721**	**4.057**		**49**	**6**
2002 AW	3/18/2032	153	188	40.036	5.339		267	2
2007 UY1	8/23/2032	87	237	11.271	3.315		91	2
2009 TP	10/12/2032	149	182	47.718	3.897		67	6
2007 UY1	5/14/2033	178	301	37.073	6.664		91	2
2007 YF	**12/1/2033**	**118**	**150**	**33.282**	**3.748**		**38**	**5**
2006 BZ147	**2/28/2034**	**89**	**120**	**22.954**	**2.528**		**28**	**3**
2006 FH36	**3/27/2034**	**106**	**157**	**25.577**	**3.725**		**90**	**3**
2007 YF	**11/29/2034**	**87**	**163**	**13.481**	**3.494**		**38**	**5**
2006 BZ147	**2/6/2035**	**55**	**53**	**5.682**	**0.997**		**28**	**3**
2009 TP	**5/9/2035**	**85**	**89**	**21.561**	**2.588**		**67**	**6**
2005 GE60	6/10/2035	185	222	46.535	6.263		130	4
1998 XN17	11/27/2035	183	219	49.317	5.730		113	2
2002 CD	5/2/2036	156	345	15.382	8.184	C[52]	294	1
2001 TE2	9/25/2036	180	300	39.069	6.484		362	0

[a]IMLEO given for deep space vehicle only. The separate crew launch adds 35 t.
[b]Diameter approximated from absolute visual magnitude assuming 15% albedo unless otherwise referenced

Table 4. 540 Day Missions

Designation	Launch Date	DSV[a] IMLEO (t)	Power (kW)	C_3 (km²/s²)	SEP ΔV (km/s)	Spectral Type	Diameter (m)[b]	Orbit Code
2004 MN4	**10/13/2019**	**93**	**125**	**12.385**	**3.696**	**Sq[45]**	**270[46]**	**0**
2003 SD220	7/4/2020	192	232	33.706	7.687		1457	1
2001 CC21	12/4/2020	146	190	24.373	6.301	L[50]	711	0
2002 OA22	**3/27/2021**	**125**	**160**	**20.946**	**5.348**		**473**	**1**
1998 MW5	6/24/2021	165	278	18.399	7.994	Sq[50]	516	2
2006 SY5	**9/1/2021**	**91**	**109**	**13.112**	**3.451**		**90[47]**	**3**
2001 CC21	**12/18/2021**	**100**	**133**	**10.868**	**4.684**	L[50]	711	**0**
2006 GB	**3/30/2022**	**122**	**157**	**22.579**	**4.863**		**304**	**2**
2000 EE104	10/27/2022	163	200	32.720	6.180		318	0
2006 SY5	**3/4/2023**	**96**	**129**	**14.558**	**3.730**		**90[47]**	**3**
1998 MW5	6/27/2023	223	294	37.584	8.330	Sq[50]	516	2
2008 EV5	**12/28/2023**	**81**	**72**	**16.642**	**1.977**	**C[48]**	**450[49]**	**0**
1992 BF	1/21/2024	210	266	36.620	8.013	Xc[50]	510[47]	0
2004 FM17	3/22/2024	165	276	20.673	7.663		493	1
2001 CC21	**6/10/2024**	**129**	**164**	**18.324**	**6.060**	**L[50]**	711	**0**
1989 UQ	**8/22/2024**	**117**	**151**	**18.117**	**5.131**	**B[50]**	**730[47]**	**0**
2001 CC21	**5/30/2025**	**107**	**141**	**14.248**	**4.838**	**L[50]**	711	**0**
1999 AQ10	8/23/2025	130	165	23.173	5.362	S[50]	295	0
1991 JW	**5/16/2026**	**108**	**127**	**23.506**	**3.584**	**S[51]**	**500**	**0**
2001 TE2	9/21/2026	167	238	23.128	7.673		362	0
1991 JW	**11/20/2026**	**99**	**187**	**11.218**	**4.124**	**S[51]**	**500**	**0**
2004 MN4	**10/30/2027**	**86**	**117**	**8.764**	**3.517**	**Sq[45]**	**270[46]**	**0**
1991 JW	**11/19/2027**	**105**	**138**	**17.169**	**4.192**	**S[51]**	**500**	**0**
2001 TE2	3/18/2028	145	182	28.255	5.741		362	0
1992 BF	8/9/2028	149	295	16.309	7.046	Xc[50]	510[47]	0
2003 GS	10/16/2028	212	252	39.757	7.741		549	0
2004 FM17	3/21/2029	173	293	21.467	7.952		493	1
2006 SF6	**5/15/2029**	**135**	**171**	**26.435**	**5.297**		**360**	**2**
2002 OA22	**3/16/2030**	**132**	**167**	**22.658**	**5.627**		**473**	**1**
1989 UQ	**6/10/2030**	**126**	**160**	**23.338**	**5.034**	**B[50]**	**730[47]**	**0**
2001 QC34	12/29/2030	217	256	49.634	6.524	Q[53]	378	0
1989 UQ	**8/18/2031**	**118**	**152**	**18.716**	**5.081**	**B[50]**	**730[47]**	**0**
2001 QC34	1/12/2032	160	267	19.356	7.530	Q[53]	378	0
1999 JU3	6/28/2032	229	297	34.937	9.006	Cg[50]	980[54]	0
2002 OA22	**9/12/2032**	**119**	**154**	**19.570**	**5.085**		**473**	**1**
2002 CD	**10/3/2032**	**90**	**122**	**13.475**	**3.279**	**C[52]**	**294**	**1**
2000 HA24	10/18/2032	198	238	37.139	7.470		569	0
2002 CD	**10/5/2033**	**88**	**120**	**12.157**	**3.265**	**C[52]**	**294**	**1**
1996 FG3	2/22/2034	213	300	35.538	8.089	C[50]	1900[47]	0
1999 AQ10	**8/14/2034**	**131**	**166**	**22.783**	**5.522**	**S[50]**	**295**	**0**
1996 FG3	2/5/2035	184	343	21.215	8.305	C[50]	1900[47]	0
1999 RQ36	9/14/2035	141	176	29.843	5.170	B[55]	580[56]	0

[a]IMLEO given for deep space vehicle only. The separate crew launch adds 35 t.
[b]Diameter approximated from absolute visual magnitude assuming 15% albedo unless otherwise referenced

Table 5. 720 Day Missions

Designation	Launch Date	DSV[a] IMLEO (t)	Power (kW)	C_3 (km^2/s^2)	SEP ΔV (km/s)	Spectral Type	Diameter (m)[b]	Orbit Code
1999 JU3	6/16/2019	183	246	13.635	9.253	Cg[50]	980[54]	0
2003 UC20	**11/17/2019**	**149**	**151**	**22.175**	**6.287**	**C[52]**	**813**	**0**
2003 CY18	7/31/2020	210	278	46.093	5.701		861	0
1982 HR	10/4/2020	205	463	18.151	8.499		300[57]	0
1996 GT	11/4/2020	145	364	19.039	5.085	Xk[50]	880	0
1989 FB	4/6/2021	246	392	32.251	8.895		1300[57]	0
2000 HA24	**8/7/2021**	**148**	**185**	**17.150**	**6.741**		**569**	**0**
2003 SD220	**12/16/2021**	**161**	**174**	**28.997**	**5.999**		**1457**	**1**
1996 FG3	**1/12/2022**	**159**	**198**	**17.153**	**7.467**	**C[50]**	**1900[47]**	**0**
2002 NW16	7/10/2022	233	499	25.449	8.660		887	0
1996 GT	10/15/2022	172	244	34.822	5.356	Xk[50]	880	0
1996 FG3	**4/10/2023**	**165**	**204**	**16.818**	**7.866**	**C[50]**	**1900[47]**	**0**
1982 HR	10/6/2024	205	453	18.471	8.536		300[57]	0
2003 SD220	**12/22/2024**	**176**	**179**	**27.573**	**7.131**		**1457**	**1**
1999 FP59	9/10/2026	175	427	30.830	5.012		835	0
2002 RW25	**9/11/2026**	**136**	**131**	**18.472**	**6.021**		**606**	**1**
2004 OB	11/8/2026	171	422	18.734	6.645	C[52]	601	1
2003 SD220	7/4/2027	250	368	23.216	10.494		1457	1
2000 EX106	1/24/2028	232	448	24.951	8.998	S[50]	621[47]	0
2007 HF44	**12/13/2028**	**134**	**169**	**28.979**	**3.934**		**498**	**3**
2000 EX106	2/10/2029	181	222	22.091	8.026	S[50]	621[47]	0
2002 RW25	**9/12/2029**	**136**	**147**	**17.432**	**6.062**		**606**	**1**
1998 WT24	12/8/2029	210	237	43.140	6.403	E[58]	420[58]	0
1991 VH	2/21/2030	243	289	27.703	10.014	Sk[59]	1120[47]	0
2002 TD60	6/2/2030	159	397	9.922	7.318		501	0
2003 UC20	**12/2/2030**	**141**	**120**	**21.641**	**6.023**	**C[52]**	**813**	**0**
2007 HF44	**12/10/2030**	**133**	**168**	**28.674**	**3.886**		**498**	**3**
2002 TD60	6/1/2031	191	298	21.386	8.233		501	0
1998 YN1	5/5/2032	205	427	28.650	7.144		862	0
2000 HA24	**7/30/2032**	**149**	**187**	**16.396**	**6.939**		**569**	**0**
2002 RW25	**9/13/2032**	**136**	**162**	**15.908**	**6.155**		**606**	**1**
1992 SL	9/14/2032	203	487	33.354	5.957		903	0
2003 UC20	**12/3/2032**	**144**	**144**	**19.694**	**6.320**	**C[52]**	**813**	**0**
1998 WT24	12/12/2032	205	246	32.594	7.690	E[58]	420[58]	0
2003 SD220	7/7/2033	251	337	27.542	10.106		1457	1
1999 VG22	2/24/2034	184	315	34.623	5.727		662	1
2002 RW25	**9/13/2035**	**136**	**159**	**15.774**	**6.216**		**606**	**1**
1998 WT24	12/14/2035	209	252	27.064	8.694	E[58]	420[58]	0
1999 VG22	1/29/2036	146	277	23.158	5.098		662	1
2000 EX106	2/12/2036	173	213	20.514	7.825	S[50]	621[47]	0
2001 QC34	**7/6/2036**	**144**	**182**	**11.508**	**7.373**	**Q[53]**	**378**	**0**
1994 CN2	9/6/2036	144	363	16.482	5.416		1668	1

[a]IMLEO given for deep space vehicle only. The separate crew launch adds 35 t.
[b]Diameter approximated from absolute visual magnitude assuming 15% albedo unless otherwise referenced

Individual mission examples

The list of targets generated from an accessibility study provides an overview of which target characteristics can be associated with a given set of technologies. A NEA exploration campaign emerges from this overview by choosing a sequence of missions that can accomplish the objectives for human spaceflight. Flexibility is introduced to the exploration program by designing multiple target sequences that account for delays in technology development, changes to the mission schedule, and shifts in overall program objectives and policy. However, the current design of mission sequences is necessarily incomplete given the dearth of information available for most targets.[17] Nevertheless, we provide example mission sets with different technology options assuming that the first asteroid mission occurs in the 2020s and that the overall objective of the NEA campaign is to develop a proficiency in deep space that leads to the human exploration of Mars. A diverse catalogue of mission sequences provides the flexibility necessary to adapt to an evolving development path to Mars.

We believe that the most exciting and productive NEA missions push technology to a midpoint between current designs and Mars capability and explore asteroids that are at least a few hundred meters across. Four such examples are provided in Figure 2, where an IMLEO of 150 t (including crew launch) and flight time of 540 days are half the Mars-orbital requirements and 150 kW is a fifth of the Mars design.[44] The variety of launch years to these targets provides the flexibility to complete an important step towards Mars as soon as the technology can be developed.

While these advanced missions are attractive for their exploration value, we do not suggest that the first long-duration test flights occur on a NEA mission. Instead, the assembly of the DSV in high-Earth orbit and exploration of the Moon from lunar orbit provide productive and meaningful missions that can qualify vehicles for deep space while the astronauts remain only a few days from Earth. Even if the first asteroid mission is designed to last only a few months, cislunar test flights provide more robust abort options than deep space NEA excursions. The key technological barrier does not appear to be launching mass to orbit or high-power SEP systems, but instead the mitigation of radiation hazards. Many propose NEA excursions with limited mission duration,[8–16] which limits the cumulative radiation dose. (Alternatively, additional radiation shielding provides a prophylactic against radiation exposure during longer missions.) While the environmental effects on humans in deep space remains a key issue, there are many options for NEA exploration with mission durations of a year or less. If a 300 kW SEP system is developed then 2006 FH36 and 2004 MN4 provide 270-day missions to sizable targets in 2020 and 2029, respectively. These missions are portrayed in Figure 3, where the same SEP system and launch vehicles combined with an upgraded habitat provide one-year mission to 1991 JW in 2027. If a 300 kW SEP system is not developed, several options for one-year durations still exist at lower power levels where a mission to 1999 RA32 in 2024 is given as an example.

Alternatively, if more resources are allocated to developing deep space habitation as opposed to launch vehicle capacity and SEP systems with ISS-sized arrays, then a different set of missions emerge. In Figure 4 a 100 t DSV with a 130-kW SEP stage provides an opportunity to explore 2008 EV4 in 2024. Alternatively, a mission with much smaller IMLEO and power is available to the much smaller target 2000 SG344 in 2028 (and again in 2029) following a more languid technology development schedule. Further development of two-year habitats enables a steady launch cadence to relatively large objects with 150-kW systems as exemplified by the 2002 RW25 and 2003 UC20 missions in 2029 and 2030.

Provided a set of missions with a variety of targets and technologies, a NEO exploration program can be designed to progress from cislunar capability up to the threshold of Mars exploration. A notional sequence in Figure 5 begins with a six-month, low mass, low power mission to 2007 XB23 in 2024. We note that this mission is exceptional, but serves as a proof of concept for the mission architecture using limited exploration capability. As new NEAs are detected, it is assumed that missions with similar trajectories will be available in multiple launch years with better characterized and potentially larger targets. Alternatively, the capability to survive up to a year in deep space could be developed during cislunar and lunar missions, which dramatically increases the variety of known accessible targets. A 330-day mission with moderate mass and power requirements to Apophis (2004 MN4) could then occur in 2029. Following this mission, any of the NEAs in Figure 2 would make a respectable next target, or the development of higher power and launch capability enables a 500-day mission to 1996 FG3 in 2034. This NEA makes an attractive target because it is large, potentially primitive, and has a satellite. The addition of a binary adds significant complexity to the mission, which would have to be considered in context of eventual Mars (including Phobos and Deimos) exploration objectives. The final mission in Figure 5 is to the relatively large Mars-crossing asteroid 1994 CN2. This trajectory is unique in that it remains outside of Earth's orbit for the duration of the mission, and may provide the closest analogue to a Mars orbital mission.

The opportunities depicted in Figure 2–Figure 5 provide a small subset of the example mission sequences that can be created from the target lists in Table 2–Table 5. Further, these target lists represent a hand-picked portion of the steadily growing catalogue of NEAs that are accessible with different technology options. Depending on how technology development for deep space evolves, there are myriad combinations of missions that create a flexible campaign to explore NEAs. While the population of currently known asteroids that provide short duration missions is relatively anemic, there is a variety of enticing missions for flight times of one to two years. As human spaceflight transitions to deep space exploration, NEAs provide many options to push farther from Earth and closer to Mars.

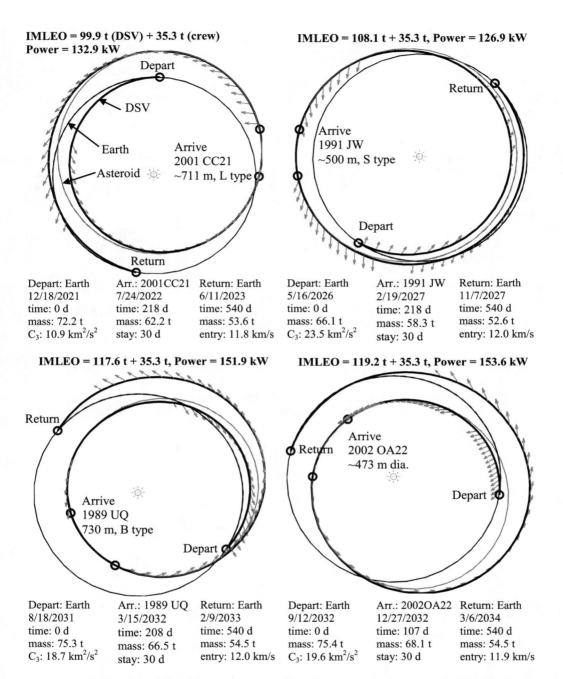

IMLEO = 99.9 t (DSV) + 35.3 t (crew)
Power = 132.9 kW

Depart

DSV

Earth

Asteroid

Arrive
2001 CC21
~711 m, L type

Return

Depart: Earth	Arr.: 2001CC21	Return: Earth
12/18/2021	7/24/2022	6/11/2023
time: 0 d	time: 218 d	time: 540 d
mass: 72.2 t	mass: 62.2 t	mass: 53.6 t
C_3: 10.9 km^2/s^2	stay: 30 d	entry: 11.8 km/s

IMLEO = 108.1 t + 35.3 t, Power = 126.9 kW

Return

Arrive
1991 JW
~500 m, S type

Depart

Depart: Earth	Arr.: 1991 JW	Return: Earth
5/16/2026	2/19/2027	11/7/2027
time: 0 d	time: 218 d	time: 540 d
mass: 66.1 t	mass: 58.3 t	mass: 52.6 t
C_3: 23.5 km^2/s^2	stay: 30 d	entry: 12.0 km/s

IMLEO = 117.6 t + 35.3 t, Power = 151.9 kW

Return

Arrive
1989 UQ
730 m, B type

Depart

Depart: Earth	Arr.: 1989 UQ	Return: Earth
8/18/2031	3/15/2032	2/9/2033
time: 0 d	time: 208 d	time: 540 d
mass: 75.3 t	mass: 66.5 t	mass: 54.5 t
C_3: 18.7 km^2/s^2	stay: 30 d	entry: 12.0 km/s

IMLEO = 119.2 t + 35.3 t, Power = 153.6 kW

Arrive
2002 OA22
~473 m dia.

Return

Depart

Depart: Earth	Arr.: 2002OA22	Return: Earth
9/12/2032	12/27/2032	3/6/2034
time: 0 d	time: 107 d	time: 540 d
mass: 75.4 t	mass: 68.1 t	mass: 54.5 t
C_3: 19.6 km^2/s^2	stay: 30 d	entry: 11.9 km/s

Figure 2 Multiple NEAs 500 m or larger become accessible with 150 t IMLEO, 150 kW SEP power, and 540 day flight time.

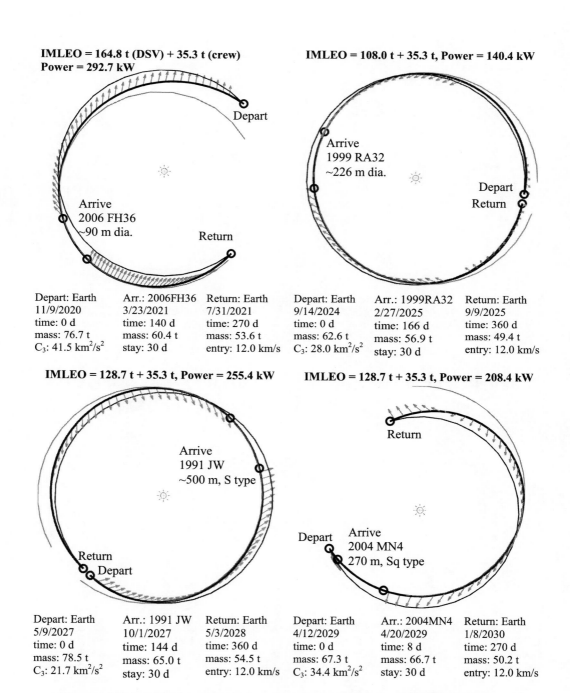

IMLEO = 164.8 t (DSV) + 35.3 t (crew)
Power = 292.7 kW

Depart

Arrive
2006 FH36
~90 m dia.

Return

Depart: Earth	Arr.: 2006FH36	Return: Earth
11/9/2020	3/23/2021	7/31/2021
time: 0 d	time: 140 d	time: 270 d
mass: 76.7 t	mass: 60.4 t	mass: 53.6 t
C_3: 41.5 km^2/s^2	stay: 30 d	entry: 12.0 km/s

IMLEO = 108.0 t + 35.3 t, Power = 140.4 kW

Arrive
1999 RA32
~226 m dia.

Depart
Return

Depart: Earth	Arr.: 1999RA32	Return: Earth
9/14/2024	2/27/2025	9/9/2025
time: 0 d	time: 166 d	time: 360 d
mass: 62.6 t	mass: 56.9 t	mass: 49.4 t
C_3: 28.0 km^2/s^2	stay: 30 d	entry: 12.0 km/s

IMLEO = 128.7 t + 35.3 t, Power = 255.4 kW

Arrive
1991 JW
~500 m, S type

Return
Depart

Depart: Earth	Arr.: 1991 JW	Return: Earth
5/9/2027	10/1/2027	5/3/2028
time: 0 d	time: 144 d	time: 360 d
mass: 78.5 t	mass: 65.0 t	mass: 54.5 t
C_3: 21.7 km^2/s^2	stay: 30 d	entry: 12.0 km/s

IMLEO = 128.7 t + 35.3 t, Power = 208.4 kW

Return

Depart
Arrive
2004 MN4
270 m, Sq type

Depart: Earth	Arr.: 2004MN4	Return: Earth
4/12/2029	4/20/2029	1/8/2030
time: 0 d	time: 8 d	time: 270 d
mass: 67.3 t	mass: 66.7 t	mass: 50.2 t
C_3: 34.4 km^2/s^2	stay: 30 d	entry: 12.0 km/s

Figure 3 Mission durations of one year or less occur regularly with 300 kW SEP systems.

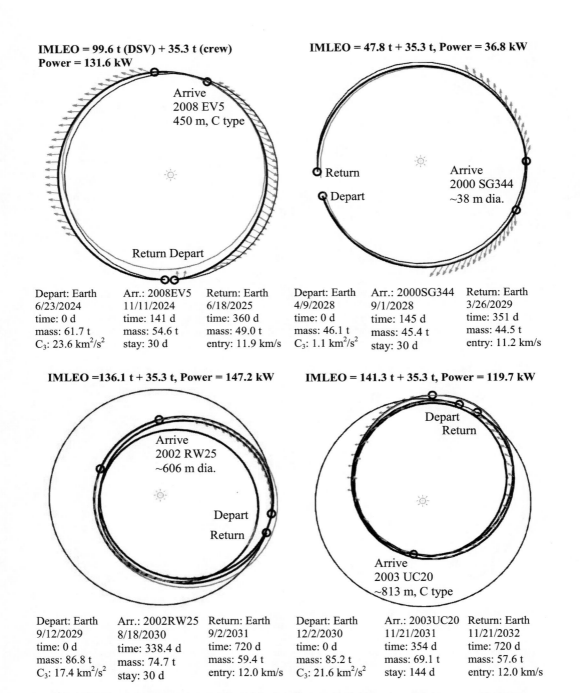

IMLEO = 99.6 t (DSV) + 35.3 t (crew)
Power = 131.6 kW

Arrive
2008 EV5
450 m, C type

Return Depart

IMLEO = 47.8 t + 35.3 t, Power = 36.8 kW

Return

Depart

Arrive
2000 SG344
~38 m dia.

Depart: Earth	Arr.: 2008EV5	Return: Earth	Depart: Earth	Arr.: 2000SG344	Return: Earth
6/23/2024	11/11/2024	6/18/2025	4/9/2028	9/1/2028	3/26/2029
time: 0 d	time: 141 d	time: 360 d	time: 0 d	time: 145 d	time: 351 d
mass: 61.7 t	mass: 54.6 t	mass: 49.0 t	mass: 46.1 t	mass: 45.4 t	mass: 44.5 t
C_3: 23.6 km^2/s^2	stay: 30 d	entry: 11.9 km/s	C_3: 1.1 km^2/s^2	stay: 30 d	entry: 11.2 km/s

IMLEO =136.1 t + 35.3 t, Power = 147.2 kW

Arrive
2002 RW25
~606 m dia.

Depart

Return

IMLEO = 141.3 t + 35.3 t, Power = 119.7 kW

Depart
Return

Arrive
2003 UC20
~813 m, C type

Depart: Earth	Arr.: 2002RW25	Return: Earth	Depart: Earth	Arr.: 2003UC20	Return: Earth
9/12/2029	8/18/2030	9/2/2031	12/2/2030	11/21/2031	11/21/2032
time: 0 d	time: 338.4 d	time: 720 d	time: 0 d	time: 354 d	time: 720 d
mass: 86.8 t	mass: 74.7 t	mass: 59.4 t	mass: 85.2 t	mass: 69.1 t	mass: 57.6 t
C_3: 17.4 km^2/s^2	stay: 30 d	entry: 12.0 km/s	C_3: 21.6 km^2/s^2	stay: 144 d	entry: 12.0 km/s

Figure 4 A variety of NEA characteristics and mission durations exist for SEP power below 150 kW.

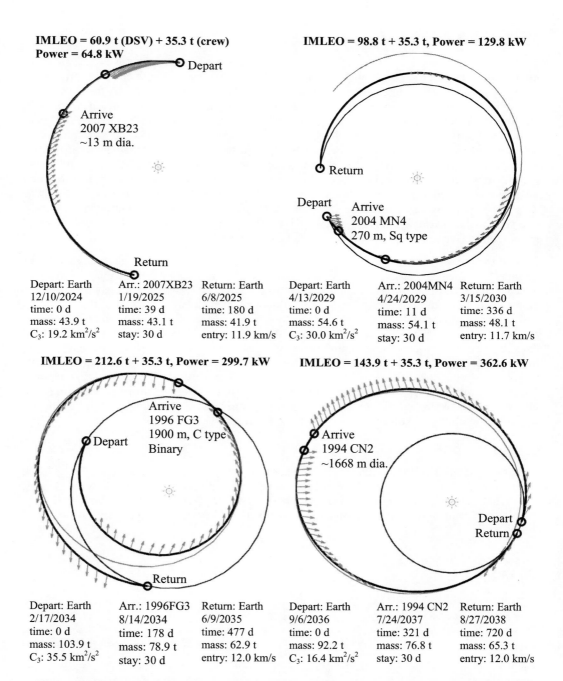

IMLEO = 60.9 t (DSV) + 35.3 t (crew)
Power = 64.8 kW

Depart

Arrive
2007 XB23
~13 m dia.

Return

IMLEO = 98.8 t + 35.3 t, Power = 129.8 kW

Return

Depart   Arrive
2004 MN4
270 m, Sq type

Depart: Earth	Arr.: 2007XB23	Return: Earth	Depart: Earth	Arr.: 2004MN4	Return: Earth
12/10/2024	1/19/2025	6/8/2025	4/13/2029	4/24/2029	3/15/2030
time: 0 d	time: 39 d	time: 180 d	time: 0 d	time: 11 d	time: 336 d
mass: 43.9 t	mass: 43.1 t	mass: 41.9 t	mass: 54.6 t	mass: 54.1 t	mass: 48.1 t
C_3: 19.2 km^2/s^2	stay: 30 d	entry: 11.9 km/s	C_3: 30.0 km^2/s^2	stay: 30 d	entry: 11.7 km/s

IMLEO = 212.6 t + 35.3 t, Power = 299.7 kW

Arrive
1996 FG3
1900 m, C type
Binary

Depart

Return

IMLEO = 143.9 t + 35.3 t, Power = 362.6 kW

Arrive
1994 CN2
~1668 m dia.

Depart
Return

Depart: Earth	Arr.: 1996FG3	Return: Earth	Depart: Earth	Arr.: 1994 CN2	Return: Earth
2/17/2034	8/14/2034	6/9/2035	9/6/2036	7/24/2037	8/27/2038
time: 0 d	time: 178 d	time: 477 d	time: 0 d	time: 321 d	time: 720 d
mass: 103.9 t	mass: 78.9 t	mass: 62.9 t	mass: 92.2 t	mass: 76.8 t	mass: 65.3 t
C_3: 35.5 km^2/s^2	stay: 30 d	entry: 12.0 km/s	C_3: 16.4 km^2/s^2	stay: 30 d	entry: 12.0 km/s

Figure 5 Mission targets become increasingly more attractive as exploration capability matures.

CONCLUSIONS

The hybrid combination of a high thrust Earth departure stage with a high power SEP stage for interplanetary flight produces a much larger set of NEA missions than with chemical propulsion alone. A progressively wider selection of larger asteroids become accessible as the SEP power level or mission flight time increases, suggesting a NEA exploration campaign that incrementally develops technologies to a level needed for the eventual exploration of Mars. The individual missions of this campaign could be combined into multiple sequences that connect a path from cislunar space to Mars orbital missions, where each step adjusts to evolving technological capabilities and variable program objectives. The design of such a NEA campaign calls for a range of launch opportunities from those requiring limited technology, to initiate deep space exploration, and those with advanced technology to establish the capability needed to explore objects as distant as Mars. The target characteristics associated with each phase in the mission sequence are strongly correlated to the mission duration. Missions with 180-day flight time and relatively low mass and power requirements are rare, but do exist sporadically over multiple years.

Both the hybrid SEP architecture and impulsive ΔV architectures have limited target sets for missions of 270 days or shorter. Accessible targets with shorter flight times are mostly limited to objects that are less than 100 m in diameter and have poorly resolved orbits, simply because they are the majority of known NEAs. For one-year missions, a much larger fraction of the NEA population becomes accessible, and multiple launch opportunities to objects larger than 100 m with suitably defined orbits become possible. At a 540-day mission duration the accessible population expands dramatically, generating multiple opportunities to 500 m objects with a diversity of taxonomic types. The list of currently known NEAs includes many kilometer-sized targets accessible with two-year flight times and 400 kW SEP systems, a capability which brings NEA exploration to the threshold of Mars exploration. An entire spectrum of asteroid missions exists between the most accessible targets and the most challenging destinations, providing multiple options to establish a flexible and evolvable human exploration program.

ACKNOWLEDGMENTS

Our investigation of the "Electric Path" has been inspired, encouraged, and enhanced by Mark Adler, Buzz Aldrin, John Baker, John Brophy, Bret Drake, Rich Hofer, Jay Polk, Mike Sander, and Brent Sherwood. This research was carried out at the Jet Propulsion Laboratory, California Institute of Technology, under a contract with the National Aeronautics and Space Administration.

REFERENCES

[1] Augustine, N.R., "Seeking a Human Spaceflight Program Worthy of a Great Nation," Final report of the Review of U.S. Human Spaceflight Plans Committee, October 2009.

[2] Obama, B.H., "Remarks by the President on Space Exploration in the 21st Century," John F. Kennedy Space Center, April 15, 2010, (http://www.whitehouse.gov/the-pressoffice/remarks-president-space-exploration-21st-century).

[3] Smith, E., Northrup Space Laboratories, Hawthorne, California, "A Manned Flyby Mission to [433] Eros," February 1966.

[4] Niehoff, J. C., "Round-Trip Mission Requirements for Asteroids 1976AA and 1973EC," *Icarus*, Vol. 31, No. 4, August 1977, pp. 430–438.

[5] Shoemaker, E. M. and Helin, E. F., "Earth-Approaching Asteroids as Targets for Exploration," In *Asteroids: An Exploration Assessment*, NASA CP-2053, January 1978, pp. 245–256.

[6] Davis, D. R., Friedlander, A. L., and Jones, T. D., "Role of Near-Earth Asteroids in the Space Exploration Initiative," In *Resources of Near-Earth Space*, U. of Arizona Press, 1993, pp. 619–655.

[7] Borowski, S. K., Dudzinski, L.A., and McGuire, M. L., "Artificial Gravity Human Exploration Missions to Mars and Near-Earth Asteroids Using Bimodal NTR Propulsion," Paper AIAA 2000-3115, July 2000.

[8] Jones, T. et al., "The Next Giant Leap: Human Exploration and Utilization of Near-Earth Objects," *The Future of Solar System Exploration 2003-2013*, ASP Conference Series, 272, 2002, pp. 141–154.

[9] Korsmeyer, D. J., Landis, R. R., and Abell, P. A., "Into the Beyond: A Crewed Mission to a Near-Earth Object," *Acta Astronautica, 63*, 2008, pp. 213–220.

[10] Abell, P. A. et al., "Scientific Exploration of Near-Earth Objects via the Orion Crew Exploration Vehicle," *Meteoritics & Planetary Science*, Vol. 44, No. 12, 2009, pp. 1825–1836.

[11] Landis, R. R. et al., "Piloted Operations at a Near-Earth Object," *Acta Astronautica, 65*, 2009, pp. 1689–1697.

[12] Gil-Fernandez, J, Cadenas, R., and Graziano, M., "Analysis of Manned Missions to Near-Earth Asteroids," Paper AAS 10-243, AAS/AIAA Space Flight Mechanics Meeting, San Diego, CA, February 14–17, 2010.

[13] Zimmerman, D., Wagner, S., and Wie, B., "The First Human Asteroid Mission: Target Selection and Conceptual Mission Design," Paper AIAA 2010-8730, August 2010.

[14] Barbee, B. W. et al., "A Comprehensive Ongoing Survey of the Near-Earth Asteroid Population for Human Mission Accessibility," Paper AIAA 2010-8368, August 2010.

[15] Hopkins, J.B., and Dissel, A.F., "Plymouth Rock: Early Humans Missions to Near Earth Asteroids Using Orion Spacecraft," Paper: AIAA 2010-8608, September 2010.

[16] Adamo, D. R. et al., "Asteroid Destinations Accessible for Human Exploration: A Preliminary Survey in Mid-2009," *Journal of Spacecraft and Rockets*, Vol. 47, No. 6, 2010, pp. 994–1002.

[17] "Target NEO: Open Global Community NEO Workshop Report," George Washington University, Washington, D.C., May 2011, (http://www.targetneo.org/pdfs/TargetNEOWorkshopReport.pdf).

[18] Stuhlinger, E., "Electrical Propulsion System for Space Ships with Nuclear Power Source," *Journal of the Astronautical Sciences*, Part I, Vol. 2, winter 1955, pp.149–152; Part II, Vol. 3, spring 1956, pp.11–14; Part III, Vol. 3, summer 1956, p.33.

[19] Irving, J. H. and Blum, E. K., "Comparative Performance of Ballistic and Low-Thrust Vehicle for Flight to Mars," *Vistas in Astronautics*, Vol. II, Pergamon Press, 1959, pp.191–218.

[20] Donahue, B. B. and Cupples, M. L., "Comparative Analysis of Current NASA Human Mars Mission Architectures," *Journal of Spacecraft and Rockets*, Vol. 38, No. 5, 2001, pp.745–751.

[21] Landau, D. and Longuski, J. M., "Comparative Assessment of Human-Mars-Mission Technologies and Architectures," *Acta Astronautica*, Vol. 65, June 2009, pp. 893–911.

[22] Brophy, J.R., et al., "300-kW Solar Electric Propulsion System Configuration for Human Exploration of Near-Earth Asteroids," Paper AIAA-2011-5514, 47th AIAA/ASME/SAE/ASEE Joint Propulsion Conference & Exhibit, San Diego, CA, August 20011.

[23] *Laying the Foundation for Space Solar Power: An Assessment of NASA's Space Solar Power Investment Strategy*, National Academy Press, Washington, D.C., 2001, p. 35.

[24] Strange, N. et al., "Solar Electric Propulsion for a Flexible Path of Human Exploration," Paper IAC-10-A5.2.4., Oct. 2010.

[25] Landau, D. and Strange, N., "Human Exploration of Near-Earth Asteroids via Solar Electric Propulsion," in *Proceedings of the 21st AAS/AIAA Space Flight Mechanics Meeting*, New Orleans, LA, 13-17 February 2011. Paper AAS 11-102.

[26] "Orion Crew Exploration Vehicle," NASA Fact Sheet, FS–2008–07–031–GRC, January 2009.

[27] Drake, B. G. (ed.), "Human Exploration of Mars Design Reference Architecture 5.0," Tech. Rep. NASA-SP-2009-566, NASA, July 2009, (http://www.nasa.gov/pdf/373665main_NASA-SP-2009-566.pdf).

[28] NASA STD-3000 Man Systems Integration Standards, Revision B, July 1995, (http://msis.jsc.nasa.gov/).

[29] Kennedy, Kriss, "Lessons from TransHab: An Architect's Experience," Paper AIAA 2002-6105, October 2002.

[30] Guest, A.N., Hofstetter, W.K., Wooster, P.D., "Interplanetary Transfer Vehicle Concepts for Near-Term Human Exploration Missions Beyond Low Earth Orbit," Paper: AIAA 2010-8641, September 2010.

[31] Russell, J.F., "Environmental Control and Life Support Considerations for a Human Mission to Near-Earth Asteroids", Paper: AIAA-2010-8650, August 2010.

[32] Larson, W.J. and Pranke, L.K., *Human Spaceflight: Mission Analysis and Design*, McGraw-Hill, New York, 1999, pp. 240, 771-790.

[33] Spence, B., "High-Performance Elastically Self-Deployed Roll-Out Solar Array," NASA SBIR Proposal 08-1 S3.03-8644, 2008 (http://deployablespacesystems.com).

[34] Donahue, B., "Solar Electric and Nuclear Thermal Propulsion Architectures for Human Mars Missions Beginning in 2033," Paper: AIAA 2010-6819, July 2010.

[35] Spence, B. et al., "UltraFlex-175 Solar Array Technology Maturation Achievements for NASA's New Millennium Program (NMP) Space Technology 8 (ST8)," IEEE Photovoltaic Energy Conversion Conference, Waikoloa, HI, May 2006.

[36] Klaus, K., Smith, D.B., Kapla, M.S., "Outer Planet Science Missions Enabled by Solar Power," Abstract Contribution No. 1533, Lunar and Planetary Science Conference, March 2010, p. 1076.

[37] Manzella, D., Jankovsky, R., Hofer, R., "Laboratory Model 50 kW Hall Thruster," Paper AIAA 2002-3676, July 2002.

[38] Peterson et al., "The Performance and Wear Characterization of a High-Power High-Isp NASA Hall Thruster," Paper AIAA 2005-4243, July 2005.

[39] Brown, D.L., Beal, B.E., Haas, J.M., "Air Force Research Laboratory High Power Electric Propulsion Technology Development," 2010 IEEE Aerospace Conference, Big Sky, MT, March 2010.

[40] Mikellides, I.G. et al., "Magnetic Shielding of the Acceleration Channel Walls in a Long-Life Hall Thruster," *Physics of Plasmas*, 18, 033501 (2011).

[41] Gooding, R.H. "A procedure for the solution of Lambert's orbital boundary-value problem. *Celestial Mechanics and Dynamical Astronomy*, Vol. 48, No. 2, 1990, pp.145–165.

[42] Sims, J. A. et al., "Implementation of a Low-Thrust Trajectory Optimization Algorithm for Preliminary Design," AIAA/AAS Astrodynamics Specialist Conference, Paper AIAA 2006-6746, August 2006.

[43] Landau, D. et al., "Electric Propulsion System Selection Process for Interplanetary Missions," *Journal of Spacecraft and Rockets*, 48, 3, May–June 2011, pp. 467–476.

[44] Strange, N. et al., "Human Missions to Phobos and Deimos Using Combined Chemical and Solar Electric Propulsion," AIAA/ASME/SAE/ASEE Joint Propulsion Conference, Paper AIAA-5663, August 2011.

[45] Binzel, R. P. et al., "Spectral Properties and Composition of Potentially Hazardous Asteroid (99942) Apophis," *Icarus*, Vol. 200, No. 2, April 2009, pp. 480–485.

[46] Delbo, M., Cellino, A., and Tedesco, E. F., "Albedo and Size Determination of Potentially Hazardous Asteroids: (99942) Apophis," *Icarus*, Vol. 188, No. 1, May 2007, pp. 266–269.

[47] Mueller, M. et al., "Physical Characterization of 65 Potential Spacecraft Target Asteroids," *The Astronomical Journal*, Vol. 41, No. 109, April 2011, pp. 1–9.

[48] Somers, J. M. et al., "Optical Characterization of Planetary Radar Targets, Low-ΔV, and potentially Hazardous Asteroids: Results from 2009–2010," Abstract 13.16, American Astronomical Society DPS Meeting #42, 2010, p. 1055.

[49] Busch, M. W. et al., "Determining Asteroid Spin States Using Radar Speckles," *Icarus*, Vol. 209, No. 2, October 2010, pp. 535–541.

[50] Binzel, R. P. et al., "Dynamical and Compositional Assessment of Near-Earth Object Mission Targets," *Meteoritics & Planetary Science*, Vol. 39, No. 3, 2004, pp. 351–366.

[51] Reddy, V. et al., "Mineralogical Characterization of Potential Targets for the ASTEX Mission Scenario," *Planetary and Space Science*, Vol. 59, No. 8, June 2011, pp. 772–778.

[52] Abe, M. et al., "Ground-Based Observation of Post-Hayabusa Mission Targets," Abstract 1638, Lunar and Planetary Science XXXVIII, 2007.

[53] Vilas, F., "Spectral Characteristics of Hayabusa 2 Near-Earth Asteroid Targets 162173 1999 JU3 and 2001 QC34," *The Astronomical Journal*, Vol. 135, April 2008, pp. 1101–1105.

[54] Abe, M. et al., "Ground-Based Observational Campaign for Asteroid 162173 1999 JU3," Abstract 1594, Lunar and Planetary Science XXXIX, 2008.

[55] Campins, H. et al., "The Origin of Asteroid 101955 (1999 RQ_{36})," *The Astrophysical Journal Letters,* Vol. 721, Spetember 2010, pp. L53–L57.

[56] Nolan M. et al., "The Shape and Spin of 101955 (1999 RQ36) from Arecibo and Goldstone Radar Imaging," Abstract 13.06, American Astronomical Society DPS Meeting #39, 2007, p. 433.

[57] Gehrels, T., (ed.), *Hazards Due to Comets and Asteroids*, U. of Arizona Press, 1995, pp. 540–543.

[58] Kiselev, N. N., "Polarimetry of Near-Earth Asteroid 33342 (1998 WT24). Synthetic Phase Angle Dependence of Polarization for the E-Type Asteroids," *Proceedings of Asteroids, Comets, Meteors*, ACM International Conference, Berlin, July–August 2002, pp.887–890.

[59] Bus, S. J. and Binzel, R. P., "Phase II of the Small Main-Belt Asteroid Spectroscopic Survey: A Feature Based Taxonomy," *Icarus*, Vol. 158, No. 1, July 2002, pp. 146–177.

ORBIT OPTIONS FOR AN ORION-CLASS SPACECRAFT MISSION TO A NEAR-EARTH OBJECT

Nathan C. Shupe[*] and Daniel J. Scheeres[†]

This study seeks to identify candidate orbit options for a crewed mission to a Near-Earth Object (NEO) using an Orion-class spacecraft. A model including multiple perturbations (solar radiation pressure, solar gravity, non-spherical mass distribution of the central body) to two-body dynamics is constructed to numerically integrate the motion of a satellite in close proximity to a small body in an elliptical orbit about the Sun. Simulations about NEOs possessing various physical parameters (size, shape, rotation period) are then used to empirically develop general guidelines for establishing orbits of an Orion-class spacecraft about a NEO.

INTRODUCTION

Early in the next decade, a set of crewed flights will test and prove the systems required for exploration beyond low Earth orbit. And by 2025, we expect new spacecraft designed for long journeys to allow us to begin the first-ever crewed missions beyond the Moon into deep space. So we'll start – we'll start by sending astronauts to an asteroid for the first time in history. By the mid-2030s, I believe we can send humans to orbit Mars and return them safely to Earth. And a landing on Mars will follow. And I expect to be around to see it.

In this excerpt from a speech given on April 15, 2010 at the John F. Kennedy Space Center, President Barack Obama outlined several of the milestones from his vision for the future of U.S. human spaceflight. Among the objectives identified by the President was the goal to complete by the middle of the next decade the first-ever manned mission outside of cis-lunar space. The target of this mission will be a nearby asteroid, selected from the population of small-body objects in close proximity to the Earth known as Near-Earth Objects (NEOs).

The impetus for the inclusion of a manned NEO mission in the President's spaceflight vision came from the final report issued by the Review of U.S. Human Spaceflight Plans Committee.[1] Among its findings, the committee reported that Mars is the best candidate for the ultimate destination of human spaceflight, and that return missions to the Moon would likely be required in order to verify the systems and procedures for landing, ascent and surface operations. However, recognizing that missions to Mars will be much longer in duration and distance than missions to the Moon, the committee proposed an incremental buildup to a full-up manned mission to Mars by scheduling several intermediate missions of increasing duration, the targets for which lie outside of lunar orbit. These missions would provide the opportunity to carefully and thoroughly investigate the impacts of deep-space travel, including the long-term effects of radiation exposure and a zero-gravity environment on astronauts. NEOs were included among the destinations suggested for these missions because of the magnitude of their expected science return, as well as their likely utility in future deep space operations.

The concept of a manned mission to a NEO was first explored as part of the Space Exploration Initiative announced by President George H. W. Bush in 1989. Though the initiative only included objectives for establishing an Earth-orbiting space station, a permanent lunar base, and a manned mission to Mars, a follow-on

---

[*]Master of Science Graduate, Department of Aerospace Engineering Sciences, University of Colorado at Boulder, Boulder, CO 80309.

[†]A. Richard Seebass Endowed Chair Professor, Department of Aerospace Engineering Sciences, University of Colorado at Boulder, 429 UCB, Boulder, CO 80309.

study published in 1993 argued that manned missions to NEOs could serve as important precursors to the ultimate Mars mission and identified a number of candidate NEO targets.[2] Since that time, there have been several studies which have investigated potential NEO targets for a manned mission, including a 2002 study by former astronaut Tom Jones et al.[3] One of the most recent studies was commissioned by the Constellation Program Advanced Projects Office in 2006-2007 to examine the feasibility of sending the Orion Crew Exploration Vehicle (CEV) to a NEO.[4] This research focused on the identification of potential NEO targets for launch scenarios using various configurations of the Ares and Evolved Expendable Launch Vehicle systems. The study concluded that a number of suitable candidates for a manned mission exist in the current NEO database, and that the number of candidates will continue to increase as more NEOs are discovered in future surveys of the asteroid population.

The objective of this paper is to pick up where the previous Constellation study left off by investigating the available orbit options for an Orion-class spacecraft in close proximity to a NEO. Even though the Constellation Program was effectively canceled by the NASA Authorization Act of 2010 (S. 3729), it is assumed that the spacecraft which will ultimately be used for the President's proposed mission to a NEO will likely closely resemble the Orion CEV from the Constellation Program. Consequently, the spacecraft used for the simulations in this paper is referred to as an Orion-class spacecraft because it is modeled to have physical properties (mass, cross-sectional area) similar to that of the true Orion CEV.

MODEL

NEO orbit model

The unperturbed Keplerian orbit of the NEO about the Sun is given by the trajectory equation:

$$d = \frac{P}{1 + E \cos \nu},$$

(1)

where d is the distance measured from the Sun to the NEO, P and E are the semi-latus rectum and eccentricity parameters of the NEO Keplerian orbit respectively, and ν is the true anomaly angle measured from the periapsis direction to the position vector of the NEO in the Sun-centered inertial frame. The angular velocity, or time rate of change of the true anomaly angle, of the NEO is related to its angular momentum h by:

$$\dot{\nu} = \frac{h}{d^2}.$$

(2)

By substituting $h = \sqrt{\mu_\odot P}$, where $\mu_\odot \approx 1.327 \times 10^{11}$ km^3/s^2 is the gravitational parameter for the Sun, Eq. 2 can be rewritten as:

$$\dot{\nu} = \frac{\sqrt{\mu_\odot P}}{d^2}.$$

(3)

The angular velocity vector is given by $\mathbf{\Omega} = \dot{\nu}\hat{\mathbf{z}}$ where $\hat{\mathbf{z}}$ is a unit vector normal to the orbit plane and aligned with the angular momentum vector, $\mathbf{h} = \mathbf{d} \times \dot{\mathbf{d}}$. The $\hat{\mathbf{x}}$ unit vector points in the perihelion direction, and the final unit vector, $\hat{\mathbf{y}} = \hat{\mathbf{z}} \times \hat{\mathbf{x}}$, completes the orthogonal basis set for the Sun-centered inertial reference frame $\mathcal{N} = \{\mathcal{O}, \hat{\mathbf{x}}, \hat{\mathbf{y}}, \hat{\mathbf{z}}\}$, where $\mathcal{O}$ is the frame origin. Two other reference frames are defined, both anchored to the NEO center of mass position as the NEO orbits the Sun. The first of these NEO-centered frames is defined to be fixed inertially relative to the NEO and is denoted as $\mathcal{N}' = \{\mathcal{O}', \hat{\mathbf{x}}, \hat{\mathbf{y}}, \hat{\mathbf{z}}\}$. Though this frame is non-rotating, it is not truly inertial, since the frame origin $\mathcal{O}'$ is accelerated according to the motion of the NEO about the Sun. The second NEO-centered frame is defined to rotate with the NEO position vector, and is denoted as $\mathcal{B} = \{\mathcal{O}', \hat{\mathbf{d}}, \hat{\mathbf{z}} \times \hat{\mathbf{d}}, \hat{\mathbf{z}}\}$ where $\hat{\mathbf{d}}$ is a unit vector directed along the Sun-NEO position vector $\mathbf{d}$. A schematic of the Sun-NEO-satellite system is depicted in Figure 1.

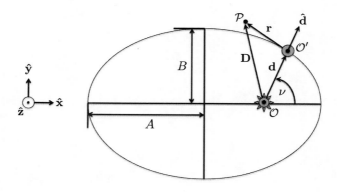

Figure 1. Notional schematic of the Sun-NEO-satellite system. The Sun is located at point $\mathcal{O}$, the NEO at point $\mathcal{O}'$, and the satellite at point $\mathcal{P}$. The Sun-centered inertial frame is denoted as $\mathcal{N} = \{\mathcal{O}, \hat{\mathbf{x}}, \hat{\mathbf{y}}, \hat{\mathbf{z}}\}$, the NEO-centered non-rotating frame as $\mathcal{N}' = \{\mathcal{O}', \hat{\mathbf{x}}, \hat{\mathbf{y}}, \hat{\mathbf{z}}\}$, and the NEO-centered rotating frame as $\mathcal{B} = \{\mathcal{O}', \hat{\mathbf{d}}, \hat{\mathbf{z}} \times \hat{\mathbf{d}}, \hat{\mathbf{z}}\}$.

NEO gravity model

The acceleration due to NEO gravity is modeled as the composite of the inertial two-body acceleration and a perturbation due to the non-spherical mass distribution of the NEO. The functional form of this model is:

$$\mathbf{a}_{\text{2body}} + \mathbf{a}_{\text{mdist}} = -\frac{\mu_{\text{N}}}{|\mathbf{r}|^3}\mathbf{r} + \frac{\partial R}{\partial \mathbf{r}}, \tag{4}$$

where $\mu_{\text{N}} = GM$ is the gravitational parameter for a NEO of mass M, $\mathbf{r} = \mathbf{D} - \mathbf{d}$ is the position vector of the satellite measured relative to the NEO position, and R is the potential due to the 2nd order and degree gravitational field perturbation.

Non-spherical mass distribution Precise mass estimates are not available for nearly all known NEOs (Eros and Itokawa are the only exceptions in the JPL small body database), but given their small size it is fair to assume that their masses are many orders of magnitude smaller than other celestial bodies in our solar system. Because their masses are so small, the gravitational fields of NEOs are far too weak to overcome rigid body forces in order to achieve a spherical shape consistent with a hydrostatic equilibrium state (pressure forces exactly balancing gravitational forces). Consequently, the true shapes of NEOs are likely to depart significantly from spheres. To model the perturbing acceleration associated with a non-spherical distribution of the NEO mass, a simple tri-axial ellipsoid model is assumed for the NEO shape. A NEO-centered fixed (rotating) reference frame is defined to be aligned with the principal body axes and is denoted $\mathcal{R} = \{\mathcal{O}', \hat{\mathbf{s}}, \hat{\mathbf{q}}, \hat{\mathbf{p}}\}$.

Because the $\mathcal{R}$ frame is aligned with the principal body axes, all off-diagonal elements of the inertia matrix evaluate to zero. If the mass density function is constant throughout the mass distribution ($\rho(r) = \rho$), then the diagonal elements of the inertia matrix are given as:

$$
\begin{aligned}
I_{11} &= \frac{M}{5}(q^2 + p^2), \\
I_{22} &= \frac{M}{5}(p^2 + s^2), \\
I_{33} &= \frac{M}{5}(s^2 + q^2),
\end{aligned}
\tag{5}
$$

where $\{s, q, p\}$ are the semi-principal axes of the ellipsoid and $M = \rho V = \rho \frac{4}{3}\pi s p q$ is the total mass of the ellipsoid. The second order and degree gravity coefficients for the ellipsoid are related to its inertia moments by:[5]

$$
C_{20} = -\frac{1}{2}(2I_z - I_x - I_y),
\tag{6}
$$

$$
C_{22} = \frac{1}{4}(I_y - I_x),
\tag{7}
$$

where $[I_x, I_y, I_z] = \frac{1}{M}[I_{11}, I_{22}, I_{33}]$ are the mass-normalized moments of inertia. Note that the other gravity coefficents – $C_{10}, C_{11}, S_{11}, C_{21}, S_{21}, S_{22}$ – all evaluate to zero because the NEO reference frame has been defined to be anchored at the NEO center of mass and oriented along the principal axes of inertia of the NEO body.[6,7] The potential due to the 2nd order and degree gravitational field perturbation is given for the general case of the ellipsoid polar axis offset from the polar axis $\hat{\mathbf{z}}$ of the reference coordinate frame:[5]

$$
R = -\frac{\mu_N}{2r^3}C_{20}\left[1 - 3(\hat{\mathbf{r}} \cdot \hat{\mathbf{p}})^2\right] + \frac{3\mu_N}{r^3}C_{22}\left[(\hat{\mathbf{r}} \cdot \hat{\mathbf{s}})^2 - (\hat{\mathbf{r}} \cdot \hat{\mathbf{q}})^2\right].
\tag{8}
$$

The ellipsoid polar axis $\hat{\mathbf{p}}$, defined as the axis about which the body inertia is greatest, is expressed in $\mathcal{N}'$ frame components as:

$$
\hat{\mathbf{p}} = \sin\beta\sin\alpha\hat{\mathbf{x}} - \sin\beta\cos\alpha\hat{\mathbf{y}} + \cos\beta\hat{\mathbf{z}},
\tag{9}
$$

where $\beta = \cos^{-1}(\hat{\mathbf{p}} \cdot \hat{\mathbf{z}})$ measures the obliquity and $\alpha = \cos^{-1}\left(\frac{(\hat{\mathbf{z}} \times \hat{\mathbf{p}}) \cdot \hat{\mathbf{x}}}{|\hat{\mathbf{z}} \times \hat{\mathbf{p}}|}\right)$ measures the right ascension of the $\hat{\mathbf{p}}$ direction. The polar axis is assumed to be inertially fixed, constantly oriented in the direction specified by Equation (9). The NEO is assumed to rotate uniformly and exclusively about its polar axis, at a rate of $\omega = 2\pi/P$ (rad/sec) where P (sec) is the period of the NEO rotation. The combined rotation which transforms the $\mathcal{N}'$ frame to the $\mathcal{R}$ frame is a (3-1-3) Euler rotation, given by:

$$
[RN'] = [M_3(\omega t)][M_1(\beta)][M_3(\alpha)],
\tag{10}
$$

where ωt (rad) is the angle swept out by the NEO rotation over a period of t seconds and $[M_i(\theta)]$ is a rotation matrix for a single-axis rotation of angle θ about reference frame axis i.

Third body gravity model

The third body perturbing the motion of the NEO-orbiting satellite is the Sun. The form of this perturbing acceleration is:[6]

$$
\mathbf{a}_{3\text{body}} = \mu_\odot\left(\frac{\mathbf{d}}{|\mathbf{d}|^3} - \frac{\mathbf{d} + \mathbf{r}}{|\mathbf{d} + \mathbf{r}|^3}\right),
\tag{11}
$$

where $\mathbf{d} + \mathbf{r} = \mathbf{D}$ is the position vector of the satellite and $\mathbf{d}$ the position vector of the NEO, both measured relative to the Sun's position. This first term in Equation (11) is the acceleration of the NEO and the second term is the acceleration of the satellite, both due to the Sun's gravity.

Solar radiation pressure model

To model the pressure force due to incident solar radiation, the satellite is assumed to be a flat plate with its surface normal oriented perpendicular to the direction of the incident photon flux. In this simple model, the acceleration due to solar radiation pressure is given by:

$$\mathbf{a}_{\text{SRP}} = \frac{L_\odot}{4\pi c} \frac{c_{\text{R}}}{B} \frac{\mathbf{d} + \mathbf{r}}{|\mathbf{d} + \mathbf{r}|^3}, \tag{12}$$

where $L_\odot = 3.839 \times 10^{26}$ W is the time-averaged luminosity (or power) of the Sun, $c \approx 2.99792 \times 10^8$ m/s is the speed of light constant, $B = m/A_{\perp\odot}$ (kg/m^2) is the mass to area ratio of the body, and c_{R} is the reflectivity:

$$c_{\text{R}} = \begin{cases} 0, & \text{transparent} \\ 1, & \text{blackbody} \\ 2, & \text{mirror} \end{cases} . \tag{13}$$

Equations of motion

The acceleration of the satellite as measured in the non-rotating reference frame $\mathcal{N}'$ is found by summing the contributions from two-body gravity, non-spherical mass distribution, solar gravity, and solar radiation pressure.

$$\begin{aligned} \ddot{\mathbf{r}} &= \mathbf{a}_{\text{2body}} + \mathbf{a}_{\text{3body}} + \mathbf{a}_{\text{SRP}} + \mathbf{a}_{\text{mdist}} \\ &= \left[-\mu_{\text{N}} \frac{\mathbf{r}}{|\mathbf{r}|^3} + \left(\frac{L_\odot}{4\pi c} \frac{c_{\text{R}}}{B} - \mu_\odot \right) \frac{\mathbf{d} + \mathbf{r}}{|\mathbf{d} + \mathbf{r}|^3} + \frac{\partial R}{\partial \mathbf{r}} \right] - \left[-\mu_\odot \frac{\mathbf{d}}{|\mathbf{d}|^3} \right] \\ &= [\ddot{\mathbf{D}}] - [\ddot{\mathbf{d}}] \end{aligned} \tag{14}$$

Therefore, the acceleration of the satellite as measured in the $\mathcal{N}'$ frame is found to be the difference of the inertial acceleration of the satellite location, point $\mathcal{P}$, and the $\mathcal{N}'$ frame origin, point $\mathcal{O}'$, both measured in the inertial $\mathcal{N}$ frame centered at the Sun.

Model parameters

The software implementation of the model described in the previous sections allows for nearly every parameter to be specified as a run-time input (with the exception of the orbit elements describing the orientation of the NEO orbit relative to the inertial $\mathcal{N}$ frame, since that frame is defined to be aligned with the NEO heliocentric orbit). For the purposes of this study, some of these parameters were chosen to remain fixed (see Table 1) while others were allowed to vary (see Table 2). Future research in this area of study could investigate how the behavior of the candidate orbits identified in this paper would be affected by changes to one or more of the fixed parameters.

Initial conditions

The satellite motion about the NEO is integrated in a non-rotating frame, which allows the initial conditions for the satellite orbit to be expressed as orbit elements instead of Cartesian position and velocity vectors. Expressing the initial state in orbit elements facilitates the design of useful orbits, as it is often much easier to track and make adjustments to orbits expressed in orbit elements. In particular, a class of orbits that remain frozen relative to the rotating $\mathcal{B}$ frame can be quickly designed using orbit elements for the initial conditions.

Two families of orbits discussed previously in the literature are found to maintain a fixed or *frozen* orientation relative to the Sun-NEO line.[5,9] These orbits would be desirable for a manned mission to a NEO because they are stable in the presence of a strong solar radiation pressure perturbation. The safety of the spacecraft and the astronauts is put at risk if perpetual thruster firings are required to maintain the orbit about the NEO,

Table 1. Model Fixed Parameters

Object	Parameter	Value	Notes
NEO	ρ (g/cc)	2.0	Representative; the majority of known asteroid densities are 2.5 g/cc or less[8]
	α (deg)	45	Arbitrary if propagating for a full NEO orbit; should allow the satellite to sample every azimuth angle
	β (deg)	45	Representative; should be varied in future work
	A (AU)	1.05	Representative; selected from the two-dimensional distribution of semi-major axis and eccentricity for the orbits of all Potentially Hazardous Asteroids (PHAs) in the JPL Small Body Database
	E	0.15	Same as above
	I (deg)	0	$\mathcal{N}$ frame $\hat{\mathbf{z}}$ is aligned with NEO orbit $\hat{\mathbf{h}}$
	RAAN (deg)	0	RAAN is undefined for an equatorial orbit
	ω_p (deg)	0	ω_p is undefined for an equatorial orbit
	ν (deg)	270	Arbitrary if propagating for a full NEO orbit
Orion-Class Spacecraft	M (kg)	20000	CEV Capsule[a]+ Service Module (dry mass + propellant)[b]
	$A_{\perp\odot}$ (m^2)	50	Capsule cross-section + Solar Array area[a]
	c_R	1	Blackbody
Astronaut	M (kg)	220	175 lb Body + Shuttle-class space suit[c]
	$A_{\perp\odot}$ (m^2)	0.9	1.8 m height x 0.5 m width
	c_R	1	Blackbody

[a] http://www.nasa.gov/pdf/156298main_orion_handout.pdf
[b] http://microgravity.grc.nasa.gov/Orion/ServiceModule/index.php
[c] http://history.nasa.gov/spacesuits.pdf

Table 2. Model Free Parameters

Object	Parameter	Description
NEO	$[s, p, q]$ (m) P (hr)	Ellipsoid semi-principal axes Rotation period
Satellite	a (m) e i (deg) RAAN (deg) ω_p (deg) ν (deg)	Semi-major axis Eccentricity Inclination Right ascension of ascending node Argument of periapsis True anomaly angle

so an orbit which is designed to be naturally stable in this environment provides a significant mitigation of this risk.

The first family of frozen orbits are referred to as Terminator Frozen Orbits, and are so named because the satellite orbits in a plane perpendicular to the Sun-NEO line known as the terminator plane. For these orbits, if the angular momentum vector $\hat{\mathbf{h}}$ points toward the Sun, then periapsis points in the $+\hat{\mathbf{z}}$ direction. If, however, the angular momentum vector $\hat{\mathbf{h}}$ points away from the Sun, then periapsis points in the $-\hat{\mathbf{z}}$ direction.

The second family of orbits are called Ecliptic Frozen Orbits because the satellite orbits the NEO in the ecliptic plane, which is the plane of the NEO's orbit about the Sun. For these orbits, periapsis can point either toward or away from the Sun, along the Sun-NEO line described by $\hat{\mathbf{d}}$.

ANALYSIS

Stability definition

Before proceeding with analyses of the orbit studies conducted with the numerical model described in the previous section, it is necessary to define what stability means for satellite orbits about a small body within the context of this study. A rigorous definition of stability such as that which would be used for a control problem (e.g. Lagrange, Lyapunov, etc.) is not applied to these cases. Instead, a stable small body orbit is defined rather generally as a satellite trajectory for which the osculating elements of its orbit can be used to provide a reasonably accurate estimate of the position (and velocity) of the satellite position at a later time. Consequently, it is possible to have an orbit bound to the small body (the motion is dominated by gravitational attraction of the small body) which is unstable, provided its osculating orbit elements do not remain *close* to their initial values. The size of the region describing how *close* the elements must be to their initial values in order to be considered stable is subjective and can vary depending on the context of the case being analyzed. However, the goal in each case remains the same: to find orbits which are both bound to the small body and stable in the presence of multiple perturbing forces.

Limiting radii

Analytical limits have been derived elsewhere in the literature for maintaining stable orbits in the presence of perturbations to the two-body dynamics. In general, these limits provide useful design parameters for building orbits in the small body system. However, it is important to note that because these limits are derived for a small body system with a single perturbation force, an orbit constructed to meet all of the limits is not guaranteed to remain stable in a small body system modeled with multiple perturbing forces.

Maximum semi-major axis limit due to solar radiation pressure The limit on the osculating semi-major axis for stability in the presence of a constant (in magnitude and direction) solar radiation pressure force for a circular terminator orbit about a point mass is given as:[5]

$$a \leq \frac{\sqrt{3}}{4} \sqrt{\frac{4\pi c}{L_\odot} \frac{d^2 B \mu}{c_R}} = a_{\max}. \tag{15}$$

Though this limit is derived in the context of a non-rotating and non-translating reference frame, it approaches the true limit for the general case of a small body in an elliptical orbit about the Sun, provided the solar radiation pressure force is strong.[5]

Assuming a NEO of sphere-equivalent radius R_N and constant mass density ρ, Equation (15) can be written as:

$$a_{\max} = \pi d \sqrt{\frac{cG}{L_\odot} \frac{B \rho R_N^3}{c_R}}. \tag{16}$$

To investigate the behavior of this equation, some characteristic values are chosen for several of the independent parameters. The reflectivity is set to 1 for a blackbody, and two mass/area ratio values are tested: one for an Orion-class spacecraft and another for an astronaut. The results are shown in Figure 2.

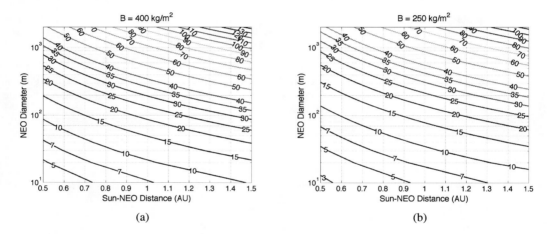

Figure 2. Contour plots of $a_{\max}/R_N$ as computed by Eq. 16 for (a) an Orion-class spacecraft and (b) an astronaut wearing a Shuttle-class space suit. Note that the NEO is assumed to have a constant mass density of $\rho = 2.0$ g/cc and the reflectivity of the satellite (spacecraft or astronaut) is assumed to be 1 (blackbody). For a given NEO size and Sun-NEO distance, the maximum limit on the semi-major axis is smaller for an orbiting astronaut than for an Orion-class spacecraft because the astronaut's mass to area ratio is smaller than that of the spacecraft.

Minimum semi-major axis limit due to NEO ellipticity A minimum limit on the semi-major axis to guard against the destabilization of an orbit about a NEO due to the ellipticity of the NEO body is given as:[5]

$$a > \frac{3}{2} r_{\text{res}} = a_{\min}, \tag{17}$$

where

$$r_{\text{res}} = \left(\frac{P^2 \mu_N}{4\pi^2} \right)^{1/3} \tag{18}$$

662

is the resonance radius; the radius at which the gravitational acceleration due to NEO gravity is equal to the centripetal acceleration of its rotation. This minimum limit on the semi-major axis was derived from the results of a previous study[10] where stable and unstable orbits were found empirically as a function of two parameters: the initial orbit semi-major axis normalized by the resonance radius, and a second parameter defined as

$$\chi \equiv \frac{I_z - I_x}{r_{\text{res}}^2}. \tag{19}$$

χ can be thought of as a shape parameter, measuring the degree to which the shape of the NEO departs from a sphere. A χ value of 0 indicates that the NEO is a perfect sphere, and as χ increases the shape of the NEO becomes increasingly stretched along its s axis.

To study the behavior of Equation (17), the expression for the resonance radius in Equation (18) is rewritten for the case of a NEO of constant mass density ρ and sphere-equivalent radius R_N:

$$r_{\text{res}} = R_N \left(\frac{G}{3\pi} P^2 \rho \right)^{1/3}. \tag{20}$$

When the equation for the resonance radius is expressed in this form, it is clear that the value of the resonance radius depends on only two free parameters (assuming the mass density is fixed): the NEO sphere-equivalent radius and the rotation period. Note that there is no dependence on the actual shape of the NEO, so that the resonance radius can be the same for NEOs of any shape provided their sphere-equivalent radii (and therefore their masses) are equal. Since a_{min} is directly proportional to r_{res}, these dependencies also apply to a_{min}. The qualitative dependencies of a_{min} on the rotation period and size of the NEO are given in Table 3.

By substituting Equation (20) into Equation (17) and then dividing by the NEO sphere-equivalent radius, the ratio of a_{min} to R_N is found to be directly proportional to $P^{2/3}$. A plot of this distance ratio versus the NEO rotation period is shown in Figure 3.

Because the χ parameter is a function of the body moments of inertia, the shape of the NEO matters when computing this quantity. The shape of an ellipsoid is fully described by the ratio of its s axis to its q axis, $s : q$, provided the ratio of the q and p axes is constrained to unity. Assuming the NEO to be orbited has such a shape, then its mass is given by:

$$M = \rho \frac{4}{3} \pi \frac{s^3}{(s : q)^2}, \tag{21}$$

where

$$\frac{s}{(s : q)^{2/3}} = R_N \tag{22}$$

is the relationship between the ellipsoid dimensions and the sphere-equivalent radius. Substituting this expression for the NEO mass in Equation (18) and replacing I_z and I_x in Equation (19) with the expressions from Equation (5) yields a new expression for χ:

$$\chi = \frac{1}{5} \left(\frac{3\pi (s : q)^2}{G \rho P^2} \right)^{2/3} \left(1 - \frac{1}{(s : q)^2} \right). \tag{23}$$

Inspection of Equation (23) reveals that the value of χ is independent of the size of the NEO s axis and dependent only on the parameters P and $s : q$. Thus, χ can have the same value for NEOs of various sizes provided $s : q$ and P are held constant between them. To demonstrate the quantitative dependence of χ on these free parameters, contours of equal χ are plotted against representative ranges of P and $s : q$ in Figure 3. A summary of the qualitative dependencies of χ on these parameters is given in Table 3.

663

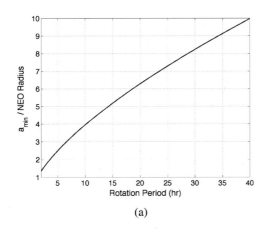 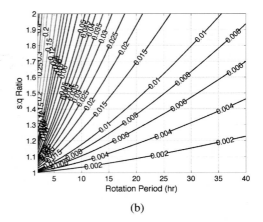

| | (a) | | (b) |

Figure 3. Plots of (a) $a_{\min}/R_N$ as computed by Equations (17) and (20); and (b) equal contours of χ as computed by Equation (23). Note that the NEO is assumed to have a constant mass density of $\rho = 2.0$ g/cc.

Table 3. Dependence of $a_{\min}$ and χ on NEO parameters

Increasing...	$a_{\min}$	χ
P	Increases	Decreases
$s:q$[†]	Constant	Increases
s[‡]	Increases	Constant

[†]Assumes total NEO mass is held constant.
[‡]Assumes the $s:q$ ratio is held constant.

Numerical Studies

Using the NEO+satellite orbit model and the fixed NEO and Orion parameters listed in Table 1, several numerical studies were conducted with the objective to answer some of the most pressing questions regarding the feasibility and viability of orbiting the target body for a manned mission to a NEO. For each study, the spacecraft and NEO motion were propagated for one full revolution of the NEO orbit about the Sun unless the spacecraft escaped from NEO orbit or impacted the surface prior to the end of the propagation interval.

How small of a NEO can be orbited? To investigate how small of a NEO an Orion-class spacecraft could stably orbit, simulations were conducted sequentially against NEOs of progressively smaller size. In each case, the spacecraft state was initialized to establish a terminator frozen orbit of size $a_0 = a_{\max}$. The purpose of maximizing the orbit size was to minimize the effect of the non-spherical mass distribution on the orbit. It was assumed that if the spacecraft could not stably orbit at the maximum distance permitted by the solar radiation pressure perturbation, then it probably couldn't establish a stable orbit at a distance closer to the NEO where the effects of the mass distribution would be greater. A shape distribution study of asteroid families found that a $s:q$ ratio of ≈ 1.2 is the most common in the observable asteroid population,[11] so each NEO is constrained to have this $s:q$ ratio and $q:p = 1$. Finally, the NEO rotation period for each simulation was set to 15 hours, both because a previous study indicated that targets for manned missions should have $P > 10$ hours,[4] and also because the range of the effects due to the non-spherical distribution is extended for a longer NEO rotation period.

The results of the simulations showed that Orion-class spacecraft could establish a stable orbit about every NEO tested, including the smallest having semi-principal axes $10 \times 8.3 \times 8.3$ m. Though the results seem to indicate that even smaller NEOs could theoretically be orbited by an Orion-class spacecraft, nothing smaller was tested for two reasons: (1) it seems unlikely that a manned mission would be planned to a NEO much smaller than ≈ 20 m in diameter; and (2) for smaller NEOs the mass would begin to approach the mass of the Orion-class spacecraft and would therefore increasingly necessitate the inclusion of the acceleration of the spacecraft on the NEO in the orbit model.

Since an Orion-class spacecraft was found to be able to achieve orbit about the smallest NEO at the maximum distance permitted by the solar radiation pressure perturbation, several other simulations were executed in order to determine how much closer the spacecraft could get to the NEO and still maintain a stable orbit. One other simulation was also run to verify that the spacecraft would escape NEO orbit if placed into an initial orbit having $a_0 > a_{max} \approx 71$ m. The integrated trajectories from these simulations are shown in Figure 4. The spacecraft initialized outside of a_{max} escapes NEO orbit as expected, but contrary to expectations the spacecraft orbits established inside of $a_{min} \approx 46$ m remain relatively stable over the full NEO orbit. The orbit initialized at $a_0 = 25$ m does eventually impact the NEO surface, but only after a period of 200 days, which is significantly longer than the likely duration of a manned mission to the NEO.

The χ parameter for this NEO ($s : q = 1.2$, $P = 15$ hr) is calculated to be approximately 0.007, which has been shown empirically to correspond to stable orbits for nearly all values of $(a/r_{res})^{3/2}$.[10] This explains why orbits below a_{min} remained stable for this NEO: the perturbation due to the NEO ellipticity was too weak to destabilize them. Since the value of χ increases with a decreasing rotation period or increasing $s : q$ ratio, these NEO parameters were adjusted to see whether the Orion-class spacecraft orbits below a_{min} would remain stable.

To investigate whether a more elongated small NEO could destabilize the stable low altitude orbits found in the previous section, the $s : q$ ratio of the small NEO was increased to 2.0. The dimension of the s axis was solved for given the constraint that the total volume of the new NEO must equal that of the previous NEO modeled. All other physical parameters of the NEO (rotation period, mass density, etc.) were left unchanged. Because the total volume, and therefore the total mass, of the NEO was held fixed, the value of a_{min} was held constant at ≈ 46 m. However, the larger $s : q$ ratio causes the χ value to increase to 0.032, which has been shown empirically to correspond to very few stable orbits.[10] To confirm this expectation, a simulation was conducted for an Orion-class spacecraft initialized in a terminator frozen orbit of size $a_0 = 35$ m about the elongated NEO (see Figure 5). After a period of 20 days, the orbit begins to destabilize, and after 60 days the spacecraft escapes NEO orbit. This result indicates that the a_{min} threshold for orbits about a NEO becomes more firm as the NEO becomes more elongated (higher $s : q$ ratio). Thus, the interesting a_{max} to NEO surface orbit stability observed for the first small NEO tested appears to be a consequence of its rounder shape.

The other NEO parameter that can be adjusted to increase the χ value for the NEO is the rotation period. χ is inversely proportional to $P^{4/3}$, so decreasing P results in increasing χ. The rotation period of the NEO was set to 10 hours, while all other values for the physical parameters of the NEO were held constant from the previous test cases. The shorter rotation period for this NEO leads to a smaller value for the minimum semi-major axis threshold – $a_{min} \approx 35$ m – and a larger value for the shape parameter – $\chi = 0.011$. These new values imply that the threshold orbit size for guarding against ellipticity effects is lower for this NEO, but at the same time the strength of those effects within the threshold distance are stronger than they were for the previous small NEO. To test this behavior, an Orion-class spacecraft was initialized in a terminator frozen orbit with the same semi-major axis as the smallest orbit tested previously. The results of the simulation (see Figure 6) show that this low altitude orbit impacts the surface much more quickly for the more rapidly rotating NEO.

Are there NEOs that Orion cannot orbit? The previous test cases have shown that a wide range of NEOs could potentially be orbited by an Orion-class spacecraft, which begs the question: are there any NEOs which cannot be orbited? Theoretically, the answer to this question is yes, provided the parameters of the system are configured such that the value of a_{min} exceeds that of a_{max}. Figure 7 shows contours of a_{max}/a_{min} plotted

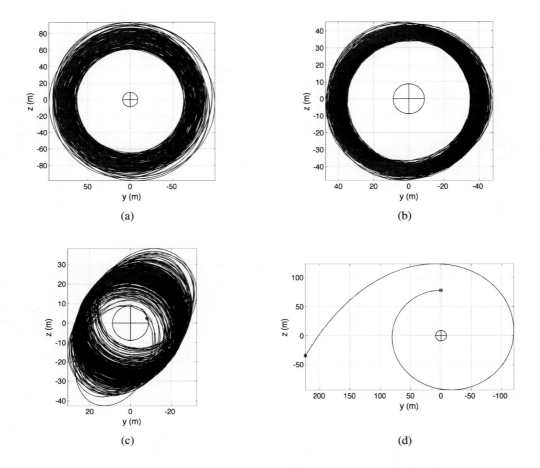

Figure 4. **Integrated trajectories for an Orion-class spacecraft orbiting a small NEO** ($[s, q, p] = [10.0, 8.3, 8.3]$ **m**): **(a)** $a_0 = a_{\max} \approx 71$ **m**; **(b)** $a_0 = 40$ **m** $< a_{\min}$; **(c)** $a_0 = 25$ **m** $<< a_{\min}$; **(d)** $a_0 = 80$ **m** $> a_{\max}$. **The images are the trajectories as seen by an observer on the negative x-axis of the $\mathcal{B}$ frame (the Sun is behind the observer). Because $\chi \approx 0.007$ is so low for this NEO ($P = 15$ hr, $s : q = 1.2$), the ellipticity effects due to the non-spherical mass distribution of the NEO are weak. For case (c), the spacecraft orbits just slightly above the NEO surface and does eventually impact, but only after orbiting the NEO for a period of 196 days. In contrast to the mass distribution perturbation, the perturbation due to solar radiation pressure is found to have the ability to destabilize the orbit quite quickly. Increasing the semi-major axis just slightly above the maximum stability limit results in escape from NEO orbit in less than 7 days.**

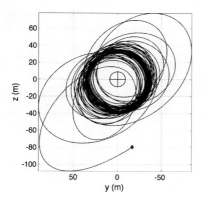
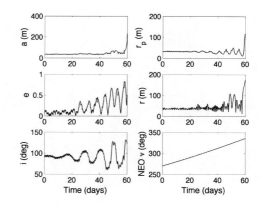

Figure 5. Results from the simulation of an Orion-class spacecraft orbiting a small NEO ($[s, q, p] = [14, 7, 7]$ m) in a terminator frozen orbit initialized with $a_0 = 35$ m $< a_{\min}$. The ellipticity effects, which are stronger for this NEO due to its more elongated shape, begin to destabilize the orbit after only 20 days and lead to escape after 60 days.

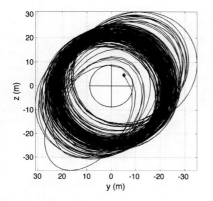
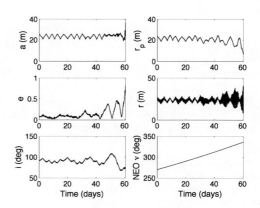

Figure 6. Results from the simulation of an Orion-class spacecraft orbiting a small NEO ($[s, q, p] = [10, 8.3, 8.3]$ m) in a terminator frozen orbit initialized with $a_0 = 25$ m $< a_{\min}$. The ellipticity effects, which are stronger for this NEO due to its shorter rotation period, cause the spacecraft to impact the surface after 60 days.

for a wide range of rotation periods and NEO diameters. The plot clearly shows that NEOs with long rotation periods can have $a_{\min} > a_{\max}$, and that the rotation period at which this threshold is crossed is shorter for smaller NEOs and longer for larger NEOs.

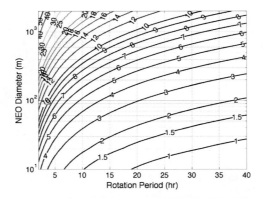

Figure 7. Contours of $a_{\max}/a_{\min}$. The plot shows that NEOs with a small diameter and a long rotation period can have a value for this ratio of less than one. In principle, these NEOs cannot be orbited by Orion, though depending on the shape of the NEO, and thus the value of χ, the ellipticity perturbation may be weak enough to allow stability over extended periods. The assumptions used to produce this plot are: the NEO has a constant mass density of $\rho = 2.0$ g/cc; $a_{\max}$ is evaluated at the perihelion distance of the heliocentric orbit specified in Table 1; and the satellite is an Orion-class spacecraft with $B = 400$ kg/m^2.

Recall that the previous test cases showed that the degree to which the the $a_{\min}$ constraint is *firm* depends on the shape of the NEO. For rounder, more spherical NEOs, orbits having a semi-major axis smaller than the minimum threshold can remain stable in the presence of ellipticity effects. Thus, provided that the mass and rotation period of a NEO cause it to fall in the region where $a_{\min} > a_{\max}$, it is possible that this NEO could still be stably orbited if its shape is not too elongated. To test this hypothesis, a numerical simulation was run for an Orion-class spacecraft orbiting a small, very slowly rotating NEO. The NEO $s : q$ ratio was initially set to 4.0 to demonstrate that no orbits were possible, and then decreased to 3.0 to show that a rounder NEO could be orbited provided all other parameters were held constant. The results of these simulations are shown in Figure 8.

Why terminator frozen orbits? The results of the previous test cases showed that a terminator frozen orbit can be long-term stable provided that the semi-major axis falls within the maximum and minimum limits for stability. However, given that an Orion-class spacecraft has such a high mass to area ratio compared to other spacecraft, it seems reasonable that other types of orbits could also be stable in the NEO environment. In particular, one of simplest alternatives would be a circular orbit at an arbitrary orientation relative to the NEO. A numerical simulation was conducted to test the viability of such an orbit, which was initialized to have a semi-major axis of 3 km, an inclination of $45°$ relative to the ecliptic plane, and an azimuth of $45°$ relative to the terminator plane. The NEO is modeled as a uniformly rotating ellipsoid with $s : q$ ratio of 2.0, s axis of 200 m, and a rotation period of 15 hours. The simulation results for the circular orbit propagation are shown in Figure 9 along with the results for a terminator frozen orbit having the same initial semi-major axis. The spacecraft initialized in the circular orbit follows a highly perturbed but bounded trajectory until it finally escapes 146 days after the propagation epoch, while the terminator frozen orbit remains stable for the full cycle of the NEO orbit. While the trajectory for the initial circular orbit does remain bounded for a period likely much greater than the duration of any manned mission, the rapid variation of its osculating orbit elements would not be desirable for such a mission. The terminator frozen orbit, on the other hand, provides a stable trajectory useful for both conducting scientific studies of the NEO as well as for staging astronaut

EVAs to the NEO surface. Therefore, owing partly to Orion's high mass to area ratio, it is possible to achieve and temporarily maintain a non-frozen orbit about a small body. However, while this orbit can remain bound to the NEO for a period of time, its osculating elements will vary rapidly and therefore it is not be an ideal candidate for meeting the objectives of a manned mission.

To this point, ecliptic frozen orbits have been excluded from all of the simulation test cases in favor of terminator frozen orbits. To understand why this has been the case, it is important to consider how each family of frozen orbits adjusts as the strength of the solar radiation pressure perturbation varies. The parameter ψ is used to describe the strength of this perturbation and is given by:

$$
\begin{aligned}
\Lambda &= \frac{3L_\odot}{8B\pi c}\sqrt{\frac{a}{P\mu_N\mu_\odot}}, \\
\psi &= \tan^{-1}\Lambda.
\end{aligned}
\tag{24}
$$

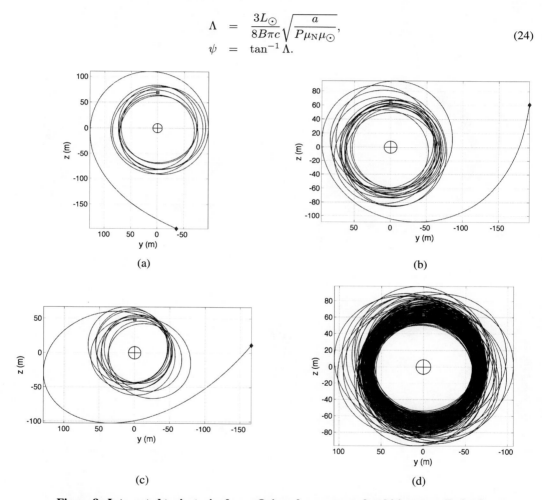

(a)

(b)

(c)

(d)

Figure 8. Integrated trajectories for an Orion-class spacecraft orbiting a small, slowly rotating NEO: (a) $s : q = 4.0$, $a_0 = a_{\max}$; **(b)** $s : q = 4.0$, $a_0 = 65$ m; **(c)** $s : q = 4.0$, $a_0 = 50$ m; **(d)** $s : q = 3.0$, $a_0 = 65$ m. **In all cases, the** s **axis dimension of the NEO is solved for given the ellipsoid** $s : q$ **ratio and the constraint that the total volume equals that of the NEO from the first test case. The rotation period is 35 hr, which causes** $a_{\min}$ **to grow beyond** $a_{\max}$ **consistent with Figure 7. For cases (a) - (c),** $\chi = 0.032$, **and for (d)** $\chi = 0.021$. **As shown in panels (a) - (c), the NEO with** $s : q = 4.0$ **cannot be orbited by Orion at any distance. However, (d) shows that the NEO with** $s : q = 3.0$ **can be orbited despite the fact that** $a_{\min} > a_{\max}$. **This is because the value of** χ, **and thus the strength of the ellipticity perturbation, is low enough to permit the orbit to remain stable over the period of one NEO orbit about the Sun.**

Equation (24) shows that ψ is a function of both NEO and satellite parameters. Since the orbit of the NEO and the mass to area ratio of the satellite have been fixed in our model, the only parameters which can be adjusted to change the value of ψ are the satellite orbit semi-major axis a and the NEO gravitational parameter μ_N. Since ψ is proportional to $\sqrt{a}$ and inversely proportional to $\sqrt{\mu_N}$, ψ grows larger for larger orbits about the NEO or less massive (i.e. smaller sized) NEOs. Given that the value of Λ can only vary between 0 and 1, the solar radiation pressure perturbation grows weak as $\psi \to 0$ and strong as $\psi \to \pi/2$. The frozen orbit eccentricity is computed from the ψ parameter as follows:

$$e = \begin{cases} \cos\psi, & \text{terminator frozen orbit} \\ \sin\psi, & \text{ecliptic frozen orbit} \end{cases} \tag{25}$$

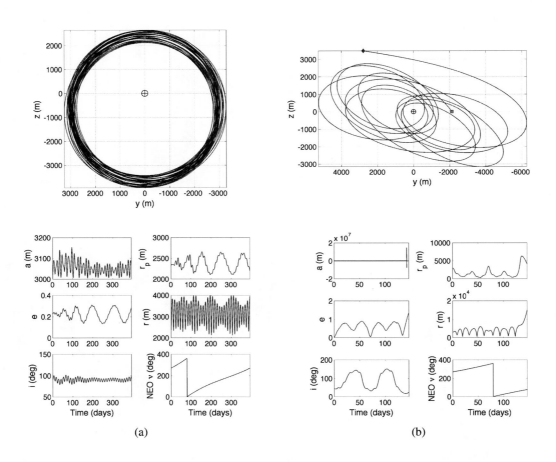

Figure 9. **Integrated trajectories for an Orion-class spacecraft orbiting about a medium NEO ($[s, q, p] = [200, 100, 100]$ m): (a) terminator frozen orbit with $\hat{h}$ directed toward the Sun; (b) circular orbit rotated $45°$ out of the terminator plane and inclined $45°$ above the ecliptic plane. Both orbits are initialized with a semi-major axis of $a_0 = 3$ km. The spacecraft in the terminator frozen orbit is found to remain bound and stable throughout the propagation interval, while the spacecraft in the inclined circular orbit escapes after 146 days.**

670

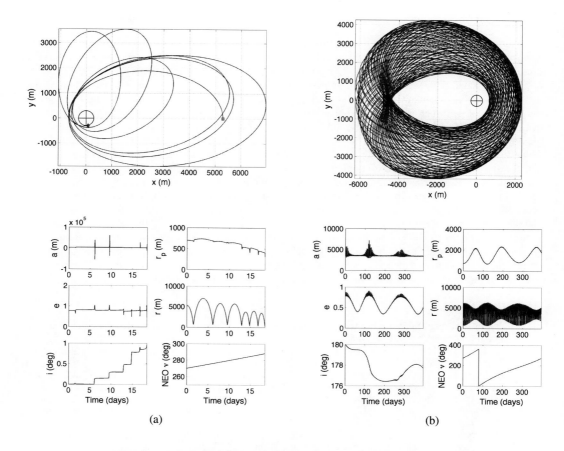

Figure 10. Ecliptic frozen orbit trajectories for an Orion-class spacecraft orbiting a medium-sized NEO ($[s, q, p] = [476, 238, 238]$ m). The images in the top row are the trajectories as seen by an observer on the positive z-axis of the $\mathcal{B}$ frame (the Sun is to the left and below the observer). The orbit is initialized with a semi-major axis of $a_0 = 3$ km, which sets a periapsis radius of ≈ 700 m. Since periapsis for the frozen orbit lies below the limit for guarding against ellipticity effects ($a_{\min} \approx 1.55$ km), the motion is significantly perturbed by the non-spherical mass distribution during each periapsis passage. The prograde orbit quickly destabilizes, and results in surface impact after 18 days. The retrograde orbit, however, does not impact the surface and remains bound to the NEO throughout the propagation interval.

As the strength of the solar radiation pressure perturbation increases, a terminator frozen orbit approaches a circular orbit while an ecliptic frozen orbit tends toward a parabolic trajectory. For this reason, ecliptic frozen orbits are not preferred for strongly perturbed situations, since in these situations they will be highly eccentric with a low altitude for periapsis. This is undesirable because the orbit can become destabilized during periapsis passage if the NEO mass distribution is not spherical. Figure 10 shows simulation results for prograde and retrograde orbits modeled about a medium-sized NEO characterized by the parameters $s : q = 2$, $s \approx 476$ m and $P = 15$ hours. The retrograde ecliptic frozen orbit does seem to show a higher resilience to the influence of the other perturbations, however its osculating elements still vary too much to be considered a suitable candidate for a manned mission.

CONCLUSIONS

A numerical model – including the perturbative effects of solar radiation pressure, solar gravity and a non-spherical mass distribution for the central body – was constructed to simulate orbital trajectories in close proximity to a small solar system body. Using this model, analytically-derived limits on the size of a stable orbit about a small body were confirmed numerically. For the particular application of a manned mission to a NEO, it was found that an Orion-class spacecraft can generally achieve a stable orbit about a NEO despite the presence of perturbations to the two-body dynamics. The range of distances over which the spacecraft can orbit the NEO depends on the size and shape of the NEO, as well as the period of its rotation. The maximum limit on the semi-major axis size in the presence of the solar radiation pressure perturbation is found to be quite rigid, and increases in value with the NEO mass. The minimum limit on the semi-major axis threshold for guarding against ellipticity effects is found to more flexible, depending on the strength of the perturbation as quantified by the χ parameter. As the rotation period increases or the NEO shape becomes increasingly round, the perturbation due to the NEO ellipticity becomes increasingly weak and orbit stability is maintained for longer periods for orbits having semi-major axes less than $a_{\min}$. If the NEO is small enough and the rotation period long enough, the value of $a_{\min}$ can exceed that of $a_{\max}$. If the ellipticity perturbation is strong enough, these NEOs cannot be orbited at any distance. Finally, terminator frozen orbits have been shown to be the best orbit option a manned mission to a NEO. Their stability in the presence of multiple perturbation sources makes them the ideal solution for achieving a safe trajectory about the NEO from which science observations can be made of the NEO and astronaut EVAs can be launched to the surface.

REFERENCES

[1] "Seeking a Human Spaceflight Program Worthy of a Great Nation," tech. rep., Review of U.S. Human Spaceflight Plans Committee, 2009.

[2] D. R. Davis, A. L. Friedlander, and T. D. Jones, *Role of near-Earth asteroids in the space exploration initiative.*, pp. 619–655. 1993.

[3] T. D. Jones, D. R. Davis, D. D. Durda, R. Farquhar, L. Gefert, K. Hack, W. K. Hartmann, R. Jedicke, J. S. Lewis, S. Love, M. V. Sykes, and F. Vilas, "The Next Giant Leap: Human Exploration and Utilization of Near-Earth Objects," *The Future of Solar System Exploration (2003-2013) – First Decadal Study contributions* (M. V. Sykes, ed.), Vol. 272 of *Astronomical Society of the Pacific Conference Series*, Aug. 2002, pp. 141–154.

[4] D. J. Korsmeyer, R. R. Landis, and P. A. Abell, "Into the Beyond: A Crewed Mission to a Near-Earth Object," *Acta Astronautica*, Vol. 63, July-August 2008, pp. 213–220.

[5] D. J. Scheeres, "Orbit mechanics about small asteroids," 20th International Symposium on Space Flight Dynamics, September 2007.

[6] D. J. Vallado, *Fundamentals of Astrodynamics and Applications.* Space Technology Library, 3rd ed., 2007.

[7] N. A. Chuikova, "The Gravitational Field and Figure of the Moon.," *Soviet Astronomy*, Vol. 12, June 1969, p. 1021.

[8] D. T. Britt, D. Yeomans, K. Housen, and G. Consolmagno, "Asteroid Density, Porosity, and Structure," *Asteroids III*, 2002, pp. 485–500.

[9] D. J. Scheeres, "Satellite Dynamics about Small Bodies: Averaged Solar Radiation Pressure Effects," *Journal of Astronautical Sciences*, Vol. 47, No. 1, 1999, pp. 25–46.

[10] W. Hu and D. J. Scheeres, "Numerical determination of stability regions for orbital motion in uniformly rotating second degree and order gravity fields," *Planetary and Space Science*, Vol. 52, July 2004, pp. 685–692, 10.1016/j.pss.2004.01.003.

[11] G. M. Szabó and L. L. Kiss, "The shape distribution of asteroid families: Evidence for evolution driven by small impacts," *Icarus*, Vol. 196, July 2008, pp. 135–143, 10.1016/j.icarus.2008.01.019.

SMALL-BODY GRAVITATIONAL FIELD
APPROXIMATION METHODS

Parv Patel,[*] Robert Phillips[†] and Bogdan Udrea[‡]

Small celestial bodies such as comets and asteroids are the target of space exploration missions which have invigorated noticeable interest in aerospace communities for nearby orbit designs. Among the requirements for planning such missions
is an accurate model of their gravitational fields which serves even the most irregularly shaped bodies. This paper offers alternative approaches for generating
gravity models of these bodies by using size-varying element approximations. The
geometric models are explained and are evaluated for modeling and computational
performance. Each gravity model is compared with that of a tetrahedron model to
verify accuracy and reliability for practical applications.

INTRODUCTION

In recent years, scholars have studied small celestial bodies and have offered various methods
for simulating their external gravitational fields. Included in a range of gravity models published
recently are Park's finite cube and finite sphere models, Anderson's finite offset sphere with correction spheres model, and Jones's cubed-sphere model.[1,2,3] These models generally rely on either
finite element analysis or spherical and ellipsoidal harmonics in order to approximate the geometry
of irregularly-shaped bodies, as these definitions are compatible with simple gravitational potential analysis and with today's computational resources. Finite element analysis is selected as the
approach for synthesizing the gravity models explored in this paper.

These models are unique in their goal to approximate irregular geometries while maintaining
the same level of accuracy as finite element models, with the least number of constant-density and
maximum-volume sphere and ellipsoid elements. In turn, each model strives to decrease the computational runtime to reckon the gravitational attractions. Graviational field simulation is demanded
by mission planning operations and furthermore by onboard spacecraft computers for navigation
and control functions within their environment.

The four finite variable-element models are the variable sphere, ellipsoid, inscribed ellipsoid, and
overscribed ellipsoid models, implementing either sphere or ellipsoid elements, or a combination
of the two. After elaborating on the function of each geometric model, their performances are
compared. The following section discusses the analytical formulae utilized for the computation of
the external gravitational acceleration, and then each gravity model is demonstrated. For accuracy
verification, a constant-density tetrahedron gravity model serves as a truth model with which the
gravitational acceleration components of each model are compared. Development and simulation
of these models is performed in MATLAB.

---

[*]Undergraduate Student, Embry-Riddle Aeronautical University, Daytona Beach, FL 32114; patelp4@my.erau.edu
[†]Undergraduate Student, Embry-Riddle Aeronautical University, Daytona Beach, FL 32114; phillir1@my.erau.edu
[‡]Assistant Professor, Embry-Riddle Aeronautical University, Daytona Beach, FL 32114; udreab@erau.edu

GEOMETRIC APPROXIMATION

The four gravity models presented in this paper revolve around the goal to account for the most volume by using the fewest finite sphere and/or ellipsoid elements. Accordingly, the maximum-volume finite elements must be determined to fulfill this requirement. This is performed by using optimization algorithms to generate each element's information, defining the element within the body, updating the available space inside of the body, and then repeating the process for as many elements as desired. For consistency throughout this paper and comparison with well-established modeling work, the asteroid 25143 Itokawa is investigated.

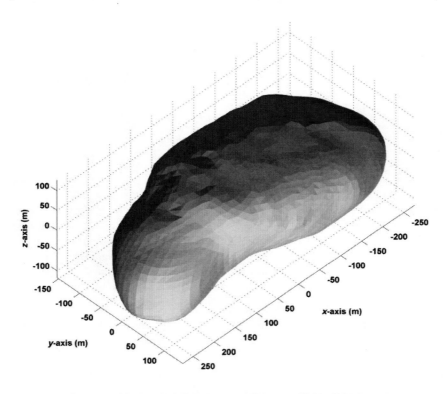

Figure 1. Shaded 25143 Itokawa surface manifold (4285 facets).

The studied surface model of Itokawa contains 2144 surface points which define its 4285 surface facets, while its resolution may be increased by generating surface points at the center of each facet.[4] Prior to the definition of any elements within the body, a three-dimensional grid of linearly-spaced interior points must be generated within the body. A rectangular prism of finite points encompasses this surface model, and then a function called `InPolyhedronTest` * filters the points such that all reside within the body.[5] The resultant interior points serve as candidate geometric centroids for any element that may be defined within the body. Varying a *grid density parameter* affects the number of points which comprise the grid, or the grid density, heavily impacting both the accuracy of the gravity models and their computational runtime.

---

*MATLAB® *inpolyhedron.m* function file may be downloaded from: http://www.advancedmcode.org/in-polyhedron-test.html

674

Modeling capability and computational runtime are two measurements of performance that are frequently used to gauge how effectively a model approximates the geometry of the body. Certainly a model which approximates the body poorly is not expected to portray accurate external gravitational acceleration. Modeling capability is measured by calculating the percentage of the body's accepted volume that is modeled by finite elements, or the *volumetric efficiency*, given by

$$\eta_m \equiv \sum_{k \in N_E} \frac{4}{3}\pi a_k b_k c_k \left(\sum_{t \in N_t} \frac{|\mathbf{A}_t \times (\mathbf{B}_t \cdot \mathbf{C}_t)|}{6} \right)^{-1} \times 100\% \tag{1}$$

where the net volume of all elements is given in the first summation term. The parameters a_k, b_k, c_k represent the semiaxes of the kth element and the case $a_k = b_k = c_k$ denotes a kth sphere element.

The accepted volume of the body, as shown in the latter summation term of Equation 1, is found by summing the volume of tetrahedra whose bases are equivalent to the surface facets as interpreted from the corresponding shape file. The parameters $\mathbf{A}_t$, $\mathbf{B}_t$, and $\mathbf{C}_t$ specify the 1-by-3 edge vectors from a tth tetrahedron's apex to its first, second, and third base vertices, respectively. The universal tetrahedron apex is the origin of the shape file coordinate system. Note that, for bodies which exhibit concave geometry, a limitation exists in calculating the exact volume of the body via the summation of tetrahedron volumes in this fashion. Edge vectors are permitted to pass through free space which does not belong to the body's surface manifold, typically occurring near the concave regions of an irregular body. Nonetheless, this calculation remains a sufficient method for approximating the body's accepted volume solely for the purpose of gauging a model's volumetric efficiency.

Because these models intend to rapidly approximate the body, computational runtime is useful for measuring their practical feasibility. The computational runtime encapsulates the entire geometric model definition and is measured by using MATLAB's functions `tic` and `toc`.[*]

Factors known to substantially affect both the computational runtime and the modeling capability (and subsequently the accuracy of a gravity model) are the number of surface points (determined by the body's surface manifold resolution and increased with additionally defined ellipsoid elements) and the grid density. Increasing the grid density allows for a model to approach a more accurate characterization of the body; however, the gain in accuracy may or may not outweigh the penalty experienced in computational runtime.

Variable Sphere Model

Finite sphere elements of varying radii approximate the shape of the small-body by implementing this variable sphere model. An infimum optimization algorithm ensures that each successive sphere element is of maximum-volume and does not exit the body. The minimum-distances from each interior point to all of the body's surface points are calculated and assigned to the corresponding interior point. Thereafter, the interior point which holds the maximum of minimum-distances is selected as the geometric centroid of the maximum-volume sphere element, whose radius is equal to the assigned minimum-distance. After defining the first sphere element, logical shortcuts are implemented to decrease runtime. Illustrated in Figure 3(c) is the 2500-element model of Itokawa,

---

[*]The computational runtimes depends on the computer's performance specifications and hence are subject to change from machine to machine; the analysed data discussed in the paper are measured by a PC with an Intel® Core™ 2 Duo Processor E8500 @ 3.16GHz 3.17GHz, 4GB RAM with a 64-bit Operating System type.

whose sphere elements extend from 104.8m to 3.9m in radius and altogether achieve an 83.3% volumetric efficiency.

The performance of the variable sphere model, as it varies with a linear increase of the grid density parameter, is tabulated in Table 1. Holding the number of sphere elements constant, both the number of interior points and the computational runtime increase exponentially. While increasing the number of interior points improves accuracy, the volumetric efficiency tends to reach a limit.

Table 1. Variable sphere model (2500 elements)

Grid Density Parameter	Number of Interior Points	Volumetric Efficiency	Computational Runtime
50	13407	72.2%	3.433 sec
100	108768	78.7%	29.82 sec
150	368491	81.1%	108.3 sec
200	874964	82.5%	264.9 sec
250	1710808	83.3%	525.9 sec

The histogram located in Figure 2 depicts the frequency distribution of 2500 sphere elements (taken from the variable sphere model) which fall into 115 logarithmically plotted radius intervals. Agreeing with the very nature of the sphere element definition algorithm, sparse sphere elements are defined by a radius larger than 10m. As the number of sphere elements increases, the radius (and thus the volume contributed) per element decreases exponentially. In light of this relationship, it is possible to preserve some amount of computational runtime without too severely affecting the resultant volumetric efficiency.

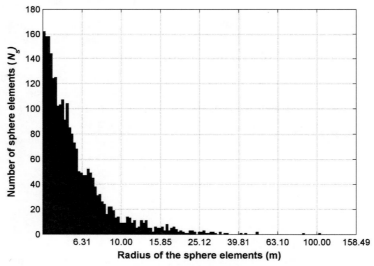

Figure 2. Sphere element radius histogram (2500 elements).

Variable Ellipsoid Model

Frequently it is useful to implement varying triaxial ellipsoid elements for approximating a body whose shape resembles that of an ellipsoid. This model is designed to account for more volume per element, in comparison to the variable sphere model. To exercise adaptability within the body, the ellipsoid elements are free to vary in location, orientation, and length along their semiaxes.

676

The primary stage of the element definition algorithm borrows fundamental techniques from the variable sphere model. Minimum-distances are calculated and assigned as mentioned before, and then the interior points along with their minimum-distances are sorted according to descending minimum-distances.

A range (starting with the first, infimum point) of the sorted interior points is selected to form a *parent cluster* in which each point comprising it lies directly next to another interior point. Another *child cluster*, derived from the parent cluster, is formulated based on each interior point's minimum-distance variation with respect to the infimum distance. The maximum allowable percentage of variation is termed as the *size-cutoff*, as it limits the number of points for the child cluster. This child cluster of points is utilized in conjunction with a function called `MinVolEllipse`.* Making use of an algorithm developed by Leonid Kanchiyan, this function determines the shape information for the minimum-volume ellipsoid which encompasses a set of points, different from the optimal solution by a pre-specified tolerance.[6] This method is chosen because it provides key geometric attributes that represent the ellipsoid in a short time, generally on the order of one second.[†]

Once the information for the minimum-volume ellipsoid is obtained, the maximum semiaxis lengths are determined. A scanning is performed and the ellipsoid is expanded appropriately, whose new shape details define the maximum-volume ellipsoid element. Figure 3(d) demonstrates the 2-element model of Itokawa, consuming a total of 63.9% of its volume. A clustering problem has limited the model to only two elements. The parent cluster becomes scattered throughout the remaining geometry of the body, and the size-cutoff, which dictates the child cluster, requires adjustment for each element. Adhering to this methodology necessitates deeper cluster analysis; so, in its current state, the variable ellipsoid model is insufficient for geometric approximation.

The variable ellipsoid models' runtimes listed in Table 2 drastically increase as the grid density parameter increases. This is attributed to the time necessary for updating the remaining interior points after each element definition. The robust function `InPolyhedronTest` is used in order to identify interior points within an ellipsoid, becoming a prolonged process for high grid densities.

Table 2. Variable ellipsoid model (2 elements)

Grid Density Parameter	Number of Interior Points	Volumetric Efficiency	Computational Runtime
50	13407	62.3%	7.942 sec
100	108768	62.9%	72.69 sec
150	368491	63.4%	571.7 sec
200	874964	63.8%	1312 sec
250	1710808	63.9%	2491 sec

Variable Inscribed Ellipsoid Model

Employing a combination of spheres and one ellipsoid, this model exhibits improved volumetric efficiency and favorable simplicity. One ellipsoid element first inscribes the body's interior, supplemented by sphere elements which characterize the remaining volume. Contrary to the previous model, the parent cluster dispersion quandary is avoided and an equal number of sphere elements (in comparison to the 2500-element variable sphere model of Itokawa) can be devoted to the more

---

*MATLAB® *minvolellipse.m* function file may be downloaded from: http://www.mathworks.com/matlabcentral/-file-exchange/9542-minimum-volume-enclosing-ellipsoid

[†]The generated ellipsoidal element is represented in a solution matrix, to which a *singular value decomposition* is employed to obtain the ellipsoid's semiaxes a, b, c corresponding to the generated diagonal matrix (Σ) and its orientation matrix (V^*).

677

intricate volumetric interior. Again, the gravitational acceleration components of both the inscribed ellipsoid and the spheres are combined for a field of points. Seen in Figure 3(e), the 2501-element variable inscribed ellipsoid model of Itokawa consumes 87.9% of the true volume.

The variable inscribed ellipsoid model offers improved volumetric efficiency in exchange for a mild runtime penalty, as seen in Table 3. Like the variable ellipsoid model, this model requires additional time to update the available space after defining the first ellipsoid element.

Table 3. Variable inscribed ellipsoid model (2501 elements)

Grid Density Parameter	Number of Interior Points	Volumetric Efficiency	Computational Runtime
50	13407	78.4%	8.467 sec
100	108768	83.6%	52.32 sec
150	368491	86.4%	174.7 sec
200	874964	87.6%	420.6 sec
250	1710808	87.9%	840.1 sec

Variable Overscribed Ellipsoid Model

Like most finite element models, the aforementioned models are forms of additive modeling, where all finite elements are combined to comprise the entire body. Working in the reverse manner, the variable overscribed ellipsoid model exhibits variable sphere elements whose gravitational attractions subtract from those of an ellipsoid element which encompasses, or overscribes, the body.

The first phase for defining this model employs the `MinVolEllipse` function in order to generate a minimum-volume ellipsoid that overscribes the investigated body, leaving a shell of space between the surface of the body and that of the generated ellipsoid. In doing so the volume of the entire body is consumed, simultaneously accounting for extra volume not belonging to the body. Following, the implemented second phase corrects for this overcompensation of volume by defining a multitude of maximum-volume sphere elements in this shell, thereby interpreted as volume subtracted from the ellipsoid. Increasing the number of subtraction spheres reduces the overshoot extrema volume toward unity.

Respecting the removal of shell volume from the overscribed ellipsoid, the gravitational acceleration calculation follows suit. The gravitational pull exerted by all sphere elements, for the entire field of points, is subtracted from that by the overscribed ellipsoid. Figure 3(f) shows the model of Itokawa after 2500 sphere elements have been defined inside of the shell, achieving a volumetric efficiency of 123%.

Referring to Table 4, the performance of the variable overscribed ellipsoid model behaves oppositely in comparison to the previous models. That is to say, increasing the grid density parameter results in a unity-bound decrease in volumetric efficiency. The listed computational runtimes reflect not only a relationship with the number of interior points but also a toll taken by generating and filtering them inside of the shell.

Table 4. Variable overscribed ellipsoid model (2501 elements)

Grid Density Parameter	Number of Interior Points	Volumetric Efficiency	Computational Runtime
50	13407	135%	74.81 sec
100	108768	128%	139.3 sec
150	368491	126%	316.9 sec
200	874964	124%	676.7 sec
250	1710808	123%	1245 sec

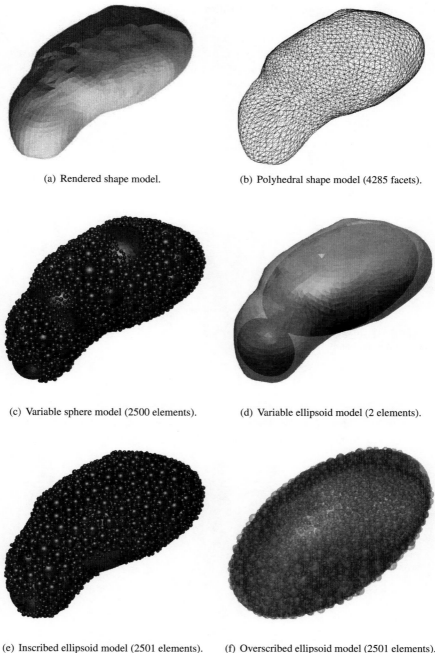

(a) Rendered shape model.

(b) Polyhedral shape model (4285 facets).

(c) Variable sphere model (2500 elements).

(d) Variable ellipsoid model (2 elements).

(e) Inscribed ellipsoid model (2501 elements).

(f) Overscribed ellipsoid model (2501 elements).

Figure 3. Geometric illustrations of variable element models of small-body Itokawa. The volumetric efficiencies achieved by the configurations 3(c), 3(d), 3(e) and 3(f) are 83.3%, 63.9%, 87.9% and 123%, respectively. While 3(e) best characterizes the geometry of the body, it does not necessarily offer the most accurate gravity model. As discussed in the gravity model verification section, an inappropriate concentration of mass causes unexpected discrepancies for models 3(e) and 3(f).

Volumetric Efficiency and Computational Runtime

The net volumetric efficiencies per element are depicted for all models in Figure 4. Note that the variable ellipsoid model is currently limited to just two elements. At this point, the variable inscribed ellipsoid model tends to return the most favorable volumetric efficiency.

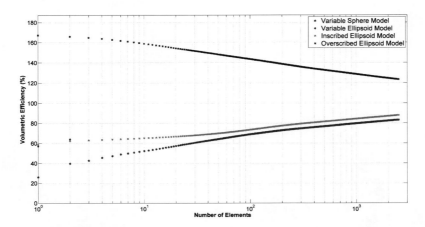

Figure 4. Dependence of the volumetric efficiencies on the number of elements of examined variable element gravity models.

As seen in Figure 5, the computational runtimes for each model is plotted with respect to the grid density parameter. For all models, a compromise is established between volumetric efficiency and computational runtime. However, after the number of elements continues beyond one thousand, the amount of volume contributed by each element tends to become relatively insignificant.

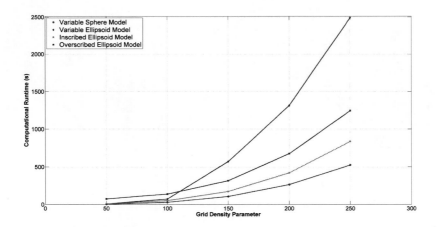

Figure 5. Computational performance for defining the variable element geometric models with respect to the grid density parameter.

GRAVITATIONAL ATTRACTION OF FINITE ELEMENTS

Simulation of the presented gravity models calls for the computation of the net gravitational acceleration of sphere and/or ellipsoid elements which model the body. The gravitational acceleration exerted at an external field point $r(x, y, z)$ is achieved via differentiation (by manner of the gradient operator) of the effective gravitational potential function examined at the locale. The following sections elaborate on the analytical formulations for simulation of the gravitational field acceleration of a small celestial body. A major assumption governing the gravity model formulation asserts equivalence of the density parameter for all elements. The field of points $r(x, y, z)$ aligned with the body's center of mass have been generated in a 500m-by-500m range with a 25m precision, for all gravity models.

Model Density Correction

Depending on the body of interest, these models may lack the ability to reach a volumetric efficiency of unity without incredible computational resources, which results in a loss of mass represented by these models. Compensating for the missing mass, a density correction

$$\rho_m \equiv \left[\rho_b \sum_{t \in N_t} \frac{|\mathbf{A}_t \times (\mathbf{B}_t \cdot \mathbf{C}_t)|}{6} \right] \left(\sum_{k \in N_E} \frac{4}{3} \pi a_k b_k c_k \right)^{-1} \tag{2}$$

replaces the body's accepted density ρ_b, returning the modeled mass to unity. Note that this correction may cause unfavorable mass concentrations for low volumetric efficiencies.

Gravitational Attraction of Constant-Density Finite Spheres

Employment of the variable element gravity models consisting of sphere elements necessitates the calculation of the gravitational potential and acceleration of the sphere elements. Treating the elements as finite spheres of constant density, the gravitational potential and gravitational acceleration as demonstrated by Park et. al[1] are:

$$U_s(\mathbf{r}) = \sum_{i \in N_s} \frac{4}{3} \pi r_{si}^3 G \rho_m \frac{1}{\|\mathbf{r} - \mathbf{r}_i\|} \tag{3}$$

and

$$\frac{\partial U_s}{\partial \mathbf{r}} = \sum_{i \in N_s} -\frac{4}{3} \pi r_{si}^3 G \rho_m \frac{\mathbf{r} - \mathbf{r}_i}{\|\mathbf{r} - \mathbf{r}_i\|} \tag{4}$$

here $\mathbf{r}_i$ and r_{si} represent the center coordinate pointing vector (relative to the global coordinate system situated at the origin of the polyhedron shape model) and the radius of the ith finite sphere element, correspondingly. The total gravitational attraction at a field point $\mathbf{r}$ approximated in this manner is thereby a straightforward computational task and its simulation within terse MATLAB script is immediate.

Gravitational Attraction of Constant-Density Triaxial Ellipsoids

Casotto et al.[7] exemplifies the calculation of gravitational potential and acceleration for a finite triaxial ellipsoid, at an examined field point. The formulae are updated to satisfy the translational characteristics of the ellipsoid for a given external field of points. In order to accommodate the rotational attributes of an ellipsoid, the calculated gravitational acceleration components can be multiplied with an appropriate rotation matrix to obtain those with respect to the body.

Here U_e is the gravitational potential and a_x, a_y, a_z are the gravitational acceleration components due to the homogeneous j^{th} ellipsoid of density ρ_m and semiaxes a_j, b_j, c_j that for convience we take to satisfy the order relationship $a_j \geq b_j \geq c_j$, with mass $M = \frac{4}{3}\rho_m \pi a_j b_j c_j$ and center $[x_{c_j}, y_{c_j}, z_{c_j}]$ at an external field point $r(x, y, z)$:

$$U_e = \sum_{j \in N_e} \frac{3}{2}GM\{A(u) + B(u)(x - x_{c_j})^2 + C(u)(y - y_{c_j})^2 + D(u)(z - z_{c_j})^2\} \quad (5)$$

and

$$a_x = \sum_{j \in N_e} 3GMB(u)(x - x_{c_j}), \quad (6)$$

$$a_y = \sum_{j \in N_e} 3GMC(u)(y - y_{c_j}), \quad (7)$$

$$a_z = \sum_{j \in N_e} 3GMD(u)(z - z_{c_j}), \quad (8)$$

where,

$$A(u) = \frac{F(\varphi_u)}{\sqrt{a_j^2 - c_j^2}} \quad (9)$$

$$B(u) = \frac{E(\varphi_u) - F(\varphi_u)}{k^2(a_j^2 - c_j^2)^{\frac{3}{2}}} \quad (10)$$

$$C(u) = \frac{1}{(a_j^2 - c_j^2)^{\frac{3}{2}}}\left[\frac{F(\varphi_u)}{k^2} - \frac{E(\varphi_u)}{k^2(1 - k^2)} + \frac{1}{1 - k^2}\sqrt{\frac{a_j^2 - c_j^2}{a_j^2 + u}\frac{c_j^2 + u}{b_j^2 + u}}\right] \quad (11)$$

$$D(u) = \frac{E(\varphi_u) - \sqrt{\frac{a_j^2 - c_j^2}{a_j^2 + u}\frac{b_j^2 + u}{c_j^2 + u}}}{(1 - k^2)(a_j^2 - c_j^2)^{\frac{3}{2}}} . \quad (12)$$

In the above formulae $F(\varphi_u)$ and $E(\varphi_u)$ are incomplete elliptic integrals of first and second kinds, respectively, given by

$$F(\varphi_u) = F(\varphi_u, k) = \int_0^{\varphi_u} \frac{1}{\sqrt{1 - k^2 \sin^2 \theta}} \; d\theta \tag{13}$$

$$E(\varphi_u) = E(\varphi_u, k) = \int_0^{\varphi_u} \sqrt{1 - k^2 \sin^2 \theta} \; d\theta \tag{14}$$

whose modulus k and amplitude φ_u are

$$k^2 = \frac{a_j^2 - b_j^2}{a_j^2 - c_j^2} \tag{15}$$

$$\varphi_u = \sin^{-1} \sqrt{\frac{a_j^2 - c_j^2}{a_j^2 + u}} \; . \tag{16}$$

The parameter u is the largest root of the cubic equation

$$\frac{(x - x_{c_j})^2}{a_j^2 + u} + \frac{(y - y_{c_j})^2}{b_j^2 + u} + \frac{(z - z_{c_j})^2}{c_j^2 + u} = 1 \tag{17}$$

The desired solution can be acquired by solving the following equation

$$u_3 + a_1 u^2 + a_2 u + a_3 = 0 \tag{18}$$

where

$$a_1 = a_j^2 + b_j^2 + c_j^2 - (x - x_{c_j})^2 - (y - y_{c_j})^2 - (z - z_{c_j})^2 \tag{19}$$

$$a_2 = a_j^2 b_j^2 + a_j^2 c_j^2 + b_j^2 c_j^2 - (b_j^2 + c_j^2)(x - x_{c_j})^2 - (a_j^2 + c_j^2)(y - y_{c_j})^2 - (a_j^2 + b_j^2)(z - z_{c_j})^2 \tag{20}$$

$$a_3 = a_j^2 b_j^2 c_j^2 - b_j^2 c_j^2 (x - x_{c_j})^2 - a_j^2 c_j^2 (y - y_{c_j})^2 - a_j^2 b_j^2 (z - z_{c_j})^2 \; . \tag{21}$$

For the calculation of the gravitational acceleration components it is not necessary to account for the dependence of u on the field points coordinates $r(x, y, z)$.[7,8]

GRAVITATIONAL FIELD SIMULATION

Gravitational attraction of all models are computed using finite analytical formulation for sphere and triaxial ellipsoid elements as discussed in the previous section. The following figures show the computed gravitational field for all each model, with a 500m range at 25m precision.

Variable Sphere Gravity Model

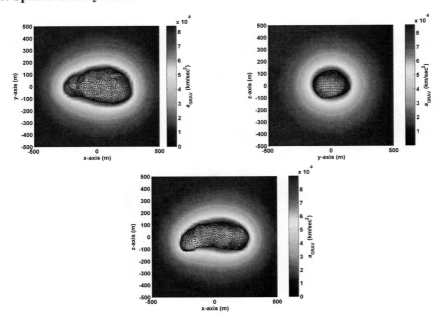

Figure 6. Attraction magnitude for variable sphere model (2500 elements).

Variable Ellipsoid Gravity Model

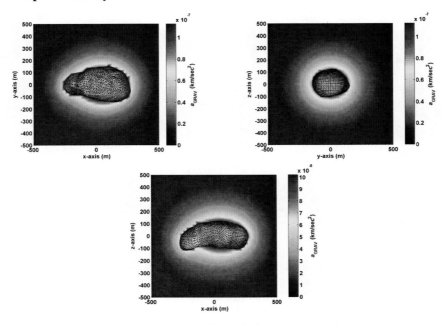

Figure 7. Attraction magnitude for variable ellipsoid model (2 elements).

Variable Inscribed Ellipsoid Gravity Model

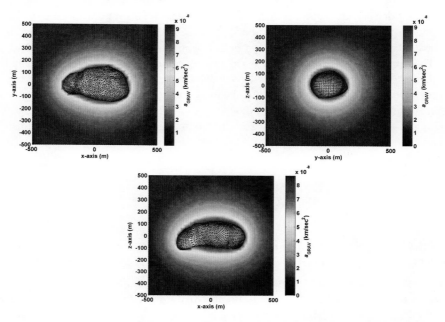

Figure 8.   Attraction magnitude for variable inscribed ellipsoid model (2501 elements).

Variable Overscribed Ellipsoid Gravity Model

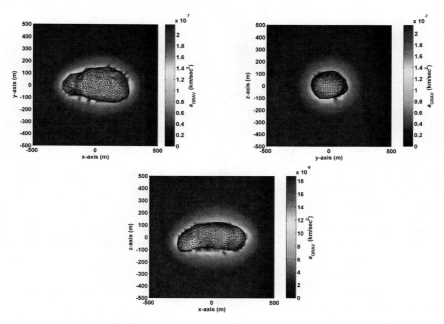

Figure 9.   Attraction magnitude for variable overscribed ellipsoid model (2501 elements).

GRAVITY MODEL VERIFICATION

The constant-density tetrahedron gravity model accounts for the entire volume of the body of interest; so, its gravitational field approximation is expected to accurately characterize the actual gravitational attraction of the body, resulting in its selection for an agreeable truth model for comparison. The comparisons of gravitational attraction at each field point are computed using Equation 22.[1] While the tetrahedron gravity model is a valuable and accurate model, its required runtime and script complexity render it unfeasible for use aboard a satellite for real-time trajectory calculations. On the other hand, these variable-element models are incapable of attaining an exact 100% volumetric efficiency, allowing for deviations from the optimal gravitational field approximation. It is their relatively quick runtimes complimented by their simplistic scripts that ultimately have driven the design of these models.

$$\lambda(\mathbf{r}) \equiv \frac{\|\partial U_t/\partial \mathbf{r} - \partial U_m/\partial \mathbf{r}\|}{\|\partial U_t/\partial \mathbf{r}\|} \times 100\% \tag{22}$$

wherein $\partial U_t/\partial \mathbf{r}$ and $\partial U_m/\partial \mathbf{r}$ denote the gravitational attraction vectors generated by the tetrahedron model and variable element model, respectively, at the field coordinate designated by $\mathbf{r}$.

The percent error of the gravitational attraction between the variable sphere gravity model and the tetrahedron gravity model is depicted in Figure 10. Observed in the x-y plane is a maximum error of about 6% in the gravitational acceleration components distributed over a small region close to the surface of Itokawa. The y-z plane shows a maximum error of 2.5%, and, in the x-z plane, 4%. Field points lying further away from the body's surface typically suffer a modest penalty error, in the neighborhood of 1.5% or less.

The variable ellipsoid gravity model comparison is found in Figure 11. Given that only two ellipsoid elements comprise this model, errors as high as 25%-30% are anticipated.

Conflicting with intuition are the comparison results of the variable inscribed ellipsoid model, illustrated in Figure 12. This model accounts for an extra 4.6% of the volume of Itokawa, which is indicative of a more accurate gravity model. However, the maximum error of the x-y planes is a about 12% (twice that of the variable sphere model), located at an isolated region, and those for the both the y-z and x-z planes are 10%. This deviation in gravitational acceleration likely represents an unequal distribution of mass throughout the model. Therefore, the achieved volumetric efficiency of this model does not solely reflect the accuracy of the gravity model. The unequally distributed mass appears to be caused by the nature of the model itself; it implements one ellipsoid element to characterize the majority of the body's volume and packs some number of sphere elements about the ellipsoid element. Fundamentally, the incompatible packing of spheres against a triaxial ellipsoid results in an inappropriate concentration of mass

Figure 13 depicts the percent error between the variable overscribed ellipsoid gravity model and the tetrahedron gravity model. The maximum error in all three planes extends beyond a staggering value of 100%. Interestingly, the error distributions shown in Figure 12 (evaluated for the variable inscribed ellipsoid model) and in Figure 13 both demonstrate considerable similarity. It is reasoned that perhaps both models suffer the same penalty of inappropriately concentrated mass, due to the inability of the sphere elements to consume virtually their entire surrounding volume.

Accuracy of Variable Sphere Gravity Model

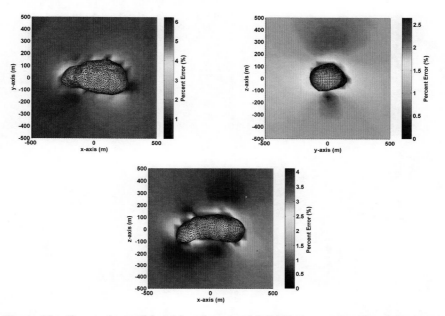

Figure 10.   Comparison of variable sphere model (2500 elements) with tetrahedron gravity model (6875 elements).

Accuracy of Variable Ellipsoid Gravity Model

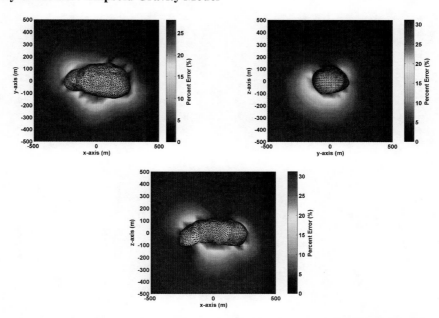

Figure 11.   Comparison of variable ellipsoid model (2 elements) with tetrahedron gravity model (6875 elements).

687

Accuracy of Variable Inscribed Ellipsoid Gravity Model

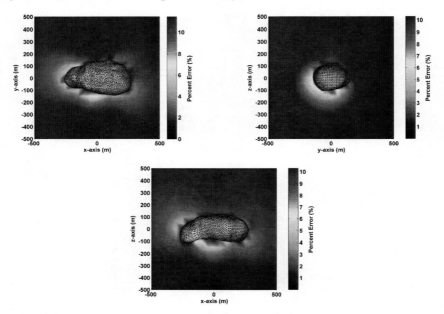

Figure 12. Comparison of variable inscribed ellipsoid model (2501 elements) with tetrahedron gravity model (6875 elements).

Accuracy of Variable Overscribed Ellipsoid Gravity Model

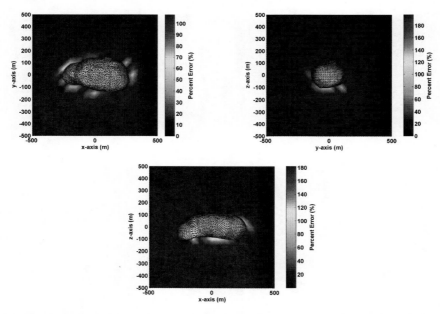

Figure 13. Comparison of variable overscribed ellipsoid model (2501 elements) with tetrahedron gravity model (6875 elements).

CONCLUSION

Presented in this paper are several unconventional size-varying finite element approaches for modeling irregularly-shaped small celestial bodies, and each model is evaluated for practicality and accuracy. The variable sphere model is shown to terminate in the shortest amount of time, and its gravity model yields sufficiently low percent error to deem it agreeable with the tetrahedron gravity model. Unable to function beyond two elements in its current state, the variable ellipsoid model's performance remains inconclusive. The variable inscribed and overscribed ellipsoid models have demonstrated inaccurate results despite their ability to claim respectable volumetric efficiency, in comparison to the variable sphere model. This lack in performance is due to the inappropriate concentration of mass at the ellipsoid element as induced by the homogenized density distribution. Overall, the variable sphere model has proven to be the most accurate and practical gravity model for aerospace applications.

ACKNOWLEDGEMENT

The authors would like to acknowledge the Aerospace Engineering Department at Embry-Riddle Aeronautical University, under which the research presented within this document was performed. Special thanks is given to Dr. Liu and Dr. Raghavan of the Mathematics Department at Embry-Riddle Aeronautical University for their assistance with the work.

NOMENCLATURE

$\mathbf{A}_t, \mathbf{B}_t, \mathbf{C}_t$	=	Coordinate vectors of the vertices of the base of tth tetrahedron, $\mathbf{D}_t = [0,0,0]$
G	=	Universal gravitational constant, $\approx 6.67428 \times 10^{-20} \text{km}^3/\text{kg/s}^2$
N_E	=	Number of elements
N_e	=	Number of ellipsoid elements
N_s	=	Number of sphere elements
N_t	=	Number of tetrahedron elements
$\mathbf{r}_i$	=	Center coordinate vector of the ith sphere element
r_{si}	=	Radius of an ith sphere element
$\mathbf{r}$	=	External field coordinate vector
U_s	=	Gravitational potential of sphere elements at field point $\mathbf{r}$
U_e	=	Gravitational potential of ellipsoid elements ($a \geq b \geq c$) at field point $\mathbf{r}$
$\partial U_s/\partial \mathbf{r}$	=	Gravitational acceleration of sphere elements at field point $\mathbf{r}$
$\partial U_t/\partial \mathbf{r}$	=	Gravitational acceleration of tetrahedron elements at field point $\mathbf{r}$
$\partial U_m/\partial \mathbf{r}$	=	Gravitational acceleration of variable element model at field point $\mathbf{r}$, $m \in \{s, e\}$
$[a_x, a_y, a_z]_e$	=	Gravitational acceleration components of ellipsoid elements at field point $\mathbf{r}$
$V_{Itokawa}$	=	Volume of 25143 asteroid Itokawa, 0.0185km^3
ρ_b	=	Density of the investigated small-body (kg/km^3)
$\rho_{Itokawa}$	=	Density of 25143 asteroid Itokawa, $1.98 \times 10^{12} \text{kg/km}^3$
ρ_m	=	*Corrected* density of variable element model (kg/km^3)
η_m	=	Volumetric efficiency of variable element model
$\lambda(\mathbf{r})$	=	Percent error between acceleration $\partial U_t/\partial \mathbf{r}$ and $\partial U_m/\partial \mathbf{r}$ at field point $\mathbf{r}$

REFERENCES

[1] R. Park, R. Werner and S. Bhaskaran, "Estimating Small-Body Gravity Field from Shape Model and Navigation Data," *Journal of Guidance, Control and Dynamics*, Vol. 33, No. 1, 2010, pp. 212–221.

[2] P. Anderson, "Validation of a Finite Sphere Gravitation Model with Applications to Comet 67P/Churyumov-Gerasimenko," AAS 11-408, 2011.

[3] B. Jones, B. George and B. Gregory, "Comparisons of the Cubed-Sphere Gravity Model with the Spherical Harmonics," *Journal of Guidance, Control and Dynamics*, Vol. 33, No. 2, 2010, pp. 415–425.

[4] "Data Archives and Transmission System," Itokawa Plate Model, [shape file], (2007), http://darts.isas.jaxa.jp/planet/project/hayabusa/shape.pl, [retrieved 8 September 2010].

[5] G. Luigi, "In-Polyhedron Test," Advanced Matlab, 15 May 2009, http://www.advancedmcode.org/in-polyhedron-test.html.

[6] N. Moshtagh, "MinVolEllipse," Matlab Central, 20 Jan 2009, http://www.mathworks.com/matlabcentral/fileexchange/9542-minimum-volume-enclosing-ellipsoid.

[7] S. Casotto and S. Musotto, "Methods for Computing the Potential of an Irregular Homogeneous Solid Body and its Gradient," AIAA 2000-4023, 2000.

[8] W. D. MacMillan, *The Theory of the Potential*. McGraw-Hill, New York. Reprinted by Dover, New York, 1958.

WHY ATENS ENJOY ENHANCED ACCESSIBILITY FOR HUMAN SPACE FLIGHT

Daniel R. Adamo[*] and Brent W. Barbee[†]

Near-Earth objects can be grouped into multiple orbit classifications, among them being the Aten group, whose members have orbits crossing Earth's with semi-major axes less than 1 astronomical unit. Atens comprise well under 10% of known near-Earth objects. This is in dramatic contrast to results from recent human space flight near-Earth object accessibility studies, where the most favorable known destinations are typically almost 50% Atens. Geocentric dynamics explain this enhanced Aten accessibility and lead to an understanding of where the most accessible near-Earth objects reside. Without a comprehensive space-based survey, however, highly accessible Atens will remain largely unknown.

INTRODUCTION

In the context of human space flight (HSF), the concept of near-Earth object (NEO) accessibility is highly subjective (Reference 1). Whether or not a particular NEO is accessible critically depends on mass, performance, and reliability of interplanetary HSF systems yet to be designed. Such systems would certainly include propulsion and crew life support with adequate shielding from both solar flares and galactic cosmic radiation. Equally critical architecture options are relevant to NEO accessibility. These options are also far from being determined and include the number of launches supporting an HSF mission, together with whether consumables are to be pre-emplaced at the destination.

Until the unknowns of HSF to NEOs come into clearer focus, the notion of *relative* accessibility is of great utility. Imagine a group of NEOs, each with nearly equal HSF merit determined from their individual characteristics relating to crew safety, scientific return, resource utilization, and planetary defense. The *more* accessible members of this group are more likely to be explored first.

A highly accessible NEO could conceivably be deferred in favor of a less accessible HSF destination because the latter is more accessible during a programmatically desirable launch season. Such a season is really yet another undetermined HSF architecture option. A launch season's duration will likely be measured in weeks, and it will be utilized at an indeterminate point almost certainly more than a decade in the future when HSF programmatic maturity is sufficient.

Furthermore, current knowledge of the NEO population relevant to HSF is far from complete. In the 100-m-diameter class of greatest interest, only a few percent of the estimated NEO population is known (Reference 2, Figure 2.4). Therefore, any known, lost, or fictitious NEO in a highly accessible orbit is a potential HSF destination of merit. Even if lost, fictitious, small, or hazardous, such a *potential* target (or another in a similar orbit) may ultimately prove to be an early HSF destination when the pertinent NEO population is more thoroughly catalogued and NEO orbits are more thoroughly maintained at high accuracy.

[*] Independent Astrodynamics Consultant, 4203 Moonlight Shadow Court, Houston, TX 77059; adamod@earthlink.net.
[†] Aerospace Engineer, Code 595, 8800 Greenbelt Road, Greenbelt MD 20771.

This paper first reviews methodology and pertinent results from NASA-sponsored research performed in late 2010 and dubbed NEO HSF Accessible Targets Study (NHATS, pronounced as "gnats"). A useful accessibility metric developed during this study is n, the tally of NHATS-compliant mission trajectory solutions detected in association with a specific NEO. The known NEO population is then surveyed to illustrate in which regions of heliocentric semi-major axis, eccentricity, and inclination (a, e, i) space NEOs with large n values are mapped. The (a, e, i) mapping is also formatted such that membership in each of four NEO orbit classifications, as defined below, is evident.

Amors have orbits everywhere superior to (outside of) Earth's. An Amor is therefore defined to have perihelion between 1.017 astronomical units (AU) and the maximum NEO value of 1.3 AU. As of 0 hrs Universal Time on 1 January 2011 (UT epoch 2011.0), Amors numbered 2855 in the Jet Propulsion Laboratory (JPL) Small-Body Database (SBDB)[*], comprising 37.7% of known NEOs.

Apollos have orbits crossing Earth's with periods greater than Earth's. An Apollo is therefore defined to have perihelion less than 1.017 AU and a greater than 1.0 AU. As of 2011.0 UT, Apollos numbered 4080 in the SBDB, comprising 53.9% of known NEOs.

Atens have orbits crossing Earth's with periods less than Earth's. An Aten is therefore defined to have aphelion greater than 0.983 AU and a less than 1.0 AU. As of 2011.0 UT, Atens numbered 618 in the SBDB, comprising 8.2% of known NEOs.

Atiras have orbits everywhere inferior to (inside of) Earth's. An Atira is therefore defined to have aphelion less than 0.983 AU. As of 2011.0 UT, Atiras numbered 11 in the SBDB, comprising 0.1% of known NEOs.

It is no surprise that the largest n values are chiefly associated with Apollos and Atens. Because these orbits cross Earth's, distance to be covered in a given round trip mission time Δt can be far less than is possible for Amors or Atiras (Reference 1, Figure 7). This Δt or the sum of mission propulsive impulse magnitudes Δv can more frequently be minimized to enhance NHATS compliance for Apollos and Atens than is generally the case for Amors and Atiras.

A less intuitive trend in NHATS results is that Atens nearly outnumber the more numerous Apollos among the most compliant NEOs as measured by n. This trend is completely out of proportion to the degree Atens are represented among the known NEO population. A theory based on geocentric NEO relative motion is presented by this paper to explain why Atens enjoy inherently greater accessibility than do Apollos.

Another trend evident from mapping into (a, e, i) space is the dearth of known NEOs at low e when $a <$ 1 AU. Underrepresentation of Atens and Atiras in the NEO catalog is at least in part attributable to observing exclusively from a perspective near Earth (Reference 2, pp. 41-49). Generally inferior Aten and Atira orbits are rarely, if ever, in Earth's night sky (Reference 2, Figure 3.5). Until a comprehensive NEO survey is conducted from an appropriate region remote from Earth, the theory developed in this paper indicates a substantial fraction of the most accessible NEOs will remain unknown. The accessibility theory developed in this paper has the potential to offer guidance in design, deployment, and operation of this survey.

PERTINENT NHATS TECHNIQUES AND RESULTS

Inaugurated by NASA in August 2010, NHATS is conceived as a means to assess the proliferation of *potential* NEO destinations accessible for HSF. Data with a NHATS pedigree reported in this paper have undergone thorough technical review by two independent research teams and are considered accurate in the context of that study's assumptions and constraints. However, readers should understand NHATS data are being disclosed in the interest of technical interchange before NASA has made any HSF architecture or NEO destination decisions based on this research. Until these decisions are made, whether or not a specific

---

[*] The SBDB may be accessed via a search engine at http://ssd.jpl.nasa.gov/sbdb_query.cgi or via a browser at http://ssd.jpl.nasa.gov/sbdb.cgi [verified 1 January 2011].

NHATS-viable NEO is accessible for HSF remains an open question. The following two sub-sections report NHATS assessment techniques and results internally reviewed and adopted by NASA prior to November 2010.

Constraints, Computations, And Criteria Identifying Viable NHATS Destinations

To be considered a viable destination under NHATS criteria, a NEO is required to be associated with at least one compliant trajectory design. Every NEO catalogued in the SBDB as of UT epoch 1.0 September 2010 (a total of 7210 with 2718 or 37.7% being Amors, 3893 or 54.0% being Apollos, 589 or 8.2% being Atens, and 10 or 0.1% being Atiras) is evaluated for compliant trajectory designs under NHATS ground rules. The trajectory design Earth departure interval (EDI) is confined to *Horizons*-internal coordinate time (CT) epochs from 1.0 January 2015 to 31.0 December 2040 to keep the evaluation task HSF-relevant and computationally manageable. *Horizons* is JPL's on-line solar system data and ephemeris computation service (Reference 3) and may be accessed at http://ssd.jpl.nasa.gov/?horizons [verified 29 December 2010].

Barbee et al document in detail the method of embedded trajectory grids used to compute NHATS trajectory designs (Reference 4). Each design consists of three segments.

The first *outbound* segment is a heliocentric conic trajectory departing Earth and arriving at the NEO destination during time interval Δt_1 such that 4 days $\leq \Delta t_1 \leq$ 358 days. The 2-dimensional array (or grid) of NHATS-permissible outbound segment EDI epochs (columns) is incremented at 6-day intervals, as are associated Δt_1 values (rows). Outbound segment departure is from a circular Earth parking orbit of geocentric radius r_{EPO} (equivalent to an orbit height 400 km above Earth's equatorial radius r_E) and requires an impulsive change-in-velocity magnitude at trans-NEO injection of Δv_{TNI}. Patched conic theory is used to compute Δv_{TNI} from the outbound segment's required Earth departure energy C_3 and Earth's reduced mass μ_E as follows.

$$\Delta v_{TNI} = \sqrt{C_3 + \frac{2\,\mu_E}{r_{EPO}}} - \sqrt{\frac{\mu_E}{r_{EPO}}} \tag{1}$$

The second *loiter* segment matches the NEO destination's trajectory as defined by *Horizons* during time interval Δt_2 between NEO arrival and departure such that 8 days $\leq \Delta t_2 \leq$ 40 days. To initiate loiter at the end of the outbound trajectory segment, an impulsive change-in-velocity magnitude of Δv_A is required at NEO destination arrival.

The third *return* segment is a heliocentric conic trajectory departing the NEO destination and arriving at Earth atmospheric entry interface during time interval Δt_3 such that 4 days $\leq \Delta t_3 \leq$ 358 days. A return segment grid of departure/arrival epochs is embedded at each element of the outbound segment's grid. The embedded grid consists of return segment NEO departure epochs (columns) incremented at 2-day intervals and associated Δt_3 values (rows) incremented at 6-day intervals. To initiate return following loiter, an impulsive change-in-velocity magnitude of Δv_D is required at NEO destination departure. A return trajectory segment is defined to arrive at a geocentric radius of r_{EI} (defined to be at a height 121.92 km above r_E) and is further constrained to a geocentric speed no more than $v_{EIX} =$ 12.5 km/s at that arrival point. Coasted geocentric Earth atmospheric entry interface speed v_{EI} is computed from geocentric asymptotic Earth return segment speed v_∞ using patched conic theory as follows.

$$v_{EI} = \sqrt{v_\infty^2 + \frac{2\,\mu_E}{r_{EI}}} \tag{2}$$

In cases where $v_{EI} > v_{EIX}$, an atmospheric braking impulse magnitude $\Delta v_{EI} = v_{EI} - v_{EIX}$ is computed. Otherwise, no such impulse is necessary and $\Delta v_{EI} \equiv 0$.

Multiple criteria must be satisfied for a trajectory design to be deemed NHATS-compliant. First, $\Delta t = \Delta t_1 + \Delta t_2 + \Delta t_3$ must not exceed 365 days to maintain radiation and microgravity exposure risks to the crew at reasonable levels. Second, C_3 must not exceed 24 km²/s² to maintain reasonable propulsive performance expectations at Earth departure when vehicle mass is likely greatest during the three trajectory design segments. Third, $\Delta v = \Delta v_{TNI} + \Delta v_A + \Delta v_D + \Delta v_{EI}$ must not exceed 12 km/s to maintain reasonable propulsive performance expectations throughout the HSF mission.

Readers familiar with current interplanetary HSF capabilities will find the foregoing NHATS trajectory design constraints and compliance criteria to border on the realm of science fiction in multiple respects. This astronautic optimism might be excessive even if reasonable state-of-the-art progress through the 2030s is assumed. Such optimism is intentional. A major NHATS objective is to determine whether or not a dedicated space-based survey is justified by the proliferation of known NEO destinations available for HSF missions. Initial NHATS compliancy processing documented here is therefore biased toward inclusion. Subsequently, NASA plans to cull this initial list of potential NEO destinations using other considerations such as physical characteristics (size, composition, spin, etc.), orbit prediction uncertainty, and accessibility with respect to HSF infrastructure capabilities during specific Earth departure seasons.

Viable NHATS Destinations With Maximum Trajectory Design Compliance

Selecting NEO HSF destinations from a known population whose physical characteristics are largely unknown is well beyond the scope of this paper. Furthermore, as noted in the Introduction, the known NEO population is but an observationally biased sample amounting to only a few percent of the whole at HSF-relevant diameters near 100 m.

In contrast to *selecting* NEO destinations for HSF (literally in the blind), *ranking* them according to their compliance with NHATS trajectory design criteria is very useful at this point. At the very least, this ranking exercise identifies a subset of known NEO orbits highly accessible for HSF. As NEO surveys continue under mandates from the U.S. Congress (Reference 2, p. 1), identifying orbit classes of higher interest will lead to more informed and cost-effective observation strategies. For example, inability to detect NEOs approaching Earth from the Sun's general direction could easily rule out 50% of all HSF mission opportunities simply because such opportunities will not be evident with sufficient time to prepare for launch.

Processing under constraints and compliance criteria outlined in the previous section has identified 666 NEOs with at least one NHATS-compliant trajectory design. Of these, 106 (15.9%) are Amors, 390 (58.6%) are Apollos, 170 (25.5%) are Atens, and none are Atiras. But a handful of barely viable trajectories over the 26-year NHATS EDI cannot qualify a potential destination as highly accessible, particularly in the context of intentionally inclusive NHATS trajectory design constraints and compliance criteria.

Table 1 ranks viable NHATS destinations in order of decreasing n, the total number of compliant trajectory solutions associated with each destination. Only the top 50 NEOs according to this ranking are included, rendering Table 1 a plausible list of the most accessible NHATS destinations. Very little characterization data are available for Table 1 NEOs, but a range of likely diameter d values in meters is provided using the following relationship based on absolute magnitude H and a likely range of albedo values ρ ranging from 0.05 to 0.25.

$$d = \frac{1,329,000}{\sqrt{\rho}} \, 10^{-0.2\,H} \qquad\qquad (3)$$

Osculating heliocentric orbit elements appearing in Table 1 (a is semi-major axis, e is eccentricity, and i is ecliptic inclination) are from the SBDB as configured 3 January 2011.

Table 1. The 50 Most Accessible NHATS Destinations Ranked According to n.

Rank	Designation	n	Likely d (m)	a (AU)	e	i (deg)	Orbit Group
1	2000 SG$_{344}$	4,153,445	29 to 66	0.977	0.067	0.1	Aten
2	1991 VG	3,524,012	6 to 12	1.027	0.049	1.4	Apollo
3	2008 EA$_9$	2,189,719	8 to 17	1.059	0.080	0.4	Apollo
4	2001 FR$_{85}$	1,991,566	33 to 75	0.983	0.028	5.2	Aten
5	2006 BZ$_{147}$	1,845,936	22 to 49	1.024	0.099	1.4	Apollo
6	2007 UN$_{12}$	1,836,008	5 to 11	1.054	0.060	0.2	Apollo
7	2008 HU$_4$	1,778,197	6 to 13	1.093	0.073	1.3	Apollo
8	2006 RH$_{120}$	1,687,566	3 to 7	1.033	0.025	0.6	Apollo

Rank	Designation	n	Likely d (m)	a (AU)	e	i (deg)	Orbit Group
9	2008 UA$_{202}$	1,419,978	3 to 8	1.033	0.068	0.3	Apollo
10	2007 VU$_6$	1,393,440	13 to 29	0.976	0.091	1.2	Aten
11	2004 QA$_{22}$	1,342,378	7 to 16	0.951	0.122	0.6	Aten
12	2009 BD	1,225,392	6 to 13	1.002	0.047	0.4	Apollo
13	1999 VX$_{25}$	1,204,010	12 to 27	0.900	0.140	1.7	Aten
14	2001 GP$_2$	1,124,586	11 to 25	1.038	0.074	1.3	Apollo
15	2008 JL$_{24}$	1,100,888	3 to 7	1.038	0.107	0.5	Apollo
16	2000 SZ$_{162}$	1,018,474	10 to 23	0.930	0.168	0.9	Aten
17	2004 VJ$_1$	1,017,841	37 to 83	0.944	0.164	1.3	Aten
18	2010 JR$_{34}$	1,011,306	8 to 17	0.960	0.145	0.7	Aten
19	2009 OS$_5$	993,890	51 to 115	1.144	0.097	1.7	Amor
20	2007 YF	892,078	30 to 66	0.953	0.120	1.7	Aten
21	1993 HD	882,148	20 to 45	1.126	0.040	0.5	Amor
22	2000 LG$_6$	869,476	4 to 9	0.917	0.111	2.8	Aten
23	2009 YR	860,265	7 to 15	0.942	0.110	0.7	Aten
24	2001 QJ$_{142}$	800,937	55 to 123	1.062	0.086	3.1	Apollo
25	2009 YF	794,499	31 to 69	0.936	0.121	1.5	Aten
26	2006 DQ$_{14}$	785,949	10 to 23	1.028	0.053	6.3	Apollo
27	1999 CG$_9$	784,795	25 to 55	1.060	0.063	5.2	Apollo
28	1999 AO$_{10}$	771,044	45 to 101	0.912	0.111	2.6	Aten
29	2008 DL$_4$	756,226	11 to 26	0.929	0.123	3.2	Aten
30	2005 LC	743,975	12 to 26	1.133	0.102	2.8	Amor
31	2008 ST	736,888	10 to 23	0.964	0.126	1.9	Aten
32	2010 JK$_1$	687,496	36 to 79	1.026	0.150	0.2	Apollo
33	2003 SM$_{84}$	685,501	76 to 169	1.126	0.082	2.8	Amor
34	2005 UV$_{64}$	682,372	13 to 28	0.958	0.116	5.4	Aten
35	2003 WT$_{153}$	676,727	7 to 15	0.894	0.178	0.4	Aten
36	2009 CV	641,350	37 to 84	1.112	0.150	1.0	Apollo
37	2006 UQ$_{216}$	631,360	9 to 21	1.104	0.162	0.5	Apollo
38	2001 BB$_{16}$	606,609	80 to 179	0.854	0.172	2.0	Aten
39	2009 DB$_{43}$	589,918	14 to 30	1.102	0.172	0.9	Apollo
40	2008 CX$_{118}$	582,718	35 to 78	1.145	0.035	2.4	Amor
41	2007 BB	564,165	7 to 16	0.932	0.142	3.5	Aten
42	2009 HC	557,435	30 to 66	1.039	0.126	3.8	Apollo
43	2006 UB$_{17}$	557,021	15 to 33	1.141	0.104	2.0	Amor
44	2004 JN$_1$	531,561	54 to 121	1.085	0.176	1.5	Apollo
45	2007 XB$_{23}$	525,765	10 to 23	1.041	0.054	8.5	Apollo
46	2009 UD	503,677	10 to 22	1.038	0.121	4.4	Apollo
47	2006 FH$_{36}$	480,108	69 to 155	0.955	0.198	1.6	Aten
48	2008 EL$_{68}$	448,257	7 to 15	1.210	0.192	0.6	Apollo
49	2008 CM$_{74}$	432,970	7 to 15	1.089	0.147	0.9	Apollo
50	2007 RC$_{20}$	430,820	13 to 28	0.955	0.198	2.8	Aten

The Table 1 breakdown according to orbit groups is 6 Amors (12.0%), 23 Apollos (46%), 21 Atens (42%), and no Atiras (0%). Compare the ratio of Apollos-to-Atens in Table 1 (23/21 = 1.095) to that in the SBDB processed by NHATS (3893/589 = 6.610). It is not intuitively obvious why this 6-fold selectivity should apply to Atens in the context of relatively high HSF accessibility. A theory applying geocentric relative motion to heliocentric NEO orbits is presented subsequently to provide an understanding of this selectivity.

Another noteworthy trend in Table 1 is that no i value exceeds 10°. When the entire list of 666 viable NHATS destinations is scanned for $i > 10°$ members, the highest ranking is the 189th, 2007 VV$_{83}$, with a diminutive $n = 54{,}819$. A necessary condition for high accessibility among NEOs is evidently i < 10°.

695

Table 2 presents the portion of each NEO orbit group having $i < 10°$ according to the SBDB as configured at 2011.0 UT.

Table 2. Portion Of Each NEO Orbit Group Meeting the $i < 10°$ Accessibility Criterion.

Orbit Group	Total Members	$i < 10°$ Members	$i < 10°$ %
Amors	2855	1331	46.6
Apollos	4080	2106	51.6
Atens	618	288	46.6
Atiras	11	4	36

The rightmost column in Table 2 is remarkable because the $i < 10°$ criterion is not dramatically more selective among some orbit groups, particularly the Atens and Atiras, than others. But low inclination in an inferior orbit does not necessarily equate to low solar elongation and poor visibility from Earth. During close Earth encounters, typically when NEOs are discovered, even an Atira with $i < 10°$ can enjoy sufficiently large solar elongation to be detectable from Earth. Such geometry can place the NEO far from the ecliptic plane from a geocentric viewpoint. Thus, the $i < 10°$ accessibility criterion imposes roughly equal selectivity among the four orbit groups. This consistency is only enhanced in the context of viable NHATS destinations because Atiras are absent.

SCOUTING FOR HIGHLY ACCESSIBLE NEO ORBITS WITH (a, e, i) PLOTS

Many small-body researchers have published plots of e as a function of a to provide insight into how groups of these objects share common dynamics. Increments in i are typically denoted on these plots by differing data point markers. These (a, e, i) plots also have utility in scouting the solar system for highly accessible NEOs (Reference 5, Figure 1). The (a, e, i) plot in Figure 1 maps every known NEO in its range with $i < 10°$ as of 2011.0 UT. As indicated in Figure 1's plot legend, filled data markers denote NEOs with $i < 5°$, and hollow data markers denote NEOs with $5° < i < 10°$. This legend also details how data markers are further associated by shape and color into pertinent Amor, Apollo, and Aten orbit groups. There are no known Atiras within the plot's range as of 2011.0 UT.

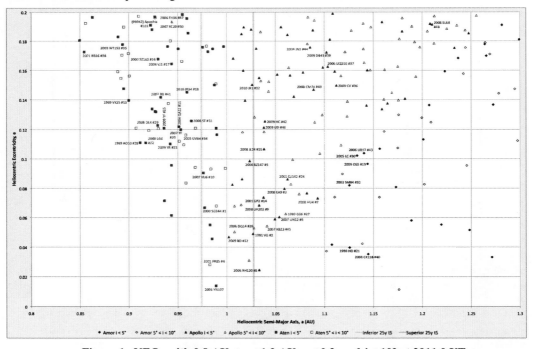

Figure 1. NEOs with 0.8 AU < a < 1.3 AU, e < 0.2, and i < 10° at 2011.0 UT.

The 50 most accessible NEOs identified by Table 1 are annotated in Figure 1, including their rank according to n. In the interest of legibility, NEO designations in Figure 1 annotations refrain from using subscripted numerals. Thus, the NEO with highest n-ranking is annotated as "2000 SG344 #1" in Figure 1.

Two NEOs not appearing in Table 1 are annotated in Figure 1. The first of these is (99942) Apophis at (a, e, i) coordinates (0.922 AU, 0.191, 3.3°). With $d = 270$ m, Apophis will become the largest NEO to encounter Earth so closely when it reaches a predicted perigee radius of 38,000 km on 13 April 2029. Because of this event, both robotic and HSF mission proposals targeting Apophis are prolific. With $n = 204,028$, however, Apophis is ranked #101 among viable NHATS destinations. Particularly when inadvertent changes to future Earth collision prospects are considered, visiting Apophis early in a NEO exploration program is ill advised. There are many more accessible and less potentially hazardous destinations warranting a visit before Apophis is considered.

The second NEO annotated in Figure 1, but absent from Table 1, is 2003 YN_{107}. At (a, e, i) coordinates (0.989 AU, 0.014, 4.3°), 2003 YN_{107} is in the most Earth-like orbit of any known NEO as of 2011.0 UT. This attribute ought to rank 2003 YN_{107} among the most accessible NHATS destinations, but its Figure 1 annotation has no rank because its n is zero. The reason 2003 YN_{107} is excluded as a viable NHATS destination lies with its synodic period t_S.

Provided a NEO of interest undergoes no close planetary encounters during an interval of interest, t_S can be computed with sufficient accuracy from NEO and Earth mean heliocentric orbit rates (ω and ω_R, respectively) as follows. Using the Sun's reduced mass μ_S, orbit rates derive directly from Kepler's third law (the square of orbit period is proportional to the cube of semi-major axis). Earth's semi-major axis in Equation (5) is approximated by $a_R = 1$ AU.

$$\omega = \sqrt{\frac{\mu_S}{a^3}} \tag{4}$$

$$\omega_R = \sqrt{\frac{\mu_S}{a_R^3}} \tag{5}$$

Synodic period is the time required for orbit rate difference to sweep out a full revolution such that the NEO "laps" Earth or vice-versa.

$$t_S = \frac{2\pi}{\left| \omega - \omega_R \right|} \tag{6}$$

In the case of 2003 YN_{107}, $a = 0.989$ AU. When Equations (4) and (6) are evaluated for 2003 YN_{107}, the synodic period is 61.6 Julian years. This t_S greatly exceeds the 26-year period during which NHATS missions lasting less than one year must be initiated. It is therefore evident that 2003 YN_{107} has slowly *phased ahead* of Earth (the Earth-Sun-NEO phase angle θ has increased from zero) since its late 2003 discovery to an extent inhibiting any NHATS-compatible trajectory during the required 1.0 January 2015 to 31.0 December 2040 UT EDI.

To indicate that portion of Figure 1 in which NEOs would have $t_S > 25$ Julian years, the plot is accompanied by two vertical loci of constant semi-major axis. The first locus is positioned inferior to a_R at a_I, and the second locus is positioned superior to a_R at a_S. Thus, the two loci bracket all Figure 1 NEOs having $t_S > 25$ Julian years. Semi-major axis values for these loci are obtained by substituting Equation (4) into Equation (6) and solving for a while ensuring the difference in orbit rate from Equation (6)'s denominator is maintained positive ($\omega - \omega_R$ for the inferior case and $\omega_R - \omega$ for the superior case) without computing an absolute value.

$$a_I = \left[\mu_S \bigg/ \left(\omega_R + \frac{2\pi}{t_S} \right)^2 \right]^{1/3} \tag{7}$$

$$a_S = \left[\mu_S \Big/ \left(\omega_R - \frac{2\pi}{t_S} \right)^2 \right]^{1/3} \tag{8}$$

When evaluated for $t_S = 25$ Julian years, Equation (7) produces $a_I = 0.974191$ AU, and Equation (8) produces $a_S = 1.027589$ AU. Note the slight asymmetry of a_I and a_S about $a_R = 1$ AU. Here is the first of four inferior/superior asymmetries documented in this paper, and they all relate to enhanced accessibility among Atens. In effect, a broader range of orbit rates exists over a given a increment *inferior* to Earth's orbit than is present over the same increment *superior* to Earth's orbit.

It is a straightforward exercise to compute heliocentric phasing of 2003 YN$_{107}$ with respect to Earth during the NHATS EDI from 1.0 January 2015 to 31.0 December 2040 UT and thereby explain the $n = 0$ result for this NEO. Phasing over this interval is shown graphically in Figure 2 by mapping the heliocentric 2003 YN$_{107}$ *Horizons* ephemeris into the Cartesian UVW coordinate system defined by Earth's heliocentric *Horizons* ephemeris using a 30-day time increment.

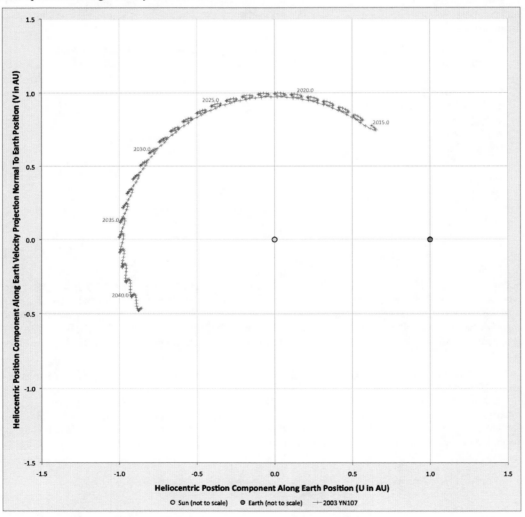

Figure 2. Heliocentric UV Plot of 2003 YN$_{107}$ Phasing During The NHATS EDI.

In Figure 2's context, the unit vector **U** is aligned with Earth's heliocentric position, **W** is aligned with Earth's heliocentric angular momentum vector, and **U** × **V** = **W** in the right-handed convention. Because Figure 2 is confined to Earth's orbit plane, it is called a heliocentric UV plot. In such a plot, Earth is fixed at heliocentric (U, V) coordinates (1, 0) AU. A NEO whose position is phased ahead of Earth (with $0 < \theta < 180°$) has a positive V-coordinate, and one behind Earth (with $-180° < \theta < 0$) has a negative V-coordinate. Figure 2's plot is annotated with 1.0 January UT epochs at 5-year intervals beginning with "2015.0". Since θ is far from zero in Figure 2, the $n = 0$ NHATS assessment for 2003 YN_{107} lends further credence to the assertion that HSF mission opportunities with minimal Δt and Δv occur only during timeframes when the NEO destination encounters Earth within 0.1 AU (Reference 1).

What would be the NHATS assessment for 2003 YN_{107} if Earth departures were confined to years 1997 through 2007? According to *Horizons*, this EDI around the time of 2003 YN_{107} discovery contains no less than 21 perigees closer than 0.1 AU. The result of this biased departure time NHATS assessment is $n = 10,141,782$, exceeding any Table 1 value by a factor of at least 2.4 (2000 SG_{344}, ranked #1, has $n = 4,153,445$). The high *intrinsic* accessibility of 2003 YN_{107}, as apparent from Figure 1, is confirmed.

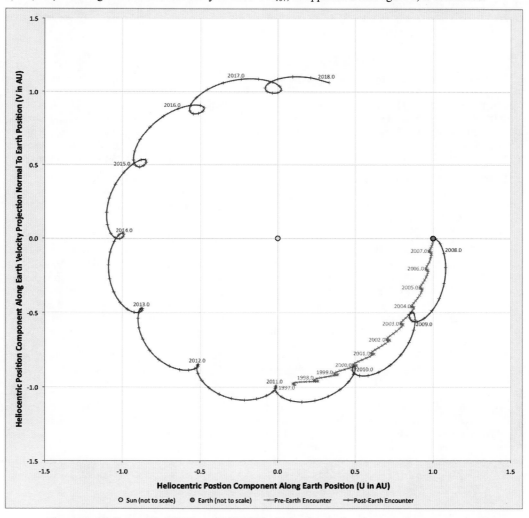

Figure 3. Heliocentric UV Plot of 2007 UN$_{12}$ Transformation from an Aten to an Apollo.

A noteworthy feature of (a, e, i) plots like Figure 1's is that some NEOs undergo dramatic coordinate shifts over time scales of months or less. Such events typically occur during a close Earth encounter and may therefore be associated with a NEO's discovery or an HSF mission opportunity. An example of dramatic (a, e, i) dynamics is provided by 2007 UN_{12}, whose Table 1 rank is #6. During the timeframe of this NEO's discovery, it encountered Earth with a perigee less than 0.000467 AU (69,900 km) on 17.6 October 2007 UT according to *Horizons*. In terms of (a, e, i) coordinates from *Horizons*, 2007 UN_{12} went from (0.992 AU, 0.010, 3.080°) on 17.0 September 2007 UT to (1.053 AU, 0.061, 0.236°) 60 days later on 16.0 November 2007 UT. As illustrated in Figure 3's UV plot, Earth gravity perturbations to the 2007 UN_{12} orbit during 2007 transformed it from that of an Aten to that of an Apollo.

As of Figure 1's 2011.0 UT osculation epoch, a series of six close Earth approaches begun in 2008 is nearing completion for 2009 BD at (a, e, i) = (1.004 AU, 0.046, 0.374°). By the earliest NHATS Earth departure epoch at 1.0 January 2015 CT, *Horizons* predicts 2009 BD's coordinates will have shifted to (1.062 AU, 0.052, 1.267°), well clear of the t_S > 25 years region in Figure 1. Of all Table 1 NEOs, 2009 BD's coordinates are by far the most dynamic over the interval from 2011.0 to 2042.0 CT, but only 2.6% of 2009 BD a variations during this interval occur after 2012.0 CT. Indeed, all Table 1 NEOs exhibit remarkably static a values during the NHATS assessment interval. At no time during this interval does a superior Table 1 NEO become inferior, nor does an inferior NEO become superior.

A THEORY OF NEO ACCESSIBILITY DYNAMICS FOR HSF

With HSF missions constrained to be round trips lasting well under a year, NEO accessibility must place a premium on minimal distance between Earth and destination in the mission timeframe. As recently documented (Reference 1), this precept has its basis in the simple "distance equals rate times time" relationship. At a given NEO distance, minimal rate (and minimal propulsive mass) generally requires maximum mission duration. Likewise, at a given mission duration, minimal propulsive mass generally requires minimal NEO distance. From the utility of (a, e, i) plots demonstrated in the previous section, a question naturally arises. Where on such plots are NEO orbits with minimal separation from Earth's to be found?

To address that question, a simplifying constraint is first imposed and retained throughout this section. The constraint fixes minimal separation from Earth's heliocentric orbit at an apsis in a NEO's heliocentric orbit. Thus, Amors and Apollos will come to minimum separation at perihelion, while Atens and Atiras will come to minimum separation at aphelion under this constraint.

The perigee-at-apsis constraint is a close approximation to actual geometry for highly accessible NEOs. At 2011.0 UT, Earth's orbit would be plotted in Figure 1 at (a, e, i) = (1.001 AU, 0.017, 0.002°) according to *Horizons*. Earth's orbit eccentricity is but 68% of the smallest e value appearing in Table 1 (2006 RH_{120}, ranked #8, has e = 0.025). Consequently, any NEO orbit encountering Earth's away from an apsis will possess a heliocentric radial velocity component generally far greater than Earth's at that location. This radial NEO motion is as detrimental to accessibility as motion out of the ecliptic plane previously identified in connection with i. Therefore, the best close Earth encounter geometry from the standpoint of HSF accessibility is generally parallel to Earth's heliocentric orbit and near a NEO orbit apsis.

In the ideal accessibility condition of zero perigee constrained to be at a NEO heliocentric apsis (ZePHA), geometric properties of a NEO's orbit ellipse give rise to Equation (9).

$$a_R = a \, (1 \pm e) \tag{9}$$

With a > 1 AU (Amors and Apollos), e is subtracted in Equation (9) to place NEO perihelion on Earth's orbit. With a < 1 AU (Atens and Atiras), e is added in Equation (9) to place NEO aphelion on Earth's orbit. A ZePHA condition is the second inferior/superior asymmetry documented in this paper. From Equation (9), $a/a_R = (1 \pm e)^{-1}$. At any given e, inferior Atens and Atiras will possess a/a_R closer to 1 AU (the semi-major axis of Earth's orbit) than the corresponding superior Amors and Apollos. Once again, accessibility of inferior NEOs is favored over superior NEOs. For the purpose of mapping a locus of ZePHA points onto an (a, e, i) plot, Equation (9) is solved for e.

$$e = \left| \frac{a_R}{a} - 1 \right| \tag{10}$$

As noted previously, NEOs such as (99942) Apophis can approach Earth very closely without being among the most accessible. The Equation (10) condition is necessary for high HSF accessibility, but it is not sufficient. A condition limiting geocentric speed is also necessary. One such condition easily mapped onto (a, e, i) plots is developed here and called the geocentric relative motion stall (GReMS). At an arbitrary heliocentric apsis distance r_X, the GReMS condition requires heliocentric tangential velocity in a NEO orbit, whose magnitude is given by the energy integral, be equal to local tangential velocity at Earth's mean orbit rate. This condition gives rise to Equation (11).

$$\sqrt{\mu_s \left(\frac{2}{r_X} - \frac{1}{a} \right)} = \omega_R \, r_X \tag{11}$$

Squaring both sides of Equation (11) leads to the following cubic in r_X.

$$\frac{\omega_R^2 \, r_X^3}{\mu_s} + \frac{r_X}{a} - 2 = 0 \tag{12}$$

The solution to this cubic can be computed as follows.

$$f_1 \equiv \frac{\omega_R^2}{\mu_s} \tag{13}$$

$$f_2 \equiv \left[9 \, a^3 f_1^2 + \sqrt{3 \, a^3 f_1^3 \left(27 \, a^3 f_1 + 1 \right)} \right]^{1/3} \tag{14}$$

$$r_X = \frac{f_2}{9^{1/3} \, a f_1} - \frac{1}{3^{1/3} \, f_2} \tag{15}$$

With this apsis solution in hand, the GReMS eccentricity corresponding to a is computed by substitution into Equation (10).

$$e = \left| \frac{r_X}{a} - 1 \right| \tag{16}$$

Numeric results from Equations (13) through (16) relevant to highly accessible NEOs appear in Table 3 for discrete a values on Figure 1's horizontal axis. Table 3's Δr column is a heliocentric conic estimate of perigee when a NEO undergoes GReMS in the $+U$ direction with zero θ ($\Delta r \equiv | r_X - a_R |$).

Table 3. GReMS Conditions Near $a = 1$ AU.

a (AU)	r_X (AU)	Δr (AU)	e
0.80	0.938567	0.061433	0.173209
0.85	0.956401	0.043599	0.125178
0.90	0.972423	0.027577	0.080470
0.95	0.986886	0.013114	0.038828
1	1	0	0
1.05	1.011940	0.011940	0.036248
1.10	1.022852	0.022852	0.070135
1.15	1.032861	0.032861	0.101860
1.20	1.042073	0.042073	0.131605

Table 3 immediately suggests a third inferior/superior asymmetry favoring Aten and Atira HSF accessibility. At a given e, the associated GReMS condition for an inferior NEO orbit will be at an a closer to Earth's semi-major axis than the corresponding GReMS a for a superior NEO orbit. For example, an inferior NEO with $e = 0.038828$ must have $a = 0.95$ AU to undergo GReMS at aphelion. But a superior NEO with $e = 0.038828$ must have $a > 1.05$ AU to undergo GReMS at perihelion.

A fourth asymmetry lurks in Table 3 within its rightmost two columns, but it requires mental interpolation to perceive. At a given e, the associated GReMS condition for an inferior NEO orbit will be at a smaller geocentric distance than the corresponding GReMS geocentric distance for a superior NEO orbit. This asymmetry is easily perceived when e is plotted as a function of Δr for inferior orbits and for superior orbits in Figure 4.

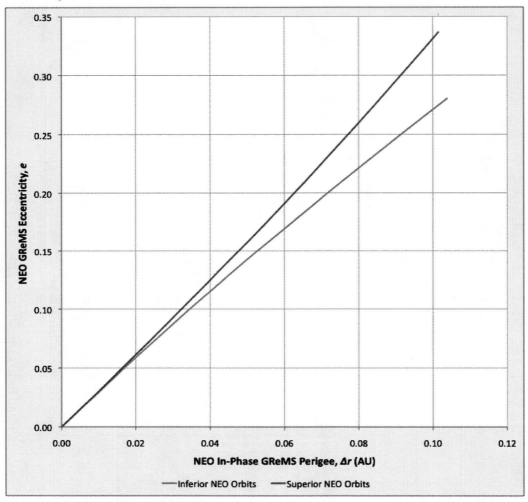

Figure 4. In-Phase GReMS Perigee Asymmetry Between Inferior & Superior NEO Orbits.

With both Table 3 asymmetries relating to e, it is important to understand their significance is undiminished by the GReMS condition's independence of e per Equations (13) through (15). This independence arises only because GReMS is defined to occur at a NEO apsis, where radial heliocentric velocity is zero. However, immediately before and after the GReMS epoch, finite radial heliocentric velocity reducing NEO accessibility *does* exist, and its negative influence *will* be enhanced according to e.

To summarize the NEO accessibility theory, a ZePHA locus is plotted using Equation (10) and a GReMS locus is plotted using Equations (13) through (16), together with the Figure 1 data and annotations, producing Figure 5. At a given e and i near zero, the ZePHA and GReMS loci plotted in Figure 5 are theorized to encompass a region of elevated NEO accessibility. Furthermore, this elevated accessibility for Atens and Atiras is enhanced with respect to that for Amors and Apollos at a given t_S, e, and i. The area bounded by the double-V of solid ZePHA and dashed GReMS Figure 5 loci is therefore termed the NEO enhanced accessibility region (NEAR). It should be noted that programmatic considerations may impose a zone of exclusion within the NEAR due to excessive t_S if a approaches a_R too closely. This "t_S cutout" is suggested by the two vertical loci in Figure 5 at a_I and a_S which enclose the region with $t_S > 25$ years.

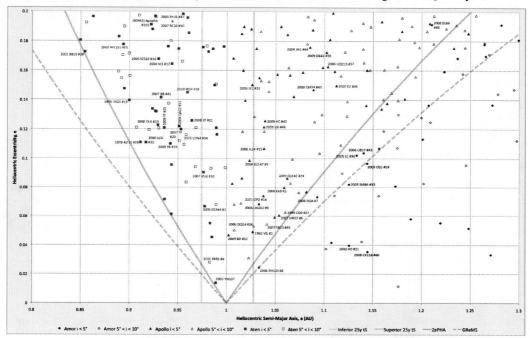

Figure 5. Theorized NEAR Bounded By ZePHA and GReMS Loci.

Because the entire ZePHA locus is defined with a_R valued at 1 AU, its superior branch only approximates the Figure 5 demarcation between Amors and Apollos. A precise demarcation would be achieved if the superior branch were to be computed with a_R valued at 1.017 AU in accord with the marginal perihelion value defining these two orbit classifications. Similarly, a precise demarcation between Atens and Atiras would be mapped onto Figure 5 (assuming Atiras actually appeared in Figure 5) if the ZePHA inferior branch were to be computed with a_R valued at 0.983 AU.

Branch-specific ZePHA computations are deemed unwarranted by these precise demarcation correlations with orbit classifications. Earth's heliocentric orbit apses impose the critical apsis values between these classifications. Thus, depending on precise argument of perihelion values, an Apollo with perihelion slightly less than 1.017 AU (or an Aten with aphelion slightly more than 0.983 AU) may not cross Earth's real orbit, even when the NEO orbit is projected onto the ecliptic plane. The notion of orbits crossing Earth's is rendered even more approximate in three-dimensional space by finite NEO ecliptic inclinations. Consequently, Equation (10) is considered an adequate ZePHA locus definition consistent with this paper's accessibility theory, whose pedigree approximates Earth's heliocentric orbit as a circle of radius 1 AU.

Although a smattering of low inclination Amors and Apollos lies superior to Figure 5's superior ZePHA branch, the Figure 5 region inferior to its inferior ZePHA branch is completely void of Atens and Atiras having $i < 10°$. Yet, if the NEO accessibility theory is credible, NEOs in proximity to the inferior ZePHA branch ought to be among the most accessible for HSF. If such NEOs were known, how would their accessibilities vary and how would these accessibilities compare with those of otherwise identical superior NEOs and those of NHATS destinations in Table 1? The following section details a simulation method to answer these questions.

USING FICTITIOUS NEOs TO ASSESS HSF ACCESSIBILITY THEORY

The baseline concept of creating plausible (but yet to be discovered) "fictitious" NEOs for accessibility assessment is facilitated in *Horizons* through User-Specified Small Bodies (USSBs). A variety of optional orbit element sets may be used to temporarily define a USSB in *Horizons*. Once defined, a USSB ephemeris may be generated with the same JPL Standard Dynamical Model (SDM) routinely supporting SBDB trajectory predictions by *Horizons*. A USSB ephemeris, together with JPL's DE405 for the Earth, is then exported by *Horizons* for HSF accessibility assessment using NHATS constraints, computations, and criteria previously documented. Inputs required to create fictitious NEO initial conditions as a USSB in *Horizons* are documented in the following subsection. To evaluate Figure 5's NEAR, fictitious NEO ephemerides are generated within sequences of constant (e, i) coordinates in which a is progressively increased.

Two deviations from the foregoing fictitious NEO baseline concept are necessary to evaluate HSF accessibility theory under minimally controlled conditions. First, as detailed subsequently, SDM perturbations to heliocentric conic motion introduce (a, e, i) dynamics often disrupting USSB long-term membership in a single NEO orbit classification. To maintain a controlled experimental relationship between orbit classification membership and HSF accessibility, USSB trajectory prediction with the SDM is therefore abandoned in favor of fictitious NEO conic (or Keplerian or two-body) heliocentric motion.

Second, as detailed subsequently, fictitious NEO orbit period resonances with Earth create significant variations in n with a due to the extended 1.0 January 2015 to 31.0 December 2040 CT EDI applicable to NHATS. These variations are effectively eliminated by using an EDI from 20.0 September 2025 to 18.0 September 2030 CT. Constraints, computations, and criteria attributable to NHATS and documented previously are otherwise preserved by accessibility assessments presented for fictitious NEOs.

Creating Fictitious NEO Initial Conditions In *Horizons*

The following osculating quantities, referenced to the Cartesian heliocentric ecliptic coordinate system at epoch J2000.0 (J2KE), are used to create fictitious NEO initial conditions in *Horizons*. The J2KE system is defined by I directed at the ascending node of Earth's orbit plane at epoch J2000.0 on the Earth mean equatorial plane of epoch J2000.0, K oriented normal to Earth's orbit plane at epoch J2000.0 (directed into the northern geocentric celestial hemisphere), and $J = K \times I$ in the right-handed convention.

EPOCH: osculating epoch Julian ephemeris date in CT. For all fictitious NEOs, the EPOCH value is selected at a vernal equinox approximately midway through the NHATS EDI from 1.0 January 2015 to 31.0 December 2040 CT. Because J2KE elements are in use, this equinox is reckoned with respect to Earth crossing the J2KE I/K plane and occurs at 20.5 March 2028 CT or 2,461,851.0 Julian ephemeris date CT according to *Horizons*. In this paper's narrative, 20.5 March 2028 CT is often referred to as a fictitious NEO's initialization epoch.

EC: the value of e specific to the fictitious NEO ephemeris sequence being generated.

MA: mean anomaly in deg. A fictitious NEO with $a \le a_R$ requires MA = 180, and a fictitious NEO with $a > a_R$ requires MA = 0.

A: the value of a in AU specific to the fictitious NEO ephemeris being generated.

OM: J2KE longitude of ascending node in deg. All fictitious NEOs use OM = 0.

W: J2KE argument of perihelion in deg. A fictitious NEO with $a \le a_R$ requires W = 0, and a fictitious NEO with $a > a_R$ requires W = 180.

IN: the value of i in deg specific to the fictitious NEO ephemeris sequence being generated.

Each Earth and fictitious NEO ephemeris assessed under NHATS constraints starts at 31.0 December 2014 CT and ends at 2.0 January 2042 CT. These ephemerides consist of geometric J2KE positions at 2-day intervals, covering all NHATS-permissible Earth departure and Earth return dates.

Noteworthy HSF accessibility consequences arise from the foregoing J2KE elements defining USSBs to *Horizons*. First, all fictitious NEOs, whether inferior or superior, are "in-phase" with Earth at the initialization epoch such that the condition $\theta = 0$ is imposed. Second, the initialization epoch always coincides with the fictitious NEO heliocentric apsis passage closer to a_R (aphelion for $a \leq a_R$ orbits; perihelion for $a > a_R$ orbits). Consistent with the previously documented accessibility theory, these two conditions ensure each fictitious NEO undergoes one of the most favorable accessibility seasons possible in its orbit. Furthermore, this season falls near the initialization epoch, approximately midway through the NHATS EDI. The season is therefore unlikely to be curtailed by assessment time limits. In this manner, a "level playing field" is created on which each fictitious NEO is equally favored to tally its highest possible n.

Maintaining Fictitious NEO Orbit Classification With Conic Heliocentric Ephemerides

Consider a fictitious NEO sequence consisting of 21 cases whose 20.5 March 2028 CT initialization epoch (a, e, i) coordinates progress according to the series (0.90 AU, 0.05, 0), (0.91 AU, 0.05, 0), …, (1.09 AU, 0.05, 0), (1.10 AU, 0.05 ,0). At the initialization epoch, this sequence of coordinates fully spans the theorized NEAR at $e = 0.05$. Table 4 lists a values among these initialization coordinates, together with the corresponding heliocentric phasing behavior relative to Earth and the resulting n accompanied by its rank within the $(a, 0.05, 0)$ sequence. Table 4 data reflect exported USSB ephemerides generated by *Horizons* with an SDM pedigree.

Table 4. NHATS Fictitious NEO Assessments at $(a, 0.05, 0)$.

Initialization a (AU)	Earth-Relative Phasing from 2015 through 2041	n/Rank
0.90	Atira (0.8988 AU $< a \leq$ 0.9000 AU)	1,426,368/19
0.91	Atira (0.9075 AU $< a \leq$ 0.9100 AU)	1,594,970/18
0.92	Atira (0.9179 AU $< a \leq$ 0.9200 AU)	1,385,650/20
0.93	Atira (0.9287 AU $< a \leq$ 0.9300 AU)	1,681,623/17
0.94	Apollo until January 2028; Aten thereafter	2,326,324/13
0.95	Geocentric distance $< \sim$250,000 km	42,954,445/1
0.96	Aten (0.9600 AU $\leq a <$ 0.9800 AU)	1,941,575/16
0.97	Aten (0.9700 AU $\leq a <$ 0.9780 AU)	2,072,537/15
0.98	Aten (0.9798 AU $< a <$ 0.9846 AU)	2,966,543/8
0.99	Aten (0.966 AU $< a <$ 0.996 AU)	4.845,413/6
1.00	Semi-periodic Aten/Apollo transitions (0.997 AU $< a <$ 1.003 AU)	30,826,237/3
1.01	Apollo until June 2030; Aten thereafter	5,128,242/5
1.02	Apollo (1.0121 AU $< a \leq$ 1.0200 AU)	3,581,938/7
1.03	Apollo (1.0147 AU $< a \leq$ 1.0300 AU)	2,786,993/11
1.04	Aten until May 2027; Apollo until July 2027; Aten until February 2028; Apollo thereafter	5,220,894/4
1.05	Geocentric distance $< \sim$250,000 km	42,855,048/2
1.06	Apollo until May 2028; Aten thereafter	2,870,959/10
1.07	Amor (1.0695 AU $< a <$ 1.0795 AU)	2,895,089/9
1.08	Amor (1.0772 AU $< a <$ 1.0845 AU)	2,488,575/12
1.09	Amor (1.0897 AU $< a <$ 1.0922 AU)	2,096,862/14
1.10	Amor (1.1000 AU$\leq a <$ 1.1015 AU)	1,191,512/21

As noted previously, many catalogued NEOs possess dynamic (a, e, i) coordinates over time intervals of months or less. Because of their Earth-like orbits, all Table 4 fictitious NEOs see appreciable Earth gravity accelerations from the SDM on one or more occasions. In 7 of these 21 cases, Earth gravity perturbations to the respective heliocentric orbits are sufficient to alter the fictitious NEO's orbit classification at least once between 2015 and 2042.

The cases at $a = 0.95$ AU and $a = 1.05$ AU spend the entire NHATS EDI in elliptic geocentric orbits well inside the Moon's. Although these cases have n tallies approaching 43 million NHATS-compliant solutions, likely near the maximum theoretically possible, they are nevertheless dynamically nonsensical. Fictitious NEO initialization intentionally results in nearly the closest possible Earth encounter for the specified (a, e, i) coordinates at the 20.5 March 2028 CT initialization epoch. Consequently, these two cases never gain kinetic energy by falling toward Earth from interplanetary space. Instead, they "materialize" inside the Moon's orbit with insufficient geocentric speed to depart Earth's vicinity.

Due chiefly to Earth gravity modeling by *Horizons*' SDM in USSB fictitious NEO ephemerides, Table 4 data fail to represent a controlled experiment in NEO accessibility, for which cases with reasonably fixed (a, e, i) coordinates are required. Even among the 14 cases remaining in one orbit classification throughout the NHATS EDI, considerable overlap in a exists between some cases during this interval. Given the presence of Earth gravity perturbations, it is remarkable that all Table 4 cases remain within $0.008 < e < 0.32$ and $i < 2.9°$ envelopes during the NHATS EDI. Limits for both envelopes are only approached by the aberrant (0.95 AU, 0.05, 0) and (1.05 AU, 0.05, 0) cases.

The solution eliminating experimental chaos due to Earth gravity perturbations is straightforward. If fictitious NEO ephemerides with a heliocentric conic trajectory pedigree are generated, static (a, e, i) coordinates are imposed. When first considered, this solution appears flawed by its blatant departure from real world dynamics, particularly for highly accessible fictitious NEOs undergoing close Earth encounters. But this departure is largely irrelevant to study of relative accessibility among NEOs. While it is true that near-captures of NEOs like 2003 YN$_{107}$ by Earth are not possible with conic fictitious NEO ephemerides, such cases are rare and confined to the programmatically unfavorable (a, e, i) region near (1 AU, 0, 0). Close Earth encounters are still possible without Earth gravity modeling, and simulated missions with the loiter segment conducted well within Earth's gravitational sphere of influence will produce optimistic accessibility results. Such missions are also rare, and only those targeting NEO destinations with relatively small n would fail to remain NHATS-compliant if Earth gravity were to be modeled. Earth gravity is largely irrelevant to the spacecraft trajectory in close Earth encounter cases because outbound and return segments traverse short geocentric distances.

As an illustration of heliocentric conic fictitious NEO ephemerides applied to NHATS, consider the formerly problematic case with initial (a, e, i) coordinates (0.95 AU, 0.05, 0). Table 5 lists conic ephemeris geocentric distance values for this case at standard NHATS ephemeris epochs and at the fictitious NEO initialization epoch. The time interval spanned by Table 5 is during the only Earth approach of this conic fictitious NEO closer than 0.1 AU throughout the NHATS EDI.

Table 5. Earth Close Approach by Conic Fictitious NEO Ephemeris at (0.95 AU, 0.05, 0).

Epoch (CT)	Geocentric Distance (km)
8.0 March 2028	1,151,673
10.0 March 2028	990,663
12.0 March 2028	830,224
14.0 March 2028	670,908
16.0 March 2028	514,627
18.0 March 2028	366,959
20.0 March 2028	246,247
20.5 March 2028	225,816
22.0 March 2028	208,334
24.0 March 2028	288,127
26.0 March 2028	423,039
28.0 March 2028	574,632
30.0 March 2028	731,669
1.0 April 2028	890,454
3.0 April 2028	1,049,654

In the NHATS context, a fictitious NEO ephemeris provides Lambert boundary values, together with velocities permitting Δv_A and Δv_D to be computed. If this ephemeris fails to account for Earth gravity, its function is not significantly compromised. Even in the rare case of a close Earth approach well inside the Moon's orbit, Table 5 indicates the period of significant geocentric speed errors is measured in weeks. Consequently, all fictitious NEO accessibility data presented hereinafter reflect Reference 6 heliocentric conic trajectory modeling using μ_S and *Horizons* J2KE initial conditions.

706

Smoothing n Versus a For Fictitious NEOs In Period-Resonant Orbits With Earth's

Assessments under NHATS demonstrate that heliocentric conic fictitious NEO orbits in period resonances with Earth's orbit can strongly influence n. Local maxima in n as a function of a arise consistently in resonant cases because of the in-phase $\theta = 0$ condition imposed on each fictitious NEO at the initialization epoch. With this epoch selected about midway through the 26-year NHATS EDI, any resonant case with $t_S < 13$ years will be in-phase with Earth at least three times during that interval. As previously noted, any relatively accessible NEO will tend to tally copious NHATS-compatible trajectory solutions whenever it is nearly in-phase with Earth.

The a value corresponding to exactly j heliocentric revolutions completed by a NEO during the same t_S in which Earth completes exactly k heliocentric revolutions is easily computed according to Equations (17) and (18). This condition is termed a $j : k$ resonance. For reference purposes, Tables 6a and 6b contain resonant a values in AU for $0 < j < 13$ and $0 < k < 13$.

$$\omega = \frac{j\,\omega_R}{k} \tag{17}$$

$$a = \left[\frac{\mu_S}{\omega^2}\right]^{1/3} \tag{18}$$

Table 6a. a **Values in AU Leading to** $j < 13 : k < 7$ **NEO Resonances with Earth.**

j	\multicolumn{6}{c}{k}					
	1	2	3	4	5	6
1	1	1.5874010	2.0800838	2.5198421	2.9240177	3.3019272
2	0.6299605	1	1.3103706	1.5874010	1.8420157	2.0800838
3	0.4807498	0.7631428	1	1.2114137	1.4057211	1.5874010
4	0.3968502	0.6299605	0.8254818	1	1.1603972	1.3103706
5	0.3419951	0.5428835	0.7113786	0.8617738	1	1.1292432
6	0.3028534	0.4807498	0.6299605	0.7631428	0.8855488	1
7	0.2732758	0.4337984	0.5684367	0.6886120	0.7990635	0.9023370
8	0.25	0.3968502	0.5200209	0.6299605	0.7310044	0.8254818
9	0.2311204	0.3668808	0.4807498	0.5823869	0.6758002	0.7631428
10	0.2154434	0.3419951	0.4481404	0.5428835	0.6299605	0.7113786
11	0.2021800	0.3209407	0.4205513	0.5094616	0.5911779	0.6675836
12	0.1907857	0.3028534	0.3968502	0.4807498	0.5578607	0.6299605

Table 6b. a **Values in AU Leading to** $j < 13 : 6 < k < 13$ **NEO Resonances with Earth.**

j	\multicolumn{6}{c}{k}					
	7	8	9	10	11	12
1	3.6593057	4	4.3267487	4.6415888	4.9460874	5.2414827
2	2.3052181	2.5198421	2.7256808	2.9240177	3.1158398	3.3019272
3	1.7592106	1.9229994	2.0800838	2.2314431	2.3778308	2.5198421
4	1.4521964	1.5874010	1.7170713	1.8420157	1.9628561	2.0800838
5	1.2514649	1.3679807	1.4797272	1.5874010	1.6915381	1.7925618
6	1.1082332	1.2114137	1.3103706	1.4057211	1.4979395	1.5874010
7	1	1.0931035	1.1823960	1.2684342	1.3516464	1.4323708
8	0.9148264	1	1.0816871	1.1603972	1.2365218	1.3103706
9	0.8457402	0.9244816	1	1.0727659	1.1431418	1.2114137
10	0.7883735	0.8617738	0.9321697	1	1.0656022	1.1292432
11	0.7398384	0.8087200	0.8747820	0.9384364	1	1.0597230
12	0.6981432	0.7631428	0.8254818	0.8855488	0.9436427	1

Figure 6 is an n versus a plot for an $(a, 0.10, 0)$ fictitious NEO sequence spanning the theorized NEAR and covering the 26-year NHATS EDI. Correlation between annotated resonant conditions in this plot and local maxima in n is highly evident. This plot is also annotated with a values satisfying $t_S = 25$ years, together with GReMS and ZePHA conditions at $e = 0.10$. Figure 6 local maxima in n can be turned into local minima simply by initializing fictitious NEOs such that MA = 0 for $a \leq a_R$ and MA = 180 for $a > a_R$, while initializing W = 180 for $a \leq a_R$ and W = 0 for $a > a_R$. Excepting the 1 : 1 resonance maximum, all extrema in the $(a, 0.10, 0)$ sequence can be suppressed by collapsing the NHATS EDI from 26 years to the 5 years centered on the fictitious NEO initialization epoch. In this manner, even Figure 6 resonances with the smallest $k > 1$ (6 : 5 and 4 : 5) cannot achieve a $\theta = 0$ in-phase condition other than at the fictitious NEO initialization epoch.

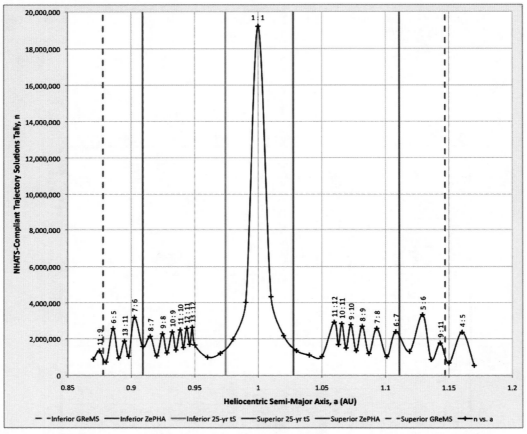

Figure 6. A 26-Year EDI n Versus a Plot for the Fictitious NEO Sequence at $(a, 0.10, 0)$.

708

Smoothing effects of the 5-year EDI on the n versus a plot at $(a, 0.10, 0)$ are evident in Figure 7. This smoothing permits more critical accessibility comparisons between inferior and superior fictitious NEOs at similar t_S, also equivalent to resonant cases at the same k when $|j - k| = 1$. Enhanced inferior accessibility, expected from theory with respect to equivalent superior cases, is not evident in Figure 7. Additional research will be necessary to reconcile this apparent contradiction.

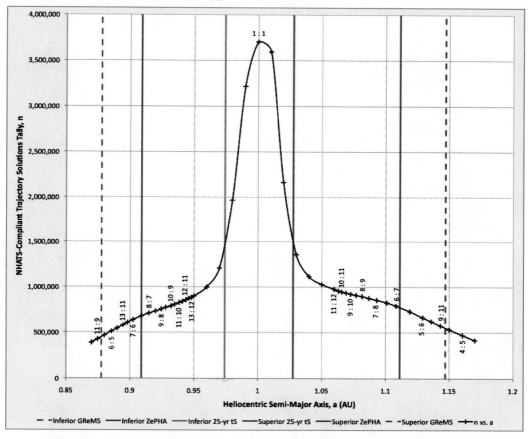

Figure 7. A 5-Year EDI n Versus a Plot for the Fictitious NEO Sequence at $(a, 0.10, 0)$.

CONCLUSIONS

Empirical NHATS-derived evidence has been presented and correlated with a theory identifying regions in heliocentric (a, e, i) space offering relatively high NEO accessibility for HSF. Of the 50 most accessible NEOs according to the NHATS metric n, only 4 (ranked #19, #21, #33, and #40) from the superior Amor orbit classification fail to lie within the theorized NEAR. In addition, no NEO with an n-ranking in the NHATS "top 50" exhibits a t_S significantly greater than the 26-year NHATS EDI during that interval, creating a "programmatic cutout" through the NEAR's central region in an e versus a plot (see Figure 5).

Inferior of the ZePHA condition partially defining the NEAR's inferior boundary, there are no known NEOs at $e < 0.2$ and $i < 10°$ as of epoch 2011.0. Close to the corresponding superior NEAR boundary, members of the Apollo orbit classification enjoy NHATS n-rankings as high as #6, #7, and #8 (see Figure 5). The dearth of inferior NEOs with potentially high accessibility is almost certainly an artifact of attempting to observe them from vantages exclusively near Earth. Knowing inferior NEAR limits in heliocentric (a, e, i) space can help guide design, deployment, and operation of future NEO survey instrumentation located in deep space.

Ongoing work to corroborate NEO accessibility theory by systematically assessing fictitious NEO sequences has been reported. This work is far from complete and is already known to entail non-intuitive techniques such as heliocentric conic fictitious NEO orbit modeling and a curtailed NHATS EDI. According to HSF accessibility theory, multiple orbit dynamics asymmetries favor an inferior NEO's accessibility with respect to an equivalent superior NEO's. Confirmation of this enhanced accessibility through controlled fictitious NEO assessments awaits additional research. It may be necessary to further modify NHATS destination viability criteria or to perform discrete trajectory design assessments under highly controlled conditions to achieve this confirmation. In discrete designs, assessments would use mission-specific metrics such as Δv or initial mass in low Earth orbit (with an assumed architecture) as substitutes for n.

ACKNOWLEDGMENTS

The authors are indebted to Dr. Lindley Johnson, Program Manager of NASA's Near Earth Objects Observation Program, for his leadership and guidance during the genesis of NHATS. Experiments with fictitious NEOs were enabled through timely and effective *Horizons* software maintenance rendered by Jon Giorgini of JPL's Solar System Dynamics Group.

REFERENCES

[1] Adamo, D. R., Giorgini, J. D., Abell, P. A., and Landis, R. R., "Asteroid Destinations Accessible For Human Exploration: A Preliminary Survey in Mid-2009", *Journal of Spacecraft and Rockets*, Vol. 47, No. 6, AIAA, Washington, D.C., 2010, pp. 994-1002.

[2] National Research Council Committee to Review Near-Earth Object Surveys and Hazard Mitigation Strategies, *Defending Planet Earth: Near-Earth Object Surveys and Hazard Mitigation Strategies: Final Report*, The National Academies Press, Washington, D.C., 2010.

[3] Giorgini, J. D., Yeomans, D. K., Chamberlin, A. B., Chodas, P. W., Jacobson, R. A., Keesey, M. S., Lieske, J. H., Ostro, S. J., Standish, E. M., and Wimberly, R. N., "JPL's On-Line Solar System Data Service," *Bulletin of the American Astronomical Society*, Vol. 28, No. 3, 1996, p. 1158.

[4] Barbee, B. W., Esposito, T., Piñon, E. III, Hur-Diaz, S., Mink, R. G., and Adamo, D. R., "A Comprehensive Ongoing Survey of the Near-Earth Asteroid Population for Human Mission Accessibility", *Proceedings of the AIAA/AAS Guidance, Navigation, and Control Conference 2 - 5 August 2010, Toronto, Ontario Canada*, Paper 2010-8368, AIAA, Washington, D.C., 2010.

[5] Hopkins, J. B. and Dissel, A. F., "Plymouth Rock: An Early Human Mission to Near-Earth Asteroids Using Orion Spacecraft", *Proceedings of the AIAA Space 2010 Conference and Exposition 30 August - 2 September 2010, Anaheim, California*, Paper 2010-8608, AIAA, Washington, D.C., 2010.

[6] Adamo, D. R., "A Precision Orbit Predictor Optimized For Complex Trajectory Operations", *Volume 116 of the Advances in the Astronautical Sciences Series, AAS/AIAA Astrodynamics Conference 2003*, Paper AAS 03-665, Univelt, San Diego, California, 2003.

TRAJECTORY OPTIMIZATION I

SESSION 6

Chair: David Dunham
                                                    KinetX, Inc.

The following paper was presented in Session 17:

AAS 11-452

The following paper was not available for publication:

AAS 11-458
(Paper Withdrawn)

HYPERSONIC, AERODYNAMICALLY CONTROLLED, PATH CONSTRAINED REENTRY OPTIMIZATION USING PSEUDOSPECTRAL METHODS

Christopher L. Ranieri[*] and Anil V. Rao[†]

Hypersonic, aerodynamically controlled reentries are optimized with the *General Pseudospectral Optimal Control Software* (GPOPS). The reentries presented in this paper incorporate state and control path constraints and interior waypoint constraints to address heating, stability, and no-fly zone constraints. By examining multiple reentry profiles, GPOPS was used to determine the booster size needed to safely complete the desired mission objectives without being significantly oversized. GPOPS's newly developed mesh refinement scheme is used to adaptively adjust the mesh size and spacing to increase solution accuracy. The accuracy improvements afforded by the mesh refinement scheme are highlighted and the solution process is compared with past efforts on this problem using a different tool, SOCS.

INTRODUCTION

A numerical optimization study of aerodynamically controlled atmospheric entry trajectories is performed using pseudospectral methods. Specifically, this study considers a hypersonic reentry vehicle that is launched from the continental US, separates with sub-orbital velocity from the booster upon engine burnout (out of the atmosphere), and then coasts until atmospheric entry. During the entry phase, the reentry vehicle is controlled using angle of attack to manage the downrange distance covered. It also can use bank angle control for energy management, maneuvering, and to provide cross-range capability.

Similar reentries have been studied extensively in past works. The Space Shuttle reentry is a perfect hypersonic reentry example and similar problems are often solved as standard test problems for optimization tools.[1,2] Research has also been published on next generation reusable launch vehicles. In particular, trimmed flight regimes[3,4] and the effects winds can have on a reentry profile with heating constraints[5] have been examined. Additionally, general heat rate constrained reentries have been explored in References 6 and 7, and a parametric study of the sensitivity of reentries to acceptable heating rates, vehicle mass, and drag coefficients was presented in Reference 8. These papers are similar in scope to the problems presented but do not fully encompass the flight regimes and constraints particular to this study.

---

[*] Senior Member of the Technical Staff, Flight Mechanics Department, The Aerospace Corporation, P.O. Box 92957-M/S M4/957, Los Angeles CA, 90009-2957, USA, 310-336-3496, christopher.l.ranieri@aero.org.

[†] Assistant Professor, University of Florida, P.O. Box 116, Gainesville, FL 32611-6250, USA, 352-392-5523, anilvrao@ufl.edu

Entry scenarios most similar to those found in this study have been examined in detail in recent work using the *General Pseudospectral Optimal Control Software* (GPOPS).[9,10,11,12,13] GPOPS[2,14] is an open-source optimal control software package. This study uses those previous efforts as the main foundation for this research. It also implements the lessons learned and guidelines developed in Reference 15 to fly realistic entry profiles that satisfy a wide range of operational and physical vehicle constraints. The research of Reference 15 was performed using the Sparse Optimal Control Software (SOCS)[16] package and solved highly constrained hypersonic reentry trajectories subject to competing constraints derived from mission requirements and vehicle capabilities. SOCS is a commercial product available for purchase. This paper continues the prior efforts but uses GPOPS instead of SOCS.

The paper first will describe the relevant equations of motion and the set up of the optimization tools used. Next, the paper will present and solve reentry scenarios where new missions are explored using the same reentry vehicle used in Reference 15. The goal was to determine the appropriate booster size needed to complete the prescribed mission without being significantly oversized. Two different boosters are considered.

In addition to describing the key features of the optimal trajectories and how these features affect the choice of the booster, the paper will also highlight the capabilities and recent improvements in GPOPS. The newly developed *hp*-adaptive version of GPOPS[17] running with the NLP solver SNOPT[18] is used. The *hp*-adaptive version of GPOPS implements the Radau pseudospectral method as described extensively in References 19 and 20. Prior GPOPS versions used the Gauss pseudospectral method. Path constraints, multiple phases, interior point event constraints, and free initial conditions are all GPOPS capabilities implemented in this analysis.

After detailing the methods used with GPOPS to find and shape acceptable reentries and select the appropriate booster, GPOPS' newly developed mesh refinement scheme is examined. A qualitative example of the accuracy improvement from the refinement is provided where a reentry generated by GPOPS is flown out with explicit integration. It is shown that with successive refinements, the meshes used by GPOPS increase modeling accuracy, provide a more complete control time history, and allow the independent fly-out reentry to converge to the GPOPS reentry.

The final aspect of the paper will focus on a qualitative comparison between SOCS and GPOPS as both tools have now been used to solve similar, challenging problems. Both software programs are highly capable of solving general optimal control problems. It is noted, however, that the mathematical methods between SOCS and GPOPS differ significantly, leading to different solutions with each program. The qualitative differences observed when using both GPOPS and SOCS on the hypersonic reentries under consideration are described.

TRAJECTORY AND OPTIMIZATION SETUP

Optimization Tool Setup and Interfaces

For a particular mission scenario, the trajectory is first solved with The Aerospace Corporation's Trajectory Optimization Program (TOP)[21] which optimizes both the launch ascent and aerodynamically controlled hypersonic reentry portions of the trajectories as a single problem. TOP is a capable, multi-function optimization tool with many built-in dynamics models and other available subroutines. It uses explicit numerical integration and a direct shooting method with piecewise control profiles that are optimized with a parameter optimization method. However, it has limited flexibility in how it models the controls and struggles with highly path constrained problems.[15] If it is determined that more analysis capability is needed beyond what TOP can provide for a particular mission, the problem is re-solved with GPOPS.

For these stressing reentries, the vehicle state at the reentry point from the best TOP trajectory is used as the initial state for the GPOPS reentry vector. GPOPS then is used to find an acceptable reentry profile from this fixed reentry point. The same approach was used in Reference 15 with TOP and SOCS and works for most scenarios examined. Additionally, once patched with the GPOPS reentry trajectory, the TOP ascent and exo-atmospheric coast phases provide a complete, continuous trajectory solution from liftoff to the end of the reentry.

This two-part approach is justified due to the complexity of the booster models used in TOP. The TOP booster phase is complex and involves significant table interpolations. This complexity led to the ascent phase not being modeled in GPOPS for this study or in SOCS in Reference 15. Typically the TOP reentry point for the best end-to-end TOP solution is good enough for in-depth reentry analysis performed by GPOPS or SOCS. If an acceptable reentry cannot be found with the nominal TOP reentry point, GPOPS is used with TOP to iteratively adjust the reentry point until an acceptable full mission profile is found or the solution space is exhausted. Examples of this process will be presented although most scenarios work fine with TOP's nominal reentry state.

In addition to using TOP to calculate the reentry state vector, GPOPS uses the best TOP trajectory as an initial guess of the time histories for all states. GPOPS interpolates the discrete data points of the best TOP reentry to generate state and control estimates for GPOPS's initial mesh.

The GPOPS reentries are broken down into multiple phases. These phases are used to break the entire reentry into smaller duration segments that are linked to form a continuous reentry. The phase boundaries allow the user to place interior point constraints on the states or controls at discrete times. The multiple phases also allow for different dynamics and path constraints to be utilized in each phase as needed, including different path box constraints on the states and controls. Typically for this analysis, four to six GPOPS phases are used to describe a reentry.

The equations of motion used by GPOPS are neither non-dimensionalized nor scaled. However, GPOPS has its own auto-scaling feature that normalizes each state and control variable based on the minimum and maximum box limits provided in each phase of the problem.[14] Additionally, the use of multiple phases provides benefits for scaling the problem. The different scaling of the states and controls when multiple phases are used allows the NLP problem to be scaled more efficiently than a single scaling factor for the entire reentry. This permits the scaling to be more appropriately tailored for the different regimes experienced during the reentry.

Equations of Motion and Basic Constraint Definition

The intrinsic states of Reference 22 are modified in this GPOPS application to include the effects of J_2 and the effects of a rotating Earth. The state is defined by: altitude over an oblate earth (h), Longitude (θ), Geocentric Latitude (Φ), Earth Relative Speed (V), Geocentric Relative Flight Path Angle (γ), and Geocentric Relative Azimuth (Az). In addition to the above states utilized by GPOPS, four other states were analyzed. The first two, the pitch angle of attack and bank angle, could be considered controls (and are in TOP). This allows path constraints to be place on the attitude angle rates in addition to constraints on the angles themselves. The last two states are the vehicle downrange distance from launch site and the DKR heating model.[23] The complete state vector (**x**) and equations of motion used by GPOPS are shown in Eq. (1).

$$\mathbf{x} = \begin{bmatrix} h \\ \theta \\ \phi \\ V \\ \gamma \\ Az \\ \beta \\ \alpha \\ range \\ heating \end{bmatrix} \qquad \dot{\mathbf{x}} = \begin{bmatrix} V\sin\gamma + \dfrac{a_e C_{esq} V \cos\gamma\cos Az\cos\phi\sin\phi}{r(1+C_{esq}\sin^2\gamma)^{1.5}} \\[4mm] \dfrac{V\cos\gamma\sin Az}{r\cos\phi} \\[4mm] \dfrac{V\cos\gamma\cos Az}{r} \\[4mm] \left(\begin{array}{c} -D - Gx\sin\gamma + \cos\gamma(G_y\sin Az + G_z\cos Az) + \\ \omega^2 r\cos\phi(\sin\gamma\cos\phi - \cos\gamma\cos Az\sin\phi) \end{array}\right) \\[6mm] \left(\begin{array}{c} \left(\dfrac{V}{r}-\dfrac{G_x}{V}\right)\cos\gamma - \dfrac{\sin\gamma}{V}(G_y\sin Az + G_z\cos Az - L\cos\beta) + \\ \dfrac{\omega^2 r\cos\phi}{V}(\cos\phi\cos\gamma + \sin\phi\cos Az\sin\gamma) + 2\omega\sin Az\cos\phi \end{array}\right) \\[6mm] \left(\begin{array}{c} \dfrac{V}{r}\cos\gamma\tan\phi\sin Az + \dfrac{(G_y\cos Az - G_z\sin Az - L\sin\beta)}{V\cos\gamma} + \\ \dfrac{\omega^2 r}{V\cos\gamma}(\cos\phi\sin\phi\sin Az) - 2\omega(\cos Az\cos\phi\tan\gamma - \sin\phi) \end{array}\right) \\[6mm] u_{c1} \\[2mm] u_{c2} \\[2mm] \dfrac{V\cos\gamma(r-h)}{r} \\[4mm] Q_0 * V^{3.15}\sqrt{\rho} \end{bmatrix} \qquad (1)$$

The heating rate coefficient, Q_0, is defined in Reference 23. The term, ω, is the Earth's angular rotation rate, a_e and a_p are the radius of the Earth at the equator and poles respectively and:

$$C_{esq} = 1 - \left(\frac{a_p}{a_e}\right)^2 \qquad (2)$$

For the reentry vehicle under consideration, the aerodynamic coefficients c_L and c_D can be found via a four-dimensional table look up that has altitude, Mach number (M), and angle of attack (α) as the independent variables. Additionally, there are different tables for turbulent or laminar flight. The same database was used in Reference 15. However, for the GPOPS implementation, one level of interpolation was removed in favor of polynomial curve fit approximations to the data versus angle of attack. This choice improved GPOPS run-time and convergence characteristics. GPOPS and TOP employ a four-dimensional linear interpolation scheme to determine the appropriate coefficients at each evaluation of Eq. (1). The density, ρ, is found from the 1962 US standard atmosphere model which is a smooth function of the vehicle's altitude above the oblate Earth. The vehicle's radius magnitude, r, is determined from the oblate Earth model as:

$$r = h + \frac{a_p}{\sqrt{\left(\dfrac{a_p}{a_e}\right)^2 + C_{esq}\sin^2\phi}} \qquad (3)$$

716

$$L = 0.5\rho * c_L * A_{ref} V^2$$
$$D = 0.5\rho * c_D * A_{ref} V^2 \tag{4}$$

The non-aerodynamic external forces (**G**) acting on the vehicle include J_2 perturbations. The external non-aerodynamic forces are expressed in a rotating radial coordinate system where the x-axis is along the outward radius vector, the y-axis is along the direction of motion and orthogonal to the x-axis, and the z-axis completes the right handed system.

$$\mathbf{G} = \begin{bmatrix} \dfrac{\mu}{r^2}\left\{ 1 - 1.5 J_2 \left(\dfrac{a_e}{r}\right)^2 (3\sin^2\phi - 1) \right\} \\ 0 \\ -3 J_2 \dfrac{\mu}{r^2}\left(\dfrac{a_e}{r}\right)^2 \sin\phi\cos\phi \end{bmatrix} \tag{5}$$

The pitch angle of attack was constrained to be between a minimum and maximum value. The two GPOPS controls are the angular body attitude rates. Using rates avoids wrapping issues and allows constraints to be placed on the rates to ensure that the angles do not change unrealistically.

$$\mathbf{u}_c = \begin{bmatrix} \dot{\beta} \\ \dot{\alpha} \end{bmatrix} \tag{6}$$

All trajectories in this analysis target a minimum of five terminal conditions at the end of the reentry profile as shown in Eq. (7). The constraints enforce a particular final orientation at a specific Earth location with a specified relative velocity.

$$\mathbf{z}(t_f) = \begin{bmatrix} h = h^* \\ \theta = \theta^* \\ \phi = \phi^* \\ V = V^* \\ \gamma < \gamma^* \end{bmatrix} \tag{7}$$

Other constraints on bank angles, downrange distance, g-loading, and altitude regimes are also imposed on the reentries. The specifics of these constraints and their impact on the trajectories are not detailed here. Constraints on angle of attack are detailed in the example below. The relevant and stressing constraints will be discussed and their impact on the reentries will be highlighted.

Guidelines to Finding an Acceptable Reentry Profile

Reference 15 describes an iterative process with the trajectory design work performed by SOCS and subject matter experts in heating, stability, and ablation effects. That effort helped establish a set of acceptable parameters and guidelines for reentry profiles with acceptable characteristics in all of these disciplines. Those guidelines are employed in shaping the trajectories found in this GPOPS study. All trajectories found with GPOPS are analyzed in-depth in each subsystem area to verify their acceptable performance. It is important to note that the iterative analysis of Reference 15 indicated that the DKR heating model was insufficient in modeling the heating performance of the vehicle as the sole design parameter. Instead, that heating model must be combined with other constraints to find a reentry acceptable for heating.

The main finding of the previous effort was to maximize laminar flow while minimizing both the total heat load and the peak stagnation point heating rate. Secondary peak heating rates may also need to be constrained, depending on the reentry profile. These goals are achieved via a combination of path constraints on the heating rate, end point constraints on the total heat load, and path constraints on the acceptable altitude regimes for given Mach numbers throughout the reentry. These vehicle-driven constraints are combined with mission-driven constraints (e.g. over-flight constraints) to find the most realistic and flyable reentries possible.

One important item to note is that both the GPOPS and SOCS implementations utilized to date do not actually optimize a particular performance function like time or total heat load. The large set of constraints imposed on these problems means that once a feasible solution is found that has acceptable performance in all subsystems, the analysis is complete. Optimization is sometimes used to drive states or controls at initial or final times and/or at phase breaks to desired values, but the purpose is solely to help satisfy constraints, not extremize a performance parameter.

Scaled Results

All results presented are scaled such that both the x- and y-axes range from approximately zero to one. The actual dimensional units are divided by scale factors to find these scaled results. The scale factors used are not provided to prevent disclosure of the actual performance characteristics of the vehicle under consideration. However, the scaled examples presented still provide clear examples of how effective GPOPS is in improving basic trajectories found by TOP. They also demonstrate that GPOPS can incorporate a variety of path and event constraints to shape trajectories as desired. The scaled results also still clearly demonstrate the importance of GPOPS's mesh refinement scheme and show how it can adaptively improve the accuracy of a given solution, even for highly constrained trajectories.

Results are scaled using the same scale factors used in Reference 15 where they are also not revealed. This allows direct comparison to results presented not only in this paper but also in Reference 15. As examples of the naming convention used, Distance Units are labeled DU and Time Units are labeled TU. These scaled unit examples are not exhaustive of the units used in paper.

PROBLEM DESCRIPTION

The exact problem under consideration is very stressing from overflight and heating standpoints. The goal was to reach a specific longitude target over the Eastern Mediterranean Sea. There are at least three sharp turns that need to be made in relatively quick order to traverse the entire Mediterranean Sea and avoid all landmasses. These two driving constraints are actually competing constraints since overflight maneuvers are best affected by performing atmospheric dives to quickly change the trajectory's path. However, deep dives and higher dynamic pressures increase heating with higher atmospheric densities and earlier possible turbulent transitions. A balance must be struck in which the required dynamic pressures for the overflight maneuvers can be found in such a way that the heating increases are not excessive.

The goal of this particular study was to find the appropriate booster size that can complete this reentry without being significantly oversized. This reentry scenario is the most stressing of the range of possible scenarios under consideration and therefore is the driving factor in the booster sizing. The Mediterranean Sea solution presented in Reference 15 is basically the same mission presented here with two main differences. The payload carried by the booster in this case is half (by mass) the payload carried in the prior study. Reference 15's booster carried two separate but equally sized reentry vehicles while this reentry only launches a single reentry vehicle. All of the reentry vehicles themselves have the same size, shape and aerodynamics. As a result, the booster used in Reference 15 is significantly oversized for the problem solved here.

Two new boosters were examined and will be labeled simply "Booster 1" and "Booster 2." "Booster 1" is the less capable launcher of the two new boosters. The booster used in Reference 15 will be labeled "Booster SOCS." The TOP reentries for both new boosters were able to reach the desired final Earth location but both were significantly short of the desired final velocity, did not satisfy the overflight constraints, and significantly violated the heating guidelines for safe flight. Therefore, GPOPS was used to determine if the reentries from these new boosters could be modified to satisfy all of the relevant constraints.

It should be noted that the analysis in Reference 15 found that the reentry point provided by "Booster SOCS" allows an acceptable reentry in all subsystems. Therefore, the reentry states found by "Booster 1" or "Booster 2" should aim for the vicinity of the "Booster SOCS" states.

Booster 1

It was quickly determined that "Booster 1" would not likely provide enough performance to achieve this mission. The downrange distance from the launch site to the reentry point for the TOP trajectory was almost 40% less than the reentry point provided by "Booster SOCS". In addition to the shortfall with the reentry state, the final velocity of the TOP trajectory was only 70% of the desired value. Regardless, GPOPS was still used to determine if Booster 1 could possibly achieve the mission objectives.

Using GPOPS, a trajectory was found using the nominal "Booster 1" reentry state where the desired final velocity value is achieved and the heating characteristics are acceptable. Some of the overflight constraints were also achieved but only two of the three major turns needed could be completed while also not violating the heating constraints.

GPOPS was then used to investigate how close the reentry state was from a state that could provide an acceptable reentry. This investigation was performed by allowing the reentry state to vary in GPOPS within proscribed limits from the nominal reentry state provided by TOP. These limits were progressively increased in size until a reentry was found in GPOPS that satisfied all mission constraints (terminal, overflight, heating, stability, etc.). Each new GPOPS run or "restart" used an initial guess based on the converged trajectory from the prior GPOPS run. The final results are hence referred to as the "Booster 1 Relaxed" case and the altitude curves for this GPOPS solution and the original TOP reentry are seen in Figure 1.

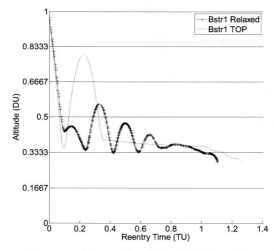

Figure 1: Altitude vs. Time (Booster 1 TOP and Booster 1 Relaxed)

The final acceptable reentry state cut the range deficit between the "Booster SOCS" reentry state and the "Booster 1" reentry state from ~40% to ~20%. The boost-only phase for "Booster 1" was re-run in TOP to attempt to target this new point. However, "Booster 1" did not have the capability to come anywhere close to this adjusted reentry state, indicating that "Booster 1" was not adequately sized for this mission.

From a GPOPS-perspective, this analysis was successful. It demonstrated that similar reentries to Reference 15 could be found where very stressing overflight and heating constraints can be applied simultaneously with GPOPS. Exact implementation details and the effects of these constraints will be shown explicitly for Booster 2 scenarios.

Booster 2

For "Booster 2," TOP again was not able to find an acceptable solution, significantly violating heating and overflight constraints along with terminal constraints on final velocity (~44% short). However, "Booster 2" is more capable than "Booster 1." The nominal TOP "Booster 2" reentry state downrange distance was only 7% less than the "Booster SOCS" case. Based on the successful reentry found for the "Booster 1 Relaxed" case, the nominal TOP "Booster 2" reentry state seemed promising.

GPOPS used the "Booster 1 Relaxed" case as the initial guess for the "Booster 2" reentry. This choice was made as the "Booster 1 Relaxed" solution already satisfied all the relevant problem constraints even though a disconnect existed between the "Booster 2" and "Booster 1 Relaxed" reentry points. GPOPS then forced the initial conditions to match TOP's "Booster 2" reentry state by letting the initial conditions float. Several GPOPS "restarts" were run where the limits on the initial conditions were adjusted to slowly force the "Booster 1 Relaxed" values to match the "Booster 2" values while still maintaining all the other relevant constraints.

The altitude curve for the "Booster 2" and the "Booster 1 Relaxed" reentries are shown in Figure 2, demonstrating how GPOPS morphed the "Booster 1 Relaxed" altitude time history due to the differences in the reentry states.

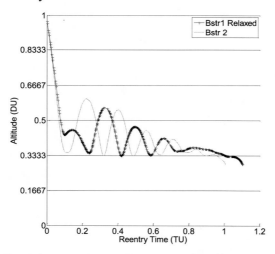

Figure 2: Altitude vs. Time (Booster 1 Relaxed and Booster 2)

Although the downrange distance was better, other aspects of the "Booster 2" reentry state, such as the velocity vector, were worse than the "Booster 1 Relaxed" case. In-depth heating analysis showed that the GPOPS "Booster 2" reentry was slightly too stressing from a heating stand-point. In particular, "Booster 2's" higher reentry velocity results in a second dive with too high of a Mach number, indicating a likely turbulent transition and significantly increased heating. Efforts were made using both GPOPS and SOCS to improve the heating characteristics to no avail.

However, since the nominal reentry state had much more range than "Booster 1," additional effort was used to improve the reentry state to lower the heating. TOP was used to re-target the reentry state to minimize the difference between the reentry state that "Booster 2" can provide and the "Booster SOCS" reentry state. TOP was able to get "Booster 2" to a new reentry state that was very close to the "Booster SOCS" reentry state. In fact, the largest deviation from the "Booster SOCS" reentry states was only 0.8% difference. This new reentry state will be labeled "Booster 2 Adj." GPOPS was again successfully used in a "restart" fashion to morph the "Booster 2" trajectory such that it matched the "Booster 2 Adj." reentry state while still respecting all of the relevant heating and overflight constraints.

Relevant reentry points are shown in Figure 3, clearly showing how far the original "Booster 1" reentry point is from the "Booster SOCS" reentry. Additionally, the "Booster SOCS" and "Booster 2 Adj." reentry points are shown to be almost identical. Figure 4 shows the altitude curve for the "Booster 2 Adj." and the original "Booster 2" reentry. The new solution is clearly better for heating characteristics. The first and second dive altitudes have been increased and the total time of flight has been decreased.

The "Booster 2 Adj." altitude curve is compared to the "Booster SOCS" solution from Reference 15 in Figure 5, showing that both reentries are very similar. This is to be expected due to their almost identical reentry states.

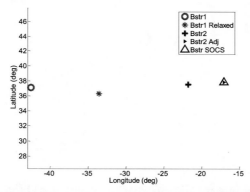

Figure 3: Reentry Points for Various GPOPS/TOP/SOCS Trajectories

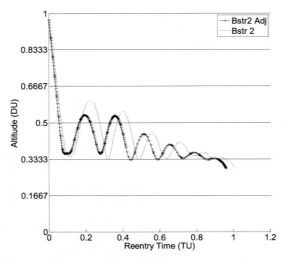

Figure 4: Altitude vs. Time (Booster 2 and Booster 2 Adjusted)

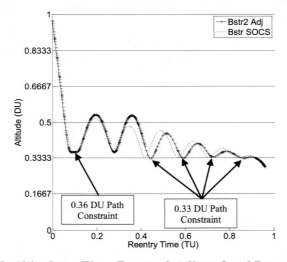

Figure 5: Altitude vs. Time (Booster 2 Adjusted and Booster SOCS)

Figure 6 shows a snapshot of the portion of the trajectory around the Mediterranean Sea for the original "Booster 1" TOP solution. It can be seen that overflight constraints are violated significantly for Northern Africa and the Straits of Gibraltar is clipped. Figure 7 shows the same region for the "Booster 2" TOP solution where most of Northern Africa is avoided. Tunisia is clipped and Crete and Cyprus are over-flown. Recall that both of these TOP solutions also have significant heating and terminal constraint violations. Figure 8 shows the same map region for the final "Booster 2 Adj." solution that satisfies ALL relevant problem constraints on overflight, heating, stability, etc. Figure 9 shows a zoomed in view of the central Mediterranean Sea where the reentry vehicle performs maneuvers to stay north of North Africa followed by reverse turns to the south to avoid Sicily, mainland Italy, and Crete.

Figure 6: Booster 1 TOP Mediterranean Sea Flight

Figure 7: Booster 2 TOP Mediterranean Sea Flight

Figure 8: Booster 2 Adjusted GPOPS Mediterranean Sea Flight

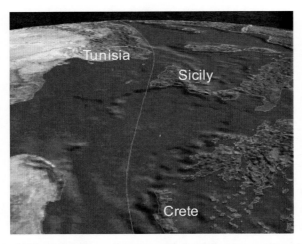

Figure 9: Central Mediterranean Sea Overflight Maneuvers (Booster 2 Adjusted)

The enforcement process for overflight and heating constraints are summarized here but are described in more detail in Reference 15. Even though two different optimization programs (SOCS and GPOPS) are used, the methods for implementing these constraints are almost identical. Overflight constraints are enforced via interior point event constraints between optimization phases. These constraints are coined "keyhole" constraints in which the vehicle must pass through a small longitude/latitude box at certain time regions of the reentry. The size, shape, and timing of these "keyholes" are adjusted via the "restart" process described above and in Reference 15 until the trajectory is shaped as desired and all overflight constraints are met.

Heating constraints are enforced via path constraints on the acceptable altitude ranges in each phase of the reentry. Figure 5 shows that the limits, particularly the lower limit of 0.33 DU for the last two-thirds of the reentry, are encountered multiple times in the final reentry solution for both the "Booster SOCS" and "Booster 2 Adj" reentries. Additionally, lower limits for altitude path constraints of 0.37 DU are encountered for the first two dives for the "Booster 2 Adj." reentry. Both reentries spend significant amount of time riding this path constraint during the first dive. This period corresponds to the passage of the Straits of Gibraltar where the vehicle is banking during the dive to avoid flying over North Africa.

Path constraints on the heating rate are also employed to ensure that the peak heating rate from the first dive is not too extreme. Different limits are used in later mission phases to ensure that the secondary dives are also manageable. "Booster 2" and "Booster 2 Adj" heating rates can be seen in Figure 10, clearly showing the improvement the final GPOPS solution has over the nominal "Booster 2" case. The first and second peaks in the heating rate are reduced. The second peak in particular is the peak that was too high for the nominal "Booster 2" reentry.

Comparison of the "Booster SOCS" and "Booster 2 Adj" heating rate curves shows very similar performance in Figure 11. The second peak is slightly higher for "Booster 2 Adj" which dives slightly deeper than the "Booster SOCS" reentry. Figure 12 shows that the integrated heating for "Booster 2 Adj." actually is slightly less than the result found for "Booster SOCS."

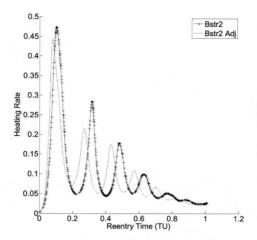

Figure 10: Heating Rates vs. Time (Booster 2 and Booster 2 Adjusted)

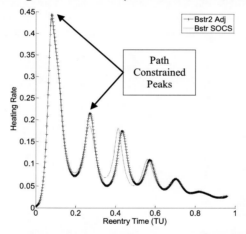

Figure 11: Heating Rate vs. Time (Booster 2 Adjusted and Booster SOCS)

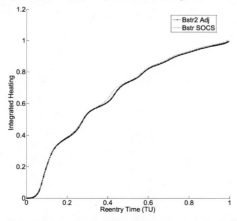

Figure 12: Integrated Heating vs. Time (Booster 2 Adjusted and Booster SOCS)

The aero-controls (bank and angle of attack angles) are shown in Figure 13 and Figure 14. These plots show that the "Booster 2 Adj." and "Booster SOCS" reentries employ similar attitude angles. Figure 15 shows the stability constraints on acceptable angle of attack. The vehicle has a range between a general minimum and maximum angle of attack but the trimmable region in which the vehicle can achieve stable flight is a smaller and constantly changing subset of this larger region. As described in Reference 15, the stable/trimmable angle of attack limits are determined by three dimensional tabular interpolations versus altitude and Mach number. Some reentries ride these path constraints more than others as shown in Reference 15. Similar stability constraints have also been enforced in References 3 and 4 implemented in a different fashion.

The path constraints are implemented implicitly by checking the angle of attack chosen by GPOPS to ensure that it lies within the acceptable region. If the angle of attack is outside the acceptable region then the differential equations and path constraints are evaluated using the boundary of the permitted range of angles. The actual GPOPS value for angle of attack is not changed. There are two distinct periods highlighted in Figure 15 where this constraint is active. The "Constrained" curve is the actual value used in the GPOPS differential equations. The "Unconstrained" curve is the actual GPOPS state value for angle of attack. This same approach is used with SOCS in Reference 15. Attempts were made with both tools to employ and enforce actual path constraints but this negatively impacted convergence characteristics for both tools. The difficulty in implementing the explicit path constraints may be due to the tabular nature of the constraint surfaces.

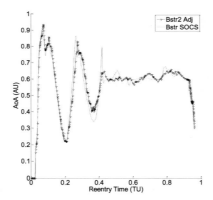

Figure 13: Angle of Attack vs. Time (Booster 2 Adjusted and Booster SOCS)

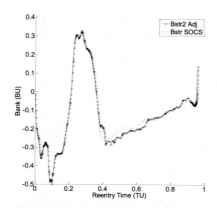

Figure 14: Bank Angle vs. Time (Booster 2 Adjusted and Booster SOCS)

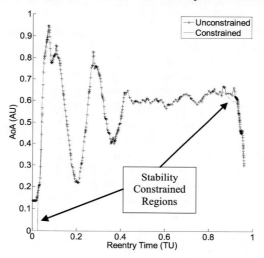

Figure 15: Angle of Attack vs. Time (Stability Constraints)

GPOPS FLY-OUT AND MESH REFINEMENT

After GPOPS has shaped the trajectory as best as possible, a validity check of the GPOPS trajectory was performed to ensure that the GPOPS angular control profile would generate the same trajectory when flown independently in TOP. This "fly-out" starts from the given reentry state and explicitly integrates the trajectory in TOP forward in time, interpolating the GPOPS aero-control angle time history. The aero-controls provided to TOP are based on a spline interpolation of the GPOPS angles. Once the TOP "fly-out" finished, the terminal states for both GPOPS and TOP runs were compared to ensure they closely matched. Additionally, the time-histories of both solutions were plotted to ensure they matched at all times.

This "fly-out" process clearly demonstrates the importance of GPOPS's mesh refinement scheme. Placement of the node points is crucial to the trajectory accuracy. The mesh size and distribution for the initial mesh is specified by the user who inputs the number and order of the polynomials used in each phase of the problem along with the number and distribution of the phases. The distribution of the node points is then determined by pseudospectral method used by GPOPS.

Unfortunately, the node points on an initial mesh may not be placed in the most appropriate regions, particularly those with faster dynamics or active path constraints.

Rather than using a brute force approach with a large number of node points on a single mesh, a more effective approach starts with a coarse initial mesh. Converging solution to the problem posed with the coarse initial mesh is easier, especially if the initial guess provided is not accurate. GPOPS analyzes the initial mesh and once the corresponding NLP problem converges, GPOPS's *hp*-adaptive mesh refinement routine initiates. Based on specified values for mesh size growth rate and requested tolerances, GPOPS adds polynomials and/or increases the order of the polynomials used to create a new mesh with better accuracy to the real dynamics. This is performed by interpolating between GPOPS node points and re-evaluating the dynamics constraints. Regions with large deficit constraint errors receive more node points in subsequent meshes. Multiple mesh refinements are performed until these constraints meet the user-specified tolerances.

The following figures demonstrate the accuracy improvements due to the mesh refinement. Each shows the converged GPOPS altitude time history and the time history found in TOP using the GPOPS time history of the aero-controls. Figure 16 shows the TOP fly-out based on a single mesh GPOPS solution where the number and order of the approximating polynomials is completely user-specified. The GPOPS and TOP solutions diverge one-third of the way into the reentry. The errors expand significantly over the rest of the solution indicating a poor mesh. Figure 17 shows the GPOPS and TOP reentries after one mesh refinement which has added node points and shifted their placement. In this case, the two solutions follow the same trends throughout the reentry although there is some divergence on the last third of the reentries.

Figure 18 shows the results after two mesh refinements. The GPOPS and TOP solutions have converged to the same solution. In this case, sufficient GPOPS node points have been used and placed appropriately. In particular, this can be seen at the bottom of the third dive where a path constraint is active. Examining all three "fly-out" figures, there are few node points on the first two figures at this dive but many points have been placed at this dive in the final figure. The mesh refinement process clearly improves the accuracy of the GPOPS solutions and allows users to take a GPOPS solution to other tools and generate the same trajectories.

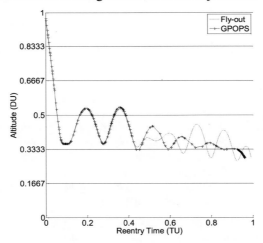

Figure 16: Altitude vs. Time (Fly-out, 0 mesh refinements)

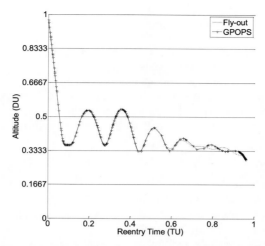

Figure 17: Altitude vs. Time (Fly-out, 1 mesh refinement)

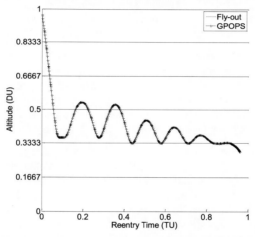

Figure 18: Altitude vs. Time (Fly-out, 2 mesh refinements)

Table 1 provides statistics for all three mesh refinement cases including the total number of node points, the total number of polynomials used, and the CPU run time. The analysis was performed on a laptop with an Intel Core2 Duo CPU T9400 2.53 GHz/2.53 GHz processors with 2.96 GB of RAM running MATLAB v7.10.0 (R2010a) on Windows XP.

Table 1: Mesh Refinement Characteristics

Case	Total # of Polys.	Total # of Node Points	Total # of Variables	Total # of Constraints	Major Iterations on Final Mesh	Total CPU Run Time (sec)
Figure 16	80	160	1992	1682	10	158.8
Figure 17	80	275	3864	3267	5	599.8
Figure 18	195	469	6012	5090	2	1045.5

GPOPS AND SOCS INSIGHTS

Similar reentries have now been solved with two different optimization tools, SOCS and GPOPS. Although the exact problems under the same conditions and constraints have not been solved simultaneously with both tools, the experience gained in using both tools on extremely similar problems highlights some of their qualitative differences. Both tools are very capable and have their own unique "pluses" and "minuses." It should be noted that these insights are based on observations gained only from solving the particular aerodynamically controlled reentries posed in this study. The performance characteristics of both tools may be different on other problems.

- **Problem Setup and Implementation**: GPOPS's MATLAB interface is much easier to learn and apply to new problems than SOCS's FORTRAN interface. This observation comes from a user with a stronger FORTRAN than MATLAB background.

- **Overall Capabilities/Functionality**: Although SOCS provides many other capabilities including a parameter estimation tool, for the complex, highly-constrained problems solved in this study and in Reference 15, both GPOPS and SOCS provide the same functionality and can implement the same types of constraint sets needed.

- **Run Time**: For the problems under consideration, to get an accurate, fully mesh-refined solution, SOCS typically takes one to five minutes while GPOPS typically takes 10-20 minutes. GPOPS's MATLAB interface may slow it down compared to the compiled nature of SOCS.

- **Handling of Aerodynamic Data**: Although both tools ideally would not use tabular data, in some cases, these are necessary. SOCS was able to handle the multi-dimensional aero tables used for this vehicle. GPOPS would not converge using the same multi-level interpolations. One level had to be replaced with a polynomial curve fit to get convergence. In general, the tabular interpolations are one of the main factors that slowed GPOPS down compared to SOCS. This may also partially be a function of SNOPT versus SOCS's NLP code.

- **Mesh Refinement Robustness and Accuracy**: With one fixed set of mesh refinement tolerances and parameters, SOCS has consistently found solutions that satisfy the "fly-out" analysis. The GPOPS mesh refinement parameters have to be adjusted from problem to problem to strike a balance between run time and required accuracy. It was found that GPOPS was best used in a "restart" fashion with only moderately tight tolerances (to get run times under 10 minutes) until the solution was shaped as desired. Only then should tolerances be tightened.

- **Initial Mesh Convergence**: GPOPS seems to be much less sensitive to the accuracy of the initial guess, making it easier for a user to solve a complicated problem from scratch.

- **"Restart" Robustness and Flexibility**: GPOPS is more robust than SOCS when used in the "restart" manner. Larger steps can be made with GPOPS when walking a set of constraints (such as the overflight waypoint/keyhole targets) to their desired values. This reduces the number of "restarts" needed with GPOPS than SOCS, helping to balance the longer GPOPS run times for a given problem. Additionally, GPOPS is more flexible in allowing the initial conditions to float than SOCS, at least for these reentry problems. This functionality was key to this analysis as multiple reentries were found in GPOPS by adjusting the reentry states.

CONCLUSIONS/DISCUSSION

Aerodynamically controlled, hypersonic reentries have been found using GPOPS that impose a variety of realistic and detailed event and path constraints. These constraints make the trajectories actually flyable by the vehicle under consideration from a heating and stability perspective, while also taking into account operational concerns such as no-fly zones. Examples were presented that show how GPOPS significantly improved initial guess solutions provided by TOP and utilized more encompassing constraint sets than TOP provides. Using GPOPS, the appropriate booster size needed for the desired missions was determined.

Multiple GPOPS reentries were analyzed for different reentry states provided by the boosters under consideration. GPOPS was also used in conjunction with TOP in an iterative process to adjust reentry states until a reentry point was found that allowed a full end-to-end mission to be flown that satisfied all relevant constraints. Path constraints on the heating rate and acceptable altitude regimes were imposed. The limits of these path constraints were adjusted using GPOPS's phase structure to allow varying limits due to changing reentry dynamics. "Implicit" path constraints on angle of attack for stability constraints were also used. Interior and terminal event constraints on heat load and waypoint/keyhole constraints were incorporated. All of these constraints were eventually satisfied by taking the initial TOP reentries and walking them to their desired profiles via a "restart" process.

In addition to finding an acceptable reentry profile to allow the appropriate sizing of a booster, the paper highlights the mesh refinement capabilities of GPOPS. The mesh refinement was clearly shown to improve the accuracy in which GPOPS models a given trajectory. Additionally, GPOPS was qualitatively compared with the SOCS optimization tool that has previously been used to solve similar problems. Both tools have now been shown to be capable of solving these problems and both have their pluses and minuses in the actual use and implementation. Overall, GPOPS provides a range of functionality and capabilities that allow it to solve some of the most complicated reentry optimization problems.

ACKNOWLEDGEMENTS

The authors would like to thank Nicholas Martin and Kristina Kipp for their help in running TOP reentries, JinWook Lee and Han Sik Lee for their heating analysis, and Omar Amrani for his stability analysis. Additional acknowledgement is due to AFRL personnel Lt. Col. Timothy Jorris and Franklin Friedl for their pioneering efforts in employing GPOPS on hypersonic reentries.

REFERENCES

[1] Betts, J.T., Practical Methods for Optimal Control Using Nonlinear Programming (Advances in Design and Control), Society for Industrial Mathematics, Second Edition, 2010.

[2] Rao, A. V., Benson, D. A., Darby, C. L., Patterson, M. A., Sanders, I., and Huntington, G. T., "Algorithm: GPOPS, A MATLAB Software for Solving Multiple-Phase Optimal Control Problems Using the Gauss Pseudospectral Method," *ACM Transactions on Mathematical Software*, Vol. 37, No. 2, April – June 2010, Article 22, 39 pages.

[3] Shaffer, P. J., Ross, I. M., Oppenheimer, M. W., Doman, D. B., and Bollino, K. P., "Fault-Tolerant Optimal Trajectory Generation for Reusable Launch Vehicles," *Journal of Guidance, Control, and Dynamics*, Vol. 30, No. 6, Nov-Dec 2007, pp 1794-1802.

[4] Fahroo, F. and Doman, D.,"A Direct Method for Approach and Landing Trajectory Reshaping with Failure Effect Estimation," *Proceedings of 2004 AIAA Guidance, Navigation, and Control Conference*, Aug. 2004, AIAA 2004-4772.

[5] Bollino, K. P., Ross, I. M., and Doman, D. B., "Optimal Nonlinear Feedback Guidance for Reentry Vehicles," *Proceedings of the AIAA Guidance, Navigation, and Control Conference and Exhibit*, Keystone, CO, Aug 2006, AIAA 2006-6074.

[6] Shen, Z. and Lu, P., "Onboard Generation of Three-Dimensional Constrained Entry Trajectories," *Journal of Guidance, Control, and Dynamics*, Vol. 26, No. 1, Jan-Feb 2003, pp111-121.

[7] Josselyn, S., and Ross, I. M., "Rapid Verification Method for the Trajectory Optimization of Reentry Vehicles" *Journal of Guidance, Control, and Dynamics*, Vol. 26, No. 3, May-June 2003, pp 505-508.

[8] Josselyn, S., and Ross, I. M., "Sensitivity Analysis for Rapid Prototyping of Entry Vehicles," *Journal of Spacecraft and Rockets*, Vol. 43, No. 4, July-August 2006, pp 836-841.

[9] Jorris, T.R., Schulz, C.S., and Rexius, S., "Improvements in Pseudospectral Based Hypersonic Vehicle Trajectory Generation via Enhanced Aerothermal Protection Methods," *Proceedings of the 19th AAS/AIAA Space Flight Mechanics Meeting*, Savannah, GA, Feb. 2009, AAS 09-219.

[10] Jorris, T.R., Schulz, C.S., and Rexius, S.,"Bang-Bang Trajectory Optimization Using Autonomous Phase Placement and Mesh Refinement Satisfying Waypoints and No-Fly Zone Constraints," *Proceedings of the 20th AAS/AIAA Space Flight Mechanics Meeting*, San Diego, CA, Feb. 2010, AAS 10-115.

[11] Jorris, T.R. and Cobb, R.G., "Three-Dimensional Trajectory Optimization Satisfying Waypoint and No-Fly Zone Constraints," *Journal of Guidance, Control, and Dynamics*, Vol. 32, No. 2, March-April 2009, pp 551-572.

[12] Jorris, T.R., Schulz, C.S., Friedl, F.R., and Rao, A.V.," Constrained Trajectory Optimization Using Pseudospectral Methods," *Proceedings of the AIAA Atmospheric Flight Mechanics Conference and Exhibit*, Honolulu, HI, Aug. 2008, AIAA 2008-6218.

[13] Jorris, T.R. and Cobb, R.G., "Multiple Method 2-D Trajectory Optimization Satisfying Waypoints and No-Fly Zone Constraints," *Journal of Guidance, Control, and Dynamics*, Vol. 31, No. 3, May-June 2008, pp 543-553.

[14] Rao, A.V., Benson, D.A., Darby, C., et al., "GPOPS, The Open-Source Pseudospectral Optimal Control Software," http://www.gpops.org, February 2010.

[15] Ranieri, C.L., "Hypersonic, Aerodynamically Controlled, Path Constrained Reentry Optimization in SOCS," *Proceedings of the 21th AAS/AIAA Space Flight Mechanics Meeting*, New Orleans, LA, Feb. 2011, AAS 11-242.

[16] Betts, J., *SOCS – Sparse Optimal Control Software User Manual*, Release 6.4.9, Boeing. Referenced February 12, 2009.

[17] Darby, C. L., Hager, W. W., and Rao, A. V., "A Variable-Order Adaptive Pseudospectral Method for Solving Optimal Control Problems," *Journal of Spacecraft and Rockets*, Accepted for Publication, November 2010.

[18] Gill, P. E., Murray, W., and Saunders, M. A., "SNOPT: An SQP Algorithm for Large-Scale Constrained Optimization," *SIAM Review*, Vol. 47, No. 1, January 2002, pp. 99 – 131.

[19] Garg, D., Patterson, M. A., Darby, C. L., Francolin, C., Huntington, G. T., Hager, W. W., and Rao, A. V., "Direct Trajectory Optimization and Costate Estimation of Finite-Horizon and Infinite-Horizon Optimal Control Problems via a Radau Pseudospectral Method," *Computational Optimization and Applications*, Published Online, 6 October 2009, DOI 10.1007/s10589-009-9291-0.

[20] Garg, D., Patterson, M. A., Hager, W. W., Rao, A. V., Benson, D. A., and Huntington, G. T., "A Unified Framework for the Numerical Solution of Optimal Control Problems Using Pseudospectral Methods," *Automatica*, Vol. 46, No. 11, November 2011, pp. 1843 - 1851.

[21] Shaw, M. A., and Fruth, G., Trajectory Optimization Program (TOP) User Manual, Version 2.0a, August 6, 2004, Flight Mechanics Department, The Aerospace Corporation.

[22] Vinh, N.X., "Optimal Trajectories in Atmospheric Flight," Elsevier Publishing Co., 1981.

[23] R.W. Detra, N.H. Kemp and F.R. Riddell, "Addendum to heat transfer to satellite vehicles reentering the atmosphere," *Jet Propulsion* 27 (1957) (12), pp. 1256–1257.

A DESIGN METHOD
FOR LOW ALTITUDE, NEAR-EQUATORIAL LUNAR ORBITS

Laura Plice[*] and Tim Craychee[†]

In 2013 the Lunar Atmosphere & Dust Environment Explorer (LADEE) mission will return to an orbital regime not visited since Apollo. The lunar orbit required for LADEE poses unique challenges to the mission designer: low, retrograde, near circular, near equatorial, 100 days duration, with the line of apsides aligned near the solar terminator. Due to the close proximity to the surface, the lunar gravity creates havoc on the LADEE orbit, perturbing the eccentricity and line of apsides while the semi-major axis remains largely unchanged. LADEE uses a novel, visual approach to allow the orbit designer to predict altitude decay and shifts in argument of periapsis and to plan orbit maintenance maneuvers.

INTRODUCTION

The Lunar Atmosphere and Dust Environment Explorer (LADEE) project is a NASA mission that will orbit the Moon's equator with the goal of characterizing the atmosphere and dust environment of the Moon[1]. LADEE will launch on a Minotaur V launch vehicle from the Wallops Flight Facility in Virginia in May 2013. The trans-lunar trajectory uses a phasing loop strategy to accommodate launch dispersions and efficiently raise apogee to lunar distance. After capture at the Moon through three lunar orbit insertion maneuvers, LADEE will enter lunar orbit, where it will be commissioned and begin its mission.

The National Research Council report, "The Scientific Context for Exploration of the Moon" (also referred to as the SCEM Report)[2], lists among its major goals:

a. Determine the global density, composition, and time variability of the fragile lunar atmosphere before it is perturbed by further human activity

b. Determine the size, charge, and spatial distribution of electrostatically transported dust grains and assess their likely effects on lunar exploration and lunar-based astronomy.

LADEE science orbit requirements combine with launch vehicle, spacecraft, and mission design limitations to pose significant lunar orbit design constraints.

- Retrograde, with low inclination (*i*) relative to the equator (155° - 180°)

- Low altitude (50 km average altitude or lower desired)

- 100 days Science Phase, preceded by 30 days in Checkout Phase and followed by zero or more days of Decommissioning

- Limited arrival dates at the moon (approximately 1-2 days per lunar month)

---

[*] LADEE Flight Dynamics Lead, Logyx, LLC, NASA Ames Research Center MS 240-5, Moffett Field, CA 94035.
[†] Senior Aerospace Engineer, Applied Defense Solutions, 8171 Maple Lawn Blvd, Fulton, MD, 20759

- Only two initial RAAN placement options for each trans-lunar design
- Very constrained delta-v budget allocation
  - Nominally 120 m/s for 100 days' Science orbit maintenance
- Beta angle restricted to -21.5° to 6°.
- Science operations relate to sunlight conditions; favored data collection at passage over surface sunrise terminator, however, low altitudes also desired throughout.
  - 50 km maximum altitude over sunrise terminator

LADEE's lunar orbit requirements exclude frozen orbits as possible candidates. Folta & Quinn[3] sum up their findings: "There exist real solutions only when $i > 39.23°$. There are no closed-form analytical solutions for frozen orbits below this value of critical inclination." Similarly, Elipe & Lara's results do not address LADEE's needs[4]. They assume, "that the density of the moon admits axial symmetry," and limit potential model zonals to degree 7. LADEE's investigations of the lunar gravitational field show anything but symmetry.

Unmanned lunar missions favor polar orbits for their enhanced coverage of the entire surface. Perhaps the most similar lunar orbit would be that of Apollo but LADEE has a much longer mission duration, much tighter propellant limitations, and of course higher tolerance for risk. Table 1 compares best available data on several lunar missions[5]. In summary, the LADEE orbit has not been done before.

Table 1 - Lunar Missions for Comparison

Mission	Altitude (km)	Inclination (deg)	Duration (days)
LADEE	250 x 250 Commissioning 50 x 250 Science Commissioning 50 x 50 Science	155 – 180	≥ 30 ≥ 10 ≥ 100
LRO	50 x 50	Polar	yrs
LCROSS	The LCROSS trajectory is an unsuitable solution for LADEE's mission goals.		
Chandrayaan	100 x 100	Polar	312
SELENE	100 x 100	Polar	608
Lunar Prospector	100 x 100 Nominal 30 x 30 Extended	Polar	570
Clementine	2200 x 4600	Polar	~60
Lunar Orbiter I - III	40 x 1850	12 – 20	80 - 385
Apollo	180 x 190 62 x 70	~148	2 ½
Particle & Field Sub-satellites (Apollo 15 & 16)	100 x 140 90 x 130	151 169	30 180

This paper presents a visualization tool for supporting the design of low, near-equatorial, near-circular lunar orbits, first with an introduction to the design method, followed by a description of the implementation approach. LADEE models lunar orbits using Analytical Graphics' STK/Astrogator propagator,[6] a variable-step-size numerical integrator of Cowell's equations of motion. LADEE's lunar design to date uses LP150q and LP100k gravity models[7], usually at degree and order 50. Earth & Sun are included in the gravity model.

OBSERVED PERTURBATIONS ON LOW, NEAR-EQUATORIAL LUNAR ORBITS

Low, near-circular lunar orbits at low inclinations exhibit perturbations in shape (eccentricity, e, but not semimajor axis, a) and orientation of the line of apsides (argument of periapsis, ω). Passage over the lunar mascons often increases e, here termed "decircularization," however some orientations to the lunar mass cause other effects. The periapsis vector trends to favored directions relative to the lunar body. Figure 1 through Figure 4 show examples. The orbit sketches are figurative characterizations depicting the effect of gravitational perturbations on the orbit, drawn in a very exaggerated scale.

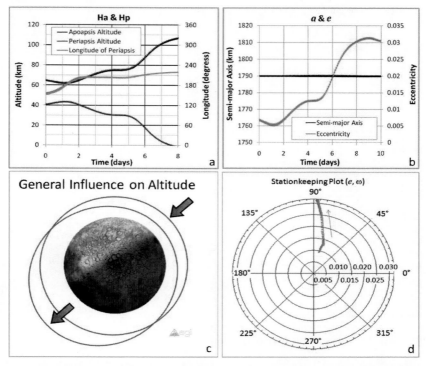

Figure 1. "Decircularizing" Perturbations. a) Periapsis altitude decreases while apoapsis altitude increases, with very little change in the line of apsides. b) Increase in eccentricity with near-constant semi-major axis. c) Near circular orbit (green) becomes more eccentric (red). d) Significant change in eccentricity with small change in the argument of periapsis.

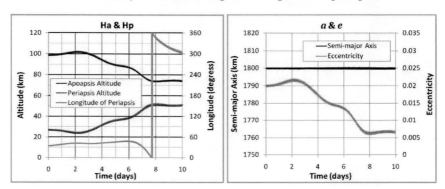

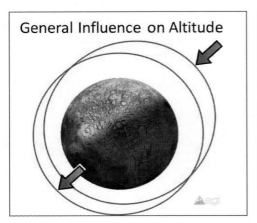
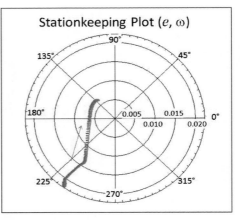

Figure 2. Circularizing Trend

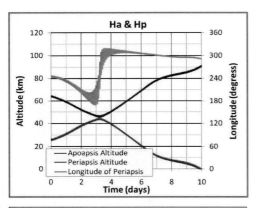
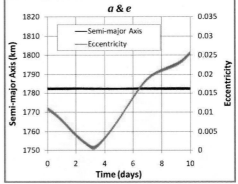

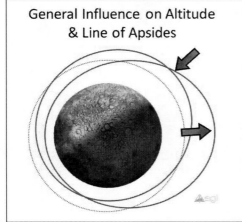
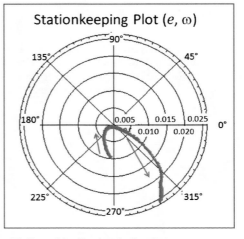

Figure 3. Circularization Followed by Decircularization

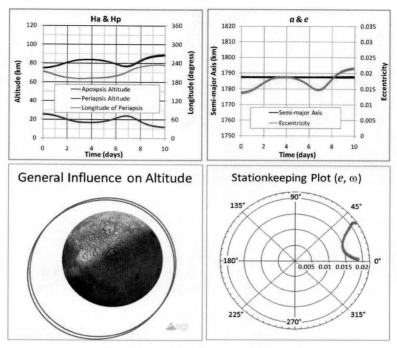

Figure 4. Relatively Stable Orbit

THE CONTOUR MAP DESIGN METHOD

Altitude Decay in Relation to Mascons

For analytical purposes, selenographic longitude (Moon-centered, fixed coordinates) represents the location relative to mascons. Selenographic longitude has the prime meridian facing the Earth and measures positively around the right-handed fixed lunar coordinate system. East lunar longitudes are positive in the ±180° scale, though 0 – 360° is the standard for the LADEE project.

The moon's gravity field tends to drive the periapsis to particular regions of lunar longitude, and from there, eccentricity increases until the periapsis impacts the surface. Because both the gravitational effects and science goals are dictated in relation to the moon's features, LADEE designs use a moon-fixed reference frame.

Initial investigations into a broad range of parameters discovered that five are the strongest design drivers: periapsis & apoapsis altitude (alternatively a & e), inclination, selenographic longitude of ascending node (RAAN + epoch), and selenographic longitude of periapsis (represents ω).

Contour Map Grid Framework

The LADEE Contour Map is and abstract design space where both the x and the y axes refer to lunar longitude. The x-axis is the selenographic longitude of the ascending node ("LAN" or "SLAN"). The y-axis is the selenographic longitude of periapsis ("LOP" or "SLOP"). The grid points all represent the same initial apsis altitudes (h_p & h_a). Each plot has fixed i and epoch, while varying the right ascension of the ascending node (Ω) and ω. Figure 5 illustrates the grid coverage of LAN and LOP, showing periapsis vectors as red arrows (for the SLAN=0° case).

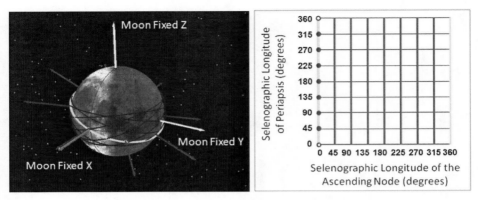

Figure 5. Abstract Design Space for 160° Inclination

Periapsis Decay Layer

Figure 6 adds the first data layer to the grid established in Figure 5, using an example 25 x 75 km orbit at 160° inclination. With initial conditions defined at grid points, the increments of LAN on the x-axis determine the duration of orbit propagation. The combined rate of the moon's rotation (approximately 13 degrees/day) and the precession of the line of nodes create a rate of change in LAN that is typically about 11.5 degrees/day. A 45° change in LAN takes approximately 4 days. Color codes in the data layer contours use a standardized correlation to the altitude change in the periapsis over the time span defined by the grid spacing. The color scheme derives from topographic maps and creates an intuitive portrayal of highs, lows, and neutral areas.

For example, the deep blue color shows cases where an orbit with initial conditions at the SLAN & SLOP coordinates will experience periapsis altitude decay between 30 and 35 km in four days, while the medium green color indicates conditions where the periapsis altitude will increase 10 to 15 km in four days. Since only e changes and a remains nearly constant, there is an implied opposite change in apoapsis altitude very close to the same magnitude.

The periapsis decay contours predict short term eccentricity changes for any orientation of the line of nodes and the line of apsides at low inclinations. Figure 6 identifies example configurations similar to the trends depicted in Figures 1 through 4.

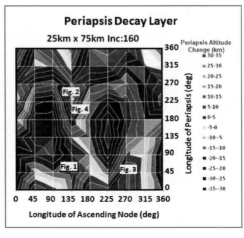

Figure 6. Periapsis Decay Layer Example

738

Periapsis Shift Layer

The second data layer (Figure 7) shows the change in the line of apsides during the propagation time period. Each grid point of LAN and LOP coordinates establishes the initial conditions in Ω and ω. The trend lines shown in black begin at their right-hand starting conditions on grid points and end on the next lower increment in LAN, or to the left on the x-axis. The motion of the y-coordinate and the resultant left-hand endpoint are the results of gravitational perturbations on the line of apsides.

Using the progression of the LAN as the duration for propagation allows the x-axis to represent time. Figure 7a propagates over a 45 degree increment, approximately 4 days, while Figure 7b uses a 30 degree change in LAN or approximately 2 ½ days. Longer propagations can achieve greater changes in eccentricity, color-coded as larger changes in periapsis altitude, while shorter propagations show finer granularity. The change in periapsis altitude over the propagation timeframe appears in the color code mapped at the starting grid point. The shift in the direction of the periapsis vector over the same time interval reflects in black data points which track from the starting grid point to the endpoint on the termination LAN.

For low inclination orbits, gravitational perturbations tend to draw the periapsis vector to favored orientations relative to the lunar mascons, depending on the location of the nodes. Figure 7 below shows two slightly different inclinations, both with strong trends in the resulting periapsis direction.

Each Contour Map has fixed initial values of epoch, i, h_p & h_a (for a & e). The data layers cover the complete range of LAN & LOP (for Ω & ω). True anomaly (υ) cycles many times during the time period of each propagation in the plot. Comparison across different initial conditions in a, e, & i requires multiple Contour Maps. Since the perturbative effects are relative to the lunar mass, there are no apparent variations among starting epochs.

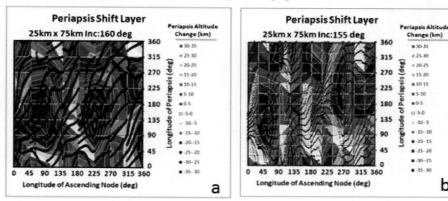

Figure 7. Periapsis Shift Layer in Increments of 45 degrees (a) and 30 degrees (b)

Figure 8 shows cases at LADEE's 160 degree design inclination with semi major axes from 1775 to 1863 km, periapsis altitudes of 25, 50, and 75 km, and apoapsis altitudes in 25 km increments. Eccentricities have approximate increments of 0.007. A circular orbit would have no periapsis to plot on the y-axis so the color contours for altitude decay would appear as vertical bands. The upper left hand plot of Figure 8 begins the trend away from that bounding condition in eccentricity. The lowest eccentricity cases shown in Figure 8 all undergo similar effects from gravitational perturbations: most configurations decay rapidly and draw the periapsis vector to a narrow range of longitudes.

With greater eccentricities, some configurations of orbits resist the gravitational perturbations. Increasing semi-major axes have diminishing influence from the mascons. Without perturbations, the periapsis orientation layer would be only diagonal lines from upper right to lower left, showing constant argument of periapsis. Higher orbit altitudes (lower right hand plot in Figure 8) begin to approach this uniform bounding condition.

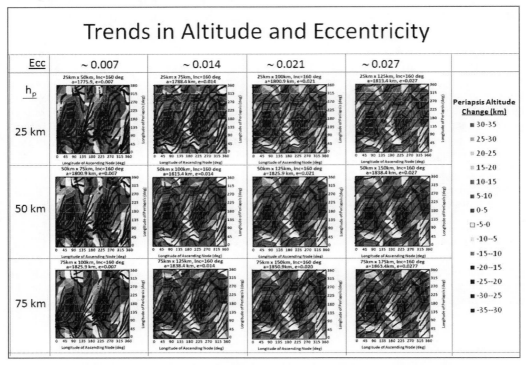

Figure 8. Contour Maps Varying Altitude and Eccentricity

The strongest source of variability in the Contour Maps comes from orbit inclination. An equatorial orbit, either 0° or 180°, would have no ascending node so contours would appear as horizontal bands. For near-equatorial orbits, increments in longitude of periapsis are nearly equal to increments in argument of periapsis; as the orbit inclines away from the equator, longitudes along the orbit track become uneven in spacing and ω is more useful as a grid reference in the Contour Map.

The y-axis in Figure 9 is argument of periapsis rather than longitude of periapsis. Now the periapsis decay layer is oriented about 45° offset from the standard Contour Map. The periapsis shift lines map relative to horizontal (for constant argument of periapsis), rather than relative to diagonal.

Figure 9 uses this slightly different version of the periapsis shift layer to show inclination cases in 15 degree increments for direct, near-polar, and retrograde orbits. All plots in Figure 9 have the same starting altitudes, 25 x 75 km. As with the standard plot, time progresses from right to left, with initial conditions renewed at each grid point.

Close to the equator, the periapsis shifts toward configurations with strong altitude decay and, at low altitude, impact quickly follows. As the inclination approaches polar, the periapsis shift

740

lines don't concentrate to specific regions of the plot, allowing altitude perturbations to counter orbit lowering with raising trends.

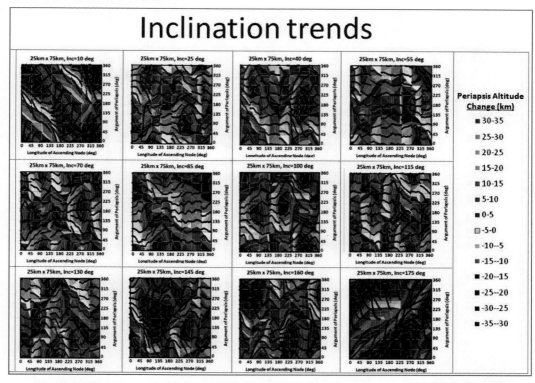

Figure 9. Argument of Periapsis Version of Contour Maps Showing Trends in Inclination (Using Alternate Contour Map with Argument of Periapsis instead of Longitude of Periapsis)

Figure 10 below shows an example 40 x 60 km orbit inclined 89 degrees. Even though the orbit is nearly circular (e=0.0055), there is no consistent decay in the 30 day propagation period. The most similar Contour Map in Figure 9 above is for 85 degrees inclination and shows that periapsis shift perturbations do not concentrate in configurations with strong altitude decay.

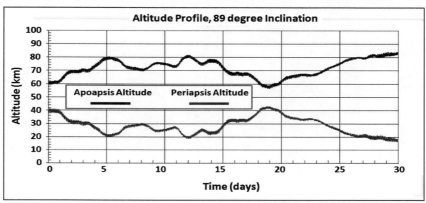

Figure 10. Example Polar Orbit Altitude Profile

Mission Design Layers

With the Contour Map as a tool for visualizing the gravitational perturbations on low orbits, it is possible to choose combinations of orbital elements which provide the most stable orbits and to design maneuvers to avoid the strongest perturbations. Where the lower layers include 64 (or 144) repeated propagations with unique combinations of initial conditions, in Figure 11 the mission design layer shows the history of a single orbit in orange. The orange line maps the trajectory of the design case periapsis orientation over time in (LAN, LOP) coordinates. In LADEE mission design, the spacecraft orbit's LAN data correlates to time, from right to left on the x-axis.

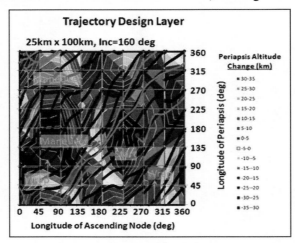

Figure 11. Trajectory Design Layer

Altitude characteristics of the design orbit are near 25 x 100 km when the orange line follows the black lines; the orange trajectory deviates from the pattern of perturbations laid out in black when other altitudes occur. Design activities use multiple Contour Maps to cover relevant altitude combinations. Altitude change maneuvers occur to maintain mission constraints and are not apparent on the Contour Map. Maneuvers that shift the line of apsides appear as discontinuities in the history of the periapsis vector. Propulsive maneuvers can reposition the periapsis vertically on the Contour Map (Figure 13c), but horizontal shifts, representing changes to the node, are prohibitively expensive in delta-v.

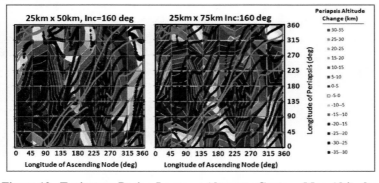

Figure 12. Trajectory Design Layer on Alternate Contour Map Altitudes

The most advantageous design for delta-v use stays near the border between regions of increasing and decreasing periapsis altitude. Figure 13 shows an example case designed for conservation of delta-v, with a design goal of maintaining altitudes near 50 km and 100 km, for h_p and h_a, respectively. Altitude adjustments use in-track maneuvers at the apsides. There are several methods for shifting the line of apsides; for simplicity, apsis shift maneuvers are shown in Figure 13a, c, & d as discontinuities in the longitude of periapsis and modeled here as a circularization burn followed immediately by a apoapsis raising burn to establish a new periapsis, appearing as single point anomalies in the altitude of apoapsis, semi major axis, and eccentricity plots (Figure 13a, b, & d).

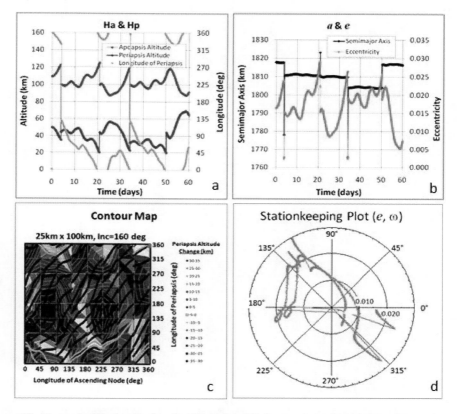

Figure 13. Example Mission Design for Minimizing Delta-v. a) Apsis Altitudes & Longitude, b) Semi-major Axis and Eccentricity, c) Contour map, d) Station-keeping Plot (e vs. ω)

LADEE mission design involves one additional design layer, the sunrise terminator (Figure 14). The rapid decay of circular orbits, combined with the science requirement for sunrise terminator crossings below 50 km altitude, creates the necessity to use a slightly eccentric orbit and keep the periapsis near the sunrise terminator. The longitude of the sunrise terminator becomes the target longitude for the periapsis, as displayed on the y-axis of the Contour Map. The moon's rotation wraps the sunrise terminator across the range of longitudes each lunar cycle. The sunrise terminator layer on the Contour Map uses the longitude of LADEE's ascending node for the abscissa and the time-correlated longitude of the sunrise terminator for the ordinate. Figure 14 shows the location of the sunrise terminator over the four lunar cycles of LADEE mission designs.

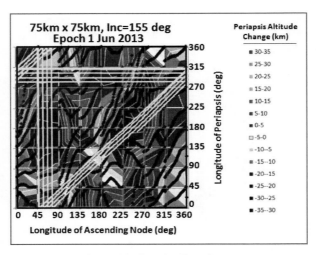

Figure 14. Sunrise Terminator

The geometry of the sunrise terminator on the Contour Map varies with mission epoch (Figure 15). LADEE trans-lunar trajectory design uses the same Earth-Moon geometry for each candidate launch month (March – October, 2013), creating a progression of terminator longitudes for the same LAN in different months.

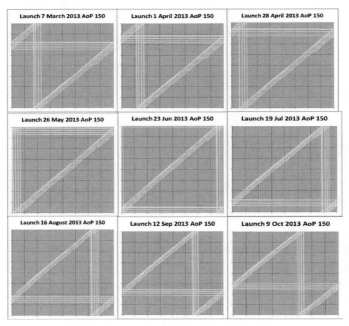

Figure 15. Sunrise Terminator for Potential LADEE Mission Start Dates

The design process using the Contour Map visual tool culminates in LADEE's baseline lunar orbit which uses perturbative trends to balance the orientation of the line of apsides with conservation of propulsive altitude maintenance. Figure 16 shows the time history of LADEE's periapsis relative to the sunrise terminator.

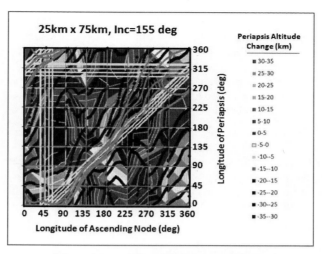

Figure 16. LADEE Baseline Lunar Orbit

Figure 17 adds graphical information about the LADEE baseline design, showing conformance to design requirements:

- Minimum 100 days duration
- Orbit inclination within 25° of retrograde equatorial (baseline 157°)
- Altitude at sunrise terminator crossing < 50 km except for brief, allowable interruptions
- Periapsis altitude maintaining a safety margin above decay to impact (4 days)
- Apoapsis altitude below 150 km for at least 95% of the Science Phase
- Maintenance maneuvers within propellant budget (not shown)
- Periapsis orientation near the sunrise terminator
- Operational goal of minimizing the number of maneuvers needed

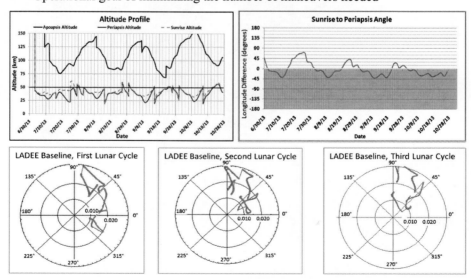

Figure 17. LADEE Baseline Lunar Orbit Data

SOFTWARE IMPLEMENTATION

The design space illustrated in Figure 5 lays out an n X n grid which represents an n squared number of cases that are needed just to create one set of plots (decay plus periapsis shift). Using the example in Figure 5 which has a step size of 45 degrees, n becomes 8 and the number of cases becomes 64. For a higher level of fidelity the number of cases becomes 144 with a step size of 30 degrees. With the significant number of cases that need to be run for just one set of plots, the need for an automatic approach became imperative.

The automatic approach, known as the Periselene Orientation Optimization Program (PO^2P), utilizes the tools and process that originated as manual steps and replaces them with code. The PO^2P integrates with STK, STK/Astrogator, and MS Excel via their respective APIs (Application Programming Interfaces) to execute, gather data, store, and eventually plot each case for a particular run. Initially designed as a prototype, the PO^2P has evolved into a tool that meets a series of needs for the LADEE mission.

Manual Grid Creation

The manual approach was a time intensive process to create the Contour Map periapsis decay and shift layers. Each Contour Map took approximately one week for computation of the necessary cases, including propagation runs (usually 64 cases), collection of the data, the plotting of the data and the overlay of the individual layers that compose the design layer. An example of a manual design layer can be seen in Figure 18 where the Periapsis Decay, Periapsis Shift, and the Solar Terminator layers are depicted, using the default Excel color scheme.

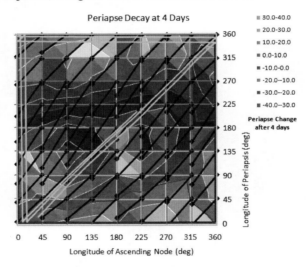

Figure 18. Example Contour Map via the Manual Process

In early research, the manual process for creating the periapsis decay and periapsis shift layers used manual inputs to initialize the orbital elements in STK/Astrogator. Trial and error established the RAAN input value for the desired LAN reference. From there, RAAN and AOP increments covered the entire grid.

In addition to the trial and error method there were several assumptions that were incorporated. Those assumptions were:

- The inclination was close enough to equatorial that 45 degrees of AOP would be 45 degrees of SLOP
- During propagation of the spacecraft's orbit, four days of propagation represented approximately 45 degrees of change in SLAN
- The periapsis shift was observable from the initial and final points to define its behavior

The time that the user spent creating the design layer manually and the ever growing number of configurations to evaluate created the need for an automatic approach.

PO²P Requirements

The purpose of the PO2P is to simplify and standardize the way that the user creates the visualization layers and replace the need for significant user interaction. Once the requirements were established, implementation followed a set of builds that allowed the user to provide feedback, verification, and new requirements as needed to support the rapid prototyping approach. The main high level requirements that drove the design of the PO²P were:

- Automate the creation of the Contour Map via the same tools as the manual prototype (STK and MS Excel)
- Simplify the user's interaction and involvement in the creation of the Contour Map
- Improve, where applicable and necessary, the creation of the Contour Map
- Incorporate a template scenario to be associated with the PO²P to standardize the creation of the Contour Map
- Provide a prototype tool as soon as possible to the analysts to support pre-launch mission analysis and design

Implementation

The PO²P uses Microsoft's Visual Studio application and employs VB.Net to interact with STK and Microsoft Excel via their Application Programming Interfaces (APIs). The PO²P re-uses previously developed libraries that simplify and standardize routine interactions with STK and STK/Astrogator. Lastly, the PO²P also incorporates a template scenario which is necessary for proper operations.

Template Scenario

In order to standardize the automation of the Contour Map, the PO²P utilizes a STK "template scenario". The template scenario simplifies the process of running the individual cases that make up the Periapsis Decay and Periapsis Shift layers. The incorporation of the template scenario simplified four main areas:

- An automated method for calculating input AOP from the desired SLOP
- The elimination of the trial and error method for finding SLAN by varying the RAAN initial state value
- Refinement of the correlation between propagation time and change in SLAN
- Reducing the memory storage footprint of each Contour Map

By utilizing the template scenario, scenario setup is minimized, allowing the PO²P to quickly determine the AOP initial state value by using the differential corrector inside of STK/Astrogator.

The template scenario varies the initial AOP as a control inside of the differential corrector with the goal of achieving the SLOP for a particular Contour Map case. The PO²P and the template scenario work together for each case where the PO²P defines and sets the particular SLOP value dependent on case being run and the template scenario's differential corrector iterates to find the appropriate value for AOP. One benefit of this implementation is that by utilizing the differential corrector, the value for SLOP will always be within a predefined tolerance, in this case 0.001 degrees. Where in the manual process the error between actual SLOP value and desired SLOP value is mostly likely going to be larger depending on how much effort the user can put into refining the value.

The template scenario includes propagator settings that also remove the assumption that the four days of propagation is equivalent to 45 degrees of change in SLAN. These have been defined to stop at the true change in SLAN (i.e. 45 degrees). This condition for stopping is defined as a custom angle which defines the SLAN value. As the individual case is run the satellite propagates until the SLAN value reaches the desired stopping condition. In order for the individual cases to be run accurately the PO^{2}P updates the stopping condition value. This stopping condition also has a defined tolerance which guarantees that each of the n x n cases are uniform to one another.

Framework Element

The PO^{2}P utilizes a framework architecture as part of its interaction with STK and STK/Astrogator. The PO^{2}P made use of two different frameworks, one for STK and one for STK/Astrogator. The design, depicted in Figure 19, behind the development of the individual framework elements is to simplify, standardize, and reutilize algorithms and development that has been conducted in the past to allow for the quick development and prototyping of tools without having to rewrite, relearn, and rehash previously conducted work.

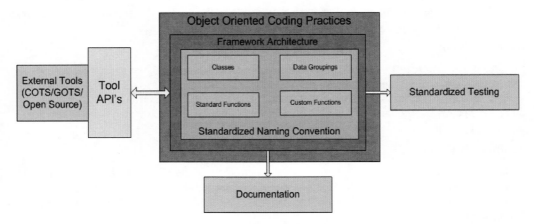

Figure 19. Framework Philosophy

The incorporation of the framework elements significantly reduced the development time in creating the first version of the PO^{2}P, which allowed the tool to be successful from multiple standpoints. Not only did the frameworks save development time, but they also reduced the debugging time by limiting the potential places were problems could occur. Each framework component has its own test and verification process and this process is executed before a new version of a layer is released. The time savings allowed the PO^{2}P development team to meet and exceed which was the last requirement.

Plot Layering

The Contour Map consists of four layers, Periapsis Decay, Periapsis Shift, Solar Terminator, and Mission. These layers are plotted on top of one another. Without the layering, the individual plots, shown in Figure 20, require practice to interpret independently. Additionally, if the plots are askew the probability of misinterpreting the plots increases. Due to these factors, the correct placement and layering of the plots is a critical piece of functionality inside the PO^{2}P. This implementation was one of the most difficult development items.

The problem of correctly layering the plots arises due to the way that MS Excel performs and handles its plotting and the objects inside of an individual chart. Inside any standard MS Excel chart there is a chart area (the container for all other areas), plot area, a legend area, axes areas, and a title area. Additionally, since there are three separate layers plotted in Figure 16 there are three individual MS Excel plots. Only in the base layer, Periapsis Decay, are the individual Excel plot areas shown. In the remaining layers, Periapsis Shift and Mission, only the data points are visible, with the other areas transparent.

In order to correctly organize the various layers, the PO^{2}P locks the placement of the base layer, Periapsis Decay, and uses its location to determine the placement of the remaining layers.

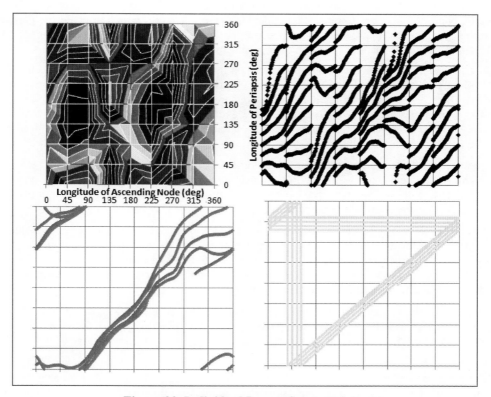

Figure 20. Individual Layers Separated Apart

Benefits

The PO^{2}P has further enhanced the manual approach initially used to create the Contour Maps. The majority of these benefits were expected based on the requirements that defined the PO^{2}P

749

design. However, there were some additional benefits that became apparent during the development, testing, and use of the PO^{2}P.

The first of additional benefits is the significant reduction in time to create one Contour Map. As stated above, it originally took on average about a week to create just one Contour Map. Use of the PO^{2}P reduces this time to approximately 40 minutes. This improvement has facilitated the creation of a reference library of Contour Maps to be available for the design process.

Additionally the development team believes that further reductions are possible, since a large majority of the time goes into processing and plotting the data inside of MS Excel. IT may be possible, by switching to a different graphing package, the total time required to create a Contour Map could reduce to 15 to 20 minutes.

A great example of the time saving was realized in the creation of Figure 9. As part of the figure there are twelve plots, using the manual method those plots would have taken several weeks to create. PO^{2}P generated the plots comprising the Figure 9 in approximately 7 hours.

The second benefit is the increased accuracy of the tool. The biggest improvement is the stopping condition change from the standard four day propagation which affected the periapsis shift plot. The manual approach was overestimating the shift in periapsis compared to the PO^{2}P. This is only due to the manual approach over propagating.

In addition to the accuracy benefit, there is the third improvement of standardization of the PO^{2}P plots which is closely tied to the accuracy advantage. This becomes very evident when viewing Figure 9. One can very quickly see the differences between the various plots in Figure 9. For the manual approach it would be up to the creator of the plots to ensure that the individual plots are standardized requiring more valuable time and thus increasing the time that it takes to complete just one Contour Map.

Additionally there is standardization of the process and the computed tolerances of each run. For a change to occur, the user of the PO^{2}P must make a conscious decision and perform an action. Whereas with the manual approach something might change just due to human error (time is running out, a procedure not being followed correctly, or the user has become tired).

The fourth benefit is reuse. As described in the Framework section there are pieces that the PO^{2}P utilizes from past missions and programs. By reusing this past development work as well as lessons learned, the risk involved in the creation of the PO^{2}P was drastically reduced. This has allowed the tool to grow from the original purpose of investigation to a tool that supports analysis, design, and will be available if needed in operations.

The PO^{2}P also has incorporated some of its lessons learned and development as part of the Framework which will be used for other aspects of the LADEE mission. By continually doing this the Framework itself evolves such that the next mission benefits from the rest.

The last benefit is additional insight. By comparing Figure 18 and Figure 7 and focusing on the Periapsis Shift layer, one can see a difference between the original way of viewing the data and the current method. Periapsis trends now also include data points throughout the propagation period, rather than just the endpoints. The current method allows the user to see the exact behavior of the periapsis shift and the intended or unintended consequences depending on the starting point. The view resulting from the manual method did not give insights into these areas. The current view allows mission planners to use the periapsis shift to its greatest potential when designing the overall mission plan.

CONCLUSION

The LADEE science mission poses unique requirements and constraints on the lunar orbit design. The Contour Map offers an innovative design approach which is in use on the LADEE project for visualizing the perturbative effects of the lunar gravitational field and for planning maintenance maneuvers. The PO2P Tool is a streamlined implementation approach; combining STK/Astrogator and Excel affords the user rapid, convenient production of plots for any needed configuration.

ACKNOWLEDGMENTS

LADEE Flight Dynamics is a team effort and the current design work would not be possible without the invaluable contributions of Ken Galal, John Carrico, Mike Loucks, Lisa Policastri, Craig Nickel, and Adam Bedrossian. Thanks always to the late Professor Harm Buning, whose many students of orbital mechanics included Mercury, Gemini, and Apollo astronauts.

REFERENCES

[1]B. Hine, et al. "The Lunar Atmosphere and Dust Environment Explorer (LADEE) Mission." 2010 IEEE Aerospace Conference, Big Sky, Montana, March 6-13, 2010.

[2]NASA Science Definition Team (SDT) for the Lunar Atmosphere And Dust Environment Explorer (LADEE) Study Report, May 21, 2008. http://lunarscience.arc.nasa.gov/files/LADEE_SDT_Report.pdf

[3]Folta, D. & D. Quinn, 2006 "Lunar Frozen Orbits", **AIAA 2006-6749**, *AIAA/AAS, Astrodynamics Conference and Exhibit,* Keystone, CO.

[4]Elipe A., and Lara, M. "Frozen Orbits about the Moon", Journal of Guidance, Control, and Dynamics, Vol 26. no2, March-April 2003.

[5]Internet sources & pers. comm.

[6]STK, A Technical Summary, Analytical Graphics, Inc. February 2010.

[7]Konopliv, A. S., et al. 2001. Recent Gravity Models as a Result of the Lunar Prospector Mission. *Icarus* **150**, 1–18. http://trs-new.jpl.nasa.gov/dspace/bitstream/2014/15597/1/00-1301.pdf

NEW DYNAMIC MODEL FOR LUNAR PROBE
AND ITS APPLICATION TO QUASI-PERIODIC ORBIT
ABOUT THE TRANSLUNAR LIBRATION POINT

Yingjing Qian,[*] Inseok Hwang,[†] Wuxing Jing[‡] and Jian Wei[§]

A new dynamic model with the standard ephemerides that describes the relative motion of a lunar probe in a rotating coordinate system is presented. By using the ephemerides, the description for the real physical situation is more precise. Compared with other high-order models, the complexity of the proposed model is lower. More specifically, the proposed model considers the influences of direct and indirect Sun's perturbation, and the eccentricity of the Moon's orbit. It also provides a solution without a truncation error. Further, a lunar L2 quasiperiodic orbit design is presented as an application of the proposed model. The initial conditions are calculated by using the Lindstedt-Poincare technique. An iteration method which introduces the Sun's influence gradually and the differential correction are utilized to adjust the initial conditions.

I. INTRODUCTION

The five Lagrangian points were first found by Euler and Lagrange in the Restricted Three-body Problem (R3BP). In the last 20 years, periodic orbits in the three-body regime have successfully served as the basis for trajectory design in various missions[1~7], from ISEE-3 to the more recent Genesis mission. Farquhar [1], Hill [7] , Brown [8], Szebehely [9] , Howell [2], etc. have made great contributions to the Lagrangian point dynamics. Conley [10], Koon [11], McInnes[12] , Parker[13] , etc. extended the applications of the Lagrangian points , such as solar sail, low energy transfer orbits.

Mostly the motion of lunar probe can be described in inertial coordinate systems, but when it comes to the mission based on Lagrangian points or R3BP, rotating coordinates could be a better option. Therefore, this paper aims at deriving an accurate dynamic model in a rotating coordinate system for further Lagrangian point research.

Since the Restricted Three-body Problem (R3BP) is the basic model for Lagrangian point missions, most papers follow the three basic assumptions in the R3BP which can be summarized as

[*] Visiting Scholar, School of Aeronautics and Astronautics, Purdue University, PhD Student, School of Astronautics engineering, Harbin Institute of Technology, 701 W. Stadium Ave ARMS 3132,West Lafayette, IN 47907-2045. qian14@purdue.edu.
[†] Associate Professor, School of Aeronautics and Astronautics, Purdue University, 701 W. Stadium Ave ARMS 3211,West Lafayette, IN 47907-2045. AIAA Senior Member. ihwang@purdue.edu
[‡] Professor, Department of Astronautics Engineering , Harbin Institute of Technology, 92 W Dazhi St Mailbox 330. 150001.
[§] PhD Student, School of Aeronautics and Astronautics, Purdue University, 701 W. Stadium Ave ARMS 3132,West Lafayette, IN 47907-2045. wei15@purdue.edu.

follows: (i) the two primaries have circular or elliptical orbits about their barycenter, (ii) the barycenter of the two primaries is an inertial point, and (iii) the plane defined by the circular or elliptical orbits of the primaries is inertial. For the Sun-Earth-satellite system, the R3BP model is good, because we can consider the Sun and the Earth-Moon barycenter as two primaries; however, when it comes to the Earth-Moon-satellite system, those three assumptions could become three drawbacks because the influence of the Sun on the Earth and the Moon is no longer negligible. The influence of the Sun can be classified into two categories: one is the direct influence called solar gravity which is reflected on the motion of a probe, and the other is the indirect influence reflected on the motion of the two primaries which will finally affect the motion of a lunar probe. The indirect influence can be shown in the following aspects. Firstly, the orbit of the Moon around the Earth is not a strict ellipse, but it has a variable eccentricity (1/15~1/23). This is contradictory to Assumption (i). In addition, the barycenter of the Earth-Moon system is no longer an inertial point, but a point moving on an elliptical orbit around the Sun, which is against Assumption (ii). Last but not least, the Moon's orbit does not lie on an inertial plane, but lies on a plane with nutation (average period 173 days) and precession (average period 18.6 years), which is against Assumption (iii). From the facts presented above, the three assumptions of the R3BP could cause large errors for the Earth-Moon-satellite system in the real physical situation.

Since the 1960s, a lot of work has been done to improve the R3BP model. Tapley[14] et al. considered the Sun's influence on the triangular Lagrangian points in the Earth-Moon system and proposed a four-body dynamic model which considered the angle between the ecliptic plane and the Moon's orbital plane, but the precession and the eccentricity of the Moon's orbit were still not taken into account. Schechter [15] improved Tapley's work and took the precession of the Moon's orbit into account, but his research was based on the assumption that the Moon's eccentricity equals zero. Nicholson[16] considered the Sun's influence on the collinear Lagrangian points and developed a dynamic model based on the assumption that the angle between the ecliptic plane and the Moon's orbital plane is zero and both the Moon's orbit and the Sun's orbit are circular. Farquhar[1] et al. systematically studied the existence of periodic orbits near the translunar Lagrangian point L2 in the Earth-Moon system, and derived a dynamic model relative to L2 which includes solar influence; however, the expression for solar influence considered was only a fourth order approximation of the accurate formula and the parameters used to express the Moon's orbit were average parameters, which means there might be truncation errors and roundoff errors. In addition, the Sun's influence was not considered in the calculation of the position of L2.

In order to more accurately describe the motion of a probe in the true physical situation, we develop a more accurate dynamic model with the standard ephemerides, which takes the Sun's gravitational influence into full consideration.

The rest of this paper is organized as follows. In Section II, the derivation of a precise dynamic model with the standard ephemerides in the geocentric rotating coordinate system is presented. In Section III, we illustrate an application of the proposed model, with an example of the lunar L2 quasi-periodic orbit design. Conclusions are given in Section IV.

II. DERIVATION OF THE DYNAMIC MODEL WITH THE STANDARD EPHEMERIDES

Coordinate systems

In this section, the derivation of a dynamic model with the standard ephemerides in the Geocentric rotating coordinate system (GRC) is presented. To start with, we introduce the definition of the two coordinate systems as shown in Table 1.

Table 1. Coordinate Systems.

Name	Origin	X-axis definition	Z-axis definition	Y-axis definition
J2000 Geocentric Equatorial Coordinate System (J2000) $O-XYZ$	Center of the Earth O	Pointing to the vernal equinox at noon on January 1st 2000 X	Pointing to the North Pole at this time Z	Completing the right-handed coordinate system Y
Geocentric Rotating Coordinate System (GRC) $O-xyz$	Center of the Earth O	Pointing to the center of the Moon $\hat{x}$	Pointing to the instantaneous direction of the Moon's orbital angular momentum $\hat{z}$	Completing the right-handed coordinate system $\hat{y}$

The coordinate system $O-XYZ$ is considered as an inertial coordinate system in this paper, so the absolute angular velocity of the rotating coordinate system $O-xyz$ is the angular velocity relative to the J2000, which is denoted by ω. The unit vectors of the coordinate system $O-xyz$ are denoted by $\hat{x}, \hat{y},$ and $\hat{z}$, and their derivatives relative to the J2000 coordinate system are denoted by $\dot{\hat{x}}, \dot{\hat{y}},$ and $\dot{\hat{z}}$, respectively.

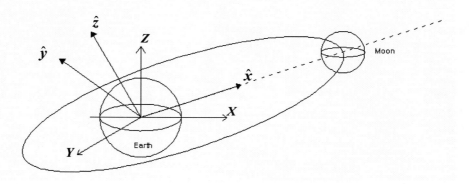

Figure 1. The J2000 coordinate system and the Geocentric rotating coordinate system.

The angular velocity of the GRC relative to the J2000

Since the indirect influence of the Sun affects the motion of the two primaries which will finally affect the motion of a probe, it is necessary to find an accurate expression for the motion of the two primaries. In this paper, we choose the standard ephemerides in the J2000.

In order to use the standard ephemerides in the GRC, we derive an accurate relationship between the GRC and the J2000 by using the dynamic equations of the Moon in the J2000 shown in Eq. (1), the definition of the GRC and the relationship between the angular velocity ω of the GRC relative to the J2000 and the unit vectors $\hat{x}, \hat{y},$ and $\hat{z}$ shown in Eq. (2)[17]:

$$\ddot{r}_M = -\frac{\mu_E + \mu_M}{r_M^3} r_M + \mu_S \left(\frac{r_M - r_S}{r_{MS}^3} - \frac{r_S}{r_S^3} \right) \tag{1}$$

where r_S and r_M are the Sun's position vector and the Moon's position vector relative to the center of the Earth, respectively; μ_E, μ_M and μ_S are the gravitational constants for the Earth, the Moon and the Sun, respectively. We define $r_M = \|r_M\|$, $r_S = \|r_S\|$ and $r_{MS} = \|r_S - r_M\|$.

$$\omega = \frac{1}{2}\left(\hat{x} \times \dot{\hat{x}} + \hat{y} \times \dot{\hat{y}} + \hat{z} \times \dot{\hat{z}} \right) \tag{2}$$

According to the definition of the GRC, the following equations can be derived:

$$\hat{x} = \frac{r_M}{r_M}, \hat{z} = \frac{h_M}{h_M}, \hat{y} = \frac{h_M \times r_M}{h_M r_M} \tag{3}$$

where the h_M is the Moon's orbital angular momentum and $h_M = r_M \times \dot{r}_M$, $h_M = \|h_M\|$.

Considering Eq. (1) and Eq. (3), Eq.(2) can be rewritten with the ephemerides in the GRC,

$$\omega = \left[\frac{r_M}{h_M^2}\left(\frac{\mu_S}{r_{MS}^3} - \frac{\mu_S}{r_S^3} \right)(r_S \cdot h_M) \right]\hat{x} + \frac{h_M}{r_M^2}\hat{z} \tag{4}$$

Compared with Farquhar's[18] expression of ω which uses the Moon's orbital average parameters and has truncation errors, the proposed model, which is a simple yet accurate expression of the angular velocity of the GRC, contains the Sun's and the Moon's orbit parameters which can be directly computed from the Sun's and the Moon's ephemerides in the standard coordinate system J2000 (such as the DE405 ephemerides).

In the literature, the Moon's orbital angular momentum $h_M = r_M \times \dot{r}_M$ is usually taken as a constant. However, the h_M is changing continuously with a changing rate which can be expressed as follows:

$$\dot{h}_M = \frac{h_M \cdot \dot{h}_M}{h_M} = \left(\frac{\mu_S}{r_{MS}^3} - \frac{\mu_S}{r_S^3} \right)\frac{(r_M \times r_S) \cdot h_M}{h_M} = \left(\frac{\mu_S}{r_{MS}^3} - \frac{\mu_S}{r_S^3} \right) r_M (r_S \cdot \hat{y}) \tag{5}$$

Derivation of Dynamic Model

If the non-spherical gravitational influence of the Earth and the disturbances of other planets are neglected, the lunar dynamic model in the J2000 coordinate system is:

$$\ddot{r}_P = -\frac{\mu_E}{r_P^3} r_P + \mu_M \left(\frac{r_M - r_P}{r_{PM}^3} - \frac{r_M}{r_M^3} \right) + \mu_S \left(\frac{r_S - r_P}{r_{PS}^3} - \frac{r_S}{r_S^3} \right) \tag{6}$$

where r_P is the position vector from the center of mass of the Earth to the lunar probe, and $r_{PM} = \|r_M - r_P\|$, $r_{PS} = \|r_S - r_P\|$.

We define $r_P \triangleq x\hat{x} + y\hat{y} + z\hat{z}$, $\dot{r}_P^b \triangleq \dot{x}\hat{x} + \dot{y}\hat{y} + \dot{z}\hat{z}$, $\ddot{r}_P^b \triangleq \ddot{x}\hat{x} + \ddot{y}\hat{y} + \ddot{z}\hat{z}$, where $\dot{r}_P^b$ and $\ddot{r}_P^b$ are the relative speed and the relative acceleration in the GRC. The result from the combination of Eq. (6) and Eq.(5) is as follows:

$$\ddot{r}_P^b = -2\omega \times \dot{r}_P^b - \omega \times (\omega \times r_P) - \dot{\omega} \times r_P - \frac{\mu_E}{r_P^3} r_P + \mu_M \left(\frac{r_M - r_P}{r_{PM}^3} - \frac{r_M}{r_M^3} \right) + \mu_S \left(\frac{r_S - r_P}{r_{PS}^3} - \frac{r_S}{r_S^3} \right) \quad (7)$$

where r_P is the position vector from the center of mass of the Earth to the lunar probe. Then, we substitute the expression of ω in Eq. (4) into the dynamic equation of a lunar probe in Eq. (7).

$$\begin{cases} \ddot{x} = 2\omega_z \dot{y} + \omega_z^2 x - \omega_x \omega_z z + \dot{\omega}_z y - \left(\frac{\mu_E}{r_P^3} + \frac{\mu_M}{r_{PM}^3} + \frac{\mu_S}{r_{PS}^3} \right) x + \left(\frac{\mu_M}{r_{PM}^3} - \frac{\mu_M}{r_M^3} \right) r_M + \left(\frac{\mu_S}{r_{PS}^3} - \frac{\mu_S}{r_S^3} \right) r_{Sx}, \\[2ex] \ddot{y} = 2\omega_x \dot{z} - 2\omega_z \dot{x} - \left(\omega_x^2 + \omega_z^2 \right) y + \dot{\omega}_z z - \omega_z x - \left(\frac{\mu_E}{r_P^3} + \frac{\mu_M}{r_{PM}^3} + \frac{\mu_S}{r_{PS}^3} \right) y + \left(\frac{\mu_S}{r_{PS}^3} - \frac{\mu_S}{r_S^3} \right) r_{Sy}, \\[2ex] \ddot{z} = -2\omega_x \dot{y} + \omega_x^2 x - \omega_x \omega_z z + \dot{\omega}_x y - \left(\frac{\mu_E}{r_P^3} + \frac{\mu_M}{r_{PM}^3} + \frac{\mu_S}{r_{PS}^3} \right) z + \left(\frac{\mu_S}{r_{PS}^3} - \frac{\mu_S}{r_S^3} \right) r_{Sz}, \end{cases} \quad (8)$$

where

$$\omega_x = \frac{r_M}{h_M} \left(\frac{\mu_S}{r_{MS}^3} - \frac{\mu_S}{r_S^3} \right) r_{Sz}, \omega_z = \frac{h_M}{r_M^2}$$

$$r_{Sx} = r_S \cdot \frac{r_M}{r_M}, r_{Sy} = r_S \cdot \frac{h_M \times r_M}{r_M h_M}, r_{Sz} = r_S \cdot \frac{h_M}{h_M}$$

Since the dot product is irrelevant to the coordinates, the Sun and the Moon orbital parameters can be directly calculated with the Sun's and Moon's ephemerides in the standard coordinate system J2000.

Relationship between the proposed model and restricted three-body model

If we do not consider the solar gravity ($\mu_S = 0, \omega_x = 0, \dot{\omega}_x = 0$), Eq(8) can be simplified as:

$$\begin{cases} \ddot{x} = 2\omega_z \dot{y} + \dot{\omega}_z y + \omega_z^2 x - \left(\frac{\mu_E}{r_P^3} + \frac{\mu_M}{r_{PM}^3} \right) x + \left(\omega_z^2 - \frac{\mu_M}{r_M^3} \right) r_M \\[2ex] \ddot{y} = -2\omega_z \dot{x} + \omega_z^2 y - \dot{\omega}_z x - \left(\frac{\mu_E}{r_P^3} + \frac{\mu_M}{r_{PM}^3} \right) y \\[2ex] \ddot{z} = -\left(\frac{\mu_E}{r_P^3} + \frac{\mu_M}{r_{PM}^3} \right) z \end{cases} \quad (9)$$

where

757

$$\omega_z = \sqrt{\frac{(\mu_E + \mu_M)a_M(1-e_M^2)}{r_M^3}} \qquad r_M = \frac{a_M(1-e_M^2)}{1+e_M\cos\theta_M}$$

of which a_M, e_M and θ_M are the average semi-major axis of the lunar orbit, eccentricity and true anomaly, respectively. It is not difficult to find that Eq. (9) is a simplified dynamic model for the elliptical R3BP in the GRC.

Moreover, if we don't consider the solar gravity and the eccentricity of the Moon's orbit ($\mu_S = 0, \omega_x = 0, \dot\omega_x = 0, \dot\omega_z = 0$), Eq(8) can be simplified as:

$$\begin{cases} \ddot{x} = 2\Omega\dot{y} + \Omega^2 x - \left(\dfrac{\mu_E}{r_P^3} + \dfrac{\mu_M}{r_{PM}^3}\right)x + \left(\dfrac{\mu_M}{r_{PM}^3} - \dfrac{\mu_M}{r_M^3}\right)r_M \\[3mm] \ddot{y} = -2\Omega\dot{x} + \Omega^2 y - \left(\dfrac{\mu_E}{r_P^3} + \dfrac{\mu_M}{r_{PM}^3}\right)y \\[3mm] \ddot{z} = -\left(\dfrac{\mu_E}{r_P^3} + \dfrac{\mu_M}{r_{PM}^3}\right)z \end{cases} \qquad (10)$$

where, $\Omega = \sqrt{\dfrac{(\mu_E + \mu_M)}{l^3}}$, of which l is the distance between the Earth and the Moon.

Eq(10) is a simplified dynamic model for the circular R3BP in the GRC.

It is clear that the dynamic model proposed in this paper is a more general model which has the circular and elliptical R3BP models as special cases. During the process of deriving the proposed model, we do not use those three assumptions for the R3BP or add other equations to represent the motion of primary bodies; instead, we use the standard ephemerides which provide more accurate and brief expressions of the motions of primary bodies.

III. LUNAR L2 QUASI-PERIODIC ORBIT DESIGN WITH NEW DYNAMIC MODEL

Eq(8) can be used as easily as other models in the applications around the libration points. In this section, we consider the lunar L2 quasi-periodic orbit design as an example to investigate the performance of the proposed dynamic model in detail. Previous studies on the lunar L2 quasi-periodic orbit has achieved many successes, such as numerical determination of Lissajous trajectories in the R3BP [19], solutions in the restricted four-body problem [20,21], and Lyapunov and halo orbits about L2 [22]. However, they either do not consider the Sun's indirect influence or both the Sun's indirect and direct influence. Thus, if we place a probe into space with the initial condition calculated by previous models, the probe will diverge soon. Otherwise, it will require more fuel to overcome the Sun's influence in order to keep the probe in the designed orbit in a real physical situation.

Coordinate systems and their relationship

Because the proposed model is in the GRC while the quasi-periodic orbits are always shown in the L2 rotating coordinate system, we need to define a new coordinate system and introduce the relationship between the L2 rotating coordinate system and the GRC

1). L2 rotating coordinates

The new coordinate system is defined shown in Table 2.

Table 2. New Coordinate Systems.

Name	Origin	X-axis definition	Z-axis definition	Y-axis definition
L2 Rotating Coordinate System (LRC) $O_{L2} - \widetilde{xyz}$	L2 point which moves along the line joining the Earth and the Moon O_{L2}	Pointing to the center of the Moon $\tilde{x}$	Pointing to the instantaneous direction of the Moon's orbital angular momentum $\tilde{z}$	Completing the right-handed coordinate system $\tilde{y}$

Since this coordinate system $O_{L2} - \widetilde{xyz}$ is parallel to the GRC $O - xyz$, the angular velocity relative to the J2000 of the LRC is the same as the GRC, which is also denoted by ω. The unit vectors of the coordinate system $O_{L2} - \widetilde{xyz}$ are denoted by $\tilde{x}, \tilde{y}$, and $\tilde{z}$, and their time derivatives relative to the J2000 coordinate system are denoted as $\dot{\tilde{x}}, \dot{\tilde{y}}$, and $\dot{\tilde{z}}$, respectively.

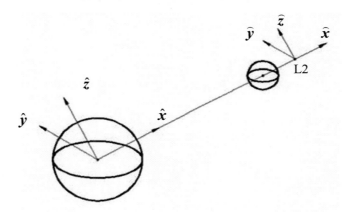

Figure 2. The Geocentric rotating coordinate system and the L2 rotating coordinate system

2) Relationship between the LRC and the GRC

Compared with the definition of the GRC in Table 1, it seems that we only move the origin from the center of the Earth to the L2 point and the transforming relationship should be easily computed by moving "certain distance" from the Earth center to the L2 point. However, the L2 point moves along the line joining the Earth and the Moon all the time. In other words, we do not know the "certain distance". If we want to find the relationship between the LRC and the GRC, we need to know the distance from the L2 point to the center of the Earth. A numerical method used to find the L2 point during a designed time interval in the proposed model is an iteration method adapted from the work of Jing[17] which is described in Appendix B.

a. Relationship in the real physical situation

If $\mathbf{r}, \mathbf{v}$ are the vectors in the GRC and $\mathbf{R}, \mathbf{V}$ are the same vectors expressed in the LRC, due to the movement of L2 point, the relationship between those vectors can be expressed as follows:

$$\mathbf{r} = \mathbf{R} + \mathbf{R_{L2}} = \mathbf{R} + \delta \mathbf{R}_m$$

$$\mathbf{v} = \mathbf{V} + \frac{\mathbf{V_{L2}} \cdot \mathbf{R_{L2}}}{R_{L2}} = \mathbf{V} + \delta \frac{\mathbf{V}_m \cdot \mathbf{R}_m}{R_m} = \mathbf{V} + \delta \frac{v_m \cdot r_m}{R_m} \qquad (11)$$

where $\mathbf{R_{L2}} = [R_{L2}, 0, 0]^T$ is the expression for the position vector from the center of the Earth to the L2 point in the GRC and R_{L2} is the distance between the L2 point and the center of Earth; $\mathbf{V_{L2}}$ is the velocity of the L2 point; $\mathbf{R_m} = [R_m, 0, 0]^T$ where R_m is the distance between the center of the Moon and the center of the Earth in the GRC; $\mathbf{V_m}$ is the velocity of the Moon in the GRC; and v_m, r_m are the standard ephemerides in the J2000. It is not easy for us to know the $\mathbf{R_m}$ and $\mathbf{V_m}$ in the GRC, but we can use $\mathbf{V}_m \cdot \mathbf{R}_m = v_m \cdot r_m$ since the dot product is irrelevant to the coordinate system. R_{L2}, R_m and δ are not constants because of the Sun's influence. The computation of R_{L2}, R_m and δ are shown in Appendix B.

According to the relationship presented above, the proposed model contains the standard ephemerides, and the calculation of the accurate L2 point correlates to the initial time and the time interval. We set the initial time which is 12pm Oct. 1st 2012(GTM) in this paper and the time interval is 1 day. Then, between 12pm Oct. 1st 2012 to 12pm Oct. 2nd 2012, δ equals to 1.16783259631133.

b. Relationship in the circular R3BP

The relationship between the GRC and the LRC based on the circular R3BP can be described as follow:

If $\mathbf{r}, \mathbf{v}$ are the vectors in the GRC and $\mathbf{R}, \mathbf{V}$ are the same vectors expressed in the LRC, the relationship between those vectors can be expressed as follows:

$$\mathbf{r} = \mathbf{R} + \mathbf{R_{L2}} = \mathbf{R} + \lambda \mathbf{R}_m$$

$$\mathbf{v} = \mathbf{V} \qquad (12)$$

where $\mathbf{R_{L2}} = [R_{L2}, 0, 0]^T$ with R_{L2} that is the distance between L2 point and the center of Earth; $\mathbf{R_m} = [R_m, 0, 0]^T$ and R_m that is the distance between the center of the Moon and the center of the Earth; when $\mu_E / \mu_M = 81.3006559788989$, the λ equals to 1.1678326832682341647 which is the same as Farquhar[1] and Nicholson[6]'s results. λ is always a constant and the computation of which is presented in Appendix A.

Initial Conditions

To initialize the designing process, a reference trajectory is required. For "initial guess" trajectories, we use a halo orbit from the circular R3BP which is rotated and scaled to fit the proposed model. The initial conditions from third-order solutions in the circular R3BP are used as an initial approximate solution here.

The following analysis follows the Lindstedt-Poincare technique and the work of Richardson [23]. The process of designing a lunar halo orbit includes three steps:

Step 1: Simplifying the proposed model into the circular R3BP form, which is as shown in Eq. (10). Then translate the origin of Eq. (10) into the L2 point. The distance from the L2 point to the center of the Earth is calculated under the circular R3BP model.

A simplified model in the LRC is as follows:

$$\begin{cases} \ddot{\tilde{x}} = 2\omega_z \dot{\tilde{y}} + \omega_z^2 \tilde{x} - \mu_E (\dfrac{\tilde{x}-\tilde{x}_E}{r_{PE}^3} + \dfrac{\tilde{x}_E}{r_{LE}^3}) - \mu_M (\dfrac{\tilde{x}-\tilde{x}_M}{r_{PM}^3} + \dfrac{\tilde{x}_M}{r_{LM}^3}) \\[2mm] \ddot{\tilde{y}} = -2\omega_z \dot{\tilde{x}} + \omega_z^2 \tilde{y} - \mu_E (\dfrac{\tilde{y}-\tilde{y}_E}{r_{PE}^3} + \dfrac{\tilde{y}_E}{r_{LE}^3}) - \mu_M (\dfrac{\tilde{y}-\tilde{y}_M}{r_{PM}^3} + \dfrac{\tilde{y}_M}{r_{LM}^3}) \\[2mm] \ddot{\tilde{z}} = -\mu_E (\dfrac{\tilde{z}-\tilde{z}_E}{r_{PE}^3} + \dfrac{\tilde{z}_E}{r_{LE}^3}) - \mu_M (\dfrac{\tilde{z}-\tilde{z}_M}{r_{PM}^3} + \dfrac{\tilde{z}_M}{r_{LM}^3}) \end{cases} \tag{13}$$

Step 2: Normalization of the simplified model.

Firstly, we consider the distance between the Moon and the Earth as a unit distance, and use the non-dimensional mass and time units. Then, we consider the distance between the Moon and the L2 point as a unit distance. Finally, we expand it and keep the terms up to the third order. Eq.(13) becomes Eq. (14), which will be used later.

$$\begin{cases} \xi'' - 2\eta' - \xi = 2c_2\xi + \dfrac{3}{2}c_3(2\xi^2 - \eta^2 - \zeta^2) + 2c_4(3\xi^2 - 3\eta^2 - 3\zeta^2)\xi \\[2mm] \eta'' + 2\xi' - \eta = -c_2\eta - 3c_3\xi\eta - \dfrac{3}{2}c_4(4\xi^2 - \eta^2 - \zeta^2)\eta \\[2mm] \zeta'' = -c_2\zeta - 3c_3\xi\zeta - \dfrac{3}{2}c_4(4\xi^2 - \eta^2 - \zeta^2)\zeta \end{cases} \tag{14}$$

where,

$$\xi = \frac{\tilde{\xi}}{\tilde{\rho}_{ml}}, \eta = \frac{\tilde{\eta}}{\tilde{\rho}_{ml}}, \zeta = \frac{\tilde{\zeta}}{\tilde{\rho}_{ml}}$$

$$\tilde{\xi} = \frac{\tilde{x}}{l}, \tilde{\eta} = \frac{\tilde{y}}{l}, \tilde{\zeta} = \frac{\tilde{z}}{l}, \tilde{\rho}_{pm} = \frac{r_{PM}}{l}, \tilde{\rho}_{pe} = \frac{r_{PE}}{l}, \tilde{\rho}_{ml} = \frac{|\tilde{x}_M|}{l}, \tilde{\rho}_{el} = \frac{|\tilde{x}_E|}{l}$$

$$c_l = \frac{1-\mu}{\tilde{\rho}_{ml}^3} \cdot (-1)^l (\frac{\tilde{\rho}_{ml}}{\tilde{\rho}_{el}})^{l+1} + (-1)^l \frac{\mu}{\tilde{\rho}_{ml}^3} = (-1)^l \left[\frac{(1-\mu)\tilde{\rho}_{ml}^{l-2}}{\tilde{\rho}_{el}^{l+1}} + \frac{\mu}{\tilde{\rho}_{ml}^3} \right]$$

$$\mu = \frac{m_m}{m_m + m_e}, \tau = \omega t, (\dot{x}) = \frac{dx}{dt} = \omega \frac{dx}{d\tau} = (x)'$$

Step 3: Calculation of the initial conditions by Lindstedt-Poincare Technique.

Generally speaking, it is a formidable task to derive an analytic solution to the differential equations Eq. (14). However, perturbation theory[23] and the Lindstedt-Poincare technique offer a way to generate approximate initial values, which can be further used in the adjustment procedure to obtain periodic orbits. By following the Lindstedt-Poincare technique and D. L. Richardson's work, we can obtain the third order approximation to the solution of Eq. (15):

$$
\begin{cases}
\overset{*}{\xi}(\tau) = c_\xi^{20} A_\xi{}^2 + c_\xi^{21} A_\zeta{}^2 - A_\xi \cos(\omega_{\xi\eta} \overset{*}{\tau} + \phi_1) + (c_\xi^{22} A_\xi{}^2 - c_\xi^{23} A_\zeta{}^2)\cos(2\omega_{\xi\eta} \overset{*}{\tau} + 2\phi_1) \\
\qquad + (c_\xi^{30} A_\xi{}^3 - c_\xi^{31} A_\xi A_\zeta{}^2)\cos(3\omega_{\xi\eta} \overset{*}{\tau} + 3\phi_1) \\
\overset{*}{\eta}(\tau) = kA_\xi \sin(\omega_{\xi\eta} \overset{*}{\tau} + \phi_1) + (c_\eta^{20} A_\xi{}^2 - c_\eta^{21} A_\zeta{}^2)\sin(2\omega_{\xi\eta} \overset{*}{\tau} + 2\phi_1) \\
\qquad + (c_\eta^{30} A_\xi{}^3 - c_\eta^{31} A_\xi A_\zeta{}^2)\sin(3\omega_{\xi\eta} \overset{*}{\tau} + 3\phi_1) + (c_\eta^{32} A_\xi{}^3 - (c_\eta^{33} - c_\eta^{34})A_\xi A_\zeta{}^2)\sin(\omega_{\xi\eta} \overset{*}{\tau} + \phi_1) \\
\overset{*}{\zeta}(\tau) = (2-n)[A_\zeta \cos(\omega_{\xi\eta} \overset{*}{\tau} + \phi_1) + c_\zeta^{20} A_\xi A_\zeta \cos(2\omega_{\xi\eta} \overset{*}{\tau} + 2\phi_1 - 3) \\
\qquad + (c_\zeta^{31} A_\xi{}^2 A_\zeta - c_\zeta^{30} A_\zeta{}^3)\cos(3\omega_{\xi\eta} \overset{*}{\tau} + 3\phi_1)]
\end{cases}
\tag{15}
$$

Where c_ξ^{ij}, c_η^{ij}, c_ζ^{ij}, are constants as given in Appendix C and A_ζ A_ξ ϕ_1 $\omega_{\xi\eta}$ are the parameters for this equation.

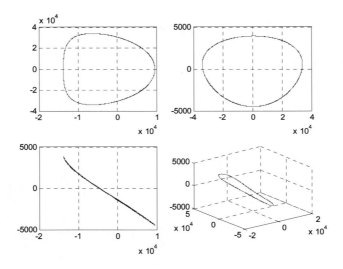

Figure 3. Nominal Halo Orbit.

The first guesses r_0, v_0 of the initial conditions for the lunar L2 halo orbit obtained by setting $\tau* = 0$ are sufficiently close to the exact initial conditions under circular R3BP. By taking $A_z = 5000km$ ($A_\zeta = 0.061837$), $n = 1$ and changing $\tau*$ in Eq.(15), we can find the periodic halo orbit shown in Figure 3.

Adjustment for initial conditions with the proposed model

In the circular R3BP model, adjustment for the initial condition is easy to accomplish by using the differential correction process with the stopping criterion that the trajectory of the probe crosses the xz-plane perpendicularly, i.e., $v_x = 0$ and $v_z = 0$ at the xz-plane. When it comes to our proposed model which considers the Sun's influence, the halo orbit may not exist, and therefore the original stopping criterion is not appropriate. If we want to use the same method to modify the initial conditions r_0, v_0, we need to find another appropriate stopping criterion. What affects the stopping criterion mostly is the Sun's influence.

From Eq. (8), we can find that the influence of the Sun is determined by its position vector r_S and its gravitational constant μ_S. Given a specific time, the position vector of the Sun is determined by the standard ephemerides, for example, at 12:00:00 pm on Oct. 1st 2012, $r_S = \begin{bmatrix} -1.480206243571720 \times 10^8, -2.082346072056160e \times 10^7, -9.026737751424652 \times 10^6 \end{bmatrix}^T$ km in the J2000. However, how much the Sun's influence affects the Sun-Earth-Moon-satellite system is determined by its gravitational constant μ_S. And the Sun's gravitational constant is the one we can artificially assign to be lower than the real μ_S. Therefore, we propose an iteration method which introduces the Sun's influence gradually[20]. The steps of our proposed numerical iteration method are given below.

Step 1: We assume that the artificially assigned Sun's constant of gravitation μ_S' is zero. Accordingly, the proposed model is actually an elliptical R3BP model. A differential correction process is used to slightly modify the first guess of the initial conditions r_0, v_0. We record the new initial solution denoted by r_1, v_1 and the new v_{x1} and v_{z1} at the xz-plane which will be used as the initial state and the final state respectively for the next iteration of differential correction.

Step 2: We slightly increase the assumed value of μ_S'. Taking r_1, v_1 and v_{x1}, v_{z1} as the initial and final states, we repeat the differential correction process to obtain the new initial condition r_2, v_2 and new final condition v_{x2}, v_{z2}.

Step 3: We repeat Step 2 until μ_S' reaches the real μ_S. The newest initial conditions are denoted by r_n, v_n.

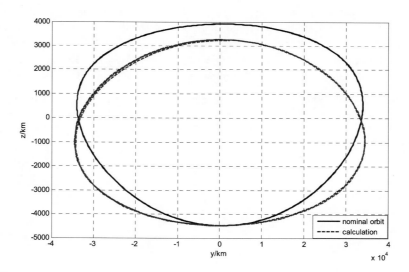

Figure 4. Simulation Result when artificially assigned μ_S' equals zero.

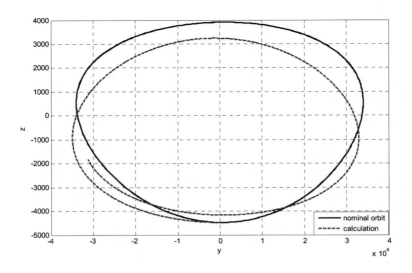

Figure 5. Simulation result when μ_S' equals to the real μ_S.

Simulation with STK

One way to compare the accuracy of those sets of initial conditions from the R3BP model and our proposed model is to numerically integrate them using STK for the same time period. Of these two sets of initial conditions, the one which can make the probe move around L2 for a longer time is more accurate.

The simulation results are shown in Figure 6 and Figure 7. The blue point labeled EM_L2 is the translunar Lagrangian point L2 in the Sun-Earth-Moon-satellite system. The trajectory labeled L2_proposed is generated by integrating our dynamic equations with the initial conditions r_n, v_n obtained from the proposed model, and the trajectory denoted by L2_R3BP is generated by integrating our dynamic equations with the initial conditions r_0, v_0 obtained from the R3BP model.

The simulation results show that if we use the result obtained from the R3BP as the initial conditions of the probe, its orbit will diverge very quickly. However, when using the initial conditions obtained from the proposed model, the probe will maintain a quasi-periodic orbit for about three periods before it diverges.

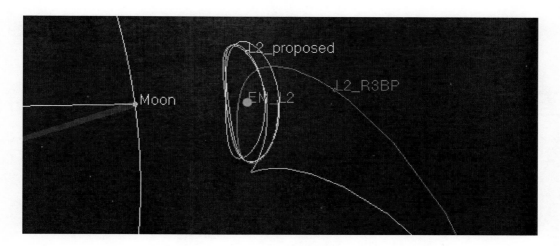

Figure 6. Orbits generated by STK using different initial conditions obtained from the R3BP and the proposed model (viewed from the X-Z Plane).

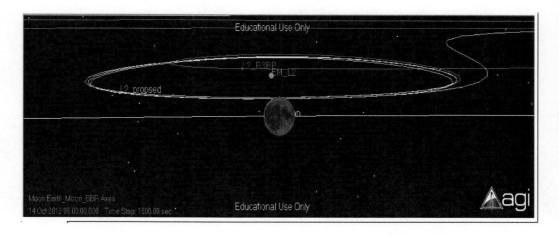

Figure 7. Orbits generated by STK using different initial conditions obtained from the R3BP and the proposed model (viewed from the Y-Z Plane).

CONCLUSIONS

The contributions of this paper can be summarized as follows:

a) A new dynamic model for lunar probe for lunar probe with the standard ephemerides has been derived and it has been shown that the proposed model is more precise. Compared with other high-order models, the complexity of the proposed model is lower. More specifically, the proposed model takes the influence of direct solar perturbation, indirect solar perturbation and the eccentricity of the Moon's orbit into account.

b) The derivation of the proposed model shows that the model presented in this paper is a more general model which has the circular and elliptical R3BP models as special cases.

c) The lunar L2 quasi-periodic orbit design has been taken as an example to investigate the performance. The orbit design procedure of designing shows that the proposed model is convenient for applications about the Lagrangian points and can provide more accurate initial condition results.

d) Although this paper has only been concerned with orbits around the translunar libration point, the types of solutions obtained herein are quite general. And thus, proposed model also can be used to find a continuous libration trajectory using numerical methods.

NOTATION

ω	angular velocity of the geocentric rotating coordinate
r_S, r_M	the Sun's position vector and the Moon's position vector relative to the center of the Earth in the J2000 inertial coordinate , respectively;
r_{MS}	the position vector from the Sun to the Moon in the J2000; $r_{MS} = \|r_{MS}\|$
μ_E	the gravitational constant for the Earth
μ_M	the gravitational constant for the Moon
μ_S	the gravitational constant for the Sun
h_M	Moon's orbital angular momentum per unit mass
r_P	position vector from the center of mass of the Earth to lunar probe
$\dot{r}_P^b$, $\ddot{r}_P^b$	relative speed and relative acceleration in the geocentric rotating coordinate system
a_M	the average semi-major axis of lunar orbit
e_M	the average eccentricity of lunar orbit
θ_M	the true anomaly of lunar orbit
l	the distance between the Earth and the Moon
$\tilde{x}_M, \tilde{y}_M, \tilde{z}_M$	the Moon's vector in the L2 point rotating coordinate
$\tilde{x}_E, \tilde{y}_E, \tilde{z}_E$	the Earth's vector in the L2 point rotating coordinate
r_{PE}, r_{PM}	the distance from the Earth to lunar probe and the distance from the Moon to lunar probe in L2 point rotating coordinate, respectively
r_{LE}, r_{LM}	the distance from the Earth to the L2 point and the distance from the Moon to the L2 point in the L2 point rotating coordinate, respectively
$\tilde{\xi}, \tilde{\eta}, \tilde{\zeta}$	the lunar probe vector in the non-dimensional coordinate when we consider the l as a unit distance
$\tilde{\rho}_{pm}$, $\tilde{\rho}_{pe}$	the distance from the Earth to lunar probe and the distance from the Moon to probe in the non-dimensional coordinate when we consider l as a unit distance

$$\tilde{\rho}_{ml}, \tilde{\rho}_{el} \quad \text{the distance from the Earth to the L2 point and the distance from the Moon to the L2 point}$$

$\tilde{\rho}_{ml}, \tilde{\rho}_{el}$ the distance from the Earth to the L2 point and the distance from the Moon to the L2 point in the non-dimensional coordinate when we consider l as a unit distance

ξ, η, ζ the lunar probe vector in the non-dimensional coordinate when we consider l and the distance between the Moon and the L2 point as unit distances.

ρ_{pm}, ρ_{pe} the distance from the Earth to lunar probe and the distance from the Moon to lunar probe in the non-dimensional coordinate when we consider l and the distance between the Moon and the L2 point as unit distances.

c_l Legendre Polynomials in the expanded equation.

$A_\zeta \ A_\xi \ \phi_1 \ \omega_{\xi\eta}$ Parameters in Eq. (15).

APPENDIX A: CALCULATION OF L2 POINT WITH RESTRICTED THREE-BODY PROBLEM MODEL

Assuming $\left[\bar{\lambda} r_m(t), 0, 0, \bar{\lambda} \dot{r}_m(t), 0, 0 \right]$ is one solution to the elliptical R3BP model Eq. (9). Then, we can have

$$\bar{\lambda} \ddot{r}_M = \omega_z^2 \bar{\lambda} r_M - \left(\frac{\mu_E}{r_P^3} + \frac{\mu_M}{r_{PM}^3} \right) \bar{\lambda} r_M + \left(\omega_z^2 - \frac{\mu_M}{r_M^3} \right) r_M \tag{A1}$$

Eq. (A2) is the dynamic model of the Moon in the GRC without considering the Sun's influence.

$$\ddot{r}_M = \omega_z^2 r_M - \frac{\mu_E + \mu_M}{r_M^3} r_M \tag{A2}$$

Therefore, the necessary condition for Eq. (A1) is as follow:

$$\mu_E + \mu_M - \frac{\mu_E}{|\bar{\lambda}|^3} + \left[\frac{1 - \bar{\lambda}}{\left| (1 - \bar{\lambda}) \right|^3} \right] \frac{\mu_M}{\bar{\lambda}} = 0 \tag{A3}$$

Eq. (A3) is uncorrelated with t but relevant to the μ_E / μ_M which is 81.3006559788989 here. By solving Eq. (A3), we can obtain the classic L_2 and the result is $\bar{\lambda} = 1.167832682341647$ which we call it as classical L_2 point, in other words, the position of L_2 point in the GRC is $\left[1.167832682341647 r_m(t), 0, 0, 1.167832682341647 \dot{r}_m(t), 0, 0 \right]$.

Particularly, in the R3BP model, $r_m(t)$ is a constant. Therefore, the L_2 point is constant.

APPENDIX B: CALCULATION OF L2 POINT WITH RESTRICTED THREE-BODY PROBLEM MODEL

We assume that Eq. (8) has initial conditions $[x(t_0), y(t_0), z(t_0), \dot{x}(t_0), \dot{y}(t_0), \dot{z}(t_0)]$ which equal to $[\delta r_m(t_0), 0, 0, \delta \dot{r}_m(t_0), 0, 0]$. With these initial conditions, Eq. (8) has solutions $[x, y, z, \dot{x}, \dot{y}, \dot{z}]$ and δ is a constant to be determined. If we have an appropriate initial λ', then the solution $P = [x, y, z]^T$ should be around the Lagrangian point $L_2 = [\delta r_m(t_0), 0, 0]^T$. With the influence of the Sun, in order to make sure that P will move around the L2 point, we need to minimize the function as follow:

$$J(\delta, t, \Delta t) = \int_{t_0}^{t_0 + \Delta t} (P - L)^T (P - L) d\tau + (P(\Delta t) - L(\Delta t))^T (P(\Delta t) - L(\Delta t)) \Delta t \qquad \text{(B1)}$$

Where λ' is relevant to both t and Δt. Generally, during a space mission, t and Δt are fixed. Therefore, we can give an iteration method while minimizing the $J(\lambda', t, \Delta t)$ as follow:

$$\delta_{i+1} = \delta_i - \frac{J(\delta_i, t, \Delta t)}{J(\delta_i + \Delta\delta, t, \Delta t) - J(\delta_i, t, \Delta t)} \Delta\delta \qquad (i = 1, 2, ...) \qquad \text{(B2)}$$

where $\Delta\delta$ is a tiny positive number and Δt is variable.

The derivative of Eq. (B1) is

$$\dot{J}(\delta, t, \Delta t) = 2(P(t) - L(t))^T (P(t) - L(t)) + 2(P(t) - L(t))^T (P(t) - L(t))t \qquad \text{(B3)}$$

Therefore, combing Eq. (B3) and Eq. (8), we can obtain a new system which can be integrated from t_0 to $t_0 + \Delta t$, and we also know $J(\lambda', t, 0) = 0$.

We set the initial time which is 12pm Oct. 1st 2012(GTM) in this paper and the time interval is 1 day. We can obtain $\delta = 1.16783259631133$.

APPENDIX C: PARAMETERS

$$\omega_\zeta = \sqrt{c_2}$$

$$\omega_{\xi\eta} = \sqrt{\frac{1}{2}(2 - c_2 + \sqrt{9c_2^2 - 8c_2})}$$

$$k = \frac{\omega_{\xi\eta}^2 + 1 + 2c_2}{2\omega_{\xi\eta}} = \frac{2\omega_{\xi\eta}}{\omega_{\xi\eta}^2 + 1 - c_2}$$

$$\chi_1 = 16\omega_{\xi\eta}^4 + 4\omega_{\xi\eta}^2(c_2 - 2) - 2c_2^2 + c_2 + 1$$

$$\chi_2 = 81\omega_{\xi\eta}^4 + 9\omega_{\xi\eta}^2(c_2 - 2) - 2c_2^2 + c_2 + 1$$

$$\chi_3 = 2\omega_{\xi\eta}[\omega_{\xi\eta}(1 + k^2) - 2k]$$

$$c_\xi^{20} = \frac{3c_3(k^2 - 2)}{4(1 + 2c_2)}$$

$$c_\xi^{22} = -\frac{3\omega_{\xi\eta}c_3}{4k\chi_1}(3k^3\omega_{\xi\eta} - 6k(k - \omega_{\xi\eta}) + 4)$$

$$c_\eta^{20} = -\frac{3\omega_{\xi\eta}c_3}{2\chi_1}(3\omega_{\xi\eta}k - 4) \qquad\qquad c_\xi^{21} = \frac{3c_3}{4(1 + 2c_2)}$$

$$c_\xi^{23} = -\frac{3\omega_{\xi\eta}c_3}{4k\chi_1}(2 + 3\omega_{\xi\eta}k) \qquad\qquad c_\eta^{21} = \frac{3\omega_{\xi\eta}c_3}{\chi_1}$$

$$c_\zeta^{20} = -\frac{c_3}{2\omega_{\xi\eta}^2}$$

$$v_2^1 = \frac{1}{\chi_3}[\frac{3}{2}c_3(2c_\xi^{20}(k^2 - 2) - c_\xi^{22}(k^2 + 2) - 2kc_\eta^{20}) - \frac{3}{8}c_4(3k^4 - 8k^2 + 8)]$$

$$v_2^2 = \frac{1}{\chi_3}[\frac{3}{2}c_3(2c_\xi^{21}(k^2 - 2) + c_\xi^{23}(k^2 + 2) - 2kc_\eta^{21} + 5c_\zeta^{20}) + \frac{3}{8}c_4(12 - k^2)]$$

$$\nu_1 = 2\nu_2^1 \omega_{\xi\eta}^{\ 2} - \frac{3}{2} c_3 (2c_\xi^{20} + c_\xi^{22} + 5c_\zeta^{20}) - \frac{3}{8} c_4 (12 - k^2)$$

$$\nu_2 = 2\nu_2^2 \omega_{\xi\eta}^{\ 2} + \frac{3}{2} c_3 (c_\xi^{23} - 2c_\xi^{21}) + \frac{9}{8} c_4$$

$$\delta = \omega_{\xi\eta}^{\ 2} - c_2 = \omega_{\xi\eta}^{\ 2} - \omega_\zeta^{\ 2}$$

$$c_\xi^{30} = -\frac{9\omega_{\xi\eta}}{\chi_2} [c_3 (kc_\eta^{22} - c_\eta^{20}) + kc_4 (1 + \frac{1}{4} k^2)] + \frac{9\omega_{\xi\eta}^{\ 2} + 1 - c_2}{2\chi_2} [3c_3 (2c_\xi^{22} - kc_\eta^{20}) + c_4 (2 + 3k^2)]$$

$$c_\xi^{31} = -\frac{9\omega_{\xi\eta}}{4\chi_2} [4c_3 (kc_\xi^{23} - c_\eta^{21}) + kc_4] - \frac{3(9\omega_{\xi\eta}^{\ 2} + 1 - c_2)}{2\chi_2} [c_3 (kc_\eta^{21} + c_\zeta^{20} - 2c_\xi^{23}) - c_4]$$

$$c_\eta^{30} = \frac{1}{\chi_2} [3\omega_{\xi\eta} (3c_3 (kc_\eta^{20} - 2c_\xi^{22}) - c_4 (2 + 3k^2)) + (9\omega_{\xi\eta}^{\ 2} + 1 + 2c_2)(12c_3 (kc_\xi^{22} - c_\eta^{20}) + 3c_4 k (4 + k^2))/8)]$$

$$c_\eta^{31} = \frac{1}{\chi_2} [3\omega_{\xi\eta} (3c_3 (kc_\eta^{21} + c_\zeta^{20} - 2c_\xi^{23}) - 3c_4) + (9\omega_{\xi\eta}^{\ 2} + 1 + 2c_2)(12c_3 (kc_\xi^{23} - c_\eta^{21}) + 3c_4 k/8)]$$

$$c_\eta^{32} = -\frac{k}{16\omega_{\xi\eta}} [12c_3 (c_\eta^{20} - 2kc_\xi^{20} + kc_\xi^{22}) + 3c_4 k (3k^2 - 4) + 16\nu_2^1 \omega_{\xi\eta} (\omega_{\xi\eta} k - 1)]$$

$$c_\eta^{33} = \frac{k}{8\omega_{\xi\eta}} [12c_3 kc_\xi^{21} - 3c_4 k - 8\nu_2^2 \omega_{\xi\eta} (\omega_{\xi\eta} k - 1)]$$

$$c_\eta^{34} = -\frac{k}{16\omega_{\xi\eta}} [12c_3 (c_\eta^{21} + kc_\xi^{23}) + 3c_4 k]$$

$$c_\zeta^{30} = \frac{3}{64\omega_{\xi\eta}^{\ 2}} (4c_3 c_\xi^{23} + c_4)$$

$$c_\zeta^{31} = \frac{3}{64\omega_{\xi\eta}^{\ 2}} [4c_3 (c_\xi^{22} - c_\zeta^{20}) + c_4 (4 + k^2)] .$$

REFERENCES

1. R. W. Farquhar, "The Control and Use of Libration-Point Satellites", Ph.D. Dissertation, Department of Aeronautics and Astronautics, Stanford University, Stanford, CA, July 1968.
2. K.C. Howell and H.J. Pernicka, "Station Keeping Method for Libration Point Trajectories", *Journal of Guidance, Control, and Dynamics*, Vol. 16, No. 1, January-February 1993, pp. 151-159.
3. C. Sim, G. Gmez, J. Llibre, R. Martnez, and R. Rodrquez, "On the Optimal Station Keeping Control of Halo Orbits", *Acta Astronautica*, Vol. 15, No 6/7, 1987, pp.391-397.
4. G. Gmez, W.S. Koon, M.W. Lo, J.E. Marsden, J. Masdemont, and S.D. Ross, " Invariant Manifolds, the Spatial Three-body Problem and Space Mission Design", AAS 01-301.
5. W.S. Evans "Natural Environment near the Sun/Earth-Moon L2 Libration Point", Marshall Space Flight Center. Alabama
6. I. M. Ross, King, J. T. and F. Fahroo, "Designing Optimal Spacecraft Formations," Proceedings of the AIAA/AAS Astrodynamics Conference, AIAA-2002-4635, Monterey, CA, 5-8 August 2002.
7. G. W. Hill, "Researches in the Lunar Theory". *American Journal of Mathematics*, 1878(1): 129-147
8. E. Brown, *An Introductory Treatise on the Lunar Theory*. New York: Dover Publications, Inc., 1960
9. V. Szebehely, *Theory of Orbits: The Restricted Problem of Three Bodies*. New York: Academic Press, Inc., 1967
10. C. Conley, "Low energy transit orbits in the restricted three body problem". *SIAM Journal on Applied Mathematics*, 1968, 16(4): pp. 732-746
11. W.S. Koon, M. W. Lo and J. E. Marsden. "Low energy transfer to the Moon". *Celestial Mechanic*. 2001, 81(1): pp. 63-73
12. H. Baoyin and C.R. Mcinnes, "Solar Polar Orbiter: A Solar Sail Technology Reference Study". *Celestial Mechanics and Dynamical Astronomy*. 2006. 94(2): pp.155-171,

13. J. S. Parker and G. H. Born. Modeling A Low Energy Ballistic Lunar Transfer using Dynamical Systems Theory. *Journal of Spacecr Rockets*, 2008, 45(6): pp. 1269-1281

14. B. D. Tapley and J. M. Lewallen. "Solar Influence on Satellite Motion near the Stable Earth-Moon Libration Points." *AIAA Journal*, 1964, 2(4): pp. 728-732

15. H.B. Schechter, "Three-Dimensional Nonlinear Stability Analysis of the Sun-Perturbed Earth-Moon Equilateral Points". *AIAA Journal*, 1968, 6(7): 12231-228

16. F. T. Nicholson. "Effect of Solar Perturbation on Motion near the Collinear Earth-Moon Libration Points". *AIAA Journal*, 1967, 5(12): pp. 2237-2241

17. W. Jing and C. Gao. "Relative Dynamics Model of A Lunar Probe and its Application". *Scientia Sinica Phys, Mech & Astron*, 2010, 40(4), pp.462-470

18. R. W. Farquhar, "A Quasi-periodic orbit about the translunar libration". *Celestial Mechanic*, 1973, 7: pp.458-473

19. K. C. Howell, "A Numerical Determination of Lissajous Trajectories in the Restricted Three-body Problem"

20. K. C. Howell and D. B. Spencer. "Periodic Orbits in the Restricted Four-body Problem". *Acta Astronautica*, 1986, 13(8): pp.473-479.

21. L. Mohn and J. Kevorkian, "Some Limiting Cases of the Restricted Four-body Problem". *Astronomical Journal*, 1967, 72(8): pp. 959-963

22. M. Kim, "Lyapunov and Quasi-periodic Orbits about L2". AAS 01-324

23. D. L Richardson, "Analytic Construction of Periodic Orbits about the Collinear Points," *Celestial Mechanics*, Vol. 22, 1980, pp. 241-253.

24. H. Keric, W. Lo Martin and G. H. Born. "Liaison Navigation in the Sun-Earth-Moon Four-body Problem." Paper AAS 06-221, AAS/AIAA Astrodynamics Specialist Conference.

LUNAR-RESONANT TRAJECTORY DESIGN FOR THE INTERSTELLAR BOUNDARY EXPLORER (IBEX) EXTENDED MISSION

John Carrico Jr., [*] Donald Dichmann, [†] Lisa Policastri, [‡] John Carrico III, [§]
Timothy Craychee, [**] John Ferreira, [††] Marissa Intelisano, [‡‡] Ryan Lebois, [§§]
Mike Loucks, [***] Travis Schrift [†††] and Ryan Sherman [‡‡‡]

This paper describes the trajectory design and analysis performed to ensure the success of the IBEX extended mission. In order to minimize the radiation dose, improve science collection, and avoid long eclipses, the authors designed a transfer to a new orbit with a period of about 9.1 days, which yields a 3:1 resonance with the Moon's orbit. In June 2011, the IBEX flight team commanded IBEX to perform three maneuvers which successfully transferred IBEX to this new lunar-resonant orbit. This paper gives the details of the analysis, the trade-offs that were made, and the constraints that governed the operations.

INTRODUCTION

The Interstellar Boundary Explorer (IBEX)[1,2,3,4] successfully launched on October 19th, 2008. The trajectory design and operations for the nominal mission has been described previously[5,6,7,8,9]. IBEX's original cislunar orbit had an approximately eight-day period with a high eccentricity of about 0.9. This orbit was therefore greatly influenced by the gravitational effects of the Moon and the Sun, which caused radical variations in the altitude of each perigee and orbit inclination. Because of these perturbations, the orbit was very difficult to predict; previously presented work demonstrated that uncertainties in the orbit determination and modeling prevent accurate numerical integration of the trajectory much beyond 3.5 years.

The nominal IBEX mission lasted two years and was successfully completed in February 2011. For IBEX to continue into its extended mission some orbit changes were required to avoid violating altitude

---

[*] Principal Astrodynamics Specialist, Applied Defense Solutions, Inc., 8171 Maple Lawn Blvd. Suite 210, Fulton, MD 20759, JCarrico@AppliedDefense.com.
[†] Principal Engineering Specialist, Applied Defense Solutions Inc., DDichmann@AppliedDefense.com
[‡] Senior Aerospace Engineer, Applied Defense Solutions Inc., LPolicastri@AppliedDefense.com
[§] Engineer, Applied Defense Solutions Inc., JPCarrico@AppliedDefense.com
[**] Senior Aerospace Engineer, Applied Defense Solutions Inc., TCraychee@AppliedDefense.com
[††] Aerospace Engineer, Applied Defense Solutions Inc., JFerreira@AppliedDefense.com
[‡‡] Aerospace Engineer, Applied Defense Solutions Inc., MIntelisano@AppliedDefense.com
[§§] Aerospace Engineer, Applied Defense Solutions Inc., RLebois@AppliedDefense.com
[***] Principal Astrodynamics Scientist, Space Exploration Engineering Co., 687 Chinook Way, Friday Harbor, WA 98250, Loucks@see.com.
[†††] Aerospace Engineer, Applied Defense Solutions Inc., TSchrift@AppliedDefense.com
[‡‡‡] Aerospace Engineer, Applied Defense Solutions Inc., RSherman@AppliedDefense.com

and eclipse mission constraints. With limited remaining fuel, the maneuver magnitudes had to be minimized. In addition, the number of Orbit Maintenance Maneuvers had to be minimized because any orbit maneuvers interrupt science operations. The following sections describe how a new orbit was developed and analyzed for IBEX's extended mission phase. We also briefly describe the operations that we performed to place IBEX into this new orbit.

NOMINAL SCIENCE MISSION ORBIT

The primary mission orbit was the result of three post-launch orbit raising maneuvers[10] which ended in November, 2008. The resulting orbit shown in Figure 1 was used until June 2011, and was designed to be inertially fixed so that the 2-year nominal mission could collect statistics to create the map of the Interstellar Boundary. The Earth is in the center of the figure, the white circle is the Moon's orbit, and the teal line is in the direction of the helionose. (The helionose is the tip of the bow shock where the solar wind collides with the interstellar wind.) The orbit shown is the definitive orbit from orbit determination during the IBEX nominal mission.

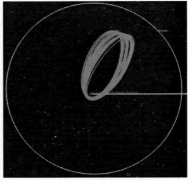

Figure 1. Nominal Trajectory in Geocentric Inertial Coordinate Frame

In Figure 2 an alternative view of this same nominal orbit reveals how the orbit plane changes due to the strong gravitational perturbations from the Moon.

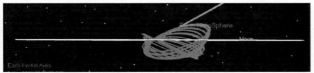

Figure 2. Nominal Trajectory in Geocentric Inertial Coordinate Frame (Edge on to Lunar Plane)

By portraying the same orbit in the Earth-Moon Rotating coordinate frame—where the line between the Earth and Moon is held fixed and is used as one of the axes—the proximity of the apogees relative to the Moon can be clearly seen, as shown in Figure 3. (Note the white line between the Earth in the center and the Moon at the top.) For reference, Figure 4 shows the same orbit in the Earth-Sun Rotating coordinate frame. The yellow radial line on the left half of the figure is drawn between the Earth in the center of the figure and the Sun (not in the picture). A projection of the Earth's shadow is visible on the right half of the figure, opposite the Earth-Sun line.

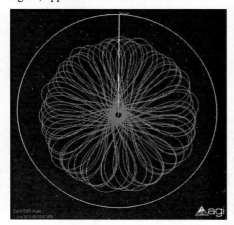

Figure 3. Nominal Trajectory in Earth-Moon Rotating Coordinate Frame

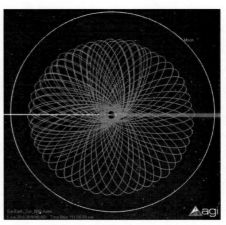

Figure 4. Nominal Trajectory in Earth-Sun Rotating Coordinate Frame

Due to the strong and repeated perturbations from the Moon's gravity, the nominal mission trajectory was unpredictable in the long term. Figure 5 shows the perigee radius history resulting from Monte Carlo simulation of the primary orbit. The orbit has a time window of predictability of about 2.5 years from Jun 2010 to Mar 2013, after which the various perigee radius values diverge. Although this lack of long-term predictability was fine for the nominal mission, it made it impossible to predict the ΔV—and therefore the fuel—needed for future station-keeping. The inability to predict the orbit also prohibited the prediction of mission-ending eclipses and low altitudes beyond about 2.5 years, which made an estimate of the spacecraft lifetime impossible, and hindered planning efforts for an extended mission.

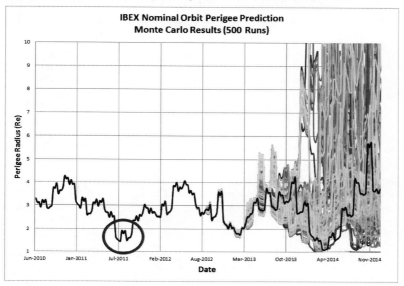

Figure 5. Monte Carlo simulation results: Perigee radius prediction showing low perigees in the red circle and demonstrating the inability to predict orbit evolution beyond 2.5 years.

ORBIT CONSIDERATIONS FOR EXTENDED MISSION

In choosing an extended mission orbit, various operational requirements and design guidelines influenced which types of orbits were considered and, eventually, which of the many feasible orbits were downselected to the final decision. Along with the improved stability over the current orbit, the new orbit meets the requirements and guidelines described below.

Limit eclipse durations. Due to spacecraft power limitations it is required that the satellite is not subjected to any eclipse over four hours in duration (calculated as a proxy for power as 30% penumbra duration + umbra duration). This condition was only a requirement for the first ten years of the extended mission, though it was desirable for the entire mission. This was the driving requirement for changing the orbit because the spacecraft was going to experience a 5-hour eclipse in 2012 and an 8-hour eclipse in 2013.

Minimize radiation dose. In order to minimize the satellite's exposure to radiation in the Van Allen radiation belts, the design guideline was that the orbit perigee radius should be above 2.3 Earth Radii (Re) from the center of the Earth, and the higher the better. Several low perigees that would occur in July, 2011 are shown circled in red in Figure 5.

Point apogee toward helionose. For improved science data, the design guidelines stated that vector from the Earth towards apogee should rotate clockwise (as seen looking down on the Earth from above the Earth's north pole). This would allow IBEX to collect more science observations in area of the sky map that the nominal mission wasn't able to observe well. (Since the nominal mission orbit was inertially fixed the Earth blocked a lot of the same region of the sky during the 2-year mission.)

Maximize science collection time. The design guidelines called for maximizing the time at apogee to improve science data by giving more time to observe each region of the sky, while still meeting spacecraft-ground communication requirements. The higher the apogee the more time the spacecraft spends at apogee.

Maintain communications. Maintain communications during Orbit Maintenance Maneuvers near apogee, and maintain sufficient communications to downlink science data near perigee throughout the extended mission.

OPERATIONAL CONSTRAINTS THAT AFFECTED ORBIT SELECTION

There were operational constraints that also affected the selection of the final orbit since they put limitations on the types of orbit transfers that could be performed. Several of these are described below.

Minimize the number of times IBEX needs to be repointed and spun-up. IBEX is a spin-stabilized spacecraft usually spinning at 4 revolutions per minute (rpm) during science mode. The orbit maneuvers, however, must be executed at 22 rpm for attitude stability. The process to align the engines with the thrust axis requires a repointing attitude maneuver, then a spin-up to 22 rpm. After the maneuver(s) a spin-down back to 4 rpm is needed and then a repoint back towards the Sun is performed. In addition to the fact that the spin-change and re-pointing maneuvers use fuel, there are operational costs and risks performing these non-nominal activities. Therefore the number of maneuvers to transfer to the extended mission orbit was kept to a minimum. It is less risky, however, if several maneuvers are performed in the same thrust direction, which yielded some more options.

Minimize fuel use. IBEX had about 16.3 kg of fuel remaining at the end of the nominal mission. We, along with other members of the flight team, decided to allocate about 10 kg for the maneuvers to transfer to the new orbit, which was the equivalent of about 260 m/s of ΔV. The remaining usable fuel would be saved for the spin-change maneuvers and repointing the spacecraft for the orbit maneuvers as well as for the routine attitude precession maneuvers needed each orbit when collecting science observations.

600-second maximum maneuver duration. The original specification of the engines limited the duration of any single maneuver to 600 seconds. Although this was not a hard limit, and investigation showed that the spacecraft could survive a longer maneuver, there was less risk to the spacecraft if the maneuvers were never longer than the specification. (During the initial orbit raising after launch the longest maneuver was 600 seconds in duration.)

Spin axis-to-Sun angle limits. Since the solar arrays reside on the +z face of the spacecraft, the spin axis vector (along the +z axis) is required to be within 45 degrees of the sun at the time of each apogee maneuver to maintain sufficient power. During maneuvers, thrust is along the spin axis. However, to avoid large maneuver inefficiencies, the maneuvers needed to be performed with the spin-axis near the orbit inertial velocity vector at the time of the maneuver(s). Because of the desire to minimize the number of times IBEX would need to be spun-up, this sun angle limitation had to apply over the entire time the spacecraft was at 22 rpm.

ORBIT SELECTION TRADE STUDY

At first we explored a wide variety of missions that might meet the requirements and constraints. We looked at Earth-Moon libration point orbits, lunar orbits, and some that were outside the Moon's orbit. We investigated using strong lunar gravity assists to dramatically change the orbit. It became evident that the communication limitations would require that the perigee radius be no greater than about 15 to 20 Re. We then started looking at a variety of cislunar orbits. Based on some pre-launch analysis and subsequent investigation we recognized that an orbit resonant with the Moon allows the apogee to be kept away from the Moon, stabilizing the orbit and reducing the propellant required to maintain the orbit.

Orbit resonance plays an essential role in the dynamics of the solar system: the planets, moons and asteroids[11]. For example, the Lagrange points are in 1:1 resonance with the primary bodies. Moreover, in our solar system, the L4 and L5 points are stable in the Circular Restricted 3-Body Problem. Several studies has exploited resonance in the Earth-Mars and Earth-Moon "cycler" trajectories[12,13].

In 1963 the satellite IMP-A (NSSDC ID: 1963-046A [*], also known as "Explorer 18" and "IMP 1") was placed into a 4,395 km perigee by 192,003 km apogee orbit; the orbit period was 5,606 minutes, which is about a 7:1 resonance with the lunar orbit. Some missions have used lunar resonant orbits for short time spans[14,15,16] mainly to phase with the Moon to achieve a desired gravity assist geometry. A. Kogan proposed using a 2:1 orbit with the apogees aligned directly on the Earth-Moon line for the Regatta-D mission[17]. The perigee radius of the Regatta-D orbit was designed to be 22.5 Re so that the apogee radius was inside the Moon's orbit, about 50 to 53 Re. At the time of this writing we have not found any satellite mission that has used or proposed the 3:1 resonant orbit to achieve long-term stability. We would be very interested in any information on this that the reader may have.

Using a resonant orbit for IBEX made the orbit easier to predict for a longer time. The simplest resonances to achieve from the nominal orbit with the limited ΔV allocation were near 2:1 and 3:1. One of the 2:1 resonant orbits considered is shown in Figure 6, and a 3:1 is shown in Figure 7. These are shown in the Earth-Moon rotating frame which has the Earth at the center and the Moon at the top.

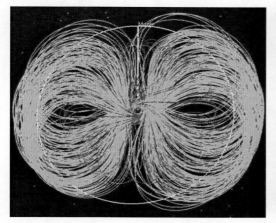

Figure 6. Orbit with 2:1 resonance with lunar orbit. The nominal apogee location is 90 deg away from the Earth-Moon line, in the vertical direction.

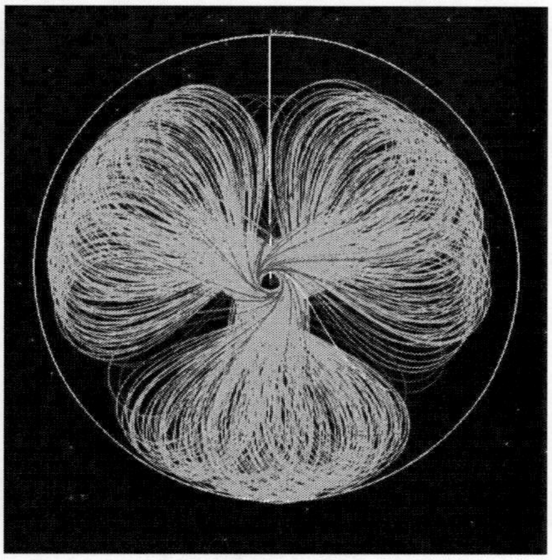

Figure 7. Orbit with 3:1 resonance with lunar orbit

While the 2:1 resonant orbit would meet mission requirements, the 3:1 resonant orbit was preferable for a few reasons. First, apogee radius for the 3:1 orbit is much lower, allowing for communications at apogee. In addition, while the higher apogee of the 2:1 orbit seemed better for science, modeling by the mission scientists of the expected science from a 2:1 orbit did not yield significantly better statistics than the 3:1. Furthermore, to transfer to the 2:1 orbit also required more ΔV than to the 3:1 orbit, and the 2:1 orbit was harder to target. These were the main reasons the team settled on the 3:1 orbit.

Another consideration was the selection of a 3:1 orbit that achieved the desired apsidal rotation to move apogee in the direction of the helionose. Studies showed that the apsidal rate did not depend significantly on the Sun perturbation or the Earth's non-spherical gravity field. It was shown that the apsidal rate depended strongly on the perigee radius, as shown in Figure 8 and Figure 9. It was also shown that a comparable orbit in the Circular Restricted 3-Body Problem exhibited similar qualitative behavior, although with

---

[*] National Space Science Data Center, http://nssdc.gsfc.nasa.gov/nmc/spacecraftDisplay.do?id=1963-046A, captured July, 2011

only about half the apsidal rate values seen in Figure 9. From this figure it was decided that an initial perigee radius of at least 7 Re would achieve this science goal.

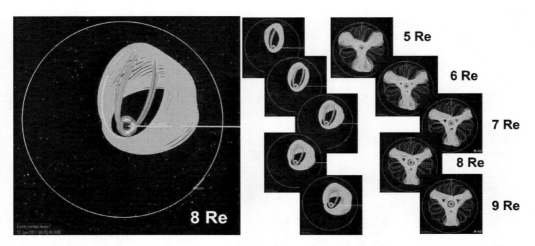

Figure 8. Rotation of the Line of Apsides as a Function of Perigee Radius Shown in Inertial and Earth-Moon Rotating Frames.

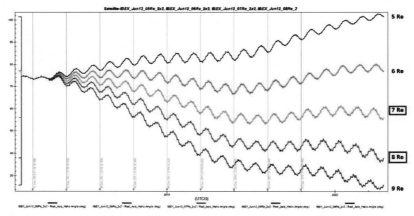

Figure 9. The Angle between the Apogee and the Helionose as a Function of Perigee Radius. The orbits with perigee radius in the range 7 to 8 Re yielded the desired angle and produced the best overall performance.

The perigee radius histories from several 3:1 orbits are shown in Figure 10 with initial perigee radii ranging from 7.0 to 8.0 Re in 0.1 Re steps. The x-axis is time and starts before the maneuvers in June and goes for 10 years. The y-axis is the radius of perigee and goes from about 2 Re to almost 15 Re. The perigee radius after the transfer to the new orbit stays well above the 2 Re limit yielding acceptable radiation levels, but as the insert shows, some of the perigees would dip below the geostationary orbit radius early in the extended mission. Staying above the geostationary orbit belt (geobelt) saves a lot of conjunction assessment and possible collision avoidance work in operations since the geobelt is so crowded with other spacecraft. Therefore trajectories with an initial orbit radius above about 7.3 Re were preferred.

While it was determined that a near 3:1 resonant orbit best met the extended mission requirements, that still left a range of periods near 9.1 days from which to choose. It turned out that a driver of the choice of orbit period was the limit on eclipse durations. It was a significant challenge to develop a way to assess whether the eclipse constraint would be satisfied for a range of periods over the first ten years of the extended mission duration.

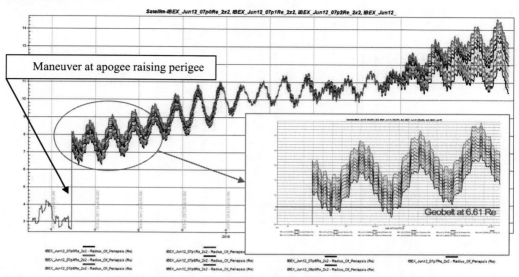

Figure 10. 10-Year Perigee Radius Evolution as a Function of Initial Perigee Radius (from 7.0 Re to 8.0 Re), with Zoomed-in View Showing First Few Years Compared to Geobelt.

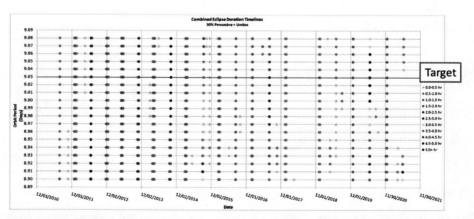

Figure 11. Eclipse Duration Predictions as a Function of Target Orbit Period. The color of each circle indicated the maximum eclipse duration for an orbit with the period on the vertical axis, during the year indicated on the horizontal axis. The significance of each color is shown in the legend on the right side of the plot; green is less than 3 hours, yellow between 3 and 3.5, orange between 3.5 and 4, and red over 4 hours.

Ultimately a very effective graphical technique was developed, shown in Figure 11. In this plot the vertical axis shows the orbit period, the horizontal axis indicates the year, and the color of the circle at each grid point indicates the maximum eclipse duration encountered during that year. By scanning the circles across the horizontal line for a given period, one can quickly determine how well the constraint is met.

These plots became the center of decision making for both analysis and operations; they proved to be an effective communication and collaborative tool for choosing a strategy. For some of the early orbits in the trade study there wasn't a single orbit period that had less than four hour eclipse durations for 10 years into the future. Using these plots we were able to design a series of maneuvers, every few years, to work around the long eclipses. Based on the analysis of Figure 11, the team selected an initial orbit period of 9.03 days.

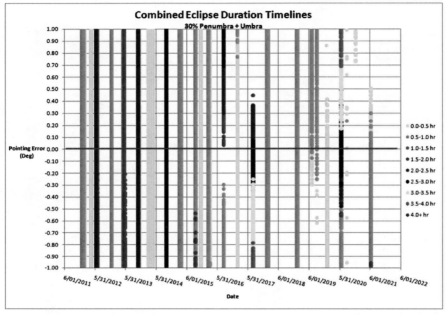

Figure 12. Eclipse Plot showing Monte Carlo Results. The simulation results were sorted in increasing order of pointing error, and plotted with date on the x axis and pointing error on the y axis.

This same graphical approach was adapted in Figure 12, to analyze the effect of thruster pointing error during the orbit maneuvers on resulting eclipse durations. A Monte Carlo simulation was performed varying the initial state based on the 6x6 orbit state error covariance, ΔV magnitude and pointing error. The eclipse durations were then sorted in order of increasing pointing error, as shown in Figure 12. This demonstrated that, for this orbit, we could predict the duration of eclipses after seven years to about one minute, and after ten years to less than thirty-five minutes. By sorting the Monte Carlo simulation results we also discovered the need for a tight pointing tolerance on the thrust vector. Figure 12 shows that if the pointing error could be controlled within about 0.15 degrees then eclipses greater than three hours could be avoided for at least ten years.

MANEUVER SEQUENCE TRADE STUDY

To achieve the chosen orbit, it was important to select a maneuver sequence that allowed for adequate orbit determination between maneuvers to calibrate the achieved thrust. As mentioned above, prior to the first maneuver it would be necessary to spin up the spacecraft from 4 rpm used for science collection to 22 rpm for stable pointing during maneuvers. Following the maneuvers, spin down would be performed to return to the 4 rpm rate. Several possible maneuver sequences were considered.

The first issue is the number of maneuvers. It would be possible to plan a single maneuver at perigee to change the orbit period. This would be the most fuel efficient way to change the orbit period, however it would not raise perigee, causing the spacecraft to continue to receive high radiation doses. To achieve both a desired orbit period and perigee radius a two-maneuver sequence could be performed: a maneuver at apogee to raise perigee, and then a maneuver at perigee to achieve the desired orbit period. However, that plan would require several orbit revolutions after the first maneuver to obtain adequate orbit determination to plan the next maneuver at perigee. If the perigee maneuver were performed first followed by an apogee maneuver, then the two maneuvers need to be planned together in a "2-by-2" targeting problem to achieve both goals of orbit period and perigee radius simultaneously. This was possible but made the operations planning complex, especially to recover from a non-nominal maneuver.

In addition, due to the requirement that IBEX maintain an inertially fixed pointing throughout all of the maneuvers, a perigee maneuver in addition to the apogee maneuver would require the use of IBEX's opposite 22N thruster. Since neither engine had been fired in over two years, there is added operational risk associated with using both thrusters as opposed to just one, and any calibration information gained off of the first maneuver would not reduce uncertainty in the second maneuver.

We eventually found it was possible to perform a single maneuver at apogee to achieve a new orbit that met mission requirements, as long as the perigee radius was raised enough to get the orbit period near 9.1 days. The perigee radius required to achieve this period turned out to be slightly higher than 8 Re, which was higher than needed to get above the geobelt and to rotate the line of apsides towards the helionose. It was decided that the small amount of extra ΔV to achieve a higher radius of perigee by maneuvering only at apogee was worth the simplification of operations that resulted from avoiding a perigee maneuver.

The orbit finally selected for the extended mission is shown in Figure 13 in an inertial frame and in Figure 14 in the Earth-Moon Rotating frame.

 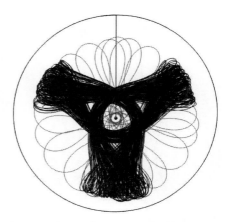

Figure 13. Nominal Mission (in Green) and Extended Mission (Blue) orbits shown in inertial space.

Figure 14. Extended mission orbit in the Earth-Moon rotating frame, with the Moon at the top of the plot.

In addition to the number of maneuvers, the timing of the maneuver was also important. To transfer from the nominal mission orbit to the 3:1 resonant orbit, the maneuver had to be performed at an apogee that was close to the desired orbit in the Earth-Moon frame. This meant the apogee had to be either 60 degrees in front of or behind the Earth-Moon line, or 180 degrees away (in opposition). The opportunity to transfer at a desired apogee happens about once a month: The line of apsides takes about four or five orbits to rotate 120 degrees in the Earth-Moon frame, and the orbit period is between seven and eight days. However, the constraint on the angle between the Sun and the spin axis meant that inertial velocity vector at the maneuver apogee had to be less than 45 degrees from the Sun. (Because IBEX has a thruster on both sides of the spacecraft the Sun could also have been near the anti-velocity direction.) The apogees with viable velocity vector directions can be seen at the top and bottom of Figure 4, where the tangents at apogee are nearly parallel with the Earth-Sun line. These two constraints on the apogee— at a specific orientation in the Earth-Moon geometry and the inertial velocity aligned towards the Sun—led to only a few maneuver opportunities before the low perigee in July 2011. In order to give ourselves and others in the flight team enough time to develop procedures and analyze the effects and impact of the new orbit on operations, the opportunity for the maneuvers in June 2011 was selected.

Even though the orbit transfer from the nominal mission orbit to the extended mission orbit could be accomplished in one maneuver, that maneuver would have to be close to 1800 seconds in duration. Since this was about three times the limit of a 600-second burn, the flight team decided to keep the risk low and perform three separate maneuvers. Using three maneuvers also gave the flight dynamics team an opportunity to calibrate the engine after the first maneuver before executing the rest of the ΔV. Since the engine that would be used to perform this maneuver had only been fired once right after launch, the desire to have tracking data for maneuver calibration after the first maneuver was added as a goal.

The flight team analyzed many possible transfer sequences ranging from all maneuvers at one apogee to each maneuver at its own apogee, and investigated backup and contingency plans for each possible sequence. The desire to calibrate the engine after the first maneuver led to the decision to put an orbit between the first and second maneuvers. The second and third maneuvers were performed at the same apogee to minimize the risk to the spacecraft due to the changing Sun angle: If trajectory correction maneuvers (TCMs) were needed at the following apogees, the spin vector-to-Sun angle would no longer satisfy the 45 degree constraint, since the Sun moves about a degree per day in the geocentric inertial frame. Placing two maneuvers at one apogee also yielded the benefit that science operations could resume sooner. Therefore the team decided to perform a sequence of three maneuvers, all at apogee, with the first maneuver at one apogee followed by two maneuvers near the next apogee, 8 days later, as indicated in Figure 15.

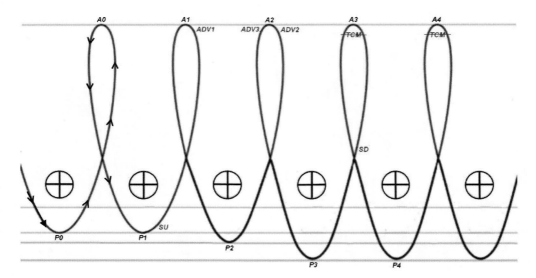

Figure 15. Schematic representation of the orbit maneuver transfer sequence, with alternate perigees and apogees drawn from left to right to denote their evolution in time. The spin-up (SU) to 22 rpm was performed near the first perigee (P1) of the sequence which was on 5 June 2011. The first apogee (A1) was on 9 June 2011; A2 on 17 June; and Spin-Down (SD) on 22 June. The first Apogee ΔV (ADV) maneuver occurred near A1 with the next two maneuvers at A2. Possible Trajectory Corrections Maneuvers (TCM) were to occur at A3 (26 June) or A4 (5 July), but were not needed.

ENGINE MODEL DEVELOPMENT

During IBEX early operations, the three orbit-raising maneuvers behaved differently than expected from the predictive model that gave engine thrust and specific impulse (I_{sp}) as polynomial functions of tank pressure. The IBEX Flight Dynamics Group developed a tool to fit polynomial coefficients to the available flight data based on the tank pressure drop from telemetry for each maneuver and the observed ΔV from orbit determination. In order to rectify the model with the observations the model had to include separate effects due to the propulsion system and the individual thrusters. However it was determined the data from the three maneuvers were not sufficient to obtain a good fit. Based on this analysis, the staff at Southwest Research Institute (SwRI) and the system engineers at Orbital Sciences performed a detailed engineering analysis of the engine and developed a set of tables of thrust and I_{sp} as a function of time from ignition for each maneuver. We used these successfully in maneuver planning and operations in June 2011.

There was also an issue that heaters on the spacecraft would come on, based on the measured temperature, to prevent the propellant from becoming too cold. The heating also caused the tank pressure to increase enough to significantly change thruster performance (by a few percent). However, an analysis of the telemetered pressure data did not show any regular pattern that would allow us to predict tank pressure 12 hours in advance in order to accurately plan a maneuver. Ultimately, the flight team decided that they could relax the settings of the control law for the heater to prevent the heater from coming on during an orbit maneuver, while still assuring that the propellant would not get too cold.

After the first maneuver, ADV1, we calibrated the engine and determined a thrust scale factor that was close to that observed during IBEX early operations. After this scale factor was applied, the second and third maneuvers performed within one percent of the plan. This precision enabled the flight team to waive off any subsequent TCMs and return to science collection more quickly by adopting an accelerated schedule.

Sensitivity to Maneuver Modeling Errors

The long term stability of the extended mission orbit was highly dependent on the ability of the maneuvers to achieve the desired orbit period. To determine how accurately the final orbit could be achieved, we performed a Monte Carlo analysis. It was necessary to consider uncertainty in the orbit state prior to the maneuver sequence along with the uncertainty in the maneuver execution. Since the thrust magnitude is a function of tank pressure, the uncertainty in the tank pressure had to be considered. This analysis used the original engine model of temperature and I_{sp} as a function of pressure. The key source of tank pressure uncertainty was the irregular pattern of heater activation. We decided to generate a probability distribution for the observed pressure values, and used this as a basis for random draws in the Monte Carlo simulation. The pressure modeling also accounted for the expected tank pressure drop after each Orbit Maintenance Maneuver, as well as the repointing maneuvers to be performed prior to the first maneuver. In addition to the Monte Carlo simulations, several "envelope" cases were simulated to model extreme but plausible cases. The two key performance parameters for this study were that the initial orbit period be within 0.01 days of 8.8 days (which was the target at the time of the study) and that the total propellant mass used, including spin up, spin down and repointing, be less than 10.3 kg. The results of the Monte Carlo simulation are summarized in Table 1 below. Some extreme cases did slightly exceed the design goal. It was decided that the performance would meet mission criteria when the new engine model became available.

Parameter	Envelope Minimum	Monte Carlo Minimum	Monte Carlo Maximum	Envelope Maximum	Total Spread	Monte Carlo Spread
Achieved orbit period (days)	8.7862	8.7973	8.8046	8.8128	0.02661	0.0073
Fuel Used (kg)		10.2655	10.3837			0.1182

Table 1. Results of Engine Sensitivity Monte Carlo and Envelope Simulations.

Plots of the orbit element evolution for the envelope cases showed remarkably little variation among the draws, demonstrating the stability of this orbit, and the robustness to the expected engine model uncertainties. For example, Figure 16 shows the evolution of the apogee radius over 10 years; the differences are just larger than the line width itself.

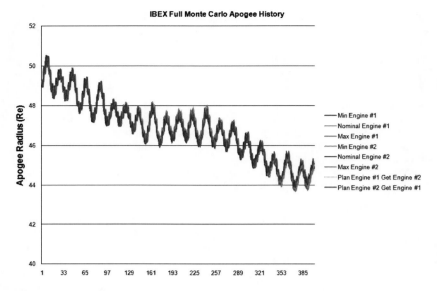

Figure 16. Evolution of apogee radius over time, for the envelope cases, where time is measured in number of orbit revolutions with average period 9.1 days. All cases show the same trend and nearly identical values.

COMMUNICATIONS

There were two key communications issues: the need for communications during the three Orbit Maintenance Maneuvers at apogee, and the need for communications during the extended mission. Communications analyses was performed using a high-fidelity link margin model, including antenna gain patterns, to determine whether there would be adequate link margin. An attitude model representative of the anticipated 10-year extended mission attitude plan was also used in order to accurately identify downlink opportunities. For the maneuvers at apogee, ground station coverage was required for real-time telemetry monitoring. Only the ground station at Hawaii was known to be able to close the link with the spacecraft at apogee at even the lowest data rate of 2 kilosymbols per second (ksps). For this reason, the times of the three maneuvers were chosen to ensure that the spacecraft would be in view of that station.

For extended mission operations the key concern is the ability to downlink science data. These contacts are performed around perigee, at a range of less than 25 Re, so any of the three ground stations can be used. A science data downlink requires adequate link margin for at least 45 minutes at 320 ksps or 90 minutes at 160 ksps. A perigee is considered to be missed if there is nowhere in the perigee region, from true anomaly 270 deg to 110 deg, with the required link margin and duration to downlink science data. Analysis showed that, for the entire 10 years of extended operations, none of the 402 perigees would be missed at a 160 ksps data rate for a minimum required link margin of 3 dB. For a data rate of 320 ksps, 29 of the 402 perigees would be missed; however, since science data can be downlinked at either the 320 ksps or the 160 ksps data rate, there is never an orbit without the opportunity to downlink the data.

STAR TRACKER OUTAGES

For attitude determination, IBEX uses a star tracker that is canted off the negative spin axis of the spacecraft. However, Due to regular repointing maneuvers to align the positive spin axis near the sun, there are periods when the star tracker experiences outages because it is pointed too near the Earth or Moon for a fraction of each rotation. During the primary mission, repointing maneuvers occurred once an orbit. In the extended mission, due to the longer orbit period, repointing occurs twice an orbit: once 10 hours before apogee, and once six hours before perigee near 280 deg true anomaly. These attitude maneuvers were modeled for 10 years of extended mission operations to determine the expected average and maximum star tracker outages in the extended mission orbit. Simulations show that during the first ten years of extended operations, the longest outage during which the star tracker is less than 100% valid lasts 8.1 days, while the average less than 100% valid outage duration is 1.62 days. These results are acceptable to the project when compared to the 1.58 day average outage experienced during the nominal science mission.

SUMMARY OF EXTENDED MISSION ORBIT

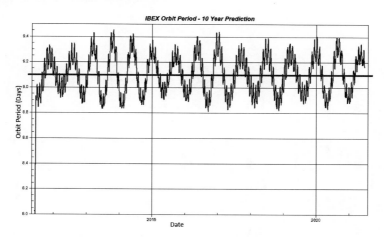

Figure 17. Keplerian orbit period evolution for the extended mission.

The transfer maneuver operations were completed in June 2011. Figure 13 and Figure 14 show the nominal mission orbit in green and the new extended mission orbit in blue. The maneuver calibration was successful and no TCMs were needed. The resulting orbit was nearly indistinguishable from the planned orbit. Figure 17 shows the predicted instantaneous orbit period predicted for the next ten years. The figure shows that the orbit period oscillates around the ideal 3:1 resonant orbit period of 9.1 days, shown with the blue line.

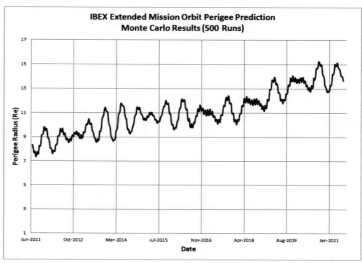

Figure 18. Evolution of perigee radius over time, for the envelope cases, as a function of time. All cases show the same trend and nearly identical values.

At the time of this writing, IBEX has gone through several orbits since the transfer maneuvers. Using the orbit state error covariance from orbit determination we ran a Monte Carlo simulation to verify that the orbit would evolve as predicted. The simulation also modeled the uncertainty in the magnitude of the re-pointing maneuvers which will occur twice an orbit. Figure 18 shows that the orbit seems very stable over a ten-year interval, especially as compared to the IBEX nominal science orbit as shown in Figure 5.

Figure 19 shows the eclipse duration results for the same Monte Carlo simulation, and demonstrates that there will be no eclipses longer than 3.5 hours for the next ten years, surpassing mission requirements.

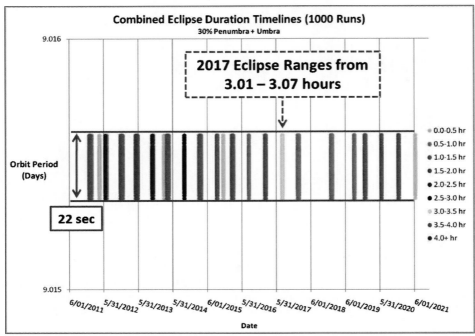

Figure 19. Eclipse history for the extended mission orbit. An analysis of orbit state uncertainty showed that the uncertainty in the resulting orbit period was 22 sec, well within the limits allowed to achieve maximum shadow duration of just over 3 hours.

DYNAMICAL SYSTEMS ANALYSIS

To better understand the remarkable stability of the new IBEX orbit, we decided to analyze the dynamics in the simpler setting of the Circular Restricted 3-Body Problem (CR3BP). The CR3BP, formulated in the frame rotating with the primary bodies, is a Hamiltonian system[18]. This analysis was performed in Matlab using the ode45 numerical integrator. The first step was to compute a symmetric periodic orbit in the CR3BP that is close to the IBEX orbit, using differential correction and employing the Mirror Theorem[19]. The period of this orbit in the CR3BP frame is T = 27.26 days. We next computed the monodromy matrix for the periodic orbit, which is the state transition matrix after one orbit period of the periodic orbit—which is about 3 of the inertial orbits—and computed the Floquet multipliers, which are the eigenvalues of the monodromy matrix. For a periodic solution in a Hamiltonian system, two of the Floquet multipliers must equal one[20]. The other Floquet multipliers were found to be the complex conjugate pairs $0.8119 \pm i\, 0.5838$ and $0.9997 \pm i\, 0.0232$. Because all of the multipliers have modulus one, and because there is a complete set of eigenvectors, we know this periodic solution is neutrally stable. That is, in the linearized dynamics, a nearby solution will always remain nearby. (This is consistent with our experience with the numerically integrated full-force model orbits; slight changes to the initial orbit period did not cause large deviations in the trajectory, even after ten years.) We also note that $0.8119 \pm i\, 0.5838 =$

$\exp(i2\pi/k_1)$ and $0.9997 \pm i\, 0.0232 = exp(i2\pi/k_2)$, where $k_1 = 10.08$ and $k_2 = 270.8$. We can infer that the dynamics near the periodic orbit are quasi-periodic oscillations, with periods $k_1 T = 275.1$ days or about 9 months, and $k_{12} T = 7392.7$ days or about 20 years. (A quasi-periodic solution has a combination of sinusoidal components with non-commensurable periods, so the solution does not close on itself.) Figure 20 shows the evolution of the orbit inclination over 20 years for an orbit near the periodic solution in the CR3BP. As predicted by Floquet analysis, the curve exhibits oscillations with periods near 9-month and 20-year oscillations. The plot of period evolution in Figure 17 and the other orbit element plots, show predicted oscillations for the actual IBEX orbit with period close to 8 months. This indicates that the simplified CR3BP model captures some key features of the full orbit dynamics, but the specific oscillation frequency will depend on the particular orbit and force model.

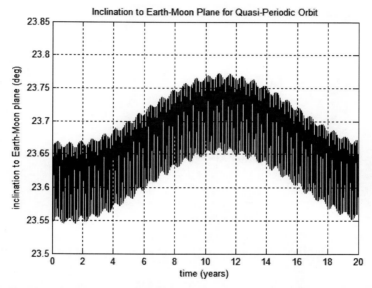

Figure 20. Twenty-year propagation of inclination to the Earth-Moon plane for an IBEX-like quasi-periodic orbit. The curve shows oscillations with period near 9 months, and a long-term oscillation with period near 20 years.

The Floquet analysis provides information about the linearized dynamics near the periodic solution, but further analysis is needed to understand the global stability. To further understand the long-term dynamics we computed the State Transition Matrix (STM) for a quasi-periodic orbit over an interval of 40 years, and computed the matrix infinity-norm at each time. The result is shown in Figure 21 below. To monitor the accuracy of the propagation we confirmed that the determinant of the STM equals 1, to within 7e-4, as expected for the conservation of phase space volume in a Hamiltonian system. Figure 21 provides a bound on the ratio of the linearized state error at time t to the initial state error, which demonstrates the long-term stability of this orbit. Over a 40 year interval, an initial error would be magnified by no more than 1300, and during most of that interval an error would be magnified by not more than a factor of 200.

It is common to employ Lyapunov exponents to quality the rate of error growth[21]. However it is apparent in Figure 21 that the error grows at far less than an exponential rate. When we did attempt to compute a Lyapunov exponent, the values trended downward over 40 years, suggesting that limit is zero. The approximate Lyapunov exponent reached a value of 0.1 per year over 40 years, equivalent to an average growth of just 10% per year.

To further understand the stability of IBEX-like orbits, we employed a Poincare map[22] in which we recorded each point where a solution crosses a particular surface or "Poincare section", in this case the x-z plane. (The x axis is from the Earth to the Moon and the z axis is along the Moon's orbit angular momentum vector.) The paper by Vaquerro and Howell[23] at this conference presents another application of Poincare maps to resonant orbits in the CR3BP. The Poincare map reduces the dynamics by one dimension, while still capturing key stability information. We generated 800 random perturbations from the initial state of the periodic orbit, and recorded the next 48 x-z plane crossings. For 400 of these draws we used "large" size normally distributed perturbations with standard deviation 1000 km in position and 10 m/sec at apogee. For the other 400 draws we used "very large" perturbations with standard deviation 10000 km in position and 100 m/sec at apogee. The large and very large perturbations are much bigger than would be expected in flight operations. The results are shown in Figure 22. (We did look at "moderate" perturbations of 100 km in position and 1 m/sec in velocity, but there was no visual difference from the periodic orbit in the Poincare map.)

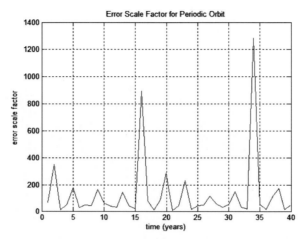

Figure 21. Error growth near IBEX-like periodic orbit in CR3BP. There is no sign of exponential error growth. The scale factor does not exceed 1300 in 40 years, and most of the time is below 300.

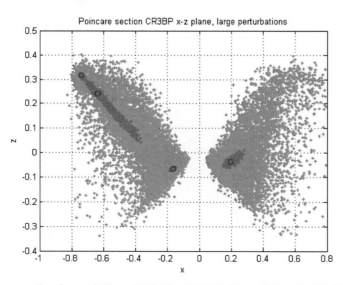

Figure 22. Poincare section for periodic orbit in the CR3BP. The primary bodies lie along the x-axis, Earth is located near the origin, the Moon is located near x = 1. The four points where the periodic orbit crosses the x-z plane are marked by red circles. The results of the large perturbations are shown in green, while the results for very large perturbations are shown in cyan.

786

The solutions for large perturbations are all quasi-periodic solutions that remain close to the periodic orbit. For example, Figure 23 shows the orbit for a large perturbation whose initial state lies near x = -0.4, z = 0.05 on the green "island" at upper left in Figure 22. Notice that the quasi-periodic orbit in Figure 23 looks similar to the actual IBEX orbit shown in Figure 14. (The x axis is positive towards the right in Figure 23 while it is positive up in Figure 14.)

The Poincare map is a further demonstration that the IBEX-like resonant orbit is stable even under perturbations orders of magnitude larger than those encountered in operations. However, as shown in very large perturbations can produce solutions very far from the nominal periodic solution. When we sample some of the initial states in cyan in Figure 22, we find a variety of solutions including some regular solutions near 5:2 resonance and near 13:4 resonance, as well as some chaotic solutions.

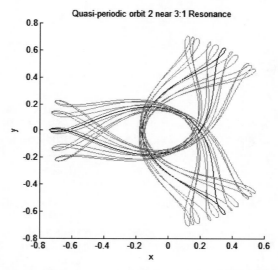

Figure 23. Quasi-periodic orbit (green) produced by a large perturbation from the nominal periodic orbit (black). The orbits are projected into the x-y plane, where the Moon lies along the plus x-axis at x = 0.985. The shape of this orbit is similar to the IBEX orbit in Figure 14, where the Moon is located on the vertical axis.

CONCLUSIONS AND FUTURE WORK

This paper describes the trajectory analysis performed in preparation for the IBEX extended mission. A detailed trade study was performed to identify an orbit that best satisfied the mission requirements, and to determine the best maneuver sequence. The orbit selection was driven by the need for limited orbit maintenance maneuvers and limited eclipse durations. A novel graphical technique was developed to help summarize eclipse durations vs. time for various orbit periods and pointing errors. (In fact, it has become so useful that we are already using this technique another mission with eclipse duration constraints.) Based on the trade study an orbit near 3:1 resonance with the Moon was chosen, which proved to be remarkably stable. A dynamical systems analysis of the orbit stability was performed in the CR3BP which demonstrated that some of the evolution and characteristics noticed with the actual IBEX orbit are consistent with those seen in the linearized dynamics model.

The pre-maneuver analysis sufficiently modeled all of the effects, enabling a successful transfer to the new mission orbit. We plan to perform further stability analysis of the families of resonant orbits. We believe this class of orbits could be used for many types of missions including space weather and space science.

ACKNOWLEDGMENTS

We would like to acknowledge the significant contributions of Dave McComas, Nathan Schwadron, Michelle Reno, John Scherrer, and Mark Tapley, with whom we worked closely developing options for, designing, and performing operations for this new trajectory. We especially thank them for their insight, encouragement, and support as we explored many options in pursuit of creating a successful extended mission trajectory. We would also like to thank Jim Bobbett, Walker Cross, Jeff Godward, Steve Green, Bret Hautamaki, Sean Kirn, Robert Lockwood, Tim Perry, Ryan Tyler, and Sheral Wesley who contributed significantly and were critical to the success of the transfer to the extended mission orbit. We worked with them closely developing the trajectory designs, planning, and staffing long operational shifts.

This work was performed under contract to Southwest Research Institute. The IBEX mission is sponsored by the National Aeronautics and Space Administration's Small Explorer (SMEX) Program. This work was supported under contract NNG05EC85C.

REFERENCES

[1] D. McComas, L. Bartolone, W. Mills, J. Salgado, "IBEX: Interstellar Boundary Explorer," Southwest Research Institute, URL: http://ibex.swri.edu [cited February, 2009].

[2] D. McComas, et al, "The Interstellar Boundary Explorer (IBEX) Mission," Proc. Solar Wind 11 – SOHO 16 "Connecting Sun and Heliosphere," Whistler, Canada, 12 – 17 June 2005 (ESA SP-592, September 2005).

[3] D. McComas, et al, "The Interstellar Boundary Explorer (IBEX)," AIP CP719, Physics of the Outer Heliosphere: Third International IGPP Conference, Riverside, CA, ed. V. Florinski, N.V. Pogorelov, and G.P. Zank, 2004.

[4] D. McComas, et al, "The Interstellar Boundary Explorer (IBEX): Update at the end of phase B," CP 858, Physics of the Inner Heliosheath, ed. J. Heerikhuisen, V. Florinski, N.V. Pogorelov, 2006.

[5] M. Loucks, J. Carrico, M. Concha, T. Craychee, "Trajectory Design Operations for the IBEX Mission." AAS 09-134, *19th AAS/AIAA Spaceflight Mechanics Meeting*, Savannah, Georgia, USA, February 2009.

[6] L. Policastri, J. Carrico Jr., T. Craychee , T. Johnson , J. Woodburn, "Orbit Determination Operations for the Interstellar Boundary Explorer," AAS 09-135, *19th AAS/AIAA Space Flight Mechanics Meeting,* Savannah, Georgia, USA, February 2009.

[7] M. Loucks, J. Carrico, R. Tyler, "Prelaunch Trajectory Design and Analysis for the IBEX Mission." AAS 09-132, *19th AAS/AIAA Spaceflight Mechanics Meeting*, Savannah, Georgia, USA, February 2009.

[8] L. Policastri, J. Carrico, R. Lebois, "Flight Dynamics Operations for the IBEX Mission: The First Six Months," AAS 09-350, *AAS/AIAA Astrodynamics Specialist Conference*, Pittsburgh, Pennsylvania, USA, August 2009.

[9] J. Carrico Jr., L. Policastri, R. Lebois, M. Loucks, "Covariance Analysis and Operational Results for the Interstellar Boundary Explorer (IBEX)", *AAS/AIAA Astrodynamics Specialist Conference*, Toronto, Canada, August 2010.

[10] M. Loucks, J. Carrico, M. Concha, T. Craychee, "Trajectory Design Operations for the IBEX Mission," Paper No. AAS 09-134, *19th AAS/AIAA Space Flight Mechanics Meeting*, Savannah, Georgia, USA, February, 2009.

[11] C.D. Murray, S.F. Dermott, Solar System Dynamics, Cambridge, 1999.

[12] C. Uphoff, M.A. Crouch, "Lunar Cycler Orbits with Alternating Semi-Monthly Transfer Windows," AAS 91-105, AAS/AIAA Space Flight Mechanics Meeting, Houston, TX, 11-13 February 1991.

[13] D.V. Byrnes, J.M. Longuski, B. Aldrin, "Cycler Orbit between Earth and Mars," J. Spacecraft and Rockets, Vol. 30 No. 3, May-June 1993, pp. 334-336

[14] R.W. Farquhar, D.W. Dunham, "A New Trajectory Concept for Exploring the Earth's Geomagnetic Tail," Journal of Guidance and Control, Vol. 4, No. 2, 1981, pp. 192–196.

[15] D.W. Dunham, et al. "Double Lunar-Swingby Trajectories for the Spacecraft of the International Solar Terrestrial Physics Program," Advances in the Astronautical Sciences, Vol. 69, 1989, pp. 285-301

[16] H. Franz, et al. "WIND Nominal Mission Performance and Extended Mission Design," J. Astronautical Sciences, Vol. 49, No. 1, January 2001, pp. 145-167 and presented at the AIAA/AAS Astrodynamics Conference, Boston, Massachusetts, August 11, 1998.

[17] R. Farquhar, "Halo-Orbit and Lunar-Swingby Missions of the 1990s," Acta Astronautica, Vol. 24, pp. 227-234, 1991. (Presented at the 41st Congress of the International Astronautical Federation, Paper No. IAF-90-308, Dresdon, Germany, Oct. 6-12, 1990)

[18] K.R. Meyer, G.R. Hall, "Introduction to Hamiltonian Dynamical Systems and the N-Body Problem", Springer-Verlag, New York, 1992.

[19] A.E. Roy, M.V. Ovenden, "On the occurrence of commensurable mean motions in the solar system. The mirror theorem", Monthly Notices of the Royal Astronomical Society, Vol. 115, 1955, p.296.

[20] K.R. Meyer, G.R. Hall, ibid.

[21] K.T. Alligood, T.D. Sauer, J.A. Yorke, Chaos: An Introduction to Dynamical Systems, Springer, 1996.

[22] K.R. Meyer, G.R. Hall, ibid, p. 131.

[23] M. Vaquerro, K. C. Howell, "Poincare Maps and Resonant Orbits in the Circular Restricted Three-Body Problem", AAS 11-428, AAS/AIAA Astrodynamics Specialist Conference, Girdwood, Alaska, July 31-August 4, 2011

OPTIMAL EARTH-MOON TRANSFER TRAJECTORY DESIGN USING MIXED IMPULSIVE AND CONTINUOUS THRUST

Daero Lee,[*] Tae Soo No,[†] Ji Marn Lee,[‡] Gyeong Eon Jeon,[§] Ghangho Kim[**] and Sang-Kon Lee[††]

Optimal transfer trajectories based on the planar circular restricted three body problem are designed using mixed impulsive and continuous thrust. The continuous, dynamic trajectory optimization is reformulated in the form of discrete optimization problem by the method of direct transcription and collocation, and is then solved using nonlinear programming software. Two very different transfer trajectories can be obtained by different combinations of the design parameters. Furthermore, it was found that all designed trajectories permit a ballistic capture by the Moon's gravity. Finally, the required thrust profiles are presented and analyzed in detail.

INTRODUCTION

In Moon exploration, the designs of thrust system and considerations of the transfer orbit required for the Earth-Moon transfer must take precedence. In general, a Moon exploration spacecraft must make a series of maneuvers composed of translunar trajectory injection, trajectory correction maneuvers and lunar orbit injection, in that sequence[1]. The nature of this series of maneuvers is determined by the type of launch vehicle and the onboad spacecraft rockets. Consideration of the characteristics of the thrust system is essential for designing a transfer trajectory. In general, thrust systems are classified into impulsive thrust or continuous thrust. The solid rockets which use impulsive thrust are not able to control the thrust magnitude or combustion time whereas liquid rockets which use continuous thrust can. The most general methods for transfer trajectory design using multiple impulsive maneuvers[2,3] are the Hohmann transfer, Bi-elliptic Transfer, Weak Stability Boundary(WSB)[4,5] that consider the possibility of the reignition of the rocket. Recently, the research for transfer trajectory design which actively use electronic and ion thrusters has progressed. However, transfer trajectories with a spiral shape have a disadvantage that the flight time takes dozens to hundreds of days[6,7] when using low thrusters that work for long pe-

---

[*] Postdoctoral Research Associate, Wind Power Grid-Adaptive Technology Research Center, Chonbuk National University, Jeonju, Republic of Korea
Professor, Department of Aerospace Engineering, Chonbuk National University, Jeonju, Republic of Korea
† Graduate Student, Department of Aerospace Engineering, Chonbuk National University, Jeonju, Republic of Korea
‡ Graduate Student, Department of Aerospace Engineering, Chonbuk National University, Jeonju, Republic of Korea
§ Graduate Student, School of Mechanical and Aerospace Engineering, Seoul National University, Seoul, Republic of Korea
[**] Principal Researcher, Korea Aerospace Research Institute, Daejeon, Republic of Korea

riods successively. The most effective Earth-Moon orbit transfer in terms of fuel consumption is the use of a natural orbit that takes advantage of the attractions of the Earth and the Moon. Until recently a large effort to look for a natural orbit based on the circular restricted three body problem (CRTBP) so called low energy orbit[5] has been made. The research to look for this orbit numerically using weak boundary stability (WBS) or invariant manifold theory is now mature[4,8].

Pierson and Kleuver[1] found minimum-fuel planar trajectories from a circular low Earth parking orbit (LEO) to a circular low lunar parking orbit (LLO). The optimal low-thrust transfer problem studied in the classical CRTBP is solved by formulating and successively solving a hierarchy of sub-problems, resulting in a three stage approach. Kleuver and Pierson[9] extended their work on optimal planar transfers to a minimum fuel problem for a three dimensional transfer using a hybrid method. They also obtained minimum-fuel, two-dimensional and three-dimensional, Earth-Moon trajectories for a nuclear electronic propulsion spacecraft with relatively low thrust-to weight ratio[10]. Herman and Conway[11] found optimal, low thrust, Earth-moon orbit transfers with nonlinear programming for the case where the initial spacecraft Earth orbit is arbitrary and the Moon is in its actual orbit. The transfer time is relatively long (on the order of 30 days) but is minimized. Belbruno and Miele[12] proposed a method for a low energy Earth to Moon transfer trajectory design using WSB whose transfer trajectory enters the Moon mission orbit and can carry out a natural capture or so called "ballistic capture". Koon et al.[6] considered the coupled three body problem as a precursor to higher fidelity gravitational models. They constructed low energy Earth to Moon transfer trajectories executing a ballistic capture by the Moon using the invariant manifolds of the periodic orbits.

The optimization problems that are solved to find transfer trajectories are classified as either direct or indirect methods. Indirect methods may exhibit rapid convergence and requires fairly fewer function computations when compared with a direct method. Because of these advantages, much early optimization research focused on indirect methods, these methods were successfully demonstrated in several low-thrust problems[13-15]. However, indirect methods have disadvantages due to initialization difficulties for the adjoint variable of the TPBVP, the sensitivity of Euler-Lagrange equation, and discontinuity. On the other hand, direct methods convert the calculus of variation problem into a parameter optimization problem that minimizes the performance index using nonlinear programming (NLP). It also transcribes the states and controls through direct transcription and collocation[16,17] or differential inclusion[18,19]. The entire trajectory to be optimized by this direct method is represented in terms of nodes[17], and a large number of design variables.

This study proposes an optimal Earth-Moon transfer trajectory design method using mixed impulsive and continuous thrust by employing direct transcription and collocation method. The transfer time can be reduced significantly by using mixed impulsive and continuous thrust. Impulsive thrust contributes to the escape of spacecraft from the Earth's gravity field and continuous thrust contributes the translunar trajectory and the Moon mission orbit insertion or capture. The Earth-Moon transfer trajectory is governed by the planar circular restricted three-body problem (PCRTBP) considering the attractions of the Earth and the Moon simultaneously. Unlike Pierson and Kleuver's three stage approach, this study does not consider a hierarchy of sub-problems that are categorized into three stages. Instead, continuous, dynamic trajectory optimization for every stage is reformulated in the form of a discrete optimization problem by the method of direct transcription and collocation.

Various types of Earth-Moon transfer trajectories are then designed by adjusting the design parameters such as the relative weighting factor for impulsive and continuous thrust and flight time. We show the various types of transfer trajectory that escape the Earth's gravitation and enter a translunar trajectory. This study shows that a transfer trajectory design is possible which meets the condition of a non-thrust orbit insertion or a so called ballistic capture, that is, the spacecraft is placed in the Moon mission orbit by the Moon's gravity alone. Furthermore, we show the required thrust magnitude and transfer trajectory types corresponding to various Earth-Moon transfer trajectory designs in detail.

PLANAR CIRCULAR RESTRICTED THREE BODY PROBLEM

The design of the Earth-Moon transfer trajectory can be understood through three-body orbit dynamic modeling that considers the attractions of both the Earth and the Moon. This study employs the PCRTBP described in the Earth-Moon plane. The binary system composed of the Earth and the Moon, as seen in Fig. 1, is assumed to rotate with an angular rate ω about the barycenter. Since a more detailed derivation of the circular restricted three-body problem equations can be seen in References 20 and 21, the necessary equations considering the planar motion only are briefly described as below:

$$\ddot{\xi} = \xi + 2\dot{\zeta} - \frac{(1-\mu)}{\gamma_E^3}(\xi + \mu) - \frac{\mu}{\gamma_E^3}(\xi - 1 + \mu) + u_\xi \tag{1}$$

$$\ddot{\zeta} = \zeta - 2\dot{\xi} - \frac{(1-\mu)}{\gamma_E^3}\zeta - \frac{\mu}{\gamma_E^3}\zeta + u_\zeta \tag{2}$$

where

μ : Mass ratio of the restricted three-body problem

$\gamma_E = \sqrt{(\xi + \mu)^2 + \zeta^2}$: Earth-satellite distance

$\gamma_M = \sqrt{(\xi - 1 + \mu)^2 + \zeta^2}$: Moon-satellite distance

and (u_ξ, u_ζ) represent the control acceleration. It should be noted that Eqs. (1) and (2) are written in non-dimensional form where the distance unit (DU) is the distance between the Earth and the Moon, 3.844×10^5 km, and the time unit (TU) is the Moon's period divided by 2π. Thus, the velocity unit (VU) is DU/TU and the acceleration unit (ACU) is DU/TU^2.

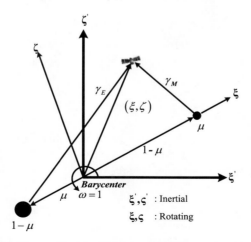

Figure 1. Planar Circular Restricted Three-Body Problem

793

PROBLEM FORMULATION FOR EARTH-MOON OPTIMAL TRANSFER TRAJECTORY

Mixed Impulsive and Continuous Thrust

In a broad sense, the Earth-Moon transfer trajectory is an orbit transfer from an Earth orbit to a Moon orbit. Hohmann and bi-elliptic transfers are the representative orbit transfer methods using impulsive thrust in the tangential directions. Hohmann and bi-elliptic describe an insertion into an Earth-centered Moon orbit. In order for spacecraft to be inserted into a Moon-centered mission orbit, an impulsive maneuver is needed at the intersection point of the Earth-Moon transfer trajectory and the Moon-centered mission orbit. In addition, there is a different type of orbit transfer method using continuous thrust. The ESA Smart-1 spacecraft launched in 2003 a successful example of using continuous thrust from a solar electric propulsion system. The transfer trajectory was one that departs from the Earth parking orbit and reaches the Moon mission orbit by extending the transfer trajectory gradually. While it is appropriate for the transport of all sorts of exploration equipment and payloads because the fuel consumption is very small, this type of transfer method using a low thrust system may take several months or years to reach the Moon mission orbit

This study employs mixed impulsive and continuous thrust to take advantage of the characteristics of impulsive and continuous thrust to find an Earth-Moon optimal transfer trajectory design. As a result, the transfer time that may take hundreds of days by different methods can be reduced by using mixed impulsive and continuous thrust. Furthermore, it is desired that the additional ΔV is not necessary for insertion into the Moon mission orbit. The impulsive thrust is just used for Earth departure and the continuous thrust is used for the translunar trajectory, shown as a dotted line in Figure 2, and insertion into the Moon mission orbit. The design problem of the Earth-Moon optimal transfer trajectory is ultimately formulated as a dynamic optimization problem. The system's governing equations for the optimal transfer trajectory design considered in this study as previously stated are the three-body orbital motion equations described by Eqs. (1) and (2). The cost function or performance index used to minimize the use of mixed impulsive and continuous thrust is defined as follows.

$$J = \alpha \Delta V_E^2 + \frac{1}{2} \int_0^{t_f} \sqrt{u_\xi^2 + u_\zeta^2}\, dt \qquad (3)$$

where ΔV_E is the impulsive velocity increment in Earth departure. $\sqrt{u_\xi^2 + u_\zeta^2}$ is the required continuous thrust magnitude during the transfer period, α is the weighting factor that determines the relative contribution from the impulsive and continuous thrust, and t_f denotes the flight time. In this work, α and t_f are treated as the design parameters.

Earth Departure Condition

Referring to Fig. 2, this study assumes that the satellite departs from the circular parking orbit of radius r_E along the tangential direction. Then, considering the velocity increment ΔV_E, the initial position and velocity of the spacecraft in the rotating, non-dimensional frame are given by

$$\xi_0 = r_E \cos(\theta_E) - \mu \qquad (4)$$

$$\zeta_0 = r_E \sin(\theta_E) \qquad (5)$$

$$\dot{\xi} = -(V_E + \Delta V_E)\sin(\theta_E) + \zeta_0 \tag{6}$$

$$\dot{\zeta} = (V_E + \Delta V_E)\cos(\theta_E) - \xi_0 \tag{7}$$

Where $V_E = \sqrt{\dfrac{1-\mu}{r_E}}$: is the spacecraft speed in the Earth parking orbit and the phase angle θ_E determines the departure position. Hence, the design variables in the Earth departure are the velocity increment ΔV_E and the phase angle θ_E.

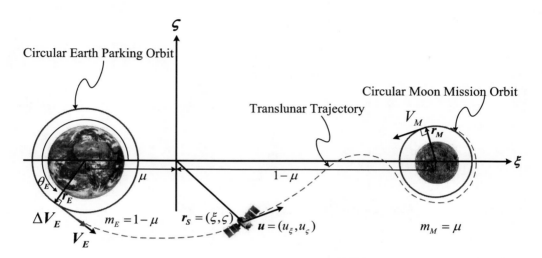

Figure 2. Earth-Moon Transfer Geometry

Moon Arrival Condition

In this study, it is desired that the spacecraft is inserted into a circular Moon-centered orbit of radius r_M. Then, the final position and velocity of the spacecraft with respect to the Moon should satisfy the following conditions:

$$\sqrt{(\xi_f - 1 + \mu)^2 + \zeta_f^2} = r_M \tag{8}$$

$$\sqrt{(\dot{\xi}_f - \zeta_f)^2 + (\dot{\zeta}_f + \xi_f)^2} = V_M \tag{9}$$

$$(\xi_f - 1 + \mu) \cdot (\dot{\xi}_f - \zeta_f) + \zeta_f \cdot (\dot{\zeta}_f + \xi_f) = 0 \tag{10}$$

where $V_M = \sqrt{\dfrac{\mu}{r_M}}$ denotes the orbital speed in the Moon mission orbit. Differently from the Earth departure, it should be noted that any additional impulsive is not used.

Transfer Trajectory Condition

During the Earth-Moon transfer, the spacecraft should obey the dynamic equations given by Eqs. (1) and (2). Here, the purpose is to find the control acceleration $\left(u_\xi, u_\varsigma\right)$ that not only minimizes the performance index defined in Eq. (3) but also makes the spacecraft satisfy the Moon arrival condition at the final time. To solve the optimization problem in this work, the direct method based on direct transcription and collocation that transcribes the optimization problem to NLP is applied. For this purpose, the continuous design variables along the time t, as seen in Figure 3, are considered as the discretized N nodes. The individual time points are called node or grid points. Therefore, the design variables are defined as follows.

$$t : t_0, t_1, t_2, \ldots, t_N \tag{11}$$

$$x(t) : x_0, x_1, x_2, \ldots, x_N \tag{12}$$

$$u(t) : u_0, u_1, u_2, \ldots, u_N \tag{13}$$

where x_i denotes the spacecraft position and velocity, and u_i represents the control acceleration at time t_i as below:

$$x_i = (\xi_i, \zeta_i, \dot{\xi}_i, \dot{\zeta}_i), \ i = 1, \ldots, N \tag{15}$$

$$u_i = (u_{\xi_i}, u_{\zeta_i}), \ i = 1, \ldots, N \tag{16}$$

Also the performance index considering the discretized design variables is slightly modified as

$$J = \alpha \Delta V_E^2 + \frac{1}{2} \sum_{i=1}^{N} \sqrt{(u_{\xi_i}^2 + u_{\zeta_i}^2)}(t_{i+1} - t_i) \tag{17}$$

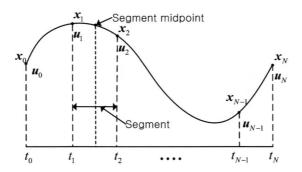

Figure 3. Discretization of Continuous Optimization Problem

Noting that the state variables x_i and control variables u_i are not independent in the sense that they should satisfy the governing equations, we also discretized Eqs. (1) and (2) using the Hermite-Simpson method[16] which represents the implicit, numerical integration as below:

$$x_i = x_{i-1} + \frac{h_i}{6}\Big[f(x_{i-1}, u_{i-1}) + 4f(y_{i,c}, u_{i,c}) + f(x_i, u_i) \Big], \quad i = 1, \ldots, N \tag{18a}$$

where $h_i = t_i - t_{i-1}$, and

$$f(x, u) = \frac{dx}{dt} \quad \text{for } t \in \Big[0, t_f\Big] \tag{18b}$$

$$y_{i,c} = \frac{1}{2}(x_{i-1} + x_i) + \frac{h_i}{8}\Big[f(x_{i-1}, u_{i-1}) - f(x_i, u_i) \Big] \tag{18c}$$

$$u_{i,c} = \frac{1}{2}(\mathbf{u}_{i-1} + \mathbf{u}_i) \tag{18d}$$

where y is the state vector at the segment midpoint and $f(x, u)$ represents the Eqs. (1) and (2) evaluated at the nodes and midpoints. Eq. (18) is ultimately the constraint equation that concatenates every design variable, and is called as a defect[16,17] by rewiring the Eq. (18) as follows.

$$\Delta_i = x_{i-1} - x_i + \frac{h_i}{6}\Big[f(x_{i-1}, u_{i-1}) + 4f(y_{i,c}, u_{i,c}) + f(x_i, u_i) \Big] \tag{19}$$

OPTIMAL TRANSFER TRAJECTORY DESIGN RESULTS AND ANALYSIS

Direct vs. Spiral Departure Trajectory Design Example

Figures 4 and 5 show the representative examples of Earth-Moon transfer trajectories obtained in this work. One may easily note that the shape of trajectories at the Earth departure phase is quite different in the sense that whether a spacecraft is directly injected into the translunar trajectory or it follows the spiral path by elevating the altitude gradually. We call the former one as a direct departure trajectory, and the latter as a spiral departure trajectory. Various trajectories can be obtained by different combinations of design parameters, that is, the relative weighting factor α and the flight time t_f.

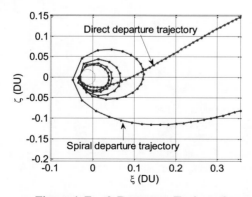

Figure 4. Earth Departure Trajectories.

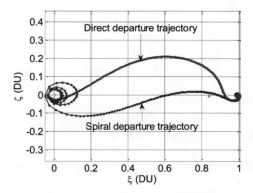

Figure 5. Earth-Moon Transfer Trajectories.

Table 1 shows the features of direct departure and spiral departure trajectories. The used flight time in this example is 6 days. It is obvious that the relative weighting factor α determines the type of Earth departure trajectory. While the impulsive velocity ΔV_E required for the direct depar-

797

ture trajectory is larger than that for the spiral departure trajectory, the continuous thrust contribution, which is expressed in the form of $\sum \sqrt{\left(u_{\xi_i}^2 + u_{\zeta_i}^2\right)} dt_i$, for the direct departure trajectory is smaller than that for the spiral departure trajectory.

Table 1. Earth-Moon Optimal Transfer Trajectory Results.

Transfer trajectory	α	ΔV_E	θ_E (deg)	$\sum \sqrt{\left(u_{\xi_i}^2 + u_{\zeta_i}^2\right)} dt_i$
Direct Departure	100	2.9025	226.81	1.4275
Spiral Departure	1000	1.5306	334.93	4.7131

Figure 6 presents the time histories of the required continuous thrusts for both of the transfer trajectories during the flight time of 6 days. The direct departure trajectory requires relatively smaller continuous thrust than the spiral departure trajectory does. It should be noted that the magnitude of continuous thrust approaches zero, and this implies that the so-called ballistic capture is achieved at the Moon arrival phase.

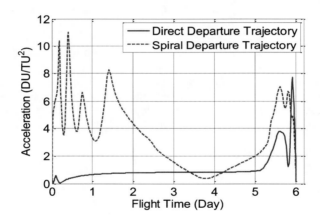

Figure 6. Continuous Thrust During Transfer.

Parametric Study

As mentioned previously, very different transfer trajectories can be designed using the different combinations of the relative weighting factor and the flight time. Since one of objectives of this study is to find an Earth-Moon transfer trajectory with reasonable flight time and smaller impulsive thrust requirement, it is important to study the effects of design parameters on the final results. The other consideration in this kind of numerical search for the optimal solution is to get a decent initial guess for iteration. In addition, the altitude of the departure and arrival orbits is an important factor that determines the numerical convergence. As such, this study applied the progressive homotpy-like[22] optimization method. For example, once an optimal trajectory has been obtained, this result is used as an initial guess to the new problem that has slightly different departure/arrival altitude, the relative weighting factor, and the flight time.

Relative Weighting Factor

For the fixed flight time of 6 days, the weighting factor α determines the shape of departure trajectory regardless of the altitude of departure and arrival orbits. Figures 7 shows the Earth-Moon transfer trajectories and the required continuous thrusts during transfer from the high altitude Earth departure orbit to the high altitude Moon arrival orbit with the flight time of 6 days. The weighting factors used are 100, 300, and 500, respectively. As the relative weighting factor α gets larger, the spacecraft immediately enters the translunar trajectory but requires larger continuous thrust during transfer. Table 2 supports this tendency clearly. From Fig. 7(b), it can be seen that the continuous thrust magnitude becomes very small at the end of flight, and this implies that the spacecraft is captured by the Moon gravity in a so-called ballistic manner.

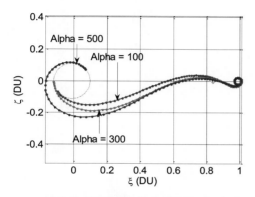 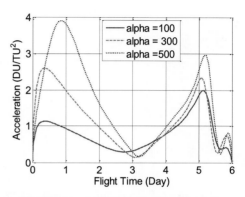

(a) **Earth-Moon Transfer Trajectories.**   (b) **Continuous Thrust During Transfer.**
Figure 7. High Altitude Earth-Moon Transfer (Direct Departure Trajectory, Parameter: Weighting Factor).

Table 2. Summary of Parametric Study Results
(High Altitude Earth-Moon Transfer, Direct Departure Trajectory, Parameter: Weighting factor).

α	ΔV_E	θ_E (deg)	$\sum \sqrt{\left(u_{\xi_i}^2 + u_{\zeta_i}^2\right)} dt_i$
100	0.8157	217.06	1.099734
200	0.6640	194.34	1.443822
300	0.5665	174.38	1.639360
400	0.4422	151.39	1.912571
500	0.2328	40.57	2.322653
600	0.1747	-0.69	2.341412
700	0.1438	-58.31	2.322671
800	0.1257	-75.71	2.333717
900	0.1153	-85.20	2.346871
1000	0.1135	-85.46	2.348997

For the low altitude departure and arrival case, the relative weighting factor α has a significant effect on the shape of transfer trajectory at the vicinity of the Moon as can be seen from Fig. 8. In this example, the altitude of both departure and arrival orbits was set to 100 km. Differently from the case of transfer between high altitude departure and arrival orbits, the relative weighting factor does not seem to cause much variations in the Earth departure trajectories but alters the trajectory shape at the Moon arrival phase as can be seen from Fig. 8(b). Figure 8(c) shows the required continuous thrust during transfer. Again in this case, the continuous thrust approaches zero as it enters the arrival orbit. From the results summarized in Table 3, the relative weighting factor does not significantly affect the velocity increment requirement for departure.

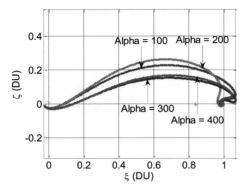

(a) Earth-Moon Transfer Trajectories.

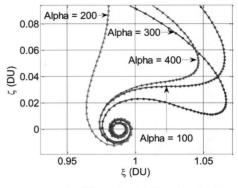

(b) Moon Arrival Trajectories.

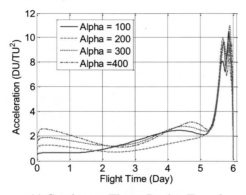

(c) Continuous Thrust During Transfer.
Figure 8. Low Altitude Earth-Moon Transfer (Direct Departure Trajectory,
Parameter: Weighting Factor).

Table 3. Summary of Parametric Study Results
(Low Altitude Earth-Moon Transfer, Direct Departure Trajectory, Parameter: Weighting factor)

α	ΔV_E	θ_E (deg)	$\sum \sqrt{\left(u_{\xi_i}^2 + u_{\zeta_i}^2\right)}dt_i$
100	3.0627	228.61	2.769626
200	3.0040	228.29	2.468709
300	2.9769	215.36	3.308720
400	2.9361	213.39	3.473532

Figures 9 shows the Earth-Moon transfer trajectories and the required continuous thrusts during transfer from the low altitude Earth departure orbit to the low altitude Moon arrival orbit with the flight time of 6 days. The used weighting factors are 500, 1000, and 1500, respectively. As the relative weighting factor α gets larger, the Earth-Moon transfer trajectories get closer L1 libration point and similar each other in the shape of Earth-Moon transfer trajectory. In addition, the required continuous thrust during transfer gets larger whereas the impulsive thrust gets smaller. The relative weighting factor α does not have a significant effect on the shape of the Earth-Moon transfer trajectories when it is larger than 1000. Table 4 supports this tendency clearly. The values of the impulsive thrust for the low altitude spiral departure in Table 4 are pretty much smaller than the values of impulsive thrust for the low altitude direct departure in Table 3. As a result, the spiral departure trajectory contributes to the less size of the launch vehicle by reducing the impulsive thrust.

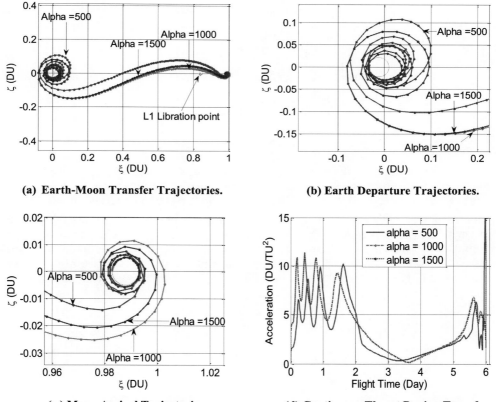

(a) Earth-Moon Transfer Trajectories.

(b) Earth Departure Trajectories.

(c) Moon Arrival Trajectories.

(d) Continuous Thrust During Transfer.

Figure 9. Low Altitude Earth-Moon Transfer (Spiral Departure Trajectory, Parameter: Weighting factor).

α	ΔV_E	θ_E (deg)	$\sum \sqrt{\left(u_{\xi_i}^2 + u_{\zeta_i}^2\right)}dt_i$
500	1.3900	210.31	4.38054
600	1.2478	174.05	4.86186
700	1.1838	168.50	5.09766
800	1.1783	167.58	5.1898
900	1.1738	166.77	5.2220
1000	1.1700	166.15	5.2712
1100	1.1652	165.55	5.2835
1200	1.1682	165.91	5.2446
1300	1.1693	166.16	5.2375
1400	1.1700	166.43	5.2375
1500	1.1702	166.59	5.1971

Flight Time

For the varying flight time, the Earth-Moon transfer trajectories are designed for the high and low altitude direct departure, and the low altitude spiral departure trajectory. For the high altitude departure and arrival case, the flight time t_f has a significant effect on the shape of transfer trajectory in the vicinity of both the Earth and Moon as can be seen from Fig. 10. The used flight times are 6, 10 and 14 days, respectively. The most influential portion of the Earth-Moon transfer trajectory on the flight time is the trajectory shape in proximity to the Moon. The spiral trajectories around the Moon orbit regardless of the Moon mission orbit occur to fit the phase of the Moon's orbital motion. It is due to the fact that certain flight time is involved before a rendezvous with

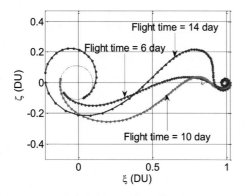

(a) Earth-Moon Transfer Trajectories.

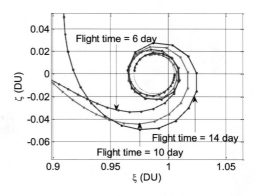

(b) Moon Arrival Trajectories.

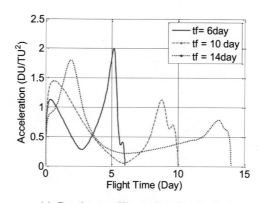

(c) Continuous Thrust During Transfer
Figure 10. High Altitude Earth-Moon Transfer (Direct Departure Trajectory,
Parameter: Flight Time).

the Moon. Again in this case, the continuous thrust approaches zero as it enters the arrival orbit. From the results summarized in Table 5, the flight time has a significantly effect on both the velocity increment requirement for departure and the continuous thrust during transfer.

Table 5. Summary of Parametric Study Results
(High Altitude Earth-Moon Transfer, Direct Departure Trajectory, Parameter: Flight Time).

t_f (day)	ΔV_E	θ_E (deg)	$\sum \sqrt{\left(u_{\xi_i}^2 + u_{\zeta_i}^2\right)} dt_i$
5.5	0.8512	222.39	1.07541
6	0.8157	217.06	1.09973
7	0.7573	203.95	1.18809
8	0.7287	197.05	1.23943
9	0.7003	183.91	1.32090
10	0.6614	166.68	1.47410
11	0.6393	150.13	1.57743
12	0.5946	112.21	1.70695
13	0.5156	13.75	1.76722
14	0.4313	-63.95	1.91507

For the low altitude departure and arrival case, the flight time t_f has a significant effect on the shape of transfer trajectory in the vicinity of the Moon as can be seen from Fig. 11 like the result shown in Fig. 8. The used flight times are 6, 7 and 8 days, respectively. In this example, the altitude of both departure and arrival orbits was also set to 100 km. Differently from the case of transfer between high altitude departure and arrival orbits, the flight time does not seem to cause much variations in the Earth departure trajectories but alters the trajectory shape at the Moon arrival phase as can be seen from Fig. 11(b). Figure 11(c) shows the required continuous thrust during transfer. Again in this case, the continuous thrust approaches zero as it enters the arrival orbit.

803

From the results summarized in Table 6, the flight time does not significantly affect the velocity increment requirement for departure.

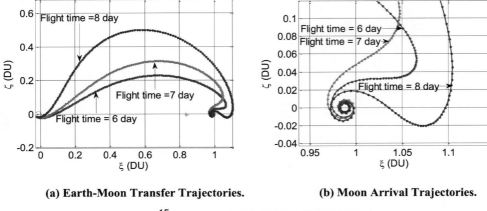

(a) Earth-Moon Transfer Trajectories.   (b) Moon Arrival Trajectories.

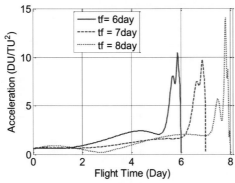

(c) Continuous Thrust During Transfer
Figure 11. Low Altitude Earth-Moon Transfer (Direct Departure Trajectory, Parameter: Flight Time).

Table 6. Summary of Parametric Study Results
(Low Altitude Earth-Moon Transfer, Direct Departure Trajectory, Parameter: Flight Time).

t_f (day)	ΔV_E	θ_E (deg)	$\sum \sqrt{\left(u_{\xi_i}^2 + u_{\zeta_i}^2\right)} dt_i$
6	3.0627	228.61	2.769626
7	3.0400	235.21	2.592188
8	3.0286	258.36	2.850455

Figures 12 shows the Earth-Moon transfer trajectories from the low altitude Earth departure orbit to the low altitude Moon arrival. The used flight times are 6, 7, 8 and 9 days, respectively. As the flight time gets longer, it is obvious that Earth departure trajectories tend to disperse further away from the Earth. In addition, the flight time has a significantly effect on velocity increment requirement for departure. This is because the spacecraft drifts in the Earth-Moon transfer trajectory by natural attraction after escaping the Earth gravitational field with a big thrust to meet the required flight time condition. Figure 12(c) shows the required continuous thrust during transfer. From the results summarized in Table 7, the flight time has a significant on the velocity increment requirement for departure. The flight time taken for the Earth-Moon transfer trajectory is an important factor to determine the performance requirements of the on board thruster in the spacecraft. If a very short flight time is required for the Earth-Moon transfer, naturally a bigger impulsive or continuous thrust is required but such a launch vehicle is not practical. On the contrary, if a very long flight time is required, there is a problem requiring a higher launch vehicle performance. The spacecraft should waste a certain time to fit the phase of the Moon with respect to the Earth. The practical problem in going to the Moon involves a rendezvous problem with the Moon a certain time after departing from the Earth. Consequently, the flight time t_f should also be considered as a very important design parameter like the relative weighting factor α.

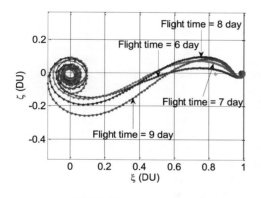

(a) Earth-Moon Transfer Trajectories.

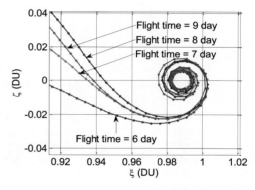

(b) Moon Arrival Trajectories.

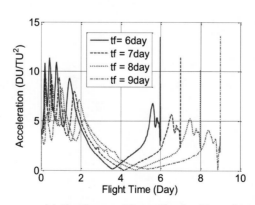

(c) Continuous Thrust During Transfer
Figure 12. Low Altitude Earth-Moon Transfer (Spiral Departure Trajectory,
Parameter: Flight Time).

Table 7. Summary of Parametric Study Results
(Low Altitude Earth-Moon Transfer, Spiral Departure Trajectory, Parameter: Flight Time).

Day	ΔV_E	θ_E (deg)	$\sum \sqrt{\left(u_{\xi_i}^2 + u_{\zeta_i}^2\right)} dt_i$
6	1.1700	166.15	5.2712
7	1.0514	139.02	4.3925
8	1.1853	118.52	5.2745
9	1.4023	92.96	4.3967

CONCLUSIONS

In this paper, results of Earth-Moon transfer trajectory studies are presented. planar, circular, restricted three body formulation is adopted to represent the system dynamics, and use of mixed thrust, that is, impulsive thrust at Earth departure, continuous thrust during Earth-Moon transfer and Moon capture is assumed. This continuous and dynamic optimization problem is reformulated as a discrete optimization one by using the method of direct transcription and collocation, and then is solved using the nonlinear programming software. As a performance index, we choose to use the sum of initial ΔV required for the departure from the Earth (parking) orbit and the continuous control acceleration needed during the transfer and insertion into the final Moon orbit. By adjusting the flight time and the weighting factor that determines the relative contribution of the impulsive thrust and the continuous acceleration, we are able to design various types of transfer trajectories. The two very different types of transfer trajectories were obtained by different combinations of the design parameters. The control acceleration during transfer becomes very small at the Moon arrival phase and this implies a ballistic capture into the Moon orbit. Other advantage due to the use of mixed thrust is that the flight time can be drastically reduced compared to the conventional low thrust orbit transfer where it requires from tens to hundreds of days for the Earth-Moon transfer.

ACKNOWLEDEGMENT

The work was supported by Korea Aerospace Research Institute through KARI's University Partnership Program.

REFERENCES

[1] B. L. Pierson and C. A. Kluever, "Three-Stage Approach to Optimal Low-Thrust Earth-Moon Trajectories," *Journal of Guidance, Control, and Dynamics*, Vol. 17, No. 6, 1994, pp. 1275-1282.

[2] M. T. Ozimek and K.C. Howell, "Low-Thrust Transfers in the Earth–Moon System, Including Applications to Libration Point Orbits," *Journal of Guidance, Control, and Dynamics*, Vol. 33, No. 2, 2010, pp. 533-549.

[3] A. Miele and S. Mancuso, "Optimal Trajectories for Earth-Moon-Earth Flight", *Acta Astronautica*, Vol. 49, No. 2, 2001, pp. 59-71.

[4] F. García and G. Gómez, "A note on weak stability boundaries", *Celestial Mechanics and Dynamical Astronomy*, 97, 2007, pp. 87-100.

[5] E. A. Belbruno and J. P. Carrico, "Calculation of Weak Stability boundary Ballistic Lunar Transfer Trajectories", *AIAA/AAS Astrodynamics Specialist Conference*, AIAA, 2000. Paper 2000-4142.

[6] G. Mingotti, F. Topputo and F. Bernelli-Zazzera, "A Method to Design Sun-Perturbed Earth-to-Moon Low-Thrust Transfers with Ballistic Capture", *XIX Congresso Nazionale AIDAA*, 2007.

[7] W.S. Koon, M.W., Lo, J. E, Marsden and S.D., Ross, "Low energy transfer to the moon", *Celestial Mechanics and Dynamical Astronomy*, Vol. 81, Issues. 1-2., 2001, pp. 63-73.

[8] F. Topputo, M. Vasile, and F. Bernelli-Zazzera, "Earth-to-Moon Low Energy Transfers Targeting L1 Hyperbolic Transit Orbits", *Annals of Academic of Sciences*, New York, vol. 1065, 2005, pp. 55-76

[9] C. A. Kluever and B. L. Pierson, "Optimal Low-Thrust Three-Dimensional Earth-Moon Trajectories," *Journal of Guidance, Control, and Dynamics*, Vol. 18, No. 4, 1994, pp. 830-837.

[10] C. A. Kluever and B. L. Pierson, "Optimal Earth-Moon Trajectories Using Nuclear Electronic Propulsion," ," *Journal of Guidance, Control, and Dynamics*, Vol. 20, No. 2, 1997, pp. 239-245.

[11] A. L. Herman and B. A. Conway, "Optimal, Low-Thrust, Earth-Moon Orbit Transfer," ," *Journal of Guidance, Control, and Dynamics*, Vol. 21, No. 1, 1998, pp. 141-147.

[12] Belbruno, E. A. and Miller, J. K. "A Ballistic Lunar Capture Trajectory for Japanese Spacecraft Hiten", Jet Propulsion Lab., JPL IOM 312/90.4- 1731.

[13] C. Ranieri and C. Ocampo, "Optimization of Round trip, Time-constrained, Finite Burn Trajectories via an Indirect Method," *Journal of Guidance, Control, and Dynamics*, Vol. 28, No. 2, 2005, pp. 306-314.

[14] C. Ranieri and C. Ocampo, "Indirect Optimization of Spiral Trajectories," *Journal of Guidance, Control, and Dynamics*, Vol. 29,No. 6, 2006, pp. 1360-1366.

[15] Russell, R., "Primer Vector Theory Applied to Global Low-Thrust Trade Studies," *Journal of Guidance, Control, and Dynamics,* Vol. 30, No. 2, 2007, pp. 460-473.

[16] P. J. Enright and B. A. Conway, "Discrete Approximations to Optimal Trajectories Using Direct Transcription and Nonlinear Programming", *Journal of Guidance, Control, and Dynamics*, Vol. 15, No. 4, 1992, pp.944-1002.

[17] C. Hargraves and S. Paris, "Direct Trajectory Optimization Using Nonlinear Programming and Collocations," *Journal of Guidance, Control, and Dynamics*, Vol. 10, No. 4,1987, pp. 338-342.

[18] B. Conway and K. Larson, "Collocation Versus Differential Inclusion in Direct Optimization,*" Journal of Guidance, Control, and Dynamics*, Vol. 21, No. 5, Sept.–Oct. 1998, pp. 780–785.

[19] J. Hargens and V. Coverstone, "Low-Thrust Interplanetary Mission Design Using Differential Inclusion," IAA/AAS Astrodynamics Specialist Conference and Exhibit, AIAA Paper 2002-4730, Aug. 2002.

[20] H. Schaub and J. L. Junkins, "Analytical Mechanics of Space Systems," American Institute of Aeronautics and Astronautics, Inc., 2nd ed., 2009.

[21] A. E. Roy, "Orbital Motion," Taylor and Francis Groups, LLC, 4th ed., 2009.

[22] B. Gray, Homotopy Theory, An Introduction to Homotopy Theory, Academic Press, INC., 1975.

AAS 11-456

PARAMETRIC STUDY OF EARTH-TO-MOON TRANSFERS WITH HYBRID PROPULSION SYSTEM AND DEDICATED LAUNCH

Giorgio Mingotti[*]

This work concerns preliminary parametric design of Earth-to-Moon transfers, exploiting both chemical (high-thrust) and solar electric (low-thrust) propulsion. Starting from a GTO to a polar orbit around the Moon, WSB trajectories with initial lunar swingby are evaluated in terms of propellant mass consumption and flight time. A dedicated launch strategy is investigated. This research has been conducted during an internship at the European Space Operations Centre, in the Mission Analysis Section, within the AstroNet framework.

INTRODUCTION

A number of possible ways to reach the Moon departing from the Earth has been found in the last years. These include transfers exploiting periodic orbits about the equilibrium points of the restricted three-body problem; transfers using the distant periodic orbits about the Moon; low energy transfers to low Moon orbit. Moreover, each of these solution can be obtained with either high- or low-thrust means. These two propulsion philosophies further widen the set of viable trajectories to reach the Moon. Moreover, the n-body problem dynamics is the subject of many recent studies. These studies exploit the natural dynamics arising in the three/four-body problem to achieve free arcs of transfers. In this framework, low energy transfers to the Moon,[1-3] as well as transfers to libration points orbits[4-9] and to distant periodic orbits,[10,11] have been designed.

More in depth, there are few space missions which have paved the present research study; starting from the rescue of the Japanese HITEN spacecraft flying along the WSB low-energy trajectories[12] to the ESA's SMART-1[13] mission, where the spacecraft reached the Moon by means of low-thrust spiral arcs flying through the L1 gateway.

In more recent years, there is the study of the upcoming ESA's NEXT [*] mission that aims at sending a spacecraft on a low polar orbit around the Moon and then release a lander; another example is the NASA's GRAIL [†] mission that will fly a twin spacecraft on a low-altitude, near-circular, polar lunar orbit. Finally, there is the preliminary study of ESA's LUMETTO mission that involves both direct and WSB low-thrust transfers to the Moon.

[*]PostDoctoral Fellow, Institut für Industriemathematik, Universität Paderborn, Warburger Str. 100, Paderborn, Germany
[*]http://www.esa.int/esaCP/SEMUV2KOXDGindex0.html
[†]http://moon.mit.edu/

Background

Low-energy transfers are achieved with impulsive maneuvers that intrinsically involve chemical propulsion. Low-thrust propulsion represents a viable option to attain further reductions of the propellant mass fraction. However, with low-thrust propulsion only, the transfer time increases excessively. In addition, in the case of Earth-Moon transfers, low-thrust propulsion is not likely used to reach the Sun-Earth WSB ; this makes the interior transfer through Earth-Moon L1 the only feasible solution in these cases (i.e. as in ESA's SMART-1[13]). An appealing option to improve the performances of low-energy transfers without increasing the transfer time is represented by the so-called *low-energy, low-thrust transfers* or *hybrid propulsion transfers*. The concept of hybrid propulsion transfer has been first observed in 2008,[14] and it has been assessed in a number of more recent works.[15–19] In brief, a hybrid propulsion transfer is described by the following sequence of steps.

— The spacecraft is launched and placed into a low-Earth parking orbit;

— An impulsive maneuver injects the spacecraft into an Earth-escape orbit toward the Sun-Earth WSB . This ballistic escape exploits the Sun-Earth-Moon gravitational interaction. The Earth-escape maneuver is accomplished by using chemical propulsion. If the initial parking orbit is elliptic, the maneuver is likely performed at the pericenter;

— From this point on (i.e., rightly after the impulsive injection) the spacecraft can only rely on its low-thrust propulsion to reach the final target orbit. The low-thrust is obtained through Solar Electric Propulsion (SEP);

— The transfer terminates when the spacecraft achieves the final mission orbit around the Moon.

Few issues arise from the sequence of events above.

A lunar gravity assist can be considered immediately after the chemical burn. This option would improve the transfers performances[20] although the inclusion of a lunar swing-by is not straightforward and depends on the mission at hand. (For instance, it can be planned only for missions having a dedicated launch).

In case of lunar gravity assist, it would be desirable to account for a small trajectory correction maneuver between the impulsive injection and the Moon encounter. When no lunar swing-bys are envisaged, possible errors in the nominal trajectory (due to not nominal impulsive injection) can be recovered in the subsequent low-thrust arcs.

To reduce the gravity losses, the impulsive injection maneuver can be split into several (e.g., two or three) low-Δv maneuvers. Although this increases the total flight time, splitting the initial injection maneuver (into a number of maneuvers) may allow for trajectory corrections. The transfer is hybrid as both chemical and SEP are used on the same platform. Nevertheless, it is worth stressing that while the duration of SEP is long (tens or hundreds of days), the chemical propulsion is used only to achieve the first translunar injection.

Using chemical propulsion along the transfer (i.e., allowing deep-space maneuvers carried out from time to time along the transfer) seems to be not convenient; the main reasons for this are given below.

- After the first injection burn, all the mass associated to the chemical propulsion subsystem (i.e., the main engine, the tanks, the feeding lines, etc.) can be ejected. In this way the low-thrust propulsion would be more effective on a higher thrust-to-mass ratio (i.e., on a system having lower-mass system);

- Allowing for deep-space maneuver asks for a more complex system. This is unnecessary as the trajectory corrections can be performed by using the SEP due to the slow dynamics characterizing the ballistic ejection and the ballistic capture. (This concept has been clearly demonstrated by ESA's SMART-1[13]).

The only exception is represented by a possible trajectory correction maneuver performed between the translunar injection and the Moon encounter in case of lunar gravity assists. Due to the short times between these two events, chemical propulsion is the only means capable of reacting to possible errors.

Motivations and Aims

The core of this work is to design brand-new Earth-to-Moon transfers assuming a hybrid propulsion system: this means that after the initial impulsive maneuver given by a chemical engine, the spacecraft can rely only on solar electric propulsion to reach the target orbit at the Moon, flying along the WSB . The main purpose of this study is to search trajectories with reduced propellant mass required to perform the transfers, also providing some assessment regarding the flight time.

More in depth, a dedicated launch strategy is considered assuming the Soyuz-Fregat as Launch Vehicle from the Guiana Space Center: three sub-orbital stages and two orbital Fregat burns lead to the injection into the GTO. As final orbit around the Moon, a polar orbit is selected.

As far as it concerns the design technique proposed, the main idea is to divide the complete transfers into few phases: these are selected according to some events defined a-priori. As dynamical model, a real ephemeris model is taken into account. The gravitational contributions of the Earth, the Moon and the Sun are considered acting on the spacecraft at the same time. As the relative position of the main celestial bodies involved changes a lot in time and has a strong effect on the designed trajectories, in order to compute conservative results, the departure period is selected when the lunar plane has the highest inclination with respect to EME.2000 (i.e. around January 2025).

Finally, two different methodological approaches are proposed in order to compute efficient Earth-to-Moon transfers, both in terms of reduced propellant mass and reasonable flight time. The first method is the *forward/forward* one: as mentioned before, the complete transfer is a-priori divided into phases (with variable duration and selected constraints); then each phase is independently optimized by means of a forward propagation from the initial to its final conditions. The algorithm reveals to be versatile and robust and a direct sensitivity analysis on the design parameters is possible. On the other side, the second approach is the *forward/backward* one: once again, the complete transfer is divided into significant phases, including the Earth escape and the Moon capture ones; then the initial phases are forward integrated, while the final one is backward integrated. The trajectory continuity is obtained solving the joint of the phases at the their boundaries, by the formulation of an iterative optimal control problem.

DESIGN TECHNIQUE

The family of transfers designed with hybrid propulsion strategy are mainly based on two propulsive philosophies combined together, which characterize the whole trajectory shape.

Earth Ballistic Departure

In an Earth-Moon hybrid propulsion transfer, a first impulse injects the spacecraft into an orbit that flies in the Sun-Earth WSB . From this region, the spacecraft reaches the Earth-Moon WSB at zero cost. If the trajectory is properly designed, the spacecraft is temporary captured by the Moon and performs a number of revolutions around it. Thus, in principle, the Moon can be reached with the initial burn only.

The Earth-Moon WSB transfers exploit the gravity gradient of the Sun in a favorable way. To do that, the transfer orbit has to be oriented in a proper way. More specifically, in a rotating frame centered at the Earth, with x-axis aligned with the Sun-Earth line, and with x growing in the anti-Sun direction, the exterior transfers can take place when the apogee lies in the II or IV quadrant. Thus, the cost of the initial impulse and the transfer time (up to the first Moon encounter) mainly depend on the following considerations.

— The orbital parameters of the departure orbit;

— The existence (or not) of a lunar gravity assist;

— The maximum distance from the Earth (i.e. the apogee of the Earth-escape orbit)

— The phasing of the Sun, the Earth, and the Moon at the departure;

— The angle between the Sun-Earth and the Earth-apogee lines.

Moon Low-thrust Arrival

For a conventional WSB transfer, reducing the time-of-flight worsens the ballistic capture at the Moon, and therefore increases the cost of the second burn. This in turn makes these short WSB transfers not convenient when conventional, chemical propulsion is used. On the other hand, due to the high specific impulse of SEP systems, short WSB transfers may become convenient when low-thrust propulsion is used to stabilize the spacecraft in a low-altitude Moon orbit. This is possible at the cost of further increasing the transfer time by the duration of the low-thrust capture arc.

The duration and the mass spent in the low-thrust capture phase depend on the following assumptions.

— The type and the number of thrusters;

— The specific impulse of the thrusters;

— The thrust magnitude;

— The nominal guidance law.

Dedicated Launch Campaign

Assuming a dedicated launch strategy, the Soyuz-Fregat (with RD-0124) is chosen as Launch Vehicle, from the CSG. Three sub-orbital stages and two orbital Fregat burns lead the spacecraft to the injection into the GTO.

The keplerian elements of the GTO are written below.

- Inclination: 7 deg;

- Perigee altitude: 250 km;

- Apogee altitude: 35786 km;

- Launched mass: 3070 kg.

Low-Thrust Engine

The engine selected for the low-thrust phases of the transfers is the Solar Electric Propulsion PPS.5000, based on the Hall Effect with Xenon as Primary fuel.

The features of the thruster are summarized below.

- Thrust available: 276 mN;

- Specific impulse: 1763 s;

- Power required: 5.0 kW;

- Mass budget: ~130 kg.

The chosen control parameters are magnitude, azimuth and elevation.

DESIGNED TRAJECTORIES

As written previously, the complete transfer structure is a-priori divided into three phases, bounded by the following four main events:

- Earth departure,

- Lunar swingby,

- Ballistic capture,

- Moon arrival.

The spacecraft can perform an initial impulsive maneuver, then only the solar electric propulsion is available on board to conclude the transfer. Table 1 shows the trajectories computed in terms of initial impulsive maneuver (ΔV and corresponding chemical propulsion mass), low-thrust and lunar-delivered masses as well as flight time.

Table 1. Optimized hybrid propulsion transfers from GTO to a polar circular orbit around the Moon; last line corresponds to the classic Hohmann transfer.

Type	ΔV_{ht} [km/s]	Prop M_{ht} [kg]	Prop M_{lt} [kg]	Del M [kg]	ΔT [days]
sol.1	0.675	626.2	424.9	2018.9	173.2
sol.2	0.675	626.2	422.0	2021.8	169.3
sol.3	0.675	626.2	374.7	2069.1	151.8
sol.4	0.675	626.2	371.6	2072.2	142.9
Imp.	0.675	1189.9	–	1880.1	4.6

Forward/Forward Approach

In this section, a sample trajectory computed following the forward/forward approach is described. Each transfer phase is independently optimized by means of a forward propagation from the initial conditions to its final constraints; the latter are properly defined with respect the mission requirement. According to this method, a direct sensitivity analysis on the design parameters is straightforward.

Departure–Swingby Phase   Assuming a dedicated launch strategy with the Soyuz-Fregat, the departure date is a free design parameter of the mission. Then, after the insertion into the GTO , the spacecraft is lead to the lunar swingby by means of an impulsive translunar maneuver. The swingby is exploited in order to change the trajectory plane from the almost GEO one to the proper one related to the ballistic capture onto a polar orbit around the Moon. Moreover, the post-swingby conditions put the spacecraft into a WSB trajectory, with the semimajor axis of its orbit around the Earth equal to the Moon one, but the pericenter above the Van Allen belts.

In this phase, the assumptions are:

— Impulsive departure;

— Launch around January 2025;

— Analytic two-body model.

The optimization variables become:

— Departure date and ΔV;

— Midcourse maneuver date;

— Swingby date and targeting;

while the optimization constraints read:

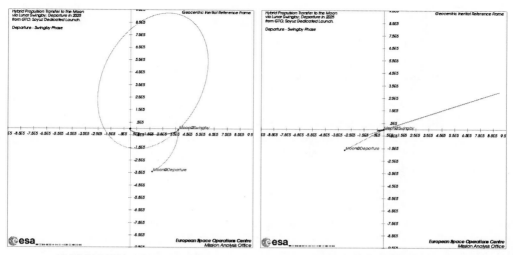

(a) EME.2000 in-plane trajectory. (b) EME.2000 out-of-plane trajectory.

Figure 1. Departure–Swingby phase trajectory plot of sol.2 of Table 1.

```
-------------- Earth Departure --------------        ---------------- Moon Swingby ----------------

------------ Spacecraft EME.2000 ------------        ------------ Spacecraft EME.2000 ------------

  MJD:     9132.2192034 = 2025/ 1/ 1  5:15:39.18        MJD:     9136.7523417 = 2025/ 1/ 5 18: 3:22.32

  Semi-major axis [km]:              24396.140          Semi-major axis [km]:             578375.905
  Eccentricity:                      .7283119           Eccentricity:                     .7367079
  Inclination [deg]:                 7.0059             Inclination [deg]:                18.4912
  R.A. of asc. node [deg]:           2.8377             R.A. of asc. node [deg]:          .5302
  Arg. of periapsis [deg]:           176.8594           Arg. of periapsis [deg]:          245.5940
  True anomaly [deg]:                .0000              True anomaly [deg]:               112.9938
  Angle wrt. v.e. [deg]:             179.6971           Angle wrt. v.e. [deg]:            359.1180
  Periapsis radius [km]:             6628.1400          Periapsis radius [km]:            152281.8285
  Apoapsis radius[km]:               42164.1400         Apoapsis radius[km]:              1004469.9815


-------------- Incoming Velocity -------------       ----------------------------------------------
                                                     Earth Departure - to - Moon Swingby
  Body: Moon                                         ----------------------------------------------
  vx [km/s]:                         .047283
  vy [km/s]:                         -.735391         --------------- Delta-V Summary ---------------
  vz [km/s]:                         -.480012
  total [km/s]:                      .879458          Translunar insertion [km/s]:        .675604
                                                      Midcourse maneuver [km/s]:          .000004
------------- Swingby Hyperbola --------------        Delta-V budget [km/s]:              .675609

  Semi-major axis [km]:              -6338.899        ---------------- Mass Summary ----------------
  Eccentricity:                      1.690539
  Inclination [deg]:                 33.771910        Earth departure [kg]:               3070.0000
  RA of ascending node [deg]:        16.757633        Moon swingby [kg]:                  2443.8175
  Argument of perigee:               205.335356       Mass consumption [kg]:              626.1825
  Hyperbolic excess vel. [km/s]:     .879458
  Pericenter radius [km]:            4377.257         ------------- Timeline Summary ---------------
  Pericenter altitude [km]:          2639.257
  Pericentre velocity [km/s]:        1.735964         Earth departure [d]:                .0000
  Semi-minor axis B [km]:            8640.276         Midcourse maneuver [d]:             4.1785
  B-T [km]:                          8571.643         Moon swingby [d]:                   4.5331
  B-R [km]:                          -1086.878        Phase duration [d]:                 4.5331
```

Figure 2. Departure–Swingby phase transfer data of sol.2 in Table 1.

- Post swingby 2:3 lunar resonance;

- Post swingby relative inclination i=10 deg.

The objective function corresponds to minimize the total ΔV.

Swingby–Capture Phase   After the lunar swingby, the spacecraft can rely only on its low-thrust propulsion to encounter again the Moon with reduced relative velocity. Exploiting explicitly the gravitational influences of the Earth, the Moon and the Sun on the spacecraft at the same time, the mathematical conditions to perform a ballistic almost-polar capture around the Moon are defined.

The ballistic capture significantly reduces the excess velocity that characterizes the hyperbolic approach. This allows the spacecraft to perform few orbits about the arrival body (a planet or a moon) at zero cost. As the capture is temporary, the spacecraft has to be maneuvered to achieve the final, stable orbit prescribed by mission requirements. It has been demonstrated that the cost needed to place the spacecraft into a given orbit may be less than the cost of typical hyperbolae pericenter injections provided that the ballistic capture is properly designed.[12]

In this phase, the assumptions are:

- Low-thrust encounter;

- Ballistic capture;

- Numerical four-body model;

- Phase subdivision in arcs.

The optimization variables become:

- Thrust magnitude within each arc;

- Thrust orientation (azimuth and elevation) within each arc;

- Encounter date;

- Capture date;

while the optimization constraints read:

- Encounter on the lunar sphere of influence;

- Capture in the lunar sphere of influence;

- Capture on a nearly polar orbit.

The objective function corresponds to maximize the final mass.

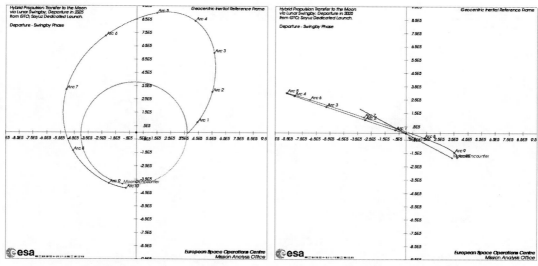

(a) EME.2000 in-plane trajectory.   (b) EME.2000 out-of-plane trajectory.

Figure 3. Swingby–Capture phase trajectory plot of sol.2 in Table 1.

```
--------------- Moon Encounter ---------------        --------------- Moon Capture ---------------

------------- Spacecraft EME.2000 -------------       ------------- Spacecraft EME.2000 -------------

MJD:     9183.8355751 = 2025/ 2/21 20: 3:13.69         MJD:     9190.8355751 = 2025/ 2/28 20: 3:13.69

Semi-major axis [km]:            1652772.061           Semi-major axis [km]:             117729.161
Eccentricity:                       .7457409           Eccentricity:                        .6782771
Inclination [deg]:                   31.9424           Inclination [deg]:                   45.8424
R.A. of asc. node [deg]:             28.3644           R.A. of asc. node [deg]:            144.7199
Arg. of periapsis [deg]:            241.9299           Arg. of periapsis [deg]:             25.9855
True anomaly [deg]:                 352.9802           True anomaly [deg]:                 324.9991
Angle wrt. v.e. [deg]:              263.2745           Angle wrt. v.e. [deg]:              135.7045
Periapsis radius [km]:           420232.3044           Periapsis radius [km]:            37876.1672
Apoapsis radius[km]:            2885311.8177           Apoapsis radius[km]:             197582.1545


-------------------------------------------           -------------------------------------------
    Moon Swingby - to - Moon Encounter                     Moon Encounter - to - Moon Capture
-------------------------------------------           -------------------------------------------


--------------- Delta-V Summary ---------------       --------------- Delta-V Summary ---------------

Delta-V budget [km/s]:               .847398          Delta-V budget [km/s]:               .000000

--------------- Mass Summary ---------------          --------------- Mass Summary ---------------

Moon swingby [kg]:                2443.8175           Moon encounter [kg]:              2326.9648
Moon encounter [kg]:              2326.9648           Moon capture [kg]:                2326.9648
Mass consumption [kg]:             116.8528           Mass consumption [kg]:                .0000

--------------- Timeline Summary ---------------      --------------- Timeline Summary ---------------

Moon swingby [d]:                    4.5331           Moon encounter [d]:                 51.6164
Moon encounter [d]:                 51.6164           Moon capture [d]:                   58.6164
Phase duration [d]:                 47.0832           Phase duration [d]:                  7.0000
```

Figure 4. Swingby–Capture phase transfer data of sol.2 in Table 1.

817

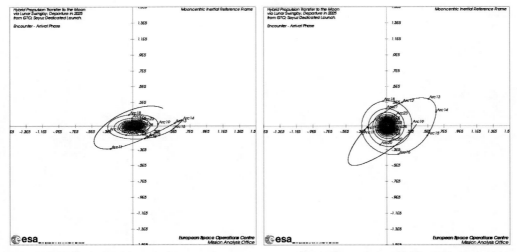

(a) MME.2000 in-plane trajectory.   (b) MME.2000 out-of-plane trajectory.

Figure 5. Capture–Arrival phase trajectory plot of sol.2 in Table 1.

Capture–Arrival Phase   Once the spacecraft is ballistically captured around the Moon, by means of the solar electric propulsion it decreases the altitude with respect to the lunar surface and it reduces the value of the eccentricity in order to reach the final target circular polar orbit with a prescribed altitude of 50 km.

In this phase, the assumptions are:

— Forward low-thrust descending;

— Numerical four-body model;

— Phase subdivision in arcs.

The optimization variables become:

— Thrust magnitude within each arc;

— Thrust orientation (azimuth and elevation) within each arc;

— Arrival date;

while the optimization constraints read:

— Nearly circular lunar orbit;

— Nearly polar lunar orbit.

818

```
---------------- Moon Arrival ---------------          ------------------------------------------------
                                                                  Moon Departure - to - Moon Arrival
------------- Spacecraft MME.2000 ------------         ------------------------------------------------

MJD:    9301.5061135 = 2025/ 6/19 12: 8:48.21          --------------- Delta-V Summary --------------

Semi-major axis [km]:           1788.000               Translunar insertion [km/s]:        .675604
Eccentricity:                   .0015563               Midcourse maneuver [km/s]:          .000004
Inclination [deg]:              89.3351                Swb-Enc Delta-V [km/s]:             .847398
R.A. of asc. node [deg]:        93.0172                Enc-Cap Delta-V [km/s]:             .000000
Arg. of periapsis [deg]:        352.5690               Cap-Arr Delta-V [km/s]:             2.24488
True anomaly [deg]:             105.2435
Angle wrt. v.e. [deg]:          190.8297               Delta-V budget [km/s]:              3.767886
Periapsis radius [km]:          1785.2173
Apoapsis radius[km]:            1790.7827              --------------- Mass Summary ----------------

------------------------------------------------        Earth departure [kg]:               3070.0000
             Moon Capture - to - Moon Arrival           Midcourse maneuver [kg]:            2443.8198
------------------------------------------------        Moon swingby [kg]:                  2443.8175
                                                        Moon encounter [kg]:                2326.9648
--------------- Delta-V Summary --------------          Moon capture [kg]:                  2326.9648
                                                        Moon arrival [kg]:                  2021.7863
Delta-V budget [km/s]:          2.248865
                                                        Mass consumption [kg]:              1048.2137
--------------- Mass Summary ----------------
                                                       -------------- Timeline Summary --------------
Moon capture [kg]:              2326.9648
Moon arrival [kg]:              2021.7863               Earth departure [d]:                .0000
Mass consumption [kg]:          305.1786               Midcourse maneuver [d]:             4.1785
                                                        Moon swingby [d]:                   4.5331
-------------- Timeline Summary --------------          Moon encounter [d]:                 51.6164
                                                        Moon capture [d]:                   58.6164
Moon arrival [d]:               58.6164                 Moon arrival [d]:                   169.2869
Moon insertion [d]:             169.2869
Phase duration [d]:             110.6705                Transfer duration [d]:              169.2869
```

Figure 6. Capture–Arrival phase transfer data of sol.2 in Table 1.

The objective function corresponds to maximize the final mass.

On the right side of Figure 6 a summary of the transfer corresponding to sol.2 in Table 1 is reported. First of all, it is possible to notice that a midcourse maneuver between the departure and the lunar swingby is considered as a free design parameter: as a result of the optimization process, it turn out that this maneuver is almost negligible. As far as concerns the transfer performances, the propellant mass required is lower than the Hohmann one (see Table 1), while the flight time is much higher. Actually, as the transfer time till the lunar capture is comparable with the classic WSB trajectories, the longest part of the journey is related to the spiral arc necessary to lower the orbit altitude around the Moon.

Forward/Backward Approach

In this section, a sample trajectory obtained following the forward/backward approach is presented. The initial phases are forward integrated, while the final one is backward integrated. The trajectory continuity is obtained solving the joint of the phases at the their boundaries, by the formulation of an iterative optimal control problem, with assigned conditions at both boundaries of the transfer.

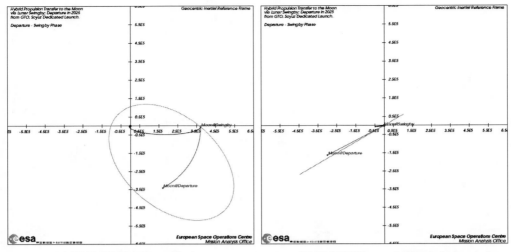

(a) EME.2000 in-plane trajectory. (b) EME.2000 out-of-plane trajectory.

Figure 7. Departure–Swingby phase trajectory plot of sol.4 in Table 1.

Departure–Swingby Phase Assuming once again a dedicated launch strategy with the Soyuz-Fregat, the departure date is a free design parameter. After the insertion into the GTO , the spacecraft is lead to the lunar swingby by means of an impulsive translunar maneuver. By means of the swingby, the trajectory plane inclination is changed from the almost GEO one to the proper one related to the ballistic capture onto a polar orbit around the Moon. The post-swingby conditions see the spacecraft into a WSB trajectory, with the semimajor axis of its orbit around the Earth larger then the Moon one and with the pericenter above the Van Allen belts.

In this phase, the assumptions are:

— Impulsive departure;

— Launch around January 2025;

— Analytic two-body model.

The optimization variables become:

— Departure date and ΔV;

— Midcourse maneuver date;

— Swingby date and targeting;

while the optimization constraints read:

— Post swingby 1:1 lunar resonance;

— Post swingby relative inclination i=6 deg.

The objective function corresponds to minimize the total ΔV.

820

```
--------------- Earth Departure ---------------          ---------------- Moon Swingby ----------------

------------ Spacecraft EME.2000 ------------          ------------- Spacecraft EME.2000 ------------

MJD:     9132.2247678 = 2025/ 1/ 1  5:23:39.94          MJD:     9136.7517710 = 2025/ 1/ 5 18: 2:33.01

Semi-major axis [km]:              24396.140          Semi-major axis [km]:              385577.176
Eccentricity:                      0.7283119          Eccentricity:                      0.7648472
Inclination [deg]:                 7.0059             Inclination [deg]:                 34.4891
R.A. of asc. node [deg]:           2.8464             R.A. of asc. node [deg]:           359.9359
Arg. of periapsis [deg]:           176.8594           Arg. of periapsis [deg]:           137.1987
True anomaly [deg]:                0.0000             True anomaly [deg]:                221.9240
Angle wrt. v.e. [deg]:             179.7058           Angle wrt. v.e. [deg]:             359.0587
Periapsis radius [km]:             6628.1400          Periapsis radius [km]:             90669.5714
Apoapsis radius[km]:               42164.1400         Apoapsis radius[km]:               680484.7812


------------- Incoming Velocity -------------          ----------------------------------------------
                                                              Earth Departure - to - Moon Swingby
Body: Moon                                             ----------------------------------------------
vx [km/s]:                         0.048778
vy [km/s]:                         -0.735394          --------------- Delta-V Summary ---------------
vz [km/s]:                         -0.480063
total [km/s]:                      0.879570           Translunar insertion [km/s]:       0.675611
                                                       Midcourse maneuver [km/s]:         0.000066
------------- Swingby Hyperbola --------------          Delta-V budget [km/s]:             0.675677

Semi-major axis [km]:              -6337.279          --------------- Mass Summary ----------------
Eccentricity:                      1.763518
Inclination [deg]:                 146.865030         Earth departure [kg]:              3070.0000
RA of ascending node [deg]:        187.542760         Moon swingby [kg]:                 2443.7636
Argument of perigee:               -142.315541        Mass consumption [kg]:             626.2364
Hyperbolic excess vel. [km/s]:     0.879570
Pericenter radius [km]:            4838.629           ------------- Timeline Summary --------------
Pericenter altitude [km]:          3100.629
Pericentre velocity [km/s]:        1.673370           Earth departure [d]:               0.0000
Semi-minor axis B [km]:            9205.423           Midcourse maneuver [d]:            1.7752
B-T [km]:                          -9199.545          Moon swingby [d]:                  4.5270
B-R [km]:                          328.916            Phase duration [d]:                4.5270
```

Figure 8. Departure–Swingby phase transfer data of sol.4 in Table 1.

Swingby–Encounter Phase   After the lunar swingby, the spacecraft can use only on its low-thrust propulsion to encounter again the Moon with reduced relative velocity. The mathematical conditions to perform a ballistic almost-polar capture around the Moon are defined taking into account explicitly the gravitational influences - at the same time - of the Earth, the Moon and the Sun on the spacecraft.

The final encounter with the Moon is searched such that the conditions of a ballistic capture implicitly arise. By means of this approach, the incoming hyperbolic velocity reduces significantly. As the capture is temporary, a manoeuver is required in order to place the spacecraft into the final, stable orbit prescribed by mission requirements. It has been proven - provided that the ballistic capture is properly designed - that the cost needed to place the spacecraft into a given orbit may be less than the cost of typical hyperbolae pericenter injections.[12]

In this phase, the assumptions are:

— Low-thrust encounter;

— Ballistic capture;

— Numerical four-body model;

821

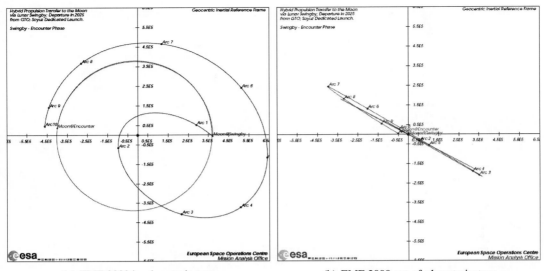

(a) EME.2000 in-plane trajectory. (b) EME.2000 out-of-plane trajectory.

Figure 9. Swingby–Capture phase trajectory plot of sol.4 in Table 1.

```
--------------- Moon Encounter ---------------      --------------- Moon Capture ---------------

------------- Spacecraft EME.2000 ------------      ------------- Spacecraft MME.2000 ------------

MJD:    9177.0801409 = 2025/ 2/15  1:55:24.18       MJD:    9181.0801409 = 2025/ 2/19  1:55:24.18

Semi-major axis [km]:        1021555.452            Semi-major axis [km]:          59204.109
Eccentricity:                  0.5453976            Eccentricity:                   0.4313978
Inclination [deg]:            35.8921               Inclination [deg]:             88.0001
R.A. of asc. node [deg]:     354.7362               R.A. of asc. node [deg]:        4.2021
Arg. of periapsis [deg]:     179.5089               Arg. of periapsis [deg]:        8.1876
True anomaly [deg]:          359.3471               True anomaly [deg]:           233.1553
Angle wrt. v.e. [deg]:       173.5922               Angle wrt. v.e. [deg]:        245.5450
Periapsis radius [km]:       464401.5332            Periapsis radius [km]:        33663.5891
Apoapsis radius[km]:         1578709.3710           Apoapsis radius[km]:          84744.6294


------------------------------------------          ------------------------------------------
    Moon Swingby - to - Moon Encounter                  Moon Encounter - to - Moon Capture
------------------------------------------          ------------------------------------------


--------------- Delta-V Summary ---------------     --------------- Delta-V Summary ---------------

Delta-V budget [km/s]:         0.805202             Delta-V budget [km/s]:          0.000000

---------------- Mass Summary ----------------      ---------------- Mass Summary ----------------

Moon swingby [kg]:           2443.7636              Moon encounter [kg]:           2331.3783
Moon encounter [kg]:         2331.3783              Moon capture [kg]:             2331.3783
Mass consumption [kg]:        112.3853              Mass consumption [kg]:            0.0000

-------------- Timeline Summary --------------      -------------- Timeline Summary --------------

Moon swingby [d]:               4.5270              Moon encouter [d]:               44.8554
Moon encounter [d]:            44.8554              Moon capture [d]:                48.8554
Phase duration [d]:            40.3284              Phase duration [d]:               4.0000
```

Figure 10. Swingby–Capture phase transfer data of sol.4 in Table 1.

— Phase subdivision in arcs.

The optimization variables become:

   — Thrust magnitude within each arc;

   — Thrust orientation (azimuth and elevation) within each arc;

   — Encounter date;

   — Capture date;

while the optimization constraints read:

   — Encounter-Arrival initial state.

The objective function corresponds to maximize the final mass.

Encounter–Arrival Phase   The last phase is designed by means of a backward integration starting from the final target circular polar orbit with a prescribed altitude of 50 km. The thrust is considered acting in the direction opposite to the velocity, in order to reach the lunar sphere of influence in minimum time, also providing the conditions of a ballistic capture.

In this phase, the assumptions are:

   — Forward low-thrust descending;

   — Numerical four-body model;

   — Phase subdivision in arcs.

The optimization variables become:

   — Thrust magnitude within each arc;

   — Thrust orientation (azimuth and elevation) within each arc;

   — Arrival date;

while the optimization constraints read:

   — Nearly circular lunar orbit;

   — Nearly polar lunar orbit.

The objective function corresponds to minimize the flight time.

A summary of the transfer corresponding to sol.4 in Table 1 is reported on the right side of Figure 12. First of all, it is possible to notice, as in the case of sol.2, that the optimization process forces the midcourse maneuver between the departure and the lunar swingby to be almost negligible. As far as concerns the transfer performances, the propellant mass required is lower than the Hohmann one (see Table 1), while the flight time is much higher. Once again, the transfer time till the lunar capture is comparable with the classic WSB trajectories, while the longest part of the journey is related to the spiral arc necessary to lower the orbit altitude around the Moon.

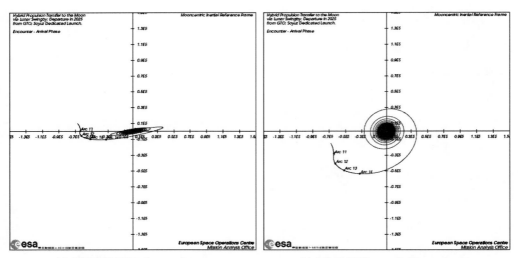

(a) MME.2000 in-plane trajectory.   (b) MME.2000 out-of-plane trajectory.

Figure 11. Capture–Arrival phase trajectory plot of sol.4 in Table 1.

```
--------------- Moon Arrival ---------------

------------ Spacecraft MME.2000 -----------

MJD:    9275.0801409 = 2025/ 5/24  1:55:24.18

Semi-major axis [km]:               1788.000
Eccentricity:                     0.0002130
Inclination [deg]:                 90.1205
R.A. of asc. node [deg]:            9.5482
Arg. of periapsis [deg]:           27.4886
True anomaly [deg]:                53.6886
Angle wrt. v.e. [deg]:             90.7254
Periapsis radius [km]:           1787.6191
Apoapsis radius[km]:             1788.3804


-------------------------------------------
        Moon Capture - to - Moon Arrival
-------------------------------------------

--------------- Delta-V Summary -------------

Delta-V budget [km/s]:             1.939246

--------------- Mass Summary ----------------

Moon capture [kg]:               2331.3783
Moon arrival [kg]:               2072.1693
Mass consumption [kg]:            259.2090

-------------- Timeline Summary -------------

Moon capture [d]:                  48.8554
Moon arrival [d]:                 142.8554
Phase duration [d]:                94.0000
```

```
-------------------------------------------
        Earth Departure - to - Moon Arrival
-------------------------------------------

--------------- Delta-V Summary -------------

Translunar insertion [km/s]:        0.675611
Midcourse maneuver [km/s]:         0.000066
Swb-Enc Delta-V [km/s]:            0.805202
Enc-Cap budget [km/s]:             0.000000
Cap-Arr budget [km/s]:             1.939246

Delta-V budget [km/s]:             3.420125

--------------- Mass Summary ----------------

Earth departure [kg]:            3070.0000
Moon swingby [kg]:               2443.7636
Moon encounter [kg]:             2331.3783
Moon capture [kg]:               2331.3783
Moon arrival [kg]:               2072.1693

Mass consumption [kg]:            997.8307

-------------- Timeline Summary -------------

Earth departure [d]:                0.0000
Midcourse maneuver [d]:             1.7752
Moon swingby [d]:                   4.5270
Moon encouter [d]:                 44.8554
Moon capture [d]:                  48.8554
Moon arrival [d]:                 142.8554

Transfer duration [d]:            142.8554
```

Figure 12. Capture–Arrival phase transfer data of sol.4 in Table 1.

824

ACKNOWLEDGMENTS

The author would like to acknowledge Mr. M.Khan and Mr. J.Schoenmaekers for their useful suggestion and their valid support during his internship at the European Space Operations Centre, in the Mission Analysis Section.

CONCLUSIONS

This work concerns preliminary parametric design of Earth-to-Moon transfers, exploiting both chemical (high-thrust) and solar electric (low-thrust) propulsion. Starting from a GTO, assuming a dedicated launch strategy, several trajectories to a polar orbit around the Moon, with initial lunar swingby, are evaluated in terms of propellant mass consumption and flight time. Two different mathematical approaches have been developed, the forward/forward one and the forward/backward one. The application of the first leads to a straightforward sensitivity analysis on the design parameters.

REFERENCES

[1] W. Koon, M. Lo, J. Marsden, and S. Ross, "Low Energy Transfer to the Moon," *Celestial Mechanics and Dynamical Astronomy*, Vol. 81, 2001, pp. 63–73.

[2] M. Lo and M. Chung, "Lunar Sample Return via the Interplanetary Superhighway," *AIAA/AAS Conference*, Vol. 886, 2002, pp. 100–110.

[3] J. Parker and M. Lo, "Shoot The Moon 3D," *Advances in the Astronautical Sciences*, Vol. 123, 2006.

[4] G. Gómez, J. Masdemont, and J. Mondelo, "A Dynamical System Approach for the Analysis of the SOHO Mission," *Third International Symposium on Spacecraft Flight Dynamics, European Space Agency, Darmstadt, Germany*, 1991, pp. 449–454.

[5] K. Howell, B. Barden, and M. Lo, "Application of Dynamical Systems Theory to Trajectory Design for a Libration Point Mission," *Journal of Astronautical Sciences*, Vol. 45, No. 2, 1997, pp. 161–178.

[6] M. Lo, B. Williams, W. Bollman, D. Han, Y. Hahn, J. Bell, E. Hirst, R. Corwin, P. Hong, K. Howell, B. Barden, and R. Wilson, "Genesis mission design," *The Journal of the Astronautical Sciences*, Vol. 49, 2001, pp. 169–184.

[7] J. Parker, "Families of Low-Energy Lunar Halo Transfers," *AAS/AIAA Spaceflight Dynamics Conference*, Vol. 90, 2006, pp. 1–20.

[8] L. Mingtao and Z. Jianhua, "Impulsive Lunar Halo Transfers Using the Stable Manifolds and Lunar Flybys," *Acta Astronautica*, Vol. 66, 2010, pp. 1481–1492.

[9] M. Ozimek and K. Howell, "Low-Thrust Transfers in the Earth-Moon System, Including Applications to Libration Point Orbits," *Journal of Guidance, Control, and Dynamics*, Vol. 33, 2010.

[10] M. Lo and J. Parker, "Unstable Resonant Orbits near Earth and their Applications in Planetary Missions," *AIAA/AAS Conference*, Vol. 5304, 2007.

[11] X. Ming and X. Shijie, "Exploration of Distant Retrograde Orbits Around Moon," *Acta Astronautica*, Vol. 65, No. 5-6, 2009, pp. 853–860.

[12] E. Belbruno and J. Miller, "Sun-Perturbed Earth-to-Moon Transfers with Ballistic Capture," *Journal of Guidance Control and Dynamics*, Vol. 16, 1993, pp. 770–775.

[13] J. Schoenmaekers, D. Horas, and J. Pulido, "SMART-1: With Solar Electric Propulsion to the Moon," *Proceedings of the 16th International Symposium on Space Flight Dynamics*, 2007.

[14] G. Mingotti, F. Topputo, and F. Bernelli-Zazzera, "A Hybrid Propulsion Approach to Design Earth-To-moon Transfers with Ballistic Capture," *5th New Trends in Astrodynamics and Applications, Milano, Italy, 30 June-2 July*, 2008.

[15] G. Mingotti, F. Topputo, and F. Bernelli-Zazzera, "Low-energy, low-thrust transfers to the Moon," *Celestial Mechanics and Dynamical Astronomy*, Vol. 105, No. 1-3, 2009, pp. 61–74.

[16] G. Mingotti, F. Topputo, and F. Bernelli-Zazzera, "Low-Thrust, Invariant-Manifolds Trajectories to Halo Orbits," *XX Congresso nazionale AIDAA, Milano, Italia, 29 June.-3 July*, 2009.

[17] G. Mingotti, F. Topputo, and F. Bernelli-Zazzera, "Dynamical Systems, Optimal Control and Space Trajectory Design," *5th International Meeting on Celestial Mechanics (CelMecV), Viterbo, Italy, 6–12 Sept.*, 2009.

[18] G. Mingotti, F. Topputo, and F. Bernelli-Zazzera, "Numerical Methods to Design Low-Energy, Low-Thrust Sun-Perturbed Transfers to the Moon," *Proceedings of 49th Israel Annual Conference on Aerospace Sciences, Tel Aviv–Haifa, Israel*, 2009.

[19] G. Mingotti, F. Topputo, and F. Bernelli-Zazzera, "Efficient Invariant-Manifold, Low-Thrust Planar Trajectories to the Moon," *3rd Conference on Nonlinear Science and Complexity, Ankara, Turkey, 28-31 July*, 2010.

[20] G. Mingotti and F. Topputo, "Ways to the Moon: A Survey," *21st AAS/AIAA Space Flight Mechanics Meeting, New Orleans, LA, USA, 13-17 Feb.*, 2011.

RESEARCH OF THE FREE-RETURN TRAJECTORIES
BETWEEN THE EARTH-MOON

Qinqin Luo,[*] Jianfeng Yin[†] and Chao Han[‡]

A new design method for the free-return lunar flyby trajectories between the Earth and the Moon is developed in this paper. The pseudostate theory is adopted to get the initial result of the free-return trajectory. On the basis of the initial result, an improved differential-correction method is employed to find the final solution in a more complicated dynamic model. The global features of the free-return lunar flyby trajectories are studied via the design method proposed in this paper, and some valuable results are obtained.

INTRODUCTION

Since the sixties of last century, the free-return lunar flyby orbit has drawn much attention due to its special characteristics. After the only one maneuver at the injection point near the Earth, the probe is injected impulsively into the free-return trajectory from a low Earth parking orbit. Then, the probe performs a flyby around the Moon with a fixed perilune altitude and return to the vicinity of the Earth with some specified reentry conditions. Free-return lunar flyby trajectory is very useful in the lunar exploration activities.

Free-return lunar flyby trajectory has been studied by many scholars since Apollo era. Schwaniger discussed the symmetrical free-return lunar flyby trajectories on the basis of the symmetry of the circular restricted three body system (CRTBS)[1]. Based on the work of Schwaniger, Jesick proposed an algorithm to construct the symmetrical free-return lunar flyby trajectories in the CRTBS[2]. The free-return lunar flyby trajectories were classified by Penzo in many ways[3]. It is very helpful for understanding the free-return lunar flyby trajectories. Johnson defined a translunar perigee surface which is composed of the perigees of the free-return lunar flyby trajectories, and this tool was used to studied the free-return trajectories with fixed launch azimuth[4]. A gradient method for obtaining free-return lunar flyby trajectories was proposed by Green[5]. The constraints on the trajectory were dealt with through a penalty function. Battin also given a preliminary design algorithm for the free-return lunar flyby trajectories based on the patched-conic technique[6]. Byrnes[7] developed a three-body Lambert problem solution algorithm based on the pseudostate theory[8] which is composed of two conic Lambert problem and a seven dimensional diffe-

---

[*] Ph.D. Candidate, School of Astronautics, Beihang University, Beijing 100191, China.
[†] Ph.D. Candidate, School of Astronautics, Beihang University, Beijing 100191, China.
[‡] Professor, School of Astronautics, Beihang University, Beijing 100191, China.

rential correction. It can be used for the free-return trajectories preliminary design and other more complicated problems, such as the multiple flyby trajectories design[9].

Usually, the free-return lunar flyby trajectories design method is divided into two steps. First, an initial result is found via a preliminary design algorithm based on the patched-conic technique. Then, the final solution which corresponds to a more complicated dynamic model is obtained through the differential-correction method. Because of the poor initial result and the high sensitivity of the free-return lunar flyby trajectories, it is very difficult to get a convergence solution in the second step. So, generally, a two phases iterative algorithm and the B-plane parameters are utilized to make the convergence easier.

A new preliminary design algorithm based on the pseudostate theory[8] is proposed in this paper. This new algorithm can get a better initial result for the free-return lunar flyby trajectory. On the basis of this better initial result, the differential-correction method with only one phase can be employed to find the final solution efficiently. A algorithm to calculate the second-order state transition matrix is also developed in this paper. With the second-order state transition matrix, an improved differential-correction method is used to get a faster convergence speed and a larger convergence domain.

The paper is organized as follows. After a brief introduction about the quasi-Lambert's problem with fixed flight-direction angle constraint and the pseudostate theory, the preliminary design algorithm and final solution searching algorithm are developed. On the basis of the method proposed in this paper, the free-return lunar flyby trajectories are explored intensively. The algorithm to calculate state transition matrix and the second-order state transition matrix are described in the Appendix.

THE QUASI-LAMBERT'S PROBLEM WITH FIXED FLIGHT-DIRECTION ANGLE CONSTRAINT

The two-point boundary value problem of Kepler orbit has drawn much attention due to its extensive application in many aerospace fields, such as orbit determination, trajectory optimization, and spacecraft guidance, among others. Generally, in practical applications, as shown in Figure 1, the Kepler orbit boundary problem can be described with variables r_1, r_2, θ, γ_1, γ_2 and Δt_{12}.

Let O be the center of the gravity field, P_1 and P_2 be the initial point and final point on the orbit that corresponding to time t_1 and t_2, respectively. $\Delta t_{12} = t_2 - t_1$ is the flight time from P_1 to P_2. r_1 and r_2 are the radial distances of P_1 and P_2 to the center of gravity field, respectively. θ is the transfer angle between the vectors $\vec{r}_1$ and $\vec{r}_2$ with respect to O. γ_1 and γ_2 are the angle between the velocity vector and the position vector (also called flight-direction angle) at P_1 and P_2 respectively. Usually, six independent parameters are required to determine an orbit in the three-dimensional space. However, two of them can be eliminated if the orbit plane is predetermined by other constraints. Therefore, only four independent parameters are needed to determine the orbit. An example would be, the two angle variables and two time variables in the orbit determination problem previously studied by Gauss[10].

Lambert's problem is one of the most famous Kepler orbit boundary problem. Lambert's problem can be defined as finding a Kepler orbit that allows a transfer between two given radius vector in a specified flight time. So, the Kepler orbit is determined according to r_1, r_2, θ and

Δt_{12}. Lambert's problem has been successfully applied in the near-Earth and deep space orbit design, orbit determination and other fields.

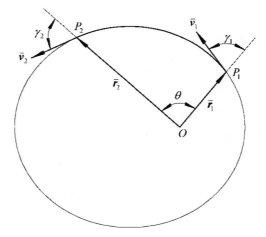

Figure 1. Geometric configuration of the two-point boundary value problem in the Kepler orbit.

But, in lunar transfer trajectory design, the problem of determining a Kepler orbit based on r_1, r_2, γ_1 and Δt_{12} is frequently encountered. For instance, we need to find a lunar transfer trajectory starting from the perigee, which means $\gamma_1 = \pi/2$, and arriving on the Moon in a specified time interval. A more complicated example is the return trajectory from the Moon which has a strict limitation on the reentry angle when the probe enters Earth's atmosphere because of the requirement for thermal protection. This is actually a constraint on flight-direction angle. We refer to this kind of problem as quasi-Lambert's problem with fixed flight-direction angle constraint. Thus, this problem can be stated as solving a Kepler orbit with a fixed flight-direction angle at the initial point, having a specified time and connecting two points only assigned radial distances. Compared with Lambert's problem, quasi-Lambert's problem with fixed flight-direction angle constraint relaxes the constraint on the transfer angle from P_1 to P_2. However, it adds the constraint on the flight-direction angle at P_1 instead.

A double-nested iterative method was invented by Ramanan to solve this problem during the lunar transfer orbit design[11]. However, his method only works in the situation that $\gamma_1 = \pi/2$. Furthermore, large amount of computation is required due to the double-nested iteration. Another method for this problem is proposed in reference 12. This method only need one-level iteration, and it is appropriate to the cases that $\gamma_1 \in (0, \pi)$.

THE PSEUDOSTATE THEORY

The pseudostate theory was developed for the approximation of three-body trajectory[7]. It is particularly suitable for the typical lunar transfer trajectory which transfers from the Earth to the Moon in 3 to 5 days. For the typical lunar transfer trajectory, its error magnitude is only 20 percent as great as the patched-conic orbit error.

Considering Earth-Moon-probe three-body system, the probe has no influence on the motion of the Earth and the Moon. All forces except the central gravitational forces of the Earth and the Moon are ignored. The geocentric states of probe at initial time t_I and later time t_k are $\Sigma_I = (t_I, \bar{R}_I, \bar{V}_I)$ and $\Sigma_k = (t_k, \bar{R}_k, \bar{V}_k)$, respectively. The selenocentric state corresponding to t_k is $\sigma_k = (t_k, \bar{r}_k, \bar{v}_k)$. Let $\Sigma_m = (t_k, \bar{R}_m, \bar{V}_m)$ be the geocentric state of the Moon at t_k. The relationship between Σ_k and σ_k is

$$\begin{cases} \bar{R}_k = \bar{r}_k + \bar{R}_m \\ \bar{V}_k = \bar{v}_k + \bar{V}_m \end{cases} \tag{1}$$

At time t_k, a moon-centered pseudostate transformation sphere (PTS) is defined. The radius of the PTS is R_{PTS}. Assuming that $\bar{R}_I$ is outside the PTS and $\bar{R}_K$ is inside the PTS.

Then, as shown in figure 2, the method of calculating Σ_k according to Σ_I is as follows.

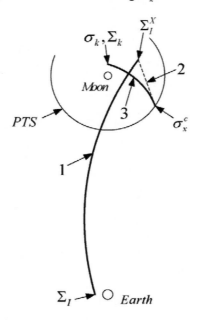

Figure 2. The pseudostate theory.

1. Geocentric conic. The pesudostate $\Sigma_I^X = (t_k, \bar{R}_I^X, \bar{V}_I^X)$ is obtained by propagating the initial state Σ_I in the central gravitational field of the Earth from t_I to t_k.

2. Linear back propagation section. The selenocentric state $\sigma_I^X = (t_k, \bar{r}_I^X, \bar{v}_I^X)$ corresponding to Σ_I^X is calculated. Then $\sigma_x^c = (t_x^c, \bar{r}_x^c, \bar{v}_x^c)$ is obtained through the following equations

$$\begin{cases} \bar{r}_x^c = \bar{r}_I^x + (t_x^c - t_k)\bar{v}_I^x \\ \bar{v}_x^c = \bar{v}_I^x \end{cases} \tag{2}$$

t_x^c is determined by the constraints that $\left\| \bar{r}_x^c \right\| = R_{PTS}$ and $t_x^c < t_k$.

3. Selenocentric conic. The selenocentric state σ_k is obtained by propagating the σ_x^c in the central gravitational field of the Moon from t_x^c to t_k. Then the geocentric state Σ_k is calculated via Eq. (1).

The method is appropriate to the case that σ_k is a preperilune state. If σ_k is a postperilune state, the calculation process should be divided into two phases, preperilune phase and postperilune phase. The postperilune phase can be calculated as the same as the method proposed above, but in a reverse order.

THE CONSTRAINTS ON THE FREE-RETURN LUNAR FLYBY ORBIT

In a lunar transfer trajectory, if the injection time and transfer time are specified, the whole trajectory is determined by the initial state. Hence, it is a six-dimensional system.

Let i_{EM} be the angle of inclination of the outbound trajectory plane with respect to the equatorial plane of the Earth, and R_0 be the perigee radius of the outbound trajectory. i_{EM} and R_0 are determined by the launch vehicle. The injection point is chosen as the perigee of the outbound trajectory. It means the flight direction angle at the injection point is 90 degrees. There are three constraints on the injection point.

The perilune radius r_p is given for the specific lunar exploration mission. The time of arrival at the perilune is also specified. There are two constraints on the perilune.

Because of the requirement for thermal protection when the probe entries Earth's atmosphere, there is a strict limitation on the reentry angle γ_E. The altitude of reentry point is usually 120 km. But, the reentry time is not fixed. So, there is only one constraint on the reentry point.

Now, the mathematical description of the six constraints on the free-return lunar flyby trajectory is given. The injection time is t_0, and the time of perilune arrival (TPA) is t_p. The transfer time from the perigee to the perilune is $t_{EM} = t_p - t_0$. The geocentric state of the perigee point is denoted by $\vec{R}_0$ and $\vec{V}_0$. The selenocentric state at t_p is $\vec{r}_p$ and $\vec{v}_p$. The geocentric state of reentry point is $\vec{R}_E$ and $\vec{V}_E$. The six constraints on the free-return trajectory can be state as

$$\begin{cases} \|\vec{R}_0\| = R_0 \\ \vec{R}_0 \cdot \vec{V}_0 = 0 \\ \vec{Z} \cdot (\vec{R}_0 \times \vec{V}_0) = \cos i_{EL} \\ \|\vec{r}_p\| = r_p \\ \vec{r}_p \cdot \vec{v}_p = 0 \\ \vec{R}_E \cdot \vec{V}_E = \cos \gamma_E \end{cases} \qquad (3)$$

where $\vec{Z}$ is the unit vector of the z axis of the geocentric equatorial inertial coordinate system.

PRELIMINARY DESIGN ALGORITHM

On the basis of pseudostate theory, a preliminary design algorithm to find an initial result of the free-return lunar flyby trajectory is proposed in this section. The result meets the constraints which are listed in Eq. (3).

The concrete steps of the preliminary design algorithm are as follows:

1. The geocentric state of the Moon $\vec{R}_m$ and $\vec{V}_m$ at TPA t_p is calculated.

2. Let the iterative variables $\vec{R}_{S1}$ and $\vec{R}_{S2}$ both be $\vec{R}_m$.

3. The outbound trajectory plane is adjusted to contain the vector $\vec{R}_{S1}$. There are two situations corresponding to ascending outbound trajectory and descending outbound trajectory, respectively.

4. The geocentric conic orbit transfer from perigee to $\vec{R}_{S1}$ in a specified time t_{EL} is determined by solving the quasi-Lambert's problem with fixed flight-direction angle constraint. The geocentric velocity vector $\vec{V}_{S1}$ at $\vec{R}_{S1}$ is obtained. The corresponding selenocentric velocity vector is $\vec{v}_{S1} = \vec{V}_{S1} - \vec{V}_m$, and the magnitude is v_{S1}.

5. An appropriate initial value is chosen for the return time from the perilune to the reentry point t_{ME}.

6. The geocentric return orbit transfer from $\vec{R}_{S2}$ to the reentry point with a specified reentry angle in the time t_{ME} is found by solving the quasi-Lambert's problem with fixed flight-direction angle constraint. It should be noted that the plane of the return orbit is not determined. So, the geocentric velocity vector $\vec{V}_{S2}$ at $\vec{R}_{S2}$ cannot yet be obtained except the magnitude V_{S2} and the angle between $\vec{R}_{S2}$ and $\vec{V}_{S2}$. The magnitude of the selenocentric velocity vector $\vec{v}_{S2} = \vec{V}_{S2} - \vec{V}_m$ is denoted by v_{S2}. Then, the plane of the return orbit is rotated around $\vec{R}_{S2}$ to make v_{S2} equals v_{S1}.

Assuming that the angle between $\vec{V}_{S2}$ and $\vec{V}_m$ is β, the following equation can be got from the law of cosines for plane triangle.

$$\cos\beta = \frac{V_{S2}^2 + V_m^2 - v_{S2}^2}{2V_{S2}V_m} \tag{4}$$

The angle between $\vec{R}_{S2}$ and $\vec{V}_m$ is α, and the angle between the plane of return orbit and the plane which composed by $\vec{R}_{S2}$ and $\vec{V}_m$ is denoted by ϕ. According to the spherical law of cosines, the following equation is obtained.

$$\cos\phi = \frac{\cos\beta + \cos\delta\cos\alpha}{\sin\delta\sin\alpha} \tag{5}$$

There are two solutions for ϕ which correspond to the ascending return trajectory and descending return trajectory. A right-handed coordinate system $o-xyz$ is defined. $\vec{R}_{S2}/\|\vec{R}_{S2}\|$ is the x axis, and $-\vec{R}_{S2}\times\vec{V}_m/\|\vec{R}_{S2}\times\vec{V}_m\|$ is the z axis. The coordinate of $\vec{V}_{S2}$ in the coordinate system $o-xyz$ is $[V_{S2}\cos\delta, V_{S2}\sin\delta\cos\phi, V_{S2}\sin\delta\sin\phi]$ which meets $v_{S2}=v_{S1}$.

7. $\vec{v}_{S1}$ and $\vec{v}_{S2}$ are the selenocentric velocity vectors at the PTS entry point and exit point, respectively. The selenocentric position vectors of these two points are denoted by $\vec{r}_{S1}$ and $\vec{r}_{S2}$,

respectively. The angle between $\bar{v}_{S1}$ and $\bar{v}_{S2}$ is $\pi - 2C$, and the angle between $\bar{r}_{S1}$ and $\bar{v}_{S1}$ is denoted by γ_{S1}. $\gamma_{S1} > \pi/2$, because of $\bar{r}_{S1}$ is a preperilune position vector. Let r_{ps} and v_{ps} be the corresponding perilune radius and perilune velocity, respectively. According to conservation of energy and conservation of angle momentum, the following equations are obtained.

$$\frac{1}{2}v_{S1}^2 - \frac{\mu_m}{r_{S1}} = \frac{1}{2}v_{ps}^2 - \frac{\mu_m}{r_{ps}} \tag{6}$$

$$r_{ps}v_{ps} = r_{S1}v_{S1}\sin\gamma_{S1} \tag{7}$$

For the conic, one gets

$$r_{S1}\cot\frac{\pi}{2} + r_{ps}\cot\gamma_{S1} = (r_{ps} - r_{S1})\cot\frac{\gamma_{S1} - C}{2}$$

$$\Rightarrow r_{ps} = \frac{r_{S1}\cot\dfrac{\gamma_{S1} - C}{2}}{\cot\dfrac{\gamma_{S1} - C}{2} - \cot\gamma_{S1}} \tag{8}$$

Then, an iterative algorithm to calculate the corresponding perilune radius r_{ps} is developed.

Assuming that $\bar{v}_{S1}$ and $\bar{v}_{S2}$ are parallel to the two asymptotes of the selenocentric hyperbola orbit respectively, the approximation of the eccentricity of this orbit is $e = \sec C$. Hence, the initial value of the perilune radius is $r_{ps1} = \mu_m(e-1)/v_{S1}^2$. Then, v_{ps} is obtained via Eq. (6), and γ_{S1} is calculated via Eq. (7). Following that, r_{ps2} is calculated via Eq. (8). r_{ps2} is assigned to r_{ps1}. Repeating the above operations until the difference between r_{ps1} and r_{ps2} is small enough. r_{ps1} is the result of the perilune radius r_{ps} corresponding to $\bar{v}_{S1}$ and $\bar{v}_{S2}$.

8. The return time t_{ME} is systematically adjusted and steps 6, 7 are repeated until $r_{ps} = r_p$. The velocity at perilune is v_{ps}.

9. The unit vector $\bar{h}$ is calculated by $\bar{h} = \bar{v}_{S1} \times \bar{v}_{S2}/\|\bar{v}_{S1} \times \bar{v}_{S2}\|$. The unit vectors $\bar{v}$ and $\bar{w}$ are defined as $\bar{v} = \bar{v}_{S1}/v_{S1}$ and $\bar{w} = \bar{v} \times \bar{h}$. Let $X = r_{ps}v_{ps}/r_{S1}$ and $Y = -(r_{S1}^2 - X^2)^{1/2}$, then $\bar{r}_{S1} = X\bar{v} + Y\bar{w}$. The flight time from the PTS entry point to the perilune is denoted by t_{PTS}, and it is calculated according to $\bar{r}_{S1}$ and $\bar{v}_{S1}$. $\bar{R}_{S1}$ is updated via the following equation

$$\bar{R}_{S1} = \bar{R}_m + \bar{r}_{S1} + t_{PTS}\bar{v}_{S1} \tag{9}$$

$\bar{R}_{S2}$ is updated via the similar method.

10. The steps 3-9 are repeated until $\bar{R}_{S1}$ and $\bar{R}_{S2}$ converge.

This method can be used to get a preliminary free-return lunar flyby trajectory design result with fourfold ambiguity in the orientation of the outbound and return orbital planes.

SEARCHING ALGORITHM FOR THE FINAL SOLUTION

The searching algorithm for the final solution is given in this section.

The iterative variable is chosen as $\bar{p} = [V_0, \Omega, \omega]^T$, where V_0 is the magnitude of the injection velocity vector, Ω is the osculating right ascension of ascending node at the injection point, and

ω is the osculating argument of perigee at the injection point. The objective variable is chosen as $\bar{q} = [q_1, q_2, q_3]^T = [r_p^t, \gamma_p^t, \gamma_E^t]^T$. r_p^t and γ_p^t are the selenocentric radius and the selenocentric flight-direction angle at t_p, respectively. γ_E^t is the geocentric flight-direction angle at the reentry point. The expected objective variable is $\bar{q}_{Expect} = [r_p, \pi/2, \gamma_E]^T$. $\bar{q}$ is a function of $\bar{p}$ as

$$\bar{q} = H(\bar{p}) \tag{10}$$

Variation of the Eq.(10) is

$$\delta\bar{q} = \nabla H \delta\bar{p} = \frac{\partial\bar{q}}{\partial\bar{p}^T}\delta\bar{p} \tag{11}$$

$\nabla H = \partial\bar{q}/\partial\bar{p}^T$, the sensitivity matrix is calculated through numerical integration, and the details are described in Appendix. If $\bar{p}$ is given, $\delta\bar{q} = \bar{q}_{Expect} - \bar{q}$, the difference between the expect objective variable and the corresponding objective variable can be obtained. Then, the differential-correction method is employed to calculate the searching direction and step length. Through Eq. (11), one gets

$$\delta\bar{p} = \nabla H^{-1}\delta\bar{q} \tag{12}$$

For the most cases, a convergence solution can be obtained through the differential-correction method. But, in some special situations, this method will be failure because of the high sensitivity. Then, an improved differential-correction method is used to solve the problem. By doing a second-order Taylor series expansion around $\bar{p}$, $\bar{q}$ can be approximated as

$$\bar{q} = H(\bar{p} + \delta\bar{p}) \approx H(\bar{p}) + \nabla H \delta\bar{p} + \frac{1}{2}\nabla^2 H (I \otimes \delta\bar{p})\delta\bar{p} \tag{13}$$

where $\otimes$ means Kronecker product, $\nabla^2 H$ is the second-order sensitivity matrix and is defined as follows.

$$\nabla^2 H = \frac{\partial\nabla H}{\partial\bar{p}^T} \tag{14}$$

The method to calculate $\nabla^2 H$ can be found in Appendix. Combining Eqs. (12) and (13), the searching direction and step length are obtained by the following equation.

$$\delta\bar{p} = \left(\nabla H + \frac{1}{2}\nabla^2 H \left(I \otimes \left(\nabla H^{-1}\delta\bar{q}\right)\right)\right)^{-1}\delta\bar{q} \tag{15}$$

The improved differential-correction method has a faster convergence speed and larger convergence domain than the differential-correction method.

EXAMPLE AND ANALYSIS

To validate the algorithm, a typical example is given. The perilune time is Julian day 2455353. The transfer time from the perigee to the perilune is 70 hours. The perigee altitude is 270 km. The osculating inclination of perigee is 30 degrees. The perilune altitude is 100 km. The altitude of reentry point is 120 km, and reentry angle is -6 degrees. The four solutions which are obtained via the algorithm proposed in this paper are shown in figure 3. The thicker line is the outbound trajectory, and the thinner line is the return trajectory.1

The free-return trajectory between the Earth and the Moon is actually a lunar flyby trajectory. The smaller the perilune altitude is, the larger change between the selenocentric PTS entry velocity vector and the selenocentric PTS exit velocity vector will be. So, when the selenocentric PTS entry velocity vector is specified, if the perilune altitude is too small or too large, the selenocentric PTS exit velocity vector will be unreasonable. It means that there is an admissible interval for the perilune altitude. Intuitively speaking, when the magnitude of the selenocentric PTS entry velocity vector becomes larger, the feasible perilune altitude will be smaller.

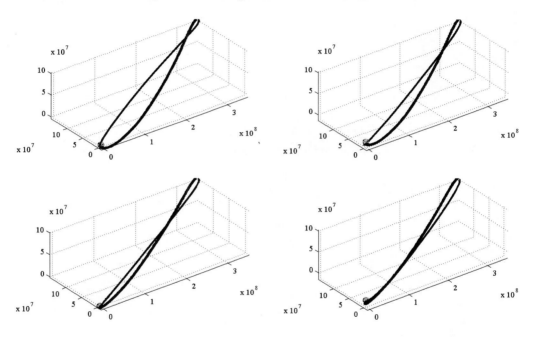

Figure 3. Four solutions with different orientation of the outbound and return orbital planes.

To verified this, an example is given. The TPA t_p are chosen as four moments in one month. The corresponding Earth-Moon distances are 402 thousand km, 392 thousand km, 372 thousand km, and 370 thousand km, respectively. The minimum and maximum of the feasible perilune altitude vs. the transfer time t_{EM} are shown in figure 4. Figure 4(a) and 4(b) are the minimum and maximum of the perilune altitude, respectively. As shown in the figure, the extrema of the perilune altitude monotonically increase with the transfer time t_{EM}. There is a negative correlation between the transfer time t_{EM} and the PTS entry velocity. As the discussion before, the smaller the PTS entry velocity is, the larger the perilune altitude will be. So, when the transfer time t_{EM} increases, the extrema of the perilune altitude will also become larger. The relationship between the Earth-Moon distance and the perilune altitude is more complicated. The extrema of the perilune altitude monotonically decrease with the Earth-Moon distance at the vicinity of the Moon's apogee. But, at the vicinity of the Moon's perigee, the trend tends to be reversed when the transfer time t_{EM} gets larger.

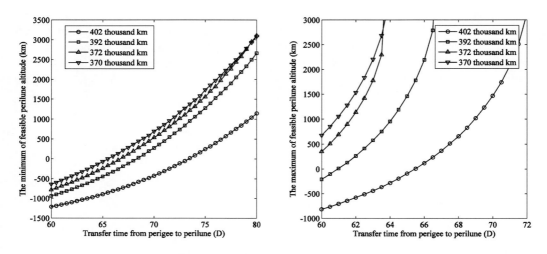

Figure 4. The minimum and maximum of feasible perilune altitude vs. the transfer time t_{EM}.

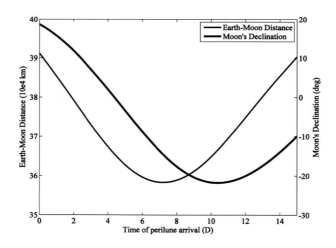

Figure 5. Geometry relationship between the Earth and the Moon.

In order to analyse the global features of the free-return lunar flyby trajectories, a huge amount of examples are calculated, with the TPA varying in a half month, the transfer time t_{EM} ranging from 55 to 73 hours. Other specified constrains are the same as the example given at the beginning of this section.

The geometry relationship between the Earth and the Moon during the range of TPA is shown in figure 5. The range of the Earth-Moon distance is from 360 to 390 thousand km, and the minimum point is located at roughly 7 days of TPA. The range of the Moon's declination is from -20 to 20 degrees, and the minimum point is located at roughly 10.3 days of TPA. The intersection of the two curves is located at about 9 days of TPA. Some important parameters of the free-return trajectory are displayed in the following figures. The thicker lines are the boundaries of admissible region, and the thinner lines are contours. The magnitude of the parameter is represented by gray value.

The return time t_{ME} and the total transfer time t_{EME} are displayed in figure 6. Figure 6(a) corresponds to the return time t_{ME} and Fig. 6(b) corresponds to the total transfer time t_{EME}. It is easy to found that, when the transfer time t_{EM} gets smaller, the return time t_{ME} will become larger. As the conclution mentioned later, decreasing of the transfer time t_{EM} will lead to increasing of the lunar flyby velocity. Hence, the difference between the direction of the velocity vectors before and after the lunar flyby will become smaller. It means that the probe tends to leave the Earth after the lunar flyby, and more return time is needed. Whereas, the total transfer time t_{EME} nearly does not depend on the transfer time t_{EM}, which means that t_{EME} is almost a constant for a specified TPA. It is clearly that the minimum points of both the parameters are roughly located at 7 days of TPA which corresponds to the minimum point of the Earth-Moon distance. So, both the two parameters are mainly affected by the Earth-Moon distance. There is a positive correlation between them.

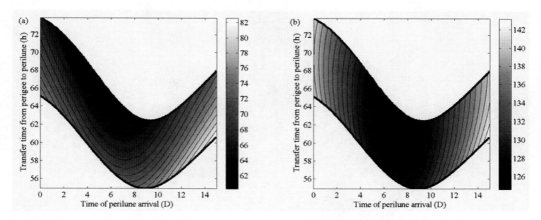

Figure 6. The return time t_{ME} (h) and total transfer time t_{EME} (h).

The geocentric perigee velocity, selenocentric perilune velocity, and geocentric reentry velocity are demonstrated in figures 7-9, respectively. As shown in the figures, the perigee velocity and perilune velocity monotonically decrease with t_{EM}. But, there is an inverse relationship between the reentry velocity and t_{EM}. It is consistent with the previous conclusion that when the transfer time t_{EM} gets larger, the return time t_{ME} will become smaller. Then, according to the theorem of image trajectories in the Earth-Moon system[13], the corresponding reentry velocity will increase with the transfer time t_{EM}. The contours are employed to analyse the influence of the Earth-Moon geometry on these parameters. The perigee velocity contours are similar to the Earth-Moon distance curve. So, the perigee velocity is mainly affected by the Earth-Moon distance. It monotonically increases with the Earth-Moon distance. According to the shape of the perilune velocity contours, there is a more complicated relationship between the perilune velocity and the Earth-Moon geometry. Based on the slope of the reentry velocity contours, it can be concluded that Earth-Moon geometry has a weak impact on the reentry velocity.

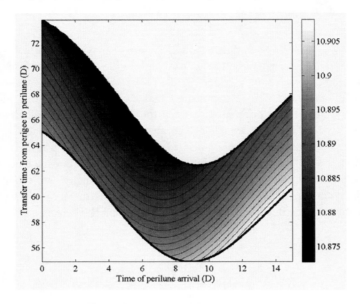

Figure 7. Geocentric perigee velocity (km/s).

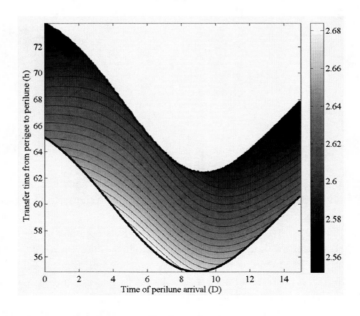

Figure 8. Selenocentric perilune velocity (km/s).

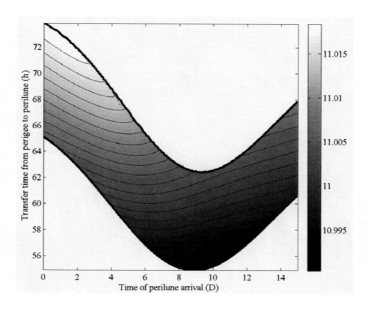

Figure 9. Geocentric reentry velocity (km/s).

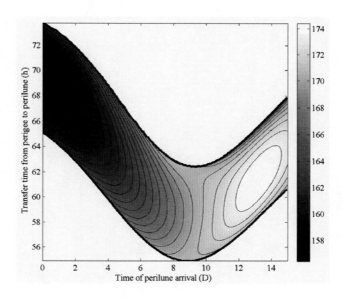

Figure 10. The inclination of the perilune (deg).

The inclination of perilune with respect to the lunar equator is shown in figure 10. There is a complicated regularity in the variation trend of the inclination which depends on transfer time t_{EM}, the Earth-Moon distance, and the Moon declination. The range of the inclination is from 156 to 174 degrees. Hence, the free-return lunar flyby trajectories are retrograde trajectories with re-

839

spect to the Moon, and the coverage of the trajectories is the low-latitude regions of the Moon. According to the distribution of the contours, the admissible area in the figure can be divided into two parts, left part and right part. The adjacent boundary of these two parts is located at roughly 9 days of TPA. There is an approximate concave quadratic relationship between the inclination of the perilune and the transfer time t_{EM} in the left part. But, in the right part, it is an approximate convex quadratic relationship between them.

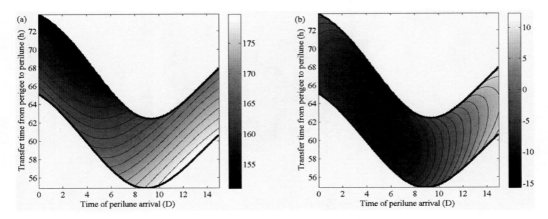

Figure 11. The selenographic longitude and latitude of the perilune (deg).

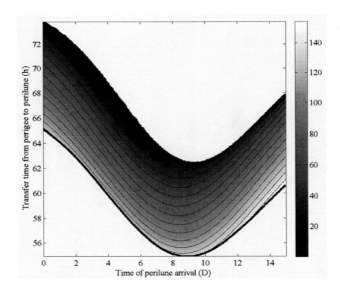

Figure 12. The inclination of the reentry point (deg).

The selenographic position of the perilune is shown in figure 11. Fig. 11(a) corresponds to the selenographic longitude, and Fig. 11(b) corresponds to the selenographic latitude. The distribution region of the perilune is located at the back side of the Moon, low latitude area. Because of

840

the Moon's shelter, it is impossible to contact with the Earth at the perilune. Hence, the perilune breaking has to be implemented automatically.

The location of landing point on the Earth is determined by the osculating inclination and the geographic position of the reentry point. So, it is necessary to study the characteristics of them. The inclination of the reentry point is described in figure 12. The range of the inclination is from 0 to 160 degrees. There is an approximately linear monotonically decreasing relationship between the inclination of the reentry point and the transfer time t_{EM}. Whereas, the inclination is basically positively correlated with the Earth-Moon distance and the Moon's declination.

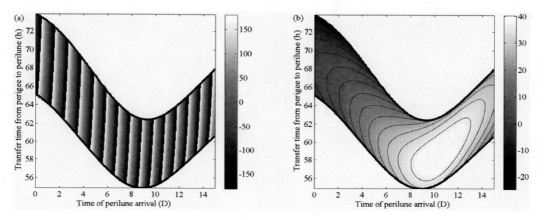

Figure 13. The geographic longitude and latitude of the reentry point (deg).

The plots of the geographic longitude and latitude of the reentry point is displayed in figure 13. Fig. 13(a) corresponds to the geographic longitude, and Fig. 13(b) corresponds to the geographic latitude. It is obvious that there is a periodic variation in the behavior of longitude with 24 hours period which is caused by the Earth's rotation. The range of latitude is from -30 to 40 degrees. The latitude is mainly affected by the transfer time t_{EM} and the Moon's declination. It monotonically decreases with the Moon's declination. The maximum of latitude corresponds to the minimum of the Moon's declination. There is an approximate convex quadratic relationship between the latitude of reentry point and the transfer time t_{EM}.

For a better description of the geometry relationship between the reentry point and the Earth-Moon system, the Earth-Moon synodic coordinate system is adopted. The origin of the synodic coordinate system is located at the Earth center, the x axis points from the Earth center to the Moon center, the z axis is parallel to angular momentum vector of the Moon, and the y axis is determined by right-hand rule. Then, the longitude and latitude of the reentry point are recomputed in the Earth-Moon synodic coordinate system corresponding to the TPA. The results are shown in figure 14.

Fig. 14(a) corresponds to the longitude, and Fig. 14(b) corresponds to the latitude. The longitude is normalized to the interval between 0 and 360 degrees. The range of longitude is roughly from 140 to 190 degrees, and the range of latitude is from -15 to 22 degrees. Hence, the location of the reentry points are mainly distributed at the far side of the Earth with respect to the Moon, vicinity of the Earth-Moon line. The reentry points corresponding to a specified TPA form an arc in the Earth-Moon synodic system, and location of the arc depends on the TPA.

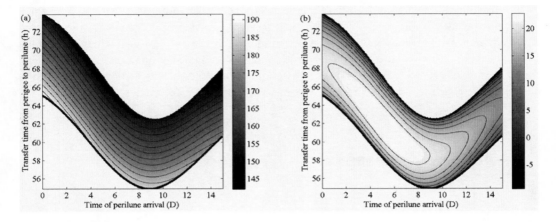

Figure 14. The longitude and latitude of the reentry point in synodic coordinate system (deg).

CONCLUSION

A new preliminary design algorithm based on the pseudostate theory is developed to obtain the preliminary design result of the free-return lunar flyby trajectory in this paper. Compared with the result which is obtained by the traditional preliminary design algorithm based on the patched-conic technique, a better preliminary design result can be got because of the good three-body trajectories approximation of the pseudostate theory. It makes the searching for the final solution becomes easier.

On the basis of the preliminary design result, the final solution in a more complicated dynamic model is obtained via an improved differential-correction method. It has a faster convergence speed and a larger convergence domain.

The characteristics of the free-return lunar flyby trajectories are studied via the algorithm developed in this paper. Some valuable results are obtained.

REFERENCES

1 A.J. Schwaniger, "Trajectories in the Earth-Moon Space with Symmetrical Free Return Properties", Technical Note D-1833, 1963.

2 M. Jesick and C. Ocampo, "Automated Generation of Symmetric Lunar Free-Return Trajectories", Journal of Guidance, Control and Dynamics, Vol. 34, No. 1, 2011, pp.98-106.

3 P.A. Penzo, "An Analysis of Free-Flight Circumlunar Trajectories", AIAA Paper No. 63-404, AIAA Astrodynamics conference Yale University, New Haven, Connecticut, August 19-21, 1963.

4 F. Johnson, JR., "Free Return Circumlunar Trajectories From Launch Windows with Fixed Launch Azimuths", AIAA Paper No. 63-406, AIAA Astrodynamics conference Yale University, New Haven, Connecticut, August 19-21, 1963.

5 B.S. Green and N. Lewin, "A Gradient Method for Obtaining Circumlunar Trajectories", AIAA Paper No. 63-401, AIAA Astrodynamics conference Yale University, New Haven, Connecticut, August 19-21, 1963.

6 R.H. Battin, "An Introduction to the Mathematics and Methods of Astrodynamics", AIAA Education Series, AIAA, New York, 1987, pp. 437-442.

7 D. V. Byrnes, "Application of the Pseudostate Theory to the Three-Body Lambert Problem", Journal of the Astronautical Sciences, Vol. 37, 1989, pp. 221-232.

8 S.W. Wilson, Jr., "A Pseudostate Theory for the Approximation of Three-Body Trajectories", TRW Note No. 69-FMT-765(11176-H304-R0-00), August 15, 1969.

9 L. A. D'Amario, D. V. Byrnes, L. L. Sackett and R. H. Stanford, "Optimization of Multiple Flyby Trajectories", AAS Paper No. 79-162, AAS/AIAA Astrodynamics Specialists Conference, Provincetown, Mass, June 1979.

10 O. Montenbruck and E. Gill, "Satellite Orbits: Models, Methods and Applications", Springer-verlag, Berlin, 2000, pp. 39-46.

11 R.V. Ramanan, "Integrate Algorithm for Lunar Transfer Trajectories Using a Pseudostate Technique", Journal of Guidance, Control and Dynamics, Vol. 25, No. 5, 2002, pp.946-952.

12 Q. Luo, Z. Meng and C. Han, "Solution Algorithm to a Quasi-Lambert's Problem with Fixed Flight-Direction Angle Constraint", Celestial Mechanics and Dynamical Astronomy, Vol. 109, No. 4, 2011, pp. 409-427.

13 A. Miele, "Theorem of Image Trajectories in Earth-Moon Space", Acta Astronaut, Vol. 6, No. 5, 1960, pp. 225-232

APPENDIX

The geocentric state at the starting time t_0 is denoted by $\bar{X}_0 = [\bar{R}_0^T, \bar{V}_0^T]^T$, and the geocentric state at time t is denoted by $\bar{X} = [\bar{R}^T, \bar{V}^T]^T$. The sensitivity matrix, ∇H, can be expended as

$$\nabla H = \frac{\partial \bar{q}}{\partial \bar{p}^T} = \frac{\partial \bar{q}}{\partial \bar{X}^T} \frac{\partial \bar{X}}{\partial \bar{X}_0^T} \frac{\partial \bar{X}_0}{\partial \bar{p}^T} \qquad (16)$$

$\partial \bar{X} / \partial \bar{X}_0^T$ is the state transition matrix and is denoted by M. It can be expressed as

$$M = \frac{\partial \bar{X}}{\partial \bar{X}_0^T} = \begin{bmatrix} \dfrac{\partial \bar{R}}{\partial \bar{X}_0^T} \\ \dfrac{\partial \bar{V}}{\partial \bar{X}_0^T} \end{bmatrix} = \begin{bmatrix} M_1 \\ M_2 \end{bmatrix} \qquad (17)$$

The time derivative of the matrix M can be written as

$$\dot{M} = \begin{bmatrix} \dot{M}_1 \\ \dot{M}_2 \end{bmatrix} = \begin{bmatrix} \dfrac{\partial \vec{V}}{\partial \vec{X}_0^T} \\ \dfrac{\partial \vec{g}}{\partial \vec{X}_0^T} \end{bmatrix} = \begin{bmatrix} M_2 \\ \dfrac{\partial \vec{g}}{\partial \vec{R}^T} M_1 \end{bmatrix} \tag{18}$$

The symbol • means the time derivative, and $\vec{g}$ is the acceleration corresponding to $\vec{X}$. The initial condition of state transition matrix is a unit matrix. Then, M is computed by the definite integral of Eq. (18) from the time t_0 to t. It should be noted that M is a contemporaneous variation. So, for the reentry point, it must take account of the time variation to calculated state transition matrix.

By substituting Eq. (16) into Eq. (14), the following is obtained.

$$\nabla^2 H = \frac{\partial \left(\dfrac{\partial \vec{q}}{\partial \vec{X}^T} \dfrac{\partial \vec{X}}{\partial \vec{X}_0^T} \dfrac{\partial \vec{X}_0}{\partial \vec{p}^T} \right)}{\partial \vec{p}^T} = \frac{\partial \left(\dfrac{\partial \vec{q}}{\partial \vec{X}^T} \dfrac{\partial \vec{X}}{\partial \vec{X}_0^T} \right)}{\partial \vec{p}^T} \left(I \otimes \frac{\partial \vec{X}_0}{\partial \vec{p}^T} \right) + \frac{\partial \vec{q}}{\partial \vec{X}^T} \frac{\partial \vec{X}}{\partial \vec{X}_0^T} \frac{\partial^2 \vec{X}_0}{\partial \vec{p}^{T2}}$$

$$= \left(\frac{\partial^2 \vec{q}}{\partial \vec{X}^T \partial \vec{p}^T} \left(I \otimes \frac{\partial \vec{X}}{\partial \vec{X}_0^T} \right) + \frac{\partial \vec{q}}{\partial \vec{X}^T} \frac{\partial^2 \vec{X}}{\partial \vec{X}_0^T \partial \vec{p}^T} \right) \left(I \otimes \frac{\partial \vec{X}_0}{\partial \vec{p}^T} \right) + \frac{\partial \vec{q}}{\partial \vec{X}^T} \frac{\partial \vec{X}}{\partial \vec{X}_0^T} \frac{\partial^2 \vec{X}_0}{\partial \vec{p}^{T2}} \tag{19}$$

Let symbol Q represents the matrix $\partial \vec{q}/\partial \vec{X}^T$. Q_j is the jth column of Q, and Q can be expressed as $Q = [Q_j]_j$. The term, $\partial^2 \vec{X}_0/\partial \vec{p}^{T2}$, can be easily calculated by a analytic expression.

The term, $\partial^2 \vec{q}/\partial \vec{X}^T \partial \vec{p}^T$, is extended as

$$\frac{\partial^2 \vec{q}}{\partial \vec{X}^T \partial \vec{p}^T} = \frac{\partial Q}{\partial \vec{p}^T} = \left[\frac{\partial Q_j}{\partial \vec{X}_0^T} \right]_j \frac{\partial \left(I \otimes \vec{X}_0 \right)}{\partial \vec{p}^T}$$

$$= \left[\frac{\partial Q_j}{\partial \vec{X}^T} \frac{\partial X}{\partial \vec{X}_0^T} \right]_j \frac{\partial \left(I \otimes \vec{X}_0 \right)}{\partial \vec{p}^T} \tag{20}$$

The term, $\partial^2 \vec{X}/\partial \vec{X}_0^T \partial \vec{p}^T$, is extended as

$$\frac{\partial^2 \vec{X}}{\partial \vec{X}_0^T \partial \vec{p}^T} = \frac{\partial M}{\partial \vec{p}^T} = \frac{\partial M}{\partial \vec{X}_0^T} \frac{\partial \left(I \otimes \vec{X}_0 \right)}{\partial \vec{p}^T} \tag{21}$$

The time derivative of $\partial M/\partial \vec{X}_0^T$ is

$$\frac{\dot{\partial M}}{\partial \vec{X}_0^T} = \begin{bmatrix} \dfrac{\partial \dot{M}_1}{\partial \vec{X}_0^T} \\ \dfrac{\partial \dot{M}_2}{\partial \vec{X}_0^T} \end{bmatrix} = \begin{bmatrix} \dfrac{\partial \dot{M}_2}{\partial \vec{X}_0^T} \\ \dfrac{\partial \left(\dfrac{\partial \vec{g}}{\partial \vec{R}^T} M_1 \right)}{\partial \vec{X}_0^T} \end{bmatrix} \tag{22}$$

where

844

$$\frac{\partial \dot{\boldsymbol{M}}_2}{\partial \bar{\boldsymbol{X}}_0^T} = \frac{\partial \left(\dfrac{\partial \bar{\boldsymbol{g}}}{\partial \bar{\boldsymbol{R}}^T} \boldsymbol{M}_1 \right)}{\partial \bar{\boldsymbol{X}}_0^T} = \frac{\partial^2 \bar{\boldsymbol{g}}}{\partial \bar{\boldsymbol{R}}^T \partial \bar{\boldsymbol{X}}_0^T} \left(I \otimes \boldsymbol{M}_1 \right) + \frac{\partial \bar{\boldsymbol{g}}}{\partial \bar{\boldsymbol{R}}^T} \frac{\partial \boldsymbol{M}_1}{\partial \bar{\boldsymbol{X}}_0^T} \tag{23}$$

and

$$\frac{\partial^2 \bar{\boldsymbol{g}}}{\partial \bar{\boldsymbol{R}}^T \partial \bar{\boldsymbol{X}}_0^T} = \frac{\partial^2 \bar{\boldsymbol{g}}}{\partial \bar{\boldsymbol{R}}^{T2}} \frac{\partial \left(I \otimes \bar{\boldsymbol{R}} \right)}{\partial \bar{\boldsymbol{X}}_0^T} \tag{24}$$

The initial condition of second-order state transition matrix is a zero matrix. Then, $\partial \boldsymbol{M} / \partial \bar{\boldsymbol{X}}_0^T$ is computed by the definite integral of Eq. (22) from the time t_0 to t. Here is the same point should be noted that $\partial \boldsymbol{M} / \partial \bar{\boldsymbol{X}}_0^T$ is a contemporaneous variation, and for the reentry point, it must take account of the time variation.

TARGETING LOW-ENERGY TRANSFERS
TO LOW LUNAR ORBIT

Jeffrey S. Parker[*] and Rodney L. Anderson[*]

A targeting scheme is presented to build trajectories from a specified Earth parking orbit to a specified low lunar orbit via a low-energy transfer and up to two maneuvers. The total transfer ΔV is characterized as a function of the Earth parking orbit inclination and the departure date for transfers to each given low lunar orbit. The transfer ΔV cost is characterized for transfers constructed to low lunar polar orbits with any longitude of ascending node and for transfers that arrive at the Moon at any given time during a month.

INTRODUCTION

Modern trajectory design techniques have enabled the construction of new classes of low-energy trajectories that spacecraft may take to transfer between the Earth and the Moon. The Japanese Hiten mission is recognized as the first spacecraft to traverse a low-energy transfer from an orbit about the Earth to an orbit about the Moon.[1,2] The two ARTEMIS spacecraft recently navigated two very different low-energy transfers from their orbits about the Earth to lunar libration orbits near the Moon.[3,4] Both Hiten and ARTEMIS were extended missions that were enabled by their fuel-efficient low-energy transfers. The two GRAIL spacecraft are the first vehicles expecting to launch onto low-energy transfers as part of their primary mission, illustrated in Figure 1; they are also the first vehicles to transfer directly to low lunar orbits via low-energy transfers.[5–7] The success of Hiten, ARTEMIS, and hopefully GRAIL, have provided impetus to explore the trade space of low-energy lunar transfers in the expectation that such trajectories will continue to enable future missions.

Low-energy transfers between the Earth and the Moon are useful for a number of compelling reasons. First, a spacecraft following a practical low-energy transfer requires less fuel to achieve the same orbit than it would when following a conventional, 3–6 day direct transfer. The lunar orbit insertion maneuver is at least 100 m/s smaller when the spacecraft's destination is a 100 km circular orbit about the Moon.[8] The fuel savings are much more significant for spacecraft traveling to lunar libration orbits and other high three-body orbits, where spacecraft may save upwards of 500 m/s of the required ΔV of a conventional transfer.[9–12] Low-energy transfers typically require 2–3 months more transfer duration than direct transfers. While this may be a disadvantage for missions with human passengers, it is a characteristic that carries several advantages for robotic missions. A spacecraft traversing a low-energy transfer may typically wait a week before performing a maneuver,[6] giving the spacecraft ample time to be checked out and prepare for its cruise operations. This also provides the spacecraft navigators ample time to achieve a stable solution of the spacecraft's orbit without requiring more than a handful of tracking stations. In addition, with several months of

---

[*]Member of Technical Staff, Jet Propulsion Laboratory, California Institute of Technology, M/S 301-121, 4800 Oak Grove Dr., Pasadena, CA 91109

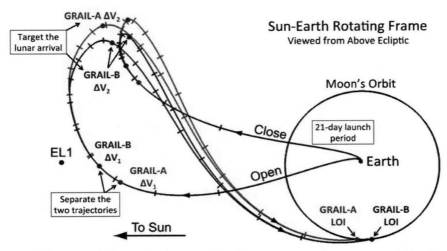

Figure 1. An illustration of GRAIL's mission design, including a 21-day launch period and two deterministic maneuvers for both GRAIL-A and GRAIL-B, designed to separate their lunar orbit insertion times by 25 hours. Graphic courtesy of Roncoli and Fujii.[5]

transfer time a mission may be designed that places multiple spacecraft into different orbits at the Moon using a single launch vehicle without requiring a large amount of fuel. The GRAIL mission is one practical example: GRAIL's two spacecraft are launched aboard the same Delta II rocket and each performs two deterministic maneuvers during their trans-lunar cruises to separate their lunar arrival times by 25 hours.[5,6] This separation is a benefit to the spacecraft operations team. Finally, another compelling reason to use a low-energy transfer for a robotic mission to the Moon is that one can construct a realistic 21-day launch period using minimal fuel, as will be demonstrated in this paper. GRAIL's mission involves at least 21 launch opportunities, such that any launch date sends the two spacecraft on two transfers that arrive at the Moon on the same two dates, again separated by 25 hours. Conventional lunar transfers can achieve the same result, though they typically require numerous Earth phasing orbits and/or lunar flybys that add complexity and radiation exposure to the mission.

Numerous researchers have explored the trade space of low-energy lunar transfers since the 1960s using a variety of different techniques. In 1968, Charles Conley was among the first people to demonstrate that a trajectory may be designed to place a spacecraft in an orbit temporarily captured by the Moon without requiring an orbit insertion maneuver.[13] His technique takes advantage of dynamical systems tools found in the planar circular restricted three-body problem. Later, in 1990, Belbruno and Miller developed a targeting technique to design a low-energy trajectory for the Hiten mission.[1] Ivashkin is among many other people to employ similarly useful targeting techniques to generate low-energy lunar transfers.[14,15] Since 2000, several authors have continued to explore the dynamical systems methodology that Conley explored to generate low-energy transfers.[16] No practical methods have ever been found to analytically generate a low-energy transfer; hence, all progress to date has involved some sort of numerical or iterative technique to build the transfers.

Recent work has begun to systematically survey the trade space of low-energy lunar transfers by building entirely ballistic transfers between the Earth and (1) lunar libration orbits,[9–11] (2) low lunar orbits,[8] and (3) the lunar surface.[17,18] These surveys have produced many thousands of lunar transfers that require no deterministic maneuvers whatsoever during their trans-lunar cruise. However, these transfers depart the Earth from particular Earth orbits and arrive at the Moon in a specified way, neither of which may be desirable for a practical mission. A previous paper studied the problem of transferring from a specified 28.5° circular low Earth orbit (LEO) to a particular lunar libration orbit using 1–3 maneuvers.[12] That paper presented a robust algorithm to generate a practical transfer, but it focused on only a handful of transfers to lunar libration orbits; it did not establish any statistically significant trends to predict the cost of an arbitrary transfer.

The work presented here is an extension of the research presented in these previous papers. The targeting algorithm presented in this paper is a modification of the algorithm used in Reference 12, applied to the problem of constructing a useful transfer from a specified LEO parking orbit to one of the transfers presented in Reference 8, each of which arrived at the Moon in 100-km circular polar lunar orbits. Details of these procedures are described in the next sections.

The purpose of this paper is to characterize the ΔV cost needed to connect a particular low-energy lunar transfer, i.e., one with a desirable lunar approach, with a specified LEO parking orbit at the Earth departure point. The work presented here characterizes the ΔV cost needed to generate a realistic, 21-day launch period for a collection of 288 low-energy transfers from 28.5° LEO parking orbits to polar lunar orbits. This effectively identifies the ΔV cost needed to implement a low-energy transfer, taking it from a theoretical study to a practical trajectory.

METHODOLOGY

Each low-energy transfer constructed in this paper departs the Earth, coasts to the Moon, and inserts directly into a circular 100 km polar orbit about the Moon. This lunar orbit is akin to the mapping orbits of several spacecraft, including Lunar Prospector,[19] Kaguya/SELENE,[20] Chang'e 1,[21] Chandrayaan-1,[22] the Lunar Reconnaissance Orbiter,[23] and GRAIL.[5] Figure 2 illustrates an example 84-day low-energy transfer. The following sections provide more information about each phase of this example low-energy transfer and how it compares with other lunar transfers.

Earth Parking Orbit The low-energy lunar transfers designed here depart the Earth from 185-km circular parking orbits. Unless otherwise noted, the parking orbits have inclinations of 28.5° in the EME2000 coordinate frame, i.e., an inertial frame aligned with the Earth's mean equator on January 1, 2000 at 12:00:00 UTC. This inclination corresponds to an easterly launch from Cape Canaveral, Florida. For the purposes of this paper, the actual launch time and its bearing on the orientation of the surface of the Earth is not considered; hence, Cape Canaveral is not constrained to be beneath the parking orbit. Adjusting the launch time by as many as 12 hours typically only has a slight impact on the trajectory and its corresponding launch period.

Trans-Lunar Injection The Trans-Lunar Injection (TLI) is modeled as an impulsive ΔV tangent to the parking orbit. This maneuver is typically performed by the launch vehicle. The launch vehicle's target C_3 value is typically in the range of -0.7 to -0.4 km^2/s^2, where C_3 is a parameter equal to twice the target specific energy. Since this target is negative, the resulting orbit is still captured by the Earth. If the trajectory is designed to implement a lunar gravity assist on the way out to the long cruise, then the launch target may be reduced to a C_3 of approximately -2 km^2/s^2.

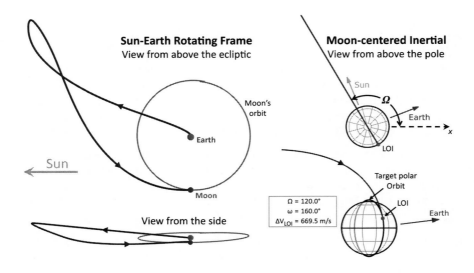

Figure 2. An example 84-day low-energy transfer between the Earth and a 100 km circular polar lunar orbit.

Launch vehicles typically target the right ascension and declination of the outbound asymptote for interplanetary missions to other planets. Since a low-energy lunar transfer is still captured by the Earth there is no outbound asymptote; hence, the GRAIL targets include the right ascension and declination of the instantaneous apogee vector at the target interface time.[5]

Trans-Lunar Cruise A spacecraft's trans-lunar cruise on its low-energy lunar transfer takes it beyond the orbit of the Moon and typically in a direction toward either the second or fourth quadrant in the Sun-Earth synodic coordinate system.[24] The spacecraft typically ventures 1–2 million kilometers away from the Earth, where the Sun's gravity becomes very influential. As the spacecraft traverses its apogee the Sun's gravity constantly pulls on it, raising the spacecraft's perigee altitude. By the time the spacecraft begins to return to the Earth its perigee has risen high enough that it encounters the Moon. Further, the trajectory is designed to place the spacecraft on a lunar encounter trajectory. The GRAIL mission design involves two deterministic maneuvers and three statistical maneuvers for each spacecraft to navigate its trans-lunar cruise.[6] The transfers in this paper may include up to two deterministic maneuvers performed during the trans-lunar cruise. These maneuvers are constrained to be further than four days from any other maneuver.

Lunar Orbit Insertion The Lunar Orbit Insertion (LOI) is modeled as an impulsive ΔV that inserts the spacecraft directly into the target 100 km circular lunar orbit. A typical lunar mission inserts into a large temporary *capture* orbit before descending into the final target orbit. This sort of mission design reduces gravity losses and protects the spacecraft in the event of an overburn. The LOI is not required to be tangent to the target orbit in this study if a small plane change would reduce the total transfer ΔV of the mission.

Target Lunar Orbit   The target lunar orbits in this paper are 100-km circular polar orbits, defined in a coordinate frame that is centered at the Moon and aligned with the lunar spin axis. The z-axis extends from the center of the Moon toward its northern spin-axis pole at the time of the LOI; the x-axis extends toward the point where the Moon's equatorial plane ascends through the Earth's J2000 equatorial plane; the y-axis completes the right-handed coordinate frame.[25] The x-axis points within 3.77° of Earth's vernal equinox at any given time. It may be the case that a mission's design requires an elliptical lunar orbit such that its orientation about the Moon is a mission requirement; for instance, a mission may be designed to place a communication satellite into an elliptical orbit with its apoapse over the lunar south pole. In this paper, the LOI is performed at the orbit's periapse point and the orbit's orientation, i.e., its argument of periapsis and longitude of ascending node, is specified and fixed. In this way, one may target a particular lunar orbit and study the ΔV costs required to insert into that orbit.

Models

All trajectories generated in this study are propagated using the DIVA propagator, which implements a variable order Adams method.[26] The state integration tolerance has been set to 1×10^{-10}.

The gravity model includes the Sun, Earth, and Moon at all times, modeled as point-masses with GM values of approximately 1.327124×10^{11} km^3/s^2, 3.986004×10^5 km^3/s^2, and 4.902800×10^3 km^3/s^2, respectively. The positions of each body are estimated using JPL's DE421 Planetary Ephemerides.[27] The mean radius of the Earth and Moon are assumed to be 6378.1363 km and 1737.4 km, respectively.

The optimization package SNOPT (Sparse Nonlinear OPTimizer)[28, 29] is used in this research to adjust the values of parameters in a system in order to identify solutions that require minimal amounts of fuel. The algorithm is highly effective at identifying local minima in the state space of systems such as those encountered here, where the state space involves smooth nonlinear objective functions. The algorithm does not necessarily converge on the global minimum; hence it is common that the routine is executed with several sets of initial conditions to improve the probability that it encounters the optimal solution.

Designing each Transfer

Each lunar mission is constructed here using a straightforward procedure that is described as follows.

Step 1.   First, a target lunar orbit is selected and a reference low-energy lunar transfer is constructed. The transfers used here have been taken from the surveys presented in Reference 8.

Each target low lunar orbit is constructed here by setting its semi-major axis to 1837.4 km, its eccentricity to zero, and its inclination to 90°, as described previously. This defines a circular, polar orbit with an altitude of approximately 100 km. Its longitude of ascending node, Ω, and argument of periapse, ω, are selected from the surveys and can take on a wide variety of combinations.

An impulsive, tangential lunar orbit insertion is applied at the orbit's periapse point on a specified date. The LOI ΔV magnitude is taken from the surveys. It is set to generate a trajectory that originates at the Earth via a simple low-energy transfer: one that contains no close lunar encounters or Earth phasing orbits. The ΔV value is at least 640 m/s and is the

Table 1.   A summary of the performance parameters of several example simple low-energy lunar transfers. None of these transfers includes any Earth phasing orbits or lunar flybys.

Traj #	Ω (deg)	ω (deg)	ΔV_{LOI} (m/s)	Duration (days)	LEO Inclination (deg) Equatorial	Ecliptic	C_3 (km^2/s^2)
1	120.0	169.2	669.3	83.483	29.441	6.129	-0.723
2	120.0	103.8	692.1	85.287	25.688	34.778	-0.723
3	120.0	70.2	743.9	93.598	57.654	74.955	-0.667
4	120.0	225.3	716.0	93.621	134.322	112.840	-0.657
5	120.0	99.9	697.5	110.060	83.127	61.624	-0.697
6	120.0	186.9	673.2	122.715	23.941	3.088	-0.712

least ΔV needed to construct a transfer that requires fewer than 160 days to reach an altitude of 1000 km or less above the Earth when propagated backward in time. Table 1 summarizes several example transfers that target low lunar orbits that each have an Ω of 120°, taken from a survey found in Reference 8.

Each reference trajectory generated in this study has no maneuvers and does not target any particular Earth orbit when propagated backward in time.

Step 2.   Second, the mission's LEO parking orbit and Trans-Lunar Injection time are specified. The LEO parking orbits used in this paper are all 185-km circular orbits with inclinations of 28.5°, as previously described. The orbit's node, Ω_{LEO}, and the location of the TLI maneuver about the orbit, ν_{LEO}, are permitted to vary; the TLI is performed tangent to the orbit.

Step 3.   The low-energy transfer is adjusted to have a perigee that coincides with the time of the TLI. This is performed by using SNOPT to determine the smallest change in the LOI $\overrightarrow{\Delta V}$ that results in a new low-energy transfer that originates at the Earth on the date of the TLI, or at least one that has a perigee on that date even if the perigee altitude is higher than 1000 km.

Step 4.   The radius of the low-energy transfer with respect to the Earth at a time 20 days after the TLI is noted. The TLI ΔV magnitude, ΔV_{TLI}, is set to a value that takes the Earth-departure trajectory out to that distance at that time, using some initial guess for the orientation of the parking orbit at that time. The spacecraft is beyond the orbit of the Moon by that time, assuming no Earth phasing orbits, and not yet at its apogee.

Step 5.   The optimization algorithm SNOPT is used to identify the values of Ω_{LEO} and ν_{LEO} that minimize the difference in position between the Earth-departure and the target low-energy transfer at a time 20 days after TLI. After convergence, the algorithm is repeated, this time permitting ΔV_{TLI} to vary as well. It is typically the case that the Earth-departure trajectory will intersect the target low-energy transfer at that time when all three variables are permitted to vary, though it is not necessary.

Step 6.   Two deterministic maneuvers are added to the trajectory: TCM1 at a time 21 days after TLI, and TCM2 at a time halfway between TCM1 and LOI. It is intentional that the first maneuver be placed near 20 days but not at a value of 20 days in order to improve the performance of the optimization algorithm in the next step.[12]

Step 7.   The SNOPT algorithm is implemented again to converge on an end-to-end trajectory between the specified LEO parking orbit and the specified low lunar orbit, minimizing the total transfer ΔV. This optimization includes eight variables: the three Earth-departure parameters Ω_{LEO}, ν_{LEO}, and ΔV_{TLI}, the dates of the two trans-lunar maneuvers t_{TCM1} and t_{TCM2}, and the three components of the LOI ΔV, namely, ΔV_{LOI}^x, ΔV_{LOI}^y, and ΔV_{LOI}^z. When the eight parameters are adjusted, an Earth-departure trajectory is generated out to the time of TCM1, a lunar-arrival trajectory is generated backward in time from LOI to the time of TCM2, and a bridge trajectory is generated connecting TCM1 and TCM2 using a single-shooting differential corrector.[12,30] The optimization algorithm is set to minimize the sum of the maneuvers that are typically required by the spacecraft, namely, the sum of ΔV_{TCM1}, ΔV_{TCM2}, and ΔV_{LOI}, but not the TLI ΔV. The dates of the TLI and LOI are fixed, and the dates of TCM1 and TCM2 are constrained to be at least four days from any other maneuver to facilitate relaxed spaceflight operations.

When the optimizer has converged, the performance of the trajectory compared with the reference low-energy transfer is recorded. It is often the case that the differential corrector will converge on a local minimum and not the global minimum; hence, this process is repeated with adjustments in the eight parameters to identify the lowest local minimum possible. This will be discussed more later.

To summarize, this procedure constructs a practical, two-burn, low-energy lunar transfer between a specified Earth departure and a specified lunar arrival. The altitude, eccentricity, and inclination of the Earth parking orbit are specified and fixed, as is the date of the Trans-Lunar Injection maneuver. The target lunar orbit, the LOI position, and the LOI date are all specified and fixed. The TLI maneuver is constrained to be tangential to the parking orbit, though the orientation of the parking orbit may vary; the LOI maneuver is not constrained to be tangential. Finally, the dates of two trans-lunar maneuvers and their ΔV values are permitted to vary.

AN EXAMPLE LUNAR MISSION

This section demonstrates the process of generating a practical low-energy lunar transfer. A reference lunar transfer has been selected from the surveys presented in Reference 8, including a target lunar orbit and LOI date. Several key parameters of this mission are summarized in Table 2. The resulting low-energy lunar transfer, illustrated in Figure 3, has a transfer duration of 101.6 days, naturally originating at the Earth on April 1, 2010 at 05:27 UTC. The reference Trans-Lunar Injection has a TLI ΔV magnitude of approximately 3195.635 m/s, corresponding to a C_3 of -0.713003 km^2/s^2, and it departs from a circular 185-km LEO parking orbit with an inclination of approximately 38.305°.

Table 2. A summary of the parameters used to generate the reference low-energy lunar transfer used in the example lunar mission.

Parameter	Value
Target Lunar Orbit Ω	257.430 deg
Target Lunar Orbit ω	48.268 deg
Date of LOI	July 11, 2010 at 19:41 UTC
ΔV_{LOI}	649.00 m/s

To illustrate the entire process of building a practical lunar transfer, we will set the Earth departure to take place from a parking orbit at an inclination of 28.5° one day later than the reference

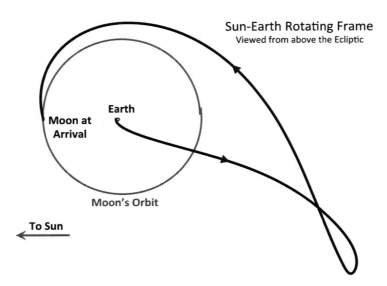

Sun-Earth Rotating Frame
Viewed from above the Ecliptic

Earth

Moon at
Arrival

Moon's Orbit

To Sun

Figure 3. An illustration of the example reference low-energy lunar transfer, shown in the Sun-Earth rotating frame from above the ecliptic, where the Sun is fixed to the left.

trajectory's departure on April 2, 2010 at 05:27 UTC. A launch vehicle may certainly target a departure at an inclination of 38.3°, but the performance loss is typically significant. The procedure outlined here results in a small increase of onboard propellant to make the adjustment.

Table 3 tracks the values of the eight control variables and the transfer ΔV cost as the lunar mission is constructed, following the steps outlined above. The reference trajectory is summarized in Step #1: the only control variables set are the components of the LOI ΔV. Step #2 does not change any control variables and is hence not shown. Step #3 illustrates the small change in the components of the LOI ΔV vector that are required to shift the timing of the trajectory's perigee to coincide with the TLI maneuver. The adjustment amounts to a difference of only 3.3 cm/s in the LOI ΔV magnitude. Although this new trajectory's perigee occurs on April 2, 2010 at 5:27 UTC, the

Table 3. The history of the example lunar transfer's control variables as the mission is constructed, where Δt_{TCM1} is the duration of time between TLI and TCM1 and Δt_{TCM2} is the duration of time between TCM1 and TCM2.

| Step # | TLI Parameters | | | TCM1 | | TCM2 | | LOI | Total Transfer |
	Ω deg	ν deg	ΔV m/s	Δt days	ΔV m/s	Δt days	ΔV m/s	ΔV_x, ΔV_y, and ΔV_z m/s, EME2000	ΔV, m/s
1	-	-	-	-	-	-	-	-87.728, -271.090, -583.108	-
3	-	-	-	-	-	-	-	-87.732, -271.103, -583.138	-
4	0.00	0.00	3197.44	-	-	-	-	-87.732, -271.103, -583.138	-
5	-25.00	27.18	3196.77	-	-	-	-	-87.732, -271.103, -583.138	-
6	-25.00	27.18	3196.77	21.00	26.10	34.84	6.37	-87.732, -271.103, -583.138	681.500
7	-25.08	27.32	3196.79	20.63	24.09	34.86	0.00	-87.736, -271.118, -583.167	673.155

perigee altitude is no longer 185 km but has risen to about 5200 km. Steps #4 – #6 construct initial guesses for the departure parameters and place two deterministic maneuvers en route to construct a complete end-to-end trajectory. Finally, Step #7 includes the full optimization, where all eight parameters are permitted to vary and the transfer ΔV is minimized.

During Step #4, initial guesses for Ω_{TLI} and ν_{TLI} are needed. In this example they are both set to $0°$, however, it has been observed that the entire procedure may converge to different local minima using different combinations of initial guesses for these parameters. There are often two local minima that correspond to the typical *short* and *long* coasts for the Earth departure. In addition, the process often converges on different local minima depending on the propagation duration of the initial Earth departure. In this research, we have opted to perform Steps #4 – #6 numerous times with different initial guesses and then send only the best one or two trajectories into Step #7. This process ensures that the majority of local minima are explored without spending too much time in Step #7, which is by far the most computationally demanding step. It is likely that additional small improvements may be made, but this procedure generates a reliable estimate of the minimum transfer ΔV given a reference lunar transfer.

One can see in the final row of Table 3 that the optimizer has converged on a solution that drove the second deterministic ΔV to zero. This is typical behavior for this algorithm when the trajectory is not required to change far from the reference, i.e., when the date of the TLI is within a few days of the reference trajectory and/or when the LEO parking orbit's inclination is within several degrees of the reference trajectory's perigee inclination.

Figure 4 illustrates the difference between the Earth departures of the reference trajectory and the final, targeted lunar transfer generated here. The inclination change and the shift in the TLI departure date are compensated by the $\sim$24.1 m/s of trans-lunar ΔV. Figure 5 shows a comparison of the final transfer and the reference transfer, viewed from above the ecliptic in the Sun-Earth rotating frame. One can see that the geometry and the general features of the final transfer have not changed significantly during the procedure.

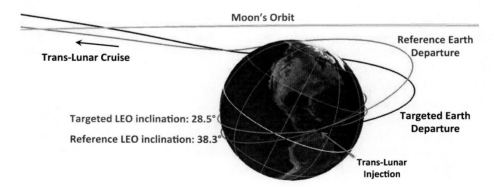

Figure 4. The targeted Earth departure compared with the reference Earth departure.

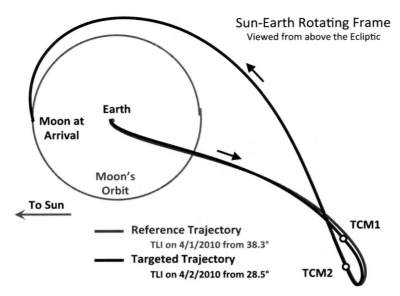

Figure 5. The final targeted lunar transfer compared to the reference transfer, viewed in the Sun-Earth rotating frame from above the ecliptic.

BUILDING A LAUNCH PERIOD

The process described above may be repeated for each day in a wide range of dates to identify a practical launch period. The total transfer ΔV typically rises as the TLI date is adjusted further from a reference trajectory's TLI date. In this research, we search 30 days on either side of the reference trajectory's TLI date and identify a practical 21-day launch period within those 61 days. The 21 days of opportunities do not have to be consecutive, though they are typically collected in either one or two segments. Since low-energy transfers travel beyond the orbit of the Moon, they may interact with the Moon as they pass by, even if they pass by at a great distance. The Moon may boost or reduce the spacecraft's energy as it passes by, depending on the geometry; typically there is a point in a launch period where the geometry switches.

Figure 6 illustrates the transfer ΔV cost required to target the reference lunar transfer studied in the previous section as a function of TLI date. Each transfer has been generated using the procedure outlined previously, but with a different TLI date. The trajectories that launch 5–6 days prior to the reference transfer are significantly perturbed by the Moon, though not perturbed enough to break the launch period into two segments. One can see that the least expensive 21-day launch period requires a transfer ΔV of approximately 706.2 m/s.

REFERENCE TRANSFERS

A total of 288 reference transfers have been used to generate lunar missions with realistic, 21-day launch periods, each starting from a 28.5° LEO parking orbit. These reference trajectories have been randomly sampled from low-ΔV, simple, low-energy transfers presented in the surveys found in Reference 8. The trajectories target low lunar orbits with any longitude of ascending node and with any argument of periapsis, though the combination of those parameters must yield

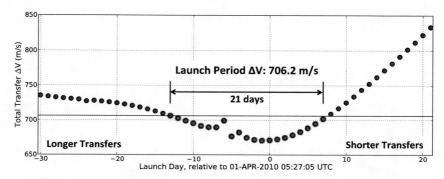

Figure 6. An example 21-day launch period, constructed using the reference lunar transfer presented in Figure 3.

a satisfactory reference transfer. The transfers arrive at the Moon at any of 8 arrival times evenly distributed across a synodic month between July 11, 2010 at 19:41 UTC and August 6, 2010 at 20:37 UTC. The majority of the reference transfers sampled here implement lunar orbit insertion maneuvers with magnitudes between 640 m/s and 750 m/s, though reference transfers have been sampled with LOI ΔV values as high as 1080 m/s. Finally, reference transfers have been sampled with transfer durations between 65 and 160 days. This collection of reference transfers makes no assumptions about what sort of mission a designer may be interested in, except that each transfer is simple, i.e., it includes no Earth phasing orbits nor lunar flybys, and each transfer targets a polar lunar orbit.

RESULTS

In general, the algorithms described in this paper generate successful launch periods with similar characteristics. Figure 7 illustrates the total transfer ΔV of several example launch periods that have been generated from these reference transfers. One notices that many of these launch periods include a single main convex ΔV minimum, from which a 21-day launch period is easily identified. Other ΔV curves include two or more local minima. The launch periods are designed to have at most two gaps, where each gap must be less than 14 days in extent. A particular lunar mission may have different requirements, which may improve the launch period's cost.

It has been found that most 21-day launch periods among the 288 missions studied include the reference launch date, though there are many examples that do not, including two of those shown in Figure 7. In some cases a practical launch period may have extended further than 30 days from the reference launch date and required less total ΔV. There are often sudden jumps in the transfer ΔV curves, which are caused by the Moon's perturbation as the spacecraft departs the Earth. Since each transfer in a particular launch period departs the Earth in approximately the same direction, the Moon passes near the transfer's outbound leg about once every synodic month. Some transfers do not experience any significant perturbations due to their out-of-plane motion.

Figure 8 illustrates the range of the transfer ΔV values that are contained in each 21-day launch period as a function of their reference transfer ΔV. As an example, the launch period illustrated in Figure 6 was generated using a reference transfer with a ΔV of 649 m/s (the ordinate of the plots in Figure 8) and the resulting launch period included missions that had transfer ΔV values

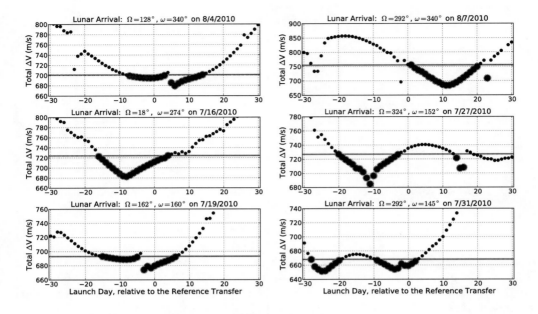

Figure 7. Several example curves that illustrate the post-TLI ΔV cost of transferring from a 28.5° LEO parking orbit at different TLI dates to a given reference low-energy transfer, including a highlighted 21-day launch period in each case.

between 670.6 and 706.2 m/s. One can see that the majority of transfers studied here have reference transfer ΔV values less than 750 m/s, though the transfers sampled include those with reference ΔV values up to 1080 m/s. The launch period ΔV range often starts above the mission's reference ΔV since each mission starts from a 28.5° LEO parking orbit and the reference transfer typically

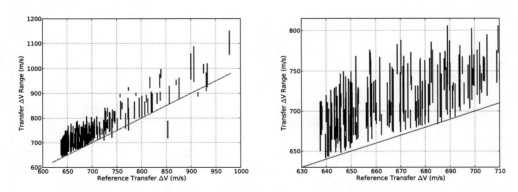

Figure 8. The range of transfer ΔV values contained in each 21-day launch period as a function of the reference transfer ΔV. The plot on the right shows an exploded view of the low-ΔV transfers.

departs from some other inclination. In a few cases, and one extreme case, the launch period ΔV range starts below the reference ΔV. This is often possible when the reference transfer has a natural Earth departure far from 28.5° and a change in the transfer duration reduces the total ΔV. The plots in Figure 8 clearly illustrate that the ΔV cost of establishing a 21-day launch period is highly dependent on the reference transfer's total ΔV. The launch period ΔV cost of these 288 example transfers requires approximately 71.67 ± 29.71 m/s (1σ) more deterministic ΔV than the transfer's reference ΔV.

The launch periods studied here include missions that depart the Earth on 21 different days and the launch period ΔV cost is the ΔV of the most expensive transfer in that set. The departure days do not need to be consecutive, as described earlier. In general, increasing the number of launch days included in a launch period increases the ΔV cost of the mission. Figure 9 shows a plot of the change in the launch period ΔV cost of the 288 missions studied here as one adds more days to each mission's launch period, relative to the case where each mission has only a single launch day. The line of best fit through these data indicate that on average it requires approximately 2.480 m/s per launch day to add days to a mission's launch period. There is a significant jump in the launch period ΔV when one moves from a 1-day launch period to a 2-day launch period. This is due to the fact that the Moon's perturbations often produce a single launch day with remarkably low ΔV requirements. The change in a launch period's required ΔV would be more smooth if the effects of lunar perturbations on the Earth-departure leg were ignored.

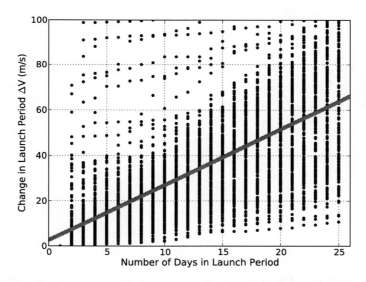

Figure 9. The change in the launch period ΔV cost of the 288 missions studied here as a function of the number of days in the launch period. The linear trend has a slope of 2.480 m/s per launch day.

It has been noted when studying Figure 7 that a launch period does not necessarily include the reference launch date. However, it is expected that the transfer duration of a reference trajectory may be used to predict a mission's actual transfer duration. Figure 10 tracks the range of transfer durations within each 21-day launch period studied here as a function of the mission's reference transfer

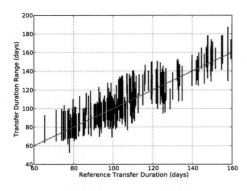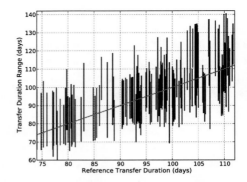

Figure 10. The range of transfer durations contained in each 21-day launch period as a function of the reference transfer duration. The plot on the right shows an exploded view, focused on transfer durations between 75 and 115 days.

duration. One can see that the range of transfer durations is indeed correlated with the reference transfer duration. Furthermore, it has been found that the maximum transfer duration of the 288 launch periods is approximately 15.95 ± 8.66 days longer than the mission's reference duration, the minimum transfer duration is approximately 10.91 ± 7.75 days shorter than the reference duration, and the total number of days between the first and final launch date of a given launch period may be estimated at approximately 26.86 ± 6.95 days. Hence, one may predict that a mission's launch period will include 21 of about 27 days, centered on a date several days earlier than the reference launch date, if one constructs a 21-day launch period using the same rules invoked here.

Figure 11 tracks the range of ΔV costs associated with each launch period as a function of the duration of the mission's reference transfer. One can see that there is a wide spread of transfer ΔV across the range of durations. As the reference transfer duration drops below 90 days, the launch

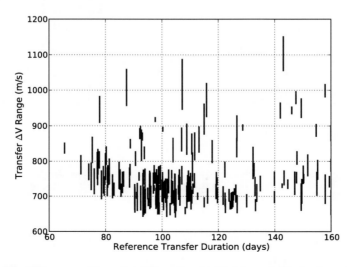

Figure 11. The range of transfer ΔV costs contained in each 21-day launch period as a function of the reference transfer's duration.

period ΔV cost climbs, which makes sense because there is less time to perform maneuvers during the shorter transfers. Beyond 90 days, there are launch periods with low ΔV requirements for any transfer duration.

It is expected that the launch period's ΔV cost is dependent upon the reference transfer's natural Earth departure inclination. It is hypothesized that a reference transfer that departs the Earth with an inclination near $28.5°$ will generate a launch period that requires less total ΔV than a reference transfer that departs the Earth with an inclination far different. Figure 12 tracks the launch period ΔV cost of the 288 missions constructed here as a function of their reference departure inclination values. The right plot in Figure 12 observes the range of transfer ΔV values as a function of the difference between the reference departure inclination value and the target $28.5°$ value. A line has been fit to the maximum ΔV for each launch period using a least-squares approach, which yields the relationship:

$$\text{Launch Period } \Delta V \sim (0.470 \text{ m/s/deg}) \times x + 756.5 \text{ m/s},$$

where x is equal to the absolute value of the difference between the reference departure inclination and $28.5°$. The sample set of lunar transfers includes low-ΔV and high-ΔV missions, which may swamp any significant relationship between the launch period's ΔV cost and the reference departure inclination. Nevertheless, it is very interesting to observe that the launch period's ΔV cost does not present a strong correlation with the reference departure inclination.

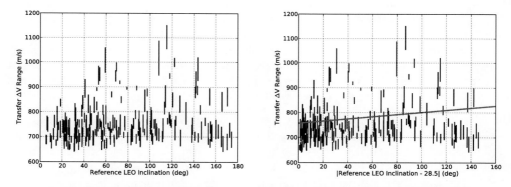

Figure 12. The range of transfer ΔV costs contained in each 21-day launch period as a function of the reference transfer's Earth departure inclination (left) and the absolute value of the difference between the reference inclination and $28.5°$ (right).

To further test the relationship of a launch period to the reference LEO inclination, each launch period's ΔV has been reduced by its reference ΔV so that each launch period may be more closely compared. Figure 13 shows the same two plots as shown in Figure 12, but with each mission's reference ΔV subtracted from its launch period ΔV range. One can see that the launch period ΔV is not well-correlated with the reference departure inclination. The linear fit has a slope of only 0.206 m/s per degree of inclination away from $28.5°$. It appears that a 21-day launch period absorbs most of the ΔV penalty associated with inclination variations. The natural Earth departure inclination of a transfer certainly varies with transfer duration, and it has already been noticed that the launch period is often not centered about the reference transfer's TLI date. This result is useful, because it indicates that the natural Earth departure inclination is not a good predictor of the launch period ΔV requirement of a reference transfer. The relationship of the low-energy transfer ΔV and the TLI inclination will be further explored in the next section.

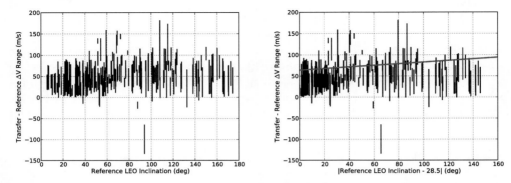

Figure 13. The same two plots as shown in Figure 12, but with each mission's reference ΔV subtracted from its 21-day launch period ΔV range.

Varying the LEO Inclination

The results presented previously in this paper have only considered missions that begin in a LEO parking orbit at an inclination of 28.5° relative to the equator, corresponding to launch sites such as Cape Canaveral, Florida. Spacecraft missions certainly depart the Earth from other launch sites; launch vehicles from those sites typically deliver the most mass to low Earth orbit if they launch into a parking orbit at an inclination approximately equal to their launch site's latitude. Hence, it is of interest to determine the ΔV cost required to depart the Earth from any LEO inclination and transfer to the same lunar orbit using a particular low-energy reference transfer.

The algorithms described in this paper have been used to generate missions that depart the Earth from LEO parking orbits at a wide range of inclinations and then target the same reference low-energy transfer discussed earlier (described in Table 2 and illustrated in Figure 3). The reference trajectory naturally departs the Earth on April 1st, 2010 from an orbital inclination of approximately 38.305°; hence, a mission that departs the Earth at that time from that orbit requires no deterministic maneuvers en route to the Moon. Upon arrival at the Moon, the reference trajectory requires a 649.0 m/s orbit insertion maneuver to impulsively enter the desired 100-km circular lunar orbit. Any mission that departs the Earth from a different inclination will require deterministic TCMs and/or a different orbit insertion maneuver.

Figure 14 illustrates how the deterministic ΔV varies for missions that depart the Earth at different LEO inclination values and target the same lunar orbit. The dates and times of the trans-lunar injection and lunar orbit insertion are fixed. The total transfer ΔV is shown on the left and the difference between each mission's total ΔV compared to the reference transfer's total ΔV is shown on the right. One can see that the ΔV cost of the mission rises as a function of the difference between the mission's departure inclination and the reference transfer's departure inclination. The cost is approximately 0.97 m/s per degree of inclination change for missions with LEO inclinations greater than 20 degrees. The transfer cost increases much more rapidly as a mission's departure approaches equatorial. As the departure inclination drops, the system gradually loses a degree of freedom: the

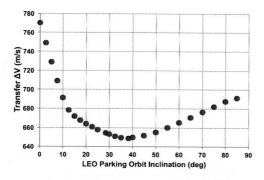 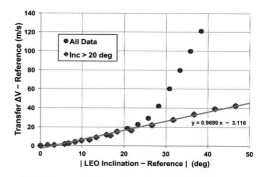

Figure 14. Left: the total transfer ΔV for missions that depart the Earth on April 1, 2010 at different inclinations and arrive at the same reference lunar orbit. Right: the difference in the total transfer ΔV for these missions compared with the reference low-energy transfer, which departs at an inclination of 38.305°.

LEO parking orbit's ascending node becomes less influential on the geometry of the departure. The ascending node is no longer defined for equatorial departures, and the lunar transfer requires over 120 m/s more deterministic ΔV than the reference transfer.

As Figure 14 illustrates, the total ΔV of a mission to the reference lunar orbit is minimized if the LEO parking orbit has an inclination of 38.305°, provided that the trans-lunar injection is performed on April 1st, 2010. If the TLI date is shifted, then the optimal LEO inclination is likely to shift as well. Hence, the ΔV cost of a full 21-day launch period cannot be strictly predicted by observing the difference in inclination between a desired LEO parking orbit and the reference departure.

Figure 15 illustrates three launch periods, corresponding to missions that depart from LEO parking orbits with inclinations of 20, 50, and 80 degrees. One can see that the launch period shifts in time, illustrating that the transfer duration may significantly alter the reference trajectory's natural departure inclination. Figure 16 illustrates the total transfer ΔV for each launch opportunity of a 21-day launch period departing from a wide range of departure inclinations. One can see that the launch period ΔV is dramatically higher for low inclinations, and the ΔV changes very little from one inclination to another for higher inclination values. It is interesting that the missions with higher inclinations require less ΔV than missions near the reference transfer's departure inclination. The low-ΔV points in the lower-left part of the plot correspond to brief opportunities in those launch periods when the Moon passes through an ideal location in its orbit to reduce the transfer ΔV.

CONCLUSIONS

This study has randomly sampled 288 different low-energy transfers between the Earth and polar orbits about the Moon and has constructed practical 21-day launch periods for each of them, using a 28.5° LEO parking orbit and no more than two deterministic maneuvers. The lunar orbits have a wide range of geometries, though they are all polar and have an altitude of approximately 100 km. The reference low-energy transfers include no Earth phasing orbits nor close lunar flybys and require between 65 and 160 days of transfer duration. Each mission has been constructed by using a sequence of steps, varying eight parameters to minimize the transfer ΔV cost. The eight variable parameters include the parking orbit's ascending node, the trans-lunar injection's location in the parking orbit, the trans-lunar injection's ΔV, the times of two deterministic maneuvers en

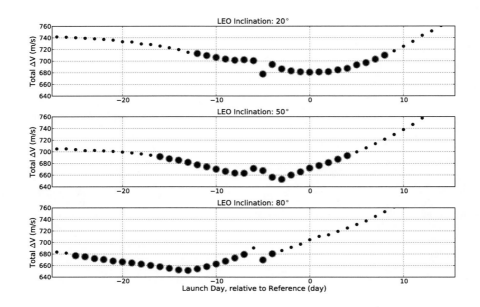

Figure 15. Three launch periods for missions to the reference lunar orbit, where each launch period is designed to accommodate a specific LEO inclination; namely, 20° (top), 50° (middle), and 80° (bottom). The Moon perturbs the outbound trajectories for those missions that launch about 5 days before the reference transfer.

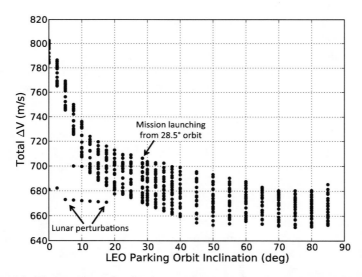

Figure 16. The total transfer ΔV for each opportunity of a 21-day launch period for missions to the reference lunar orbit departing from LEO parking orbits with varying inclination values.

route to the Moon, and three components of the lunar orbit insertion maneuver. All other aspects of the transfer are fixed when building a particular mission.

Several conclusions may be easily drawn from the results presented in this paper. First of all, the cost of a launch period is obviously dependent on the number of launch days in the period. The transfers constructed here demonstrate that it costs on average approximately 2.5 m/s per day added to a launch period; hence, the average 21-day launch period requires about 50 m/s more deterministic ΔV than a 1-day launch period for a given transfer. The cost of establishing a 21-day launch period to the 288 reference transfers studied in this paper is approximately 71.7 ± 29.7 m/s (1σ), where the additional ΔV above and beyond the 50 m/s is required to accommodate a departure from a $28.5°$ LEO parking orbit. The 21 opportunities in the launch period may be on 21 consecutive days, and frequently are, but typically include one or two gaps. The average launch period for these 288 missions requires a total of 27 days; the vast majority of the launch periods may be contained within 40 days. Finally, it has been found that there is no significant trend between the total launch period ΔV for these 288 missions and their reference departure inclination values or their reference transfer durations, except for short transfers with durations below 90 days.

An additional study has been performed to observe how a mission's ΔV changes as a function of the particular LEO inclination selected. A mission that departs at a particular time requires approximately 0.97 m/s more transfer ΔV per degree of inclination change performed, assuming that the departure inclination is above $20°$. The total transfer ΔV cost increases dramatically as the departure inclination approaches $0°$. These trends change when considering a full 21-day launch period. The required launch period ΔV is still high for missions that depart from nearly equatorial LEO parking orbits, but the variation in the launch period ΔV is reduced for missions that depart at higher inclinations.

The work presented in this paper is useful for mission designers to gain an understanding about the transfer ΔV costs associated with establishing a realistic 21-day launch period from a desirable departure to a particular low-energy lunar transfer.

Acknowledgements

This work could not have been performed without the support of Ted Sweetser, whose efforts made this work possible. The authors would also like to thank Ted and Roby Wilson for their valuable feedback during the editing of this paper.

The research presented in this paper has been carried out at the Jet Propulsion Laboratory, California Institute of Technology, under a contract with the National Aeronautics and Space Administration. Copyright 2011 California Institute of Technology. Government sponsorship acknowledged.

REFERENCES

[1] E. A. Belbruno and J. Miller, "A Ballistic Lunar Capture Trajectory for the Japanese Spacecraft Hiten," Tech. Rep. IOM 312/90.4-1731-EAB, JPL, California Institute of Technology, 1990.

[2] K. Uesugi, "Japanese first double Lunar swingby mission 'HITEN'," *Acta Astronautica*, Vol. 25, No. 7, 1991, pp. 347–355.

[3] S. B. Broschart, M. J. Chung, S. J. Hatch, J. H. Ma, T. H. Sweetser, S. S. Weinstein-Weiss, and V. Angelopoulos, "Preliminary Trajectory Design for the ARTEMIS Lunar Mission," *AAS/AIAA Astrodynamics Specialist Conference*, No. AAS 09-382, Pittsburgh, Pennsylvania, AAS/AIAA, August 9–13, 2009.

[4] M. Woodard, D. Folta, and D. Woodfork, "ARTEMIS: The First Mission to the Lunar Libration Orbits," *21st International Symposium on Space Flight Dynamics*, Toulouse, France, Centre National d'Études Spatiales, September 28 – October 2, 2009.

[5] R. B. Roncoli and K. K. Fujii, "Mission Design Overview for the Gravity Recovery and Interior Laboratory (GRAIL) Mission," *AIAA/AAS Astrodynamics Specialist Conference*, No. AIAA 2010-8383, Toronto, Ontario, Canada, AIAA/AAS, August 2–5, 2010.

[6] M. J. Chung, S. J. Hatch, J. A. Kangas, S. M. Long, R. B. Roncoli, and T. H. Sweetser, "Trans-Lunar Cruise Trajectory Design of GRAIL (Gravity Recovery and Interior Laboratory) Mission," *AIAA/AAS Astrodynamics Specialist Conference*, No. AIAA 2010-8384, Toronto, Ontario, Canada, AIAA/AAS, August 2–5, 2010.

[7] S. J. Hatch, R. B. Roncoli, and T. H. Sweetser, "GRAIL Trajectory Design: Lunar Orbit Insertion through Science," *AIAA/AAS Astrodynamics Specialist Conference*, No. AIAA 2010-8385, Toronto, Ontario, Canada, AIAA/AAS, August 2–5, 2010.

[8] J. S. Parker, R. L. Anderson, and A. Peterson, "A Survey of Ballistic Transfers to Low Lunar Orbit," *AAS/AIAA Space Flight Mechanics Meeting*, No. AAS 11-277, New Orleans, LA, AAS/AIAA, Feb 13–17, 2011.

[9] J. S. Parker, *Low-Energy Ballistic Lunar Transfers*. PhD thesis, University of Colorado, Boulder, Colorado, 2007.

[10] J. S. Parker and G. H. Born, "Modeling a Low-Energy Ballistic Lunar Transfer Using Dynamical Systems Theory," *Journal of Spacecraft and Rockets*, Vol. 45, Nov–Dec 2008, pp. 1269–1281.

[11] J. S. Parker, "Low-Energy Ballistic Transfers to Lunar Halo Orbits," *AAS/AIAA Astrodynamics Specialist Conference*, No. AAS 09-443, Pittsburgh, Pennsylvania, AAS/AIAA, August 9–13, 2009.

[12] J. S. Parker, "Targeting Low-Energy Ballistic Lunar Transfers," *American Astronautical Society, George H. Born Special Symposium*, Boulder, Colorado, AAS, May 13–14, 2010.

[13] C. Conley, "Low Energy Transit Orbits in the Restricted Three Body Problem," *SIAM Journal Appl. Math.*, Vol. 16, No. 4, 1968, pp. 732–746.

[14] V. V. Ivashkin, "On Trajectories of the Earth-Moon Flight of a Particle with its Temporary Capture by the Moon," *Doklady Physics, Mechanics*, Vol. 47, No. 11, 2002, pp. 825–827.

[15] V. V. Ivashkin, "On Particle's Trajectories of Moon-to-Earth Space Flights with the Gravitational Escape from the Lunar Attraction," *Doklady Physics, Mechanics*, Vol. 49, No. 9, 2004, pp. 539–542.

[16] W. S. Koon, M. W. Lo, J. E. Marsden, and S. D. Ross, "Shoot the Moon," *AAS/AIAA Spaceflight Mechanics 2000*, Vol. 105, part 2, AAS/AIAA, 2000, pp. 1017–1030.

[17] R. L. Anderson and J. S. Parker, "A Survey of Ballistic Transfers to the Lunar Surface," *AAS/AIAA Space Flight Mechanics Meeting*, No. AAS 11-278, New Orleans, LA, AAS/AIAA, Feb 13–17, 2011.

[18] E. M. Alessi, G. Gómez, and J. J. Masdemont, "Leaving the Moon by Means of Invariant Manifolds of Libration Point Orbits," *Communications in Nonlinear Science and Numerical Simulation*, Vol. 14, December 2009, pp. 4153–4167.

[19] L. Lozier, K. Galal, D. Folta, and M. Beckman, "Lunar Prospector Mission Design and Trajectory Support," *AAS/AIAA Spaceflight Dynamics Conference*, No. AAS 98-323, AAS/AIAA, 1998.

[20] A. Matsuoka and C. T. Russell, eds., *The Kaguya Mission to the Moon*. New York, NY: Springer, first ed., 2011.

[21] NASA, "NASA National Space Science Data Center (NSSDC) Lunar and Planetary Home Page," August 2006.

[22] J. N. Goswami and M. Annadurai, "Chandrayaan-1: India's First Planetary Science Mission to the Moon," *Current Science; Special Section: Chandrayaan-1*, Vol. 96, 25 February 2009, pp. 486–491.

[23] M. Beckman, "Mission Design for the Lunar Reconnaissance Orbiter," *29th Annual AAS Guidance and Control Conference*, No. AAS 07-057, Breckenridge, CO, AAS, 2007.

[24] V. Szebehely, *Theory of Orbits: The Restricted Problem of Three Bodies*. New York: Academic Press, 1967.

[25] R. B. Roncoli, "Lunar Constants and Models Document," Tech. Rep. JPL D-32296, Jet Propulsion Laboratory, California Institute of Technology, September 2005.

[26] F. T. Krogh, "Variable Order Adams Method for Ordinary Differential Equations," tech. rep., California Institute of Technology, 2010 Math à la Carte, Inc., http://mathalacarte.com/cb/mom.fcg/ya64, Tujunga, California, October 1975.

[27] W. M. Folkner, J. G. Williams, and D. H. Boggs, "The Planetary and Lunar Ephemeris DE 421," Tech. Rep. IOM 343R–08–003, Jet Propulsion Laboratory, California Institute of Technology, March 2008. ftp://naif.jpl.nasa.gov/pub/naif/generic_kernels/spk/planets/ de421_announcement.pdf.

[28] P. E. Gill, W. Murray, and M. A. Saunders, "User's Guide for SNOPT 7.1: A Fortran Package for Large-Scale Nonlinear Programming," Tech. Rep. Numerical Analysis Report NA 04-1, Department of Mathematics, University of California, San Diego, La Jolla, CA, 2004.

[29] P. E. Gill, W. Murray, and M. A. Saunders, "SNOPT: An SQP Algorithm for Large-Scale Constrained Optimization," *SIAM Review*, Vol. 47, No. 1, 2005, pp. 99–131.

[30] R. S. Wilson and K. C. Howell, "Trajectory Design in the Sun-Earth-Moon System Using Lunar Gravity Assists," *Journal of Spacecraft and Rockets*, Vol. 35, No. 2, 1998, pp. 191–198.

ATMOSPHERIC ENTRY GUIDANCE VIA MULTIPLE SLIDING SURFACES CONTROL FOR MARS PRECISION LANDING

Scott Selnick,[*] Roberto Furfaro[†] and Daniel R. Wibben[‡]

Improving Mars landing accuracy will require the implementation of robust, closed-loop guidance schemes for the entry portion of the atmospheric flight. A novel non-linear atmospheric entry guidance law has been developed for a class of low-lift landers similar to the one expected to be flown in the upcoming Mars Science Laboratory (MSL) mission. Here we proposed a Multiple Sliding Surface Guidance (MSSG) approach for Mars entry guidance. The presented guidance scheme is based on a higher order sliding mode control theory adapted to account for (1) the specific 2-sliding mode order exhibited by the longitudinal motion of the entry vehicle guided, using bank angle variations and (2) the ability of the system to reach the sliding surface in a finite time. Contrary to more standard methods designed to track a drag-based profile as a function of the range-to-go, the proposed scheme does not require any off-line trajectory generation and therefore it is suitable for real-time implementation. The global stability nature of the MSSG law is proven by using a Lyapunov-based approach. A parametric study has been conducted to understand the behavior of such class of trajectories as a function of the guidance parameters. The MSSG algorithm targeting ability is analyzed through a set of Monte Carlo simulations where the guidance law is required to operate under off-nominal conditions. Simulation results show good performance under perturbations and parameter uncertainties.

INTRODUCTION

The next generation of Mars landers will require advanced Guidance, Navigation and Control (GNC) capabilities to satisfy more stringent landing requirements. The latter are imposed by the desire to explore specific surface locales that have the potential to yield the highest scientific returns. For example, the landing site selection for the next Mars Science Laboratory (MSL) mission is driven by the probability of yielding important geological and exobiological information. The need for highly specific and more ambitious science requirements stimulates the development of novel guidance systems that can deliver rovers and/or landers on the Mars surface with

---

[*] Systems Engineer II, Guidance Design & Performance, Raytheon Missile Systems, postal, 1151 E. Hermans Rd, Tucson AZ 85734.

[†] Assistant Professor, Department of Systems and Industrial Engineering, University of Arizona, 1127 E. Roger Way, Tucson Arizona, 85721, USA

[‡] Graduate Student, Department of Systems and Industrial Engineering, University of Arizona, 1127 E. Roger Way, Tucson Arizona, 85721, USA

unprecedented precision. A typical Mars descent profile is characterized by a sequence of three phases, namely Entry, Descent and Landing (EDL[1]). In particular, the entry phase consists in a guided or unguided hypersonic deceleration of the lander from the entry interface (typically 125 km and 5.6 km/sec) until the parachute is deployed (typically 10 km altitude and 470 m/sec). All of the six past successful Mars landing missions, including the latest Phoenix Mission to Mars[1], had a mission descent profile with an entry phase designed to implement a ballistic (i.e., unguided) hypersonic deceleration. Whereas the approach was simple to implement, it resulted in large error ellipses (hundreds of kilometers). The newest MSL system[2] is designed to implement an active entry guidance algorithm which will likely result in an accuracy of 10 km or less. Clearly, closed-loop entry guidance is required to achieve even better landing precision, e.g., pin-point landing (< 100 m). For the entry phase of low Lift-to-Drag ratio (L/D) vehicles, any closed loop guidance system relies on the bank angle to provide active trajectory control. Therefore, a bank angle program must be determined and actively implemented to achieve the desired targeting performances. Generally, schemes for atmospheric entry guidance are divided into major categories, i.e., a) reference trajectory tracking methods and b) predictive trajectory planning methods. In the first case[3,4], a reference trajectory, generally optimal according to some specified criterion, is computed on the ground and stored on the on-board computer. The on-board guidance system is responsible for removing any errors that can arise from deviation of the nominal path (e.g. entry interface errors, deviation from a nominal density profile etc.). In the second case[5,6], no trajectory is pre-programmed, but the actual path and the bank angle program computed in real-time using prediction techniques.

In this paper, we present a novel and robust guidance approach for the entry portion of the Mars EDL phase. We propose a non-linear guidance scheme called Multiple Sliding Surface Guidance (MSSG) that computes a bank angle program as a function of the current state and the targeted final entry phase point. MSSG has its foundation on Higher Order Sliding Control (HOSC) mode theory[7,8]. The theory is based on the idea of using sliding surfaces with higher relative degree, to generate on-line targeting trajectories that are guaranteed to be globally stable under bounded perturbations. It is shown that sliding surfaces that are appropriate for the guidance of the Mars lander longitudinal motion have a second relative degree, meaning that the control variable appears at the second derivative of the selected surface. The first sliding surface is defined such that it behaves as a non-linear first order system and it is designed to reach the desired terminal state in a finite time (time of flight). The bank angle program is determined by deriving a guidance law that drives to zero a second sliding surface in a finite time generally smaller than the desired time of flight. The second surface is concatenated to the first surface: as the bank angle forces the second sliding mode to zero, the first surface dynamics has the required conditions for the lander to reach the desired state.

The paper is organized as follows: First, the Mars entry longitudinal guidance problem is formulated. After a brief introduction to the sliding control theory and the higher order sliding control mode, the guidance algorithm is formulated. The Longitudinal guidance algorithm is next analyzed along with a parametric study of the guidance parameters. Afterwards, both the lateral and longitudinal guidance laws are implemented in a three degrees of freedom simulation. Both guidance parameter optimization and Monte Carlo analysis is presented.

LONGITUDINAL GUIDANCE PROBLEM FORMULATION

Here, we consider the general Mars entry guidance problem which can be formulated as follows: given the current state of the entry vehicle (i.e. translational motion), determine a bank angle program that meets the requirements of achieving a prescribed range and speed. The initial focus will be on the longitudinal guidance formulation.

Equations of Motion

The Mars-relative longitudinal translational state of a low L/D vehicle can be represented by four states, i.e., a) downrange (R), b) radial distance from the center of mars (r), c) velocity magnitude (V) and d) flight path angle (γ). Neglecting the Coriolis and centrifugal terms due to Mars rotation and effect of the wind, the equation of motion can now be stated as follows:

$$\dot{R} = V cos\gamma \tag{1}$$

$$\dot{r} = V sin\gamma \tag{2}$$

$$\dot{V} = -D - g(r)sin\gamma \tag{3}$$

$$\dot{\gamma} = \frac{1}{V}\left[L cos\sigma - \left(g(r) - \frac{V^2}{r}\right)cos\gamma\right] \tag{4}$$

$$L = \frac{1}{2}\frac{\rho S c_L}{m}V^2 \tag{5}$$

$$D = \frac{1}{2}\frac{\rho S c_D}{m}V^2 \tag{6}$$

$$g(r) = \frac{\mu_M}{r^2} \tag{7}$$

The other variables appearing on Eq. (1)-(4) are lift acceleration (L), drag acceleration (D), bank angle (σ) and gravitational acceleration (g). L, D and $g(r)$ are formally defined in Eq. (5)-(7) where ρ is the atmospheric density, S is a surface reference, m is the lander mass, μ_M is the Mars gravitational parameter and c_L and c_D are lift and drag coefficients, respectively. Finally, the cosine of the bank angle is the parameter employed to control the longitudinal motions. The overall goal is to design and test a MSSG algorithm that generates a bank angle program that guides the lander to the desired target point during the entry portion of the descent.

NON-LINEAR GUIDANCE LAWS DEVELOPMENT

Sliding Control Theory for Systems of Higher Relative Degree

The sliding control methodology is an elementary approach to robust control[9]. Intuitively, it is based on the observation that it is much easier to control non-linear 1st order systems subjected to uncertain parameters than nth-order systems usually described by nth-order differential equations. Generally, if a transformation is found such that an nth-order problem can be replaced in a 1st order problem, a perfect performance can be in principle achieved in presence of parameter inaccuracy. However, such higher performance is paid by the need of higher control activity.

Consider the following single-input nth-order dynamical system:

$$\frac{d^n}{dt^n}x = f(\mathbf{x}) + b(\mathbf{x})u \tag{8}$$

Here x is the scalar output, u is the control variable and $\mathbf{x} = \left[x, \dot{x}, \ldots\ldots, x^{(n)}\right]^T$ is the state vector whose components are the derivative of the scalar output (up to the n-1 derivative). Both f($\mathbf{x}$), which describes the non-linear system dynamics, and the control gain b($\mathbf{x}$) are not assumed to be exactly known. However, if both f(x) and b(x) have a known upper bound, the sliding control goal is to get the state x to track the desired state $x_d = \left[x_d, \dot{x}_d, \dots \dots, x_d^{(n)} \right]^T$ in presence of model uncertainties. The time-varying sliding surface is defined as function of the tracking error $\tilde{x} = x - x_d$ by the following scalar equation:

$$s(x,t) = (\frac{d}{dt} + \lambda)^{n-1} \tilde{x} = 0 \qquad (9)$$

For example, if n = 2 we obtain:

$$s(x,t) = \dot{\tilde{x}} + \lambda \tilde{x} = 0 \qquad (10)$$

With the definitions in Eq. (9) and Eq. (10), the tracking problem is reduced to the problem of forcing the dynamical system in Eq. (8) to remain on the time-varying sliding surface. Clearly, tracking an n-dimensional vector x_d has been reduced to the problem of keeping the scalar sliding surface to zero, i.e., the problem has been reduced to a 1st order stabilization problem in the sliding surfaces. The simplified 1st order stabilization problem can be now achieved by selecting a control law such that outside the sliding surface, the following is satisfied:

$$\frac{1}{2} \frac{d}{dt} s^2 \leq -\eta |s| \qquad (11)$$

Here, η is a strictly positive constant. Eq. (11), also called "sliding condition", explicitly states that the distance from the sliding surface decreases along all system trajectories. Generally, constructing a control law that satisfies the sliding condition is fairly straightforward. For example, using the Lyapunov direct method[10] one can select a candidate Lyapunov function as follows:

$$V(s) = \frac{1}{2} s^T s \qquad (12)$$

With V(0) = 0 and V(s) > 0 for s > 0. By taking the derivative of Eq. (12), it is easily concluded that the sliding condition (Eq. (11)) is satisfied. The control law is generally obtained by substituting the sliding control definition, Eq. (12), and the system dynamical equations, Eq. (8), into Eq. (11).

Constraining the system to "slide" on the surface defined by Eq. (6) can be maintained only at the price of higher control activity. Indeed, once the surface is reached, the sliding mode requires that a specific law is implemented such that the dynamical system "slides" along the surface until the zero point is achieved. However, because of the finite time response of the actuators, fast control switching may be needed. The latter is one major drawback of the methodology as high–frequency control switching may cause chattering. Additionally, the methodology can be applied only if the system is of relative degree one, i.e. the controller explicitly appears on the first derivative of the sliding surface (Eq. (8)). If the system under consideration has higher relative degree, the application of HOSC mode can be useful to eliminate chattering yet maintain robustness of the controller in a highly uncertain environment. Here, the following definition is introduced.

Definition: Consider a smooth dynamical system with a smooth output s(x) (sliding function). Then, provided that $s, \dot{s}, \ddot{s}, \dots, s^{r-1}$ are continuous and that $s = \dot{s} = \ddot{s} = \cdots = s^{r-1} = 0$, then the motion on the set $\{s, \dot{s}, \ddot{s}, \dots, s^{r-1}\} = \{0,0,0,\dots,0\}$ is said to exist on an r-sliding mode.

870

As it will be shown shortly, the dynamics of the entry vehicle landing problem is such that the bank angle command shows up at the second derivative of a properly defined sliding vector. Thus, 2-sliding control principles can be applied to take advantage of such properties and completely eliminate chattering. Recently, HOSC has been one of the central topics of modern non-linear control theory[8]. Indeed, asymptotically stable higher-order sliding modes appear naturally in systems that are traditionally treated with conventional sliding-mode control[11]. Whereas theoretical studies on the finite-convergence properties of arbitrary-order sliding mode control are currently underway[7]. 2-sliding controllers have been already applied in practical problems of interest in space and aerospace applications including missile guidance[12,13] and reentry terminal guidance[14] as well as lunar landing guidance[15]. Importantly, Harl and Balakrishnan[14] set the stage on how to apply HOSC principles for terminal landing guidance problems. The key point is to guarantee that the sliding surface and its derivative will go to zero in a finite time while ensuring that the sliding surface will not cross zero until the final time. In contrast with one of the most popular approach described by Levant[8] where 2-sliding homogeneous control can "twist" around the sliding surface zeroing it out in a finite time, such approach is not suitable for guidance applications as the problem is considered over when the sliding surface is crossed. Notably, the design of robust sliding-based guidance algorithms where the sliding surface is reached in finite time for the first time at the landing location has been recently demonstrated for lunar landing[15].

The proposed MSSG for Mars entry vehicle landing is designed around the principles of HOSC. The overall approach to MSSG development is to employ the notion that the motion of the guided vehicle during the powered descent and landing toward the red planet is forced to exist in a 2-sliding mode. Next section describes how the proposed guidance law is derived.

Multiple Sliding Surface Guidance (MSSG) approach for Mars Entry longitudinal control

Here, the goal is to develop a novel non-linear guidance approach for the Mars entry phase based on the application of recent advancements in HOSC theory mentioned on the previous section. The overall objective is to derive a guidance law (bank angle program) that is a) robust against parameters uncertainties, and b) guarantees good targeting performances at the end of the entry phase. The guidance model employed to develop the multiple surface sliding guidance algorithm is longitudinal descent model described by Eq. (1)-(7).

The overall approach to the entry guidance development relies on the notion that the longitudinal motion of the guided entry vehicle may be forced to exist in a 2-sliding mode. For a class of sliding surfaces that are of interest to guidance problem under investigation, the dynamics of the system is such that the sliding surfaces are of order two. Let us define the first sliding surface in the following way:

$$s_1 = (r - r_d) + \dot{r}_d(t_f - t) \tag{13}$$

Where $(t_f - t)$ or time-to-go is defined as follows:

$$(t_f - t) = t_{go} = \frac{1}{v}\sqrt{(r - r_d)^2 + (R - R_d)^2} \tag{14}$$

Here, r_d is the desired (target) altitude and R_d is the desired (target) range. Taking the derivative of s_1, we obtain:

$$\dot{s}_1 = \dot{r} - \dot{r}_d \qquad (15)$$

In this case, the longitudinal entry guidance problem can be formulated as a standard control problem: Find the bank angle command such that, in a finite time t_f, both sliding surface and its derivative are driven to zero, i.e., $s_1 \to 0$ and $\dot{s}_1 \to 0$. Importantly, the sliding surface is of relative degree 2. Indeed, taking the derivative of Eq. (15) one obtains:

$$\ddot{s}_1 = \ddot{r} = -Dsin\gamma - g(r) + \frac{v^2}{r}cos^2\gamma + (Lcos\gamma)cos\sigma \qquad (16)$$

The guidance goal is achieved by a backstepping approach where $\dot{s}_1$ is set to be the virtual controller and determined in such a way that the first sliding surface is driven to zero in a finite time. The virtual controlled can be conveniently selected in the following way:

$$\dot{s}_1 = -\frac{\lambda}{(t_f-t)}s_1 \qquad (17)$$

The parameter λ is a guidance gain that determines the rate of convergence of the first surface to zero. The virtual controller $\dot{s}_1$ is globally stable and can be proven via Lyapunov second method. Indeed, consider the following candidate Lyapunov function:

$$V_1 = \frac{1}{2}s_1^2 \qquad (18)$$

It is easily verified that the function defined in Eq. (18) has the flowing properties:

$$
\begin{aligned}
V_1(0) &= 0 \quad if \; s_1 = 0 \\
V_1(s_1) &> 0 \quad \forall \, s_1 \neq 0 \\
V_1(s_1) &\to \infty \quad if \; s_1 \to \infty
\end{aligned} \qquad (19)
$$

To show global stability, we can find the conditions under which the virtual controller makes the time derivative of the Lyapunov function negative everywhere:

$$\dot{V}_1 = s_1\dot{s}_1 = -\frac{\lambda}{(t_f-t)}s_1^2 < 0 \qquad (20)$$

If and only if $\lambda > 0$. Nevertheless, a more stringent condition is required to ensure that the sliding surface and its derivative approach zero in a finite time. The time-behavior of the sliding surface and its derivative can be determined analytically by applying separation of variable to Eq. (17) and integrating:

$$\frac{ds_1}{s_1} = -\frac{\lambda dt}{t_f-t} \qquad (21)$$

$$log(s_1) = \lambda log(t_f - t) + C \qquad (22)$$

The constant of integration can be obtained by imposing the initial condition $s_1(0) = s_{10}$ and taking the exponential of both sides:

872

$$s_1(t) = s_1(t_f - t)^\lambda \qquad (23)$$

The derivative can be easily computed analytically as well:

$$\dot{s}_1(t) = \lambda s_1(t_f - t)^{\lambda-1} \qquad (24)$$

The condition $\lambda > 0$ ensures that the first surface is reached in a finite time t_f. However, to impose the requirement that both surface and derivative go to zero in a finite time, λ must be greater than 1.

At the time where the entry phase is initiated, the lander state, i.e., position and velocity are such that Eq. (17) is not satisfied. Moreover, to derive a meaningful guidance algorithm, the virtual controller must be related to the bank angle command. The link is determined by defining a second sliding surface. The latter is defined such that a bank command angle can be found that while driving and maintaining the second surface to zero, the first surface and its derivative are guaranteed to converge to zero in a finite time. The second sliding surface vector is defined in the following way:

$$s_2 = \dot{s}_1 + \frac{\lambda}{(t_f - t)} s_1 = 0 \qquad (25)$$

The surface defined in Eq. (25) is of relative degree 1 with respect to the bank angle command, i.e., the cosine of the bank angle appears at the first derivative of the second surface:

$$\dot{s}_2 = \ddot{s}_1 + \frac{\lambda}{(t_f - t)} \dot{s}_1 + \frac{\lambda}{(t_f - t)^2} s_1 \qquad (26)$$

Using Eq. (26), it is explicitly found that:

$$\dot{s}_2 = -D\sin\gamma - g(r) + \frac{v^2}{r}\cos^2\gamma + (L\cos\gamma)\cos\sigma + \frac{\lambda}{(t_f - t)}\dot{s}_1 + \frac{\lambda}{(t_f - t)^2} s_1 \qquad (27)$$

The closed-loop bank angle command can be determined using the Lyapunov second method. Let us define a second Lyapunov candidate function as follows:

$$V_2 = \frac{1}{2} s_2^2 \qquad (28)$$

The candidate Lyapunov function is quadratic on the second surface and satisfies conditions similar to the one expressed in Eq. (19). Its time-derivative can be explicitly determined:

$$\dot{V}_2 = s_2 \dot{s}_2 = s_2 \left\{ -D\sin\gamma - g(r) + \frac{v^2}{r}\cos^2\gamma + (L\cos\gamma)\cos\sigma + \lambda\frac{(t_f - t)\dot{s}_1 + s_1}{(t_f - t)^2} \right\} \qquad (29)$$

Remembering that $t_{go} = t_f - t$ and using Eq. (29), the bank angle command is found to be:

$$\sigma = \cos^{-1}\left\{ \frac{1}{L\cos\gamma}\left[-D\sin\gamma - g(r) + \frac{v^2}{r}\cos^2\gamma + \frac{\lambda}{t_{go}^2}(\dot{s}_1 t_{go} + s_1) \right] - \Phi sgn(s_2) \right\} \qquad (30)$$

Where Φ is defined as follows:

$$\Phi = \frac{|s_2(0)|}{t_f^*} \tag{31}$$

The MSSG algorithm is represented by Eq.(30). It is easy to show that the second sliding surface defined in Eq. (25) is driven to zero in a finite time $t_f^* < t_f$. The dynamics of the second sliding surface can be determined analytically. By inserting the MSSG law (Eq. (30)) into Eq. (27), one obtains:

$$\dot{s}_2 = -\Phi \mathrm{sgn}(s_2) \tag{32}$$

Since s_2 does not change sign before reaching the surface, Eq. (32) can be easily integrated:

$$s_2(t) = s_2(0) - \frac{|s_2(0)|}{t_F^*} t \tag{33}$$

As clearly demonstrated, the second sliding surface goes to zero as $t \to t_f^*$.

The MSSG is shown to be globally stable. By virtue of Eq. (30), the derivative of the candidate Lyapunov function becomes:

$$\dot{V}_2 = s_2 \dot{s}_2 = -\Phi s_2 \mathrm{sgn}(s_2) = -\Phi|s_2| < 0 \tag{34}$$

Which is negative everywhere as long as $\Phi > 0$. The second Lyapunov function is therefore decrescent and by virtue of the Lyapunov stability theorem for non-autonomous systems $s_2 \to 0$ as $t \to t_f^*$. Consequently, as the zero of the second surface is reached and maintained, $s_1, \dot{s}_1 \to 0$ as $t \to t_f$.

NON-LINEAR GUIDANCE LAWS EXTENSTION INTO 3 DIMENSIONS

Next, we consider the full 3-D Mars entry guidance problem. The latter can be formulated by determining the full three-dimensional equations of motions for the entry vehicle and considering two separate guidance problems, i.e. longitudinal and lateral guidance. The correct separation between the two guidance modes requires a) finding of a new way to define the range for the longitudinal guidance and b) providing additional lateral guidance logic to control the crossrange error.

The full three dimensional Mars-relative translational state of a low L/D vehicle can be represented by six states. These states are longitude (θ), latitude, (ϕ), radial distance from the center of mars (r), the velocity magnitude (V), the flight path angle (γ) and the heading angle (χ). Heading is defined as a clockwise rotation angle starting at due north[5]. Neglecting the Coriolis and centrifugal terms due to Mars rotation as well as the effect of the wind, and assuming that Mars is a perfect sphere, the equations of motion can be stated as follows:

$$\dot{\theta} = \frac{V \cos\gamma \sin\chi}{r\cos\phi} \tag{35}$$

$$\dot{\phi} = \frac{V \cos \gamma \, \cos \chi}{r} \tag{36}$$

$$\dot{r} = V \sin \gamma \tag{37}$$

$$\dot{V} = -D - g(r) \sin \gamma \tag{38}$$

$$\dot{\gamma} = \frac{1}{V}\left[L \cos \sigma - \left(g(r) - \frac{V^2}{r} \right) \cos \gamma \right] \tag{39}$$

$$\dot{\chi} = \frac{1}{V}\left[\frac{L \sin \sigma}{\cos \gamma} + \left(\frac{V^2}{r} \right) \cos \gamma \sin \chi \, \tan \phi \right] \tag{40}$$

Lift and drag acceleration as well as gravitational acceleration have been defined in Eq. (5)-(7). The MSSG algorithm maintains the same structure as derived in the previous section. However, a new definition of range is needed as in 3-D case; it has been replaced by longitude and latitude states. To compensate for this, the range is defined as the great circle distance from the target point relative to the vehicles current position. By using Vincenty's Formula[16], in the special case of a perfect sphere, the equation for the great circle distance can be found as follows:

$$Range = (r)\arctan\left(\frac{\sqrt{(\cos \phi_t \sin \Delta\theta)^2 + (\cos \phi_i \sin \phi_t - \sin \phi_i \cos \phi_t \cos \Delta\theta)^2}}{\sin \phi_i \sin \phi_t + \cos \phi_i \cos \phi_t \cos \Delta\theta} \right) \tag{41}$$

Lateral guidance law development

Solution of the full Mars entry guidance problem via closed-loop bank angle command requires the implementation of an appropriate lateral guidance logic. The Lateral Guidance (LG) law was developed by implementing a switching logic to change the sign of the bank angle command[5]. This is known as a bank reversal. Whenever a dead band boundary, given in terms of the heading error, is reached, the bank angle reversal is activated. The heading error is defined as the angle between the line connecting the vehicle, the target projected onto the local horizontal plane and the velocity vector projected onto the same plane[5]. The projection of the velocity vector onto the local horizontal plane is written as follows:

$$\boldsymbol{V}_P = V \cos \gamma \begin{bmatrix} -\cos \theta \sin \phi \cos \chi - \sin \theta \sin \chi \\ -\sin \theta \sin \varphi \cos \chi + \cos \theta \sin \chi \\ \cos \phi \cos \chi \end{bmatrix} \tag{42}$$

The projection of the current vehicle position, X_t to the target position X_c is given by:

$$\Delta = X_t - X_c = X_t - r \begin{bmatrix} \cos \theta \cos \phi \\ \sin \theta \cos \phi \\ \sin \phi \end{bmatrix} \tag{43}$$

Its projection into the local horizontal plane is then given by:

$$\Delta_p = \left(\frac{X_c}{\|X_c\|} \times \Delta \right) \times \frac{X_c}{\|X_c\|} \tag{44}$$

Finally, by using Eq. (42)-(44), heading error can be calculated:

$$\Delta\chi = \cos^{-1}\left(\frac{V_P}{\|V_P\|}\cdot\frac{\Delta_p}{\|\Delta_p\|}\right) \tag{45}$$

The heading error expressed in Eq. (45) is only valid for positive angles. Nevertheless, the dead band zone is always given in terms of the absolute value of the heading error regardless its sign. The dead band zone is defined as a symmetric corridor with a maximum $\Delta\chi$ as a function of range. When the heading error reaches this maximum, a bank angle reversal is commanded. This will induce a limit cycle that will keep the heading error within the allowable bounds.

LONGITUDINAL GUIDANCE PARAMETRIC ANALYSIS

The longitudinal entry phase motion of the lander guided by the proposed MSSG algorithm is analyzed first. A two degree of freedom simulation was implemented in a MATLAB® environment. Here, the Mars-relative longitudinal, MSSG-guided, trajectories of a low L/D vehicle are simulated to provide an initial understanding of the guidance algorithm as function of the guidance parameters. In such simulations, a specific range and altitude are targeted. In addition to the equations of motions defined in Eq. (1)-(4), an additional first order delay model was introduced to simulate the vehicle's attitude delay experienced to implement the desired bank angle command. The first order delay was modeled as followed:

$$\dot{\sigma} = \frac{\sigma_c - \sigma}{\tau} \tag{46}$$

A time constant (τ) of 1 sec was chosen for these runs. A Martian atmosphere as described by Sehnal[17] was used to compute the lift and drag accelerations as function of altitude and velocity (Eq. (5)-(6)). For these specific MSSG tests, it was desired to evaluate the guidance performances at the near extremes for which the lander will have to take out close to all initial velocity and hit the desired range. The simulations assume that the lander is already on a course that will take it into the atmosphere. For these initial tests, the initial velocity was set to 6 km/s at an initial downrange of 0 and altitude 126 km with an initial flight path angle of -14.5 degrees. The simulations are stopped when the lander reaches an altitude of 1 km.

Two simulations were then run in this initial test campaign. One simulation set the desired final downrange to be 800 km and the other one 550 km. In both simulations, the guidance parameters were tuned for a small miss in the desired range. The results show 400 meters of miss for a desired final range of 800 km and 900 m for a desired range of 550 km. Figure 1 and 3 show sample of trajectories for both scenarios. In both simulations, a guidance gain λ of 4.19 and a t_r^* value of 240 were used to drive the lander to the desired target point. Importantly, as shown in the 800 km desired range scenario, MSSG does not need special logic for a skip entry trajectory to extend the range of the lander. Bank angle commands and actual implementation are reported in figure 2 and 4.

Next, a systematic analysis of the longitudinal targeting performances as function guidance parameters employed in the MSSG algorithm (see Eq. (30)) has been executed. The MSSG law depends critically on t_f^* and λ. Assuming a desired range of 800 km and a final desired velocity of 600 m/sec, the $t_f^* - \lambda$ parameter space has been partitioned in a set of finite points with coor-

876

dinates described by $\left(t_{f_i}^*, \lambda_i\right)$. For each point, a simulation has been executed and the miss range recorded. Figure 5 shows the resulting contour plot representing the miss range as function of the guidance parameters. Interestingly, the region of lowest miss appears to be in a single valley on the contour plot. Nevertheless, the lowest valley is surrounded by many other valleys (local minima) which may make it difficult to determine the global minimum. Further investigation is needed to see if this same valley structure appears for different desired ranges and velocities. However, a guidance gain λ of 4.19 and a t_f^* value of 240 may be good guidance parameters to use to drive the lander to the desired target point.

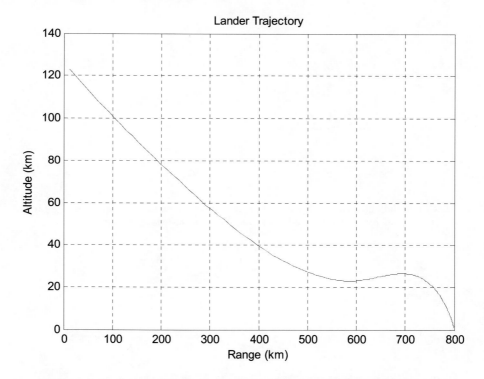

Figure 1: Trajectory for a desired range of 800 km and velocity of 600 m/s

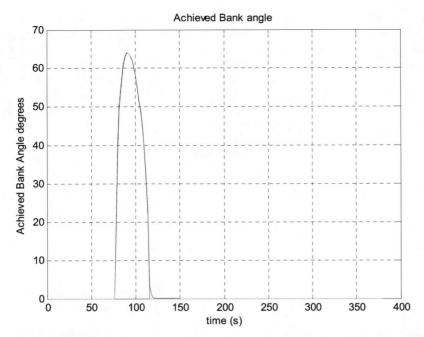

Figure 2: Command and response with first order attitude for a desired range of 800 km and velocity of 600 m/s, red is commanded and blue is achieved

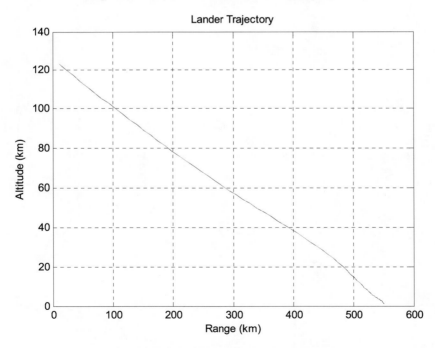

Figure 3: Trajectory for a desired range of 550 km and velocity of 600 m/s

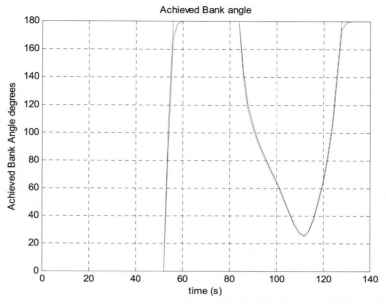

Figure 4: Command and response with first order attitude for a desired range of 550 km and velocity of 600m/s, red is commanded and blue is achieved

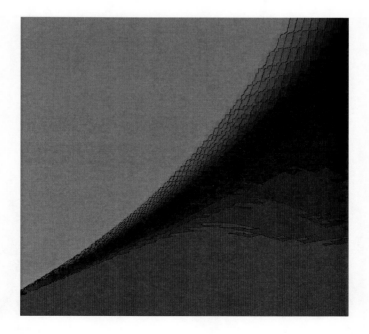

Figure 5: Contour plot of gain, t_f^*, and miss for desired range of 800 km and velocity of 600 m/s

MSSG FULL 3-D IMPLEMENTATION: GAIN OPTIMIZATION AND MONTE CARLO SIMULATIONS

MSSG parameters optimization

As discussed in the previous section and as it can be seen in figure 5, the miss distance contour plot shows many local minimum. One of these local minimum could possibly be the global minimum that is the desired couple of guidance parameters that minimize the miss range distance.

To find the global minimum, a differential evolution optimization algorithm from Price and Storm[18] written in Matlab © was used. The goal is to minimize the miss distance of the reentry vehicle at specified altitude while meeting the velocity constraints. For analysis, the MSSG algorithm was implemented into a three-degree-of-freedom (3DOF) Mars entry simulation (Eq. (35)-(40)). For each $\left(t_{fi}^*, \lambda_i\right)$ pair, the simulation is run with a closed-loop bank command angle generated by Eq. (30) and the miss range distance recorded. The terminal velocity was constrained to be 600 m/sec. The Differential Evolution algorithm searches the guidance parameter space and determines the pair of parameters that minimizes the miss range distance. A local gradient optimizer was subsequently used to further refine the search. For a set of initial conditions shown in Table 1, the optimal guidance parameters were found to be $\left(t_{fOPT}^*, \lambda_{OPT}\right) =$ (330.7514 sec, 9.368). The minimum miss range distance for a nominal run with these values was 151 m, occurring an altitude of 7.0 km.

Table 1: Simulation Conditions and Parameters

Parameters	Values
ϕ_i, deg	4.90
θ_i, deg	154.97
h_i, km	243.27
V_i, m/s	6555.85
γ_i, deg	-19.84
χ_i, deg	107.85
ϕ_t, deg	-0.04
θ_t, deg	174.95
h_t, km	1.00
V_t, m/s	600
S, m2	12.8825
m, kg	2200
L/D	0.247
CD	1.45
τ, sec	1.0
λ	9.368
t_f^*, sec	330.7514
Δt, sec	2.00
$\Delta\chi_1$, deg	6.00
$\Delta\chi_2$, deg	3.00
$\Delta\chi_3$, deg	1.50

MSSG FULL 3-D IMPLEMENTATION: MONTE CARLO SIMULATIONS

To evaluate the robustness of the MSSG algorithm, a 1000-run Monte Carlo study has been performed. In this set of Monte Carlo simulations three parameters were varied according to a normal distribution as shown in Table 2, i.e., the initial flight path angle (FPA), the coefficient of drag (C_D), and atmospheric density, similar to what has implemented by Kleuver[19]. The parameters are sampled from such Gaussian distribution to simulate errors and perturbations in the estimations and initial state of the system and evaluate how the guidance algorithm performs under off-nominal conditions. The initial FPA dispersion is $\pm$ 0.34 degrees (3 standard deviations), which is consistent with the MSL analysis[20]. The drag coefficient and density perturbations were modeled as constant factors held constant across the entire entry. The drag coefficient dispersion is modeled as $\pm$ 30% while the dispersion of the atmospheric density is set at $\pm$ 40%. Each of the dispersions represents 3 standard deviations from the nominal values. The Guidance Cycle is being updated every 2 seconds.

Table 2: Dispersion parameters used in the Monte Carlo Simulations

	Mean Value	Standard Dev.
Flight Path Angle(γ_i)	-19.84 deg	0.113 deg
Drag Coefficient (C_d)	1.45	0.145
Atmospheric density	Sehnal Mars Atmosphere profile[17]	13.3%

Figure 6-10 shows the results of the 1000-run Monte Carlo analysis. Figure 6 shows the landing dispersion. It can be seen in the 99.73 % of the runs, three standard deviations from the mean, are under 14.18 km. The mean rms miss distance of the runs is 4.3285 km with a standard deviation of 3.28 km. Figure 7 shows a cross section of the trajectories resulting from the runs, displaying range vs. altitude. The stopping condition for all runs is implemented whenever the lander either reaches an altitude of 6 km or reaches a velocity of 600 m/s. Such final desired stopping conditions are set by constraints imposed by the parachute deployment, which is limited by dynamic pressure and Mach number limits.

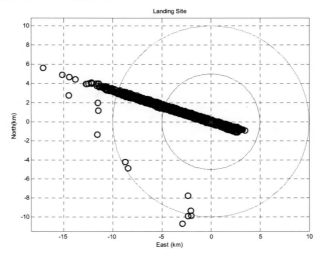

Figure 6: Landing dispersion with 10 km and 5 km landing dispersion ellipse for 1000 Monte Carlo runs

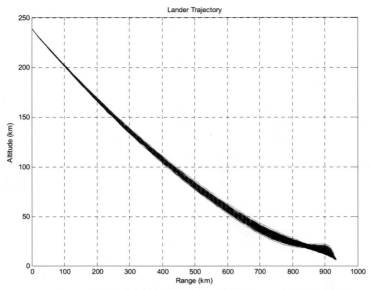

Figure 7: Lander trajectory for 1000 Monte Carlo runs

Figure 8 shows the cumulative density function of the rms miss range distance for all 1000 Monte Carlo runs. A few outliers can be seen at very high miss distances, which can be attributed to these cases have the combination of both low C_D and density values for that particular run. Additionally, in Figure 9 the cumulative density function of the final altitude is shown. Only about 20% of the runs stop because of reaching the minimum altitude while the maximum miss from the desired altitude is only 14 km more in altitude.

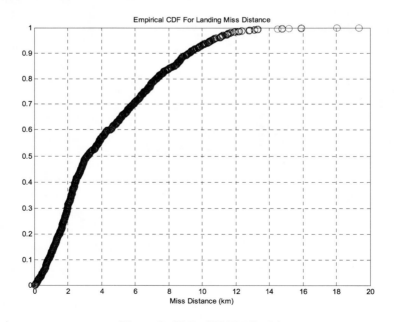

Figure 8: CDF of RMS Miss Distance

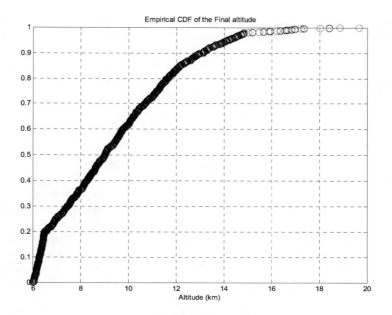

Figure 9: CDF of The final altitude

Figure 9 shows a single sample case of the bank angle command and what is achieved due to attitude dynamics delays. The blue line in the plot represents the desired bank angle that is computed by the guidance system, while the red line is the actual achieved bank angle based on the bank angle dynamics and time constant that have been implemented to provide more realistic results. This is a good representation of all the Monte Carlo runs, as it is possible to see the activity of the bank angle reversal logic at work two separate times in this run. All of the 1000 runs performed showed similar results.

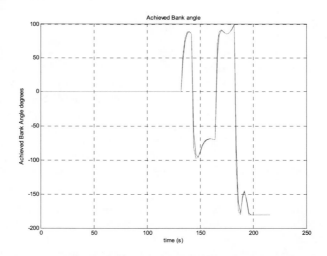

Figure 10: Sample Case Bank Angle Dynamics

While the performance is considered to be good with the current nonlinear guidance and bank angle reversal logic, it is believed that better performance can be achieved by looking into an optimal strategy for bank angle reversal. Another option to improve performance could be to look into a design that considers both the longitudinal and lateral dynamics into a unified non-linear guidance law. Future studies could include these as well as looking into other ways to make the guidance law more robust.

CONCLUSIONS

A novel non-linear guidance algorithm for Mars hypersonic entry has been presented. The proposed Multiple Sliding Surface Guidance algorithm has been developed to provide a closed-loop bank angle program that is robust against perturbations and parameters uncertainties. MSSG relies on the principles of higher order sliding control theory. Since the sliding control problem is of relative degree 2, i.e., the controller appears in the second derivative of the first sliding function, two sliding surfaces can be connected to provide a robust guidance algorithm. More specifically, the second surface is designed such that a bank angle program is found that is a) globally stable and b) drives the second surface to zero in a finite time (generally less than the overall time of flight). Under this condition, the first surface (error in position) and its derivative (error in velocity) are driven to zero, reaching the desired targeted position at the end of time of flight. High control activity is avoided because the algorithm is designed to reach the sliding surface for the first time and with its zero value at the end of the flight. The derived MSSG law is robust against perturbations and possesses a higher degree of flexibility. Indeed, the algorithm does not track any off-line, pre-computed desired trajectory. However, it does requires, to generate feasible guided trajectories, only the specification current state and the targeted final state as well as proper guidance parameters. The initial parametric analysis of the longitudinal guidance implementation (2-D analysis) showed that if the guidance parameters are properly tuned, the residual guidance error can be reduced to hundreds of meters. Such results represent a vast improvement over previously Mars missions, which exhibited an EDL profile with unguided hypersonic deceleration resulting in large landing error ellipses. The three-dimensional analysis of the guided entry problem required the implementation of a later guidance logic coupled with the MSSG-derived longitudinal guidance. Building on the results obtained from the 2-D parametric analysis to get insight on the structure of the miss range function which exhibits many local minima, it has been shown that the optimal tuning of the guidance parameters for the 3-D entry guidance problem may be achieved by using a global optimizer. A differential evolution algorithm coupled with a gradient-based local optimizer has been employed to determine the optimal values of λ and t_r^* that minimize the miss range distance. The proposed MSSG algorithm has been tested on more realistic scenarios to evaluate its performances under uncertain and perturbed conditions. A set of 1000 Monte Carlo simulations have been executed by perturbing the initial entry phase and the current environmental conditions experienced by the lander during the guided hypersonic deceleration. The analysis of the statistical results of the Monte Carlo runs shows that the MSSG algorithm performs well under perturbations and make is suitable for real-time implementation.

Future research will be directed to find ways to improve the performance of the proposed guidance law. For example, whereas the single longitudinal implementation shows remarkable accuracy improvements, the coupling with the specified dead-band lateral control logic degrades the overall targeting performances. Research will be directed to explore ways to consider both lateral and longitudinal guidance logic into a unified non-linear, sliding-based guidance law.

REFERENCES

[1]Shotwell, R, 2005, Phoenix—the first Mars Scout mission, *Acta Astronautica*, Volume 57, Issue 2-8, p. 121-134.

[2]Steltzner, A. D., Kipp, D. M., Chen, A., Burkhart, P. D.,Guernsey, C. S., Mendeck, G. F., Mitcheltree, R. A., Powell, R. W., Rivellini, T. P., San Martin, A. M., Way, D. W., 2006, Mars Science Laboratory Entry, Descent, and Landing System, *IEEE Aerospace Conference* Paper No. 2006-1497, Big Sky, MT, Mar. 2006.

[3]Carman, G. L., Ives, D. G., and Geller, D. K., 1998, Apollo-Derived Mars Precision Lander Guidance," *AIAA Paper* 98-4570, Aug. 1998.

[4]Mendeck, G. F., and Carman, G. L., 2002, Guidance Design for Mars Smart Landers Using the Entry Terminal Point Controller, *AIAA Paper* 2002- 4502, Aug. 2002.

[5]Tu, K.-Y., Munir, M. S., Mease, K. D., and Bayard, D. S., 2000, Drag-Based Predictive Tracking Guidance for Mars Precision Landing, *Journal of Guidance, Control, and Dynamics*, Vol. 23, No. 4, 2000, pp. 620–628.

[6]Lu, P., 2008, Predictor-Corrector Entry Guidance for Low Lifting Vehicles, *Journal of Guidance, Control, and Dynamics*, 2008, 31: 1067–1075

[7]Levant, A., Higher-order sliding modes, differentiation and output feedback control. *International Journal of Control*, 76(9/10), 924–941, 2003.

[8]Levant, A., "Construction Principles of 2-Sliding Mode Design," Automatica, Vol. 43, No. 4, 2007, pp. 576–586.

[9]Slotine, J., and Li, W., *Applied Nonlinear Control*, Prentice Hall, 1991.

[10]Vincent, T., L., and Grantham, W., J., *Nonlinear and Optimal Control Systems*, Wiley, 1997.

[11]Fridman, L., Chattering analysis in sliding mode systems with inertial sensors. *International Journal of Control*, 76(9/10), 906–912, 2003.

[12]Shtessel, Y. B., & Shkolnikov, I. A., Aeronautical and space vehicle control in dynamic sliding manifolds. *International Journal of Control*, 76(9/10), 1000–1017, 2003.

[13]Y. Shtessel, I. Shkolnikov and A. Levant, "Guidance and Control of Missile Interceptor Using Second Order Sliding Modes," *IEEE Transactions on Aerospace and Electronic Systems*, Vol. 45, No. 1, 2009, pp. 110-124.

[14]Harl, N., and Balakrishnan, S., N., Reentry Terminal Guidance Through Sliding Control Mode, Journal of Guidance, Control and Dynamics, Vol. 33, No. 1, January–February 2010.

[15] Furfaro, R., Selnick, S., Cupples, M., L., Cribb, M., W., Nonlinear Sliding Guidance Algorithms for Precision Lunar Landing, American Astronautical Society, AAS paper 167, Feb 2011

[16]Vincenty, Thaddeus (1975-04-01). "Direct and Inverse Solutions of Geodesics on the Ellipsoid with Application of Nested Equations". Survey Review (Kingston Road, Tolworth, Surrey: Directorate of Overseas Surveys) 23 (176): 88–93. http://www.ngs.noaa.gov/PUBS_LIB/inverse.pdf. Retrieved 2008-07-21.

[17]Sehnal, L., 1989, Analytical Models of Mars' Atmosphere Density, *Astronomical Institutes of Czechoslovakia*, Bulletin (ISSN 0004-6248), Vol. 41, No. 2, March 1990, p. 115–117

[18]Price, Kenneth and Storn, Rainer et al. "Differential Evolution (DE) for Continuous Function Optimization" http://www.icsi.berkeley.edu/~storn/code.html. Retrieved 2011-07-10.

[19]Kluever, C.A, "Entry Guidance Performance for Mars Precisions Landing", *Journal of Guidance, Control, and Dynamics"*, Vol. 31, No. 6, November-December 2008, pp. 1537-1544.

[20]Lockwood, M.K., Powell, R.W., Sutton, K., Prabhu, R.K., Graves, C. A., Epp, C. D., and Carman, G.L., "Entry Configurations and performance Comparisons for the Mars Smart Lander," *Journal of Spacecraft and Rocket*, Vol. 43, No. 2, 2006, pp. 258-269.

FORMATION FLYING I

SESSION 7

Chair: Dr. Aaron Trask
                                                        Apogee Integration

The following papers were not available for publication:

AAS 11-460
    (Paper Withdrawn)

AAS 11-461
    (Paper Withdrawn)

AAS 11-468
    (Paper Withdrawn)

AAS 11-469
    (Paper Withdrawn)

AN OPERATIONAL METHODOLOGY
FOR LARGE SCALE DEPLOYMENT OF NANOSATELLITES
INTO LOW EARTH ORBIT[*]

Justin A. Atchison,[†] Aaron Q. Rogers[‡] and Steven J. Buckley[§]

The on-orbit deployment of large numbers of nanosatellites is cast in terms of the relative motion equations, augmented with differential drag. Using this framework, we develop a methodology for minimizing the likelihood of recontact or interference among the deployed nanosatellites. This approach is applied to the Operationally Responsive Space Office's Launch Enabler Mission, which is planning to deliver 25 small payloads to orbit in the mid-late 2012 timeframe. By strategically varying the deployment order, timing, and launch vehicle attitude, we demonstrate net separation amongst each of the nano-satellites for the first three weeks, as validated by high fidelity simulations.

INTRODUCTION

Advances over the past decade in highly reliable commercial electronics, miniaturization techniques, and materials have enabled a new class of small "nanosatellites," loosely defined as satellites having a total mass of 50 kg or less[1], that now afford the capability to execute a broad array of meaningful science and technology missions[2]. A subset of this system-class, CubeSats, are canonically defined as single unit (1U) spacecraft with nominal stowed volume of 10x10x10 cm and mass of about one kilogram[3]. Capitalizing on significant, otherwise unused launch vehicle (LV) volume and lift mass capability, the first CubeSats were launched as opportunistic rideshares in 2000. To facilitate their manifest, CubeSats have utilized containerized deployers like the Poly Picosatellite Orbital Deployer (P-POD) developed by California Polytechnic State University[4]. The P-POD is the foundational CubeSat encapsulated deployment system capable of delivering any combination of three 1U spacecraft. Through these launches, confidence was established such that they could be safely and readily incorporated into the LV and mission plan without impact to the primary payload. Catalyzed by these successes in dramatically lowering the cost and programmatic barriers to space access, there is growing global interest to find further ways to increase nanosatellite launch accommodation to quantities well in excess of 10 free-flyer deployments per mission. As part of its Launch Enabler Mission, the Operationally Responsive Space (ORS) Office is currently planning to deliver 25 small payloads to orbit, including 19 free-flyer cube/nanosatellites in the mid-late 2012 timeframe. To accommodate this unprecedented record manifest, the mission will employ two versions of the NanoSatellite Launch Adapter System (NLAS)[5], shown in Figure 1, developed by NASA Ames Research Center. The second, evolutionary wafer design, called the CubeStack, is being developed by LoadPath Engineering

[*] DISTRIBUTION STATEMENT A. Approved for Public Release on 7 July 2011. Distribution is Unlimited.

[†] Senior Mission Design Engineer, Space Department, The Johns Hopkins University Applied Physics Laboratory, 11100 Johns Hopkins Road, Laurel, MD 20723.

[‡] Senior System Engineer, Space Department, The Johns Hopkins University Applied Physics Laboratory.

[§] Chief Engineer, Launch and Range, Operationally Responsive Space Office, 3548 Aberdeen Drive SE, Kirtland AFB, NM 87117.

under a small business innovative research (SBIR) contract with the ORS Office. These adapters can integrate the P-POD or other compatible dispenser such as the Ames' M100, to accommodate up to a total of 24U in single spacecraft increments in individual combinations as large as 6U. A primary challenge of this mission is the safe deployment and mitigation of satellite close-approaches (CA) across early-orbit operations.

The deployment design is challenging because many of the relevant parameters are inherently uncertain. The mission combines many unique satellites from different organizations, and the final manifest will continuously evolve in order to prevent individual satellite schedule slips from affecting the whole mission. Of foremost concern are the different relative satellite ballistic coefficients and deployment velocities conferred by the dispensers incorporated in the NLAS. Most CubeSats have little-to-no attitude control, at least for the first few orbits. They also typically have no on-board propulsion. Their orbits will evolve due to natural dynamics only. Once on orbit, it is not uncommon for CubeSats to initiate deployments and attain larger volumes. For example, a 3U CubeSat may have a solar panel on each of four faces that unfolds as the CubeSat is deployed, or potentially release a stowed antenna. The presence of deployables implies that the standard values for stowed volume and mass do not necessarily correspond to a standard on-orbit value. That is, the on-orbit area-to-mass ratio for each CubeSat depends on its deployed configuration.

The CubeSats (in their respective dispensers) are loaded into slots within the wafers as depicted in Figure 2. The wafers are sized to fit within the diameter of the launch-vehicle fairing, and below a primary payload. Each wafer contains volume for up to eight dispensers, each capable of accommodating three 1U CubeSats or some combination thereof. These dispensers are organized as two sets of four opposing systems. For the Launch Enabler Mission, two of these wafers will be stacked on top of each other. They can be arbitrarily oriented relative to each other by a clocking angle, ϕ. The wafer is designed to be able to accommodate a variety of CubeSat shapes and groupings. For example, using the M100 a single, monolithic 6U CubeSat can be accommodated. The wafer slots are depicted in Figure 3, which shows three 1U CubeSats within a single slot. When a command is given, the release door is opened and a set of springs ejects the CubeSats. The springs are each passive, and are pre-compressed prior to launch. In this image, the CubeSats are deployed as a triplet; with an intermediate separation spring between each adjacent CubeSat.

The deployment process is open-loop and uses a pre-defined time-tagged sequence. For the Launch Enabler Mission, the two wafers are being populated with CubeSats from different organizations, so it is desirable that each wafer deploy each of its CubeSats independently. When the final deployment occurs on the first wafer, an electrical signal will be sent to the second wafer to begin its deployment.

Figure 1. The NASA Ames Nanosatellite Launch Adapter System (NLAS) shown with both Cal-Poly P-POD and Ames' M100 CubeSat dispenser system[5]

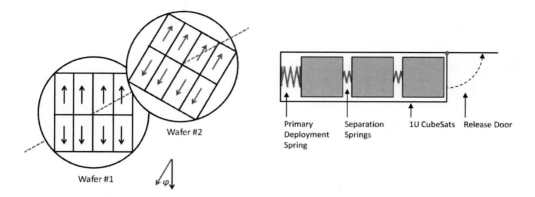

Figure 2. Notional top view of two wafers　　　**Figure 3. Side view of P-POD with 3 CubeSats**

The springs in the wafer slots offer a fixed (or well-characterized) deployment Δv. The mass of the LV and wafers is much larger than the mass of the deployed CubeSat. As a result, the spring is assumed to impart momentum only to the CubeSat. The deployment Δv is therefore only dependent on the deployed CubeSat's mass. The potential energy of the spring is transferred into the kinetic energy of the deployed CubeSat. This energy balance yields the CubeSat's effective Δv as a function of its mass and the spring constant, which is taken to be fixed. For pairs and triples of CubeSats, it is straightforward to derive the relative separation δv associated with the smaller separation springs. However, this analysis assumes a fixed value of δv, given the absence of high-fidelity data.

Moreover, the deployment sequencing is challenging because the process depends on the limited LV primary power from on-board batteries, which constrains the total sequence duration to approximately ten minutes. During this time the LV attitude control is principally limited to body rate management, obligating deployments to be conducted from an "inertial hold" mode. At present, the specific LV has not been selected for this particular mission, so these constraints are generalized to a reference system that is representative of the envisioned LV solution that will be utilized.

Given these uncertainties, challenges and constraints, we discuss a proposed methodology for designing a deployment concept of operations that minimizes the likelihood of recontact or interference during critical early-orbit operations. The methodology is formulated using a classic relative motion framework augmented with aerodynamic drag acceleration. We offer simulations of a representative manifest and parameter-set from the Launch Enabler Mission in an effort to evaluate the effectiveness of these strategies.

RELATIVE MOTION

Close-proximity orbit mechanics are best accommodated using a relative motion framework. Relative motion can be described in terms of the Clohessy-Wiltshire-Hill (CWH) equations, which are derived in a number of references, for example Vallado[6]. These equations model the motion between two nearby satellites in circular orbits. The motion of one satellite, the follower, is expressed in a set of coordinates fixed to a reference satellite. The local frame is defined by the reference satellite's orbit (e.g. local-vertical/local-horizontal). This analysis uses the *RSW* (also called the *RTN*) frame[6], which is defined by the radial *R* and orbit normal *W* directions. The second direction *S* is the cross-product that completes the right-handed system. This *S* direction is the along-track (or transverse) direction and is collinear with the velocity for circular orbits. These equations consider a point-mass gravity field only. This is a fair approximation so long as the radii of the satellites are nearly equal and the simulation timescales are on the order of days.

The CWH equations are differential equations in terms of three coordinates (*x,y,z*) aligned with the *R, S* and *W* axes respectively, which locate the follower satellite. Given the reference satellite's mean angular velocity n, the homogeneous (unforced) solution to the CWH equations as a function of time t, which is the time that has elapsed since the values of x_0, y_0, z_0 and $\dot{x}_0$, $\dot{y}_0$, $\dot{z}_0$ were given, is[6]

$$
\begin{bmatrix} x_h(t) \\ y_h(t) \\ z_h(t) \end{bmatrix} = \begin{bmatrix} 4-3cos(nt) & 0 & 0 \\ 6(sin(nt)-nt) & 1 & 0 \\ 0 & 0 & cos(nt) \end{bmatrix} \begin{bmatrix} x_0 \\ y_0 \\ z_0 \end{bmatrix} + \left(\frac{1}{n}\right) \begin{bmatrix} sin(nt) & 2(1-cos(nt)) & 0 \\ 2(cos(nt)-1) & 4sin(nt)-3nt & 0 \\ 0 & 0 & sin(nt) \end{bmatrix} \begin{bmatrix} \dot{x}_0 \\ \dot{y}_0 \\ \dot{z}_0 \end{bmatrix} \quad (1)
$$

In this analysis, $\dot{x}_0$, $\dot{y}_0$, $\dot{z}_0$ are associated with a relative deployment velocity Δv. These unforced dynamics consist of periodic motion in the x (radial) and z (orbit-normal) directions, and linearly growing periodic motion in the y (along-track) direction. The z-coordinate dynamics are uncoupled from the x- and y-coordinates. Finally, the equations are linear, so that a change in sign of the initial condition corresponds to a change in sign of the resultant motion.

The deployment process considers the case where x_0, y_0, and z_0 are each zero, and the deployment springs supply a value of Δv_x, Δv_y, and Δv_z. The unperturbed deployment CWH equations are then

$$
\begin{bmatrix} x_h(t) \\ y_h(t) \\ z_h(t) \end{bmatrix} = \left(\frac{1}{n}\right) \begin{bmatrix} sin(nt) & 2(1-cos(nt)) & 0 \\ 2(cos(nt)-1) & 4sin(nt)-3nt & 0 \\ 0 & 0 & sin(nt) \end{bmatrix} \begin{bmatrix} \Delta v_x \\ \Delta v_y \\ \Delta v_z \end{bmatrix}. \quad (2)
$$

With this framework, one can evaluate the relative motion resulting from a Δv aligned with each of the three directions: x_0, y_0, and z_0.

- If the spring's Δv is supplied in the $\hat{z}$ direction only, the resultant follower motion is periodic with twice the orbital frequency. At each half-orbit, the leader and the follower will have a CA. This is analogous (and in some cases, the same as) to two orbits with slightly differing inclinations.
- If the spring's Δv is supplied in the $\hat{x}$ direction, the resultant follower motion is periodic with the orbit frequency. The two satellites will CA as they approach the original point of deployment each period. For an initially circular orbit, the radial Δv changes only the eccentricity of the follower's orbit.
- If the spring's Δv is supplied in the $\hat{y}$ direction, the resultant motion is a combination of periodic and secular terms. The periodicity goes with the orbit period. The secular term is an along-track drift. An along-track Δv changes both the eccentricity and the semimajor axis of the follower orbit, implying that a difference in periods will drive a continuous separation over time. The CWH equations show that an initial non-zero Δv_y drives a drift rate whose magnitude is three times this value

$$
dy = 3\Delta v_y(0) \quad (3)
$$

The direction of the along-track drift differs from the direction of the Δv. That is, a follower spacecraft that is deployed with an initial Δv in the $+y$ direction will at first move forward with respect to the leader but will soon after cross over and behind the leader. This can be explained in terms of the change in energy of the follower. An instantaneous increase in the follower's velocity corresponds to a higher energy and therefore an orbit with a larger semimajor axis and period. As the follower continues in this longer period orbit, it will be passed below by the shorter-period leader.

For very long timescales, the follower and leader will eventually have a CA at their synodic period[6]

$$
P_s = \frac{P_L P_F}{|P_L - P_F|}. \quad (4)
$$

For separation Δv's on the order of m/s, this CA time occurs months in the future. Given that this analysis is focused on early deployment operations, this unavoidable effect is neglected.

For the case of Δv directed along a combination of the relative coordinate directions, the resultant follower motion is similar to the above cases. Here, the direction is described in terms of two angles (γ,θ) and a polarity $p = \pm 1$.

$$\Delta\hat{\mathbf{v}} = p \begin{bmatrix} \sin\gamma\ \cos\theta \\ \cos\gamma\ \cos\theta \\ \sin\theta \end{bmatrix}$$ (5)

These angles are illustrated in Figure 4 in terms of a coordinate system aligned with the relative motion frame. Note that γ is measured positive counterclockwise.

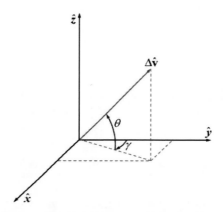

Figure 4. Deployment direction in the relative motion coordinate system

There are two cases considered here: cross-track/in-plane combinations and along-track/in-track combinations. The first case is defined by a non-zero θ. Here, a component of the deployment Δv lies in the $\hat{z}$ direction. It turns out that the resulting motion is simply the linear combination of the two uncombined cases. This simplicity results from the independence of the two coordinates in the CWH equations. The second case considers a non-zero γ, which implies that Δv has components in both the $\hat{x}$ and $\hat{y}$ directions. This case is illustrated in Figure 5, which gives the simulated motion in the x,y plane over a period for four simulated deployment directions: $\gamma = 0°$, $30°$, $60°$, and $90°$. The $\gamma = 0°$ case represents pure along-track Δv, and the $\gamma = 90°$ case represents pure radial Δv. The two intermediate cases do not produce qualitatively different behaviors.

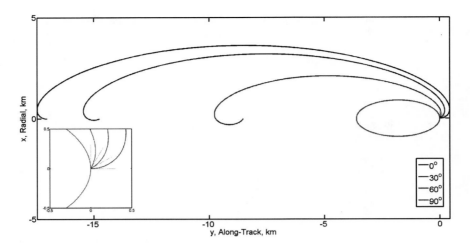

Figure 5. Relative motion for a combination of along-track and radial Δv in the x, y plane, defined using γ. The inset gives a close-up view with the deployment directions.

Relevance of Frames

The relative motion equations are given in a local frame that is defined by the orbit of the leader satellite, or in this case: the wafers that are fixed to the LV. The LV will nominally hold an inertial attitude. That is, its attitude control system will receive an inertial heading (e.g. a star), and then supply the torques necessary to maintain that heading. In an inertial frame, the along-track direction is rotating (with the orbit period). Two followers that are deployed in the same inertial heading with the same magnitude Δv will have different resultant motions depending on when they were deployed. This behavior is illustrated in Figure 6, which depicts the relative frame x and y vectors at three different points within an orbit. The red vector represents an inertial heading in the plane of the orbit ($\theta_0 = 0$). The angle between this vector and the y axis is defined as γ. This angle is seen to grow with the mean motion, and will make a complete revolution each period.

$$\gamma(t) = \gamma_0 + nt \, cos\theta_0 \qquad (6)$$

So, though the motion is best described in the relative frame, the deployment Δv's will be aligned with inertial fixed axes.

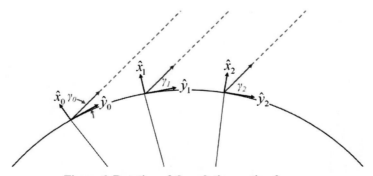

Figure 6. Rotation of the relative motion frame

If some epoch is defined with an initial angle γ_0, one can compute the future relative Δv directions:

$$\Delta v_x = |\Delta v| \sin(\gamma_0 + nt) \cos \theta_0 \tag{7}$$

$$\Delta v_y = |\Delta v| \cos(\gamma_0 + nt) \cos \theta_0. \tag{8}$$

As an illustration, one could prescribe $\gamma_0 = 0$ and $\theta = 0$ and observe the behavior of Figure 5 over the course of a quarter of an orbit, deploying at $nt = 0°$, $30°$, $60°$, and $90°$.

Aerodynamic Drag

Satellites orbiting through Earth's atmosphere experience atmospheric drag, an acceleration that opposes the motion of the satellite and has the form[6]

$$a_{Drag} = -\frac{1}{2} \left(\frac{C_D A}{m} \right) \rho v^2 \, \hat{v} \tag{9}$$

where C_D is the drag coefficient, A is the frontal area, m is the mass of the satellite, ρ is the atmospheric density, and v is the spacecraft's velocity with respect to the atmosphere. The term in parentheses is the inverse of the *ballistic coefficient* $C_B = m/(C_D A)$, a term that is commonly used to define the spacecraft dependent properties. Drag has the effect of reducing the total energy of the satellite's orbit. As energy is removed, the orbital semimajor axis decreases and the satellite "falls" to a lower orbit. At this lower altitude, the satellite's velocity increases.

For dissimilar satellites, differential drag can accumulate and drive relative separation between the satellites. Defining δa_{Drag} as the difference in the magnitude of drag between the reference and follower satellites,

$$\delta a_{Drag} = \left(a_{Drag} \right)_{Ref} - \left(a_{Drag} \right)_{Follower} \tag{10}$$

one can compute the drag-induced particular solutions to the CWH equations. For satellites in nearly the same orbit, the velocities and atmospheric density will be nearly identical. Therefore, δa_{Drag} is driven almost entirely by differences in the satellite ballistic coefficients.

The velocity of Earth's atmosphere is typically much smaller than the velocity of an orbiting satellite, so its value is neglected in this analysis. For a circular orbit, the velocity lies in the along-track direction, $y \parallel v$. With this assumption, one can derive the particular solution to the perturbed dynamics[7]

$$\begin{bmatrix} x_p(t) \\ y_p(t) \\ z_p(t) \end{bmatrix} = \frac{2\delta a_{Drag}}{n} \begin{bmatrix} t - \frac{1}{n} \sin(nt) \\ -\frac{3n}{4} t^2 + \frac{2}{n} \left(1 - \cos(nt) \right) \\ 0 \end{bmatrix}. \tag{11}$$

This equation describes a combination of periodic motion in x and y (with frequency n, corresponding to the orbital motion), as well as a linear growth in x and quadratic growth in y. The signs of the terms on the right hand side verify that a follower satellite will drift forward ($+y$) and downward ($-x$) if its drag exceeds the reference satellite. The quadratic nature of the drift in y suggests that large relative motions can accumulate over sufficient timescales, even for small δa_{Drag} values.

The perturbed relative dynamics can be expressed completely by summing the homogeneous solution given in Eq. 1 and the particular solution given in Eq. 11. For the case of deployment, the total solution is given by:

$$\begin{bmatrix} x(t) \\ y(t) \\ z(t) \end{bmatrix} = \left(\frac{1}{n}\right) \begin{bmatrix} sin(nt) & 2(1 - cos(nt)) & 0 \\ 2(cos(nt) - 1) & 4sin(nt) - 3nt & 0 \\ 0 & 0 & sin(nt) \end{bmatrix} \begin{bmatrix} \Delta v_x \\ \Delta v_y \\ \Delta v_z \end{bmatrix} + \left(\frac{2\delta a_{Drag}}{n}\right) \begin{bmatrix} t - \frac{1}{n}sin(nt) \\ -\frac{3n}{4}t^2 + \frac{2}{n}(1 - cos(nt)) \\ 0 \end{bmatrix}. \quad (12)$$

Again, the independent variable t is referenced to the epoch at which Δv_x, Δv_y, and Δv_z are given, which in this case is the time of deployment. Neglecting oscillatory terms, the along-track position is given by

$$y(t) = (-3\dot{y}_0 t) + \left(-\frac{3}{2}\delta a_{Drag} t^2\right). \quad (13)$$

Setting $y(t)$ to zero yields the close approach time t_{CA} associated with aerodynamic drag.

$$t_{CA} = \frac{2\dot{y}_0}{-\delta a_{Drag}} \quad (14)$$

A positive value of t_{CA} indicates that a CA will occur in the future. This would represent a case in which the follower was deployed to drift rearward, but drag accumulated and caused it drift forward (or vice versa). This case is simulated in Figure 7, in which the follower drifts rearward until differential drag accumulates and reverses its motion. Differential drag will continue to accelerate the follower forward. Note that the separation distances in Figure 7a don't necessarily go to zero because altitude is varying as well.

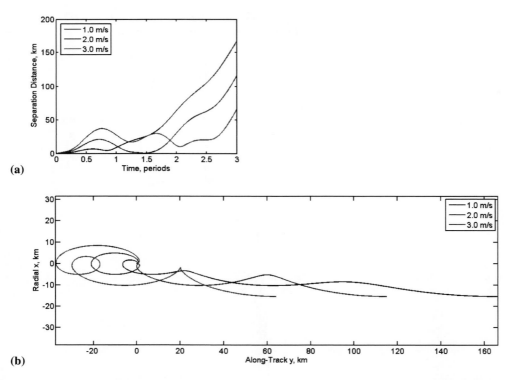

(a)

(b)

Figure 7. (a) Separation distance time-history for an along-track Δv with δa_{Drag} = -0.0005 m/s², and (b) the corresponding relative motion in the x, y plane.

DEPLOYMENT STRATEGY

The deployment strategy must consider the motions of each of the deployed nanosatellites with respect to each other. It also must accommodate mission-specific constraints and practical margins of uncertainty. The design parameters in the deployment process are deployment order, timing, and direction. The deployment order is an integer index i ascribed to each nanosatellite that defines its position in the deployment process. The deployment timing t_i is the number of seconds after which a given nanosatellite will be deployed. The deployment direction is a unit vector defined by the angles (γ_i, θ_0) and polarity p_i. This is the vector along which the nanosatellite's initial Δv will be aligned.

The terms "forward net drift" and "backward net drift" are used to define the intended deployment direction in the along-track direction. Here, "net drift" describes the secular along-track drift direction after a few orbits. A nanosatellite must be deployed with $p_i < 0$ (which implies $\Delta v_{yi} < 0$) in order to have a forward net drift.

Sequencing by Along-Track Drift

One strategy to promote relative separation among neighboring nanosatellites is to focus on secular effects and generate an along-track relative drift between each deployment. That is, if the magnitude of Δv is decreasing with time, each deployed nanosatellite will nominally be drifting away from its neighbors. The along-track component of Δv is restated below with index i corresponding to deployment order:

$$\Delta v_{yi} = p_i |\Delta v_i| \cos(\gamma_0 + n t_i) \cos \theta_0 . \tag{15}$$

There are two indexed variables: the magnitude of the deployment Δv, and the time of deployment. The third free parameter is the initial deployment angle γ_0, which is the same for each nanosatellite. Since $\cos(\gamma)$ is a nonlinear term, its value can be adjusted to affect the relative separation rates. However, if $(\gamma_0 + n t_i)$ crosses odd multiples of $\pi/2$, it will change sign and likely result in an increased probability of CA.

A choice of γ_0, $|\Delta v_i|$, and t_i that produces a descending magnitude of Δv_{yi} by deployment will cause each deployed nanosatellite to drift away from its neighbors with time. So long as the radial periodic motions are small compared to the relative drift separation (which implies long amounts of time between deployments) and differential drag is negligible, this strategy promotes relative separation over time. This is true for nanosatellites deployed with both a forward or rearward net drift.

Accounting for Atmospheric Drag

Atmospheric drag can be incorporated using Eq. 11. The resulting effective Δv_{yi} is dependent on time, as well as the relative drag acceleration between adjacent deployments δa_{ij}

$$\Delta v_{yi}(t) = p_i |\Delta v_i| \cos(\gamma_0 + n t_i) \cos \theta_0 - \delta a_{ij}(t - t_i) . \tag{16}$$

If the sign of the terms of on the RHS differ, the follower and leader will pass each other at time t_{CA}. Passes due to atmospheric drag can be prevented by ordering the deployment sequence according to the ballistic coefficients C_{Bi}. For nanosatellites with forward drift rates, the magnitudes of C_{Bi} should be descending; for rearward drift rates, C_{Bi} should be ascending. This ordering ensures that the along-track drifts associated with Δv_y and atmospheric drag are each acting to promote separation. If this ordering is not feasible, one can then set adjacent nanosatellites to have as similar a ballistic coefficient as possible, in an effort to extend their CA times. For short-term missions, it may even be possible to extend the CA time beyond the intended operation life.

First-Period Close Approaches

Even if Δv_y decreases between deployments, it is possible to have two nanosatellites cross each other's trajectories. This can occur if the magnitude of their deployment Δv increases. This scenario is represented in Table 1 and illustrated in Figure 8, which shows the paths of two deployed nanosatellites in the RSW frame of the LV. The LV's initial attitude is $\gamma_0 = 45°$, $\theta_0 = 0$. The blue nanosatellite is deployed at time $t = 0$, with a Δv of 1.0 m/s. Six minutes later, the red nanosatellite is deployed with a Δv of 1.4 m/s. The deployment angle has rotated 15.2° by the orbital motion of the LV, yielding $\gamma(t_2) = 60.2°$. This scenario yields descending along-track Δv_y values of 0.707 m/s and 0.695 m/s; however, the two trajectories cross each other after a short period of time. This crossing represents a possible CA. Markers on the trajectories indicate the positions of the nanosatellites at 4 min. increments, and show that the blue nanosatellite narrowly leads the red nanosatellite through this crossing. Figure 9 shows the range between them as a function of time. A local minimum in the first quarter period corresponds to this first CA. The figure also illustrates that future CAs can occur at subsequent periods, since a second valley is being approached on the right-hand side.

Table 1. Sample Deployment Parameters to Generate a First-Period CA

Sat	$|\Delta v_i|$	t_i	nt_i	Δv_{yi}	Δv_{xi}	t^*	$x(t^*)$
	m/s	s	deg	m/s	m/s	s	km
Red	1.00	0	0	0.707	0.707	2420	2.71
Blue	1.40	240	15.2	0.695	1.215	2190	2.93

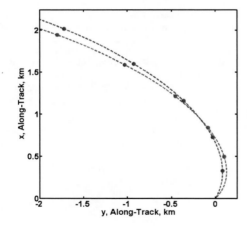 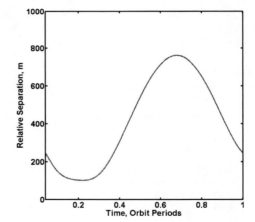

Figure 8. A Short-term CA between two sequentially deployed CubeSats. The dots indicate the CubeSat positions at 4 min. increments.

Figure 9. Relative separation between the two deployed nanosatellites.

These "first-period" CAs can be predicted using the CWH Equations. One method for predicting a crossing is to calculate the maximum radial range during the first half of the first period. This corresponds to a time when $\dot{x} = 0$. For the deployment problem $x_0, y_0 = 0$, and this term is given by

$$\dot{x}(t) = \Delta v_x \cos(nt) + 2\Delta v_y \sin(nt). \qquad (17)$$

Setting this term equal to zero, and solving for t^*, the time of maximum radial range, yields

$$t^* = \frac{1}{n}\tan\left(\frac{\Delta v_x}{2\Delta v_y}\right) + \frac{1}{n}k\pi, \quad k = 1,2,3\ldots \tag{18}$$

The first maximum occurs when $k = 1$. One can then evaluate $x(t^*)$. If sequential deployments have ascending values of $x(t^*)$, it is an indication that a trajectory crossing has occurred.

Out-of-Plane Deployments

The LV and the wafer architecture enable the deployment to use out-of-plane Δv components. The implication is that one could shift the orbit plane of each deployment. Though this may seem like a meaningful approach, multiple planes are not necessarily beneficial. Wertz argues that all co-altitude orbits always cross at only two points, and as a result, it is irrelevant whether those two points align for combinations of orbits[7]. Said another way, he argues that a constellation of polar, co-altitude satellites (such that all the orbits cross at the Earth's poles) is no more at-risk than any other constellation of co-altitude satellites. If a collision does occur, it could actually be worse for non-coplanar satellites, because their relative velocity is larger than the coplanar case.

That said, if one does choose to incorporate Δv_z, it must not overwhelm the along-track drift. Cross-track Δv produces only oscillatory motion, so changing the plane of the orbit is not enough to mitigate any CAs; it must also be accompanied by an along-track drift. However, Δv_z, which corresponds to a non-zero θ_0, decreases the effectiveness of the limited Δv_y as seen in Eq. 16. The effect of the rotating relative frame, $\cos(nt_i)$, is also decreased by $\cos(\theta_0)$. This analysis contends that along-track drift is the primary mechanism for preventing CA, so it must be given priority.

Finally for out-of-plane deployments, one must account for the location of the relative nodes between oppositely directed deployments. The relative nodes are the two points at which the orbits of the forward and rearward deployments cross. If there is no along-track drift induced between the two deployments, there is a high likelihood of CA at one of these points. That is, one must ensure relative drift (in the presence of drag) for both subsequent deployments in one direction and between opposite directions. This may be particularly challenging if all of the CubeSats are being deployed with characteristically small deployment velocities.

Overview of Deployment Strategies

There are a variety of design inputs that can be varied to generate a successful deployment strategy for an arbitrary set of nanosatellite properties:

1.) Adjust the deployment order i and direction p_i to accommodate relative drifts associated with aerodynamic drag:
   a.) Ballistic coefficients should decrease for net forward drifting deployments ($p_i < 0$) and increase for net rearward drifting deployments ($p_i > 0$).
   b.) Low ballistic coefficients nanosatellites should be deployed with a net forward drift, and high ballistic coefficient nanosatellites should be deployed with a net rearward drift.
2.) Adjust the direction, deployment order i, deployment time t_i, and initial deployment angle γ_0 such that the magnitude of $\Delta v_{yi} = |\Delta v_i|\cos(\gamma_0 + nt_i)\cos\theta_0$ decreases.
   a.) Set the deployment order and direction for each nanosatellite such that $|\Delta v_i|$ is decreasing with t_i where possible.
   b.) Increase the deployment time t_i such that Δv_{yi} is decreasing with t_i.
   c.) Vary γ_0 if necessary.
   d.) Ensure that the maximum radial range in the first period $x(t^*)$ is decreasing with subsequent deployments, in order to prevent trajectory crossings.
   e.) The magnitude of θ_0 should be kept small in order to maximize the variation in Δv_{yi}.
3.) Cross-track Δv is not necessarily helpful. If it is used, care must be taken to stagger the oppositely directed out-of-plane deployments.
   a.) Set a non-zero value for θ_0 or ϕ.

899

b.) Vary t_i for the deployments with opposite polarities p_i.

c.) Ensure that the along-track drift will not generate a future CA associated with the relative phasing Δf.

In this application, a successful deployment is characterized as a deployment in which there are minimal satellite CAs. The deployment strategy must be robust, given the high level of uncertainty inherent to this type of mission. In an effort to quantify these statements and acknowledge these uncertainties, we propose that the nominal deployment strategy will minimize the number of inter-satellite close-approaches over the first 21 days, with an emphasis on the initial 12 hours. This time-span is commensurate with the practical limitations of modeling the uncertainty inherent to the problem. A CA is defined as a period within which the distance between two CubeSats decreases below 800 m. These values are derived from practical considerations, the Space Test Program's S-26 mission deployment requirement[8], and experience with the deployment simulation environment.

APPLICATION

These strategies were developed and evaluated for the ORS Launch Enabler Mission, which will deploy 19 CubeSats of varying sizes (1U – 6U) within a 10 minute period. The following sections address representative parameters and constraints associated with this mission. The mission orbit is nominally 500 km circular, 45° inclined.

The two deployment wafers are designated by the Greek letters α and β. Each wafer has up to 8 slots, designated by a capital letter (A,B,C,...). The slots are oriented such that $\hat{A}$, the deployment direction of slot A, is nearer to the $+\hat{v}$ direction. That is, $(\hat{A} \cdot \hat{v}) > 0$. Two neighboring slots can be combined to accommodate a single 6U CubeSat. The two wafers can be "clocked" with respect to each other using ϕ. However, given the arguments of the above section, this is not considered in this analysis. That said, if one chose to incorporate this feature, one could simply substitute

$$\theta_0 = \theta_0 + \text{sign}(p_i)\frac{\phi}{2}$$

in the above equations where θ_0 currently appears.

The deployment spring properties are estimated according to Table 2. Here, 3U represents the cumulative size of the CubeSats within an individual dispenser. That is, three 1U CubeSats, each with a mass of 1.5 kg, would experience an estimated ejection Δv of 1.77 m/s, independent of the intermediate separation springs.

Table 2. Wafer Deployment Spring Δv Estimates[*]

Size	Mass, kg	Δv, m/s	Size	Mass, kg	Δv, m/s
	1.0	3.53		4.0	2.19
	2.0	2.58		6.0	2.13
3U	3.0	2.13	6U	8.0	1.86
	4.0	1.86		10.0	1.67
	5.0	1.67		12.0	1.52
	6.0	1.53		14.0	1.41

[*] Values generated by Aerospace Corporation and provided courtesy of the ORS Office.

In the absence of historic data, the intermediate separation springs are estimated to offer approximately 10 cm/s of separation δv. This value is treated as a constant, an assumption that neglects the fact that δv is proportional to the masses of the surrounding CubeSats. With this simplified model, the members of a pair of CubeSats will experience $\pm\frac{1}{2}\delta v$. For triplets, the outermost CubeSat is taken to experience $+\delta v$ and the innermost CubeSat is taken to experience $-\delta v$.

The current manifest for the ORS Launch Enabler Mission is based off of the most recent set of mass property and flight operations information provided by the participating organizations (e.g., deployed geometry, orientation, etc.). It is understood that the selection of individual CubeSats and their respective properties could likely change as the mission planning effort progresses. As a result, there is a fair amount of uncertainty in these values. Likely, the ballistic coefficient and Δv magnitudes will always have large margins of uncertainty.

When not explicitly given, we assume that each CubeSat conforms to the CubeSat standards produced by the California Polytechnic State University[3]. These standards are given below in Table 3, which establishes the maximum mass and the mean area for a CubeSat with no deployments. This analysis assumes that CubeSats take the maximum allowable mass when not otherwise specified.

A representative manifest is given in Table 4, organized by wafer and mass. Each CubeSat is identified by a number and its organization's wafer identifier. CubeSats that are grouped to deploy from a single position are identified with a lowercase postscript letter (e.g. α_{7a} and α_{7b}). CubeSat $\alpha_{1,2}$ is a special case because it has a volume of 6U and requires two adjacent slots within a wafer.

The wafer deployment architecture dictates that half of the deployment slots are oriented opposite the other half. Further, the slots on each wafer share a common line-of-action. Operationally, there is a preference to ideally deploy opposing CubeSats of equivalent mass, in a pair-wise manner so as to minimize the resultant torques conferred to the LV. This desire, however, is complicated by the requirement that certain CubeSats be located near the edge of the wafer to facilitate pre-launch accessibility: $[\alpha_5, \alpha_6, \alpha_7, \alpha_8] \in [A, D, E, H]$. This constraint also implies that two of this set of CubeSats must be deployed from one side of the wafer, while the other two CubeSats must be deployed from the opposite side of the wafer. Finally, all of wafer α must be deployed prior to deploying wafer β.

Table 3. Standard CubeSat Properties

Size	Mass, kg	Dimensions, cm	Mean Area, cm^2
1U	1.5	10 x 10 x 11.35	109
3U	4.5	10 x 10 x 34	260

Table 4. Representative CubeSat Manifest

Wafer	Designator	Size	Mass, kg	C_B, kg/m^2	$|\Delta v|$, m/s
	$\alpha_{1,2}$	6U	12.0	134	1.52
	α_3	3U	5.4	34	1.61
	α_4	3U	5.4	34	1.61
	α_5	3U	4.0	70	1.86
α	α_6	3U	4.0	70	1.86
	α_{7a}	1.5U	2.3	27	$1.77 + \delta v/2$
	α_{7b}	1.5U	2.3	27	$1.77 - \delta v/2$
	α_{8a}	1U	1.3	54	$1.86 + \delta v/2$
	α_{8b}	2U	2.6	24	$1.86 - \delta v/2$
	β_1	3U	5.5	55	1.60
	β_2	3U	4.0	36	1.86
	β_3	3U	4.0	36	1.86
	β_4	3U	4.0	36	1.86
	β_5	3U	4.0	36	1.86
β	β_6	3U	4.0	70	1.86
	β_7	3U	4.0	26	1.86
	β_{8a}	1U	1.1	46	$2.00 + \delta v$
	β_{8b}	1U	1.1	46	2.00
	β_{8c}	1U	1.2	51	$2.00 - \delta v$

RESULTS

Given the representative manifest and constraints above, two deployment scenarios have been developed and simulated. The output of this process is a choice of initial LV attitude and a table giving the time at which each CubeSat will be deployed, as well as its predicted success metrics. For atmospheric drag, the density was taken to be a fixed value of 7 x 10^{-13} kg/m^3.

Each sequence is simulated using the CWH equations in the MATLAB programming environment, which offers rapid results and follows traditional intuition. The sequence is then validated using AGI's Satellite ToolKit commercial software package. This simulation uses an adaptive 7th and 8th order Ruge-Kutta-Felberg integrator with error tolerances on the order of 10^{-13}. The environment model uses the 20x20 EGM96 Earth gravity model, the Jacchia-Roberts atmosphere model with mean solar activity, and spherical solar radiation pressure models. This choice of model complexity is meant to subject the deployment sequence to a representative Earth environment, complete with high-order accelerations.

Baseline Deployment Approach

Given the operational complexity of this mission, it may be tempting to ignore the relative motion metrics proposed here, and simply select a deployment sequence that satisfies the given constraints. This scenario is meant to serve as a baseline case that illustrates the likelihood of CAs for a straightforward deployment sequence. That is, no thought is given to relative motion or ballistic coefficient in this case. At equal time-steps, alternating CubeSats from each side of a wafer are deployed. After the first wafer has deployed its CubeSats, the sequence waits one minute and begins deploying from the second wafer. Within each wafer, the deployments are sequenced based on the location of the slots within the wafers (A,B,C...).

The initial LV attitude is given by $\gamma_0 = 10$ deg and $\theta_0 = 0$ deg. Table 5 gives the deployment sequence, organized by the deployment direction p_i for the ease of showing the separation drift rate dy_{ij} and close approach time t_{CA} relative to each CubeSat's neighbors. For example, CubeSat β_1 has a predicted separation drift rate of 0.90 m/s relative to β_7, the prior deployment in the same direction. However, β_1 is estimated to pass β_7 after approximately 16.1 days using Eq. 14 with the assumed constant atmospheric density. Negative values of relative drift imply that the satellite is drifting faster than the previous deployment in that direction. The final column gives the maximum radial displacement for each CubeSat during its first period, $x(t^*)$.

These values were numerically simulated. At each time-step, the separation between each CubeSat is computed (a total of 19 x 18 ÷ 2 distances). The time-history of these separations over 12 hours and 3 weeks are given in Figure 10 and Figure 11, respectively. As predicted by Table 5, the baseline deployment sequence is subject to many CAs within the first few hours and weeks. These CAs are associated with ascending Δv_y deployments, ascending $x(t^*)$ magnitudes, and inconsistent ballistic coefficients. It's important to note that the close approach distances are calculated at a time-step of 10 seconds, so the exact minimum is not necessarily being shown. That said, the orders-of-magnitude are sufficient to convey the argument that CAs are uncomfortably likely, with many close-approach distances on the order of 10's and 100's of meters.

Table 5. Baseline Deployment Sequence

p_i	Sat	Order	Slot	$|\Delta v_i|$ m/s	t_i s	Δv_{yi} m/s	dy_{ij} m/s	nt_i deg	C_B kg/m²	t_{CA} day	$x(t^*)$ km
	α_{8b}	1F	α-A	1.91	40	1.86	-	2.5	24.3	-	6.76
	α_{8a}	1F	α-A	1.81	40	1.77	0.29	2.5	54.2	4.9	6.41
	$\alpha_{1,2}$	2F	α-B,C	1.52	120	1.45	0.95	7.6	133.7	33.1	5.27
	α_3	3F	α-D	1.61	200	1.49	-0.11	12.7	34.4	-	5.43
+1	β_4	4F	β-A	1.86	300	1.63	-0.42	19.0	36.1	116.7	5.99
	β_7	5F	β-B	1.86	380	1.54	0.26	24.1	25.5	-	5.72
	β_1	6F	β-C	1.60	460	1.24	0.90	29.2	55.4	16.1	4.66
	β_2	7F	β-D	1.86	540	1.33	0.28	34.2	36.1	-	5.09
	α_{7a}	1R	α-E	1.82	0	-1.79	-	0.0	27.4	-	-6.49
	α_{7b}	1R	α-E	1.72	0	-1.69	0.30	0.0	27.4	-	-6.13
	α_6	2R	α-F	1.86	80	-1.80	-0.31	5.1	69.9	-	-6.52
	α_5	3R	α-G	1.86	160	-1.75	0.15	10.1	69.9	-	-6.36
	α_4	4R	α-H	1.61	240	-1.46	0.87	15.2	34.4	22.4	-5.34
-1	β_3	5R	β-E	1.86	340	-1.58	-0.39	21.6	36.1	-	-5.86
	β_6	6R	β-F	1.86	420	-1.49	0.28	26.6	69.9	-	-5.57
	β_{8b}	7R	β-G	2.10	500	-1.57	-0.23	31.7	45.9	11.4	-5.93
	β_{8a}	7R	β-G	2.00	500	-1.49	0.22	31.7	45.9	-	-5.65
	β_{8c}	7R	β-G	1.90	500	-1.42	0.22	31.7	50.5	-	-5.37
	β_5	8R	β-H	1.86	580	-1.27	0.43	36.8	36.1	21.0	-4.91

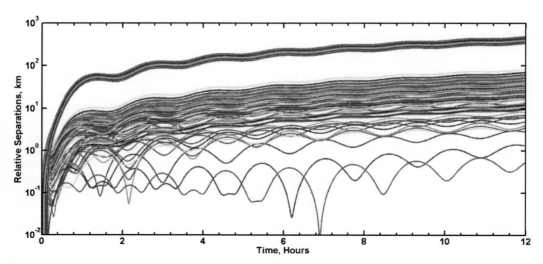

Figure 10. Baseline deployment inter-satellite separation distances over first 12 hours.

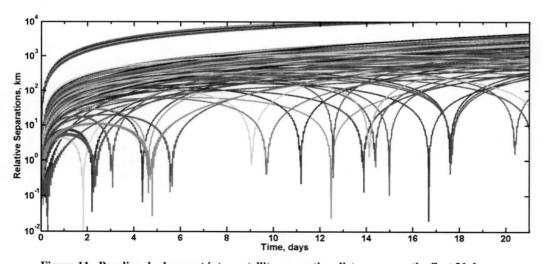

Figure 11. Baseline deployment inter-satellite separation distances over the first 21 days.

Strategic Deployment Approach

The strategic deployment sequence accounts for all of the strategies developed above, including those associated with atmospheric drag. The initial LV attitude is given by $\gamma_0 = 45$ deg and $\theta_0 = 0$ deg. The deployment sequence is given in Table 6. Here, the CubeSats are grouped and deployed such that ballistic coefficients are ordered appropriately. The CubeSats with low ballistic coefficients are deployed in front of those with high ballistic coefficients. Since some of the CubeSats must be deployed as a group from a single slot, it was impossible to order every CubeSat by ballistic coefficient. This is the case for α_{8a} and α_{8b}. In an effort to minimize the impact of these necessary CAs, the out-of-order CubeSats are timed to offer t_{CA} values greater than the 21 day window. Further, they are grouped such that they will pass as few other CubeSats as possible, given the constraints. This set of sorting requires adjustment to the initial LV angle γ_0, as well as adjustment of the individual deployment times. The deployment times are increased until subsequent Δv_{yi} values are decreasing, even though $|\Delta v_i|$ values may be increasing. This case exercises the test of $x(t^*)$, in that some sets of trajectories can potentially cross each other. Again, the deployment timing is adjusted to ensure that the magnitude of $x(t^*)$ decreases.

The simulated deployment separations are given in Figure 12 and Figure 13. The first 12 hours don't produce any CAs, verifying the condition predicted by $x(t^*)$. Likewise, the first 21 days do not indicate any CAs, although two CAs will occur shortly after. Follow-on simulations indicate that these CAs correspond to the two cases predicted in Table 6, and occur in the fourth week.

Table 6. Strategic Deployment Sequence

p_i	Sat	Order	Slot	$|\Delta v_i|$ m/s	t_i s	Δv_{yi} m/s	dy_{ij} m/s	nt_i deg	C_B kg/m^2	t_{CA} day	$x(t^*)$ km
	$\alpha_{1,2}$	1F	α-B,C	1.52	0	1.08		0.0	133.7		4.11
	α_5	2F	α-A	1.86	220	0.96	0.35	14.0	69.9	-	3.99
	α_6	3F	α-D	1.86	250	0.91	0.16	15.9	69.9	-	3.84
	β_6	4F	β-A	1.86	330	0.76	0.44	20.9	69.9	-	3.43
+1	β_1	5F	β-D	1.60	360	0.60	0.47	22.8	55.4	-	2.82
	β_{8c}	6F	β-C	2.10	570	0.32	0.84	36.1	50.5	-	2.55
	β_{8a}	6F	β-C	2.00	570	0.31	0.05	36.1	45.9	-	2.43
	β_{8b}	6F	β-C	1.90	570	0.29	0.05	36.1	45.9	-	2.31
	β_7	7F	β-B	1.86	600	0.23	0.20	38.0	25.5	-	2.12
	α_{7a}	1R	α-E	1.82	20	-1.26		1.3	27.4	-	-4.84
	α_{7b}	1R	α-E	1.72	20	-1.19	0.21	1.3	27.4	-	-4.57
	α_{8b}	2R	α-H	1.91	175	-1.07	0.37	11.1	24.3	30.5	-4.33
	α_{8a}	2R	α-H	1.81	175	-1.01	0.17	11.1	54.2	-	-4.10
-1	α_3	3R	α-F	1.61	285	-0.73	0.84	18.1	34.4	30.2	-3.17
	α_4	4R	α-G	1.61	310	-0.69	0.12	19.7	34.4	-	-3.06
	β_2	5R	β-H	1.86	450	-0.53	0.49	28.5	36.1	-	-2.83
	β_3	6R	β-G	1.86	475	-0.48	0.15	30.1	36.1	-	-2.70
	β_4	7R	β-F	1.86	500	-0.43	0.15	31.7	36.1	-	-2.58
	β_5	8R	β-E	1.86	525	-0.38	0.15	33.3	36.1	-	-2.46

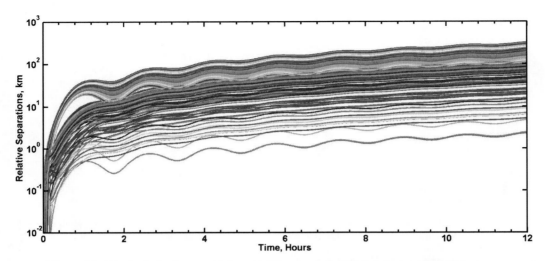

Figure 12. Strategic deployment inter-satellite separation distances over first 12 hours.

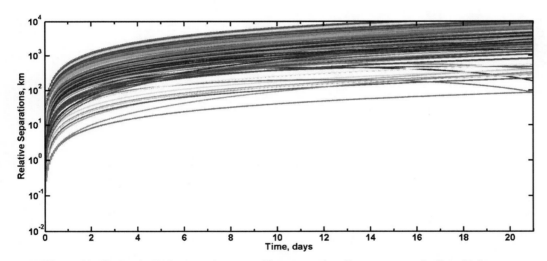

Figure 13. Strategic deployment inter-satellite separation distances over the first 21 days.

For additional intuition, Figure 14 gives the time-histories of the CubeSats over the LV's first orbit period. Dashed lines indicate the trajectories of each CubeSat. Markers indicate their positions at three instants in time: 1/3, 2/3, and 3/3 of the LV's first period. The LV's orbit is illustrated in black, with arrows indicating the radial and velocity directions. In this figure, the LV is moving to the right-hand side, such that $\alpha_{1,2}$, the CubeSat with the highest ballistic coefficient, is the furthest rearward CubeSat.

Figure 15 illustrates the layout of the CubeSats within the two wafers for this deployment sequence, as given in Table 6. This layout satisfies the deployment constraints imposed by ORS Launch Enabler Mission. The LV's velocity direction is given as a reference. The numbers at each wafer's slot correspond to the deployment order.

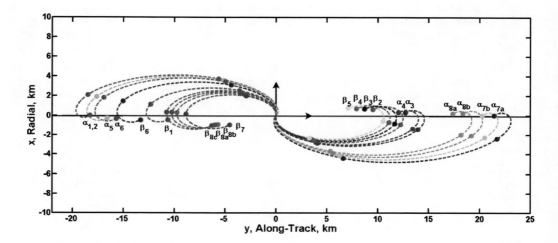

Figure 14. Relative position of the CubeSats throughout the first orbital period. The markers correspond to the positions at 1/3, 2/3 and 3/3 of the LV's period.

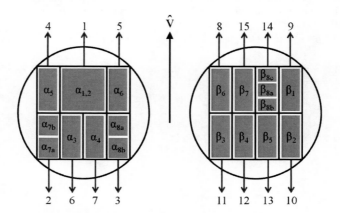

Figure 15. Wafer layout for strategic deployment sequence.

907

CONCLUSIONS

A strategic approach to deployments of large numbers of nanosatellites can decrease the likelihood of close approaches within a given time-period. Given a set of nanosatellite parameters and a set of constraints, one can methodically and deterministically develop a deployment sequence that promotes relative drift and ensures unique trajectories for each nanosatellite. For dissimilar satellites at low Earth orbit altitudes, one cannot neglect atmospheric drag.

This strategy is simulated for the ORS Launch Enabler Mission that involves the deployment of 19 CubeSats in 10 minutes, subject to a set of non-trivial constraints. A successful deployment is defined as a sequence of events lasting 21 days, in which the total number of times that two CubeSats approach within 800 m of each other is minimized. The baseline sequence yields a significant number of CAs, beginning in the first period and extending throughout the 21 day period of interest. The strategic sequence offers significant improvement, yielding no CAs within the 21 day period. Further, the total number of CAs that do occur after the 21 day period is minimized. These results validate the success and relevance of this methodology.

The next step in this research is to better accommodate uncertainty in the unknown parameters, by employing bounding cases (e.g. minimum and maximum ranges for each unknown) and Monte-Carlo simulations. Nominally, the final validation of these results will be the on-orbit demonstration planned for mid-late 2012.

ACKNOWLEDGEMENTS

This work was partially performed in support of the Operationally Responsive Space Office under SMDC contract W9113M-09-D-0001, Task-Order 18. The authors wish to thank the sponsor, as well as Gene Heyler and Bob Henderson of the Johns Hopkins University Applied Physics Laboratory.

REFERENCES

1. University Nanosat Program (UNP) *Nanosat-5 User's Guide*, UN5-0001, Feb. 2007.
2. Rogers, A. Q., and Summers, R. A., "Creating Capable Nanosatellites for Critical Space Missions," Johns Hopkins APL Tech. Dig. 29, No 3, 2010, 283-288.
3. CubeSat Design Specification: http://cubesat.atl.calpoly.edu/images/developers/cds_rev12.pdf
4. Chin, A. et al., *Standardization Promotes Flexibility: A Review of CubeSats' Success*, 2008 Responsive Space Conference, Los Angeles, CA, April 28-May 1, 2008.
5. Buckley, S., *Wafer CubeSat Dispenser*, 2010 Small Payload Rideshare Workshop, Chantilly, VA, May 18-20, 2010.
6. Vallado, D.E., *Fundamentals of Astrodynamics and Applications*, Kluwer Academic Publishers, 2nd Edition, 2004, Chapters 3.3.3, 6.8.
7. Wertz, J.R., *Orbit & Constellation Design and Management*, Microcosm Press, Hawthorne, California, 2nd Printing, 2009, Chapter 10.
8. Borowski, H., Reese, K., Motola, M., "Responsive Access to Space: Space Test Program Mission S26", IEEE *Aerospace Conference 2010*, Paper #1220.

AAS 11-463

CONTROL OF RELATIVE MOTION VIA STATE-DEPENDENT RICCATI EQUATION TECHNIQUE

Giuseppe Di Mauro,[*] Pierluigi Di Lizia[†] and Michèle Lavagna[‡]

In this paper, development of a nonlinear controller based on State-Dependent Riccati Equation (SDRE) technique is investigated to solve relative motion control problem involving in a docking operations between two Earth orbiting spacecrafts as well as in a leader-follower formation keeping mission. This method allows to generate a sub-optimal control law to regulate the tracking error in relative position and attitude. Therefore the relative translational and attitude dynamics are modeled, considering the mutual coupling due to the external gravitational torques and the nonlinearity due to Earth oblateness and air drag effects. Numerical simulations are carried out to demonstrate the effectiveness of this control formulation. Particularly, three different approaches are proposed to implement the SDRE controller, that is *Power Series Formulation*, *Kleinman-Newton* and *Quasi-Newton* algorithms, and their effects on computational cost are analyzed.

INTRODUCTION

The control problem of relative motion between multiple space systems in orbit around the Earth has provoked great interest for many years. In fact, it is essential for two important space flight applications: a) rendezvous and docking operations (RV&D) and b) formation flying (FF) keeping and manoeuvring. These applications are key elements in missions which provides in-orbit assembling of larger units, serving of low Earth spacecraft, malfunctioning satellite capturing as well as building of Distributed Space System (DSS) to accomplish various tasks, such as deep-space interferometry and terrestrial observation among others. Several approaches have been suggested as a solution to the control problem of relative motion in previous research; anyhow the majority of these techniques ignored the coupling between the rotational and translational motion due to the external disturbance torques, that is the attitude and centre of mass dynamics was separately handled. Moreover, many works exploited the linear control theory based on linearized equations of translational or rotational motion. For instance, Vaasar and Sherwood[1] used the Linear Quadratic (LQ) optimal control law for formation flying application, modeling the translational motion by Clohessy-Hill (CW) equations, whereas Sparks[2] developed a discrete-time LQ control law based on CW equation and showed the results when the J2 effect are considered. However the position and attitude relative motion involves highly nonlinear

---

[*] PhD Candidate, Aerospace Engineering Department, Politecnico di Milano, Via La Masa 34, 20156 Milano, Italy.
[†] Postdoctoral Research Fellow, Aerospace Engineering Department, Politecnico di Milano, Via La Masa 34, 20156 Milano, Italy.
[‡] Assistant Professor, Aerospace Engineering Department, Politecnico di Milano, Via La Masa 34, 20156 Milano, Italy.

kinematics and dynamics, therefore traditional linear designs might be unsuitable for accurate control, especially when large angular maneuvers are performed. Thus, some nonlinear control methodology have been explored during recent years: some of these techniques are inspired by the control theory of linear system, such as *feedback linearization* or *gain scheduling*, whereas others are inspired by stability Lyapunov theory of nonlinear system, such as *sliding mode control* and *adaptive control*. One of the highly promising and rapidly emerging methodologies for designing nonlinear controllers is the *state-dependent Riccati equation* (SDRE) approach, originally proposed by Pearson and Burghart and then described in details by Cloutier, Hammett and Beeler[3,4,6]. This method involves manipulating governing dynamic equations into a pseudo-linear non-unique form (named *SDC parameterization* or *extended linearization*) in which system matrices are given as a function of the current state and minimizing a quadratic-like performance index. An algebraic Riccati equation using the state-dependent matrices is then solved online to give a sub-optimal control law. The SDRE approach is an effective option to issues involved with solving nonlinear two-point boundary problem or Hamilton-Jacobi-Bellman partial differential equations associated to nonlinear control problem; moreover, thanks to its formulation, the SDRE method offers the same design flexibility of its linear counterpart, that is Linear Quadratic Regulator (LQR).

In this paper, the problem of driving a satellite (referred as chaser) to a target position and synchronizing its attitude with the target's attitude is treated. Particularly two typical scenarios involving relative dynamic are studied.

The contribution of this paper is to formulate the nonlinear control law based on SDRE method considering relative position attitude dynamics, mutually coupled due to the external torques, and J2 and air drag perturbing effects; moreover, three different approaches are proposed to implement the SDRE algorithm: the first one, called *Power Series Formulation*, is based on an approximation of the Algebraic Riccati Equation (ARE) solution by a series expansion, whereas the other two are based on iterative Newton's method for solving generic nonlinear system equations and are referred to *Kleinman-Newton* and *Quasi-Newton* algorithms.

BASIS OF SDRE CONTROL TECHINIQUE

Early work on SDRE was done by Pearson and Burghart, and it is well described in detail by Cloutier, Hammett and Beeler.[3,4] The SDRE is simply an extension of the constant-valued ARE used to find the optimal feedback control in the linear quadratic regulator problem.

Let consider the class of nonlinear time-invariant systems described by the following

$$\dot{x}(t) = f(x(t)) + g(x(t))u(t)$$
$$x(0) = x_0 \tag{1}$$

with the state vector $x \in \Omega \subseteq \Re^n$ and control $u \in \Re^m$, such that $f : \Re^n \to \Re^n$ and $g : \Re^n \to \Re^{n \times m}$. The SDRE method approaches the problem by mimicking the LQR formulation for linear systems. Accordingly, the system of Eq.(1) can be written in a like-linear form as follows:

$$\dot{x}(t) = A(x)x + B(x)U$$
$$x(0) = x_0 \tag{2}$$

where $f(x) = A(x)x$ and $g(x) = B(x)$. It is worth noting that the former parameterization, known as *SDC parameterization* or *extended linearization*, is possible if and only if $f(0)=0$ and $f(x)$ is continuously differentiable[5].

The optimal control problem is to find a state feedback control U which minimizes the cost functional for all possible initial conditions x_0,

$$J(x_0,U) = \frac{1}{2}\int_0^\infty (x^T Q(x)x + U^T Z(x)U)dt \qquad (3)$$

where the state and input weighting matrices are assumed state-dependent, such that $Q: \Re^n \to \Re^{nxn}$ and $Z: \Re^n \to \Re^{mxm}$, and positive semi-definite (PSD) and positive definite (PD) respectively for all x in order to ensure the local stability.[4,5]

Under the above specified conditions, an approximated solution of minimizing of the infinite-time performance criterion, J, is given by the following expression:[5]

$$U = -K(x)x$$
$$K(x) = Z^{-1}(x)B^T(x)\Pi(x) \qquad (4)$$

where $K(x) \in C^0(\Omega)$ and $\Pi(x) \in \Re^{nxn}$ is the unique, symmetric, positive-definite solution of the continuous-time state-dependent Riccati equation,

$$\Pi(x)A(x) + A^T(x)\Pi(x) - \Pi(x)B(x)Z^{-1}(x)B(x)^T \Pi(x)x + Q(x) = 0 \qquad (5)$$

Note that in order to guarantee $\Pi(x)$ be the solution of Eq.(5), the pair $\{A(x),B(x)\}$ and $\{A(x),C(x)\}$ must be point-wise stabilizable and detectable SDC parameterizations of the non-linear system (1) $\forall x \in \Omega$ [6].

Then, at every sample time, the SDRE algorithm computes the control action by solving a LQ optimal problem, considering the state-dependent dynamic matrices be constant. The main advantages of above technique are simplicity and effectiveness, since no solution of Hamiton-Jacobi-Bellman equation is required to solve the infinite-horizon non-linear regulator problem, and design flexibility due to the possibility of tuning the state and input weighting matrices, $Q(x)$ and $Z(x)$.

Techniques to Solve the SDRE Problem

The main computational step in the implementation of SDRE technique is the solution of a high-dimensional algebraic matrix Riccati equation. A closed-form solution of Eq.(5) is awkward except for few simple dynamic system; then, in most problems this equation will have to be numerically solved at each sample instant. Several numerical techniques exist for solving algebraic Riccati equations; particularly, these algorithms can be divided into two following categories: a) direct and b) iterative methods. The first of these are based on manipulation of Hamiltonian matrix (as Schur decomposition or spectral factorization), whereas the seconds can determine iteratively the solution from an initial guess. Generally, the direct methods are computationally faster than second, especially in poorly conditioned problems and in cases where a good initial guess is not available. On the other hand, the computation and storage requirements for them can be more than twice as much as that for an iterative method because the former operates on *2n* x *2n* Hamiltonian matrix for a Riccati equation of order *n*.[7] An alternative to solve an ARE at each instant time by exploiting one of the above mentioned algorithms for the SDRE implementation was proposed by Wernli and Cook[8], and then revisited by Xin et al.[9,7,10]. This approach is based on the approximation of the solution of ARE by a truncated series expansion.

In what follows, the formulation of two iterative method for ARE solution at each instant, such as *Kleinman-Newton* and *Quasi-Newton* algorithms, and the alternative approach based on series power expansion will be discussed in detail.

Power Series Formulation

This approach consists in taking a power series expansion for $\Pi(x)$ (see Eq. (5)) in terms of a temporary variable θ, such that:

$$\Pi(x) = \sum_{j=0}^{\infty} \theta^j L_j(x) \tag{6}$$

and splitting the dynamic matrices A and B into constant and state-dependent part as[9,11]

$$A(x) = A_0 + \theta \frac{\Delta A(x)}{\theta}; \qquad B(x) = B_0 + \theta \frac{\Delta B(x)}{\theta} \tag{7}$$

Substituting Eq.(6) and (7) in Eq.(5), the sub-optimal control problem is reduced to the following equations:

$$\Pi_0 A_0 + A_0^T \Pi_0 - \Pi_0 B_0 Z^{-1} B_0^T \Pi_0 + Q = 0 \tag{8}$$

$$\tilde{A}_0 = (A_0 - B_0 Z^{-1} B_0^T \Pi_0)$$

$$\Pi_n \tilde{A}_0 + \tilde{A}_0^T \Pi_n = -\frac{\Pi_{n-1} \Delta A(x)}{\theta} - \frac{\Delta A(x)^T \Pi_{n-1}}{\theta} - D_n +$$

$$+ \sum_{j=0}^{n-1} \Pi_j (B_0 Z^{-1} \frac{\Delta B(x)^T}{\theta} + \frac{\Delta B(x)}{\theta} Z^{-1} B_0 \Pi_{n-1-j}) + \tag{9}$$

$$+ \sum_{j=1}^{n-1} \Pi_j (B_0 Z^{-1} B_0^T) \Pi_{n-j} + \sum_{j=1}^{n-2} \Pi_j (\frac{\Delta B(x)}{\theta} Z^{-1} \frac{\Delta B(x)^T}{\theta}) \Pi_{n-2-j}$$

$$D_n = k_n e^{l_n t} [-\frac{\Pi_{n-1} \Delta A(x)}{\theta} - \frac{\Delta A(x)^T \Pi_{n-1}}{\theta} + \sum_{j=0}^{n-1} \Pi_j (B_0 Z^{-1} \frac{\Delta B(x)^T}{\theta} + \frac{\Delta B(x)}{\theta} Z^{-1} B_0 \Pi_{j-1}) +$$

$$+ \sum_{j=1}^{n-1} \Pi_j (B_0 Z^{-1} B_0^T) \Pi_{n-j} + \sum_{j=1}^{n-2} T_j (\frac{\Delta B(x)}{\theta} Z^{-1} \frac{\Delta B(x)^T}{\theta}) \Pi_{n-2-j}]$$

Note that increasing the number of power series used to approximate the Riccati equation solution doesn't cause necessarily an improvement of the control performance; in fact, the SDRE control offers just a sub-optimal solution for the control problem, thus a more accurate approximation of the solution may not result in a closer to optimal control. The parameter k_n and l_n must be chosen such that $k_n e^{l_n t}$ is a number closer to 1; therefore, the D_n matrix is added in the formulation to reduce large control action due to large initial state[11,14].

Finally, Eq. (9) shows that the SDRE control problem is reduced to an off-line algebraic Riccati equation solution (see Eq.(8)) plus a series of linear Lyapounv equations, which might be solved through linear algebra manipulation, such that a closed form solution can be obtained just by a matrix inverse operation. In fact, the *n-th* Eq. (8) can be rewritten as

$$\hat{A}_0 vect(\boldsymbol{\Pi}_n(\boldsymbol{x},\boldsymbol{\theta})) = vect(\boldsymbol{M}_n(\boldsymbol{x},\boldsymbol{\theta},t))$$
$$\hat{A}_0 = \boldsymbol{I}_n \otimes \tilde{A}_0 + \tilde{A}_0^T \otimes \boldsymbol{I}_n \tag{10}$$

where $\boldsymbol{M}_n$ is the matrix which includes all term on the right-hand side in Eq.(9); *vect(.)* is an operator which stacks the matrix elements in a vector form, whereas the symbol $\otimes$ represents the Kronecker product.

Note that, even through the above mentioned method is effective also when the state and input weighting matrix, $\boldsymbol{Q}$ and $\boldsymbol{Z}$, depend on the state vector $\boldsymbol{x}$, it would require more computational efforts to find the stabilizing solution, since Eq.(8) should be determined at each instant time.

Quasi-Newton Approach

The Quasi-Newton approach is an iterative technique based on Newton's algorithm exploited to solve the general nonlinear system of equations, such as ARE in Eq.(5). Differently from classical iterative Newton's method, this approach uses of Broyden's method to update directly the inverse matrix of the Jacobian.

Let rewrite Eq.(5) as

$$\boldsymbol{\Sigma}(\boldsymbol{\Pi}(\boldsymbol{x})) = \boldsymbol{\Pi}(\boldsymbol{x})A(\boldsymbol{x}) + A^T(\boldsymbol{x})\boldsymbol{\Pi}(\boldsymbol{x}) - \boldsymbol{\Pi}(\boldsymbol{x})B(\boldsymbol{x})Z^{-1}(\boldsymbol{x})B(\boldsymbol{x})^T\boldsymbol{\Pi}(\boldsymbol{x}) + Q(\boldsymbol{x}) = 0 \tag{11}$$

Therefore, the Newton's method to solve Eq.(11) results in the following iterative expression:

$$\boldsymbol{\Pi}_{i+1}(\boldsymbol{x}) = \boldsymbol{\Pi}_i(\boldsymbol{x}) - \boldsymbol{\Sigma}'^{-1}_{\boldsymbol{\Pi}(\boldsymbol{x})}(\boldsymbol{\Pi}_i(\boldsymbol{x}))\boldsymbol{\Sigma}(\boldsymbol{\Pi}_i(\boldsymbol{x}))$$
$$\boldsymbol{\Sigma}'_{\boldsymbol{\Pi}}(\boldsymbol{\Pi}_i(\boldsymbol{x}))\big(\boldsymbol{\Pi}_{i+1}(\boldsymbol{x}) - \boldsymbol{\Pi}_i(\boldsymbol{x})\big) = -\boldsymbol{\Sigma}(\boldsymbol{\Pi}_i(\boldsymbol{x})) \tag{12}$$

The first Frechet derivative reported in Eq.(12) is given by[12]

$$\boldsymbol{\Sigma}'_{\boldsymbol{\Pi}}(\boldsymbol{\Pi}(\boldsymbol{x}))Y = YA(\boldsymbol{x}) + A^T(\boldsymbol{x})Y - YB(\boldsymbol{x})Z^{-1}(\boldsymbol{x})B^T(\boldsymbol{x})\boldsymbol{\Pi}(\boldsymbol{x}) -$$
$$- \boldsymbol{\Pi}(\boldsymbol{x})B(\boldsymbol{x})Z^{-1}(\boldsymbol{x})B^T(\boldsymbol{x})Y =$$
$$= \big(A(\boldsymbol{x}) - B(\boldsymbol{x})Z^{-1}(\boldsymbol{x})B^T(\boldsymbol{x})\boldsymbol{\Pi}(\boldsymbol{x})\big)^T Y +$$
$$+ Y\big(A(\boldsymbol{x}) - B(\boldsymbol{x})Z^{-1}(\boldsymbol{x})B^T(\boldsymbol{x})\boldsymbol{\Pi}(\boldsymbol{x})\big) \tag{13}$$

Such that the second equation of Eq.(12) becomes

$$d_i = \big[\boldsymbol{\Pi}_{i+1}(\boldsymbol{x}) - \boldsymbol{\Pi}_i(\boldsymbol{x})\big]$$
$$\tilde{A}_i = \big(A(\boldsymbol{x}) - B(\boldsymbol{x})Z^{-1}(\boldsymbol{x})B^T(\boldsymbol{x})\boldsymbol{\Pi}_i(\boldsymbol{x})\big) \tag{14}$$
$$\tilde{A}_i^T d_i + d_i \tilde{A}_i = \boldsymbol{\Sigma}(\boldsymbol{\Pi}_i(\boldsymbol{x}))$$

The last of Eqs.(14) is a linear Lyapunov equation that can be rearranged as

$$H_i = \boldsymbol{I}_n \otimes \tilde{A}_i + \tilde{A}_i^T \otimes \boldsymbol{I}_n$$
$$H_i vect(d_i) = vect(\boldsymbol{\Sigma}_i) \tag{15}$$

$$vect(d_i) = H_i^{-1} vect(\boldsymbol{\Sigma}_i) \tag{16}$$

where *vect(.)* is the operator which stacks the matrix elements in a vector form, whereas the symbol $\otimes$ represents the Kronecker product. Thus, given a stabilizing symmetric initial matrix $\boldsymbol{\Pi}_0$, the descent direction vector, $vect(d_i)$ is calculated by Eq.(16) and, then, the solution of algebraic Riccati equation is updated by $vect(\boldsymbol{\Pi}_{i+1}) = vect(\boldsymbol{\Pi}_i) + vect(\boldsymbol{d}_i)$. The above algorithm should be repeated until the $\|vect(\boldsymbol{\Sigma}(\boldsymbol{\Pi}_i(\boldsymbol{x})))\|_2 < toll$ and the number of iterations is lower than maximum number of iterations set by control designer.

Finally, the $\boldsymbol{H}_i^{-1}$ can be computed by the Broyden's method[13], such that

$$\boldsymbol{H}_{i+1}^{-1} = \boldsymbol{H}_i^{-1} + \frac{\left[\left(\boldsymbol{\delta}_i - \boldsymbol{H}_i^{-1}\boldsymbol{\gamma}_i\right)\boldsymbol{\delta}_i^T \boldsymbol{H}_i^{-1}\right]}{\boldsymbol{\delta}_i^T \boldsymbol{H}_i^{-1}\boldsymbol{\gamma}_i} \tag{17}$$

$$\boldsymbol{\delta}_i = vect(\boldsymbol{\Pi}_{i+1}) - vect(\boldsymbol{\Pi}_i); \quad \boldsymbol{\gamma}_i = vect(\boldsymbol{\Sigma}(\boldsymbol{\Pi}_{i+1})) - vect(\boldsymbol{\Sigma}(\boldsymbol{\Pi}_i))$$

In order to guarantee the convergence of the method, the choice of $\boldsymbol{\Pi}_0$ must be such that all eigenvalues of $\boldsymbol{A}_0 = \left(A(\boldsymbol{x}) - B(\boldsymbol{x})Z^{-1}(\boldsymbol{x})B^T(\boldsymbol{x})\boldsymbol{\Pi}_0(\boldsymbol{x})\right)$ lie in left half of complex plane. This means that a stabilizing initial guess matrix has to be defined at each instant time. In our work, the initial guess $\boldsymbol{\Pi}_0(\boldsymbol{x}_k)$ at k-th time step has been fixed equal to ARE solution of the previous time step due to the iterative method.

Kleinmann-Newton Approach

This method, proposed by Kleinmann[14], consists of solving a sequence of Lyapounov equations deriving from the application of Newton's method for the Eq.(11).

In accordance with Eq.(12)-(13), the Newton's method can be written as[15]

$$\boldsymbol{\Sigma}'_{\Pi(\boldsymbol{x})}(\boldsymbol{\Pi}_i(\boldsymbol{x}))\boldsymbol{\Pi}_{i+1}(\boldsymbol{x}) = \boldsymbol{\Sigma}'_{\Pi(\boldsymbol{x})}(\boldsymbol{\Pi}_i(\boldsymbol{x}))\boldsymbol{\Pi}_i(\boldsymbol{x}) - \boldsymbol{\Sigma}(\boldsymbol{\Pi}_i(\boldsymbol{x})) =$$
$$= -\boldsymbol{K}_i(\boldsymbol{x})Z(\boldsymbol{x})\boldsymbol{K}_i(\boldsymbol{x}) - \boldsymbol{Q}(\boldsymbol{x})$$
$$\tilde{\boldsymbol{A}}_i = \left(A(\boldsymbol{x}) - B(\boldsymbol{x})\boldsymbol{K}_i(\boldsymbol{x})\right) \tag{18}$$
$$\tilde{\boldsymbol{A}}_i^T \boldsymbol{\Pi}_{i+1}(\boldsymbol{x}) + \boldsymbol{\Pi}_{i+1}(\boldsymbol{x})\tilde{\boldsymbol{A}}_i = -\boldsymbol{K}_i(\boldsymbol{x})Z(\boldsymbol{x})\boldsymbol{K}_i(\boldsymbol{x}) - \boldsymbol{Q}(\boldsymbol{x})$$

Eq.(18) is a linear Lyapunov equation that can be rearranged as

$$\boldsymbol{H}_i = \boldsymbol{I}_n \otimes \tilde{\boldsymbol{A}}_i + \tilde{\boldsymbol{A}}_i^T \otimes \boldsymbol{I}_n$$
$$\boldsymbol{H}_i vect(\boldsymbol{\Pi}_{i+1}) = vect(-\boldsymbol{K}_i(\boldsymbol{x})Z(\boldsymbol{x})\boldsymbol{K}_i(\boldsymbol{x}) - \boldsymbol{Q}(\boldsymbol{x})) \tag{19}$$
$$vect(\boldsymbol{\Pi}_{i+1}) = \boldsymbol{H}_i^{-1}vect(-\boldsymbol{K}_i(\boldsymbol{x})Z(\boldsymbol{x})\boldsymbol{K}_i(\boldsymbol{x}) - \boldsymbol{Q}(\boldsymbol{x}))$$

As a stabilizing feedback matrix $\boldsymbol{K}_0$ is fixed, the algorithm is repeated until the $\|vect(\boldsymbol{\Pi}_{i+1}) - vect(\boldsymbol{\Pi}_i)\|_2 < toll$ and the number of iterations is lower than maximum number of iterations set by control designer.

In order to guarantee the convergence of the method, the choice of $\boldsymbol{K}_0$ must be such that $\boldsymbol{A}_0 = \left(A(\boldsymbol{x}) - B(\boldsymbol{x})\boldsymbol{K}_0(\boldsymbol{x})\right)$ has eigenvalues with negative real part. This means that a stabilizing initial guess matrix has to be defined at each instant time. As done for the Quasi-Newton algorithm, the initial guess $\boldsymbol{K}_0(\boldsymbol{x}_k)$ at k-th time step has been chosen equal to ARE solution of the previous time step due to the method.

NON-LINEAR EQUATIONS OF MOTION

System of Reference Frame Definition

In order to describe the relative motion between two satellites, the following reference frames are defined (see Figure 1).

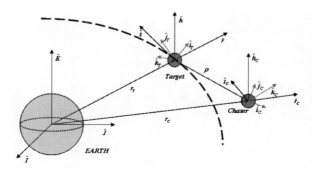

Figure 1. Main reference frames.

Earth centered inertial (ECI). This frame, named I, is centered in Earth; its $\hat{K}$ is aligned with the Earth rotation axis towards the north pole, $\hat{I}$ is directed towards the vernal equinox and $\hat{J}$ completes the right-handed orthogonal reference frame.

Orbital reference frame (ORF). This frame, named O, is centered in the centre of mass of the satellite and it has the $\hat{r}$ axis that points in zenith direction (outward direction from the centre of Earth), $\hat{h}$ is aligned with the direction of the orbital angular momentum and $\hat{t}$ completes the right-handed orthogonal reference frame. Whenever the ORF is attached to the target satellite centre of mass, it is denoted H and know as Hill reference frame.

Body reference frame (BRF). This frame, denoted B, has its origin located in the centre of mass of each spacecraft and the axes are oriented as the inertia principal axes; particularly, each $\hat{t}$ axis indicates the outward normal direction of the docking port.

Relative Translational Dynamic

In the following section the translation relative motion dynamics, including the Earth oblateness and the aerodynamic drag effects are described in detail. In fact, among the many sources of perturbations performed by the spacecrafts during a Earth mission, they are the most significant and thus they are included in the relative equations of motion.

The general orbital equations for the two spacecrafts orbiting the Earth are:

$$\frac{d^2 \boldsymbol{r}_T^H}{dt^2} = -\frac{\mu}{r_T^3} \boldsymbol{r}_T^H + \boldsymbol{f}_{J2,T}^H + \boldsymbol{f}_{drag,T}^H$$

$$\frac{d^2 \boldsymbol{r}_C^{O_C}}{dt^2} = -\frac{\mu}{r_C^3} \boldsymbol{r}_C^{O_C} + \boldsymbol{f}_{J2,C}^{O_C} + \boldsymbol{f}_{drag,C}^{O_C} \qquad (20)$$

Where $f_{J2,T}^H, f_{J2,C}^{O_C} \in \Re^3$ and $f_{drag,T}^H, f_{drag,C}^{O_C} \in \Re^3$ are the disturbance force vectors due to Earth oblateness and aerodynamic drag respectively, expressed in ORF.

Let define the position vector of the chaser centre of mass as follows:

$$\boldsymbol{\rho} = x\hat{r} + y\hat{t} + z\hat{h}$$
$$\boldsymbol{r}_C^H = \boldsymbol{r}_T^H + \boldsymbol{\rho}$$

(21)

where $\boldsymbol{\rho}$ represents the relative position vector expressed in Hill reference frame. The second order derivative of the relative position vector with respect to the Hill reference frame leads to the following expression:

$$\ddot{\boldsymbol{\rho}} = -2\boldsymbol{\omega}_{H,I}^H \wedge \dot{\boldsymbol{\rho}} - \boldsymbol{\omega}_{H,I}^H \wedge (\boldsymbol{\omega}_{H,I}^H \wedge \boldsymbol{\rho}) - \dot{\boldsymbol{\omega}}_{H,I}^H \wedge \boldsymbol{\rho} + \Delta f_{grav}^H + \Delta f_{J2}^H + \Delta f_{drag}^H + f_{control}^H$$

$$\Delta f_{grav} = (-\frac{\mu(r_T+x)}{[(r_T+x)^2+y^2+z^2]^{3/2}} + \frac{\mu r_T}{r_T^2})\hat{r} + (-\frac{\mu x}{[(r_T+x)^2+y^2+z^2]^{3/2}})\hat{t} +$$

$$+(-\frac{\mu z}{[(r_T+x)^2+y^2+z^2]^{3/2}})\hat{h}$$

(22)

$$\Delta f_{J2}^H = f_{J2,C}^H - f_{J2,T}^H$$

$$\Delta f_{drag}^H = f_{drag,C}^H - f_{drag,T}^H$$

Where μ is the Earth gravitational parameter (μ= 3.986e14 m^2/s^3), $f_{control}^H \in \Re^3$ is the vector control acceleration expressed in the Hill reference frame, $\boldsymbol{\omega}_{H,I}^H$ represents the angular velocity of the Hill reference frame with respect to the ECI frame expressed in $\boldsymbol{H}$ and $\dot{\boldsymbol{\omega}}_{H,I}^H$ is the angular acceleration of the Hill frame with respect to $\boldsymbol{H}$. In presence of orbital perturbations, $\boldsymbol{\omega}_{H,I}^H$ becomes[16,17]:

$$\boldsymbol{\omega}_{H,I}^H = \omega_r \hat{r} + \omega_t \hat{t} + \omega_h \hat{h}$$

$$\omega_r = \dot{\Omega}\sin(i)\sin(u)+\dot{i}\cos(u); \quad \omega_t = \dot{\Omega}\sin(i)\cos(u)-\dot{i}\sin(u); \quad \omega_h = \dot{\Omega}\cos(i)+\dot{u}$$

(23)

Where Ω, i, u are respectively the right ascension of the ascending node, the inclination and the anomaly of the target spacecraft orbit. According to the Lagrange-Gauss equation the above expression can be rewritten as follows:

$$\boldsymbol{\omega}_{H,I}^H = \frac{r_T f_h}{h}\hat{r} + \frac{h}{r_T^2}\hat{h}$$

(24)

Where f_h represents the total perturbing acceleration perpendicular to the target orbit plane, r_T is the distance of the centre of mass of the target satellite and h is the modulus of the orbital angular momentum. The above expression shows that the angular velocity of the Hill reference frame consists of an in-plane rotation about $\hat{h}$, plus a rotation of the orbit plane about $\hat{r}$; in fact, a rotation about $\hat{t}$ axis would not be possible because it would imply a different center of attraction from the Earth.

According to the Eq. (24), the angular acceleration $\dot{\boldsymbol{\omega}}_{H,I}^H$ can be derived as follows:

$$\dot{\boldsymbol{\omega}}_{H,I}^{H} = \left(\frac{\dot{r}_T f_h}{h} + \frac{r_T \dot{f}_h}{h} - \frac{r_T^2 f_h f_t}{h^2}\right)\hat{r} + \left(\frac{f_t}{r_T} - 2\frac{h\dot{r}_T}{r_T^3}\right)\hat{t} \qquad (25)$$

Where f_t represents the total perturbing acceleration aligned with the $\hat{t}$ axis, $\dot{r}_T$ is the derivative of the target distance and $\dot{f}_h$ is the derivative of total perturbating acceleration aligned with the $\hat{h}$ axis.

The perturbing acceleration due to J2 expressed in $\boldsymbol{H}$ can be quantified by[17]:

$$k_{J2} = -\frac{3\mu J_2 R_{Earth}^2}{2}$$

$$z_T = r_T \sin(i)\sin(u); \quad z_C = \left((r_T + x)\sin(i)\sin(u) + y\cos(u)\sin(i) + z\cos(i)\right); \quad r_C = \left[(r_T + x)^2 + y^2 + z^2\right]^{3/2}$$

$$\boldsymbol{f}_{J2,T}^{H} = \left(-\frac{5k_{J2}z_T^2}{r_T^6} + \frac{k_{J2}}{r_T^4} + \frac{2k_{J2}}{r_T^5}\sin(i)\sin(u)z_T\right)\hat{r} + \left(\frac{2k_{J2}}{r_T^5}\sin(i)\cos(u)z_T\right)\hat{t} + \left(\frac{2k_{J2}}{r_T^5}\cos(i)z_T\right)\hat{h}$$

$$\boldsymbol{f}_{J2,C}^{H} = \left(-\frac{5k_{J2}z_C^2}{r_C^7}(r_T + x) + \frac{k_{J2}z_C^2}{r_C^5}(r_T + x) + \frac{2k_{J2}}{r_C^5}\sin(i)\sin(u)z_C\right)\hat{r} +$$

$$+ \left(-\frac{5k_{J2}z_C^2 y}{r_C^7} + \frac{k_{J2}z_C^2 y}{r_C^5} + \frac{2k_{J2}}{r_C^5}\sin(i)\cos(u)z_C\right)\hat{t} + \qquad (26)$$

$$+ \left(-\frac{5k_{J2}z_C^2 z}{r_C^7} + \frac{k_{J2}z_C^2 z}{r_C^5} + \frac{2k_{J2}}{r_C^5}\cos(i)z_C\right)\hat{h}$$

where R_{EARTH} stands for the Earth radius, r_C is the distance of centre of mass of chaser, and z_C and z_T represent respectively the projections of the position vectors, r_C^I and r_T^I, on $\hat{\boldsymbol{K}}$ axis. Moreover, the perturbing acceleration due to air drag in $\boldsymbol{H}$ is computed by expressing the spacecraft absolute velocity in Hill reference frame, such that:

$$\boldsymbol{v}_T = (\dot{r}_T)\hat{r} + \frac{h}{r_T}\hat{t}$$

$$\boldsymbol{v}_C = (\dot{r}_T + \dot{x} - y\omega_h)\hat{r} + \left((\dot{r}_T + x)\omega_h + \dot{y} - z\omega_r\right)\hat{t} + (\dot{z} + y\omega_r)\hat{h}$$

$$\boldsymbol{f}_{drag,C}^{H} = -\frac{1}{2}\frac{\rho c_{d,C} A_{p,C}}{M_C}\left[\left(|\boldsymbol{v}_C|\boldsymbol{v}_C \cdot \hat{r}\right)\hat{r} + \left(|\boldsymbol{v}_C|\boldsymbol{v}_C \cdot \hat{t}\right)\hat{t}\right]$$

$$\boldsymbol{f}_{drag,T}^{H} = -\frac{1}{2}\frac{\rho c_{d,T} A_{p,T}}{M_T}\left[\left(|\boldsymbol{v}_T|\boldsymbol{v}_T \cdot \hat{r}\right)\hat{r} + \left(|\boldsymbol{v}_T|\boldsymbol{v}_T \cdot \hat{t}\right)\hat{t}\right] \qquad (27)$$

where c_d is the air drag coefficient, A_p/M is the area-mass ratio of the spacecraft and ρ is the atmosphere density which can be expressed as a function of geocentric distance of the satellite as

$$\rho(r) = \rho_0 e^{-\left(\frac{r-r_0}{H_s}\right)} \qquad (28)$$

where ρ_0 ($\rho_0 = 1.225\ kg/m^3$) is air density at sea level, r_0 is a reference distance and H_s is a scale factor[19].

Chaser Attitude Dynamic

Since the aim of the controller is attitude synchronization, such that $\hat{i}$ axis of B_C and B_T point in opposite direction, a new body reference frame attached to target centre of mass is considered. In particular, it has the $\hat{i}$ axis aligned with the opposite direction of $\hat{i}$ axis of B_T and it will be indicated as $B_{TD}{}^{*}$.

Using quaternion $\boldsymbol{q}_e = [q_{0e}, q_{1e}, q_{2e}, q_{3e}]^T$ to represent the relative attitude between the B_C and B_{TD}, the attitude kinematical equation of motion is given by[18]:

$$\dot{\boldsymbol{q}}_e = \frac{1}{2}Q(\boldsymbol{\omega}_e)\boldsymbol{q}_e$$

$$Q(\boldsymbol{\omega}_e^{B_C}) = \begin{bmatrix} 0 & -\omega_{xe} & -\omega_{ye} & -\omega_{ze} \\ \omega_{xe} & 0 & \omega_{ze} & -\omega_{ye} \\ \omega_{ye} & -\omega_{ze} & 0 & \omega_{xe} \\ \omega_{ze} & \omega_{ye} & -\omega_{xe} & 0 \end{bmatrix} \tag{29}$$

where the quaternion satisfies the normalization constraint $\boldsymbol{q}\boldsymbol{q}^T = 1$. $\boldsymbol{\omega}_e$ represents the relative angular velocity of B_C with respect to B_{TD}, such that:

$$\boldsymbol{\omega}_e^{B_C} = \boldsymbol{\omega}_{B_C,I}^{B_C} - S_{B_{TD}}^{B_C}(\boldsymbol{q}_e)\boldsymbol{\omega}_{B_{TD},I}^{B_{TD}} \tag{30}$$

where the $\boldsymbol{\omega}_{B_C,I}^{B_C}$ and $\boldsymbol{\omega}_{B_{TD},I}^{B_{TD}}$ are the angular velocity of B_C and B_{TD} with respect to I expressed respectively in B_C and B_{TD} coordinate reference systems, whereas $S_{B_{TD}}^{B_C}(\boldsymbol{q}_e)$ is the transformation matrix between B_C and B_{TD}:

In order to transform Eq.(29) in a linear-like form, let define $\boldsymbol{\zeta} = S_{B_{TD}}^{B_C}(\boldsymbol{q}_e)\boldsymbol{\omega}_{B_{TD},I}^{B_{TD}} = S_I^{B_C}(\boldsymbol{q}_{B_C})S_{B_T}^{I}(\boldsymbol{q}_{B_T})\boldsymbol{\omega}_{B_T,I}^{B_T}$; in accordance with Eq.(30) the relative angular velocity can be written as follows:

$$\begin{aligned} \omega_{xe} &= \omega_{xB_C} - \boldsymbol{a}\boldsymbol{\zeta} & \boldsymbol{a} &= \begin{bmatrix} 1 & 0 & 0 \end{bmatrix} \\ \omega_{ye} &= \omega_{yB_C} - \boldsymbol{b}\boldsymbol{\zeta} & \boldsymbol{b} &= \begin{bmatrix} 0 & 1 & 0 \end{bmatrix} \\ \omega_{ze} &= \omega_{zB_C} - \boldsymbol{c}\boldsymbol{\zeta} & \boldsymbol{c} &= \begin{bmatrix} 0 & 0 & 1 \end{bmatrix} \end{aligned} \tag{31}$$

Then, Eq.(29) becomes

$$\dot{\boldsymbol{q}}_e = \frac{1}{2}\boldsymbol{\varXi}_1\boldsymbol{q}_e + \frac{1}{2}\boldsymbol{\varXi}_2\boldsymbol{\omega}_{B_C,I}^{B_C} \tag{32}$$

Where matrices $\boldsymbol{\varXi}_1$ and $\boldsymbol{\varXi}_2$ are reported in Appendix. Finally, chaser attitude dynamics is given by:

$$\dot{\boldsymbol{\omega}}_{B_C,I}^{B_C} = \mathfrak{I}_C^{-1}\left(-\boldsymbol{\omega}_{B_C,I}^{B_C} \wedge \mathfrak{I}_C\boldsymbol{\omega}_{B_C,I}^{B_C} + \boldsymbol{T}_{grav}^{B_C} + \boldsymbol{T}_{control}^{B_C}\right) \tag{33}$$

---

* Note that transformation matrix from B_{TD} to B_T is $\boldsymbol{C} = diag\left(\begin{bmatrix} -1 & -1 & 1 \end{bmatrix}\right)$

where $\mathfrak{I}_C \in \mathfrak{R}^{3x3}$ is the chaser inertia tensor, $\boldsymbol{T}_{control}^{B_C}$ is the control torque vector expressed in $\boldsymbol{B}_C$ and $\boldsymbol{T}_{grav}^{B_C}$ represents the external torques due to gravitational field, such that results,

$$\boldsymbol{r}_C^{B_C} = \boldsymbol{S}_H^{B_C}\boldsymbol{r}_T^H + \boldsymbol{S}_H^{B_C}\boldsymbol{\rho}$$

$$\boldsymbol{T}_{grav}^{B_C} = \frac{3\mu}{r_C^5}\left(\boldsymbol{r}_C^{B_C} \wedge \mathfrak{I}_C\boldsymbol{r}_C^{B_C}\right) = \frac{3\mu}{r_C^5}\left(\boldsymbol{S}_H^{B_C}\boldsymbol{r}_T^H \wedge \mathfrak{I}_C\boldsymbol{S}_H^{B_C}\boldsymbol{\rho} + \boldsymbol{S}_H^{B_C}\boldsymbol{\rho} \wedge \mathfrak{I}_C\boldsymbol{S}_H^{B_C}\boldsymbol{\rho} - \mathfrak{I}_C\boldsymbol{S}_H^{B_C}\boldsymbol{\rho} \wedge \boldsymbol{S}_H^{B_C}\boldsymbol{\rho}\right) \quad (34)$$

where $\boldsymbol{S}_H^{B_C} = \boldsymbol{S}_I^{B_C}(q_{B_C})\boldsymbol{S}_H^I(\Omega,i,u)$, $\boldsymbol{S}_I^{B_C}(q_{B_C})$ is the transformation matrix which describes the attitude of $\boldsymbol{B}_T$ with respect to $\boldsymbol{I}$, $\boldsymbol{S}_H^I(\Omega,i,u)$ is the transformation matrix which determines the attitude of Hill reference frame with respect to $\boldsymbol{I}$ and can be defined by the classical orbital element of the target orbit[19].

SIMULATIONS AND RESULTS

In the following section, SDRE controller is designed to control the relative position and attitude of chaser spacecraft with respect to the target satellite. Particularly, the aim of the controller is to place the chaser at a fixed distance from the target centre of mass and synchronize both spacecraft body frames.

As discussed in previous sections, in order to formulate the SDRE algorithm it is necessary to rearrange the nonlinear equations of motion (see Eqs.(22)-(32)-(33)) in a linear-like form as illustrated in Eq.(2). Anyhow, in presence of state-independent terms (*bias term*), or rather when $\boldsymbol{f(0)} = \boldsymbol{0}$ condition is not verified, this SDC parameterization is not feasible. Therefore, with reference to the relative nonlinear translational equations (see Eq.(22)), the bias terms due to the gravitational and perturbing accelerations must be factorized as illustrated in Appendix (see matrix $\boldsymbol{A}_{\rho s_b}$). Note that s_b is a new stable state which satisfies $\dot{s}_b = -\lambda s_b$ ($\lambda > 0$), $s_b(0) = 1$.[5]

Moreover, in order to improve the relative position tracking performance, the SDRE controller is implemented as a integral servomechanism[20] such that the control state vector is augmented by the integral of the relative position vector,

$$\boldsymbol{X} = \left\{\boldsymbol{\rho} \quad \dot{\boldsymbol{\rho}} \quad s_b \quad \boldsymbol{\rho}_I \quad \boldsymbol{\omega}_{B_C}^{B_C} \quad \boldsymbol{q}_e\right\}^T \quad (35)$$

The feedback control law is given by

$$\boldsymbol{U} = -\boldsymbol{Z}^{-1}(\boldsymbol{X})\boldsymbol{B}^T(\boldsymbol{X})\boldsymbol{\Pi}(\boldsymbol{X})\left(\boldsymbol{X} - \boldsymbol{X}_{ref}\right)$$

$$\boldsymbol{X}_{ref} = \left[\boldsymbol{\rho}_{ref} \quad \dot{\boldsymbol{\rho}}_{ref} \quad s_b \quad \boldsymbol{\rho}_{I,ref} \quad \boldsymbol{\omega}_{B_T,I}^{B_C} \quad q_{e,ref}\right]^T \quad (36)$$

The controller aim is to position the chaser centre of mass in a fixed point placed at distance d apart on the $\hat{i}$ axis of $\boldsymbol{B}_T$, beside to synchronize the angular velocities of spacecrafts. Then, let define the reference relative position vector $\boldsymbol{\rho}_{ref}$ expressed in the Hill reference frame as

$$\boldsymbol{\rho}_{ref} = \boldsymbol{S}_I^{B_T}\boldsymbol{S}_H^I[d \quad 0 \quad 0]^T \quad (37)$$

where $\boldsymbol{S}_I^{B_T}$ is the transformation matrix which describes the attitude of $\boldsymbol{B}_T$ with respect to $\boldsymbol{I}$. In light of above, the relative reference velocity, $\dot{\boldsymbol{\rho}}_{ref}$, yields

$$\dot{\boldsymbol{\rho}}_{ref} = \boldsymbol{S}_I^H \boldsymbol{S}_{B_T}^I \left[\boldsymbol{\omega}_{B_T,I}^{B_T} \wedge \right] \begin{bmatrix} d & 0 & 0 \end{bmatrix}^T - \left[\boldsymbol{\omega}_{H,I}^H \wedge \right] \boldsymbol{\rho}_{ref} \tag{38}$$

Finally, the reference error quaternion reported in Eq.(35) is equal to $[1\ 0\ 0\ 0]^T$ which implies that the docking ports satellites are faced.

The SDC parameterization of Eqs.(22)-(32)-(33) gives

$$\dot{X} = A(X)X + B(X)U \tag{39}$$

Where elements of matrices $A(X)$ and $B(X)$ are illustrated in detail in Appendix.

In order to verify the effectiveness of the controller two scenarios are considered in what follows. In the first scenario, the chaser has to dock an uncontrolled spacecraft moving on a high eccentricity Earth orbit with a perigee altitude of 400 km and an inclination of 45°; this configuration might occur in a capturing mission for a malfunctioning satellite. Differently, the second scenario foresees the chaser keeps the relative position and attitude of a satellite moving on low circular Earth orbit with an inclination of 97.03°; this configuration might occur in building of distributed space instrument for Earth observation.

Either the SDRE problem is solved by power series formulation or one of the iterative methods the input and state weighting matrices reported in cost functional are chosen constant and equal to following, respectively for each scenario:

$$Q = diag \left(\begin{bmatrix} 1e\text{-}3, 1e\text{-}2, 1e\text{-}3, 10, 1e\text{-}5, 10, 0, 2e\text{-}2, 2e\text{-}2, 2e\text{-}2, \\ 1e\text{-}3, 1e\text{-}3, 1e\text{-}3, 1e\text{-}3, 1e\text{-}3, 1e\text{-}3, 1e\text{-}3 \end{bmatrix} \right) \qquad \textit{First Scenario} \tag{40}$$

$$Z = diag \left(\begin{bmatrix} 1.5, 1e\text{-}3, 1.5, 2e\text{-}9, 2e\text{-}9, 2e\text{-}9 \end{bmatrix} \right)$$

$$Q = diag \left(\begin{bmatrix} 1e\text{-}3, 1e\text{-}2, 1e\text{-}3, 1e\text{-}7, 1e\text{-}7, 1e\text{-}7, 0, 2e\text{-}2, 2e\text{-}2, 2e\text{-}2, \\ 1e\text{-}7, 1e\text{-}7, 1e\text{-}7, 1e\text{-}3, 1e\text{-}3, 1e\text{-}3, 1e\text{-}3 \end{bmatrix} \right) \qquad \textit{Second Scenario} \tag{41}$$

$$Z = diag \left(\begin{bmatrix} 150, 10, 150, 2e\text{-}8, 2e\text{-}8, 2e\text{-}8 \end{bmatrix} \right)$$

where $diag(.)$ indicates the diagonal matrix.

Whenever the power series formulation is exploited, the design parameters k_n and l_n shown in Eq.(9) are set to 0.999 and 0.01 respectively and a maximum number of power series equal to 2 is considered. Furthermore, maximum number of iterations is assumed equal to 12 for iterative methods.

First Scenario

The first scenario describes a capturing satellite mission, such that the uncontrolled target satellite is moving on an elliptic orbit whose classical initial orbital parameters are reported in Table 1.

Table 1. Initial classical orbital parameter of Target Satellite.

Semi-major axis	Inclination	RAAN	Arg. of Per.	Eccentricity	True Anonaly
1.9366e4 [km]	45°	0°	0	0.65	170°

The initial relative position, $\boldsymbol{\rho}$, is chosen to be $[-50\ 0\ -50]^T$ m, whereas the initial attitude, if it is represented by a set of ZXZ Euler angle rotation with reference to each orbital reference frame, is $[90°\ 20°\ 50°]^T$ for both satellites; the initial angular velocities with respect to the orbital reference frame are

$$\boldsymbol{\omega}_{B_T,H}^{B_T} = \begin{bmatrix} 10 & 10 & 10 \end{bmatrix}^T \quad [deg/s]; \quad \boldsymbol{\omega}_{B_C,O_C}^{B_C} = \begin{bmatrix} 1 & 5 & 10 \end{bmatrix}^T \quad [deg/s] \quad (42)$$

Without loss of generality, two spacecraft are assumed to be exactly alike and to have a central geometrical symmetry and an uniform mass distribution, such that the total inertia matrices are:

$$\mathfrak{I}_T = \mathfrak{I}_C = diag\left(\begin{bmatrix} 3073 & 646 & 3073 \end{bmatrix}\right) \quad [kgm^2] \quad (43)$$

The total mass of two satellites is *1000 kg*.

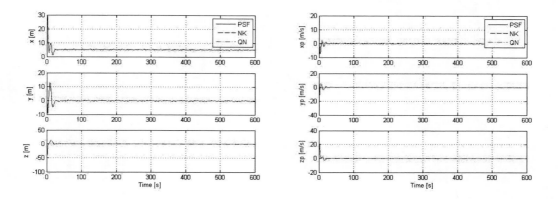

Figure 2. Relative position and velocity expressed in B_T.

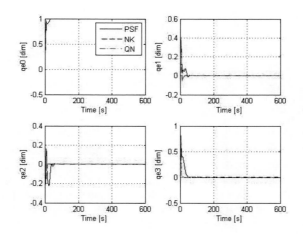

Figure 3. Quaternion error.

921

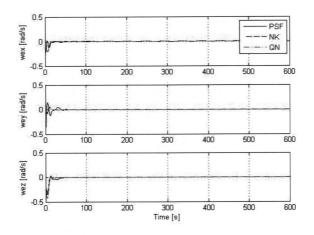

Figure 4. Relative angular velocity expressed in chaser BRF.

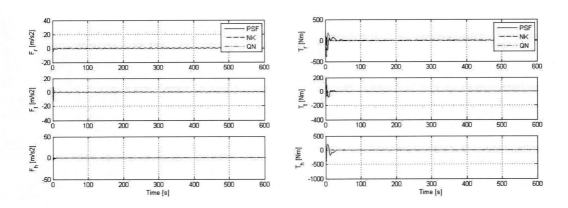

Figure 5. Control accelerations and control torques.

Figure 2 shows the relative position and velocity expressed in B_T. Note that all version of SDRE controller are able to place the chaser satellite in desired point, that is $\rho_{ref}^{B_T} = \begin{bmatrix} 5 & 0 & 0 \end{bmatrix}^T$, and cancel the relative velocity in less than 40 s. Furthermore the controller shows a good attitude tracking performance; as illustrated in Figure 3 and Figure 4 the quaternion error converges to $[1\ 0\ 0\ 0]^T$ and relative angular velocity goes to zero in less than 70 s. Figure 5 illustrates the control accelerations with reference to the Hill reference frame and the control torques expressed in B_C; it is worth noting that small oscillating accelerations and torques are kept on because a continuous control effort is required to track the attitude of the uncontrolled target satellite.

The above figures show that three algorithms implemented for SDRE formulation produce the same performances excepted for the power series algorithm which exhibits larger fluctuations in control torques.

Second Scenario

The second scenario describes a formation keeping mission. Particularly, both satellites moving on low Earth orbit are considered to match the conditions of a distributed satellite system for Earth observation. In Table 2 the classical initial orbital parameters of the target satellite are reported.

Table 2. Initial classical orbital parameter of Target Satellite.

Semi-major axis	Inclination	RAAN	Arg. of Per.	Eccentricity	True Anonaly
1.9366e4 [km]	45°	0°	0°	0.65	170°

The initial relative position, ρ, is chosen to be $[-100 \ -1200 \ -100]^T$ m, whereas the initial attitude, if it is represented by a set of ZXZ Euler angle rotation with reference to each orbital reference frame, is $[0° \ 0° \ 0°]^T$ for both satellites; the initial angular velocities with respect to the orbital reference frame are

$$\boldsymbol{\omega}_{B_T,H}^{B_T} = \begin{bmatrix} 0 & 0 & 0 \end{bmatrix}^T \quad [deg/s]; \quad \boldsymbol{\omega}_{B_C,O_C}^{B_C} = \begin{bmatrix} 2 & 2 & 2 \end{bmatrix}^T \quad [deg/s] \tag{44}$$

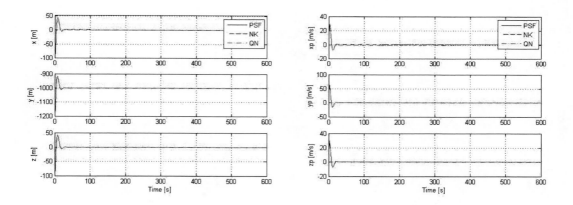

Figure 6. Relative position and velocity expressed in B_T.

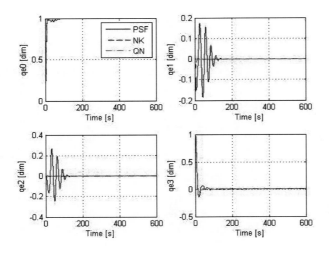

Figure 7. Quaternion error.

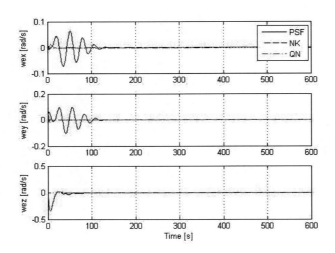

Figure 8. Relative angular velocity expressed in B_C.

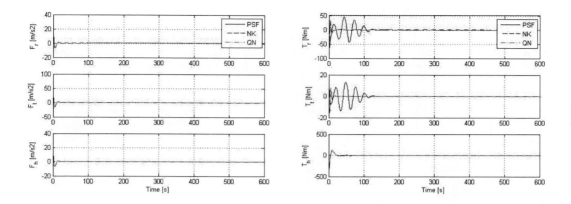

Figure 9. Control accelerations and control torques.

Figure 6 - Figure 9 illustrate the simulation results and demonstrate the accuracy of all versions of SDRE controller. In particular, whenever power series methods is exploited, the SDRE controller achieves both position tracking and attitude synchronization within 143.5 s; differently, the iterative versions of SDRE take only 60 s to reach position tracking and attitude synchronization. Therefore, this simulation shows that series power expansion (with $n = 2$) produces just an approximated solution of the sub-optimal nonlinear control problem related with the SDRE control technique.

Computational Cost Comparison

The above simulation results show the effectiveness and accuracy of the SDRE algorithm for relative motion control problem as well as the performances of three numerical techniques proposed for the SDRE formulation. In what follows, a comparison of computational cost related to these numerical methods will be carried out.

In Table 3 the time needed by MATLAB code (developed by authors) to simulate 600 s of controlled relative motion is reported. All simulations are conducted on a DualCore Pentium 2.93 GHz workstation, employing a commercial version of Windows operating system.

Table 3. Computational time needed to simulate 600 s of controlled relative motion.

Description	Power Series Formulation	Kleinman-Newton	Quasi-Newton
First Scenario	49.77 s	87.17 s	82.55 s
Second Scenario	49.07 s	68.75 s	58.9 s

As illustrated in above table, the power series formulation appears to be significantly faster than other two iterative methods for both scenarios. The iterative methods are fairly close in term of computational time: in fact, as discussed in previous section, these two algorithms are based on Newton's method; the main difference consists in using the Broyden's approximation to obtain inverse matrix $\boldsymbol{H}_i^{-1}$ (see Eqs. (16)-(19)), instead of MATLAB built-in solver for the determination of matrix inversion.

925

CONCLUSION

This paper presents an approach for controlling the relative position and attitude of two orbiting satellites around the Earth. A complete description of the relative dynamic, including the coupling between the translational and attitude motion and the perturbing effects due to Earth oblateness and air drag, has been carried out. The SDRE method has been proposed to achieve the scope; in particular, three different numerical approaches, *Power Series Formulation*, *Kleinman-Newton* and *Quasi-Newton* algorithms, are exploited for SDRE implementation and their computational cost have been compared. In order to prove the SDRE effectiveness and show the performance of the three proposed algorithms for relative motion control problem, two practical missions have been investigated: the first one matches a docking phase of a chaser with an uncontrolled satellite, whereas the second one recalls the condition occurring in a maneuver for formation flying keeping. Simulation results show efficiency of proposed control method and finally point out that better performance in term of control effort can be achieved by numerical iterative algorithms, even though they required more time to obtain the stabilizing solution.

REFERENCES

[1] R.H. Vassar, R.B. Sherwood, "Formationkeeping for a pair of satellites in a circular orbit". *Journal of Guidance, Navigation and Control*. Vol. 8, 1985, pp. 248-242.

[2] A. Sparks, "Satellite formationkeeping control in presence of gravity perturbations". *Proc. of American Control Conference*. Vol. 2, 2000, pp. 844-848.

[3] S.C. Beeler, "State-Dependent Riccati Equation Regulation of Systems with State and Control Nonlinearities". *Report No.(s): NASA/CR-2004-213245*. NIA-2004-08, 2004.

[4] K.D. Hammett, C.D. Hall and D. B. Ridgely, "Controllability Issues in Nonlinear State-Dependent Riccati Equation Control ". *Journal of Guidance, Control and Dynamics*. Vol.21, 1998.

[5] T.Cimen, "Systematic and effective design of nonlinear feedback controllers via the state-dependent Riccati equation (SDRE) method". *Annual Reviews in Control*. Vol. 34, Issue 1, 2010, pp. 32-51.

[6] J.R. Cloutier, "State-Dependent Riccati Equation Techniques: An Overview". *Proc of American Control Conference*. 1998.

[7] P.K. Menon, T. Lam, L.S. Crawford, V.H.L. Cheng,, "Real-time Computational Methods for SDRE Nonlinear Control of Missiles ". *Proc. of American Control Conference*. 2002.

[8] A. Wernli, G. Cook, "Suboptimal Control for the Nonlinear Quadratic Regulator Problem". *Automatica*. Vol. 11, 1975, pp. 75-84.

[9] M. Xin, H. Pan, "Nonlinear Optimal Control of Spacecraft Approaching a Tumbling Target". *Proc. of 2009 American Control Conference*. 2009.

[10] M. Xin, S.N. Balakrishnan, H.J.Pernicka, "Position and Attitude Control of Deep-Space Spacecraft Formation Flying Via Virtual Structure and θ-T Technique". *Journal of Dynamic System, Measurement, and Control*. Vol. 129, 2011, pp. 689-698.

[11] M. Xin, S.N. Balakrishnan, "Nonlinear Missile Autopilot Design with θ-T Technique". *Journal of Guidance Control and Dynamics*. Vol. 27, 2004, pp. 406-417.

[12] L. Cherfi, H. Abou-Kandil, H. Bouries, "Iterative Method for General Algebraic Riccati Equation". *ACSE Conference*. 2005.

[13] J. Imae, H. Sagami, T. Kobayashi, G. Zhai, "Nonlinear Control Design Method Based on State-Dependent Riccati Equation (SDRE) via Quasi-Newton Method". *43rd IEEE Conference on Decision and Control*. 2004.

[14] D.L. Kleinman, "On an Iterative Technique for Riccati Equation Computations". *IEEE Transactions on Automatic Control.* AC-13, 1969, pp. 114-115.

[15] D.L. Kleinman, "On an Iterative Technique for Riccati Equation Computations". *IEEE Transactions on Automatic Control.* 1968.

[16] J.A.Kechichian, "Motion in General Elliptic Orbit with Respect to a Dragging and Precessing Coordinate Frame". *The Journal of the Astronautical Sciences.* Vol. 46, N°1, 1998, pp.25-45.

[17] W. Chen, W. Xing, "Differential Equations of Relative Motion under the Influence of J_2 Perturbation and Air Drag". *Proc. of AIAA Space 2010 Conference & Exploration,* 2010.

[18] *Spacecraft Formation Flying: dynamic, control and navigation.* Butterworth-Heinemann. 2010.

[19] *Fundamentals of Astrodynamics and Applications.* Springer. 2nd edition. 2001.

[20] D.T. Stansbery, J.R. Cloutier, "Position and Attitude Control of a Spacecraft Using the State-Dependent Riccati Equation Technique". *Proc. of the American Control Conference,* 2000.

APPENDIX: MATRICES $A(X)$ AND $B(X)$

The matrices show in Eq.(39) are

$$A(X) = \begin{bmatrix} A_{\rho\rho} & A_{\rho\dot\rho} & A_{\rho s_b} & A_{\rho\rho_I} & A_{\rho\omega_{B_C}} & A_{\rho q_e} \\ A_{\dot\rho\rho} & A_{\dot\rho\dot\rho} & A_{\dot\rho s_b} & A_{\dot\rho\rho_I} & A_{\dot\rho\omega_{B_C}} & A_{\dot\rho q_e} \\ A_{s_b\rho} & A_{s_b\dot\rho} & A_{s_b s_b} & A_{s_b\rho_I} & A_{s_b\omega_{B_C}} & A_{s_b q_e} \\ A_{\rho_I\rho} & A_{\rho_I\dot\rho} & A_{\rho_I s_b} & A_{\rho_I\rho_I} & A_{\rho_I\omega_{B_C}} & A_{\rho_I q_e} \\ A_{\omega_{B_C}\rho} & A_{\omega_{B_C}\dot\rho} & A_{\omega_{B_C}s_b} & A_{\omega_{B_C}\rho_I} & A_{\omega_{B_C}\omega_{B_C}} & A_{\omega_{B_C}q_e} \\ A_{q_e\rho} & A_{q_e\dot\rho} & A_{q_e s_b} & A_{q_e\rho_I} & A_{q_e\omega_{B_C}} & A_{q_e q_e} \end{bmatrix} \quad B(X) = \begin{bmatrix} [0]_{3x3} & [0]_{3x3} \\ [1]_{3x3} & [0]_{3x3} \\ [0]_{1x3} & [0]_{1x3} \\ [0]_{3x3} & [0]_{3x3} \\ [0]_{3x3} & I_C^{-1} \\ [0]_{4x3} & [0]_{4x3} \end{bmatrix}$$

$$A_{\rho\rho} = A_{\rho s_b} = A_{\rho\rho_I} = A_{\rho\omega_{B_C}} = A_{\dot\rho\rho_I} = A_{\rho_I\dot\rho} = A_{\dot\rho\omega_{B_C}} = A_{\rho_I\rho_I} = A_{\rho_I\omega_{B_C}} = A_{\omega_{B_C}\dot\rho} = A_{\omega_{B_C}\rho_I} = [0]_{3x3}$$

$$A_{\rho\dot\rho} = A_{\rho_I\rho} = [1]_{3x3} \quad A_{\rho q_e} = A_{\dot\rho q_e} = A_{\rho_I q_e} = A_{\omega_{B_C}q_e} = A_{q_e\rho}^T = A_{q_e\dot\rho}^T = A_{q_e\rho_I}^T = [0]_{3x4}$$

$$A_{s_b s_b} = -0.01 \quad A_{s_b\rho} = A_{s_b\dot\rho} = A_{s_b\rho_I} = A_{s_b\omega_{B_C}} = A_{\rho_I s_b} = A_{\omega_{B_C}s_b}^T = [0]_{1x3} \quad A_{s_b q_e} = A_{q_e s_b}^T = [0]_{1x4}$$

$$A_{\dot\rho\rho} = -\left[\boldsymbol{\omega}_{H,I}^H \wedge\right]\left[\boldsymbol{\omega}_{H,I}^H \wedge\right] + \left[\dot{\boldsymbol{\omega}}_{H,I}^H \wedge\right] + \begin{bmatrix} g_{11} & g_{12} & g_{13} \\ g_{21} & g_{22} & g_{23} \\ g_{31} & g_{32} & g_{33} \end{bmatrix}$$

$$A_{\dot\rho\dot\rho} = -2\left[\boldsymbol{\omega}_{H,I}^H \wedge\right] - \frac{Cf_C|\boldsymbol{v}_C|}{2}\begin{bmatrix} 1 & 0 & 0 \\ 0 & 1 & 0 \\ 0 & 0 & 0 \end{bmatrix}$$

$$\left[\boldsymbol{\omega}_{H,I}^H \wedge\right] = \begin{bmatrix} 0 & -\omega_h & 0 \\ \omega_h & 0 & -\omega_r \\ 0 & \omega_r & 0 \end{bmatrix} \quad \left[\dot{\boldsymbol{\omega}}_{H,I}^H \wedge\right] = \begin{bmatrix} 0 & -\dot\omega_h & 0 \\ \dot\omega_h & 0 & -\dot\omega_r \\ 0 & \dot\omega_r & 0 \end{bmatrix}$$

$$g_{11} = -\frac{\mu}{r_C^3} - \frac{5k_{J2}(2r_T + x)}{r_C^7} + \frac{k_{J2}z_C}{r_C^7} + \frac{2k_{J2}(\sin(i)\sin(u))^2}{r_C^5} + \frac{k_{J2}}{r_C^5}$$

$$g_{12} = -\frac{5k_{J2}r_T \left[y(\sin(i)\sin(u))^2 + 2(r_T + x)\sin(i)^2\sin(u)\cos(u) + z\cos(i)\cos(u)\sin(i) \right]}{r_C^7} + \frac{2k_{J2}\sin(i)^2\sin(u)\cos(u)}{r_C^5}$$

$$-\frac{Cf_C|v_C|h}{2r_T^2}$$

$$g_{13} = -\frac{5k_{J2}r_T \left[z\cos(i)^2 + 2(r_T + x)\sin(i)\sin(u)\cos(i) + y\cos(i)\cos(u)\sin(i) \right]}{r_C^7} + \frac{2k_{J2}\sin(i)\sin(u)\cos(u)}{r_C^5}$$

$$g_{21} = \frac{2k_{J2}\sin(i)^2\sin(u)\cos(u)}{r_C^5} - \frac{Cf_C|v_C|h}{2r_T^2} \qquad g_{22} = -\frac{\mu}{r_C^3} - \frac{5k_{J2}z_C^2}{r_C^7} + \frac{2k_{J2}(\sin(i)\cos(u))^2}{r_C^5} + \frac{k_{J2}}{r_C^5}$$

$$g_{23} = \frac{2k_{J2}\sin(i)\cos(u)\cos(i)}{r_C^5} \qquad g_{31} = \frac{2k_{J2}\sin(i)\sin(u)\cos(i)}{r_C^5}$$

$$g_{32} = \frac{2k_{J2}\sin(i)\sin(u)\cos(i)}{r_C^5} + \frac{Cf_C|v_C|k_{J2}\sin(i)\sin(u)\cos(i)}{r_T^3 h} \qquad g_{33} = -\frac{\mu}{r_C^3} - \frac{5k_{J2}z_C^2}{r_C^7} + \frac{2k_{J2}(\cos(i))^2}{r_C^5} + \frac{k_{J2}}{r_C^5}$$

Cf_C and Cf_T are the drag coefficients with reference to chaser and target satellite respectively and are equal to

$$Cf_T = \frac{\rho_{atm}c_d A_{p,T}}{M_T} \qquad Cf_C = \frac{\rho_{atm}c_d A_{p,C}}{M_C}$$

$$A_{\omega_{B_C}\rho} = I_C^{-1}\left(\frac{3\mu}{r_C^5}\left(S_H^{B_C} r_T^H \wedge I_C S_H^{B_C} \right) + \frac{3\mu}{r_C^5}\left(S_H^{B_C}\rho \wedge I_C S_H^{B_C} \right) - \frac{3\mu}{r_C^5}\left(I_C S_H^{B_C}\rho \wedge S_H^{B_C} \right) \right)$$

$$A_{\omega_{B_C}\omega_{B_C}} = I_C^{-1}\left(-\left[\boldsymbol{\omega}_{B_C,I}^{B_C} \wedge \right] I_C \boldsymbol{\omega}_{B_C,I}^{B_C} \right); \quad A_{q_e\omega_{B_C}} = \frac{1}{2}\boldsymbol{\Xi}_2; \quad A_{q_eq_e} = \frac{1}{2}\boldsymbol{\Xi}_1$$

$$\boldsymbol{\Xi}_1 = \begin{bmatrix} -0.0001 & a\zeta & b\zeta & c\zeta \\ -a\zeta & -0.0001 & -c\zeta & b\zeta \\ -b\zeta & c\zeta & -0.0001 & -a\zeta \\ -c\zeta & -b\zeta & a\zeta & -0.0001 \end{bmatrix} \qquad \boldsymbol{\Xi}_2 = \begin{bmatrix} -q_{1e} & -q_{2e} & -q_{3e} \\ q_{0e} & -q_{3e} & q_{2e} \\ q_{3e} & q_{0e} & -q_{1e} \\ -q_{2e} & q_{1e} & q_{0e} \end{bmatrix}$$

Note that the term -0.0001 on diagonal of matrix $\boldsymbol{\Xi}_1$ is added in order to obtain a stabilizable solution for the Riccati equation $\Pi(X)$, since the satellite attitude dynamic is unstable.

CURVILINEAR COORDINATES FOR COVARIANCE AND RELATIVE MOTION OPERATIONS

David A. Vallado[*] and Salvatore Alfano[†]

Relative motion studies have traditionally focused on linearized equations, and inserting additional force models into existing formulations to achieve greater fidelity. A simpler approach may be numerically integrating the two satellite positions and then converting to a modified equi-distant cylindrical frame as necessary. Recent works have introduced some approaches for this transformation as it applies to covariance operations, with some approximations. We develop an exact transformation between Cartesian and curvilinear frames and test the results for various orbital classes. The transformation has applicability to covariance operations which we also introduce. Finally, we examine how the transformation affects graphical depiction of the covariance matrix.

INTRODUCTION

Relative motion studies have traditionally focused on linearized equations, and inserting additional force models into existing formulations to achieve greater fidelity. For very close proximity operations, this is reasonable and has been in use for many decades. Some studies use a Hills frame for large satellite displacements and this may not be accurate. A simpler approach for a wide range of satellite displacements is to numerically integrate the two satellite positions and then convert to a Hills frame as necessary. Recent literature has introduced some approaches for this transformation as it relates to covariance matrices, with some approximations. We develop an exact transformation between Cartesian and curvilinear frames and test the results for various orbital classes. The transformation has applicability to covariance operations which we also investigate. Finally, we examine how the transformation affects depiction of the covariance matrix. A summary is below.

- Characterize the accuracy of the transformation between Cartesian and a modified Equidistant Cylindrical space (Weisstien 2011) (expected sub meter level) for both position and velocity vectors. This includes exercising the transformation in both directions.

- Quantify and qualify the ability of the transformation to work on various orbital types (LEO, MEO, HEO, GEO, etc). We will analyze the operating envelope of the technique by plotting the error of the traditional Hills technique for both position and velocity vectors.

- Document the improvement in accuracy from traditional Hills solutions for each case – quantify the error introduced by Hills solutions for larger satellite separations. We will do this for full force model configurations.

Finally, we examine implications for visualization of the covariance matrix, and relative motion solutions.

---

[*] Senior Research Astrodynamicist, Analytical Graphics Inc., Center for Space Standards and Innovation, 7150 Campus Dr., Suite 260, Colorado Springs, Colorado, 80920-6522. dvallado@agi.com
[†] Senior Research Astrodynamicist, Analytical Graphics Inc., Center for Space Standards and Innovation, 7150 Campus Dr., Suite 260, Colorado Springs, Colorado, 80920-6522. salfano@agi.com

Previous studies have introduced curvilinear transformations (Hill, Alfriend, and Sabol, 2008), although they focused on the covariance propagation and orbital element aspects. We do not investigate the propagation behavior of the covariance matrix and any effects of generation via Cartesian vectors or orbital element sets. Rather, we focus on the single point in time curvilinear transformation and reverse method, including velocity vectors. The two approaches should be complimentary.

TRANSFORMATION PROCESS

The xyz system normally used for relative motion can be misleading in its portrayal of the actual relative differences. The x component is the same in both systems, but the y and z components contain differences due to the curvilinear motion. Consider an interceptor satellite whose displacement relative to the target satellite has only y and z axis components, when expressed in the relative (Hill's) frame. The traditional Hills coordinate system is shown in Fig. 1. Note that we use a target and interceptor notation where the interceptor is displaced from the target. For our applications, the interceptor represents either the other satellite that is close to the target (relative motion), or points on the instantaneous covariance about a target satellite (covariance).

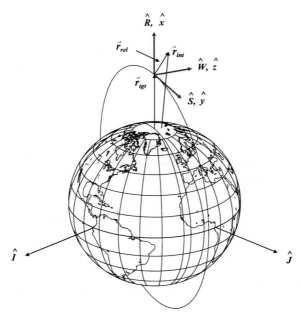

Figure 1   Hills Coordinate System. The traditional Hills coordinate system aligns with the RSW system as shown. Displacements x, y and z and their rates describe the displacements between the target and interceptor vehicles.

Figure 2 shows that this displacement actually has an x component as well, due to the curvature of the target satellite's orbit (e.g. a y displacement of 100 m is really slightly less than 100 m, and have a small negative x component).

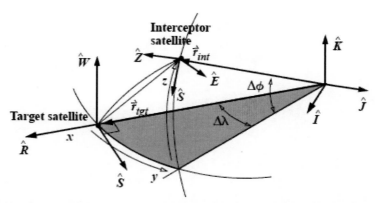

Figure 2   Relative Position of Interceptor and Target. This diagram is extremely exaggerated to illustrate the inconsistency in assuming the Hill's y and z component displacements transfer directly to Cartesian position and velocity vectors.

The question we must address is how to convert between frames—between the true vector positions, and the linearized, or relative Hill's-like equation positions. Because we also examine eccentric orbits, we modify the ***Equidistant Cylindrical*** (EQC) system (Weisstein, 2011). This system, possibly developed by Eratosthenes about 250 BC, has equal distances for polar and equatorial mappings. Using a central meridian of λ_o, the following equations apply. The reverse formulae are also given.

$$x = \lambda - \lambda_o \text{ and } \lambda = \lambda_o + x \sec(\phi)$$

$$y = \phi \tag{1}$$

We derive two transformations because for perfectly circular orbits, the RSW frame properly represents the displacements from the target satellite. The technique is derived using the EQC frame and is valid for all perfectly circular orbits. It can be used to establish the uncertainty in using Hill's equations for relative motion, and the positional displacements you would expect for various orbits. Obtaining the correct velocity components is an important aspect, and it is why we chose the EQC frame.

Elliptical orbits require a slightly different formulation because the arc length (the y distance shown in Fig. 2) is actually a function of the true anomaly. We noticed this while examining the eccentric orbit test cases, especially the Molnyia ($e = 0.7$) satellite. Although the EQC system appears to solve the problem, the distance in an elliptical orbit between two true anomaly values introduces an arc length dependency that ultimately requires an elliptic integral (as suggested by Hill, Alfriend, and Sabol, 2008). Therefore, we use a modified EQC (EQCM) notation for the coordinate system, in which we bend the frame about the target orbital path (because the uncertainty will be largest in this direction). This requires the NTW coordinate system (Vallado 2007;165) instead of the usual RSW frame.

To derive the transformations, we examine a case in which we know the target's position and velocity in Earth Centered Inertial space (ECI) and the relative interceptor position and velocity in the rotating EQCM frame. (Note that for circular orbits, this will be the traditional Hills frame) To determine the interceptor position and velocity vectors in the inertial frame, we perform a series of calculations starting from the target inertial position. Recognize that for the y and z directions, the EQCM frame lies in a curved frame in inertial space. We interchangeably use a state vector notation where X is composed of the position and velocity vectors ($\vec{r}, \vec{v}$).

Determining the velocity requires careful work. A benefit of using the EQCM frame is that the relations are more easily found for both cases (circular and eccentric). Figure 3 is needed for the formulation.

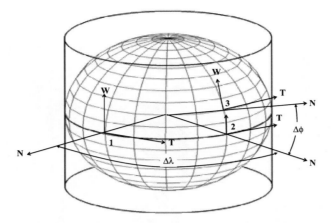

Figure 3   Elliptical Orbit Transformation. Transforming the coordinates between the target (1) and interceptor (3) requires several intermediate positions. Notice that the Earth is stretched to highlight the differences when using elliptical orbits.

The exaggeration of the sphere is because the arc length cannot be related simply by a range and angular separation ($s = r\theta$) due to the nature of the elliptical orbit.

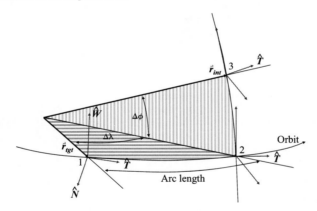

Figure 4   Arc Length Determination. Transforming the coordinates requires angles and rates of change. The various positions (1, 2, and 3) are shown in the transformation, ranging from the target (1) to the interceptor (3). The figure is exaggerated to indicate the effect and geometry of an eccentric orbit.

For circular orbits, the transformation is found using Fig. 3 (which would have no distortion for circular orbits). Here we use the EQC notation because it is compatible with the Hills frame. The RSW to SEZ transformation is used in both transformations.

$$\left[\frac{RSW}{SEZ}\right] = \begin{bmatrix} \sin(\Delta\phi)\cos(\Delta\lambda) & -\sin(\Delta\lambda) & \cos(\Delta\phi)\cos(\Delta\lambda) \\ \sin(\Delta\phi)\sin(\Delta\lambda) & \cos(\Delta\lambda) & \cos(\Delta\phi)\sin(\Delta\lambda) \\ -\cos(\Delta\phi) & 0 & \sin(\Delta\phi) \end{bmatrix} \quad (2)$$

$$EQC2ECI\left(\left[X_{tgt}\right]_{ECI}, x, y, z, \dot{x}, \dot{y}, \dot{z} \longrightarrow \left[X_{int}\right]_{ECI}\right)$$

$$\left[X_{tgt}\right]_{ECI} \longrightarrow \left[\hat{R} \mid \hat{S} \mid \hat{W}\right]$$

$$\Delta\lambda = \frac{y}{r_{tgt}} \qquad \Delta\phi = \frac{z}{r_{tgt}} \qquad \Delta\dot{\lambda}_{tgt} = \frac{\bar{v}_{tgt_{RSW}}(s)}{r_{tgt}}$$

$$\Delta\dot{\lambda}_{int} = \frac{\dot{y}}{r_{tgt}} + \Delta\dot{\lambda}_{tgt} \qquad \Delta\dot{\phi}_{int} = \frac{\dot{z}}{r_{tgt}} \qquad r_{int} = \left|\bar{r}_{tgt}\right| + x$$

$$\bar{v}_{int_{SEZ}} = \begin{bmatrix} -r_{int}\Delta\dot{\phi}_{int} \\ r_{int}\Delta\dot{\lambda}_{int}\cos(\Delta\phi) \\ \dot{x} + \bar{v}_{tgt_{RSW}}(r) \end{bmatrix} \qquad \bar{v}_{int_{RSW}} = \left[\frac{RSW}{SEZ}\right]\bar{v}_{int_{SEZ}} \qquad (3)$$

$$\bar{r}_{int_{RSW}} = \begin{bmatrix} r_{int}\cos(\Delta\phi)\cos(\Delta\lambda) \\ r_{int}\cos(\Delta\phi)\sin(\Delta\lambda) \\ r_{int}\sin(\Delta\phi) \end{bmatrix}$$

$$\left[X_{int}\right]_{ECI} = \left[\hat{R} \mid \hat{S} \mid \hat{W}\right]\left[X_{int}\right]_{RSW}$$

The reverse process uses similar formulae.

$$ECI2EQC\left(\left[X_{tgt}\right]_{ECI}, \left[X_{int}\right]_{ECI} \longrightarrow x, y, z, \dot{x}, \dot{y}, \dot{z}\right)$$

$$\left[X_{tgt}\right]_{ECI} \longrightarrow \left[\hat{R} \mid \hat{S} \mid \hat{W}\right]$$

$$\left[X_{tgt}\right]_{RSW} = \left[\hat{R} \mid \hat{S} \mid \hat{W}\right]^{T}\left[X_{tgt}\right]_{ECI}$$

$$\left[X_{int}\right]_{RSW} = \left[\hat{R} \mid \hat{S} \mid \hat{W}\right]^{T}\left[X_{int}\right]_{ECI}$$

$$\Delta\lambda = a\tan 2(\bar{r}_{int_{RSW}}(s), \bar{r}_{int_{RSW}}(r))$$

$$\Delta\phi = \sin^{-1}\left(\frac{\bar{r}_{int_{RSW}}(w)}{r_{int}}\right) \qquad \Delta\dot{\lambda}_{tgt} = \frac{\bar{v}_{tgt_{RSW}}(s)}{r_{tgt}}$$

$$\bar{r}_{int_{EQC}} = \begin{bmatrix} r_{int} - r_{tgt} \\ r_{tgt}\Delta\lambda \\ r_{tgt}\Delta\phi \end{bmatrix} = \begin{bmatrix} x \\ y \\ z \end{bmatrix} \qquad (4)$$

$$\bar{v}_{int_{SEZ}} = \left[\frac{RSW}{SEZ}\right]^{T}\bar{v}_{int_{RSW}}$$

$$\Delta\dot{\lambda}_{int} = \frac{\bar{v}_{int_{SEZ}}(e)}{r_{int}\cos(\Delta\phi)} \qquad \Delta\dot{\phi}_{int} = \frac{-\bar{v}_{int_{SEZ}}(s)}{r_{int}\cos(\Delta\phi)}$$

$$\bar{v}_{int_{EQC}} = \begin{bmatrix} \bar{v}_{int_{SEZ}}(z) - \bar{v}_{tgt_{RSW}}(r) \\ r_{tgt}\left(\Delta\dot{\lambda}_{int} - \Delta\dot{\lambda}_{tgt}\right) \\ r_{tgt}\Delta\dot{\phi}_{int} \end{bmatrix} = \begin{bmatrix} \dot{x} \\ \dot{y} \\ \dot{z} \end{bmatrix}$$

The transformation process for elliptical orbits has several steps as well, but we have to transform the vectors into the NTW coordinate frame. In Fig. 3 and 4, this is point 1. Next, we setup latitude and longitude-like transformations to relate the interceptor to the target (point 2 in Fig. 3). Finally, we rotate to a NTW frame centered at the interceptor position to find the solution. The challenge is finding the arc length from the true anomaly (and reverse).

First convert the vector to the NTW frame.

$$ECI2EQCM\left(\left[X_{tgt}\right]_{ECI},\left[X_{int}\right]_{ECI}\longrightarrow x,y,z,\dot{x},\dot{y},\dot{z}\right)$$
$$\left[X_{tgt}\right]_{ECI}\longrightarrow\left[\hat{N}\mid\hat{T}\mid\hat{W}\right]$$
$$\left[X_{tgt}\right]_{NTW}=\left[\hat{N}\mid\hat{T}\mid\hat{W}\right]^{T}\left[X_{tgt}\right]_{ECI}$$
$$\left[X_{int}\right]_{NTW}=\left[\hat{N}\mid\hat{T}\mid\hat{W}\right]^{T}\left[X_{int}\right]_{ECI}$$

(5)

Then find the rotation angles.

$$\Delta\lambda_{tgt}=a\tan 2(\vec{r}_{tgt_{NTW}}(n),\vec{r}_{tgt_{NTW}}(w))$$
$$\Delta\lambda_{int}=a\tan 2(\vec{r}_{int_{NTW}}(n),\vec{r}_{int_{NTW}}(w))$$
$$\phi_{int}=\sin^{-1}\left(\frac{\vec{r}_{int_{NTW}}(t)}{r_{int}}\right)$$

(6)

Both approaches require the orbital elements. Following notation of classical orbital elements of Vallado (2007:104), note that the eccentricity unit vector is the direction of perigee. If it doesn't exist below some tolerance, it's set to be the target unit vector.

$$\vec{h}_{tgt}=\vec{r}_{tgt_{NTW}}\times\vec{v}_{tgt_{NTW}}$$
$$p_{tgt}=\frac{h_{tgt}^{2}}{\mu}$$
$$\vec{e}_{tgt}=\frac{\vec{v}_{tgt_{NTW}}\times\vec{h}_{tgt}}{\mu}-\frac{\vec{r}_{tgt_{NTW}}}{r_{tgt}}$$
$$a_{tgt}=\frac{p_{tgt}}{1-e_{tgt}^{2}}$$

$$if\ e>0.00001$$

$$\hat{e}=\frac{\vec{e}_{tgt}}{e}$$

$$else$$

$$\hat{e}_{tgt}=\frac{\vec{r}_{tgt_{NTW}}}{r_{tgt}}$$

(7)

The arc parameters are found next.

$$\lambda_{perigee}=a\tan 2(\vec{e}_{tgt}(t),\vec{e}_{tgt}(n))$$
$$v_{start}=\Delta\lambda_{tgt}-\lambda_{perigee}$$
$$v_{end}=\Delta\lambda_{int}-\lambda_{perigee}$$

(8)

Both approaches need the equivalent target positions at point 2 in Fig. 3 and 4. Here, we use the Perifocal Coordinate system (PQW, Vallado 2007: 162-163.)

$$r_{2tgt} = \frac{p_{tgt}}{1 + e\cos(v_{end})}$$

$$\hat{P} = \hat{e}$$

$$\hat{Q} = \begin{bmatrix} 0 & 0 & 1 \end{bmatrix} \times \hat{P} \qquad (9)$$

$$\bar{r}_{2tgt_{NTW}} = r_{2tgt}\left(\cos(v_{end})\hat{P} + \sin(v_{end})\hat{Q}\right)$$

$$\bar{v}_{2tgt_{NTW}} = -\sqrt{\frac{\mu}{p_{tgt}}}\left(\sin(v_{end})\hat{P} + (e + \cos(v_{end}))\right)\hat{Q}$$

Next, adjust the NTW positions to the interceptor location. This is point 3 in Fig. 3 and 4. For the arc length calculation, we opted for a simple numerical routine rather than a full elliptic integral. Our comparison tests show this approach matches complete elliptical integrals to $1\text{x}10^{-7}$m.

$$\begin{bmatrix} \bar{r}_{2tgt} & \bar{v}_{2tgt} \end{bmatrix}_{ECI} \longrightarrow \begin{bmatrix} \hat{N} \mid \hat{T} \mid \hat{W} \end{bmatrix}$$

$$\begin{bmatrix} \bar{r}_{2tgt} & \bar{v}_{2tgt} \end{bmatrix}_{NTW} = \begin{bmatrix} \hat{N} \mid \hat{T} \mid \hat{W} \end{bmatrix}^T \begin{bmatrix} \bar{r}_{2tgt} & \bar{v}_{2tgt} \end{bmatrix}_{ECI}$$

$$[\phi] = rot2(\phi_{int})$$

$$\begin{bmatrix} X_{3int} \end{bmatrix}_{NTW} = [\phi]\begin{bmatrix} \hat{N} \mid \hat{T} \mid \hat{W} \end{bmatrix}^T \begin{bmatrix} X_{int} \end{bmatrix}_{ECI}$$

$$temp1 = elliptical\ arc\ length\ from\ true\ anomalies \qquad (10)$$

$$\bar{r}_{int_{EQCM}} = \begin{bmatrix} \bar{r}_{3int_{NTW}}(n) - \bar{r}_{2tgt_{NTW}}(n) \\ temp1 \\ \phi_{int}r_{2tgt} \end{bmatrix} = \begin{bmatrix} x \\ y \\ z \end{bmatrix}$$

$$\bar{v}_{int_{EQCM}} = \begin{bmatrix} \bar{v}_{3int_{NTW}}(n) - \bar{v}_{tgt_{NTW}}(n) \\ \bar{v}_{3int_{NTW}}(t) - \bar{v}_{2tgt_{NTW}}(t) \\ \bar{v}_{3int_{NTW}}(w) \end{bmatrix} = \begin{bmatrix} \dot{x} \\ \dot{y} \\ \dot{z} \end{bmatrix}$$

We programmed these in Matlab as eci2eqcm.m.

The reverse process is similar, but it has several subtleties and is presented separately. To find the components and rates in the EQCM frame, begin with the following.

$$EQCM2ECI\left(\begin{bmatrix} X_{tgt} \end{bmatrix}_{ECI}, x, y, z, \dot{x}, \dot{y}, \dot{z} \longrightarrow \begin{bmatrix} X_{int} \end{bmatrix}_{ECI}\right)$$

$$\begin{bmatrix} X_{tgt} \end{bmatrix}_{ECI} \longrightarrow \begin{bmatrix} \hat{N} \mid \hat{T} \mid \hat{W} \end{bmatrix} \qquad (11)$$

$$\begin{bmatrix} X_{tgt} \end{bmatrix}_{NTW} = \begin{bmatrix} \hat{N} \mid \hat{T} \mid \hat{W} \end{bmatrix}^T \begin{bmatrix} X_{tgt} \end{bmatrix}_{ECI}$$

Then find the orbital elements as in Eq. 7. The angles are found next.

$$\Delta\lambda_{tgt} = a\tan 2(\bar{r}_{tgt_{NTW}}(t), \bar{r}_{tgt_{NTW}}(n))$$

$$\lambda_{perigee} = a\tan 2(\bar{e}_{tgt}(t), \bar{e}_{tgt}(n)) \qquad (12)$$

$$v_{start} = \Delta\lambda_{tgt} - \lambda_{perigee}$$

The ending true anomaly is also found using numerical routines. This step inserts an assumption that the covariance does not extend to more than ½ an orbit. Additional work could be done to use elliptic integrals and advanced techniques, but the usefulness is limited and any operation seeking to determine probability calculations would find an answer with extremely low probability – the satellite is uncertain to within ½ an orbital revolution! Again, the routines show excellent comparison to rigorous techniques. This enables us to find

$$\Delta \lambda_{int} = v_{end} + \lambda_{perigee}$$

(13)

The next step is to form the PQW vectors as in Eq 9. We find a secondary transformation of the target vector at position 2.

$$
\begin{aligned}
\left[X_{2tgt} \right]_{ECI} &\longrightarrow \left[\hat{N} \,|\, \hat{T} \,|\, \hat{W} \right] \\
\left[X_{3tgt} \right]_{NTW} &= \left[\hat{N} \,|\, \hat{T} \,|\, \hat{W} \right]^T \left[X_{2tgt} \right]_{ECI} \\
\phi_{int} &= \sin^{-1}\left(\frac{z}{r_{2tgt_{NTW}}} \right) \\
\vec{r}_{int_{NTW}} &= \begin{bmatrix} \cos(\phi_{int})\cos(\Delta\lambda_{int}) \\ \cos(\phi_{int})\sin(\Delta\lambda_{int}) \\ \sin(\phi_{int}) \end{bmatrix}
\end{aligned}
$$

(14)

Find the final position and velocity displacements.

$$
\begin{aligned}
\left[\phi\right] &= ROT2(\phi_{int}) \\
\vec{v}_{3int_{ECI}} &= \begin{bmatrix} \dot{x} + \vec{v}_{tgt_{NTW}}(n) \\ \dot{y} + \vec{v}_{2tgt_{NTW}}(t) \\ \dot{z} \end{bmatrix} \\
\vec{v}_{2int_{ECI}} &= \left[\phi\right]\left[\hat{N} \,|\, \hat{T} \,|\, \hat{W} \right]_2^T \vec{v}_{3int_{ECI}} \\
\vec{v}_{int_{ECI}} &= \left[\hat{N} \,|\, \hat{T} \,|\, \hat{W} \right]_1^T \vec{v}_{2int_{ECI}} \\
\vec{r}_{3int_{NTW}} &= \left[\phi\right]\left[\hat{N} \,|\, \hat{T} \,|\, \hat{W} \right]_2^T \vec{r}_{int_{NTW}} \\
\vec{r}_{3uint_{NTW}}(n) &= x + \vec{r}_{2tgt_{NTW}}(n) \\
r_{scale} &= \frac{\vec{r}_{3int_{NTW}}(n)}{\vec{r}_{3uint_{NTW}}(n)} \\
\vec{r}_{1int_{NTW}} &= r_{scale}\vec{r}_{int_{NTW}} \\
\vec{r}_{int_{ECI}} &= \left[\hat{N} \,|\, \hat{T} \,|\, \hat{W} \right]_1^T \vec{r}_{1int_{NTW}}
\end{aligned}
$$

(15)

We programmed these in Matlab as eqcm2eci.m.

RESULTS

Several comparisons and analyses are possible. We can examine each position and velocity component variation from a single initial starting point displacement. We can vary the initial displacement. A comprehensive set of graphs would require a lot of space to cover so the following figures are intended only to give an indication of the magnitudes of differences you may experience.

Hill's equations are often used to study proximity flight and operations, usually from circular or near-circular orbits. The assumptions used in Hill's formulation clearly introduce error into the solution. Yet they are still widely used for initial planning. Additional realism may be inserted by using the perturbed equations of motion, but the underlying errors still remain.

We examine two-body and perturbed cases. The perturbed cases use "complete" force models. For instance, for the LEO satellites, we used a 70×70 gravitational model, NRL-MSIS00 drag, tides, solar radiation pressure, third body. For the GEOs, we reduced the gravity field size and did not include tides and atmospheric drag. In comparison, other authors have extended Hill's equations into perturbed motion (Schweighart and Sedwick, 2002). This is most often accomplished by adding the perturbing forces to the traditional Hills equations (Vallado, 2007:397) which can become quite complex.

There are several factors that affect the resulting curves, and we wish to establish the performance of the curvilinear transformation for various orbital types (LEO, MEO, HEO, GEO), and for positional and velocity differences. Cases ere tested for 10, 100, and 1000 m positional differences, and 0.01, and 0.1 m/s differences. We examine each axis individually, then all axes together with the same value. Because position and velocity differences will affect the orbit differently, we applied each velocity error to each positional choice, resulting in 6 possible combinations for each satellite orbit.

Examining the vectors that we can propagate, Fig. 5 shows the propagation and comparisons to make.

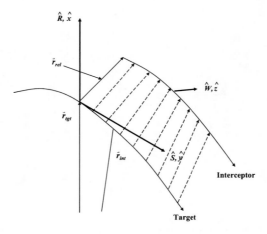

Figure 5   Initial Setup Processing. The setup uses the target Cartesian position and velocity vectors and the initial displacement (sometimes in the Hill frame, sometimes in the EQC frame) depending on the eccentricity. Both ECI vectors are propagated and the difference (in ECI) is converted to an equivalent Hills-like representation for comparison to a traditional Hills propagation.

To understand the ability of the transformation to properly model the motion and compare with the traditional Hills results, we first form the interceptor vector using the hills2eci.m. This takes the target position and velocity vectors along with the Hills displacement and forms the interceptor Cartesian vectors. The two Cartesian states are then propagated with a numerical integrator while the Hills equation is simply solved to create an ephemeris of displacements from the target satellite. The propagated target and interceptor states are then converted back to Hills space at each step. The calculated Hills (from the numerical vectors) is then differenced from the traditional Hills propagation. This comparison reveals the differences between the two approaches, and ultimately, the error in the linearization of the Hills frame.

We modify the process when examining near-circular orbits, or highly eccentric orbits. In these cases, we use the EQCM transformation because of the eccentricity component and it is used to find the interceptor initial state. The two Cartesian vectors are then used to find what an equivalent Hills initial displacement would be, noting that there is uncertainty here because Hills space is not truly defined for non-circular orbits. In the first few cases, we examine only near circular orbits with small eccentricities, as opposed to the 0.0 eccentricity in the first set of test cases.

Begin by considering an initial case where the orbit is in a nominal LEO, circular 500 km altitude orbit. We examine just the 1000 m and .1 m/s initial displacement condition. The positional differences are shown in Fig. 6. Note that the along-track component exhibit's the majority of the error. The magnitude is in blue, and represents the overall difference. The error bars approximate the error uncertainty, and are intended to give a sense of the differences over time, but without so much detail, so additional information can be plotted on each plot. The error bars are 1-sigma limits and give an idea of the variability over periods of time, without cluttering the plot with additional dynamic information.

Because the trends appear relatively constant, it's useful to reduce the volume of information to examine the results simultaneously. To accomplish this, we average each time period, here about 8 hours. Thus, we can look where the satellites are after 1, 2, 3, etc, periods to understand how much variation is in that particular time interval. That's what the green whisker plot is showing in Fig. 6.

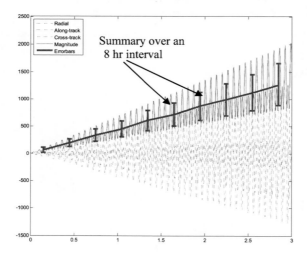

Figure 6 **Positional difference of Hills and Numerical Propagation (2-body).** The difference between a numerically generated orbit, and the Hills linearized approximation. Numerical integration results are shown for 2-body motion. The solid red line is the magnitude of the radial, along-track, cross-track (RAC) differences. The summary averages the variation over an interval of time (8 hours).

For two-body and perturbed motion, the LEO circular case results are shown in Fig 7. Note that the individual values are averaged over time interval (here about 8 hours) and the standard deviation is plotted as a whisker plot. This is intended to de-clutter the figure somewhat and give a sense of the variability of the error difference in each case. We also note the strong trending that is going on, giving us the opportunity to establish a trend line based on the time from epoch.

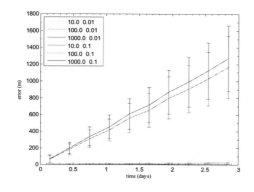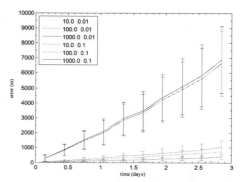

Figure 7   Positional difference of Hills and Numerical Propagation LEO Circular. The difference between a numerically generated orbit, and the Hills linearized approximation is shown. Numerical integration results are shown for 2-body and perturbed motion. The bars represent the variation during each 8 hr time interval, and the line is the average variation.

The results still appear to be reasonably linear – as we would expect because the semimajor axis is different. Thus we determined simple linear trendlines for each case. For most cases, the offset was small – although there were some exceptions, usually associated with the Perturbed cases. The rate term was our main discriminator as it was a general indicator of the error introduced by using Hills transformations for both circular and non-circular orbits. Here, the variable t is expressed in days.

For the Two-body cases, we have,

```
Case  10.0 m 0.01 m/s      p =    0.092672 (t) -  0.000198
Case  100.0 m 0.01 m/s     p =    4.445170 (t) -  0.031334
Case  1000.0 m 0.01 m/s    p =  406.292967 (t) -  2.322417
Case  10.0 m 0.1 m/s       p =    1.660938 (t) +  0.015021
Case  100.0 m 0.1 m/s      p =    9.267334 (t) -  0.020018
Case  1000.0 m 0.1 m/s     p =  443.249856 (t) -  2.269249
```

For the Perturbed case, we have,

```
Case  10.0 m 0.01 m/s      p =    36.019018 (t) -    3.924003
Case  100.0 m 0.01 m/s     p =   262.347641 (t) -   28.336312
Case  1000.0 m 0.01 m/s    p =  2327.870700 (t) -  265.931320
Case  10.0 m 0.1 m/s       p =   134.965546 (t) -   13.339106
Case  100.0 m 0.1 m/s      p =   356.080043 (t) -   39.620034
Case  1000.0 m 0.1 m/s     p =  2410.656200 (t) -  277.849673
```

Notice that the largest variation occurs for orbits with initial conditions that are far (1 km) away from the target satellite, which makes sense. The initial velocity displacements had much less effect, but they only went to 0.1 m/s in each axis.

Now examine a GPS-altitude, circular equatorial orbit. We also checked a GPS circular inclined orbit to make sure that the orbital elements had no effect on the transformations. For the two-body case, we would expect identical trendlines between the two cases, and we verified that in the simulation.

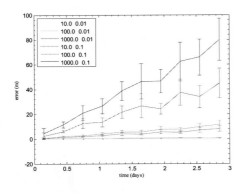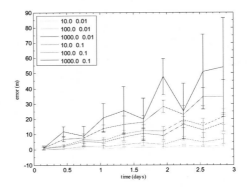

Figure 8   Positional difference of Hills and Numerical Propagation, GPS circular equatorial. The difference between a numerically generated orbit, and the Hills linearized approximation is shown. Numerical integration results are shown for 2-body and perturbed motion. The bars represent the variation during each 8 hr time interval, and the line is the average variation.

The perturbed GPS circular equatorial and inclined cases differed (as expected) due to the different positions and the different acceleration values.

For a GEO circular orbit, we have the following.

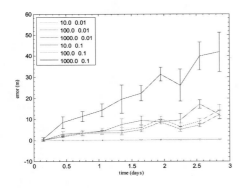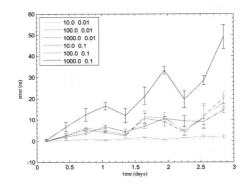

Figure 9   Positional difference of Hills and Numerical Propagation, GEO circular. The difference between a numerically generated orbit, and the Hills linearized approximation is shown. Numerical integration results are shown for 2-body and perturbed motion. The bars represent the variation during each 8 hr time interval, and the line is the average variation.

Next, we examined several satellites with small eccentricity values. These orbits should be "similar" to te circular cases because the eccentricity is relatively small in each case. For a LEO, we used a satellite with the following orbital elements. Recall that the circular LEO was at an altitude of 500 km, but also equatorial.

p km	a km	ecc	incl deg	raan deg	argp deg	nu deg	m deg
6864.9379	6864.9502	0.001336912	97.6554788	79.55466	101.98053	47.10230	46.99014

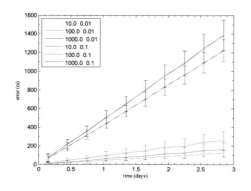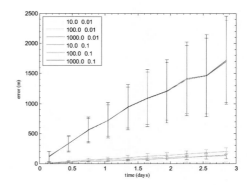

Figure 10   **Positional difference of Hills and Numerical Propagation, LEO near circular.** The difference between a numerically generated orbit, and the Hills linearized approximation is shown. Numerical integration results are shown for 2-body (left) and perturbed (right) motion. The bars represent the variation during each 8 hr time interval, and the line is the average variation.

Notice that the results are similar to the circular case, except for the perturbed results which we would expect due to the inclined nature of this nearly circular orbit.

For a small eccentricity GPS inclined orbit, we have the following orbital elements.

p km	a km	ecc	incl deg	raan deg	argp deg	nu deg	m deg
26565.5005	26565.8931	0.003844090	55.2474744	296.55617	188.46743	312.72094	313.04393

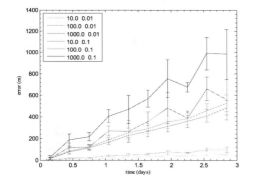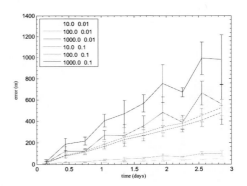

Figure 11   **Positional difference of Hills and Numerical Propagation, GPS near circular inclined.** The difference between a numerically generated orbit, and the Hills linearized approximation is shown. Numerical integration results are shown for 2-body (left) and perturbed (right) motion. The bars represent the variation during each 8 hr time interval, and the line is the average variation.

The GEO low inclination and near circular orbital elements are as follows.

p km	a km	ecc	incl deg	raan deg	argp deg	nu deg	m deg
42171.0268	42171.0298	0.000268282	0.0431571	78.14906	358.20236	119.41971	119.39293

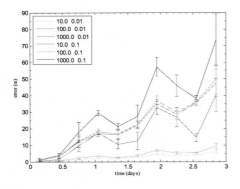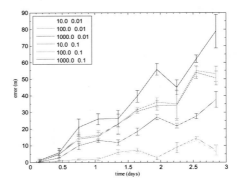

Figure 12   Positional difference of Hills and Numerical Propagation, GEO near circular. The difference between a numerically generated orbit, and the Hills linearized approximation is shown. Numerical integration results are shown for 2-body (left) and perturbed (right) motion. The bars represent the variation during each 8 hr time interval, and the line is the average variation.

If we examine more eccentric orbits, consider the following two examples. For an eccentric LEO orbit, the orbital elements are shown below. Note this is a modest eccentricity test of the eccentricity condition, which Hills equations are admittedly not designed for.

p km	a km	ecc	incl deg	raan deg	argp deg	nu deg	m deg
7982.1963	8170.9718	0.151997330	32.8682385	80.34992	117.84240	2.10039	1.52825

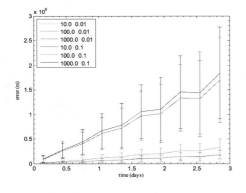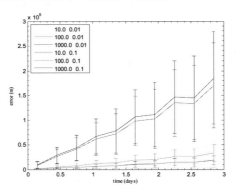

Figure 13   Positional difference of Hills and Numerical Propagation, LEO modest eccentricity. The difference between a numerically generated orbit, and the Hills linearized approximation is shown. Numerical integration results are shown for 2-body (left) and perturbed (right) motion. The bars represent the variation during each 8 hr time interval, and the line is the average variation.

For the HEO orbit, the orbital elements are shown below. Note this is a stringent test of the eccentricity condition, which Hills equations are admittedly not designed for.

p km	a km	ecc	incl deg	raan deg	argp deg	nu deg	m deg
11591.8066	25550.0883	0.739128209	62.0562099	226.25462	254.94277	263.77199	344.11265

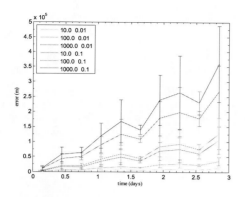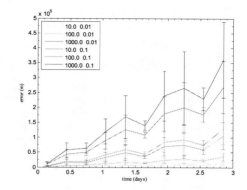

Figure 14   Positional difference of Hills and Numerical Propagation, HEO. The difference between a numerically generated orbit, and the Hills linearized approximation is shown. Numerical integration results are shown for 2-body (left) and perturbed (right) motion. The bars represent the variation during each 8 hr time interval, and the line is the average variation.

Figure 15 summarizes all the results.

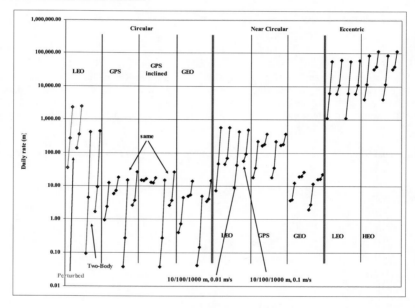

Figure 15   Rate term Positional difference of Hills and Numerical Propagation Summary. Nine cases are shown for both two-body and perturbed results. The left four cases are all circular orbits and the right five are all eccentric orbits. Each case includes 6 individual cases for initial displacements. For each case, the perturbed result is on the left and the two-body case is on the right (within each duplet). The daily rate for positional error is shown for each case. Note that the GPS circular cases are identical for the two-body equatorial and inclined cases.

We can gather a great deal of information from Fig. 15.

1.   The errors in the perturbed cases were almost always greater than the two-body cases.

2.   The results were always greater as the initial displacements were larger.

3.   As the satellite altitude increases, the errors generally go down.

943

4. The errors for circular LEO orbits can be large, even when the initial displacements are not that big (100m).

5. The near circular orbits introduced noticeable errors compared to the pure circular cases.

6. Hills equations are not designed for non circular orbits, and the errors show it!

We can also examine how the transformation affects the traditional Hills diagrams. Vallado (2007:402-408) shows sample Hills plots for a variety of initial displacements. Initial x and y displacements in velocity produce elliptical, and sliding elliptical motions respectively. Figure 16 shows the behavior using perturbed motion numerical propagation, and transforming the results to Hills space. The initial x offset is 0.5 m/s.

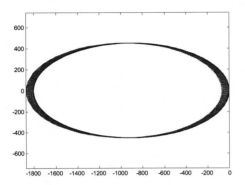 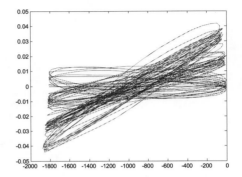

Figure 16   Hills and Perturbed Motion Hills Plot – $\dot{x}$ variation. The traditional x vs y is shown on the left, and z vs y on the right. The blue line is the Hills solution,. As time progresses (3 days) the perturbed orbit gets farther from the Hills solution, ending up nearly 400 m away at the end. The periodic motion in the z direction is also shown, and here, the Hills formulation predicts no motion, although the difference is only a fraction of a meter.

We can also examine how the results are with an initial y velocity displacement of 0.113 m/s.

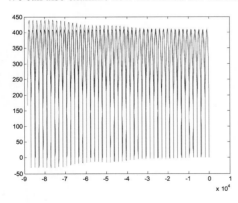 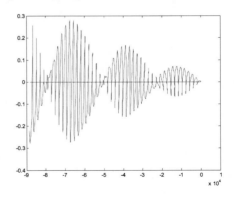

Figure 17   Hills and Perturbed Motion Hills Plot – $\dot{y}$ variation. The traditional x vs y is shown on the left, and z vs y on the right. Notice the blue line which is the Hills solution and the left figure does not have equally scaled axes so the figure is different from "usual" depictions. As time progresses (3 days) the perturbed orbit gets farther from the Hills solution, ending up nearly 400 m away at the end. The periodic motion in the z direction is also shown, and here, the Hills formulation predicts no motion, although the difference is less than a meter.

944

COVARIANCE IMPLICATIONS

The preceding analysis also applies to covariance matrices. We do not reproduce analysis that has been done for covariance propagation (Hill et al (2008, 2010), Junkins et al (1996), Sabol et al (2010), andothers). There is significant discussion about whether or not to propagate the covariance in some coordinates (or orbital elements), and then bend to the curvilinear frame, or to proceed with an Unscented Kalman Filter (UKF) approach and simply propagate in the curvilinear frame. Nevertheless, the transformations from this paper apply to any of these cases, and enables transformation to the Cartesian or curvilinear representation.

The important thing to consider is that a covariance propagated or generated from an orbit determination solution will be in a linearized frame. Consider Fig. 18. The Monte Carlo points show the true location of the covariance at the future time, but the numerically generated covariance retains a "straight" nature. The additional width of the propagated covariance accounts for some of the bending seen in the Monte Carlo representation. Notice that neither covariance is aligned with the velocity vector.

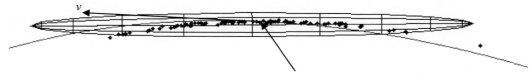

Figure 18   Covariance via Monte Carlo and Propagation. A 6×6 initial covariance is taken and propagated using standard numerical techniques. The resulting vector after nearly 4 days (wireframe box) is shown against Monte Carlo simulations (dots). Notice the misalignment with the velocity vector, and the additional width of the prorogated covariance.

We examined additional cases in Fig. 19 – a circular orbit, and a highly eccentric orbit. Even for a propagated covariance along a circular orbit (the blue wireframes in Fig. 19), the Hill transformation shows a significant bend from the velocity vector. The Monte Carlo results (red wireframes) show an even greater bend. Notice how the transformation moves the "ends" of the error ellipse, and how the eccentricity changes the thickness of the covariance ellipse, with greater eccentricity producing a thicker covariance. This is important should another satellite occupy the location on the bent portion of the covariance, but not on the linearized straight position.

Figure 19   Covariance Representations. Three examples are shown, circular, near circular, and elliptical, from the left. The covariance is propagated through time via a UKF and Monte Carlo techniques, and then bent to a linear frame. Note the discrepancy at the ends of the ellipse and that the covariance does NOT align with the velocity vector in all cases.

Clearly any graphical representation should perform the proper beinding before displaying the results or the depcition will be extremely misleading.

CONCLUSIONS

We have shown a new formulation to convert between curvilinear and Cartesian coordinate systems. A primary benefit is to simplify the process of incorporating additional force models into Hills equations solutions, but also to be general in nature to handle non-circular orbits. Errors were shown with the linearization of Hills equations for circular orbits, and several test cases demonstrated the robustness of the routines.

It appears that errors from using Hills equations can be relatively large (hundreds of meters to many kilometers) even for circular and nearly circular LEO orbits. This should be taken into account when planning missions and using these types of approaches for mission design.

We find that the covariance is not aligned with the velocity vector. This has important implications when considering covariance operations for close approaches and other operations requiring use of precise covariances. If the linearized result is used from the normal propagation of the covariance, the uncertainty will be incorrect for many regions in space.

We conclude the following about staying in the ECI frame to perform statistical operations such as conjunction analysis. First, the covariance generated from the Monte Carlo or UKF points are not centered on the unperturbed orbital position. Next, the covariance ellipse is fatter (it has a larger uncertainty and therefore a thinner density) than the EQCM ellipse. This results from trying to linearly accommodate the ECI points that clearly show a bend. Finally, we note that our transformation works only for covariances that are less than ½ an orbit revolution. Past this point, additional techniques would be needed to recover the orbital arc, and the meaning of the covariance for any actual operations would be suspect as the satellite could occupy positions in more than ½ the orbit. The resulting confidence would be extremely low.

Matlab implementations will be made available upon request as we plan additional work to further study these phenomena.

REFERENCES

Hill, K., Alfriend, and C. Sabol. 2008. Covariance-based Uncorrelated Track Association. Paper AIAA 2008-7211 presented at the AIAA/AAS Astrodynamics Specialist Conference. Honolulu, HI. August 18-21.

Hill. K., Sabol, C. and Alfriend, K.T. 2010. Comparison of Covariance-Based Track Association Approaches with Simulated Radar Data. Paper AAS 10-318 presented at the Kyle T. Alfriend Astrodynamics Symposium. Monterey, CA. May 17-19.

Hill, Keric, et al. 2010. Covariance-based Network Tasking of Optical Sensors. Paper AAS 10-150 presented at the AAS/AIAA Space Flight Mechanics Conference, February 14-17. San Diego, CA. (Also 8th USR Workshop, Maui, April 8-13, 2010, Paper S5.2).

Junkins, J.L., Akella, M.R. and Alfriend, K.T. 1996. Non-Gaussian Error Propagation in Orbital Mechanics. *Journal of the Astronautical Sciences*. Vol. 44, no. 4. pp. 541–563.

Mahalanobis, P.C. 1936. On the Generalized Distance in Statistics. Proceedings of the National Institute of Sciences of India. Vol. 2. pp. 49–55.

Park, R.S. and Scheeres, D.J. 2006. Nonlinear Mapping of Gaussian Statistics: Theory and Applications to Spacecraft Trajectory Design. *Journal of Guidance, Control, and Dynamics*. Vol. 29, no. 6. pp. 1367–1375.

Sabol, Chris, et al. 2010. Linearized Orbit Covariance Generation and Propagation Analysis via Simple Monte Carlo Simulations. Paper AAS 10-134 presented at the AAS/AIAA Space Flight Mechanics Conference, February 14-17. San Diego, CA. (Also 8th USR Workshop, Maui, April 8-13, 2010, Paper S4.1).

Seago, John H. and David A Vallado. 2010. Goodness of Fit Test for Orbit Determination. Paper AAS 10-149 presented at the AAS/AIAA Space Flight Mechanics Conference, February 14-17. San Diego, CA.

Vallado, David A. and John H. Seago. 2009. Covariance Realism. Paper AAS 09-304 presented at the AAS/AIAA Astrodynamics Specialist Conference, August 9-13. Pittsburgh, PA.

Vallado, David A. 2007. *Fundamentals of Astrodynamics and Applications*. Third Edition. Microcosm, Hawthorne, CA.

Weisstein, Eric W. June 2011. "Cylindrical Equidistant Projection." From MathWorld--A Wolfram Web Resource. http://mathworld.wolfram.com/CylindricalEquidistantProjection.html

EFFECTIVE SPHERE MODELING FOR ELECTROSTATIC FORCES ON THREE-DIMENSIONAL SPACECRAFT SHAPES

Lee E. Z. Jasper[*] and Hanspeter Schaub[†]

Satellite formations utilizing Coulomb forces are being studied due to their potential for their extremely low-fuel, low-power close formation flying control. Prior studies into Coulomb formations employ point charge or isolated sphere assumptions with well known electrostatic behavior. This is justified by having the custom Coulomb spacecraft assume near-spherical shapes to minimize charge densities for a given potential. Complex geometries, however, are the norm for existing satellite structures. This paper develops a method to model complex geometries as finite spheres. Finite element electrostatic field solutions are used to model the force interactions between a sphere and a non-spherical body. The effective sphere method is demonstrated on a sphere, a cylinder and a generic satellite structure. Force behavior is shown to match between the finite element solution and a 3D body's effective sphere for separation distances beyond 3 – 4 craft radii. Differences in the effective radii for the same non-spherical body are discussed along principal body axes and a near-elliptical distribution of effective radii are found for the case of a cylindrical shape. Finally, the nadir-aligned relative motion control of a cylinder-sphere formation is considered using the cylinder's effective radius and a voltage control strategy.

INTRODUCTION

Formation flying of spacecraft, through use of electrostatic (Coulomb) forces, have been the focus of research for many years.[1–4] Use of electrostatic forces to maintain a formation is appealing because the formation can be maintained with minimal use of fuel (I_{sp} values for relative motion control can reach up to $10^{13}s$) and low power consumption, often less than 1 Watt.[1,5] Thus, electrostatic forces allow formations to exist without the use of precious fuel and they avoid thruster exhaust plume impingement issues between spacecraft. Due to the cold and dense near-Earth plasma environment, the Debye lengths are only large enough to effectively use the Coulomb forces at high Earth and geosynchronous orbit (GEO) altitudes. However, at these high orbits, nominal minimal Debye lengths range from 180-200 meters, allowing for Coulomb spacecraft formations to be tens of meters in size.[6]

A common Coulomb formation studied is the simple two point-charge formation. This is used to study rendez-vous and docking applications,[7] virtual tethering of sensor probes to a mother craft,[8] electrostatic collision avoidance,[9] as well as creating virtual Coulomb structures.[10,11] The dynamics for two charged craft are much simpler than the complex N charged body problem. Even with the two-body problem the charge feedback control and stability development are challenging due

---

[*]Graduate Research Assistant, Aerospace Engineering Sciences Department, University of Colorado, Boulder, CO 80309-0431.

[†]Associate Professor, H. Joseph Smead Fellow, Aerospace Engineering Sciences Department, University of Colorado, Boulder, CO 80309-0431.

to the nonlinear electrostatic force actuations, and the coupling with differential gravity. This paper extends the discussion on two charged spacecraft. However, the focus is placed on finite bodies with three-dimensional shapes instead of only considering point charge models. Electrostatic properties of spherical bodies have been studied analytically for some time. Soules creates empirical models of the electrostatic forces between two finite spheres, including induced charging effects, using a modified method of images.[12] Experimental verification of such charge to voltage models of spheres is recently discussed in Reference 13. Neighboring finite bodies held at non-zero electrostatic potentials can create increased or decreased capacitance compared to the capacitance models of isolated bodies. The relation between the body size and separation distance leads to a position dependent capacitance matrix.[14, 15] With these enhanced absolute voltage to charge relationships, the charge feedback control work in prior research efforts such as References 16, 17 and 18 can be reformulated as voltage control problems.

However, most currently flying spacecraft are not spherical in shape. For the electrostatic relative orbital dynamics research, it is of interest how well the three-dimensional electrostatic fields of generally shaped bodies can be modeled without having to resort to the time-intensive and complex finite element electrostatic field solutions. This paper first investigates how to represent the electrostatic force behavior between a sphere and a general shape by representing the three-dimensional shape with an equivalent finite sphere. This allows for complex geometries, with electrostatic behavior that cannot be solved in closed form, to be approximated with spherical models with known characteristics. Two effective spheres methods are considered and compared which differ in the complexity required to evaluate the effective sphere radius. The sphere representation allows for very fast evaluations of the electrostatic forces thanks to the analytical closed form solution. The scope of this study only considers line-of-sight electrostatic force solutions between the two the center of masses. Non-aligned forces and torques are not considered in this work. Further, of interest is over what separation distance range such simplified models yield reasonable electrostatic force approximations. If a spacecraft has long solar panels extended and deployed, then small separation distances can create strong induced charge distributions between the sphere and the nearby solar panel components.

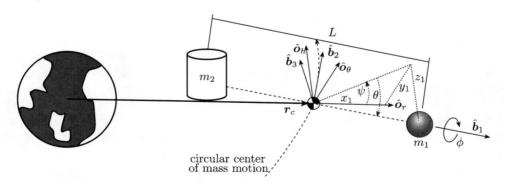

Figure 1. Illustration of a nadir-aligned charged two-craft formation.

Finally, the effects of considering finite bodies and the effective radius are demonstrated by revising the nadir-aligned charge feedback control study by Natarajan and Schaub.[8] This study uses a cylindrical body shape for one of the charged objects. Further, the prior Coulomb formation feedback control strategies utilize charge as the fundamental control variable.[19–23] This paper explores voltage control, instead of charge control, for a nominally nadir-aligned charged two-body system. Controlling the voltage is a more practical control variable as any charge emission device fundamentally controls the potential of a spacecraft, not directly charge. Reference 8 demonstrates that if both spheres are aligned in an orbit radial formation as illustrated in Figure 1, the overall formation is feedback stabilizable using only separation distance measurements. This paper investigates a modified feedback control strategy using voltages as the fundamental variable with the enhanced electrostatic force modeling.

SPHERE-SPHERE ELECTROSTATIC FORCE MODEL MODEL

Modeling of point charges uses the simple relation between voltage and charge:

$$V(q) = k_c \frac{q}{L} \tag{1}$$

where L is the separation distance, q is the point charge, and $k_c = 8.99 \cdot 10^9$ Nm^2/C^2 is the Coulomb constant. The force F between two charges q_1 and q_2 is:

$$F = -\nabla V(q_1) \cdot q_2 = k_c \frac{q_1 q_2}{L^2} \tag{2}$$

However, these equations only model point charge forces and not the inter-body electrostatic forces between general three-dimensional bodies. Specifically, when considering the case of finite bodies, any body's potential is dependent upon its own charge, as well as that of its neighbors. References 14 and 15 show that this alters Eq. (1) and changes it to:

$$V_i = k_c \frac{q_i}{r_i} + \sum_{j=1, j \neq i}^{n} k_c \frac{q_j}{L_j} \tag{3}$$

where n is the number of charged bodies. This is a linear equation and can be generalized to the matrix form:

$$\bar{V} = k_c [C_M]^{-1} \bar{q} \tag{4}$$

where $[C_M]^{-1}$ is the inverse of the position dependent capacitance matrix for the system, and assumes the following algebraic form:

$$[C_M]^{-1} = \begin{bmatrix} 1/R_1 & 1/L_{1,2} & \cdots & 1/L_{1,n} \\ 1/L_{2,1} & 1/R_2 & \cdots & \vdots \\ \vdots & \cdots & \ddots & \vdots \\ 1/L_{n,1} & \cdots & \cdots & 1/R_n \end{bmatrix} \tag{5}$$

where R_i are the spherical radii of the bodies and $L_{i,j}$ are the distances between each body. If only two craft are flying in formation, as is the main assumption in this paper, then Eq. (4) becomes:

$$\begin{bmatrix} V_1 \\ V_2 \end{bmatrix} = k_c \begin{bmatrix} 1/R_1 & 1/L_{1,2} \\ 1/L_{2,1} & 1/R_2 \end{bmatrix} \begin{bmatrix} q_1 \\ q_2 \end{bmatrix} \tag{6}$$

The notation is simplified slightly because $L_{1,2} = L_{2,1}$, which is represented from now on as $L = L_{1,2}$. Given Eq. (6), as well as the size and distance between two finite bodies, the voltages

V_i can be computed given the total charges q_i on each sphere. Or conversely, each sphere's charge can be determined if a voltage is known. This second case, having a predetermined voltage, is of particular interest because it is much easier to create a specific potential on an object than a charge. This paper assumes that the absolute voltages on both bodies are known and that the voltages are taken relative to an absolute (0V) reference at infinity. Eq. (4) therefore allows the absolute charges q_i on multiple three dimensional finite spheres to be computed based upon given potential V_i. These charges are now used to solve for the force between two bodies (Eq. (2)).

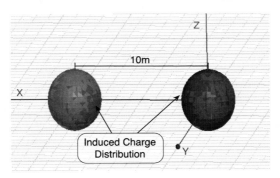

Figure 2. Sphere-sphere charge modeling.

To demonstrate the effectiveness of these analytic results, they are compared to the finite element program Maxwell3D, which solves the full Poisson's equations. As shown in Figure 2, two spheres of equal radius (2 meters) are placed at varying distances L apart. The sphere at the origin is given a fixed potential of 25kV, while the variable-distance sphere is given a -25kV fixed potential. Maxwell3D computes the center-to-center forces for each separation distance considered. The results are next compared to the analytic solution using Eq. (6) and Eq. (2).

Figure 3 demonstrates how the point charge model for the force in Eq. (2) relates to the combined capacitance model that solves for charges using Eq. (6). Once the coupled effects are taken into account, the force noticeably increases for smaller separation distances. The induced effects add onto the coupled charge force model at close distances (within about 2 - 3 craft radii). One point of interest is that the force in between the spheres is higher than originally expected with the point charge model. Therefore, when coupled capacitance is accounted for, higher forces (and possibly more control authority) occurs for a given absolute voltage.

Using the sphere-sphere model, Figure 3 shows both induced and coupled capacitance force effects of 3D shapes. Induced force effects are caused by the fact that some parts of the 3D shapes are closer than others. This makes charge concentrate on the surfaces nearest each other (Figure 2). The charge movement makes the effective separation distance smaller than the center-to-center distance used in the classical point charge equation, thus providing an increased force in relation to that of Eq. (2). The analytical sphere-sphere force model presented here uses a method developed by Soules in Reference 12 to estimate the induced effects between two spheres. When the induced behavior is taken into account, the coupled capacitance model very closely models the high-fidelity numerical results. Figure 3 demonstrates that at distances less than 3 - 4 craft radii, the coupled capacitance and induced force models are necessary to model sphere-sphere interaction. Beyond that distance, the coupled capacitance model provides a very good fit to the numerical results.

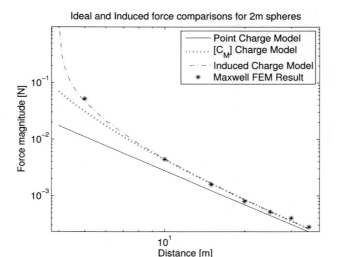

Figure 3. Ideal and Induced force comparisons for 2 m spheres.

1ST ORDER EFFECTIVE RADIUS METHOD

Algorithm Description

While the sphere-sphere electrostatic interaction is useful for demonstration purposes, it does not closely relate to the geometry of actually deployed spacecraft. Therefore, it is of interest to study generic 3D shapes and their electrostatic interaction with a spherical vehicle. It is beyond the scope of this paper to consider interactions between multiple 3D shapes. However, while non-spherical shapes are more realistic, there are no analytic solutions for describing how spherical objects will interact with another charged object. While analytical solutions for non-spherical shapes might be possible to find, they are extremely difficult to develop. Finite element codes can also be used, however, these can be computationally intensive and they do not provide a generalized perspective on the system's electrostatic force behavior.

In an effort to make complex three dimensional shapes easier to analyze, a method is developed to find a body's effective spherical radius. A complex shape is approximately modeled as a a a finite sphere by fitting its electrostatic Coulomb force characteristics to the spherical model of Eq. (4). Considering, again, the charged two-body system, Eq. (6) is used.

Figure 4 demonstrates the problem set-up for this method called the 1st-Order Effective Sphere Method. A sphere and a cylinder are placed within a small number of craft dimensions of each other. The voltages on both bodies are known and held fixed, and the spherical body's radius R_1 is known. The center-to-center force F between the two objects is computed using a finite element numerical solver, such as Maxwell3D. Knowledge of all of these parameters, including the separation distance between the two bodies, allows for the cylinder's effective sphere to be calculated using the following procedure. To calculate the effective radius R_2 of the cylinder, the three unknown parameters of the system (q_1, q_2, R_2) must be solved for simulateneously. To find

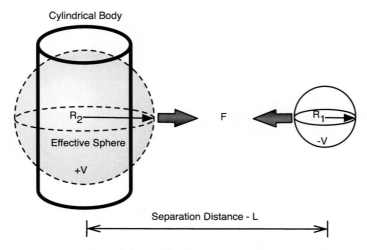

Figure 4. Example of a cylinder modeled as an effective sphere.

expressions for q_1 and q_2, Eq. (6) is separated into two equations.

$$V_1 = k_c \left(\frac{q_1}{R_1} + \frac{q_2}{L} \right) \tag{7}$$

$$V_2 = k_c \left(\frac{q_1}{L} + \frac{q_2}{R_2} \right) \tag{8}$$

Because the force F is known from the finite element solution at a particular configuration, q_2 is solved from Eq. (2) as a function of q_1:

$$q_2 = \frac{FL^2}{k_c q_1} \tag{9}$$

There are now three equations with three unknowns: q_1, q_2, R_2. Substituting Eq. (9) into Eq. (7) yields the following quadratic function of q_1:

$$0 = \frac{q_1^2}{R_1} - \frac{V_1}{k_c} q_1 + \frac{FL}{k_c} \tag{10}$$

This quadratic equation is solved for q_1. Because q_1 is now known, q_2 is solved for using Eq. (7). All parameters are now known in Eq. (8) except for the effective radius, R_2. R_2 can be easily solved for to obtain the second body's effective spherical radius:

$$R_2 = q_2 \left(\frac{V_2}{k_c} - \frac{q_1}{L} \right)^{-1} \tag{11}$$

Note that the computed effective radius is only accurate for the given geometry used in the finite element numerical solution. If the cylinder in Figure 4 is rotated relative to the sphere, different forces will be experienced, resulting in a different effective radius. Thus, this method of evaluating a 1st-order effective radius must be repeated if another relative orientation of general shape and sphere are considered. This relative orientation dependent effective radius behavior is investigated further in the following sections.

To gain some insight into the behavior of Eq. (10), q_1 is solved for using the quadratic equation:

$$q_1 = \frac{V_1 R_1}{2k_c} \pm R_1 \sqrt{\frac{1}{4}\frac{V_1}{k_c}^2 - 4\frac{FL}{R_1 k_c}} \tag{12}$$

As a simple check of this method, assume the force F is zero. Using the positive root, then the expression for q_1 simplifies to the expected single sphere voltage and charge relationship:

$$q_1 = \frac{V_1 R_1}{k_c} \tag{13}$$

For an attractive case, $F < 0$, which increases the size of q_1. For a repulsive case , $F > 0$, which decreases the size of q_1, as expected.

Because the expression for q_1 is a quadratic expression, there are two possible solutions. To understand whether the positive or negative solution for q_1 should be used, R_2 is solved for another way. R_2 can be solved for by taking Eq. (6), solving for both charges, and then plugging them into Eq. (2), which provides a quadratic equation for R_2. If this is done and the equations are solved using the physical constraints for an attractive system (i.e. $R_1 > 0$, $L > 0$, $V_1 = -V_2$ thus $F < 0$) a simplified equation for R_2 is found. This expression produces two roots, one negative and one positive. This guarantees that there will always be one physically possible solution for this method ($R_2 > 0$) and that there are no non-unique solutions.

When the effective radius is computed, a unique radius is computed for each force and separation distance tested. By evaluating the effective radius $R_{2,i}$ for a set of N separations L_i, the final 1st-order effective radius R_2 is evaluated as the mean of all evaluated radii.

$$R_2 = \frac{1}{N}\sum_{i=1}^{N} R_{2,i} \tag{14}$$

Next, appropriate ranges of separation distance for the numerical electrostatic force evaluation are considered. Due to induced charge effects and resulting larger electrostatic forces between three-dimensional bodies, short separation distances can produce effective radii that are larger than the general force trend that occurs at larger distances. Because the above effective radius evaluation for a given set of potentials and separation distance does not include the induced charge effect, the numerical finite element electrostatic force evaluations should consider separation distance larger than 3-4 craft radii. This yields an good effective sphere fit for the general shape. Further, the induced effects can be added to the effective sphere to increase the force modeling accuracy for small separation distances.

Sphere-Sphere Algorithm Verification

To demonstrate the accuracy of the 1st-order effective radius method, a sphere-sphere system (Figure 2) is considered with each sphere's radius being 2 meters. The effective radius of sphere 2 is then calculated assuming its, radius R_2, is unknown. Both spheres are given fixed equal magnitude and opposite sign potentials of $\pm$ 25kV.

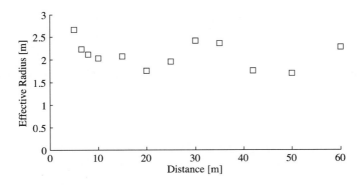

Figure 5. Effective radii calculated at different distances between two 2m spheres.

The effective radii $R_{2,i}$, calculated using Eq. (11) for each separation distance L_i, are shown in Figure 5. Induced effects on the effective radius are seen before 10m. Beyond 20m the effective radii calculations are increasingly noisy. This is caused by Maxwell3D attempting to evaluate vanishingly small electrostatic forces, resulting in relatively noisy force evaluations. Assuming this noise is random and Gaussian, its average value should equal the true effective radius. However, consider that the induced effects are not random. The effective radii computed where the induced effects are significant should be ignored. The effective radii for separation distances beyond 10m are run through a least squares fit algorithm for a zero slope line. This produces an effective radius of 2.04m, which is very close to the actual 2m sphere modeled in Maxwell3D. If all effective radii are considered including separation distances where the induced charge distribution is significant, then an increased average radius of 2.11m is computed, as expected. This shows that ignoring the effective radius data at the distances where induced force effects are significant produces more accurate effective radii, and therefore force results. In Figure 6 the relative force error is compared between the true 2m-2m sphere system, Maxwell3D's FEM results, and the two calculated effective radii. The 2.04m estimate yields only about 2 percent error while the 2.11m radii produces about 6 percent error. Again, this demonstrates that Maxwell3D produces slightly noisy force data at separation distances beyond 20m but that the average of the effective radii produced by this data gives reasonably good estimates for the behavior of the 3D shape.

Relative Orientation Dependence

Computing the effective radius of a known sphere has helped illustrate the numerical accuracy of this method, as well as justification for ignoring induced effective radii results. This knowledge is next applied to a cylinder with an unknown effective electrostatic radius. With the simple sphere-sphere scenario, the relative orientation of the two objects did not matter. With general shapes this is not true, as discussed earlier.

Considering a more complex shape, a cylinder 3 meters in radius and 12 meters in height is modeled as object 2. The sphere 1 has a radius of two meters and the vehicles are charged to $\pm$ 25kV. If the sphere moves or the cylinder rotates, the force behavior between the two bodies changes and a different effective radius R_2 must be computed. If the sphere changes position and is no longer as shown in Figure 4, but instead at an off-axis position relative to the cylinder, the

954

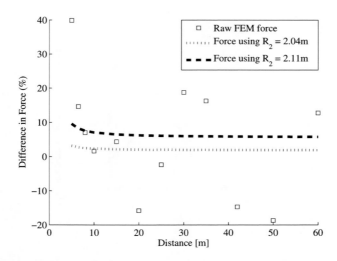

Figure 6. Relative force error between true (R_2 = 2m) and other force estimates.

charges and forces change between the two objects, graphically shown in Figure 7. As the sphere rotates about the cylinder, the effective radii is postulated to change in an elliptical pattern. To numerically illustrate this pattern, the reference sphere is placed around the cylinder at multiple points between the $\hat{c}_1$ axis to the $\hat{c}_3$ axis. Multiple separation distances between the center of the sphere and cylinder are used to calculate the effective radius for a given angle ϕ_2. An individual effective radius is calculated for each angle about the cylinder by the averaging process described above.

Figure 8 illustrates the resulting effective radii for a range of relative orientations. For the sphere-cylinder case considered, the effective radius varies as an ellipse where the major ellipse axis is the length of the long, $R_{2,3}$ axis effective radius, and the minor ellipse axis is the length of the $R_{2,1}$ effective radius. Because the numerically evaluated effective radii of a cylinder-sphere scenario appear to vary in a predictable manner, only the effective radii of a cylinder's radial and axial axes need to be determined to be able to model the electrostatic force behavior of the cylinder in the neighborhood of sphere. Due to the symmetry of the cylinder, the elliptical behavior can be expanded to an ellipsoid shape with the minor and intermediate principal axes of the ellipsoid being the same length ($R_{2,1}$). If the ellipsoid is parameterized into a local 'ellipsoid' frame shown in Figure 7, any point on the effective radius ellipsoid surface is expressed by the equations:

$$x = R_{2,1} \cos \phi_2 \cos \phi_1 \tag{15a}$$

$$y = R_{2,2} \cos \phi_2 \sin \phi_1 \tag{15b}$$

$$z = R_{2,3} \sin \phi_2 \tag{15c}$$

where the effective radius acting between the sphere and cylinder is:

$$R_2 = R_{\text{eff}} = \sqrt{x^2 + y^2 + z^2} \tag{16}$$

If the cylinder is rotating or tumbling both the orbit frame angles (θ, ψ from Figure 1) and the attitude of the cylinder need to be accounted for in Eq. (15a). Linearizing Eq. (16) for small angles

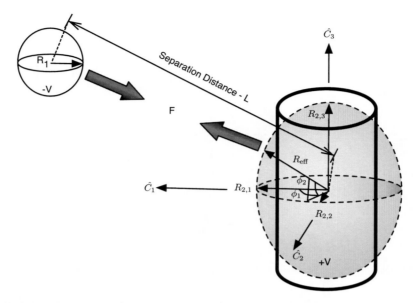

Figure 7. Ellipsoidal effective radius behavior as a sphere rotates about a cylinder.

about the principle axes of the ellipsoid, the effective radius simply becomes the radius of the given axis, i.e. $R_2 = R_{2,1} = R_{\text{eff}}$ if linearized about $\phi_1 = \phi_2 = 0$. This fact makes formation dynamics simpler if constant attitudes are held between the cylinder and sphere. Elliptical distributions of the effective radius may not occur for every 3D body geometry and should be verified for each unique geometry.

Effective Radius Robustness to Voltage Variations

The above discussion consideres many of the variables that affect the value of the effective radius. For example, separation distance, for long enough distances, provides constant effective radii. The physical orientation between two bodies changes the effective radius. However, for a cylinder-sphere scenario the radius changes in a predictable, ellipsoidal trend. Finally, the effects of changes in voltage are considered. Eq. (10) depends upon the voltage between the two craft but, it is uncertain whether changes in voltage will cause the effective radius to change. Thus, a sweep across voltages is performed holding the cylinder and sphere in the orientation seen in Figure 4. Figure 9 is obtained by changing the voltage on both bodies (equal and opposite) and then calculating the effective radius. Figure 9 numerically demonstrates that, over the ranges of voltages considered, the effective radius changes very little. The worst deviation is at 10kV and 3.8kV where the effective radius is 4.52m instead of 4.54m. Thus, the 1st-order effective sphere concept can provide realistic line-of-sight electrostatic force predictions for general shapes without having to evaluate effective radii for different voltage ranges. This makes this concept very practical to use this simplified electrostatic force instead of finite elements to compute faster than real-time control simulations.

956

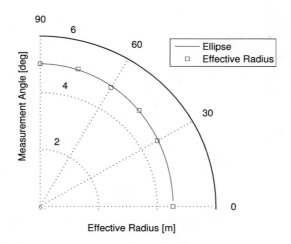

Figure 8. Polar plot for elliptical effective radius made from R_{2x} = 4.54 m and R_{2z} = 5.02 m.

0TH ORDER EFFECTIVE RADIUS METHOD

If the earlier effective radius method is considered a first-order approximation to the true electrostatic behavior of a multi-body system, then this next section discusses a simplified and less accurate 0th order approximation. The 1st-order method requires extensive and time consuming finite element solutions to be evaluated to generate the effective radius. For a cruder, but much faster, approximation of the effective radius, the outer spacecraft surface area A is simply mapped onto a spherical shape.

$$R_{2_0} = \sqrt{\frac{A}{4\pi}} \tag{17}$$

The main benefits of this method is the speed at which an effective radius can be evaluated for a general shape. However, note that this 0th-order method cannot account for relative orientation differences. Of interest is how much accuracy is sacrificed for the faster setup. Table 1 shows three different cylinder sizes that were modeled in Maxwell3D and then used with the effective radius method. This table compares electrostatic force modeling accuracy of the 1st-order method to that of the 0th-order method. Most of the force modeling difference are only a few percentage for the three cylinders considered. The largest difference is found along the cylinder symmetry axis and can reach up to 11%. This simplified model is adequate for many approximate electrostatic force evaluation where precision relative motion predictions are not required.

NUMERICAL EFFECTIVE SPHERE ACCURACY STUDY

Cylindrical-Sphere Model

To demonstrate the results from the use of the effective radius method in Eq. (11), a cylinder and spherical system is considered. A cylinder is used because it is a common space object shape. It

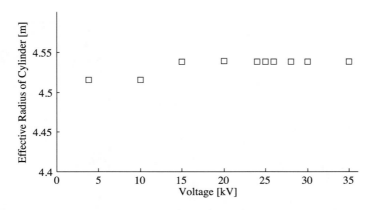

Figure 9. Effective radius for varying voltages for a cylinder and sphere along the X axis.

Table 1. Surface Area's of several cylinders and their zeroth order effective radius approximation.

Object	R [m]	H [m]	0th order R [m]	1st order R 'x' and 'y' [m]	1st order R 'z' [m]	Percent diff X, Y	Percent diff Z
Dual Spin S/C	1.85	6.8	2.83	2.78	2.62	1.77	7.42
Delta IV rocket body	2	10	3.46	3.57	3.82	3.18	10.40
Large rocket body	3	12	4.74	4.54	5.02	4.22	5.91

could be representative of a rocket body or dual-spin spacecraft, both of which can be found often near the GEO belt. Similar to the previous analysis the cylinder's dimensions are 3 meters in radius and 12 meters in height. The sphere has a radius of two meters. The cylinder has a voltage of positive 25kV and the sphere has a -25kV potential. Using Maxwell3D to find the center-to-center forces between the cylinder and sphere, the effective radius of the sphere is solved for using Eq. (9) through Eq. (11).

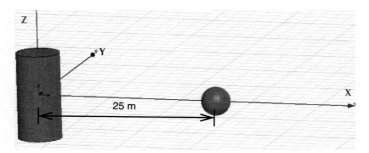

Figure 10. Sphere and cylinder geometry set-up.

Figure 11 shows the Maxwell3D results (points), and the force calculated using the effective radii method (lines). Forces created in both the X and Z axes are shown. Because the cylinder has two unique geometries as seen by the sphere, the effective radii calculated are different, but vary by

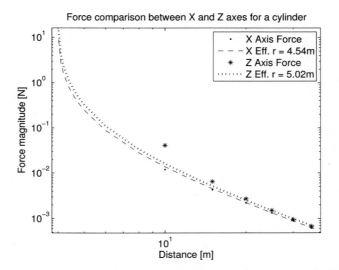

Figure 11. Force comparison between X and Z axes for a cylinder.

only about 9.5 percent. The effective sphere model does match the numerical results very well for separation distances of about 15 - 20 meters and beyond, for both axes. This demonstrates that the effective sphere method can indeed predict the behavior of a non-spherical body when separation distances are on the order of 3 - 4 craft radii away. Note that the forces in Figure 11 are plotted in a log-log scale. This was done to emphasize that the force behavior becomes nearly linear at distances beyond induced effects. This linear trend should therefore contain the dominant information about the system, including the effective radius of the cylinder. Indeed the logarithm of Eq. (2) becomes:

$$\log(F) = \log(k_c) + \log(q_1) + \log(q_2) - 2\log(L) \tag{18}$$

The effective radius method does not predict the force behavior accurately at ranges closer than 3 − 4 craft radii, where induced effects begin to dominate. Figure 11 demonstrates the model's ability to fit an effective radius to the cylinder for two distinct orientations. The effective radii shown in Figure 11 are simply the two extrema for the body and the effective radii vary as an ellipse as shown in Figure 9. While the model for the induced effects between two spheres has been included in the force computation, this model becomes less accurate for a non-spherical body primarily because the geometry of the cylinder at close separation distances, becomes much more important. Further, it can be seen in Figure 11 that the Z axis behavior begins to vary from the effective radius model much more significantly than the X axis. This is partially caused by the fact that the current effective radius model only accounts for center-to-center separation distances. However, at center-to-center separation of 10 meters, the cylinder and sphere are actually only physically separated by 2 meters due to the cylinder having a height of 6 meters above its center, and the sphere having a radius of 2 meters. Thus the two objects are physically much closer than the effective radius model computes. Future work with effective radii might attempt to account for these differences between the physical system and the approximated system. Still, beyond 3–4 craft radii, the effective radius model matches the numerical results closely.

959

Table 2. Generic satellite body dimensions.

Component	X (or radius) [m]	Y (or height) [m]	Z [m]
Body	1.8	1.7	1.75
Dishes (x2)	.85	.3	0
Solar Panels (x2)	1.75	5.4	n/a

Generic Satellite - Sphere Model

Another, more complex shape is briefly considered. Figure 12 shows a generic satellite bus with a 2 meter sphere. The satellite's dimensions are roughly 14.3 meters from solar panel tip to tip, 6 meters in height between the dishes, and 1.7 meters in width.

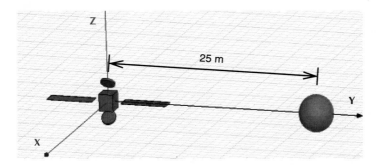

Figure 12. Generic satellite bus with a sphere.

This model represents a significantly more complex shape. Table 2 shows the dimensions used for the satellite body, not including separations between the body, dishes, and panels. Figure 13 demonstrates forces computed by the finite element and the effective radius methods. At close distances, the effective radius method poorly matches FEM results however, the models both closely match at and beyond 15 meters, just like the cylinder-sphere example in Figure 11. This demonstrates the versatility and effectiveness of the effective radius method. Even with complex geometry, the effective radius method models the force behavior between the satellite and the sphere allowing for easier force modeling behavior between complex geometries.

For a cylinder the effective radii between X and Z axes (Figure 11) vary by only about 9.5 percent. Likewise, the difference in the effective radii between the satellite's three axes (Figure 13) is only 22 percent between the Y and Z axes, and 2 percent between the X and Y axes. This shows that while geometry does change the effective radius of a body, its effects are not large as might be suspected.

Table 3 shows a 1st order versus 0th order radius calculations for the generic satellite. Along the X and Z axes, the 1st order and the 0th order methods match closely. However the Y axis, or the solar panel axis, produces noticeably different effective radii. This demonstrates that while the 0th order method can be used for rough approximation of the force behavior, for more extreme geometry, such as long extended panels, the method is not nearly as accurate as the 1st order effective radius method presented above.

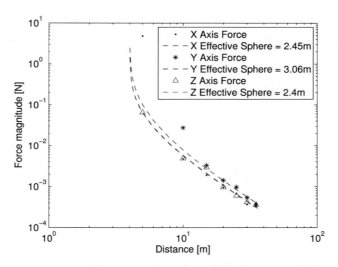

Figure 13. Force between satellite and sphere, in all three axes.

Table 3. Surface area's of a generic satellite shape and its 0th order effective radii for all three axes.

Object	0th order R [m]	1st order R 'x' [m]	1st order R 'z' [m]	1st order R 'y' [m]	Percent diff X	Percent diff Z	Percent diff Y
Generic S/C	2.33	2.40	2.45	3.06	2.91	4.90	23.86

VOLTAGE CONTROL OF A CYLINDRICAL AND SPHERICAL SPACECRAFT IN ORBIT

Most research thus far into Coulomb formation flying satellites has used a body's charge as the control parameter. However, in practice, craft potential will likely be the control parameter. Eq. (4) can be used to transfer charge control strategies to voltage control. If a two craft system is considered, Natarajan and Schaub have shown that two craft aligned in an orbit radial direction are in a stable configuration (Figure 1). They also demonstrated that the motion in the radial (L), and rotation about the in-track vector (ψ) were coupled and could be stabilized. Following the development in Reference 8, the Hill-frame dynamics are rotated into a spherical frame, which allow for some decoupling of the equations of motion. The linearized differential equation for the separation distance, in the spherical frame (L, ψ, θ) is given as:

$$\ddot{L} = \left(2\Omega\dot{\psi} + 3\Omega^2\right) L + (k_c/m_1) Q \left(1/L^2\right) [(m_1 + m_2)/m_2] \tag{19}$$

Here, $Q = q_1 q_2$ is the charge product of the two craft and Ω is the orbit mean motion. Eq. (19) developed by Reference 8 assumes two point charges in formation however this equation remains true for a cylinder and sphere system when the effective radius method is used. The fact that point charge developments can still be used by the effective sphere model, is one of the primary advantages of the effective sphere model. This is justified by the fact that the charge Q accounts for the finite size of the objects when the coupled capacitance is included in the calculation of the charge product. Using Eq. (6), the position dependent capacitance matrix can be used to get solutions for each body's net charge as a function of voltage. These charges can then be multiplied together to make $Q = f(V)$. Substituting the new charge product into Eq. (19) and linearizing the equation for small changes in separation distances and voltages, Eq. (19) becomes:

$$\delta \ddot{L} = 2L_{\text{ref}}\Omega\dot{\psi} + \left(3\Omega^2 + k_1\right)\delta L + k_2\delta V \tag{20}$$

where

$$k_1 = \frac{2R_2R_1(m_1 + m_2)(R_2^2R_1 + L_{\text{ref}}^2(2L_{\text{ref}} + 3R_1) + R_2(3L_{\text{ref}}^2 + 6L_{\text{ref}}R_1 + R_1^2))V_{\text{ref}}^2}{k_c m_1 m_2 (L_{\text{ref}}^2 - R_2R_1)^2} \tag{21}$$

and

$$k_2 = -\frac{2R_2R_1(R_2 + L_{\text{ref}})(m_1 + m_2)(L_{\text{ref}} + R_1)V_{\text{ref}}}{k_c m_1 m_2 (L_{\text{ref}}^2 - R_2R_1)^2} \tag{22}$$

Note that V_{ref} is the nominal reference voltage for the system and L_{ref} is the reference separation distance, both values are constants. Reference 8 shows that the reference charge (for a stable orientation for a given L_{ref}) is:

$$Q_{\text{ref}} = q_1 q_2 = -\frac{3\Omega^2 L_{\text{ref}}^3 m_1 m_2}{k_c(m_1 + m_2)} \tag{23}$$

The reference voltage can then be computed using Eq. (6) assuming the charges are $\pm\sqrt{|Q_{\text{ref}}|}$, respectively. This means that both Eq. (21) and Eq. (22) are constant values if the relative motion between both bodies is small and aligned along a principal axis of the cylinder/ellipsoid of Figure 7. Note that R_2 is the effective radius found from the ellipsoidal distribution from Figure 7 and Eq. (16). If the cylinder were tumbling, the sphere were rotating around the cylinder, or an off principle-axis orientation were being held, R_2 would not be constant and k_1 and k_2 would not be constant, significantly increasing the complexity of Eq. (20).

Making a feedback control law similar to the control developed by Reference 8, the voltage is given as:

$$\delta V = 1/k_2 \left(-C_1\delta L - C_2\delta\dot{L}\right) \tag{24}$$

This control yields the following linearized closed-loop separation distance dynamics:

$$\delta \ddot{L} = 2L_{\text{ref}}\Omega\dot{\psi} + \left(3\Omega^2 + k_1 - C_1\right)\delta L - C_2\delta\dot{L} \tag{25}$$

Here the positive C_1 and C_2 parameters are control gains and both proportional and derivative feedback are given to ensure asymptotic stability. The linearized equations of motion for the in-track and cross-track rotations are unchanged in Reference 8's development and are given for ease of reference:

$$\ddot{\psi} = -\left(2/L_{\text{ref}}\right)\delta L - 3\psi \tag{26}$$

$$\ddot{\theta} = -4\theta \tag{27}$$

962

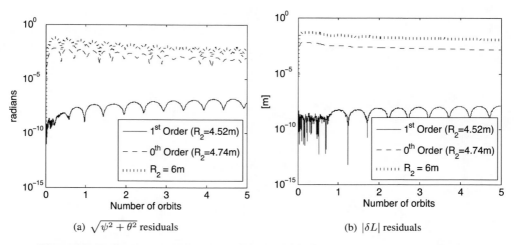

(a) $\sqrt{\psi^2 + \theta^2}$ residuals

(b) $|\delta L|$ residuals

Figure 14. Residual motions relative to a true effective sphere of $R_2 = 4.524$m at 25m separation distance.

Choosing gains C_1 and C_2 as outlined in Reference 8 results in the values:

$$C_1 = 25\Omega^2$$
$$C_2 = 9.12\Omega$$

Integrating the full nonlinear inertial equations of motion that account for coupled position dependent capacitance and a voltage based control, the behavior of the two craft system can be obtained. Here $L_{\text{ref}} = 25$m, $V_{\text{ref}} = 3750$V, $R_1 = 2$m. A range of effective radii are considered, ranging from $R_2 = 4.74$m for the 0th order method as computed in Table 1, $R_2 = 4.52$m for the 1st order method as shown in Figure 9 and $R_2 = 6$m estimating the effective radius as half the height of the cylinder. The initial separation deviation and attitude are $\delta L = .5$m, $\psi = \theta = 0.1$ rad and $\delta \dot{L} = \dot{\psi} = \dot{\theta} = 0$. Note that setting V_{ref} to 3750V is the proper reference voltage for an effective radius of 4.52m and that the other estimates will not satisfy the necessary reference charge to settle to a zero δL offset. Figure 15 demonstrates the motion of the craft from a relative reference separation distance (L_{ref}) of 25 meters and that voltage control does indeed stabilize the same configuration as the charge based control. However, small errors can be seen for the 0th order method and larger errors on the order of 2.5m for δL can be seen for the $R_2 = 6$m effective radius (overestimate).

Note that the control stabilizes the separation distance and the in-track rotation, but not the cross-track rotation. When observing the linearized analysis in Eq. (26) and Eq. (27) this behavior is apparent considering that δL occurs in Eq. (26) but not in Eq. (27), rendering the θ response that of a simply a harmonic oscillator. The continuing oscillation of ψ and δL after about 3 orbits is due to differential gravity that the linearized control does not effectively counter.

Figure 15 demonstrates how well each effective radius produces the proper forces to achieve the true inertial dynamics at 25m separation. The 'truth' model was produced by calculating the effective radius for the cylinder-sphere system at 25m separation. This effective radius ($R_{2\,\text{true}} = 4.524$m) exactly matches the steady state force at $L_{\text{ref}} = 25$m and therefore it produces the true dynamic response at 25m. Figure 14 gives a better example of how close the dynamics behave

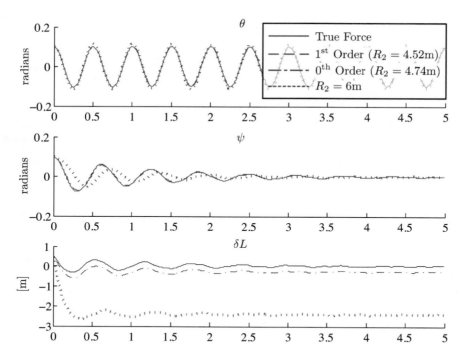

Figure 15. Voltage control craft response for different effective radii estimates.

using the approximated forces. Figure 14(a) shows the residuals for the formation orientation error measure $\sqrt{\psi^2 + \theta^2}$ and Figure 14(b) illustrates the $|\delta L|$ errors, compared to the truth simulation. This shows that basing the effective radius off of geometry dimensions alone produce largely varying force estimates. The 0th-order method produces reasonably accurate dynamics for high level analysis. Finally, the computation of the effective radii using the 1st-order method can produce force behavior that varies minimally compared to the full equations of motion demonstrating how powerful this method can be.

CONCLUSION

Prior research has modeled the Coulomb spacecraft as points or isolated spheres. This paper models complex geometries using finite spheres by calculating their effective radii through each body's force interaction with a sphere of known radius. This analysis, combined with a coupled position dependent capacitance matrix, allows for force behavior between a sphere and a 3D body to be modeled as two spheres. While the effective radius method requires *a priori* knowledge of the force behavior (in this case, through finite element modeling), the method accurately models the force interactions between two bodies making all successive calculations simpler. The electrostatic torques are not modeled with this approach. A simplified 0th-order effective sphere evaluation only uses the outer surface area to compute a radius, yielding difference ranging from 5-30% depending on the object shape and relative orientation. For a 3D body shaped like a cylinder, the effective radius changes over the body orientation in an elliptical manner. A voltage-based control illustrate the use of effective radii in enhanced control simulations.

REFERENCES

[1] J. H. Cover, W. Knauer, and H. A. Maurer, "Lightweight Reflecting Structures Utilizing Electrostatic Inflation," US Patent 3,546,706, October 1966.

[2] H. Schaub, G. G. Parker, and L. B. King, "Challenges and Prospect of Coulomb Formations," *Journal of the Astronautical Sciences*, Vol. 52, Jan.–June 2004, pp. 169–193.

[3] L. B. King, G. G. Parker, S. Deshmukh, and J.-H. Chong, "Study of Interspacecraft Coulomb Forces and Implications for Formation Flying," *AIAA Journal of Propulsion and Power*, Vol. 19, May–June 2003, pp. 497–505.

[4] L. Pettazzi, H. Krüger, S. Theil, and D. Izzo, "Electrostatic Forces for Satellite Swarm Navigation and Reconfiguration," *2nd ACT Workshop on Innovative Concepts*, ESTEC, 2008.

[5] L. B. King, G. G. Parker, S. Deshmukh, and J.-H. Chong, "Spacecraft Formation-Flying using Inter-Vehicle Coulomb Forces," tech. rep., NASA/NIAC, January 2002. http://www.niac.usra.edu.

[6] A. C. Tribble, *The Space Environment - Implications for Spacecraft Design*. Princton University Press, revised and expanded ed., 2003.

[7] A. Natarajan and H. Schaub, "Orbit-Nadir Aligned Coulomb Tether Reconfiguration Analysis," *Journal of the Astronautical Sciences*, Vol. 56, Oct. – Dec. 2008, pp. 573–592.

[8] A. Natarajan and H. Schaub, "Linear Dynamics and Stability Analysis of a Coulomb Tether Formation," *AIAA Journal of Guidance, Control, and Dynamics*, Vol. 29, July–Aug. 2006, pp. 831–839.

[9] S. Wang and H. Schaub, "Electrostatic Spacecraft Collision Avoidance Using Piece-Wise Constant Charges," *AIAA Journal of Guidance, Control, and Dynamics*, Vol. 33, Mar.–Apr. 2010, pp. 510–520, DOI:10.2514/1.44397.

[10] J. Berryman and H. Schaub, "Analytical Charge Analysis for 2- and 3-Craft Coulomb Formations," *AIAA Journal of Guidance, Control, and Dynamics*, Vol. 30, Nov.–Dec. 2007, pp. 1701–1710.

[11] S. Wang and H. Schaub, "Nonlinear Coulomb Feedback Control of a Spinning Two Spacecraft Virtual Structure," *Advances in Astronautical Sciences*, Vol. 135, American Astronautical Society, 2009, pp. 1477–1496. Paper AAS 09–393.

[12] J. A. Soules, "Precise Calculation of the Electrostatic Force Between Charged Spheres Including Induction Effects," *American Journal of Physics*, Vol. 58, 1990, pp. 1195–1199.

[13] C. R. Seubert and H. Schaub, "Electrostatic Force Model for Terrestrial Experiments on the Coulomb Testbed," *61st International Astronautical Congress*, Prague, CZ, International Astronautical Federation, Sept. 2010. Paper IAC-10.C1.1.9.

[14] W. R. Smythe, *Static and Dynamic Electricity*. McGraw–Hill, 3rd ed., 1968.

[15] J. Sliško and R. A. Brito-Orta, "On approximate formulas for the electrostatic force between two conducting spheres," *American Journal of Physics*, Vol. 66, No. 4, 1998, pp. 352–355.

[16] S. Wang and H. Schaub, "Switched Lyapunov Function Based Coulomb Control of a Triangular 3-Vehicle Cluster," *Advances in Astronautical Sciences*, Vol. 135, American Astronautical Society, 2009, pp. 1477–1496. Paper AAS 09–391.

[17] H. Schaub, "Stabilization of Satellite Motion Relative to a Coulomb Spacecraft Formation," *AIAA Journal of Guidance, Control, and Dynamics*, Vol. 28, Nov.–Dec. 2005, pp. 1231–1239.

[18] A. Natarajan and H. Schaub, "Hybrid Control of Orbit Normal and Along-Track Two-Craft Coulomb Tethers," *Aerospace Science and Technology*, Vol. 13, June–July 2009, pp. 183–191.

[19] U. Yamamoto and H. Yamakawa, "Two-Craft Coulomb-Force Formation Dynamics and Stability Analysis with Debye Length Characteristics," *AIAA/AAS Astrodynamics Specialist Conference and Exhibit*, Honolulu, Hawaii, Aug. 18–21 2008. Paper No. AIAA 2008-7361.

[20] R. Inampudi and H. Schaub, "Two-Craft Coulomb Formation Relative Equilibria about Circular Orbits and Libration Points," *AAS/AIAA Spaceflight Mechanics Meeting*, San Diego, CA, Feb. 14–18 2010. Paper AAS 10–163.

[21] H. Schaub and I. I. Hussein, "Stability and Reconfiguration Analysis of a Circulary Spinning 2-Craft Coulomb Tether," *IEEE Transactions on Aerospace and Electronic Systems*, Vol. 46, October 2010, pp. 1675–1686, doi:10.1109/AERO.2007.352670.

[22] I. I. Hussein and H. Schaub, "Stability and Control of Relative Equilibria for the Three-Spacecraft Coulomb Tether Problem," *Acta Astronautica*, Vol. 65, No. 5–6, 2009, pp. 738–754, doi:10.1016/j.actaastro.2009.03.035.

[23] C. M. Saaj, V. J. Lappas, D. J. Richie, H. Schaub, and D. Izzo, "Hybrid Propulsion System for Spacecraft Swarm Aggregation using Coulomb Force," *Journal of British Interplanetary Society*, July 2007.

AAS 11-466

RELATIVE MOTION CONTROL FOR TWO-SPACECRAFT ELECTROSTATIC ORBIT CORRECTIONS

Erik A. Hogan[*] and Hanspeter Schaub[†]

The charged relative motion dynamics and control of a two-craft system is investigated if one vehicle is performing a low-thrust orbit correction using inertial thrusters. The nominal motion is an along-track configuration where active electrostatic charge control is maintaining an attractive force between the two vehicles. In this study the charging is held fixed, and the inertial thruster of the tugging vehicle is controlled to stabilized the relative motion to a nominal fixed separation distance. Using a candidate Lyapunov function, the relative orbit control law of the tugging vehicle with respect to the passive vehicle is shown to be asymptotically stable. Analysis of the control system gains is performed in order to achieve a desired settling time and damping ratio. The effects of uncertainties in the vehicle charges are also examined. Using numerical simulation, the performance of the proposed control system is investigated for a formation in GEO. Results obtained from integration of the relative equations of motion are compared to full inertial simulations.

INTRODUCTION

Electrostatic force actuation for spacecraft formation control is a concept that is gaining significant attention in the field of formation flying.[1,2] In these Coulomb formations, active charge control is applied to generate specified inter-craft electrostatic forces that are used to manipulate the relative positions of the nodes within the formation.[3] In the presence of perturbations, such as differential gravity, these forces may be used to maintain coherence of multiple craft in close proximity.[4] Electrostatic forces have also been proposed as a method to inflate a tethered structure where individual nodes of a formation are connected by physical tethers such as cables.[5,6]

The prior work on charged relative motion dynamics of clusters of spacecraft only considers the relative motion control of a non-perturbed system.[4,7,8] The active charge control is expected to be extremely fuel efficient (I_{sp} values as high as $10^9 - 10^{12}$ seconds) and require small, Watt levels of electrical power to operate.[9] These concepts assume separation distances on the order of dozens of meters. However, an unexplored research area is how do such Coulomb spacecraft clusters perform orbit corrections. In particular, if only a sub-set of cluster elements perform inertial thrusting, then the passive cluster elements must be tugged along with the electrostatic forces. Of interest is how can the charged relative motion dynamics be stabilized, without resulting in collisions of the cluster members, while a low-thrust orbit correction is being engaged.

A related scenario is considered in in Reference 10. Here the use of electrostatic forces to tug a space debris object into a disposal orbit is investigated. Using thrusters operating on the milliNewton

---

[*]Graduate Student, Aerospace Engineering Sciences, University of Colorado at Boulder, Boulder, CO
[†]Associate Professor, H. Joseph Smead Fellow, Department of Aerospace Engineering Sciences, University of Colorado, 431 UCB, Colorado Center for Astrodynamics Research, Boulder, CO 80309-0431

level, the tug craft approaches and engages the debris object. Because the electrostatic forces do not require a physical tether to exist between tug and target, the debris object can be reorbited without requiring any physical contact. This manner of interaction is similar to the gravity tractor concept, which is suggested as a manner of modifying the trajectory of an asteroid to avoid collision with earth.[11] Once the electrostatic force is active between the tug and debris, the tug utilizes low-thrust to slowly pull the debris into a disposal orbit. Reference 10 considers the effort required to achieve a disposal orbit, and investigates how the debris orbital elements change with time under the influence of the tug. Reference 10 does not, however, consider the relative motion of the two craft during the reorbiting maneuver; nor does it propose a feedback control system for maintaing the tug and debris object in the necessary relative positions.

The current work presents the first discussion on feedback stabilizing the charged relative motion while one cluster element is performing a low-thrust orbit correction. The relative equations of motion between a tug (or chief) craft and a secondary craft (called a deputy) are developed, and a control algorithm is proposed to maintain a desired relative position using inertial thrusting on the chief only. The applications of the current study include electrostatic debris reorbiting applications, as well as maintaining an observation craft in close proximity to a main craft that can provide real time visual information. If the main craft needs to reorbit as part of its mission requirements, it may do so with the observer in tow. The following developments are made in a general way, so as to be applicable to any charged two-craft formation in orbit, whether reorbiting a debris object or maintaining an observer in close proximity. Due to the limitations of the plasma shielding of electrostatic charge, the application of the electrostatic tether reorbiting concept focuses onspacecraft in or near geosynchronous orbit.

The paper is structured as follows. First, the fundamentals of relative dynamics with respect to a slowly accelerating Hill frame are provided. The relative dynamics of the two craft in the rotating Hill frame are developed considering gravitational, electrostatic, and thruster effects. Next, a spherical coordinate frame is introduced and the equations of motion are developed in this spherical frame. The spherical frame is then used to develop a control law using Lyapunov stability analysis. Consideration of desired settling times and the nature of damping in the system response is used to select gains for the controller. After that, the effects of uncertainties in the craft charges on the control system response are investigated. Finally, numerical simulation is used to illustrate the performance of the controller in maintaining the desired relative position of chief and deputy.

RELATIVE ORBITAL DYNAMICS DURING ORBIT CHANGE MANEUVER

Hill Coordinate Frame

The Local-Vertical-Local-Horizontal (LVLH), often also referred to as the Hill coordinate frame, is briefly outlined in this section. A rectilinear Hill frame $\mathcal{H} : \{\hat{o}_r, \hat{o}_\theta, \hat{o}_h\}$ is attached to the tug (or chief) orbital position as illustrated in Figure 1. This rotating frame has it origin coincide with the tug center of mass, and the orientation is defined through

$$\hat{o}_r = \frac{r_T}{r_T}, \ \hat{o}_\theta = \hat{o}_h \times \hat{o}_r, \ \hat{o}_h = \frac{r_T \times \dot{r}_T}{|r_T \times \dot{r}_T|} \tag{1a}$$

where r_T is the inertial position vector of the chief, $\dot{r}_T$ is the inertial velocity vector, and the shorthand notation $r_T = |r_T|$ is used.

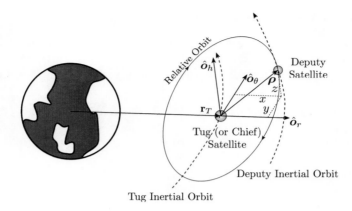

Figure 1. Illustration of Tug Rectilinear LVLH or Hill Coordinate Frame

The direction cosine matrix (DCM) of the Hill frame relative to an inertial frame, expressed through $\mathcal{N} : \{\hat{\boldsymbol{n}}_1, \hat{\boldsymbol{n}}_2, \hat{\boldsymbol{n}}_3\}$, is defined through[12]

$$[NH] = \begin{bmatrix} ^{\mathcal{N}}\hat{\boldsymbol{o}}_r & ^{\mathcal{N}}\hat{\boldsymbol{o}}_\theta & ^{\mathcal{N}}\hat{\boldsymbol{o}}_h \end{bmatrix} \tag{2}$$

Let $\boldsymbol{\omega}_{H/N}$ be the angular velocity of the Hill frame relative to the inertial frame, then Hill-frame centric deputy motion $^{\mathcal{H}}\boldsymbol{\rho}$ is translated into inertial motion $^{\mathcal{N}}\boldsymbol{r}_d$ using

$$^{\mathcal{N}}\boldsymbol{r}_d = {}^{\mathcal{N}}\boldsymbol{r}_T + [NH] \, {}^{\mathcal{H}}\boldsymbol{\rho} \tag{3}$$

where

$$^{\mathcal{H}}\boldsymbol{\rho} = \begin{bmatrix} x \\ y \\ z \end{bmatrix} \tag{4}$$

and (x, y, z) are the Hill-frame centric cartesian deputy position coordinates. The inertia and Hill-frame relative velocities are related using the transport theorem:[12]

$$^{\mathcal{N}}\dot{\boldsymbol{r}}_d = {}^{\mathcal{N}}\dot{\boldsymbol{r}}_T + [NH] \left(\frac{\mathrm{d}(^{\mathcal{H}}\boldsymbol{\rho})}{\mathrm{d}t} + {}^{\mathcal{H}}\boldsymbol{\omega}_{H/N} \times {}^{\mathcal{H}}\boldsymbol{\rho} \right) \tag{5}$$

where

$$\frac{\mathrm{d}(^{\mathcal{H}}\boldsymbol{\rho})}{\mathrm{d}t} = {}^{\mathcal{H}}\boldsymbol{\rho}' = \begin{bmatrix} \dot{x} \\ \dot{y} \\ \dot{z} \end{bmatrix} \tag{6}$$

Note the use of the short-hand notation for Hill-frame dependent time derivatives:

$$\frac{^{\mathcal{H}}\mathrm{d}(\boldsymbol{\rho})}{\mathrm{d}t} \equiv \boldsymbol{\rho}' \tag{7}$$

Relative Motion With Respect to a Constantly Accelerating Frame

Next the classical Hill frame relative orbital dynamics are revisited considering that the Hill frame is no longer on a circular orbit, but on a slowly spiraling trajectory. This study only investigates inertial thrusting to perform Semi-Major Axis (SMA) changes which require thrusting in the along-track direction.

The deputy and chief inertial position vectors are related through

$$r_d = r_T + \rho \tag{8}$$

The relative motion ρ is thus expressed through

$$\rho = r_d - r_T \tag{9}$$

Note that this is a coordinate-frame independent vector formulation of the relative motion. Taking two inertial time derivatives of Eq. (9) yields

$$\ddot{\rho} = \ddot{r}_d - \ddot{r}_T \tag{10}$$

The inertial chief or tug equations of motion are given through

$$\ddot{r}_T = -\frac{\mu}{r_T^3}r_T + \frac{F_c}{m_T} + u_T \tag{11}$$

where μ is the gravitational constant, and m_T is the chief mass. The first term of the right hand side is the gravitational acceleration, while F_c is the electrostatic force acting between tug and deputy, and u_T is the net control acceleration being produced by the chief's inertial thrusters. The inertial deputy equations of motion are

$$\ddot{r}_d = -\frac{\mu}{r_d^3}r_d - \frac{F_c}{m_d} \tag{12}$$

where m_d is the deputy mass.

Substituting Eqs. (12) and (11) into Eq. (10) yields the vector relative equations of motion

$$\ddot{\rho} = -\frac{\mu}{r_d^3}r_d + \frac{\mu}{r_T^3}r_T - \frac{F_c}{m_d} - \frac{F_c}{m_T} - u_T \tag{13}$$

Defining the control acceleration vector u as

$$u = -F_c\left(\frac{m_T + m_d}{m_T m_d}\right) - u_T \tag{14}$$

the relative EOM are rewritten as

$$\ddot{\rho} = -\frac{\mu}{r_d^3}r_d + \frac{\mu}{r_T^3}r_T + u \tag{15}$$

This algebraic form is equivalent now to the classical Clohessy-Wiltshire-Hill (CWH) equations of relative motion, where u would be the deputy control acceleration. Note that the control acceleration u contains both the impact of performing inertial thrusting, as well as the influence of the electrostatic attraction. To obtain $\ddot{\rho}$, we need to take two inertial time derivatives. The inertial derivative of ρ is

$$\dot{\rho} = \rho' + \boldsymbol{\omega}_{H/N} \times \rho \tag{16}$$

If the chief vehicle is on a circular orbit, then the orbital angular velocity vector is simply

$$\boldsymbol{\omega}_{H/N} = n\hat{o}_h \tag{17}$$

where $n = \sqrt{\mu/a^3}$ is the mean orbit rate, and a is the tug semi-major axis. However, because the tug is performing a low-thrust semi-major axis orbit change, the mean orbit rate n is not constant, but rather $n = n(t)$ is a function of time. However, the deputy reorbiting is assumed to not change the orbit plane of the deputy because only the SMA is being changed. Thus, the orbit normal direction $\hat{o}_h$ is inertially fixed, and the orbit angular velocity is written as

$$\boldsymbol{\omega}_{H/N} = n(t)\hat{o}_h \tag{18}$$

Note that the tug can maneuver relative to the deputy a general way. Thus, if charge control is turned on during general three-dimensional relative motion, then small deputy orbit plane changes are possible. However, these variations are ignorable because the nominal configuration has the tug accelerating the deputy in the positive along-track direction. This configuration provides the most efficient means to increase the semi-major axis of the deputy, and thus raise its orbit altitude.

Taking the inertial derivative of Eq. (16) yields

$$\ddot{\rho} = \rho'' + 2\boldsymbol{\omega}_{H/N} \times \rho' + \dot{\boldsymbol{\omega}}_{H/N} \times \rho + \boldsymbol{\omega}_{H/N} \times \left(\boldsymbol{\omega}_{H/N} \times \rho\right) \tag{19}$$

For the CWH equations where the chief motion is circular the orbital angular acceleration $\dot{\boldsymbol{\omega}}_{H/N}$ is set to zero and dropped from this expression. For optimal SMA corrections, the along-track acceleration a_θ of the deputy is given by

$$a_\theta = \frac{F_c}{m_d} \tag{20}$$

The orbit angular acceleration is then approximated as

$$\dot{n} = \frac{a_\theta}{r_d} \tag{21}$$

Knowing the actual along-track acceleration a_θ it would be possible to include this term. In practice determining this orbital acceleration term is non-trivial because the tug-deputy system is not aligned with the along track direction at all times. Further, the orbital acceleration requires knowledge of the exact electrostatic force between the two bodies. This is can be very challenging to obtain in practice. However, as the following analysis shows, this acceleration is a very small term that be neglected for the purpose of modeling the slowly-accelerating relative motion dynamics. Thus, the question is for what electrostatic force levels F_c^* will $\dot{n} \approx n^2$. Using Eqs. (20) and (21) we find

$$\frac{F_c^*}{m_d r_d} = \dot{n} \approx n^2 \qquad \Rightarrow \qquad F_c^* = n^2 m_d r_d \tag{22}$$

Assuming a deputy craft with the mass $m_d = 2000$ kg, and the geostationary orbit radius of about $r_d = 42{,}000$ km, we obtain

$$n = 7.335 \cdot 10^{-5} \text{ rad/s}$$
$$n^2 = 5.3801 \cdot 10^{-9} \text{ rad/s}$$

This leads to a critical acceleration force of

$$F_c^* = 451.9\ \text{N}$$

Because the expected electrostatic forces are expected to be in the milli-Newton range, the actual F_c are about 5 orders of magnitude smaller than this critical acceleration force. This justifies neglecting the difficult to measure $\dot{\boldsymbol{\omega}}_{H/N}$ in Eq. (19), resulting in the simplified relative motion acceleration expression

$$\ddot{\boldsymbol{\rho}} = \boldsymbol{\rho}'' + 2n(t)\hat{\boldsymbol{o}}_h \times \boldsymbol{\rho}' + n(t)^2 \hat{\boldsymbol{o}}_h \times (\hat{\boldsymbol{o}}_h \times \boldsymbol{\rho}) \qquad (23)$$

using Eq. (18). Note that the orbit rate $n(t)$ will decrease by about 1.1% as the deputy is reorbited from GEO to a 300 km larger super-synchronous orbit. Because the slowly varying orbit rate is easy to measure, it is kept as a time-dependent parameter in our relative equations of motion.

Next, let us refine the vector equations of motion in Eq. (7), which do not depend on a particular coordinate system, into the equivalent matrix form which provides the ordinary differential equations for the Hill frame coordinates (x, y, z). Assuming $\boldsymbol{\rho}$ is much smaller than $\boldsymbol{r}_T$, the differential gravity term is reduced to a linear form.[12] After linearizing the $\ddot{\boldsymbol{\rho}}$ term, a modified version of the classical CWH equations are obtained:

$$\ddot{x} - 2n(t)\dot{y} - 3n^2(t)x = u_x \qquad (24a)$$
$$\ddot{y} + 2n(t)\dot{x} = u_y \qquad (24b)$$
$$\ddot{z} + n^2(t)z = u_z \qquad (24c)$$

Note that the constant mean orbit rate n of the CWH equations is replaced with the osculating $n(t)$ orbit rate expression. The Coulomb forcing and inertial thrusting influence on the relative deputy motion with respect to the tug is embedded within the control acceleration $\boldsymbol{u}$ expressions.

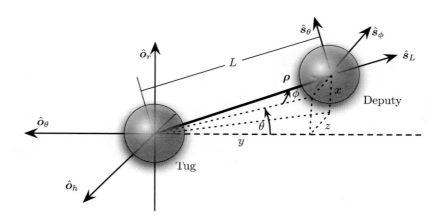

Figure 2. Illustration of the Spherical $\mathcal{S}$ Coordinate Frame

Relative Spherical Equations of Motion

The Cartesian form of the CW equations are not very convenient for the relative motion control development in that the rectilinear (x, y, z) coordinates couple both information regarding the

972

separation distance as well as the relative orientation. Instead a set of spherical relative position coordinates (L, θ, ϕ) are employed where L is the center-to-center separation distance of the tug and deputy, θ is the inplane rotation angle, and ϕ is the out of plane rotation angle. The spherical coordinate frame $\mathcal{S} : \{\hat{s}_L, \hat{s}_\theta, \hat{s}_\phi\}$ is illustrated in Figure 2.

The relative orientation angles θ and ϕ are a 3-2 Euler angle sequence with respect to the Hill frame $\mathcal{H}$. Carrying out the matrix multiplication leads to the DCM mapping from the Hill to the spherical frame:

$$[SH] = \begin{bmatrix} \cos(\phi(t))\sin(\theta(t)) & -\cos(\theta(t))\cos(\phi(t)) & -\sin(\phi(t)) \\ \cos(\theta(t)) & \sin(\theta(t)) & 0 \\ \sin(\theta(t))\sin(\phi(t)) & -\cos(\theta(t))\sin(\phi(t)) & \cos(\phi(t)) \end{bmatrix} \quad (25)$$

The $\mathcal{S}$ and $\mathcal{H}$ position coordinates are related through:

$$L = \sqrt{x^2 + y^2 + z^2} \quad (26a)$$

$$\theta = \arctan\left(\frac{x}{-y}\right) \quad (26b)$$

$$\phi = \arcsin\left(\frac{-z}{L}\right) \quad (26c)$$

and

$$\begin{bmatrix} x \\ y \\ z \end{bmatrix} = [SH]^T \begin{bmatrix} L \\ 0 \\ 0 \end{bmatrix} = \begin{bmatrix} L\sin\theta\cos\phi \\ -L\cos\theta\cos\phi \\ -L\sin\phi \end{bmatrix} \quad (27)$$

The relative motion rate coordinates are related through:

$$\begin{bmatrix} \dot{L} \\ \dot{\theta} \\ \dot{\phi} \end{bmatrix} = \begin{bmatrix} \cos(\phi)\sin(\theta) & -\cos(\theta)\cos(\phi) & -\sin(\phi) \\ \frac{\cos(\theta)\sec(\phi)}{L} & \frac{\sec(\phi)\sin(\theta)}{L} & 0 \\ -\frac{\sin(\theta)\sin(\phi)}{L} & \frac{\cos(\theta)\sin(\phi)}{L} & -\frac{\cos(\phi)}{L} \end{bmatrix} \begin{bmatrix} \dot{x} \\ \dot{y} \\ \dot{z} \end{bmatrix} \quad (28)$$

and

$$\begin{bmatrix} \dot{x} \\ \dot{y} \\ \dot{z} \end{bmatrix} = \begin{bmatrix} \sin\theta\cos\phi & L\cos\theta\cos\phi & -L\sin\theta\sin\phi \\ -\cos\theta\cos\phi & L\sin\theta\cos\phi & L\cos\theta\sin\phi \\ -\sin\phi & 0 & -L\cos\phi \end{bmatrix} \begin{bmatrix} \dot{L} \\ \dot{\theta} \\ \dot{\phi} \end{bmatrix} \quad (29)$$

Substituting the kinematic transformations in Eqs. (27) and (29) into the rectilinear EOM in Eq. (24), and performing significant algebraic simplifications, leads to the following spherical relative equations of motion:

$$\begin{bmatrix} \ddot{L} \\ \ddot{\theta} \\ \ddot{\phi} \end{bmatrix} = [F(L, \theta, \phi, \dot{L}, \dot{\theta}, \dot{\phi})] + [G(L, \phi)]\,^{\mathcal{S}}\boldsymbol{u} \quad (30)$$

where

$$
{}^{S}\boldsymbol{u} = \begin{bmatrix} u_L \\ u_\theta \\ u_\phi \end{bmatrix}
$$

$$
[F] = \begin{bmatrix} \frac{1}{4}L\left(n^2(t)\left(-6\cos(2\theta)\cos^2(\phi)+5\cos(2\phi)+1\right)+4\dot\theta\cos^2(\phi)\left(2n(t)+\dot\theta\right)+4\dot\phi^2\right) \\ \left(3n^2(t)\sin(\theta)\cos(\theta)+2\dot\phi\tan(\phi)\left(n(t)+\dot\theta\right)\right)-2\frac{\dot L}{L}\left(n(t)+\dot\theta\right) \\ \frac{1}{4}\sin(2\phi)\left(n^2(t)(3\cos(2\theta)-5)-2\dot\theta\left(2n(t)+\dot\theta\right)\right)-2\frac{\dot L}{L}\dot\phi \end{bmatrix}
$$

$$
[G] = \begin{bmatrix} 1 & 0 & 0 \\ 0 & \frac{1}{L\cos\phi} & 0 \\ 0 & 0 & -\frac{1}{L} \end{bmatrix}
$$

Note that due to the kinematics of spherical coordinates, this description is singular for large out-of-plane motions where $\phi \to \pm\pi/2$.

Electrostatic Force Model

In order to implement the dynamic model, an expression for the electrostatic force between two craft is needed. Here, the two bodies will be treated as spheres. For an isolated sphere in a vacuum, the charge to voltage relationship is

$$
V = k_T \frac{q}{R}, \tag{31}
$$

where R is the sphere radius, q is the charge on the sphere, and k_T is the Coulomb constant. When another charged object is in close proximity, this voltage to charge relationship no longer holds, as the second object will affect the charge distribution on the first. In this application, the voltages on the craft are considered to be held at constant values.

The voltages on the two spherical craft are denoted as V_1 and V_2. The potential on craft one is thus a function of the self capacitance in Eq. (31) and the potential due to the second sphere,[13]

$$
V_1 = k_T \frac{q_1}{R_1} + k_T \frac{q_2}{L}. \tag{32}
$$

The potential on craft two can be obtained in the same manner. The voltages on both spheres are linear functions of the charges, expressed as

$$
\begin{bmatrix} V_1 \\ V_2 \end{bmatrix} = k_T \begin{bmatrix} \frac{1}{R_1} & \frac{1}{L} \\ \frac{1}{L} & \frac{1}{R_2} \end{bmatrix} \begin{bmatrix} q_1 \\ q_2 \end{bmatrix} \tag{33}
$$

If the voltages on the spheres are held constant, the charges may be solved for at any point in time by inversion of Eq. (33).

This approach to charge determination given craft voltages is relatively new in the field of Coulomb formation flying, where craft have traditionally been treated as point charges. More information about using this position dependent capacitance model is given in Reference 14. Craft of arbitrary geometries will certainly not be perfect spheres. However, spherical models are more appropriate than point charge approximations as they allow for the effects of neighboring craft to be included in the charge to voltage model. Furthermore, Reference 15 provides a method for determining effective spheres for arbitrary craft geometries. Essentially, a spherical approximation is found which most closely replicates the effects of some arbitrary geometric shape. These effective sphere radii can then be used in Eq. (33) to determine the charges on the craft.

Once the charges on each craft have been determined, the electrostatic force between the craft is computed as

$$F_T = k_T \frac{q_1 q_2}{L^2}. \tag{34}$$

Note that the force acts along the line of sight vector connecting the center of the spheres. If the craft are charged to the same polarity, the force will be repulsive. If the craft are charged to opposite polarity, the force will be attractive.

RELATIVE MOTION FEEDBACK CONTROL DESIGN AND ANALYSIS

Nonlinear Control Development

For the relative control algorithm design, the equations of motion in the spherical frame are used. The spherical equations of motion are convenient because the L parameter corresponds directly to the separation distance between the craft. Careful actuation of the separation distance is critical, as it must be ensured that the two craft to do not impact each other. Consider the state vector $\boldsymbol{X} = [L \ \theta \ \phi]^T$. With a proper control law, thrusting can be used to enforce some desired relative position of chief and deputy defined in terms of the spherical coordinates. Such a control law is developed using the candidate Lyapunov function

$$V(\boldsymbol{X}, \dot{\boldsymbol{X}}) = \frac{1}{2}(\boldsymbol{X} - \boldsymbol{X}_r)^T[K](\boldsymbol{X} - \boldsymbol{X}_r) + \frac{1}{2}\dot{\boldsymbol{X}}^T\dot{\boldsymbol{X}}, \tag{35}$$

where $[K]$ is a positive definite gain matrix and $\boldsymbol{X}_r$ is a vector containing some desired steady state values for L, θ and ϕ. Taking the time-derivative of V yields

$$\dot{V}(\boldsymbol{X}, \dot{\boldsymbol{X}}) = \dot{\boldsymbol{X}}^T([K](\boldsymbol{X} - \boldsymbol{X}_r) + \ddot{\boldsymbol{X}}). \tag{36}$$

Substituting Eq. (30) in for $\ddot{\boldsymbol{X}}$, the Lyapunov function rate is expressed as

$$\dot{V}(\boldsymbol{X}, \dot{\boldsymbol{X}}) = \dot{\boldsymbol{X}}^T([K](\boldsymbol{X} - \boldsymbol{X}_r) + [F(L, \theta, \phi, \dot{L}, \dot{\theta}, \dot{\phi})] + [G(L, \phi)]\,^S\boldsymbol{u}). \tag{37}$$

To ensure stability, the Lyapunov function rate is set to the negative semidefinite form

$$\dot{V}(\boldsymbol{X}, \dot{\boldsymbol{X}}) = -\dot{\boldsymbol{X}}^T[P]\dot{\boldsymbol{X}}, \tag{38}$$

where $[P]$ is a positive definite gain matrix. Selecting $^S\boldsymbol{u}$ to be

$$^S\boldsymbol{u} = [G(L, \phi)]^{-1}\left(-[P]\dot{\boldsymbol{X}} - [K](\boldsymbol{X} - \boldsymbol{X}_r) - [F(L, \theta, \phi, \dot{L}, \dot{\theta}, \dot{\phi})]\right) \tag{39}$$

satisfies the negative semidefinite form in Eq. (38). While this ensures stability in the sense of Lyapunov, it does not guarantee asymptotic convergence to the desired reference location $\boldsymbol{X}_r$. To prove asymptotic convergence higher order derivatives of the Lyapunov function are used, which are evaluated on the set $\dot{V}(\boldsymbol{X}, \dot{\boldsymbol{X}}) = 0$.[16] The closed loop response of the system with the control developed above is

$$\ddot{\boldsymbol{X}} + [P]\dot{\boldsymbol{X}} + [K](\boldsymbol{X} - \boldsymbol{X}_r) = \boldsymbol{0}. \tag{40}$$

The second derivative of the Lyapunov function is

$$\ddot{V}(\boldsymbol{X}, \dot{\boldsymbol{X}}) = -2\dot{\boldsymbol{X}}^T[P]\ddot{\boldsymbol{X}}. \tag{41}$$

Evaluated on the set $\dot{\boldsymbol{X}} = \boldsymbol{0}$ (which corresponds to $\dot{V}(\boldsymbol{X}, \dot{\boldsymbol{X}}) = 0$), it is clear that the second derivative of the Lyapunov function is zero. Computing the third derivative yields

$$\dddot{V}(\boldsymbol{X}, \dot{\boldsymbol{X}}) = -2\ddot{\boldsymbol{X}}^T[P]\ddot{\boldsymbol{X}} - 2\dot{\boldsymbol{X}}^T[P]\dddot{\boldsymbol{X}}. \tag{42}$$

After substituting the closed loop dynamics in Eq. (40) and evaluating on the set $\dot{\boldsymbol{X}} = \boldsymbol{0}$, the third derivative of the Lyapunov function is reduced to

$$\dddot{V}(\boldsymbol{X}, \dot{\boldsymbol{X}}) = -2(\boldsymbol{X} - \boldsymbol{X}_r)^T[K]^T[P][K](\boldsymbol{X} - \boldsymbol{X}_r), \tag{43}$$

which is negative definite in terms of $\boldsymbol{X}$ due to the fact that both $[K]$ and $[P]$ are positive definite. Thus, the control law is asymptotically stabilizing. Furthermore, due to the quadratic form of both V and $\dot{V}$, it is concluded that the controller is globally asymptotically stabilizing.

The control acceleration $^S\boldsymbol{u}$ contains contributions from both the inter-craft Coulomb force and the inertial thrusters on the tug satellite,

$$^S\boldsymbol{u} = \begin{bmatrix} u_L \\ u_\theta \\ u_\phi \end{bmatrix} = {}^S\boldsymbol{F}_T\left(\frac{1}{m_T} + \frac{1}{m_d}\right) + \frac{^S\boldsymbol{T}_t}{m_T}. \tag{44}$$

Once the necessary control acceleration is known, the thrust vector is computed as

$$^S\boldsymbol{T}_t = m_T\left({}^S\boldsymbol{u} - {}^S\boldsymbol{F}_T\left(\frac{1}{m_T} + \frac{1}{m_d}\right)\right) \tag{45}$$

Gain Selection

In order for the electrostatic force to be functional as a tether, the inertial thrust magnitude must be small enough so that the craft do not pull away from each other. With an electrostatic force magnitude on the order of milliNewtons, an inertial thruster magnitude on the order of Newtons would be too large to prevent the tug and deputy from pulling away. The thrust magnitude and electrostatic force magnitude must be on the same order. Thus, it is important to select control system gains that will result in appropriate thrust levels.

If the $[K]$ and $[P]$ matrices are selected to be diagonal, the closed-loop equations of motion for each of the three coordinates decouple into the form

$$\ddot{L} + P_L\dot{L} + K_L(L - L_r) = 0 \tag{46a}$$
$$\ddot{\theta} + P_\theta\dot{\theta} + K_\theta(\theta - \theta_r) = 0 \tag{46b}$$
$$\ddot{\phi} + P_\phi\dot{\phi} + K_\phi(\phi - \phi_r) = 0. \tag{46c}$$

The response of the system will mimic a simple damped harmonic oscillator. This allows for the selection of gains to control both the damped nature of the response, and the settling time. Consider the standard harmonic oscillator equations of motion,

$$\ddot{x} + 2\zeta\omega_n\dot{x} + \omega_n^2 x = 0, \tag{47}$$

where ω_n is the natural frequency of the system and ζ is the damping coefficient. Here, a slightly underdamped response will be prescribed. To achieve this, the desired ζ value is set at 0.925 for each of the three spherical coordinates. Correspondingly, each of the P_i gains is set at $1.85\omega_n$. Note that the natural frequency of each of the coordinate responses is directly controlled by the gain K_i with the relationship $\omega_{n,i} = \sqrt{K_i}$. The values for the gains K_i are determined by choosing a desired settling time for the system. The settling time, denoted as T_s, is the time at which the response reaches and stays within two percent of its final value. From the system dynamics, the settling time is computed as[17]

$$T_s = \frac{-\ln(0.02\sqrt{1-\zeta^2})}{\zeta\omega_n}. \tag{48}$$

Because of the relationship between the feedback gains K_i and the natural frequency of the system response, the necessary gain for any desired settling time can quickly be determined. For a given settling time with the slightly underdamped response specified above, the gains for the system are

$$K_i = \left(\frac{-\ln(0.02\sqrt{1-0.925^2})}{0.925T_s}\right)^2 = \frac{27.829}{T_s^2} \tag{49a}$$

$$C_i = 1.85\sqrt{K_i}. \tag{49b}$$

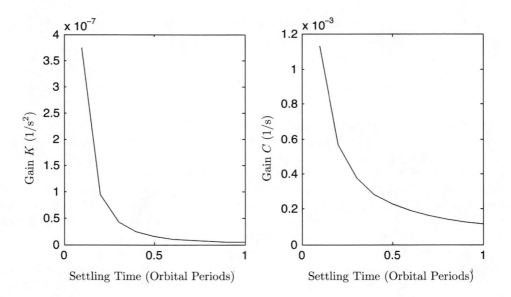

Figure 3. Effects of settling time on control system gains.

The effects of the settling time on the control system gains are readily apparent. As the settling time is increased, the gains will decrease. This is illustrated in Figure 3, which shows the gains necessary to achieve a variety of settling times with nearly critical damping. Note that the desired settling times are plotted as a fraction of a GEO orbital period. The rate of decrease for the K gain

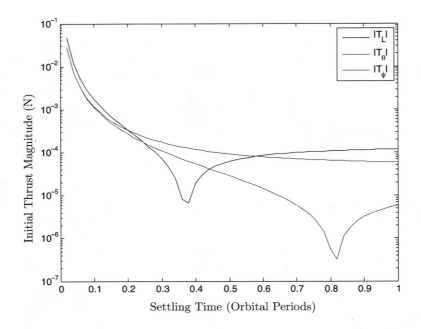

Figure 4. Effects of settling time on initial thrust magnitudes for errors of $(L - L_r) =$ **10 m,** $\theta = 10^o$**, and** $\phi = 10^o$**.**

is higher than that of the P gain. This can be attributed to the fact that K decreases as $1/T_s^2$, while C decreases as $1/T_s$. This inversely proportional decay has important implications on thruster requirements. The necessary thrust magnitudes are directly affected by these gains; if a quick settling time is desired, the required thrust magnitudes will be much higher than those for a slower settling time. To illustrate this point, consider the required initial thrust magnitude for a particular case where the initial position errors are $(L - L_r) = 10$ m, $\theta = 10^o$, and $\phi = 10^o$. Assuming the craft are stationary relative to each other at this epoch, the resulting control thrust magnitudes for this initial error are shown in Figure 3. The thrust magnitudes vary several orders of magnitude depending on the settling time, ranging from hundredths of a Newton to tens of microNewtons. When considering a baseline settling time to serve as the standard for the controller, this variation must be considered carefully. Once the parameters have converged to their desired values, the thrust in the L direction will converge to an order of magnitude on par with the Coulomb force acting between the two bodies, which will be on the order of milliNewtons. While thrust levels on the order of Newtons are certainly achievable, it would be very difficult to achieve a resolution accuracy down to the order of fractions of a milliNewton. For this reason, it is better to choose a settling time that will keep that maximum thrust level on the order of milliNewtons. Thrusters operating on this level should be able to achieve the resolution accuracy necessary to offset the Coulomb force once the relative craft positions converge to the desired locations. For this reason, a settling time of 0.1 orbital periods will be selected as the baseline settling time.

Uncertainties in Craft Charges

The control system formulation assumes that the charges on the craft are known exactly. Naturally, it is of interest to determine the effects on the control system response when the craft charges are modeled imperfectly. This is an important consideration because in actual implementation, the charges will not be known precisely. When the charges are not modeled correctly, the closed loop response of the control system for the separation distance L is

$$\ddot{L} + P_L\dot{L} + K_L(L - L_r) = \frac{k_T}{L^2}(Q_{12} - Q_{12e})\left(\frac{1}{m_T} + \frac{1}{m_d}\right), \tag{50}$$

where k_T is Coulombs constant, Q_{12} is the actual charge product (q_1q_2) of the two craft, and Q_{12e} is the estimated charge product implemented in the controller. It is desired to obtain information about where the equilibrium separation distance is with improperly modeled charges. To do so, the equilibrium conditions $\ddot{L} = \dot{L} = 0$ are applied. For compactness of notation, introduce

$$\mu = k_T\left(\frac{1}{m_T} + \frac{1}{m_d}\right) \tag{51a}$$

$$\Delta Q = (Q_{12} - Q_{12e}). \tag{51b}$$

The closed loop equilibrium positions are found by solving

$$K_L(L - L_r) = \frac{\mu}{L^2}\Delta Q.$$

With minor rearranging, a third order polynomial is obtained,

$$K_L L^3 - K_L L_r L^2 - \mu\Delta Q = 0 \tag{52}$$

The roots of this polynomial yield the equilibrium separation distance of the deputy relative to the chief. Note that only positive L values are realizable, based on the way the coordinate frame is defined. Because the L-direction is defined from the deputy to the chief, a negative L value can never be obtained. Thus, we are concerned only with the existence of positive roots of the polynomial. The existence of such roots can be determined using Descartes rule of signs.

The sign of ΔQ plays an important role in determining the existence of positive roots. First, consider the case when the control system over-predicts the craft charges. That is, the actual magnitudes of the craft charges are smaller than implemented in the control system. When this is the case, ΔQ will be positive. In the polynomial, only one sign change will occur between the L^3 and L^2 terms. As a result, it is certain that there will be one positive root, meaning the control system will drive the system to a positive L value. The magnitude of this equilibrium L is dependent on the feedback gain, the charges, and the craft masses.

Different behavior is obtained when the charges are under-predicted. When the controller assumes smaller charge magnitudes than the craft actually experience, ΔQ is negative. Now, the polynomial will have two sign changes. This means that there will be either zero or two real positive roots. The possibility of no equilibria is intriguing, as it implies the control system may fail to prevent a collision between the deputy and chief. To determine at which point the transition between zero and two positive roots occurs, the condition where Eq. (52) and its derivative both equal zero simultaneously is considered. The derivative of (52) taken with respect to L is

$$3K_L L^2 - 2K_L L_r L = 0, \tag{53}$$

which has a root at

$$L = \frac{2}{3}L_r. \tag{54}$$

Plugging this value back into the original polynomial yields the necessary gain that will ensure the existence of positive real roots. In order to ensure that an equilibrium exists in the closed loop system response, it is required that

$$K_L \geq \frac{27\mu|\Delta Q|}{4L_r^3}. \tag{55}$$

Interestingly, the requirement on the gain is dependent on the reference separation distance, L_r, and the error in the charge requirements. The required gain actually decreases with the cube of the reference distance. As a result, much higher gains are needed to ensure an equilibrium exists when the craft are desired to fly close than when they are desired to fly far apart. In order to properly bound K_L, some knowledge is needed regarding what errors may be expected in the estimation of the craft charges.

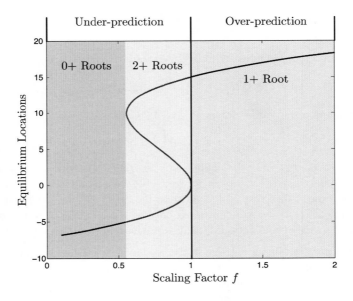

Figure 5. Effects of sweeping scaling parameter f on equilibrium locations.

To illustrate the importance of proper gain selection, equilibrium locations are determined for an example case as a function of uncertainty in the craft charges. To provide a scalable parameter representative of the severity of under- or over-prediction, the estimated charge product is defined as

$$Q_{12e} = fQ_{12}, \tag{56}$$

where f is a positive scaling parameter. When f is greater than one, the charges are overpredicted. When f is less than one, under-prediction occurs. For this study, the charge product is assumed to be $Q_{12} = -2.5 \times 10^{-11}$ C. The reference separation distance is set at $L_r = 15$ m, and the masses are $m_d = 500$ kg and $m_T = 2000$ kg. Assuming a feedback gain of $K_L = 5 \times 10^{-7}$, the scaling

Table 1. Initial spherical coordinates used in simulation

L	θ	ϕ	$\dot{L}$	$\dot{\theta}$	$\dot{\phi}$
37.03 m	-34.12°	15.67°	5.97×10^{-7} m/s	1.58×10^{-7} °/s	-2.58×10^{-7} °/s

Table 2. Parameter values used in numeric simulation

Parameter	m_T	m_d	V_T	V_d	R_T	R_d
Value	500 kg	2000 kg	25 kV	-25 kV	2 m	3 m

parameter f is swept from under-prediction to over-prediction, and the real equilibria are computed for each f value. The results are shown in Figure 5. The plot is divided into two main regions. The first is $f > 1$, which corresponds to the controller over-predicting the craft charges. As expected, only one equilibrium exists in this region. As the over-prediction becomes more severe, the location of the equilibrium configuration moves further and further away from the desired nominal position of $L = 15$ m. Note that when $f = 1$, the equilibrium falls exactly at 15 m. This corresponds to perfect prediction of the craft charges by the controller. When $f < 1$, the controller is under-predicting the actual craft charges. The region of under-prediction is subdivided into two different cases: one with two positive roots, and one with zero positive roots. As f decreases from one, the larger equilibrium location decreases from 15 meters, and a new equilibrium appears at $L = 0$ m. This new equilibrium grows from zero as the underprediction becomes more severe, until it collides with the larger equilibrium and vanishes at approximately $f = 0.55$. Note that the larger equilibrium value is stable, while the lower one is unstable. When f is lower than this value, no positive equilibria exist. This is a dangerous region to be in, as the craft may impact if nothing is done to prevent a collision.

The example shown here is not intended to represent a specific operational scenario. Rather, the parameters used to generate the plot were chosen in order to demonstrate all of the possible behavior that may occur when the charges are improperly modeled. Practically, the gain should be increased to a level where there is no region in f with zero positive roots. As K_L increases, the width of the yellow region in Figure 5 will increase as well. Likewise, this region will shrink when K_L is decreased. It is advantageous to make this region as large as possible, as it provides a wider allowable margin of error in predicting the craft charges.

The preceding results are obtained assuming the craft charges are fixed with time. This assumption is made in order to provide analytical insight into the issue of improperly modeled charges. In the actual system model, the charges change as the distance between the bodies evolves. Unfortunately, including this behavior in the analytical developments precludes the existence of useable insight. Qualitatively, however, the behavior is the same. The preceding developments provide a starting point for proper gain selection and potential outcomes that may occur with improperly modeled charges.

NUMERIC SIMULATION

To illustrate the performance of the developed control system, inertial simulations are used. Rather than integrating the linearized spherical equations of motion, the full nonlinear equations of motion, presented as Eqs. (11) and (12), are used. The linearized control developed with spherical coordinates is used to determine $\boldsymbol{u}_T$. The control system is used to raise the semi-major axis of the deputy orbit by 300 km, starting at a geosynchronous orbit radius of 42,164 km. Such a scenario is representative of raising a GEO debris object into a super-geosynchronous disposal orbit. To begin the simulation, the deputy is placed in a circular orbit with radius 42,164 km. The relative spherical coordinates between the deputy and chief at epoch are shown in Table 1. The parameter values used in the simulation are summarized in Table 2. The simulation is run until an increase in the semi-major axis of 300 km is achieved.

For the simulation, the control algorithm is implemented assuming perfect knowledge of the state and craft voltages. The electrostatic force model described in Eq. (34) is used to model the effects of the craft charging by means of the position-dependent capacitance model in Eq. (33). Note that the craft voltages, presented in Table 2, are held constant throughout the simulation. The charges vary as the relative positions of the craft change during the maneuver according to Eq. (33).

For comparison, a simulation is run where the electrostatic force is not modeled properly; rather, over-prediction of 10% in the force magnitude is considered. Because the electrostatic force is a direct function of the charge product of the craft, this is akin to over-predicting the charge product by 10%. The same parameter values are maintained for both simulations. The case with force over-prediction is run for the same length of time as the perfect-knowledge simulation. Considering the analytical developments in the preceding section, it is expected that this scenario will result in an increase in the separation distance between the craft at steady state relative to the desired nominal position.

In the control system, desired values of the spherical coordinates are needed. The target values will affect the maneuver in several different ways. Considering first the effects of the separation distance L, the maneuver time can be significantly impacted. The thrust magnitude at steady state implemented on the tugging craft is a direct function of the electrostatic force between the craft. If the craft are 5 meters apart, for example, this force is significantly larger than if the craft are 50 meters apart. Because the thrust is a direction function of the electrostatic force, larger thrust magnitudes are possible when the craft are held at smaller separation distances. Larger thrust magnitudes enable the semi-major axis of the orbit to be increased at a more rapid rate. These effects are described in further detail in Reference 10, where Gauss' variational equations are used to determine how quickly a deputy object's semi-major axis may be increased using electrostatic forces. Next, the effects of the angles θ and ϕ are considered. When both of these angles are held at zero, the deputy will follow the chief in the orbit track. When θ in non-zero and ϕ is zero, both deputy and chief occupy the same orbit plane. In this case, planar orbit maneuvers are possible, where the deputy orbit semi-major axis, eccentricity, and argument of perigee may be modified. When ϕ is non-zero, the deputy and chief are no longer in the same orbit plane. In this configuration, the deputy orbit inclination and right ascension of the ascending node may be modified, in addition to the other orbital elements. In the current study, a planar orbit raising maneuver is considered. As such, the values targeted by the controller are set at $L=12.5$ meters, $\theta = \phi = 0^o$. Note that this corresponds to the chief at 12.5 meters ahead of the deputy in the along-track direction.

To achieve the desired semi-major axis increase, slightly more than 61 days are required when perfect knowledge of the electrostatic force is available. During the same 61 day period, the 10% error in the electrostatic force magnitude leads to an increase in the semi-major axis of only 211.6 km. The evolution of the semi-major axis and eccentricity of the deputy object during the maneuver is shown in Figure 6. Note that the increase in the semi-major axis is shown, and the trend is linear. This is attributed to the fact that a constant force is applied to the deputy object in the along

982

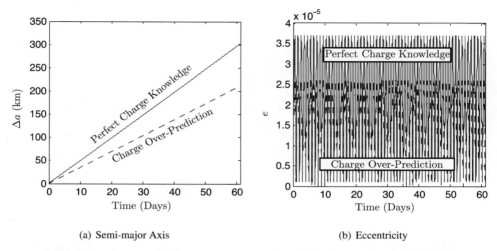

(a) Semi-major Axis   (b) Eccentricity

Figure 6. Changes in a) semi-major axis and b) eccentricity of deputy object throughout the maneuver.

track direction. As such, the rate of increase in the semi-major axis is nearly constant throughout the duration of the maneuver. The eccentricity spikes early on in the maneuver, then oscillates for the remainder. This early spike can be attributed to the initial maneuvering of the chief relative to the deputy. During this early repositioning the force on the deputy is not constant in magnitude or direction, as the electrostatic force between the craft is changing. Once the steady state relative position is achieved, the force becomes constant and the oscillation results. The decreased performance in the case of force over-prediction is attributed to the steady state conditions achieved by the controller. When this force is over-predicted, the craft settle into a separation distance larger than when the force is known perfectly. As a result the tugging force is smaller, which leads to a lower rate of change for the semi-major axis.

Initially, the deputy and chief are not in the desired relative position. There is a repositioning of the chief relative to the deputy during the early portion of the maneuver. This is illustrated by considering the evolution of the spherical coordinates during the first 12 hours, shown in Figure 7. Using the gain-selection process detailed previously, gains are chosen so that the settling time for the system is 0.1 days ($K = 3.7484 \times 10^{-7}$ 1/s^2 and $C = 1.1327 \times 10^{-3}$ 1/s). The response of the system using these gains reveals the desired settling time has been achieved. A slightly underdamped response is obtained before the chief settles into its steady-state relative position. When the electrostatic force is modeled exactly, the target is achieved. When the force is over-predicted by 10%, the desired angles are achieved but the separation distance increases to about 15 m. Once steady-state is achieved in both cases, the relative position is held throughout the duration of the maneuver. Recall that inertial simulations are used during these simulations. The spherical coordinates shown here are obtained by computing the relative position of the craft and then rotating the result into the appropriate coordinate frame.

Inspection of the spherical coordinate histories reveals the differences in performance between the two simulated cases. For both simulations the settling time is the same, as are the histories for the angles θ and ϕ. This is due to the decoupling between the coordinates in the control system. In

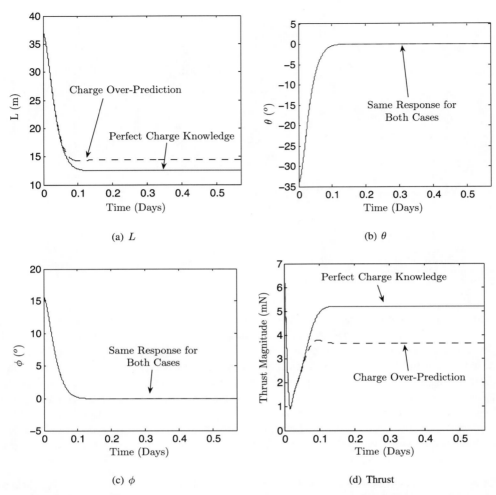

Figure 7. Evolution of spherical coordinates a) L **b)** θ **and c)** ϕ **and d) magnitude of chief thrust during the first 12 hours of the maneuver for perfect charge knowledge and over-prediction of charge product by 10%.**

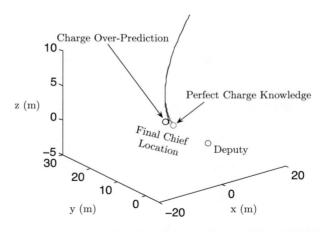

Figure 8. Relative motion of chief with respect to deputy (in Hill frame) for perfect charge knowledge and over-prediction of charge product by 2.5%.

spherical coordinates, the electrostatic force is only present in the L-direction. Thus, the feedback compensation for the electrostatic force will directly affect only this direction. Indirect effects are present in the dynamics due to the coupling of the coordinates in the equations of motion. The control system, however, effectively removes this decoupling by compensating for these dynamics in the control algorithm. Thus, errors in the electrostatic force model will manifest predominately in the L-direction with minimal deleterious effects on the desired response for the angles. Still, errors in the electrostatic force model can cause serious concerns. Here, over-prediction is considered. In this scenario, the primary effect is that the desired semi-major axis increase will take longer. A potentially more problematic scenario is when the electrostatic force is under-predicted. If the controller assumes the magnitude of the electrostatic force is less than it really is, the two craft could collide.

The magnitude of the thrust on the chief craft is shown in Figure 7(d) for the first part of the maneuver. Beyond this initial period, the magnitude remains constant at the steady value indicated on the plot. Note that the steady state value is lower for the charge over-prediction case. This corresponds to the fact that the steady-state separation distance is larger for the charge over-prediction case. As a result, the thrusters do not need as large a magnitude to compensate for the lower electrostatic force than they do when the craft are closer. The effect that this has on the overall maneuver is a lower tugging force which, in turn, does not increase the semi-major axis as readily as the case when the electrostatic force is modeled perfectly.

The relative trajectory of the chief with respect to the deputy in the Hill frame is shown in Figure 8 for both cases. The approach trajectory from the initial condition is nearly identical for the case of perfect charge knowledge and charge over-prediction. This is largely due to the same angle history achieved by the controller for both histories (see Figure 7). For a large duration of the repositioning, the separation distance history is very similar as well. It is only when the craft are within 15 meters of each other that a deviation occurs. Recall that once steady-state is achieved the relative positions of the craft remain constant in the Hill frame.

CONCLUSION

In this paper, an autonomous relative navigation control algorithm is proposed for the case when two charged spacecraft are in close proximity of each other. Denoting one craft as the chief and the other as the deputy, thrust is applied to the chief to reposition it into a desired relative position with respect to the deputy. The electrostatic force generated between the craft is then used as a contactless tug which enables the chief to tow the deputy into a different orbit. Here, a planar orbit raising maneuver is simulated to test the control algorithm, and improperly modeled charges are considered. The control algorithm demonstrates its validity by successfully repositioning the chief and achieving an increase in the deputy semi-major axis of 300 km using an electrostatic tugging force. When the charges are not modeled properly in the controller, the chief settles into a separation distance slightly larger than desired. This has minimal impact on the targeted mission, however; the only significant difference between the cases is the time needed to achieve a semi-major axis increase of 300 km. The electrostatic tug concept has been validated as a viable means for reorbiting space objects.

REFERENCES

[1] L. B. King, G. G. Parker, S. Deshmukh, and J.-H. Chong, "Spacecraft Formation-flying using Inter-vehicle Coulomb Forces," tech. rep., NASA/NIAC, http://www.niac.usra.edu, January 2002.

[2] L. B. King, G. G. Parker, S. Deshmukh, and J.-H. Chong, "Study of Interspacecraft Coulomb Forces and Implications for Formation Flying," *AIAA Journal of Propulsion and Power*, Vol. 19, No. 3, 2003, pp. 497–505.

[3] L. Pettazzi, D. Izzo, and S. Theil, "Swarm navigation and reconfiguration using electrostatic forces," *7th International Conference on Dynamics and Control of Systems and Structures in Space*, The Old Royal Naval College, Greenwich, London, England, 16-20 July 2006.

[4] A. Natarajan and H. Schaub, "Hybrid Control of Orbit Normal and Along-Track Two-Craft Coulomb Tethers," *Aerospace Science and Technology*, Vol. 13, June–July 2009, pp. 183–191.

[5] C. R. Seubert and H. Schaub, "Tethered Coulomb Structures: Prospects and Challenges," *Journal of the Astronautical Sciences*, Vol. 57, Jan.–June 2009, pp. 347–368.

[6] C. R. Seubert, S. Panosian, and H. Schaub, "Dynamic Feasibility Study of a Tethered Coulomb Structure," *AAS/AIAA Astrodynamics Specialist Conference*, Toronto, Canada, Aug. 2–5 2010.

[7] S. Wang and H. Schaub, "Nonlinear Charge Control for a Collinear Fixed Shape Three-Craft Equilibrium," *AIAA Journal of Guidance, Control, and Dynamics*, Vol. 34, Mar.–Apr. 2011, pp. 359–366.

[8] S. Wang and H. Schaub, "Switched Lyapunov Function Based Coulomb Control of a Triangular 3-Vehicle Cluster," *AAS/AIAA Astrodynamics Specialist Conference*, Pittsburgh, PA, Aug. 9–13 2009.

[9] H. Schaub, G. G. Parker, and L. B. King, "Challenges and Prospects of Coulomb Spacecraft Formation Control," *Journal of the Astronautical Sciences*, Vol. 52, No. 1-2, 2004, pp. 169–193.

[10] H. Schaub and D. F. Moorer, "Geosynchronous Large Debris Reorbiter: Challengs and Prospects," *AAS Kyle T. Alfriend Astrodynamics Symposium*, Monterey, CA, May 17–19 2010.

[11] E. T. Lu and S. G. Love, "Gravitational Tractor for Towing Asteroids," *Nature*, Vol. 438, November 2005, pp. 177–178.

[12] H. Schaub and J. L. Junkins, *Analytical Mechanics of Space Systems*. Reston, VA: AIAA Education Series, 2nd ed., October 2009.

[13] W. R. Smythe, *Static and Dynamic Electricity*. McGraw-Hill, 3rd ed., 1968.

[14] H. Schaub and L. E. Z. Jasper, "Circular Orbit Radius Control Using Electrostatic Actuation for 2-Craft Configurations," *AAS/AIAA Astrodynamics Specialist Conference*, Girdwood, Alaska, July 31 – August 4 2011. Paper AAS 11–498.

[15] L. E. Z. Jasper and H. Schaub, "Effective Sphere Modeling for Electrostatic Forces on a Three-Dimensional Spacecraft Shape," *AAS/AIAA Spaceflight Mechanics Meeting*, Girdwood, Alaska, July 31 – August 4 2011. Paper AAS 11–465.

[16] R. Mukherjee and D. Chen, "Asymptotic Stability Theorem for Autonomous Systems," *Journal of Guidance, Control, and Dynamics*, Vol. 16, 1993, pp. 961–963.

[17] N. S. Nise, *Control Systems Engineering*. Wiley, 5th ed., 2008.

NONLINEAR ANALYTICAL SOLUTION OF RELATIVE MOTION SUBJECT TO J_2 PERTURBATION USING VOLTERRA KERNELS

Ashraf Omran[*] and Brett Newman[†]

This paper introduces Volterra theory to orbit mechanics. The paper presents a novel nonlinear analytical solution for the relative motion of two satellites subject to J_2 perturbation with a circular reference orbit. First, the nonlinear equations of the relative motion are expanded in a polynomial form using the Knocker operator. Carleman bilinearization is then used to compute Volterra kernels analytically in terms of the orbit parameters and the deputy initial conditions. The resultant solution based on these analytical Volterra kernels is compared to the linear solution showing a significant reduction in the error, when the nonlinear simulation is considered as the benchmark.

INTRODUCTION

For the last few years, many techniques have been proposed to study the dynamic equations of motion for a spacecraft relative to a neighboring orbit due to the possibility of spacecraft orbiting in formation. Thus, two spacecraft can rendezvous and dock onto each other, perform inspection and servicing tasks, or orient sensors for certain mission objectives. This coordination requires an efficient technique to find solutions in order to analyze and predict the relative motion between the chaser and the target vehicles for accurate long-term simulation. Linearization was and still is the favorable method to describe the relative motion dynamics because of the simplicity of the mathematical manipulation and the capability of the linear theory to describe the motion independent of any numeric values. Study of the relative motions started with Hill when he introduced a theory to describe the relative motion of the moon with respect to the earth in [1]. Later, the Clohessy-Wiltshire (C-W) equations were developed for the relative motion of the chaser spacecraft with respect to the reference spacecraft in a circular near earth orbit [2]. The extension to the elliptical orbit is known as the Tschauner-Hempel (T-H) equations [3]. More recently published work applying the linear theory to relative motion under the influence of J_2 perturbation and air drag is given in Refs. [4-11]. Reference [4] provides a linearized model using the differential J_2 accelerations as forcing functions to the Clohessey–Wiltshire equations, but the perturbations in the mean motion and the angular rates of the chief orbit are ignored. In Ref. [5], the relative motion model accounts for the secular perturbations of the elements. However, the model in Ref. [5] ignores short-period variations and coupling terms between the out-of-plane and in-plane equations. A derivation of the short-period corrections to the mean nonsingular orbital elements is

* Research Scientist and Adjunct Assistant Professor, Dept. of Mechanical and Aerospace Engr., Old Dominion Univ., Norfolk, VA 23529, Member AAS.
† Professor, Dept. of Mechanical and Aerospace Engr., Old Dominion Univ., Norfolk, VA 23529, Senior Member AAS.

given in Ref. [6-8]. In Ref. [9], a transition matrix including the short- and long-period effects of J_2 in the case of elliptic reference orbits in a curvilinear coordinate system is offered. In Ref. [10], a set of linearized relative motion equations are derived with respect to a mean circular reference orbit by using expressions for the secular drift rates and the short-period variations of the chief's orbital elements. A general method to estimate the linearized relative orbit geometry for both circular and elliptic chief reference orbits has been recently presented in Ref. [11]. Most of these linearization models have been validated and also applied in many instances of relative navigation and control for autonomous rendezvous [12-14]. However, the usage of linear theory restricts the analysis to a small perturbation.

Volterra theory has emerged as a popular nonlinear modeling technique, primarily because of the underlying analytical framework and its extension of the impulse response concept from linear theory. Volterra theory dates back to 1887 with the first encompassing publication appearing in 1927 and later in 1958 [15-16]. An early use of this theory was made by Wiener and follow on research at the Massachusetts Institute of Technology in the area of filtering and electronic circuits [17,18]. In aeronautics, Volterra theory has been explored to a limited extent. Volterra theory has few applications to flight mechanics in the literature. For atmospheric flight dynamics, Refs. [19-20] are two notable exceptions. In these efforts, modeling the longitudinal dynamics of a high performance aircraft in limit cycling conditions has been explored via the Volterra approach. In Ref. [20], a differential form of a reduced third order Volterra series was considered. The approach proved the ability to capture the limit cycle. This work was extended in Ref. [19] to a global approach. An interesting application of Volterra theory in atmospheric flight mechanics has been presented in Ref. [21] to define nonlinear flying quality metrics analytically. However, most of these trials date back to the 1980s and early 1990s. Recently, in Refs. [22-23], the authors bring back the utilization of Volterra theory to flight mechanics through a global piecewise approach. This approach facilitates the use of Volterra theory in a piecewise fashion for strong nonlinearity. The authors in Refs. [24-25] have added another work to develop analytical closed-form solutions for the first and second order single degree of freedom system. Such analytically structured solutions provide an illumination for the source of differences between nonlinear and linear responses such as initial departure time, differences in settling times and steady value, and nonsymmetric response, which have been successfully applied to many low-order atmospheric flight and mechanical systems. From the authors' knowledge, Volterra theory has never been explored or applied to astronautics. The main goal of the current research is to explore the applicability of Volterra theory to orbit mechanics. The selected case study in this paper is the dynamic equations of motion for a spacecraft relative to a neighboring orbit.

This paper investigates the applicability of Volterra theory as an efficient nonlinear approximation technique to develop a nonlinear analytical solution for the relative motion of a spacecraft subject to J_2 perturbation in the case of a circular reference orbit. The paper is organized as follows. In Section 2, a brief discussion of Volterra theory and its mathematical origin is introduced followed by the generalized algorithm that one can use to develop the so-called Volterra kernels from the nonlinear equation of motion. Then, the governing relationships of the relative motion are set forth in a polynomial form in Section 3. Section 4 constructs the equivalent Carleman bilinearization model, which leads to closed-form expressions of the Volterra kernels for orbital relative motion dynamics. Numerical validation is presented in Section 5. Finally, the work is concluded in Section 6.

VOLTERRA THEORY

Many physical systems can be described across a set of nonlinear differential and algebraic equations between input, state, and output signals. A commonly used representation is the nonlinear state space form

$$\dot{x}(t) = f(t, x(t), u(t))$$
$$y(t) = g(t, x(t), u(t))$$

(1)

where $x \in R^n$ denotes the state vector, $u \in R^m$ the input vector, and $y \in R^p$ the output vector. Vectors $f \in R^n$ and $g \in R^p$ denote the system nonlinearities and $t \in R^1$ is time. A few nonlinear systems are exactly solvable; many others, which are not tractable analytically, can be solved by numerical integration. Although numerical techniques can provide highly accurate results, analytical type solutions are still sought. Their main advantage lies in the capability to interpret the physical meaning underneath a solution. Volterra series is one such approach, which can represent a wide range of nonlinear system behavior. The theory represents the input-output relation of a nonlinear system as an infinite sum of multi-dimensional convolution integrals.

$$y(t) = h_o(t) + \sum_{k=1}^{\infty} \int_0^\infty \int_0^\infty \ldots \int_0^\infty h_k(\tau_1, \tau_2, \ldots, \tau_k) \cdot \prod_{i=1}^k u(t - \tau_i) d\tau_i$$

(2)

In Eq. (2), $h_k(\tau_1, \tau_2, \ldots, \tau_k)$ denotes the kth order Volterra kernel. The Volterra kernels are casual symmetric functions with respect to their argument.[26]

In general kernels are of two classes: the state dependent class and the input dependent class. The only member of the state dependent class is kernel $h_o(t)$, which represents the response of the output due to the initial system state, but which also depends indirectly on the input. If the system motion is started at an equilibrium condition (both state and input values) and the equilibrium input is maintained, kernel $h_o(t)$ equals zero. On the other hand, if the state value is mismatched to the equilibrium input, or vice versa, kernel $h_o(t)$ is nonzero and can be interpreted as motion of the system from initial state to equilibrium state (stable), or the state reacting to the input. Sometimes the $h_o(t)$ response can be a sustained oscillation representing a limit cycle, or possess a divergent behavior for an unstable equilibrium. The input dependent class contains all other Volterra kernels. Those kernels represent the behavior of the system in response to any arbitrary input. In this class, each Volterra kernel is represented with the input in a multi-dimensional convolution integration. Each kernel appearing in the convolution integrals reflects a specific system behavior. Both the state and input dependent class kernels are unique for a given system. For weak nonlinearities, all higher-order kernels are seen to quickly tend to negligible values in the system representation and for a completely linear system, only $h_o(t)$ and $h_1(t,\tau)$ remain.

Since, kernels are the backbone of Volterra theory, they must be constructed by some means. Several methodologies have been addressed to estimate the Volterra kernels. Some methods are iterative and numerical in nature, identifying the nonlinear system as a black-box or gray-box. For example, one of these numerical techniques is based on linear regression or least square estimation (LSE). LSE can be cast as a recursive algorithm [20], or a non-recursive algorithm [26]. Another method to estimate Volterra kernels from the system identification point of view is provided by the use of sinusoidal or impulsive inputs [22-23]. The strategy is an extension from the use of these inputs to identify linear systems. This strategy captures only the input-output behavior of a system and disregards any internal structure. On the other hand, the usage of analytical methods have been very restricted. Lie derivatives approach has been used to compute kernels

989

analytically in Ref. [27]. This approach lacks generality since the approach constructs the kernels as a series. Each term in this series is defined as a function of Lie derivatives. Finding a closed-form result for such series is not practical. Furthermore, divergence of these derivatives may restrict any approximation definition to the series.

Three other analytical methods to develop the Volterra kernels from the nonlinear differential equation have been offered: growing exponential method, variational expansion method, and Carleman linearization method [16]. Growing exponential method provides the kernels as a set of n-dimensional Laplace transform functions. The method has been used in Ref. [28] to compute the analytical kernels for an aeroelastic two dimensional airfoil. However, the method delivers the kernels by unwieldy forms, which restricts the applicability for nonlinear characterization. Variational expansion form, also called differential form, was initially developed based on a perturbation point of view. The first remarkable application for the variational expansion method to show the capability of the method to offer a reasonable approximation for nonlinear differential systems was discussed in Ref. [29]. The method has also been employed in many flight mechanics studies, which highlights the capability of the method to capture nonlinearities imbedded in flight systems [30]. Carleman linearization or bilinearization method has been used in Ref. [31] as a system identification approach. The bilinearization method is mathematically simple and has the ability to deliver a general analytical solution for kernels. Therefore, this method is considered in the current research in order to develop an approximate Volterra kernel solution for the relative motion in the case of a reference circular orbit.

Before applying the method to any specific system, the general outline of the method to the single input case is first given to show the mechanism by which the analytical kernels can be constructed. The single input multiple output state space representation of the nonlinear affine system is defined as

$$\dot{x}(t) = F(x(t),t) + G(x(t),t)u(t)$$
$$y(t) = H(x(t),t)$$

(3)

where $x \in R^n$ denotes the state vector, $u \in R^1$ the scalar input, and $y \in R^p$ the multivariable output. Vectors $F \in R^n$, $G \in R^n$, and $H \in R^p$ denote the nonlinear analytical function in x and in t, where $t \in R^1$ is time. The system in Eq. (3) is also called a linear-analytical state equation. Carleman linearization approach can be applied to $F(x(t),t)$, $G(x(t),t)$, and $H(x(t),t)$ as

$$F(x(t),t) \approx A_1(t)x(t) + A_2(t)x^{(2)}(t) + \cdots + A_i(t)x^{(i)}(t) + \cdots$$
$$G(x(t),t) \approx B_0(t) + B_1(t)x(t) + B_2(t)x^{(2)}(t) + \cdots + B_i(t)x^{(i)}(t) + \cdots$$
$$H(x(t),t) \approx C_1(t)x(t) + C_2(t)x^{(2)}(t) + \cdots + C_i(t)x^{(i)}(t) + \cdots$$

(4)

where

$$x^{(0)}(t) = 1$$
$$x^{(1)}(t) = x$$
$$x^{(2)}(t) = x(t) \otimes x(t)$$
$$x^{(3)}(t) = x(t) \otimes x(t) \otimes x(t)$$
$$\vdots$$
$$x^{(i)}(t) = x(t)\prod_{k=1}^{i-1} \otimes x(t)$$

(5)

In Eq. (5), $\otimes$ is the Kronecker product. The Kronecker product for two matrices P and Q, where P is of dimension N_P by M_P and Q is of N_Q by M_Q, is defined as

$$P \otimes Q = \begin{bmatrix} P_{11}Q & \cdots & P_{1M_P}Q \\ \vdots & \ddots & \vdots \\ P_{N_P1}Q & \cdots & P_{N_PM_P}Q \end{bmatrix} \tag{6}$$

The resultant matrix $P \otimes Q$ has dimension ($N_P \times N_Q$) by ($M_P \times M_Q$). After considering Carleman linearization for N terms only, Eq. (3) is then given as

$$\dot{x}(t) \approx \sum_{k=1}^{N} A_k(t) x^{(k)}(t) + \sum_{k=0}^{N-1} B_k(t) x^{(k)}(t) u(t)$$

$$y(t) \approx \sum_{k=1}^{N} C_k(t) x^{(k)}(t) \tag{7}$$

The system in Eq. (7) can be formulated as a bilinear system by considering the differential equation of $x^{(i)}(t)$ as

$$\dot{x}^{(i)}(t) = \sum_{k=i}^{N} A_{i,k}(t) x^{(k)}(t) + \sum_{k=i-1}^{N-1} B_{i,k}(t) x^{(k)}(t) u(t) \tag{8}$$

where

$$A_{i,k}(t) = A_{k-i+1}(t) \left(\prod_{j=1}^{i-1} \otimes I_n \right) + I_n \otimes A_{k-i+1}(t) \left(\prod_{j=1}^{i-2} \otimes I_n \right) + \cdots + \left(\prod_{j=1}^{i-1} I_n \otimes \right) A_{k-i+1}(t)$$

$$B_{i,k}(t) = B_{k-i+1}(t) \left(\prod_{j=1}^{i-1} \otimes I_n \right) + I_n \otimes B_{k-i+1}(t) \left(\prod_{j=1}^{i-2} \otimes I_n \right) + \cdots + \left(\prod_{j=1}^{i-1} I_n \otimes \right) B_{k-i+1}(t) \tag{9}$$

and $k = i, i+1, i+2, \cdots, N$ for A_{ik}

$\quad k = i-1, i, i+1, \cdots, N-1$ for B_{ik}

In Eq. (9), there are (i-1) Kronecker products. The derivation of Eq. (9) is a sequential one. The first step of the derivation is presented as

$$\frac{d}{dt} \left[x^{(2)}(t) \right] = \frac{d}{dt} \left[x^{(1)}(t) \otimes x^{(1)}(t) \right] = \dot{x}^{(1)}(t) \otimes x^{(1)}(t) + x^{(1)}(t) \otimes \dot{x}^{(1)}(t)$$

$$\frac{d}{dt} \left[x^{(2)}(t) \right] = \left\{ \sum_{k=1}^{N-1} A_k(t) x^{(k)}(t) + \sum_{k=0}^{N-2} B_k(t) x^{(k)}(t) u(t) \right\} \otimes x^{(1)}(t) + x^{(1)}(t) \otimes \left\{ \sum_{k=1}^{N-1} A_k(t) x^{(k)}(t) + \sum_{k=0}^{N-2} B_k(t) x^{(k)}(t) u(t) \right\}$$

$$\frac{d}{dt} \left[x^{(2)}(t) \right] = \sum_{k=1}^{N-1} \left[A_k(t) \otimes I_n + I_n \otimes A_k(t) \right] x^{(k+1)}(t) + \sum_{k=0}^{N-2} \left[B_k(t) \otimes I_n + I_n \otimes B_k(t) \right] x^{(k+1)}(t) u(t)$$

$$\frac{d}{dt} \left[x^{(2)}(t) \right] \approx \sum_{k=2}^{N} A_{2,\tilde{k}}(t) x^{(\tilde{k})}(t) + \sum_{k=1}^{N-1} B_{2,\tilde{k}}(t) x^{(\tilde{k})}(t) u(t) \text{ and } \tilde{k} = k+1 \tag{10}$$

The differential equations of $x^{(i)}(t)$ for $i = 1, \ldots, N$ can be collected in a state space model as

$$\dot{x}^{\otimes}(t) = \overline{A}(t) x^{\otimes}(t) + \overline{B}_0(t) u(t) + \overline{B}_1(t) x^{\otimes}(t) u(t)$$

$$y(t) = \overline{C}(t) x^{\otimes}(t) \tag{11}$$

with

$$\overline{A}(t) = \begin{bmatrix} A_{1,1} & A_{1,2} & \cdots & A_{1,N} \\ 0 & A_{2,2} & \cdots & A_{2,N} \\ 0 & 0 & \cdots & A_{3,N} \\ \vdots & \vdots & \vdots & \vdots \\ 0 & 0 & \cdots & A_{N,N} \end{bmatrix}, \quad x^{\otimes}(t) = \begin{bmatrix} x(t) \\ x^{(2)}(t) \\ x^{(3)}(t) \\ \vdots \\ x^{(N)}(t) \end{bmatrix}, \quad \overline{B}_0(t) = \begin{bmatrix} B_{1,0} \\ 0 \\ 0 \\ \vdots \\ 0 \end{bmatrix}$$

$$\overline{B}_1(t) = \begin{bmatrix} B_{1,1} & B_{1,2} & \cdots & B_{1,N-1} & 0 \\ B_{2,1} & B_{2,2} & \cdots & B_{2,N-1} & 0 \\ 0 & B_{3,2} & \cdots & B_{3,N-1} & 0 \\ \vdots & \vdots & \vdots & \vdots & \vdots \\ 0 & 0 & \cdots & B_{N,N-1} & 0 \end{bmatrix}, \quad \overline{C}(t) = [C_1(t) \quad C_2(t) \quad \cdots \quad C_N(t)]$$

The closed-form expression for the Volterra kernels are analytically defined as

$$
\begin{aligned}
h_o(t) &= \overline{C}(t)\overline{\Phi}(t,0)x_0^{\otimes} \\
h_k(t,\tau_1,\cdots,\tau_k) &= \overline{C}(t)\overline{\Phi}(t,\tau_1)\overline{B}_1(\tau_1)\overline{\Phi}(\tau_1,\tau_2)\overline{B}_1(\tau_2)\cdots\overline{B}_1(\tau_{k-1})\overline{\Phi}(\tau_{k-1},\tau_k)\overline{B}_1(\tau_k)\overline{\Phi}(\tau_k,0)x_0^{\otimes} \\
&\quad + \overline{C}(t)\overline{\Phi}(t,\tau_1)\overline{B}_1(\tau_1)\overline{\Phi}(\tau_1,\tau_2)\overline{B}_1(\tau_2)\cdots\overline{B}_1(\tau_{k-1})\overline{\Phi}(\tau_{k-1},\tau_k)\overline{B}_0(\tau_k)
\end{aligned}
\tag{12}
$$

Note the kernels of the bilinear system are triangular ones.

RELATIVE MOTION DYNAMICS

Figure 1 describes the relative motion for the position and velocity of one satellite (a "deputy") with respect to a reference orbit (a "chief"). Two coordinate systems are used to mathematically express such a motion. The first coordinate system is the standard geocentric inertial (GCI) frame, which is located at the center of the earth and with the Z-axis parallel to the earth's rotation axis (positive to the North) and the X-axis towards the first point of Aries. The second frame is the Hill coordinate frame, which is located at the osculating chief position and where the x-axis is in the radial direction, the y-axis is in the in-track (transversal) direction, and the z-axis is in the cross-track (lateral) direction. In the case of a circular chief orbit, the position vector of the chief $\vec{R}_c$ and the deputy satellite position vector $\vec{R}_d$ are defined from the center of the earth in i_x, i_y, and i_z directions as

$$
\begin{aligned}
\vec{R}_c &= R_o i_x \\
\vec{R}_d &= \vec{R}_c + \vec{r} = (R_o + x)i_x + yi_y + zi_z
\end{aligned}
\tag{13}
$$

where $\vec{r} = [x\ y\ z]^{\mathrm{T}}$ is the relative position vector of the deputy satellite in the chief-fixed rotating coordinate system. The three components x, y, and z are respectively the radial (in i_x direction), in-track or transversal (in i_y direction), and cross-track or lateral (in i_z direction) positions.

992

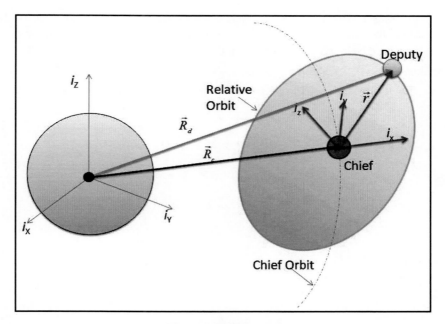

Figure 1 Relative motion

Assume that the two-body gravity effect and oblateness J_2 gravity effect are the only applied forces that the chief and deputy are exposed to. The nonlinear equation of perturbed relative motion is then

$$\ddot{\vec{r}} = -2\vec{\omega}\times\dot{\vec{r}} - \vec{\omega}\times(\vec{\omega}\times\vec{r}) - \dot{\vec{\omega}}\times\vec{r} + \vec{\nabla}F_{2B} + \vec{\nabla}F_{J_2} \tag{14}$$

The angular velocity of the Hill frame is $\vec{\omega} = [\omega_x\ \omega_y\ \omega_z]^{\mathrm{T}}$. Equation (14) has five components: the Coriolis effect $-2\vec{\omega}\times\dot{\vec{r}}$, the centripetal effect $-\vec{\omega}\times(\vec{\omega}\times\vec{r})$, the angular acceleration effect $-\dot{\vec{\omega}}\times\vec{r}$, the two-body gravity gradient effect $\vec{\nabla}F_{2B}$, and the oblateness J_2 gravity gradient effect $\vec{\nabla}F_{J_2}$. The first three components can be compounded to one vector $\vec{a}_k$ as

$$\vec{a}_K = \begin{bmatrix} \omega_y^2 + \omega_z^2 & -\omega_x\omega_y + \dot{\omega}_z & -\omega_x\omega_z - \dot{\omega}_y & 0 & 2\omega_z & -2\omega_y \\ -\omega_x\omega_y - \dot{\omega}_z & \omega_x^2 + \omega_z^2 & -\omega_z\omega_y + \dot{\omega}_x & -2\omega_z & 0 & 2\omega_x \\ -\omega_x\omega_z + \dot{\omega}_y & -\omega_z\omega_y - \dot{\omega}_x & \omega_x^2 + \omega_y^2 & 2\omega_y & -2\omega_x & 0 \end{bmatrix} \begin{bmatrix} x \\ y \\ z \\ \dot{x} \\ \dot{y} \\ \dot{z} \end{bmatrix} \tag{15}$$

The angular velocities are function of the chief orbit elements as

$$\begin{bmatrix} \omega_x \\ \omega_y \\ \omega_z \end{bmatrix} = \begin{bmatrix} 0 \\ 0 \\ \dot{\theta} \end{bmatrix} + \begin{bmatrix} C_\theta & S_\theta & 0 \\ -S_\theta & C_\theta & 0 \\ 0 & 0 & 1 \end{bmatrix} \begin{bmatrix} \dot{i} \\ 0 \\ 0 \end{bmatrix} + \begin{bmatrix} C_\theta & S_\theta & 0 \\ -S_\theta & C_\theta & 0 \\ 0 & 0 & 1 \end{bmatrix} \begin{bmatrix} 1 & 0 & 0 \\ 0 & C_i & S_i \\ 0 & -S_i & C_i \end{bmatrix} \begin{bmatrix} \dot{\Omega} \\ 0 \\ 0 \end{bmatrix} = \begin{bmatrix} \dot{\Omega}S_\theta S_i + \dot{i}C_\theta \\ \dot{\Omega}C_\theta S_i - \dot{i}S_\theta \\ \dot{\Omega}C_i + \dot{\theta} \end{bmatrix} \tag{16}$$

993

where S_j and C_j refer to sine function $\sin(j)$ and cosine function $\cos(j)$ and $j = \{\theta, i\}$. The two angles θ and i are the true latitude and inclination angle of the chief's orbit. If the J_2 gravity gradient effect $\vec{\nabla}F_{J_2}$, on the chief's orbit, is ignored, then the angular velocities are $\vec{\omega} = [0\ 0\ \dot{\theta}]^T$. The gravity gradient effect $\vec{\nabla}F_{J_2}$ makes the angular velocity variant with time. In Ref. [10], an approximate expression is developed for the angular velocity in the case of a circular chief orbit.

$$\begin{bmatrix} \omega_x \\ \omega_y \\ \omega_z \end{bmatrix} = \begin{bmatrix} 2\dot{\Omega}_o S_{i_o} S_{\bar{\theta}_o} \\ 0 \\ \dot{\Omega}_o C_{i_o} + \dot{\bar{\theta}}_o + \tfrac{3}{4} J_2 \left(\frac{R_\oplus}{\bar{R}_o} \right)^2 S_{i_o}^2 C_{2\bar{\theta}_o} \end{bmatrix} \tag{17}$$

where

$$\dot{\bar{\theta}}_o = n_o \left[1 - \tfrac{3}{2} J_2 \left(\frac{R_\oplus}{\bar{R}_o} \right)^2 \left(1 - 4C_{i_o}^2 \right) \right]$$

$$\dot{\bar{\Omega}}_o = -\tfrac{3}{2} J_2 n_o \left(\frac{R_\oplus}{\bar{R}_o} \right)^2 C_{i_o}$$

$$n_o = \sqrt{\frac{\mu}{\bar{R}_o^3}} \qquad \bar{R}_o = \bar{R} \left(1 + J_2 \left(\frac{R_\oplus}{\bar{R}_o} \right)^2 \left(\tfrac{3}{4}\left(1 - 3C_{i_o}^2 \right) + \tfrac{3}{4} S_{i_o}^2 C_{2\bar{\theta}_o} \right) \right)$$

In Eq. (17), $R_\oplus$ is the mean radius of the earth and $\bar{R}_o$ is the mean semi-major axis. By substituting from Eq. (17) into Eq. (15), the first three terms in Eq. (14) are

$$\vec{a}_K = A_k \begin{bmatrix} r \\ \dot{r} \end{bmatrix} + B_K^{J_2} \begin{bmatrix} r \\ \dot{r} \end{bmatrix} J_2 \tag{18}$$

where

$$A_k = \begin{bmatrix} n_o^2 & 0 & 0 & 0 & 2n_o & 0 \\ 0 & n_o^2 & 0 & -2n_o & 0 & 0 \\ 0 & 0 & 0 & 0 & 0 & 0 \end{bmatrix}, \qquad B_K^{J_2} = \frac{1}{2}\left(\frac{R_\oplus}{\bar{R}_o} \right)^2 \begin{bmatrix} n_o c & 0 & 3n_o^2 a & 0 & c & 0 \\ 0 & n_o c & 0 & -c & 0 & -6n_o a \\ 3n_o^2 a & 0 & 0 & 0 & 6n_o a & 0 \end{bmatrix}$$

The values of the constant a and c are

$$a = S_{2i_o} S_{\bar{\theta}_o} \quad \text{and} \quad c = 6 - C_{2\bar{\theta}_o} - \left(18 - C_{2\bar{\theta}_o} \right) C_{i_o}^2 \tag{19}$$

Note the bilinear structure in the second term in Eq. (18), when J_2 is considered as an input, is similar to Eq. (7).

The two-body gravity gradient acceleration component $\vec{\nabla}F_{2B}$ is a nonlinear function of the position. When the chief orbit is circular, this component is

$$\vec{\nabla}F_{2B} = -\mu \begin{bmatrix} \dfrac{R_o + x}{\left[(R_o + x)^2 + y^2 + z^2\right]^{3/2}} - \dfrac{1}{R_o^2} \\[4mm] \dfrac{y}{\left[(R_o + x)^2 + y^2 + z^2\right]^{3/2}} \\[4mm] \dfrac{z}{\left[(R_o + x)^2 + y^2 + z^2\right]^{3/2}} \end{bmatrix} \tag{20}$$

where μ is the gravitational parameter and R_o is the radius of the chief orbit. The nonlinearity in Eq.(20) can be approximated using Taylor's expansion up to the second order derivatives as

$$\vec{\nabla}F_{2B} \approx [A_{2B}]\begin{bmatrix} r \\ \dot{r} \end{bmatrix} + [B_{2B}]r^{[2]} \tag{21}$$

where

$$r^{[2]} = \begin{bmatrix} x^2 & y^2 & z^2 & xy & xz & yz \end{bmatrix}^T$$

$$A_{2B} = \begin{bmatrix} 2n_o^2 & 0 & 0 & 0 & 0 & 0 \\ 0 & -n_o^2 & 0 & 0 & 0 & 0 \\ 0 & 0 & -n_o^2 & 0 & 0 & 0 \end{bmatrix} \quad , \quad B_{2B} = \frac{3\mu}{2R_o^4}\begin{bmatrix} -2 & 1 & 1 & 0 & 0 & 0 \\ 0 & 0 & 0 & 2 & 0 & 0 \\ 0 & 0 & 0 & 0 & 2 & 0 \end{bmatrix}$$

Note the term $r^{[2]}$ represents additional bilinear structure between the states. The oblateness J_2 gravity gradient effect $\vec{\nabla}F_{J_2}$ is

$$\vec{\nabla}F_{J_2} = -\frac{3J_2\mu R_\oplus^2}{2}\left\{ \frac{2(\vec{R}_d \cdot \vec{n})}{R_d^5}\vec{n} + \left[1 - \frac{5(\vec{R}_d \cdot \vec{n})^2}{R_d^2}\right]\frac{\vec{R}_d}{R_d^5} - \frac{2(\vec{R}_c \cdot \vec{n})}{R_o^5}\vec{n} - \left[1 - \frac{5(\vec{R}_c \cdot \vec{n})^2}{R_o^2}\right]\frac{\vec{R}_c}{R_o^5} \right\}$$

where $\tag{22}$

$$R_d = \left|\vec{R}_d\right| = \sqrt{(R_o + x)^2 + y^2 + z^2} \quad \text{and} \quad R_o = \left|\vec{R}_c\right|$$

In Eq. (22), the unit vector $\vec{n}$ is in the Z-direction normal to the equator, which can be expressed in the Hill coordinate frame as

$$\vec{n} = (S_\theta S_i)\vec{i}_x + (C_\theta S_i)\vec{i}_y + (C_i)\vec{i}_z \tag{23}$$

Substituting from Eq. (23) into Eq. (22), the component $\vec{\nabla}F_{J_2}$ is then a nonlinear function of x, y, and z in addition to the chief orbit parameters R_o, θ, and i. Using Taylor's expansion up to the second order derivatives, the $\vec{\nabla}F_{J_2}$ gravity gradient acceleration is

$$\vec{\nabla}F_{J_2} \approx \left[B_1^{J_2}\right]\begin{bmatrix} r \\ \dot{r} \end{bmatrix}J_2 + \left[B_2^{J_2}\right]r^{[2]}J_2$$

$$B_1^{J_2} = -\frac{3\mu R_\oplus^2}{2R_o^5}\begin{bmatrix} 4\left(1-3S_i^2 S_\theta^2\right) & -4S_i^2 S_{2\theta} & -8S_{2i}S_\theta & 0 & 0 & 0 \\ -4S_i^2 S_{2\theta} & 1+2\left(1-\tfrac{1}{2}S_\theta^2\right)S_i^2 & S_{2i}C_\theta & 0 & 0 & 0 \\ -4S_{2i}S_\theta & S_{2i}C_\theta & 3-2\left(1+\tfrac{1}{2}S_\theta^2\right)S_i^2 & 0 & 0 & 0 \end{bmatrix}$$

$$B_2^{J_2} = -\frac{3\mu R_\oplus^2}{2R_o^6}\begin{bmatrix} 10\left(1-3S_i^2 S_\theta^2\right) & 10S_i^2 S_{2\theta} & 10S_{2i}S_\theta \\ -5\left(1+2\left(1-\tfrac{1}{2}S_\theta^2\right)S_i^2\right) & -\tfrac{1}{2}S_i^2 S_{2\theta} & -\tfrac{1}{2}S_{2i}S_\theta \\ -5\left(3-2\left(1-\tfrac{1}{2}S_\theta^2\right)S_i^2\right) & -\tfrac{1}{2}S_i^2 S_{2\theta} & -\tfrac{1}{2}S_{2i}S_\theta \\ 20S_i^2 S_{2\theta} & -5\left(1+2\left(1-\tfrac{1}{2}S_\theta^2\right)S_i^2\right) & -5S_{2i}C_\theta \\ 20S_{2i}S_\theta & -5S_{2i}C_\theta & -5\left(1+2\left(1-\tfrac{1}{2}S_\theta^2\right)S_i^2\right) \\ -5S_{2i}C_\theta & -5S_{2i}S_\theta & -5S_i^2 S_{2\theta} \end{bmatrix}^T \quad (24)$$

Adding all these components together, Eq. (14) yields

$$\ddot{r} = \left(A_K + A_{2B}\right)\begin{bmatrix} r \\ \dot{r} \end{bmatrix} + \left(B_K^{J_2} + B_1^{J_2}\right)\begin{bmatrix} r \\ \dot{r} \end{bmatrix}J_2 + \left(B_{2B}\right)r^{[2]} + \left(B_2^{J_2}\right)r^{[2]}J_2 \quad (25)$$

Equation (25) is a specific case of the general bilinear model expression in Eq. (7).

ANALYTICAL VOLTERRA KERNELS OF RELATIVE MOTION

Now, one can take Eq. (25) and apply the bilinearization method as listed in Section 2 in order to develop Volterra kernels of the relative motion subject to oblateness perturbation J_2. The equivalent state space model of Eq. (25) written in terms of bilinear notation is

$$\dot{X}^{(1)} = A_1 X^{(1)} + A_2 X^{[2]} + B_1 X^{(1)}J_2 + B_2 X_P^{[2]}J_2$$
$$X^{(1)} = \begin{bmatrix} x & y & z & \dot{x} & \dot{y} & \dot{z} \end{bmatrix}^T \quad (26)$$

where

$$A_1 = \begin{bmatrix} 0_{3\times3} & I_3 \\ A_K + A_{2B} \end{bmatrix} \quad, \quad A_2 = \begin{bmatrix} 0_{3\times6} \\ B_{2B} \end{bmatrix} \quad, \quad B_1 = \begin{bmatrix} 0_{3\times6} \\ B_1^{J_2} \end{bmatrix} \quad, \quad B_2 = \begin{bmatrix} 0_{3\times6} \\ B_2^{J_2} \end{bmatrix}$$

Applying the Kronecker operator directly to the vector $X^{(1)} \in R^{6\times1}$ leads to $X^{(2)} \in R^{36\times1}$ which has many redundant elements. Removing this redundancy leads to a new reduced Kronecker product vector with a square-bracket notation $X^{[2]} \in R^{21\times1}$, where

$$X^{[2]} = \begin{bmatrix} X_P^{[2]} \\ X_V^{[2]} \end{bmatrix}$$
$$X_P^{[2]} = \begin{bmatrix} x^2 & y^2 & z^2 & xy & xz & yz \end{bmatrix}^T \quad (27)$$
$$X_V^{[2]} = \begin{bmatrix} x\dot{x} & x\dot{y} & x\dot{z} & y\dot{x} & y\dot{y} & y\dot{z} & z\dot{x} & z\dot{y} & z\dot{z} & \dot{x}^2 & \dot{y}^2 & \dot{z}^2 & \dot{x}\dot{y} & \dot{x}\dot{z} & \dot{y}\dot{z} \end{bmatrix}^T$$

The new reduced Kronecker vector $X^{[2]}$ has been broken down into two sub-vectors. The first sub-vector is the position nonlinearity vector $X_P^{[2]} \in R^{6\times1}$ and the second sub-vector is the velocity nonlinearity vector $X_V^{[2]} \in R^{15\times1}$, which also includes nonlinear position-velocity coupling terms. Note $X_P^{[2]}$ appears in Eq. (26).

Differentiating the vector $X^{[2]}$ and considering Eq. (25) gives

$$\begin{bmatrix} \dot{X}^{(1)} \\ \dot{X}_P^{[2]} \\ \dot{X}_V^{[2]} \end{bmatrix} = \begin{bmatrix} A_{1,1} & A_{1,2} & 0_{6\times15} \\ 0_{6\times6} & 0_{6\times6} & A_{2,3} \\ 0_{15\times6} & A_{3,2} & A_{3,3} \end{bmatrix} \begin{bmatrix} X^{(1)} \\ X_P^{[2]} \\ X_V^{[2]} \end{bmatrix} + \begin{bmatrix} B_{1,1} & B_{1,2} & 0_{6\times15} \\ 0_{6\times6} & 0_{6\times6} & 0_{6\times15} \\ 0_{15\times6} & B_{3,2} & B_{3,3} \end{bmatrix} \begin{bmatrix} X^{(1)} \\ X_P^{[2]} \\ X_V^{[2]} \end{bmatrix} J_2 \tag{28}$$

The velocity nonlinearity vector $X_V^{[2]}$ doesn't affect the rate of change of the linear vector $X^{(1)}$ and has insignificant influence on the rate of change of the position nonlinearity vector $X_P^{[2]}$. Thus, the matrix $A_{2,3} \in R^{6\times15}$ has almost zero elements for the numerical examples to be considered. Equation (28) can be then simplified further by ignoring the coupling of the position nonlinearity vector $X_P^{[2]}$ with the rate nonlinearity vector $X_V^{[2]}$ as

$$\frac{d}{dt}\begin{bmatrix} X^{(1)} \\ X_P^{[2]} \end{bmatrix} = \begin{bmatrix} A_1 & A_2 \\ 0_{6\times6} & 0_{6\times6} \end{bmatrix}\begin{bmatrix} X^{(1)} \\ X_P^{[2]} \end{bmatrix} + \begin{bmatrix} B_1 & B_2 \\ 0_{6\times6} & 0_{6\times6} \end{bmatrix}\begin{bmatrix} X^{(1)} \\ X_P^{[2]} \end{bmatrix} J_2$$

$$\overline{C} = \begin{bmatrix} I_3 & 0_{3\times9} \end{bmatrix} \tag{29}$$

The output of the system in Eq. (29) is the position components x, y, and z. Although, the associated coefficients corresponding to the position nonlinearity vector $X_P^{[2]}$ in Eq. (29) have zero values, this vector $X_P^{[2]}$ contributes to the dynamics by its initial conditions as shown below in the kernel expressions.

The analytical Volterra kernels of the system in Eq. (29) can be evaluated using the expressions in Eq. (12). The first three kernels are

$$\begin{aligned} h_o(t) &= \overline{C}(t)\overline{\Phi}(t,0)x_0^\otimes \\ h_1(t,\tau_1) &= \overline{C}(t)\overline{\Phi}(t,\tau_1)\overline{B}_1(\tau_1)\overline{\Phi}(\tau_1,0)x_0^\otimes \\ h_2(t,\tau_1,\tau_2) &= \overline{C}(t)\overline{\Phi}(t,\tau_1)\overline{B}_1(\tau_k)\overline{\Phi}(\tau_1,\tau_2)\overline{B}_1(\tau_2)\overline{\Phi}(\tau_2,0)x_0^\otimes \end{aligned} \tag{30}$$

$$h_o(t) = \overline{C}(t)\overline{\Phi}(t,0)x_0^\otimes$$

$$h_o(t) = \begin{bmatrix} h_o^x \\ h_o^y \\ h_o^z \end{bmatrix}$$

$$= \begin{bmatrix} (4-3C_{n_o t})x_o + \frac{\dot{x}_o}{n_o}S_{n_o t} + (1-C_{n_o t})\left(\frac{2\dot{y}_o}{n_o} - \frac{3(2x_o^2-y_o^2-z_o^2)}{2R_o}\right) + \frac{6x_o y_o}{R_o}(n_o t - 2S_{n_o t}) \\ y_o - \frac{\dot{y}_o}{n_o}(3n_o t - 4S_{n_o t}) - 6x_o(n_o t - S_{n_o t}) - \frac{2\dot{y}_o}{n_o}(1-C_{n_o t}) + \frac{3(2x_o^2-y_o^2-z_o^2)}{R_o}(n_o t - 2S_{n_o t}) + \frac{3x_o y_o}{2R_o}(8-3n_o^2 t^2 - 8C_{n_o t}) \\ z_o C_{n_o t} + \frac{\dot{z}_o}{n_o}S_{n_o t} + \frac{3x_o z_o}{R_o}(1-C_{n_o t}) \end{bmatrix}$$

997

The expression of the zero order kernel $h_o(t)$ has two terms: the linear term and the nonlinear term. The linear term is a first order function of the initial values x_o, y_o, z_o and their derivatives $\dot{x}_o$, $\dot{y}_o$, and $\dot{z}_o$. This linear term is equivalent to the linear solution of the Hill equations. On the other hand, the nonlinear term includes the second order function of the initial values and their derivatives (bilinear and quadratic components). The comparison between the linear-based model of Hill's equations and the Volterra-based model of Hill's equations can be summarized in the following points.

The linear model indicates that there is no coupling between the cross-track motion and both radial and in-track motions. In other words, the motions of $x(t)$ and $y(t)$ are coupled functions of their initial conditions x_o, $\dot{x}_o$, y_o, and $\dot{y}_o$, while the motion $z(t)$ is only a function of its initial conditions z_o and $\dot{z}_o$ and uncouples with the motions in x and y directions. The Volterra-based model indicates that the three motions are coupled. For example, the motion in the z direction is a function of the initial value x_o due to the bilinear coupling term $\frac{3x_o z_o}{R_o}\left(1-C_{n,t}\right)$. Also, unlike the linear model, the Volterra-based model indicates that the initial value of the cross-track motion z_o affects the radial motion $x(t)$ and the in-track motion $y(t)$. The strength of this coupling depends on the values of the initial conditions.

The linear model shows that the motion in the x direction is a sinusoidal motion with a frequency n_o while the Volterra-based model shows that the motion in the x direction is a combination of a sinusoidal signal and ramp signal (secular term). This ramp term $\frac{6x_o y_o}{R_o}n_o t$ causes an unstable behavior for the radial motion, which is not predicted by the linear model. The direction of this unstable behavior depends on the sign of the bilinear term $x_o y_o$ (negative heads downward and positive heads upward). Also the strength of this ramp term is an indication for the rate of the instability.

Both the linear model and Volterra-based model show that the motion in the y direction is unstable sinusoidal motion with frequency n_o while the cross-track motion $z(t)$ is a sinusoidal signal with the frequency n_o. As in the case of the x direction motion, the bilinear initial condition term $x_o y_o$ increases the amount of the instability by adding t^2 to the solution of $y(t)$. In this axis, the nonlinearity can cause the direction of instability to reverse from that in the linear prediction.

The first kernel has three components: $h_1^x(t,\tau)$, $h_1^y(t,\tau)$, and $h_1^z(t,\tau)$. Each component is a two dimensional surface as a function of t and τ. The expressions of the first kernel have been omitted from the current manuscript. However, in the next section, the shapes of the first kernel's components are visualized and discussed.

NUMERICAL VALIDATION

Two numerical examples are introduced in order to validate the proposed Volterra-based analysis compared to the linear-based analysis. These two examples are taken from Ref. [10]. The values of the reference orbit elements selected in Ref. [10] and are given in Tab. 1. The difference between the two numerical examples is the value of the deputy relative initial conditions. For the first case, the deputy is set up in a projected circular orbit (PCO) with approximate radius 0.5 km with the following initial conditions.

$$x_o = -0.000288947081 \quad \text{km} \quad , \qquad \dot{x}_o = 0.000263388377 \quad \text{km/s}$$
$$y_o = 0.500033326318 \quad \text{km} \quad , \qquad \dot{y}_o = 0.000000272412 \quad \text{km/s} \qquad (31)$$
$$z_o = 0.000175666681 \quad \text{km} \quad , \qquad \dot{z}_o = 0.000527371445 \quad \text{km/s}$$

For the second case, the deputy is set up in a PCO also with approximate radius 0.5 km with the following initial conditions.

$$x_o = 0.250014418391 \quad \text{km} \qquad , \qquad \dot{x}_o = -0.000000124335 \quad \text{km/s}$$
$$y_o = 0.000198338483 \quad \text{km} \qquad , \qquad \dot{y}_o = -0.000527557529 \quad \text{km/s} \qquad (32)$$
$$z_o = 0.500288022195 \quad \text{km} \qquad , \qquad \dot{z}_o = -0.000000019840 \quad \text{km/s}$$

The first validation focuses on the zero kernel $h_o(t)$ term, which represents the solution in the case of $J_2 = 0$. This solution is the equivalent nonlinear solution of Hill's equations. Figures 2-3 show the error in the three position components between the Volterra-based model and nonlinear simulation compared to the error of the linear-based model and the nonlinear simulation in the case of $J_2 = 0$. These two test cases signify the capability of the Volterra model to develop a non-linear closed-form solution with a significant error reduction compared to the linear solution.

Table 1 Chief orbit elements

Orbit elements*	Value
R_c, km	7100
i, deg	70
θ, deg	0
Ω, deg	45

*: Zero eccentricity, undefined periapsis

Adding the effect of J_2 to the solutions requires computing the first kernel. Figure 4 shows the three first kernel components of the first case. It is clear that both the x and y first kernel components experience divergence. The rate of the divergence in the shape of the y component is much more than in the case of the x component. In the other hand, the shape of the z component first kernel is oscillatory with a very low rate of divergence. Figure 5 shows the error position in the three components between the Volterra-based model and nonlinear simulation compared to the error of the linear-based model and the nonlinear simulation. The response can be obtained from applying the convolution integral or the nonlinear state space structure of the Volterra model. Figure 6 shows the generated trajectory of the deputy using the Volterra model compared to the nonlinear simulation.

For the second case, the three components of the first kernel are shown in Fig. 7. Unlike the first case where the emphasis is put on the high amplitude value for the initial condition in the y direction ($y_o = 0.500033326318$ km), the second test case has almost zero value for the initial condition in the y direction ($y_o = 0.000198338483$ km). This reduction in the value of y_o reduces the rate of divergence of both x and y components of the first kernel. Also, it reduces the amplitude of the z component of the first kernel. Consequently, the error signals in both x and y directions of the Case II are less than the error signals in the Case I as shown in Fig. 8. On the other hand, increasing the amplitudes of z_0 and x_0 increases the divergence rate in the z component of the first kernel and consequently increases the error signal in the z direction. Figure 9 shows the generated trajectory of the deputy using the Volterra model compared to the nonlinear simulation.

The two test cases in this section provide different combinations of the initial conditions and their influences on the shape of the kernels and the error signals. For both cases, the zero order kernel along with the first order kernel show accuracy to be sufficient. An increase of the amplitude of the initial conditions may require including the second order kernel. However, the compact form of the kernels' expressions in Eq. (29) simplifies generating all of the high order kernels.

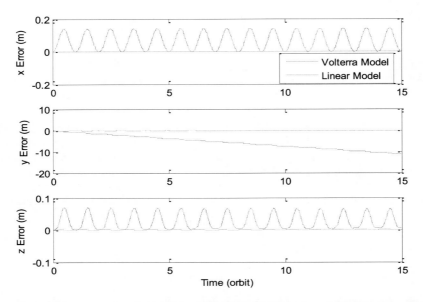

Figure 2 Errors between using Volterra-based model and linear-based model compared to the nonlinear model simulation when $J_2 = 0$ - Case I

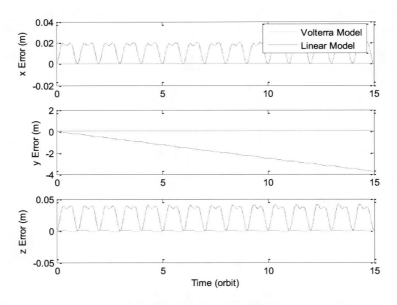

Figure 3 Errors between using Volterra-based model and linear-based model compared to the nonlinear model simulation when $J_2 = 0$ - Case II

Fig. 4-A x first kernel

Fig. 4-B y first kernel

Fig. 4-C z first kernel

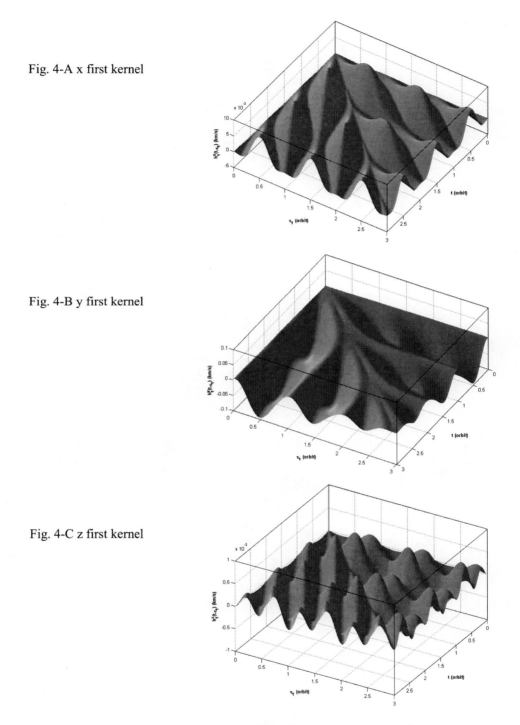

Figure 4 First kernel components for input J_2 - Case I

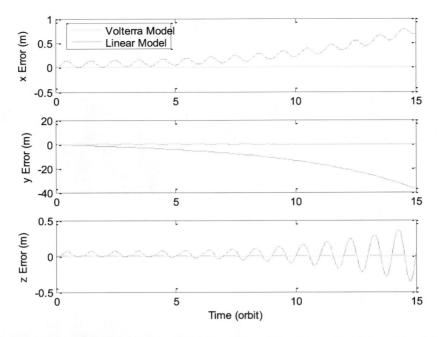

Figure 5 Errors between using Volterra-based model and linear-based model compared to the nonlinear model simulation when $J_2 \neq 0$ - Case I

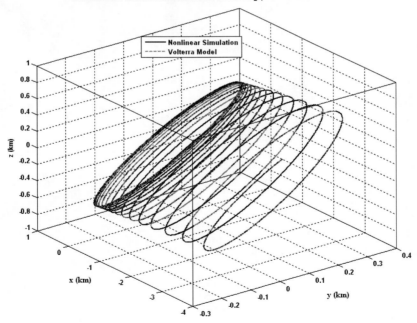

Figure 6 Orbit of the deputy for Case I

Fig. 7-A x first kernel

Fig. 7-B y first kernel

Fig. 7-C z first kernel

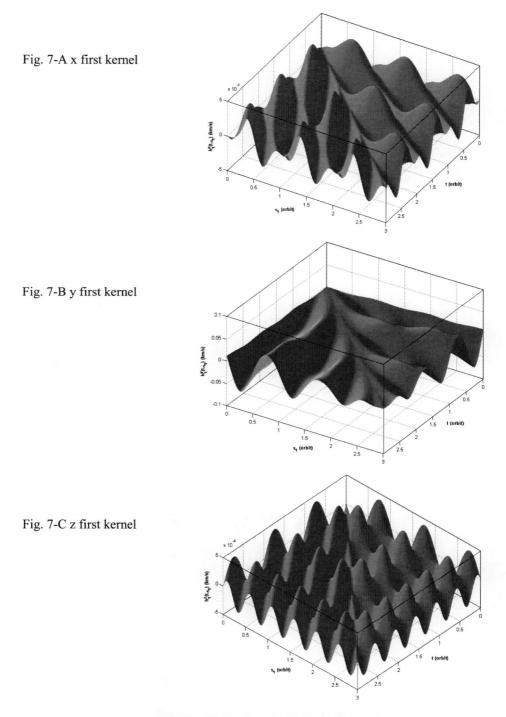

Figure 7 First kernel components for input J_2 - Case II

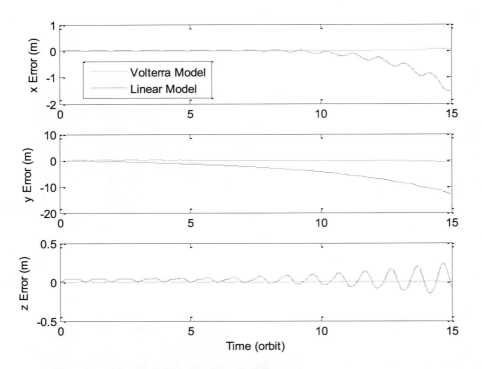

Figure 8 Errors between using Volterra-based model and linear-based model compared to the nonlinear model simulation when $J_2 \neq 0$ - Case II

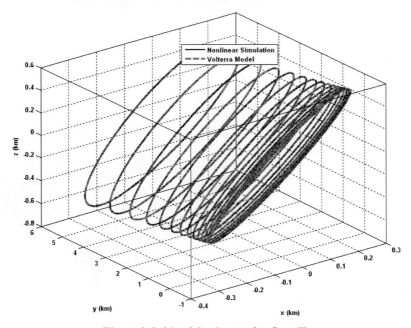

Figure 9 Orbit of the deputy for Case II

CONCLUSION

In this work, a novel nonlinear analytical solution based on Volterra theory has been developed for the relative motion subject to J_2 perturbation in the case of a circular reference orbit. A set of numerical simulations with different initial values has been used to verify the proposed Volterra approach. Compared to the previously published linear model, the Volterra-based model shows a superior reduction in the error, which is almost $1/1000$ of the error of the linear model while still retaining "Linear Like" analytical response expressions. This result makes the proposed Volterra-based model potentially more useful for rapid mission analysis and for design and evaluation of formation control strategies when compared with the linear model.

REFERENCES

1   Hill, G., "Researches in the Lunar Theory," American Journal of Mathematics, Vol. 1, No. 1, 1878, pp. 5-26.
2   Clohessy, W. and Wiltshire, R., "Terminal Guidance System for Satellite Rendezvous," Journal of the Aerospace Sciences, Vol. 27, No. 9, 1960, pp. 653-658.
3   Tschauner, J. and Hempel, P., "Rendezvous zu einem in elliptischer Bahn umlaufenden Ziel," Acta Astronautica, Vol. 11, No. 2, 1965, pp. 104-109.
4   Ross, I. M., "Linearized Dynamic Equations for Spacecraft Subject to J2 Perturbation," Journal of Guidance, Control, and Dynamics, Vol. 26, No. 4, July–August 2003, pp. 657–659.
5   Vadali, S. R., Alfriend, K. T., and Vaddi, S. S., "Hill's Equations, Mean Orbital Elements, and Formation Flying of Satellites," Advances in the Astronautical Sciences, Vol. 106, March 2000, pp. 187–204, ISBN 0877034729; also American Astronautical Society Paper 00-258, 2000.
6   Born, G. H., Goldstein, D. B., and Thompson, B., "An Analytical Theory for Orbit Determination," Journal of the Astronautical Sciences, Vol. 49, No. 2, April–June 2001, pp. 345–361.
7   Sengupta, P., Vadali, S. R., and Alfriend, K. T., "Averaged Relative Motion and Applications to Formation Flight near Perturbed Orbits," Journal of Guidance, Control, and Dynamics, Vol. 31, No. 2, 2008, pp. 258–272.
8   Izzo, D., Sabatini, M., and Valente, C., "A New Linear Model Describing Formation Flying Dynamics Under J_2 Effects," Proceedings of the 17th AIDAA National Congress, Vol. 1, Esagrafica, Rome, 2003, pp. 493–500.
9   Gim, D.-W. and Alfriend, K. T., "State Transition Matrix of Relative Motion for the Perturbed Noncircular Reference Orbit," Journal of Guidance, Control, and Dynamics, Vol. 26, No. 6, November-December 2003, pp. 956–971.
10 Vadali, S., "Model for Linearized Satellite Relative Motion about a J_2-Perturbed Mean Circular Orbit," Journal of Guidance, Control, and Dynamics, Vol. 32, No. 5, September–October 2009, pp. 1687-1691.
11 Hanspeter, S., "Relative Orbit Geometry Through Classical Orbit Element Differences," Journal of Guidance, Control, and Dynamics, Vol. 27, No. 5, September–October 2004, pp. 839-848.
12 Hablani, H. B., Tapper, M. L., and Dana-Bashian, D. J., "Guidance and Relative Navigation for Autonomous Rendezvous in a Circular Orbit," Journal of Guidance, Control, and Dynamics, Vol. 25, No 3, May-June 2002 , pp. 553-562.
13 Okasha, M. and Newman, B., "Relative Motion and Autonomous Rendezvous in Keplerian Elliptic Orbits," AIAA Guidance, Navigation, and Control Conference, 2-5 August 2010, Toronto, Ontario, Canada.
14 Tong, C., Shijie, X., and Songxia, W., "Relative Motion Control for Autonomous Rendezvous Based on Classical Orbit Element Differences," Journal of Guidance, Control, and Dynamics, Vol. 30, No. 4, July–August 2007, pp. 1003-1014.
15 Volterra, V., "Theory of Functionals and of Integral and Integro-Differential Equations," Dover, New York, 1958.
16 Rugh, W., "Nonlinear System Theory: The Volterra/Wiener Approach," John Hopkins University Press, 1981, Chapters 1-3.
17 Wiener, N., "Response of a Nonlinear Device Noise," MIT Radiation Laboratory Report No. 165, 1942.
18 Brilliant, M., "Theory of the Analysis of Nonlinear Systems," MIT Radiation Laboratory Report No. 345, 1958 (AD216-209).
19 Mohler, R., "Nonlinear Stability and Control Study of Highly Maneuverable High Performance Aircraft," OSU-ECE Report NASA 91-01, 1991.
20 Stalford, H., Baumann, W., Garrett, F., and Herdman, T., "Accurate Modeling of Nonlinear System Using Volterra Series Submodels," Proceedings of the AACC American Control Conference, Vol. 2, Minneapolis, MN, July 1987, pp. 886-891.
21 Suchomel, F., "Nonlinear Flying Qualities - One Approach," Proceedings of the AIAA Aerospace Sciences Meeting, Reno, NV, January 1987.
22 Omran A. and Newman B., "Full Envelope Nonlinear Parameter-Varying Model Approach for Atmospheric Flight Dynamics," AIAA Journal of Guidance, Control, and Dynamics, accepted.

23 Omran, A. and Newman, B., "Piecewise Global Volterra Nonlinear Modeling and Characterization for Aircraft Dynamics," Journal of Guidance, Control, and Dynamics, Vol. 32, No. 3, May-June 2009, pp. 749-759.

24 Omran, A. and Newman, B., "On Dynamical Assembly of Nonlinear Uniaxial Atmospheric Flight Mechanics," Proceedings of the AIAA Atmospheric Flight Mechanics Conference, Chicago, IL, August 2009.

25 Omran, A. and Newman, B., "Nonlinear Analytical Multi-Dimensional Convolution Solution of the Second Order System," Journal of Nonlinear Dynamics, 2010, Vol. 62, No. 4, pp. 799-819.

26 Marmarelis, Z. V., "Nonlinear Dynamic Modeling of Physiological Systems," Wiley-IEEE, New York, 2004, pp. 29-142.

27 Gray, S. and Nabet, B., "Volterra Series Analysis and Synthesis of a Neural Network for Velocity Estimation," *IEEE Transaction*, Vol. 29, April 1999, pp. 190–197.

28 Marzocca, P., Silva, P., and Librescu, L., "Nonlinear Open-/Closed-Loop Aeroelastic Analysis of Airfoils via Volterra Series," AIAA Journal, Vol. 42, No. 4, April 2004, pp. 673-686.

29 Gilbert, E., "Functional Expansions for the Response of Nonlinear Differential Systems," IEEE Transactions on Automatic Control, Vol. AC-22, 1977, pp. 909-921.

30 Baumann, W., Herdman, T., Stalford, H., and Garrett, E., "A Volterra Series Sub-model Approach to Modeling Nonlinear Aerodynamics System," Air Force Wright Aeronautical Laboratories, TM-88-FIGC, 1988.

31 Kvaternik, R. and Silva, P., "A Computational Procedure for Identifying Bilinear Representations of Nonlinear Systems Using Volterra Kernels," NASA/TM-2008-215320, 2008.